PEARSON

ALWAYS LEARNING

Raymond A. Barnett • Michael R. Ziegler • Karl E. Byleen

Calculus for Business, Economics, Life Sciences, and Social Sciences

Custom Edition for Boston University

Taken from:
Calculus, for Business, Economics, Life Sciences, and Social Sciences,
Thirteenth Edition
by Raymond A. Barnett, Michael R. Ziegler, and Karl E. Byleen

Additional Calculus Topics To Accompany Calculus, Thirteenth Edition and
College Math, Thirteenth Edition
by Raymond A. Barnett, Michael R. Ziegler, and Karl E. Byleen

Calculus for the Life Sciences, Second Edition
by Raymond N. Greenwell, Nathan P. Ritchey, and Margaret L. Lial

Taken from:

Calculus, for Business, Economics, Life Sciences, and Social Sciences, Thirteenth Edition
by Raymond A. Barnett, Michael R. Ziegler, and Karl E. Byleen
Copyright © 2015, 2011, 2008 by Pearson Education, Inc.
Boston, Massachusetts 02116

Additional Calculus Topics To Accompany Calculus, Thirteenth Edition and *College Math*, Thirteenth Edition
by Raymond A. Barnett, Michael R. Ziegler, and Karl E. Byleen
Copyright © 2015, 2011, 2008 by Pearson Education, Inc.
Boston, Massachusetts 02116

Calculus for the Life Sciences, Second Edition
by Raymond N. Greenwell, Nathan P. Ritchey, and Margaret L. Lial
Copyright © 2015, 2003 by Pearson Education, Inc.
Boston, Massachusetts 02116

This special edition published in cooperation with Pearson Learning Solutions.

All trademarks, service marks, registered trademarks, and registered service marks are the property of their respective owners and are used herein for identification purposes only.

Pearson Learning Solutions, 501 Boylston Street, Suite 900, Boston, MA 02116
A Pearson Education Company
www.pearsoned.com

Printed in the United States of America

000200010271948470

RM

ISBN 10: 1-323-04762-X
ISBN 13: 978-1-323-04762-0

CONTENTS

Taken from *Additional Calculus Topics, To Accompany Calculus*, 13E and *College Math*, 13E
by Barnett, Ziegler and Byleen

Taken from Chapter 10 of *Calculus for the Life Sciences*, Second Edition
by Greenwell, Ritchey and Lial

The following text is taken from *Calculus for Business, Economics, Life Sciences, and Social Sciences*
by Barnett, Ziegler and Byleen

PREFACE

The thirteenth edition of *Calculus for Business, Economics, Life Sciences, and Social Sciences* is designed for a one-term course in Calculus for students who have had one to two years of high school algebra or the equivalent. The book's overall approach, refined by the authors' experience with large sections of college freshmen, addresses the challenges of teaching and learning when prerequisite knowledge varies greatly from student to student.

The authors had three main goals when writing this text:

▶ To write a text that students can easily comprehend

▶ To make connections between what students are learning and how they may apply that knowledge

▶ To give flexibility to instructors to tailor a course to the needs of their students.

Many elements play a role in determining a book's effectiveness for students. Not only is it critical that the text be accurate and readable, but also, in order for a book to be effective, aspects such as the page design, the interactive nature of the presentation, and the ability to support and challenge all students have an incredible impact on how easily students comprehend the material. Here are some of the ways this text addresses the needs of students at all levels:

▶ Page layout is clean and free of potentially distracting elements.

▶ *Matched Problems* that accompany each of the completely worked examples help students gain solid knowledge of the basic topics and assess their own level of understanding before moving on.

▶ Review material (Appendix A and Chapter 1) can be used judiciously to help remedy gaps in prerequisite knowledge.

▶ A *Diagnostic Prerequisite Test* prior to Chapter 1 helps students assess their skills, while the *Basic Algebra Review* in Appendix A provides students with the content they need to remediate those skills.

▶ *Explore and Discuss* problems lead the discussion into new concepts or build upon a current topic. They help students of all levels gain better insight into the mathematical concepts through thought-provoking questions that are effective in both small and large classroom settings.

▶ Instructors are able to easily craft homework assignments that best meet the needs of their students by taking advantage of the variety of types and difficulty levels of the exercises. Exercise sets at the end of each section consist of a ***Skills Warm-up*** (four to eight problems that review prerequisite knowledge specific to that section) followed by problems divided into categories A, B, and C by level of difficulty, with level-C exercises being the most challenging.

▶ The MyMathLab course for this text is designed to help students help themselves and provide instructors with actionable information about their progress. The immediate feedback students receive when doing homework and practice in MyMathLab is invaluable, and the easily accessible e-book enhances student learning in a way that the printed page sometimes cannot.

Most important, all students get substantial experience in modeling and solving real-world problems through application examples and exercises chosen from business and economics, life sciences, and social sciences. Great care has been taken to write a book that is mathematically correct, with its emphasis on computational skills, ideas, and problem solving rather than mathematical theory.

Finally, the choice and independence of topics make the text readily adaptable to a variety of courses (see the chapter dependencies chart on page xi). This text is one of three books in the authors' college mathematics series. The others are *Finite Mathematics for Business, Economics, Life Sciences, and Social Sciences*, and *College Mathematics for Business, Economics, Life Sciences, and Social Sciences*; the latter contains selected content from the other two books. *Additional Calculus Topics*, a supplement written to accompany the Barnett/Ziegler/Byleen series, can be used in conjunction with any of these books.

New to This Edition

Fundamental to a book's effectiveness is classroom use and feedback. Now in its thirteenth edition, *Calculus for Business, Economics, Life Sciences, and Social Sciences* has had the benefit of a substantial amount of both. Improvements in this edition evolved out of the generous response from a large number of users of the last and previous editions as well as survey results from instructors, mathematics departments, course outlines, and college catalogs. In this edition,

▶ The Diagnostic Prerequisite Test has been revised to identify the specific deficiencies in prerequisite knowledge that cause students the most difficulty with calculus.

▶ Chapters 1 and 2 of the previous edition have been revised and combined to create a single introductory chapter (Chapter 1) on functions and graphs.

▶ Most exercise sets now begin with a *Skills Warm-up*—four to eight problems that review prerequisite knowledge specific to that section in a just-in-time approach. References to review material are given in the answer section of the text for the benefit of students who struggle with the warm-up problems and need a refresher.

▶ Section 6.4 has been rewritten to cover the trapezoidal rule and Simpson's rule.

▶ Examples and exercises have been given up-to-date contexts and data.

▶ Exposition has been simplified and clarified throughout the book.

▶ An Annotated Instructor's Edition is now available, providing answers to exercises directly on the page (whenever possible). *Teaching Tips* provide less-experienced instructors with insight on common student pitfalls, suggestions for how to approach a topic, or reminders of which prerequisite skills students will need. Lastly, the difficulty level of exercises is indicated only in the instructor's edition so as not to discourage students from attempting the most challenging "C" level exercises.

▶ *MyMathLab* for this text has been enhanced greatly in this revision. Most notably, a "Getting Ready for Chapter X" has been added to each chapter as an optional resource for instructors and students as a way to address the prerequisite skills that students need, and are often missing, for each chapter. Many more improvements have been made. See the detailed description on pages xiv and xv for more information.

Trusted Features

Emphasis and Style

As was stated earlier, this text is written for student comprehension. To that end, the focus has been on making the book both mathematically correct and accessible to students. Most derivations and proofs are omitted, except where their inclusion adds significant insight into a particular concept as the emphasis is on computational skills, ideas, and problem solving rather than mathematical theory. General concepts and results are typically presented only after particular cases have been discussed.

Design

One of the hallmark features of this text is the **clean, straightforward design** of its pages. Navigation is made simple with an obvious hierarchy of key topics and a judicious use of call-outs and pedagogical features. We made the decision to maintain a two-color design to help students stay focused on the mathematics and applications. Whether students start in the chapter opener or in the exercise sets, they can easily reference the content, examples, and *Conceptual Insights* they need to understand the topic at hand. Finally, a functional use of color improves the clarity of many illustrations, graphs, and explanations, and guides students through critical steps (see pages 22, 75, and 306).

Examples and Matched Problems

More than 300 completely worked examples are used to introduce concepts and to demonstrate problem-solving techniques. Many examples have multiple parts, significantly increasing the total number of worked examples. The examples are annotated using blue text to the right of each step, and the problem-solving steps are clearly identified. **To give students extra help** in working through examples, dashed boxes are used to enclose steps that are usually performed mentally and rarely mentioned in other books (see Example 4 on page 9). Though some students may not need these additional steps, many will appreciate the fact that the authors do not assume too much in the way of prior knowledge.

EXAMPLE 2   Tangent Lines Let $f(x) = (2x - 9)(x^2 + 6)$.

(A) Find the equation of the line tangent to the graph of $f(x)$ at $x = 3$.

(B) Find the value(s) of x where the tangent line is horizontal.

SOLUTION

(A) First, find $f'(x)$:

$$f'(x) = (2x - 9)(x^2 + 6)' + (x^2 + 6)(2x - 9)'$$
$$= (2x - 9)(2x) + (x^2 + 6)(2)$$

Then, find $f(3)$ and $f'(3)$:

$$f(3) = [2(3) - 9](3^2 + 6) = (-3)(15) = -45$$
$$f'(3) = [2(3) - 9]2(3) + (3^2 + 6)(2) = -18 + 30 = 12$$

Now, find the equation of the tangent line at $x = 3$:

$$y - y_1 = m(x - x_1) \quad y_1 = f(x_1) = f(3) = -45$$
$$y - (-45) = 12(x - 3) \quad m = f'(x_1) = f'(3) = 12$$
$$y = 12x - 81 \quad \text{Tangent line at } x = 3$$

(B) The tangent line is horizontal at any value of x such that $f'(x) = 0$, so

$$f'(x) = (2x - 9)2x + (x^2 + 6)2 = 0$$
$$6x^2 - 18x + 12 = 0$$
$$x^2 - 3x + 2 = 0$$
$$(x - 1)(x - 2) = 0$$
$$x = 1, 2$$

The tangent line is horizontal at $x = 1$ and at $x = 2$.

Matched Problem 2 Repeat Example 2 for $f(x) = (2x + 9)(x^2 - 12)$.

Each example is followed by a similar *Matched Problem* for the student to work while reading the material. This actively involves the student in the learning process. The answers to these matched problems are included at the end of each section for easy reference.

Explore and Discuss

Most every section contains *Explore and Discuss* problems at appropriate places to encourage students to think about a relationship or process before a result is stated or to investigate additional consequences of a development in the text. This serves to foster critical thinking and communication skills. The Explore and Discuss material can be used for in-class discussions or out-of-class group activities and is effective in both small and large class settings.

New to this edition, annotations in the instructor's edition provide tips for less-experienced instructors on how to engage students in these Explore and Discuss activities, expand on the topic, or simply guide student responses.

Explore and Discuss 1 Let $F(x) = x^2$, $S(x) = x^3$, and $f(x) = F(x)S(x) = x^5$. Which of the following is $f'(x)$?

(A) $F'(x)S'(x)$ (B) $F(x)S'(x)$

(C) $F'(x)S(x)$ (D) $F(x)S'(x) + F'(x)S(x)$

Exercise Sets

The book contains over 4,500 carefully selected and graded exercises. Many problems have multiple parts, significantly increasing the total number of exercises. Exercises are paired so that consecutive odd- and even-numbered exercises are of the same type and difficulty level. Each exercise set is designed to allow instructors to craft just the right assignment for students. Exercise sets are categorized as Skills Warm-up (review of prerequisite knowledge), and within the Annotated Instructor's Edition only, as A (routine, easy mechanics), B (more difficult mechanics), and C (difficult mechanics and some theory) to make it easy for instructors to create assignments that are appropriate for their classes. The *writing exercises*, indicated by the icon ✎, provide students with an opportunity to express their understanding of the topic in writing. Answers to all odd-numbered problems are in the back of the book.

Applications

A major objective of this book is to give the student substantial experience in modeling and solving real-world problems. Enough applications are included to convince even the most skeptical student that mathematics is really useful (see the Index of Applications at the back of the book). Almost every exercise set contains application problems, including applications from business and economics, life sciences, and social sciences. An instructor with students from all three disciplines can let them choose applications from their own field of interest; if most students are from one of the three areas, then special emphasis can be placed there. Most of the applications are simplified versions of actual real-world problems inspired by professional journals and books. No specialized experience is required to solve any of the application problems.

Additional Pedagogical Features

The following features, while helpful to any student, are particularly helpful to students enrolled in a large classroom setting where access to the instructor is more challenging or just less frequent. These features provide much-needed guidance for students as they tackle difficult concepts.

▶ **Call-out boxes** highlight important definitions, results, and step-by-step processes (see pages 57, 63–64).

► **Caution statements** appear throughout the text where student errors often occur (see pages 82, 274, and 332).

⚠ CAUTION The expression $0/0$ does not represent a real number and should never be used as the value of a limit. If a limit is a $0/0$ indeterminate form, further investigation is always required to determine whether the limit exists and to find its value if it does exist.   ▲

► **Conceptual Insights**, appearing in nearly every section, often make explicit connections to previous knowledge, but sometimes encourage students to think beyond the particular skill they are working on and attain a more enlightened view of the concepts at hand (see pages 56–57, 116, and 306).

CONCEPTUAL INSIGHT

Rather than list the points where a function is discontinuous, sometimes it is useful to state the intervals on which the function is continuous. Using the set operation **union,** denoted by $\cup$, we can express the set of points where the function in Example 1 is continuous as follows:

$$(-\infty, -4) \cup (-4, -2) \cup (-2, 1) \cup (1, 3) \cup (3, \infty)$$

► The newly revised **Diagnostic Prerequisite Test**, located at the front of the book, provides students with a tool to assess their prerequisite skills prior to taking the course. The **Basic Algebra Review**, in Appendix A, provides students with seven sections of content to help them remediate in specific areas of need. Answers to the Diagnostic Prerequisite Test are at the back of the book and reference specific sections in the Basic Algebra Review or Chapter 1 for students to use for remediation.

Graphing Calculator and Spreadsheet Technology

Although access to a graphing calculator or spreadsheets is not assumed, it is likely that many students will want to make use of this technology. To assist these students, optional graphing calculator and spreadsheet activities are included in appropriate places. These include brief discussions in the text, examples or portions of examples solved on a graphing calculator or spreadsheet, and exercises for the student to solve. For example, linear and quadratic regression are introduced in Section 1.3, and regression techniques on a graphing calculator are used at appropriate points to illustrate mathematical modeling with real data. All the optional graphing calculator material is clearly identified with the icon ⊞ and can be omitted without loss of continuity, if desired. Optional spreadsheet material is identified with the icon ▦. Graphing calculator screens displayed in the text are actual output from the TI-84 Plus graphing calculator.

Chapter Reviews

Often it is during the preparation for a chapter exam that concepts gel for students, making the chapter review material particularly important. The chapter review sections in this text include a comprehensive summary of important terms, symbols, and concepts, keyed to completely worked examples, followed by a comprehensive set of Review Exercises. Answers to Review Exercises are included at the back of the book; *each answer contains a reference to the section in which that type of problem is discussed* so students can remediate any deficiencies in their skills on their own.

Chapter Dependencies

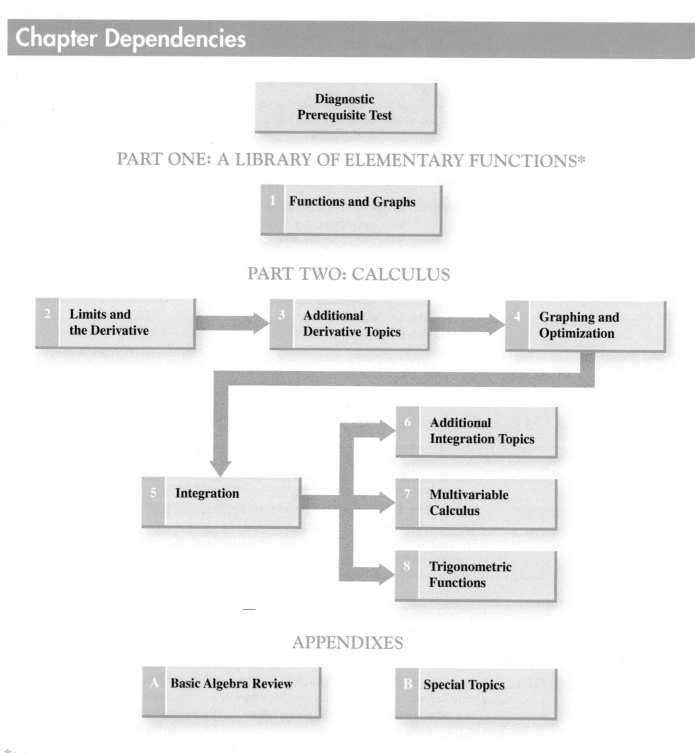

Diagnostic Prerequisite Test

PART ONE: A LIBRARY OF ELEMENTARY FUNCTIONS*

1 **Functions and Graphs**

PART TWO: CALCULUS

2 **Limits and the Derivative**

3 **Additional Derivative Topics**

4 **Graphing and Optimization**

6 **Additional Integration Topics**

5 **Integration**

7 **Multivariable Calculus**

8 **Trigonometric Functions**

APPENDIXES

A **Basic Algebra Review**

B **Special Topics**

*Selected topics from Part One may be referred to as needed in Part Two or reviewed systematically before starting Part Two.

Content

The text begins with the development of a library of elementary functions in **Chapter 1**, including their properties and applications. Many students will be familiar with most, if not all, of the material in this introductory chapter. Depending on students' preparation and the course syllabus, an instructor has several options for using the first chapter, including the following:

(i) Skip Chapter 1 and refer to it only as necessary later in the course;

(ii) Cover Section 1.3 quickly in the first week of the course, emphasizing price–demand equations, price–supply equations, and linear regression, but skip the rest of Chapter 1;

(iii) Cover Chapter 1 systematically before moving on to other chapters.

The material in Part Two (Calculus) consists of differential calculus (Chapters 2–4), integral calculus (Chapters 5 and 6), multivariable calculus (Chapter 7), and a brief discussion of differentiation and integration of trigonometric functions (Chapter 8). In general, Chapters 2–5 must be covered in sequence; however, certain sections can be omitted or given brief treatments, as pointed out in the discussion that follows (see the Chapter Dependencies chart on page xi).

▶ **Chapter 2** introduces the derivative. The first three sections cover limits (including infinite limits and limits at infinity), continuity, and the limit properties that are essential to understanding the definition of the derivative in Section 2.4. The remaining sections of the chapter cover basic rules of differentiation, differentials, and applications of derivatives in business and economics. The interplay between graphical, numerical, and algebraic concepts is emphasized here and throughout the text.

▶ In **Chapter 3** the derivatives of exponential and logarithmic functions are obtained before the product rule, quotient rule, and chain rule are introduced. Implicit differentiation is introduced in Section 3.5 and applied to related rates problems in Section 3.6. Elasticity of demand is introduced in Section 3.7. The topics in these last three sections of Chapter 3 are not referred to elsewhere in the text and can be omitted.

▶ **Chapter 4** focuses on graphing and optimization. The first two sections cover first-derivative and second-derivative graph properties. L'Hôpital's rule is discussed in Section 4.3. A graphing strategy is presented and illustrated in Section 4.4. Optimization is covered in Sections 4.5 and 4.6, including examples and problems involving end-point solutions.

▶ **Chapter 5** introduces integration. The first two sections cover antidifferentiation techniques essential to the remainder of the text. Section 5.3 discusses some applications involving differential equations that can be omitted. The definite integral is defined in terms of Riemann sums in Section 5.4 and the fundamental theorem of calculus is discussed in Section 5.5. As before, the interplay between graphical, numerical, and algebraic properties is emphasized. These two sections are also required for the remaining chapters in the text.

▶ **Chapter 6** covers additional integration topics and is organized to provide maximum flexibility for the instructor. The first section extends the area concepts introduced in Chapter 6 to the area between two curves and related applications. Section 6.2 covers three more applications of integration, and Sections 6.3 and 6.4 deal with additional methods of integration, including integration by parts, the trapezoidal rule, and Simpson's rule. Any or all of the topics in Chapter 6 can be omitted.

▶ **Chapter 7** deals with multivariable calculus. The first five sections can be covered any time after Section 4.6 has been completed. Sections 7.6 and 7.7 require the integration concepts discussed in Chapter 5.

▶ **Chapter 8** provides brief coverage of trigonometric functions that can be incorporated into the course, if desired. Section 8.1 provides a review of basic trigonometric concepts. Section 8.2 can be covered any time after Section 4.3 has been completed. Section 8.3 requires the material in Chapter 5.

▶ **Appendix A** contains a concise review of basic algebra that may be covered as part of the course or referenced as needed. As mentioned previously, **Appendix B** contains additional topics that can be covered in conjunction with certain sections in the text, if desired.

Accuracy Check

Because of the careful checking and proofing by a number of mathematics instructors (acting independently), the authors and publisher believe this book to be substantially error free. If an error should be found, the authors would be grateful if notification were sent to Karl E. Byleen, 9322 W. Garden Court, Hales Corners, WI 53130; or by e-mail to kbyleen@wi.rr.com.

Student Supplements

Student's Solutions Manual

▶ By Garret J. Etgen, University of Houston

▶ This manual contains detailed, carefully worked-out solutions to all odd-numbered section exercises and all Chapter Review exercises. Each section begins with Things to Remember, a list of key material for review.

▶ ISBN-13: 978-0-321-93173-3

Additional Calculus Topics to Accompany Calculus, 13e, and College Mathematics, 13e

▶ This separate book contains three unique chapters: Differential Equations, Taylor Polynomials and Infinite Series, and Probability and Calculus.

▶ ISBN 13: 978-0-321-93169-6; ISBN 10: 0-321-931696

Graphing Calculator Manual for Applied Math

▶ By Victoria Baker, Nicholls State University

▶ This manual contains detailed instructions for using the TI-83/TI-83 Plus/TI-84 Plus C calculators with this textbook. Instructions are organized by mathematical topics.

▶ Available in MyMathLab.

Excel Spreadsheet Manual for Applied Math

▶ By Stela Pudar-Hozo, Indiana University–Northwest

▶ This manual includes detailed instructions for using Excel spreadsheets with this textbook. Instructions are organized by mathematical topics.

▶ Available in MyMathLab.

Guided Lecture Notes

▶ By Salvatore Sciandra,
Niagara County Community College

▶ These worksheets for students contain unique examples to enforce what is taught in the lecture and/or material covered in the text. Instructor worksheets are also available and include answers.

▶ Available in MyMathLab or through Pearson Custom Publishing.

Videos with Optional Captioning

▶ The video lectures with optional captioning for this text make it easy and convenient for students to watch videos from a computer at home or on campus. The complete set is ideal for distance learning or supplemental instruction.

▶ Every example in the text is represented by a video.

▶ Available in MyMathLab.

Instructor Supplements

New! Annotated Instructor's Edition

▶ This book contains answers to all exercises in the text on the same page as the exercises whenever possible. In addition, Teaching Tips are provided for less-experienced instructors. Exercises are coded by level of difficulty only in the AIE so students are not dissuaded from trying more challenging exercises.

▶ ISBN-13: 978-0-321-92416-2

Online Instructor's Solutions Manual (downloadable)

▶ By Garret J. Etgen, University of Houston

▶ This manual contains detailed solutions to all even-numbered section problems.

▶ Available in MyMathLab or through http://www.pearsonhighered.com/educator.

Mini Lectures (downloadable)

▶ By Salvatore Sciandra,
Niagara County Community College

▶ Mini Lectures are provided for the teaching assistant, adjunct, part-time or even full-time instructor for lecture preparation by providing learning objectives, examples (and answers) not found in the text, and teaching notes.

▶ Available in MyMathLab or through http://www.pearsonhighered.com/educator.

PowerPoint® Lecture Slides

▶ These slides present key concepts and definitions from the text. They are available in MyMathLab or at http://www.pearsonhighered.com/educator.

Technology Resources

MyMathLab® Online Course
(access code required)

MyMathLab delivers **proven results** in helping individual students succeed.

▶ MyMathLab has a consistently positive impact on the quality of learning in higher education math instruction. MyMathLab can be successfully implemented in any environment—lab based, hybrid, fully online, traditional—and demonstrates the quantifiable difference that integrated usage has on student retention, subsequent success, and overall achievement.

▶ MyMathLab's comprehensive online gradebook automatically tracks your students' results on tests, quizzes, homework, and in the study plan. You can use the gradebook to quickly intervene if your students have trouble or to provide positive feedback on a job well done. The data within MyMathLab is easily exported to a variety of spreadsheet programs, such as Microsoft Excel. You can determine which points of data you want to export and then analyze the results to determine success.

MyMathLab provides **engaging experiences** that personalize, stimulate, and measure learning for each student.

▶ **Personalized Learning:** MyMathLab offers two important features that support adaptive learning—personalized homework and the adaptive study plan. These features allow your students to work on what they need to learn when it makes the most sense, maximizing their potential for understanding and success.

▶ **Exercises:** The homework and practice exercises in MyMathLab are correlated to the exercises in the textbook, and they regenerate algorithmically to give students unlimited opportunity for practice and mastery. The software offers immediate, helpful feedback when students enter incorrect answers.

▶ **Chapter-Level, Just-in-Time Remediation:** The MyMathLab course for these texts includes a short diagnostic, called Getting Ready, prior to each chapter to assess students' prerequisite knowledge. This diagnostic can then be tied to personalized homework so that each student receives a homework assignment specific to his or her prerequisite skill needs.

▶ **Multimedia Learning Aids:** Exercises include guided solutions, sample problems, animations, videos, and eText access for extra help at the point of use.

And, MyMathLab comes from an **experienced partner** with educational expertise and an eye on the future.

▶ Knowing that you are using a Pearson product means that you are using quality content. That means that our eTexts are accurate and our assessment tools work. It means we are committed to making MyMathLab as accessible as possible. MyMathLab is compatible with the JAWS 12/13 screen reader, and enables multiple-choice and free-response problem types to be read and interacted with via keyboard controls and math notation input. More information on this functionality is available at http://mymathlab.com/accessibility.

▶ Whether you are just getting started with MyMathLab or you have a question along the way, we're here to help you learn about our technologies and how to incorporate them into your course.

▶ To learn more about how MyMathLab combines proven learning applications with powerful assessment and continuously adaptive capabilities, visit www.mymathlab.com or contact your Pearson representative.

MyMathLab® Ready-to-Go Course
(access code required)

These new Ready-to-Go courses provide students with all the same great MyMathLab features but make it easier for instructors to get started. Each course includes preassigned homework and quizzes to make creating a course even simpler. In addition, these prebuilt courses include a course-level Getting Ready diagnostic that helps pinpoint student weaknesses in prerequisite skills. Ask your Pearson representative about the details for this particular course or to see a copy of this course.

MyLabsPlus®

MyLabsPlus combines proven results and engaging experiences from MyMathLab® and MyStatLab™ with convenient management tools and a dedicated services team. Designed to support growing math and statistics programs, it includes additional features such as

▶ **Batch Enrollment:** Your school can create the login name and password for every student and instructor, so everyone can be ready to start class on the first day. Automation of this process is also possible through integration with your school's Student Information System.

▶ **Login from your campus portal:** You and your students can link directly from your campus portal into your MyLabsPlus courses. A Pearson service team works with your institution to create a single sign-on experience for instructors and students.

▶ **Advanced Reporting:** MyLabsPlus advanced reporting allows instructors to review and analyze students' strengths and weaknesses by tracking their performance on tests, assignments, and tutorials. Administrators can review grades and assignments across all courses on your MyLabsPlus campus for a broad overview of program performance.

▶ **24/7 Support:** Students and instructors receive 24/7 support, 365 days a year, by email or online chat.

MyLabsPlus is available to qualified adopters. For more information, visit our website at www.mylabsplus.com or contact your Pearson representative.

MathXL® Online Course
(access code required)

MathXL is the homework and assessment engine that runs MyMathLab. (MyMathLab is MathXL plus a learning-management system.)

With MathXL, instructors can

▶ Create, edit, and assign online homework and tests using algorithmically generated exercises correlated at the objective level to the textbook.

▶ Create and assign their own online exercises and import TestGen tests for added flexibility.

▶ Maintain records of all student work tracked in MathXL's online gradebook.

With MathXL, students can

▶ Take chapter tests in MathXL and receive personalized study plans and/or personalized homework assignments based on their test results.

▶ Use the study plan and/or the homework to link directly to tutorial exercises for the objectives they need to study.

▶ Access supplemental animations and video clips directly from selected exercises.

MathXL is available to qualified adopters. For more information, visit our website at www.mathxl.com or contact your Pearson representative.

TestGen®

TestGen (www.pearsoned.com/testgen) enables instructors to build, edit, print, and administer tests using a computerized bank of questions developed to cover all the objectives of the text. TestGen is algorithmically based, allowing instructors to create multiple, but equivalent, versions of the same question or test with the click of a button. Instructors can also modify test bank questions or add new questions. The software and test bank are available for download from Pearson Education's online catalog.

Acknowledgments

In addition to the authors, many others are involved in the successful publication of a book. We wish to thank the following reviewers:

Mark Barsamian, *Ohio University*
Kathleen Coskey, *Boise State University*
Tim Doyle, *DePaul University*
J. Robson Eby, *Blinn College–Bryan Campus*
Irina Franke, *Bowling Green State University*
Andrew J. Hetzel, *Tennessee Tech University*
Timothy Kohl, *Boston University*
Dan Krulewich, *University of Missouri, Kansas City*
Scott Lewis, *Utah Valley University*
Saliha Shah, *Ventura College*
Jerimi Ann Walker, *Moraine Valley Community College*

We also express our thanks to

Mark Barsamian, Theresa Schille, J. Robson Eby, John Samons, and Gary Williams for providing a careful and thorough accuracy check of the text, problems, and answers.

Garret Etgen, Salvatore Sciandra, Victoria Baker, and Stela Pudar-Hozo for developing the supplemental materials so important to the success of a text.

All the people at Pearson Education who contributed their efforts to the production of this book.

Diagnostic Prerequisite Test

Work all of the problems in this self-test without using a calculator. Then check your work by consulting the answers in the back of the book. Where weaknesses show up, use the reference that follows each answer to find the section in the text that provides the necessary review.

1. Replace each question mark with an appropriate expression that will illustrate the use of the indicated real number property:

   (A) Commutative $(\cdot)$: $x(y + z) = ?$

   (B) Associative $(+)$: $2 + (x + y) = ?$

   (C) Distributive: $(2 + 3)x = ?$

Problems 2–6 refer to the following polynomials:

   (A) $3x - 4$ (B) $x + 2$

   (C) $2 - 3x^2$ (D) $x^3 + 8$

2. Add all four.

3. Subtract the sum of (A) and (C) from the sum of (B) and (D).

4. Multiply (C) and (D).

5. What is the degree of each polynomial?

6. What is the leading coefficient of each polynomial?

In Problems 7 and 8, perform the indicated operations and simplify.

7. $5x^2 - 3x[4 - 3(x - 2)]$

8. $(2x + y)(3x - 4y)$

In Problems 9 and 10, factor completely.

9. $x^2 + 7x + 10$

10. $x^3 - 2x^2 - 15x$

11. Write 0.35 as a fraction reduced to lowest terms.

12. Write $\dfrac{7}{8}$ in decimal form.

13. Write in scientific notation:

   (A) 4,065,000,000,000   (B) 0.0073

14. Write in standard decimal form:

   (A) 2.55×10^8 (B) 4.06×10^{-4}

15. Indicate true (T) or false (F):

   (A) A natural number is a rational number.

   (B) A number with a repeating decimal expansion is an irrational number.

16. Give an example of an integer that is not a natural number.

In Problems 17–24, simplify and write answers using positive exponents only. All variables represent positive real numbers.

17. $6(xy^3)^5$

18. $\dfrac{9u^8v^6}{3u^4v^8}$

19. $(2 \times 10^5)(3 \times 10^{-3})$

20. $(x^{-3}y^2)^{-2}$

21. $u^{5/3}u^{2/3}$

22. $(9a^4b^{-2})^{1/2}$

23. $\dfrac{5^0}{3^2} + \dfrac{3^{-2}}{2^{-2}}$

24. $(x^{1/2} + y^{1/2})^2$

In Problems 25–30, perform the indicated operation and write the answer as a simple fraction reduced to lowest terms. All variables represent positive real numbers.

25. $\dfrac{a}{b} + \dfrac{b}{a}$

26. $\dfrac{a}{bc} - \dfrac{c}{ab}$

27. $\dfrac{x^2}{y} \cdot \dfrac{y^6}{x^3}$

28. $\dfrac{x}{y^3} \div \dfrac{x^2}{y}$

29. $\dfrac{\dfrac{1}{7 + h} - \dfrac{1}{7}}{h}$

30. $\dfrac{x^{-1} + y^{-1}}{x^{-2} - y^{-2}}$

31. Each statement illustrates the use of one of the following real number properties or definitions. Indicate which one.

Commutative $(+, \cdot)$	Associative $(+, \cdot)$	Distributive
Identity $(+, \cdot)$	Inverse $(+, \cdot)$	Subtraction
Division	Negatives	Zero

   (A) $(-7) - (-5) = (-7) + [-(-5)]$

   (B) $5u + (3v + 2) = (3v + 2) + 5u$

   (C) $(5m - 2)(2m + 3) = (5m - 2)2m + (5m - 2)3$

   (D) $9 \cdot (4y) = (9 \cdot 4)y$

   (E) $\dfrac{u}{-(v - w)} = \dfrac{u}{w - v}$

   (F) $(x - y) + 0 = (x - y)$

32. Round to the nearest integer:

   (A) $\dfrac{17}{3}$ (B) $-\dfrac{5}{19}$

33. Multiplying a number x by 4 gives the same result as subtracting 4 from x. Express as an equation, and solve for x.

34. Find the slope of the line that contains the points $(3, -5)$ and $(-4, 10)$.

35. Find the x and y coordinates of the point at which the graph of $y = 7x - 4$ intersects the x axis.

36. Find the x and y coordinates of the point at which the graph of $y = 7x - 4$ intersects the y axis.

In Problems 37 and 38, factor completely.

37. $x^2 - 3xy - 10y^2$

38. $6x^2 - 17xy + 5y^2$

In Problems 39–42, write in the form $ax^p + by^q$ where a, b, p, and q are rational numbers.

39. $\dfrac{3}{x} + 4\sqrt{y}$

40. $\dfrac{8}{x^2} - \dfrac{5}{y^4}$

41. $\dfrac{2}{5x^{3/4}} - \dfrac{7}{6y^{2/3}}$

42. $\dfrac{1}{3\sqrt{x}} + \dfrac{9}{\sqrt[3]{y}}$

In Problems 43 and 44, write in the form $a + b\sqrt{c}$ where a, b, and c are rational numbers.

43. $\dfrac{1}{4 - \sqrt{2}}$

44. $\dfrac{5 - \sqrt{3}}{5 + \sqrt{3}}$

In Problems 45–50, solve for x.

45. $x^2 = 5x$

46. $3x^2 - 21 = 0$

47. $x^2 - x - 20 = 0$

48. $-6x^2 + 7x - 1 = 0$

49. $x^2 + 2x - 1 = 0$

50. $x^4 - 6x^2 + 5 = 0$

PART 1

A LIBRARY
OF ELEMENTARY
FUNCTIONS

1

Functions and Graphs

Introduction

The function concept is one of the most important ideas in mathematics. The study of mathematics beyond the elementary level requires a firm understanding of a basic list of elementary functions, their properties, and their graphs. See the inside back cover of this book for a list of the functions that form our library of elementary functions. Most functions in the list will be introduced to you by the end of Chapter 1. For example, in Section 1.3 you will learn how to apply quadratic functions to model the effect of tire pressure on mileage (see Problems 73 and 75 on page 48).

1.1 Functions

After a brief review of the Cartesian (rectangular) coordinate system in the plane and graphs of equations, we discuss the concept of function, one of the most important ideas in mathematics.

Cartesian Coordinate System

Recall that to form a **Cartesian** or **rectangular coordinate system**, we select two real number lines—one horizontal and one vertical—and let them cross through their origins as indicated in the figure below. Up and to the right are the usual choices for the positive directions. These two number lines are called the **horizontal axis** and the **vertical axis**, or, together, the **coordinate axes**. The horizontal axis is usually referred to as the *x* **axis** and the vertical axis as the *y* **axis**, and each is labeled accordingly. The coordinate axes divide the plane into four parts called **quadrants**, which are numbered counterclockwise from I to IV (see the figure).

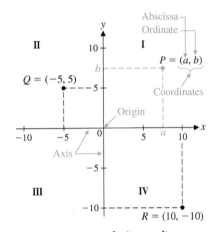

The Cartesian (rectangular) coordinate system

Now we want to assign *coordinates* to each point in the plane. Given an arbitrary point *P* in the plane, pass horizontal and vertical lines through the point (see figure). The vertical line will intersect the horizontal axis at a point with coordinate *a*, and the horizontal line will intersect the vertical axis at a point with coordinate *b*. These two numbers, written as the **ordered pair** (a, b) form the **coordinates** of the point *P*. The first coordinate, *a*, is called the **abscissa** of *P*; the second coordinate, *b*, is called the **ordinate** of *P*. The abscissa of *Q* in the figure is −5, and the ordinate of *Q* is 5. The coordinates of a point can also be referenced in terms of the axis labels. The *x* **coordinate** of *R* in the figure is 10, and the *y* **coordinate** of *R* is −10. The point with coordinates $(0, 0)$ is called the **origin**.

The procedure we have just described assigns to each point *P* in the plane a unique pair of real numbers (a, b). Conversely, if we are given an ordered pair of real numbers (a, b), then, reversing this procedure, we can determine a unique point *P* in the plane. Thus,

There is a one-to-one correspondence between the points in a plane and the elements in the set of all ordered pairs of real numbers.

This is often referred to as the **fundamental theorem of analytic geometry**.

Graphs of Equations

A solution to an equation in one variable is a number. For example, the equation $4x - 13 = 7$ has the solution $x = 5$; when 5 is substituted for *x*, the left side of the equation is equal to the right side.

A solution to an equation in two variables is an ordered pair of numbers. For example, the equation $y = 9 - x^2$ has the solution $(4, -7)$; when 4 is substituted for x and -7 is substituted for y, the left side of the equation is equal to the right side. The solution $(4, -7)$ is one of infinitely many solutions to the equation $y = 9 - x^2$. The set of all solutions of an equation is called the **solution set**. Each solution forms the coordinates of a point in a rectangular coordinate system. To **sketch the graph** of an equation in two variables, we plot sufficiently many of those points so that the shape of the graph is apparent, and then we connect those points with a smooth curve. This process is called **point-by-point plotting**.

EXAMPLE 1   Point-by-Point Plotting   Sketch the graph of each equation.

(A) $y = 9 - x^2$ (B) $x^2 = y^4$

SOLUTIONS

(A) Make up a table of solutions—that is, ordered pairs of real numbers that satisfy the given equation. For easy mental calculation, choose integer values for x.

x	-4	-3	-2	-1	0	1	2	3	4
y	-7	0	5	8	9	8	5	0	-7

After plotting these solutions, if there are any portions of the graph that are unclear, plot additional points until the shape of the graph is apparent. Then join all the plotted points with a smooth curve (Fig. 1). Arrowheads are used to indicate that the graph continues beyond the portion shown here with no significant changes in shape.

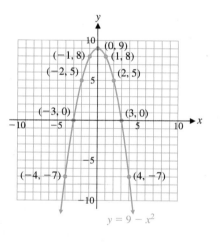

Figure 1 $y = 9 - x^2$

(B) Again we make a table of solutions—here it may be easier to choose integer values for y and calculate values for x. Note, for example, that if $y = 2$, then $x = \pm 4$; that is, the ordered pairs $(4, 2)$ and $(-4, 2)$ are both in the solution set.

x	± 9	± 4	± 1	0	± 1	± 4	± 9
y	-3	-2	-1	0	1	2	3

We plot these points and join them with a smooth curve (Fig. 2).

Matched Problem 1   Sketch the graph of each equation.

(A) $y = x^2 - 4$ (B) $y^2 = \dfrac{100}{x^2 + 1}$

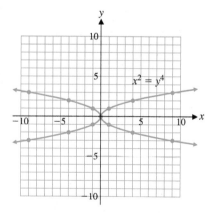

Figure 2 $x^2 = y^4$

Explore and Discuss 1   To graph the equation $y = -x^3 + 3x$, we use point-by-point plotting to obtain

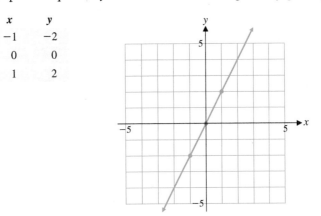

x	y
-1	-2
0	0
1	2

(A) Do you think this is the correct graph of the equation? Why or why not?

(B) Add points on the graph for $x = -2, -1.5, -0.5, 0.5, 1.5,$ and 2.

(C) Now, what do you think the graph looks like? Sketch your version of the graph, adding more points as necessary.

 (D) Graph this equation on a graphing calculator and compare it with your graph from part (C).

(A)

(B)

Figure 3

    The icon in the margin is used throughout this book to identify optional graphing calculator activities that are intended to give you additional insight into the concepts under discussion. You may have to consult the manual for your graphing calculator for the details necessary to carry out these activities. For example, to graph the equation in Explore and Discuss 1 on most graphing calculators, you must enter the equation (Fig. 3A) and the window variables (Fig. 3B).

As Explore and Discuss 1 illustrates, the shape of a graph may not be apparent from your first choice of points. Using point-by-point plotting, it may be difficult to find points in the solution set of the equation, and it may be difficult to determine when you have found enough points to understand the shape of the graph. We will supplement the technique of point-by-point plotting with a detailed analysis of several basic equations, giving you the ability to sketch graphs with accuracy and confidence.

Definition of a Function

Central to the concept of function is correspondence. You are familiar with correspondences in daily life. For example,

To each person, there corresponds an annual income.

To each item in a supermarket, there corresponds a price.

To each student, there corresponds a grade-point average.

To each day, there corresponds a maximum temperature.

For the manufacture of x items, there corresponds a cost.

For the sale of x items, there corresponds a revenue.

To each square, there corresponds an area.

To each number, there corresponds its cube.

One of the most important aspects of any science is the establishment of correspondences among various types of phenomena. Once a correspondence is known, predictions can be made. A cost analyst would like to predict costs for various levels of output in a manufacturing process; a medical researcher would like to know the correspondence between heart disease and obesity; a psychologist would like to predict the level of performance after a subject has repeated a task a given number of times; and so on.

What do all of these examples have in common? Each describes the matching of elements from one set with the elements in a second set.

Consider Tables 1–3. Tables 1 and 2 specify functions, but Table 3 does not. Why not? The definition of the term *function* will explain.

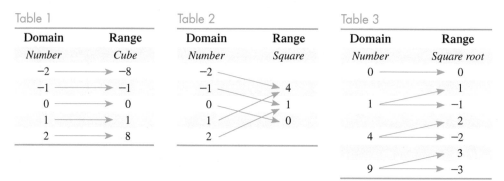

Table 1	
Domain	**Range**
Number	*Cube*
−2	−8
−1	−1
0	0
1	1
2	8

Table 2	
Domain	**Range**
Number	*Square*
−2	4
−1	1
0	0
1	
2	

Table 3	
Domain	**Range**
Number	*Square root*
0	0
	1
1	−1
	2
4	−2
	3
9	−3

DEFINITION Function

A **function** is a correspondence between two sets of elements such that to each element in the first set, there corresponds one and only one element in the second set.

The first set is called the **domain**, and the set of corresponding elements in the second set is called the **range**.

Tables 1 and 2 specify functions since to each domain value, there corresponds exactly one range value (for example, the cube of −2 is −8 and no other number). On the other hand, Table 3 does not specify a function since to at least one domain value, there corresponds more than one range value (for example, to the domain value 9, there corresponds −3 and 3, both square roots of 9).

Explore and Discuss 2   Consider the set of students enrolled in a college and the set of faculty members at that college. Suppose we define a correspondence between the two sets by saying that a student corresponds to a faculty member if the student is currently enrolled in a course taught by that faculty member. Is this correspondence a function? Discuss.

Functions Specified by Equations

Most of the functions in this book will have domains and ranges that are (infinite) sets of real numbers. The **graph** of such a function is the set of all points (x, y) in the Cartesian plane such that x is an element of the domain and y is the corresponding element in the range. The correspondence between domain and range elements is often specified by an equation in two variables. Consider, for example, the equation for the area of a rectangle with width 1 inch less than its length (Fig. 4). If x is the length, then the area y is given by

$$y = x(x - 1) \qquad x \geq 1$$

$x - 1$

x

Figure 4

For each **input** x (length), we obtain an **output** y (area). For example,

$$\text{If} \quad x = 5, \quad \text{then} \quad y = 5(5 - 1) = 5 \cdot 4 = 20.$$
$$\text{If} \quad x = 1, \quad \text{then} \quad y = 1(1 - 1) = 1 \cdot 0 = 0.$$
$$\text{If} \quad x = \sqrt{5}, \quad \text{then} \quad y = \sqrt{5}(\sqrt{5} - 1) = 5 - \sqrt{5}$$
$$\approx 2.7639.$$

The input values are domain values, and the output values are range values. The equation assigns each domain value x a range value y. The variable x is called an *independent variable* (since values can be "independently" assigned to x from the domain), and y is called a *dependent variable* (since the value of y "depends" on the value assigned to x). In general, any variable used as a placeholder for domain values is called an **independent variable**; any variable that is used as a placeholder for range values is called a **dependent variable**.

When does an equation specify a function?

DEFINITION Functions Specified by Equations

If in an equation in two variables, we get exactly one output (value for the dependent variable) for each input (value for the independent variable), then the equation specifies a function. The graph of such a function is just the graph of the specifying equation.

If we get more than one output for a given input, the equation does not specify a function.

EXAMPLE 2 Functions and Equations Determine which of the following equations specify functions with independent variable x.

(A) $4y - 3x = 8$, x a real number (B) $y^2 - x^2 = 9$, x a real number

SOLUTION

(A) Solving for the dependent variable y, we have

$$4y - 3x = 8$$
$$4y = 8 + 3x \tag{1}$$
$$y = 2 + \frac{3}{4}x$$

Since each input value x corresponds to exactly one output value $\left(y = 2 + \frac{3}{4}x\right)$, we see that equation (1) specifies a function.

(B) Solving for the dependent variable y, we have

$$y^2 - x^2 = 9$$
$$y^2 = 9 + x^2 \tag{2}$$
$$y = \pm\sqrt{9 + x^2}$$

Since $9 + x^2$ is always a positive real number for any real number x, and since each positive real number has two square roots,* then to each input value x there corresponds two output values $\left(y = -\sqrt{9 + x^2} \text{ and } y = \sqrt{9 + x^2}\right)$. For example, if $x = 4$, then equation (2) is satisfied for $y = 5$ and for $y = -5$. So equation (2) does not specify a function.

Matched Problem 2 Determine which of the following equations specify functions with independent variable x.

(A) $y^2 - x^4 = 9$, x a real number (B) $3y - 2x = 3$, x a real number

Since the graph of an equation is the graph of all the ordered pairs that satisfy the equation, it is very easy to determine whether an equation specifies a function by examining its graph. The graphs of the two equations we considered in Example 2 are shown in Figure 5.

In Figure 5A, notice that any vertical line will intersect the graph of the equation $4y - 3x = 8$ in exactly one point. This shows that to each x value, there corresponds

---

*Recall that each positive real number N has two square roots: $\sqrt{N}$, the principal square root; and $-\sqrt{N}$, the negative of the principal square root (see Appendix A, Section A.6).

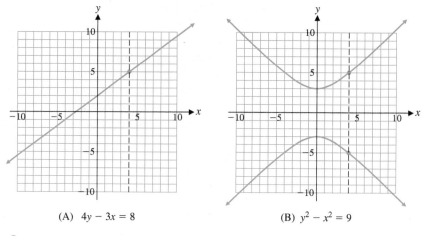

(A) $4y - 3x = 8$ (B) $y^2 - x^2 = 9$

Figure 5

exactly one y value, confirming our conclusion that this equation specifies a function. On the other hand, Figure 5B shows that there exist vertical lines that intersect the graph of $y^2 - x^2 = 9$ in two points. This indicates that there exist x values to which there correspond two different y values and verifies our conclusion that this equation does not specify a function. These observations are generalized in Theorem 1.

THEOREM 1   Vertical-Line Test for a Function

An equation specifies a function if each vertical line in the coordinate system passes through, at most, one point on the graph of the equation.

If any vertical line passes through two or more points on the graph of an equation, then the equation does not specify a function.

The function graphed in Figure 5A is an example of a *linear function*. The vertical-line test implies that equations of the form $y = mx + b$, where $m \neq 0$, specify functions; they are called **linear functions**. Similarly, equations of the form $y = b$ specify functions; they are called **constant functions**, and their graphs are horizontal lines. The vertical-line test implies that equations of the form $x = a$ do not specify functions; note that the graph of $x = a$ is a vertical line.

In Example 2, the domains were explicitly stated along with the given equations. In many cases, this will not be done. Unless stated to the contrary, we shall adhere to the following convention regarding domains and ranges for functions specified by equations:

> If a function is specified by an equation and the domain is not indicated, then we assume that the domain is the set of all real-number replacements of the independent variable (inputs) that produce real values for the dependent variable (outputs). The range is the set of all outputs corresponding to input values.

EXAMPLE 3   Finding a Domain   Find the domain of the function specified by the equation $y = \sqrt{4 - x}$, assuming that x is the independent variable.

SOLUTION   For y to be real, $4 - x$ must be greater than or equal to 0; that is,

$$4 - x \geq 0$$
$$-x \geq -4$$
$$x \leq 4 \qquad \text{Sense of inequality reverses when both sides are divided by } -1.$$

Domain: $x \leq 4$ (inequality notation) or $(-\infty, 4]$ (interval notation)

Matched Problem 3   Find the domain of the function specified by the equation $y = \sqrt{x - 2}$, assuming x is the independent variable.

Function Notation

We have seen that a function involves two sets, a domain and a range, and a correspondence that assigns to each element in the domain exactly one element in the range. Just as we use letters as names for numbers, now we will use letters as names for functions. For example, f and g may be used to name the functions specified by the equations $y = 2x + 1$ and $y = x^2 + 2x - 3$:

$$f: \quad y = 2x + 1$$
$$g: \quad y = x^2 + 2x - 3 \tag{3}$$

If x represents an element in the domain of a function f, then we frequently use the symbol

$$f(x)$$

in place of y to designate the number in the range of the function f to which x is paired (Fig. 6). This symbol does *not* represent the product of f and x. The symbol $f(x)$ is read as "f of x," "f at x," or "the value of f at x." Whenever we write $y = f(x)$, we assume that the variable x is an independent variable and that both y and $f(x)$ are dependent variables.

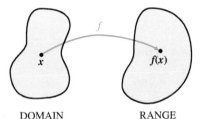

DOMAIN   RANGE

Figure 6

Using function notation, we can now write functions f and g in equation (3) as

$$f(x) = 2x + 1 \quad \text{and} \quad g(x) = x^2 + 2x - 3$$

Let us find $f(3)$ and $g(-5)$. To find $f(3)$, we replace x with 3 wherever x occurs in $f(x) = 2x + 1$ and evaluate the right side:

$$f(x) = 2x + 1$$
$$f(3) = 2 \cdot 3 + 1$$
$$= 6 + 1 = 7 \quad \text{For input 3, the output is 7.}$$

Therefore,

$$f(3) = 7 \quad \text{The function } f \text{ assigns the range value 7 to the domain value 3.}$$

To find $g(-5)$, we replace each x by -5 in $g(x) = x^2 + 2x - 3$ and evaluate the right side:

$$g(x) = x^2 + 2x - 3$$
$$g(-5) = (-5)^2 + 2(-5) - 3$$
$$= 25 - 10 - 3 = 12 \quad \text{For input } -5, \text{ the output is 12.}$$

Therefore,

$$g(-5) = 12 \quad \text{The function } g \text{ assigns the range value 12 to the domain value } -5.$$

It is very important to understand and remember the definition of $f(x)$:

For any element x in the domain of the function f, the symbol $f(x)$ represents the element in the range of f corresponding to x in the domain of f. If x is an input value, then $f(x)$ is the corresponding output value. If x is an element that is not in the domain of f, then f is *not defined at x* and $f(x)$ *does not exist.*

EXAMPLE 4 Function Evaluation For $f(x) = 12/(x - 2)$, $g(x) = 1 - x^2$, and $h(x) = \sqrt{x - 1}$, evaluate:

(A) $f(6)$ (B) $g(-2)$ (C) $h(-2)$ (D) $f(0) + g(1) - h(10)$

SOLUTION

(A) $f(6) = \dfrac{12 \quad *}{6 - 2} = \dfrac{12}{4} = 3$

(B) $g(-2) = 1 - (-2)^2 = 1 - 4 = -3$

---

*Dashed boxes are used throughout the book to represent steps that are usually performed mentally.

(C) $h(-2) = \sqrt{-2 - 1} = \sqrt{-3}$

But $\sqrt{-3}$ is not a real number. Since we have agreed to restrict the domain of a function to values of x that produce real values for the function, -2 is not in the domain of h, and $h(-2)$ does not exist.

(D) $f(0) + g(1) - h(10) = \dfrac{12}{0 - 2} + (1 - 1^2) - \sqrt{10 - 1}$

$$= \dfrac{12}{-2} + 0 - \sqrt{9}$$

$$= -6 - 3 = -9$$

Matched Problem 4 Use the functions in Example 4 to find

(A) $f(-2)$ (B) $g(-1)$ (C) $h(-8)$ (D) $\dfrac{f(3)}{h(5)}$

EXAMPLE 5 Finding Domains Find the domains of functions f, g, and h:

$$f(x) = \dfrac{12}{x - 2} \qquad g(x) = 1 - x^2 \qquad h(x) = \sqrt{x - 1}$$

SOLUTION *Domain of f:* $12/(x - 2)$ represents a real number for all replacements of x by real numbers except for $x = 2$ (division by 0 is not defined). Thus, $f(2)$ does not exist, and the domain of f is the set of all real numbers except 2. We often indicate this by writing

$$f(x) = \dfrac{12}{x - 2} \qquad x \neq 2$$

Domain of g: The domain is R, the set of all real numbers, since $1 - x^2$ represents a real number for all replacements of x by real numbers.

Domain of h: The domain is the set of all real numbers x such that $\sqrt{x - 1}$ is a real number, so

$$x - 1 \geq 0$$

$$x \geq 1 \quad \text{or, in interval notation,} \quad [1, \infty)$$

Matched Problem 5 Find the domains of functions F, G, and H:

$$F(x) = x^2 - 3x + 1 \qquad G(x) = \dfrac{5}{x + 3} \qquad H(x) = \sqrt{2 - x}$$

In addition to evaluating functions at specific numbers, it is important to be able to evaluate functions at expressions that involve one or more variables. For example, the **difference quotient**

$$\dfrac{f(x + h) - f(x)}{h} \qquad x \text{ and } x + h \text{ in the domain of } f, h \neq 0$$

is studied extensively in calculus.

CONCEPTUAL INSIGHT

In algebra, you learned to use parentheses for grouping variables. For example,

$$2(x + h) = 2x + 2h$$

Now we are using parentheses in the function symbol $f(x)$. For example, if $f(x) = x^2$, then

$$f(x + h) = (x + h)^2 = x^2 + 2xh + h^2$$

Note that $f(x) + f(h) = x^2 + h^2 \neq f(x + h)$. That is, the function name f does not distribute across the grouped variables $(x + h)$, as the "2" does in $2(x + h)$. (see Appendix A, Section A.2).

EXAMPLE 6 Using Function Notation For $f(x) = x^2 - 2x + 7$, find

(A) $f(a)$

(B) $f(a + h)$

(C) $f(a + h) - f(a)$

(D) $\dfrac{f(a + h) - f(a)}{h}$, $h \neq 0$

SOLUTION

(A) $f(a) = a^2 - 2a + 7$

(B) $f(a + h) = (a + h)^2 - 2(a + h) + 7 = a^2 + 2ah + h^2 - 2a - 2h + 7$

(C) $f(a + h) - f(a) = (a^2 + 2ah + h^2 - 2a - 2h + 7) - (a^2 - 2a + 7)$

$\qquad = 2ah + h^2 - 2h$

(D) $\dfrac{f(a + h) - f(a)}{h} = \dfrac{2ah + h^2 - 2h}{h} = \dfrac{h(2a + h - 2)}{h}$ Because $h \neq 0$, $\dfrac{h}{h} = 1$.

$\qquad = 2a + h - 2$

Matched Problem 6 Repeat Example 6 for $f(x) = x^2 - 4x + 9$.

Applications

We now turn to the important concepts of **break-even** and **profit–loss** analysis, which we will return to a number of times in this book. Any manufacturing company has **costs**, C, and **revenues**, R. The company will have a **loss** if $R < C$, will **break even** if $R = C$, and will have a **profit** if $R > C$. Costs include **fixed costs** such as plant overhead, product design, setup, and promotion; and **variable costs**, which are dependent on the number of items produced at a certain cost per item. In addition, **price–demand** functions, usually established by financial departments using historical data or sampling techniques, play an important part in profit–loss analysis. We will let x, the number of units manufactured and sold, represent the independent variable. Cost functions, revenue functions, profit functions, and price–demand functions are often stated in the following forms, where a, b, m, and n are constants determined from the context of a particular problem:

Cost Function

$$C = (\text{fixed costs}) + (\text{variable costs})$$
$$= a + bx$$

Price–Demand Function

$$p = m - nx \quad \text{x is the number of items that can be sold at \$$p$ per item.}$$

Revenue Function

$$R = (\text{number of items sold}) \times (\text{price per item})$$
$$= xp = x(m - nx)$$

Profit Function

$$P = R - C$$
$$= x(m - nx) - (a + bx)$$

Example 7 and Matched Problem 7 explore the relationships among the algebraic definition of a function, the numerical values of the function, and the graphical representation of the function. The interplay among algebraic, numeric, and graphic viewpoints is an important aspect of our treatment of functions and their use. In Example 7, we will see how a function can be used to describe data from the real world, a process that is often referred to as *mathematical modeling*. Note that the domain of such a function is determined by practical considerations within the problem.

EXAMPLE 7 Price–Demand and Revenue Modeling   A manufacturer of a popular digital camera wholesales the camera to retail outlets throughout the United States. Using statistical methods, the financial department in the company produced the price–demand data in Table 4, where p is the wholesale price per camera at which x million cameras are sold. Notice that as the price goes down, the number sold goes up.

Table 4 **Price–Demand**

x (millions)	$p(\$)$
2	87
5	68
8	53
12	37

Using special analytical techniques (regression analysis), an analyst obtained the following price–demand function to model the Table 4 data:

$$p(x) = 94.8 - 5x \qquad 1 \le x \le 15 \qquad (4)$$

(A) Plot the data in Table 4. Then sketch a graph of the price–demand function in the same coordinate system.

(B) What is the company's revenue function for this camera, and what is its domain?

(C) Complete Table 5, computing revenues to the nearest million dollars.

(D) Plot the data in Table 5. Then sketch a graph of the revenue function using these points.

(E) Plot the revenue function on a graphing calculator.

SOLUTION

(A)

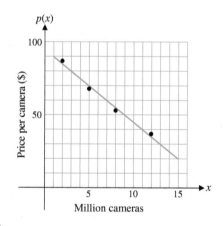

Figure 7 **Price–demand**

In Figure 7, notice that the model approximates the actual data in Table 4, and it is assumed that it gives realistic and useful results for all other values of x between 1 million and 15 million.

(B) $R(x) = xp(x) = x(94.8 - 5x)$ million dollars
Domain: $1 \le x \le 15$
[Same domain as the price–demand function, equation (4).]

(C)

Table 5 **Revenue**

x (millions)	$R(x)$ (million $\$$)
1	90
3	239
6	389
9	448
12	418
15	297

Table 5 **Revenue**

x (millions)	$R(x)$ (million $\$$)
1	90
3	
6	
9	
12	
15	

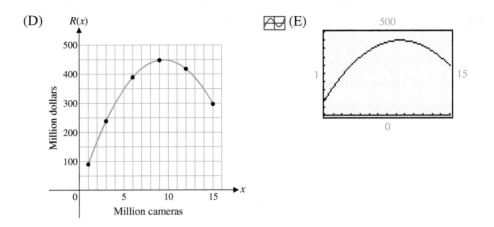

(D) and (E) graphs with axes labeled *R(x)*, Million dollars, Million cameras.

Matched Problem 7 The financial department in Example 7, using statistical techniques, produced the data in Table 6, where $C(x)$ is the cost in millions of dollars for manufacturing and selling x million cameras.

Table 6 **Cost Data**

x (millions)	$C(x)$ (million $)
1	175
5	260
8	305
12	395

Using special analytical techniques (regression analysis), an analyst produced the following cost function to model the Table 6 data:

$$C(x) = 156 + 19.7x \qquad 1 \le x \le 15 \qquad (5)$$

(A) Plot the data in Table 6. Then sketch a graph of equation (5) in the same coordinate system.

(B) Using the revenue function from Example 7(B), what is the company's profit function for this camera, and what is its domain?

(C) Complete Table 7, computing profits to the nearest million dollars.

Table 7 **Profit**

x (millions)	$P(x)$ (million $)
1	−86
3	
6	
9	
12	
15	

(D) Plot the data in Table 7. Then sketch a graph of the profit function using these points.

(E) Plot the profit function on a graphing calculator.

In Problems 1–8, use point-by-point plotting to sketch the graph of each equation.

1. $y = x + 1$

2. $x = y + 1$

3. $x = y^2$

4. $y = x^2$

5. $y = x^3$

6. $x = y^3$

7. $xy = -6$

8. $xy = 12$

Indicate whether each table in Problems 9–14 specifies a function.

9.

Domain	Range
3 →	0
5 →	1
7 →	2

10.

Domain	Range
−1 →	5
−2 →	7
−3 →	9

11.

Domain	Range
3 →	5
	6
4 →	7
5 →	8

12.

Domain	Range
8 →	0
9 →	1
	2
10 →	3

13.

Domain	Range
3 →	
6 →	5
9 →	
12 →	6

14.

Domain	Range
−2 →	
−1 →	
0 →	6
1 →	

Indicate whether each graph in Problems 15–20 specifies a function.

15.

16.

17.

18.

19.

20.

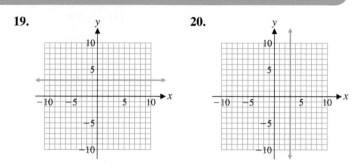

In Problems 21–28, each equation specifies a function with independent variable x. Determine whether the function is linear, constant, or neither.

21. $y - 2x = 7$

22. $y = 10 - 3x$

23. $xy - 4 = 0$

24. $x^2 - y = 8$

25. $y = 5x + \frac{1}{2}(7 - 10x)$

26. $y = \frac{2 + x}{3} + \frac{2 - x}{3}$

27. $3x + 4y = 5$

28. $9x - 2y + 6 = 0$

In Problems 29–36, use point-by-point plotting to sketch the graph of each function.

29. $f(x) = 1 - x$

30. $f(x) = \frac{x}{2} - 3$

31. $f(x) = x^2 - 1$

32. $f(x) = 3 - x^2$

33. $f(x) = 4 - x^3$

34. $f(x) = x^3 - 2$

35. $f(x) = \frac{8}{x}$

36. $f(x) = \frac{-6}{x}$

In Problems 37 and 38, the three points in the table are on the graph of the indicated function f. Do these three points provide sufficient information for you to sketch the graph of $y = f(x)$? Add more points to the table until you are satisfied that your sketch is a good representation of the graph of $y = f(x)$ for $-5 \le x \le 5$.

37.

x	−1	0	1
$f(x)$	−1	0	1

$f(x) = \dfrac{2x}{x^2 + 1}$

38.

x	0	1	2
$f(x)$	0	1	2

$f(x) = \dfrac{3x^2}{x^2 + 2}$

In Problems 39–46, use the following graph of a function f to determine x or y to the nearest integer, as indicated. Some problems may have more than one answer.

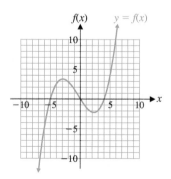

39. $y = f(-5)$ **40.** $y = f(4)$

41. $y = f(5)$ **42.** $y = f(-2)$

43. $0 = f(x)$ **44.** $3 = f(x), x < 0$

45. $-4 = f(x)$ **46.** $4 = f(x)$

In Problems 47–52, find the domain of each function.

47. $F(x) = 2x^3 - x^2 + 3$ **48.** $H(x) = 7 - 2x^2 - x^4$

49. $f(x) = \dfrac{x - 2}{x + 4}$ **50.** $g(x) = \dfrac{x + 1}{x - 2}$

51. $g(x) = \sqrt{7 - x}$ **52.** $F(x) = \dfrac{1}{\sqrt{5 + x}}$

In Problems 53–60, does the equation specify a function with independent variable x? If so, find the domain of the function. If not, find a value of x to which there corresponds more than one value of y.

53. $2x + 5y = 10$ **54.** $6x - 7y = 21$

55. $y(x + y) = 4$ **56.** $x(x + y) = 4$

57. $x^{-3} + y^3 = 27$ **58.** $x^2 + y^2 = 9$

59. $x^3 - y^2 = 0$ **60.** $\sqrt{x} - y^3 = 0$

In Problems 61–72, find and simplify the expression if $f(x) = x^2 - 4$.

61. $f(4)$ **62.** $f(-5)$

63. $f(x + 1)$ **64.** $f(x - 2)$

65. $f(-6x)$ **66.** $f(10x)$

67. $f(x^3)$ **68.** $f(\sqrt{x})$

69. $f(2) + f(h)$ **70.** $f(-3) + f(h)$

71. $f(2 + h)$ **72.** $f(-3 + h)$

73. $f(2 + h) - f(2)$ **74.** $f(-3 + h) - f(-3)$

In Problems 75–80, find and simplify each of the following, assuming $h \neq 0$ in (C).

(A) $f(x + h)$

(B) $f(x + h) - f(x)$

(C) $\dfrac{f(x + h) - f(x)}{h}$

75. $f(x) = 4x - 3$ **76.** $f(x) = -3x + 9$

77. $f(x) = 4x^2 - 7x + 6$ **78.** $f(x) = 3x^2 + 5x - 8$

79. $f(x) = x(20 - x)$ **80.** $f(x) = x(x + 40)$

Problems 81–84 refer to the area A and perimeter P of a rectangle with length l and width w (see the figure).

$$A = lw$$
$$P = 2l + 2w$$

w

l

81. The area of a rectangle is 25 sq in. Express the perimeter $P(w)$ as a function of the width w, and state the domain of this function.

82. The area of a rectangle is 81 sq in. Express the perimeter $P(l)$ as a function of the length l, and state the domain of this function.

83. The perimeter of a rectangle is 100 m. Express the area $A(l)$ as a function of the length l, and state the domain of this function.

84. The perimeter of a rectangle is 160 m. Express the area $A(w)$ as a function of the width w, and state the domain of this function.

Applications

85. Price–demand. A company manufactures memory chips for microcomputers. Its marketing research department, using statistical techniques, collected the data shown in Table 8, where p is the wholesale price per chip at which x million chips can be sold. Using special analytical techniques (regression analysis), an analyst produced the following price–demand function to model the data:

$$p(x) = 75 - 3x \qquad 1 \leq x \leq 20$$

Table 8 **Price–Demand**

x (millions)	p($)
1	72
4	63
9	48
14	33
20	15

(A) Plot the data points in Table 8, and sketch a graph of the price–demand function in the same coordinate system.

(B) What would be the estimated price per chip for a demand of 7 million chips? For a demand of 11 million chips?

86. Price–demand. A company manufactures notebook computers. Its marketing research department, using statistical techniques, collected the data shown in Table 9, where p is the wholesale price per computer at which x thousand computers can be sold. Using special analytical techniques (regression analysis), an analyst produced the following price–demand function to model the data:

$$p(x) = 2{,}000 - 60x \qquad 1 \leq x \leq 25$$

Table 9 **Price–Demand**

x (thousands)	p($)
1	1,940
8	1,520
16	1,040
21	740
25	500

(A) Plot the data points in Table 9, and sketch a graph of the price–demand function in the same coordinate system.

(B) What would be the estimated price per computer for a demand of 11,000 computers? For a demand of 18,000 computers?

87. Revenue.

(A) Using the price–demand function

$$p(x) = 75 - 3x \qquad 1 \le x \le 20$$

from Problem 85, write the company's revenue function and indicate its domain.

(B) Complete Table 10, computing revenues to the nearest million dollars.

Table 10 **Revenue**

x (millions)	R(x) (million $)
1	72
4	
8	
12	
16	
20	

(C) Plot the points from part (B) and sketch a graph of the revenue function using these points. Choose millions for the units on the horizontal and vertical axes.

88. Revenue.

(A) Using the price–demand function

$$p(x) = 2,000 - 60x \qquad 1 \le x \le 25$$

from Problem 86, write the company's revenue function and indicate its domain.

(B) Complete Table 11, computing revenues to the nearest thousand dollars.

Table 11 **Revenue**

x (thousands)	R(x) (thousand $)
1	1,940
5	
10	
15	
20	
25	

(C) Plot the points from part (B) and sketch a graph of the revenue function using these points. Choose thousands for the units on the horizontal and vertical axes.

89. Profit. The financial department for the company in Problems 85 and 87 established the following cost function for producing and selling x million memory chips:

$$C(x) = 125 + 16x \text{ million dollars}$$

(A) Write a profit function for producing and selling x million memory chips and indicate its domain.

(B) Complete Table 12, computing profits to the nearest million dollars.

Table 12 **Profit**

x (millions)	P(x) (million $)
1	−69
4	
8	
12	
16	
20	

(C) Plot the points in part (B) and sketch a graph of the profit function using these points.

90. Profit. The financial department for the company in Problems 86 and 88 established the following cost function for producing and selling x thousand notebook computers:

$$C(x) = 4,000 + 500x \text{ thousand dollars}$$

(A) Write a profit function for producing and selling x thousand notebook computers and indicate its domain.

(B) Complete Table 13, computing profits to the nearest thousand dollars.

Table 13 **Profit**

x (thousands)	P(x) (thousand $)
1	−2,560
5	
10	
15	
20	
25	

(C) Plot the points in part (B) and sketch a graph of the profit function using these points.

91. Packaging. A candy box will be made out of a piece of cardboard that measures 8 by 12 in. Equal-sized squares x inches on a side will be cut out of each corner, and then the ends and sides will be folded up to form a rectangular box.

(A) Express the volume of the box $V(x)$ in terms of x.

(B) What is the domain of the function V (determined by the physical restrictions)?

(C) Complete Table 14.

Table 14 **Volume**

x	V(x)
1	
2	
3	

(D) Plot the points in part (C) and sketch a graph of the volume function using these points.

92. Packaging. Refer to Problem 91.

(A) Table 15 shows the volume of the box for some values of x between 1 and 2. Use these values to estimate to one decimal place the value of x between 1 and 2 that would produce a box with a volume of 65 cu in.

Table 15 **Volume**

x	$V(x)$
1.1	62.524
1.2	64.512
1.3	65.988
1.4	66.976
1.5	67.5
1.6	67.584
1.7	67.252

(B) Describe how you could refine this table to estimate x to two decimal places.

(C) Carry out the refinement you described in part (B) and approximate x to two decimal places.

93. Packaging. Refer to Problems 91 and 92.

(A) Examine the graph of $V(x)$ from Problem 91D and discuss the possible locations of other values of x that would produce a box with a volume of 65 cu in.

(B) Construct a table like Table 15 to estimate any such value to one decimal place.

(C) Refine the table you constructed in part (B) to provide an approximation to two decimal places.

94. Packaging. A parcel delivery service will only deliver packages with length plus girth (distance around) not exceeding 108 in. A rectangular shipping box with square ends x inches on a side is to be used.

Length

x

Girth

(A) If the full 108 in. is to be used, express the volume of the box $V(x)$ in terms of x.

(B) What is the domain of the function V (determined by the physical restrictions)?

(C) Complete Table 16.

Table 16 **Volume**

x	$V(x)$
5	
10	
15	
20	
25	

(D) Plot the points in part (C) and sketch a graph of the volume function using these points.

95. Muscle contraction. In a study of the speed of muscle contraction in frogs under various loads, British biophysicist A. W. Hill determined that the weight w (in grams) placed on the muscle and the speed of contraction v (in centimeters per second) are approximately related by an equation of the form

$$(w + a)(v + b) = c$$

where a, b, and c are constants. Suppose that for a certain muscle, $a = 15$, $b = 1$, and $c = 90$. Express v as a function of w. Find the speed of contraction if a weight of 16 g is placed on the muscle.

96. Politics. The percentage s of seats in the House of Representatives won by Democrats and the percentage v of votes cast for Democrats (when expressed as decimal fractions) are related by the equation

$$5v - 2s = 1.4 \qquad 0 < s < 1, \quad 0.28 < v < 0.68$$

(A) Express v as a function of s and find the percentage of votes required for the Democrats to win 51% of the seats.

(B) Express s as a function of v and find the percentage of seats won if Democrats receive 51% of the votes.

Answers to Matched Problems

1. (A)   (B)

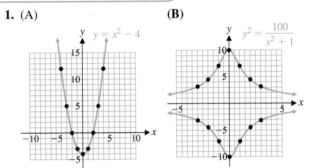

2. (A) Does not specify a function
   (B) Specifies a function
3. $x \geq 2$ (inequality notation) or $[2, \infty)$ (interval notation)
4. (A) -3 (B) 0 (C) Does not exist   (D) 6
5. Domain of F: R; domain of G: all real numbers except -3; domain of H: $x \leq 2$ (inequality notation) or $(-\infty, 2]$ (interval notation)
6. (A) $a^2 - 4a + 9$ (B) $a^2 + 2ah + h^2 - 4a - 4h + 9$
   (C) $2ah + h^2 - 4h$ (D) $2a + h - 4$
7. (A)

(B) $P(x) = R(x) - C(x)$

$= x(94.8 - 5x) - (156 + 19.7x);$

domain: $1 \le x \le 15$

(C) Table 7 **Profit**

x (millions)	$P(x)$ (million $)
1	−86
3	24
6	115
9	115
12	25
15	−155

(D)

(E)

1.2 Elementary Functions: Graphs and Transformations

- A Beginning Library of Elementary Functions
- Vertical and Horizontal Shifts
- Reflections, Stretches, and Shrinks
- Piecewise-Defined Functions

Each of the functions

$$g(x) = x^2 - 4 \qquad h(x) = (x - 4)^2 \qquad k(x) = -4x^2$$

can be expressed in terms of the function $f(x) = x^2$:

$$g(x) = f(x) - 4 \qquad h(x) = f(x - 4) \qquad k(x) = -4f(x)$$

In this section, we will see that the graphs of functions g, h, and k are closely related to the graph of function f. Insight gained by understanding these relationships will help us analyze and interpret the graphs of many different functions.

A Beginning Library of Elementary Functions

As you progress through this book, you will repeatedly encounter a small number of elementary functions. We will identify these functions, study their basic properties, and include them in a library of elementary functions (see the inside front cover). This library will become an important addition to your mathematical toolbox and can be used in any course or activity where mathematics is applied.

We begin by placing six basic functions in our library.

DEFINITION   Basic Elementary Functions

$$f(x) = x \qquad \text{Identity function}$$
$$h(x) = x^2 \qquad \text{Square function}$$
$$m(x) = x^3 \qquad \text{Cube function}$$
$$n(x) = \sqrt{x} \qquad \text{Square root function}$$
$$p(x) = \sqrt[3]{x} \qquad \text{Cube root function}$$
$$g(x) = |x| \qquad \text{Absolute value function}$$

These elementary functions can be evaluated by hand for certain values of x and with a calculator for all values of x for which they are defined.

EXAMPLE 1   Evaluating Basic Elementary Functions   Evaluate each basic elementary function at

(A) $x = 64$ (B) $x = -12.75$

Round any approximate values to four decimal places.

SOLUTION

(A) $f(64) = 64$

$h(64) = 64^2 = 4{,}096$ Use a calculator.

$m(64) = 64^3 = 262{,}144$ Use a calculator.

$n(64) = \sqrt{64} = 8$

$p(64) = \sqrt[3]{64} = 4$

$g(64) = |64| = 64$

(B) $f(-12.75) = -12.75$

$h(-12.75) = (-12.75)^2 = 162.5625$ Use a calculator.

$m(-12.75) = (-12.75)^3 \approx -2{,}072.6719$ Use a calculator.

$n(-12.75) = \sqrt{-12.75}$ Not a real number.

$p(-12.75) = \sqrt[3]{-12.75} \approx -2.3362$ Use a calculator.

$g(-12.75) = |-12.75| = 12.75$

Matched Problem 1 Evaluate each basic elementary function at

(A) $x = 729$ (B) $x = -5.25$

Round any approximate values to four decimal places.

Remark—Most computers and graphing calculators use ABS(x) to represent the absolute value function. The following representation can also be useful:

$$|x| = \sqrt{x^2}$$

Figure 1 shows the graph, range, and domain of each of the basic elementary functions.

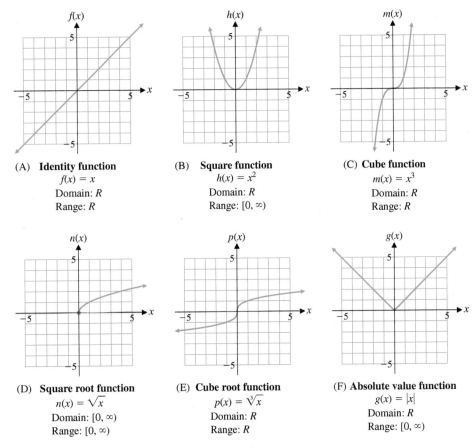

(A) **Identity function**
$f(x) = x$
Domain: R
Range: R

(B) **Square function**
$h(x) = x^2$
Domain: R
Range: $[0, \infty)$

(C) **Cube function**
$m(x) = x^3$
Domain: R
Range: R

(D) **Square root function**
$n(x) = \sqrt{x}$
Domain: $[0, \infty)$
Range: $[0, \infty)$

(E) **Cube root function**
$p(x) = \sqrt[3]{x}$
Domain: R
Range: R

(F) **Absolute value function**
$g(x) = |x|$
Domain: R
Range: $[0, \infty)$

Figure 1 **Some basic functions and their graphs***

Note: Letters used to designate these functions may vary from context to context; R is the set of all real numbers.

> **CONCEPTUAL INSIGHT**
>
> **Absolute Value** In beginning algebra, absolute value is often interpreted as distance from the origin on a real number line (see Appendix A, Section A.1).
>
> $$\text{distance} = 6 = -(-6) \quad \text{distance} = 5$$
>
> If $x < 0$, then $-x$ is the *positive* distance from the origin to x, and if $x > 0$, then x is the positive distance from the origin to x. Thus,
>
> $$|x| = \begin{cases} -x & \text{if } x < 0 \\ x & \text{if } x \geq 0 \end{cases}$$

Vertical and Horizontal Shifts

If a new function is formed by performing an operation on a given function, then the graph of the new function is called a **transformation** of the graph of the original function. For example, graphs of $y = f(x) + k$ and $y = f(x + h)$ are transformations of the graph of $y = f(x)$.

Explore and Discuss 1   Let $f(x) = x^2$.

(A) Graph $y = f(x) + k$ for $k = -4, 0$, and 2 simultaneously in the same coordinate system. Describe the relationship between the graph of $y = f(x)$ and the graph of $y = f(x) + k$ for any real number k.

(B) Graph $y = f(x + h)$ for $h = -4, 0$, and 2 simultaneously in the same coordinate system. Describe the relationship between the graph of $y = f(x)$ and the graph of $y = f(x + h)$ for any real number h.

EXAMPLE 2   Vertical and Horizontal Shifts

(A) How are the graphs of $y = |x| + 4$ and $y = |x| - 5$ related to the graph of $y = |x|$? Confirm your answer by graphing all three functions simultaneously in the same coordinate system.

(B) How are the graphs of $y = |x + 4|$ and $y = |x - 5|$ related to the graph of $y = |x|$? Confirm your answer by graphing all three functions simultaneously in the same coordinate system.

SOLUTION

(A) The graph of $y = |x| + 4$ is the same as the graph of $y = |x|$ shifted upward 4 units, and the graph of $y = |x| - 5$ is the same as the graph of $y = |x|$ shifted downward 5 units. Figure 2 confirms these conclusions. [It appears that the graph of $y = f(x) + k$ is the graph of $y = f(x)$ shifted up if k is positive and down if k is negative.]

(B) The graph of $y = |x + 4|$ is the same as the graph of $y = |x|$ shifted to the left 4 units, and the graph of $y = |x - 5|$ is the same as the graph of $y = |x|$ shifted to the right 5 units. Figure 3 confirms these conclusions. [It appears that the graph of $y = f(x + h)$ is the graph of $y = f(x)$ shifted right if h is negative and left if h is positive—the opposite of what you might expect.]

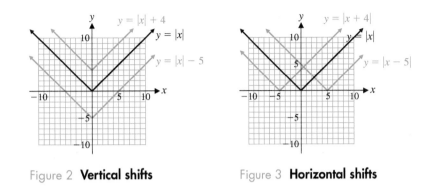

Figure 2 **Vertical shifts**   Figure 3 **Horizontal shifts**

Matched Problem 2

(A) How are the graphs of $y = \sqrt{x} + 5$ and $y = \sqrt{x} - 4$ related to the graph of $y = \sqrt{x}$? Confirm your answer by graphing all three functions simultaneously in the same coordinate system.

(B) How are the graphs of $y = \sqrt{x + 5}$ and $y = \sqrt{x - 4}$ related to the graph of $y = \sqrt{x}$? Confirm your answer by graphing all three functions simultaneously in the same coordinate system.

Comparing the graphs of $y = f(x) + k$ with the graph of $y = f(x)$, we see that the graph of $y = f(x) + k$ can be obtained from the graph of $y = f(x)$ by **vertically translating** (shifting) the graph of the latter upward k units if k is positive and downward $|k|$ units if k is negative. Comparing the graphs of $y = f(x + h)$ with the graph of $y = f(x)$, we see that the graph of $y = f(x + h)$ can be obtained from the graph of $y = f(x)$ by **horizontally translating** (shifting) the graph of the latter h units to the left if h is positive and $|h|$ units to the right if h is negative.

EXAMPLE 3   Vertical and Horizontal Translations (Shifts)   The graphs in Figure 4 are either horizontal or vertical shifts of the graph of $f(x) = x^2$. Write appropriate equations for functions H, G, M, and N in terms of f.

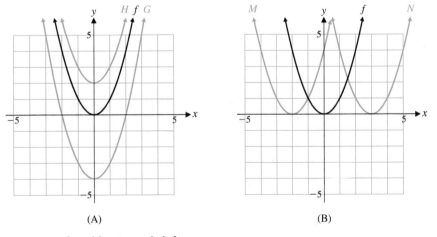

(A)   (B)

Figure 4 **Vertical and horizontal shifts**

SOLUTION Functions H and G are vertical shifts given by

$$H(x) = x^2 + 2 \qquad G(x) = x^2 - 4$$

Functions M and N are horizontal shifts given by

$$M(x) = (x + 2)^2 \qquad N(x) = (x - 3)^2$$

Matched Problem 3 The graphs in Figure 5 are either horizontal or vertical shifts of the graph of $f(x) = \sqrt[3]{x}$. Write appropriate equations for functions H, G, M, and N in terms of f.

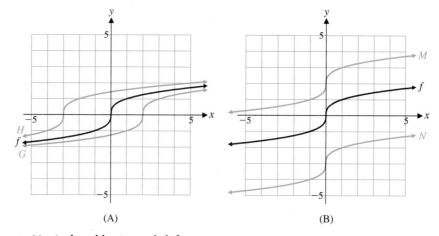

(A)   (B)

Figure 5 **Vertical and horizontal shifts**

Reflections, Stretches, and Shrinks

We now investigate how the graph of $y = Af(x)$ is related to the graph of $y = f(x)$ for different real numbers A.

Explore and Discuss 2 (A) Graph $y = Ax^2$ for $A = 1, 4$, and $\frac{1}{4}$ simultaneously in the same coordinate system.

(B) Graph $y = Ax^2$ for $A = -1, -4$, and $-\frac{1}{4}$ simultaneously in the same coordinate system.

(C) Describe the relationship between the graph of $h(x) = x^2$ and the graph of $G(x) = Ax^2$ for any real number A.

Comparing $y = Af(x)$ to $y = f(x)$, we see that the graph of $y = Af(x)$ can be obtained from the graph of $y = f(x)$ by multiplying each ordinate value of the latter by A. The result is a **vertical stretch** of the graph of $y = f(x)$ if $A > 1$, a **vertical shrink** of the graph of $y = f(x)$ if $0 < A < 1$, and a **reflection in the x axis** if $A = -1$. If A is a negative number other than -1, then the result is a combination of a reflection in the x axis and either a vertical stretch or a vertical shrink.

EXAMPLE 4   Reflections, Stretches, and Shrinks

(A) How are the graphs of $y = 2|x|$ and $y = 0.5|x|$ related to the graph of $y = |x|$? Confirm your answer by graphing all three functions simultaneously in the same coordinate system.

(B) How is the graph of $y = -2|x|$ related to the graph of $y = |x|$? Confirm your answer by graphing both functions simultaneously in the same coordinate system.

SOLUTION

(A) The graph of $y = 2|x|$ is a vertical stretch of the graph of $y = |x|$ by a factor of 2, and the graph of $y = 0.5|x|$ is a vertical shrink of the graph of $y = |x|$ by a factor of 0.5. Figure 6 confirms this conclusion.

(B) The graph of $y = -2|x|$ is a reflection in the x axis and a vertical stretch of the graph of $y = |x|$. Figure 7 confirms this conclusion.

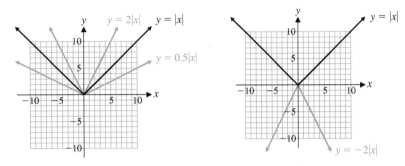

Figure 6 **Vertical stretch and shrink**   Figure 7 **Reflection and vertical stretch**

Matched Problem 4

(A) How are the graphs of $y = 2x$ and $y = 0.5x$ related to the graph of $y = x$? Confirm your answer by graphing all three functions simultaneously in the same coordinate system.

(B) How is the graph of $y = -0.5x$ related to the graph of $y = x$? Confirm your answer by graphing both functions in the same coordinate system.

The various transformations considered above are summarized in the following box for easy reference:

SUMMARY Graph Transformations

Vertical Translation:

$$y = f(x) + k \quad \begin{cases} k > 0 & \text{Shift graph of } y = f(x) \text{ up } k \text{ units.} \\ k < 0 & \text{Shift graph of } y = f(x) \text{ down } |k| \text{ units.} \end{cases}$$

Horizontal Translation:

$$y = f(x + h) \quad \begin{cases} h > 0 & \text{Shift graph of } y = f(x) \text{ left } h \text{ units.} \\ h < 0 & \text{Shift graph of } y = f(x) \text{ right } |h| \text{ units.} \end{cases}$$

Reflection:

$$y = -f(x) \quad \text{Reflect the graph of } y = f(x) \text{ in the } x \text{ axis.}$$

Vertical Stretch and Shrink:

$$y = Af(x) \quad \begin{cases} A > 1 & \text{Stretch graph of } y = f(x) \text{ vertically} \\ & \text{by multiplying each ordinate value by } A. \\ 0 < A < 1 & \text{Shrink graph of } y = f(x) \text{ vertically} \\ & \text{by multiplying each ordinate value by } A. \end{cases}$$

Explore and Discuss 3   Explain why applying any of the graph transformations in the summary box to a linear function produces another linear function.

EXAMPLE 5 Combining Graph Transformations Discuss the relationship between the graphs of $y = -|x - 3| + 1$ and $y = |x|$. Confirm your answer by graphing both functions simultaneously in the same coordinate system.

SOLUTION The graph of $y = -|x - 3| + 1$ is a reflection of the graph of $y = |x|$ in the x axis, followed by a horizontal translation of 3 units to the right and a vertical translation of 1 unit upward. Figure 8 confirms this description.

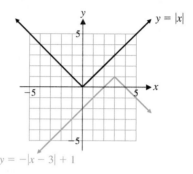

Figure 8 **Combined transformations**

Matched Problem 5 The graph of $y = G(x)$ in Figure 9 involves a reflection and a translation of the graph of $y = x^3$. Describe how the graph of function G is related to the graph of $y = x^3$ and find an equation of the function G.

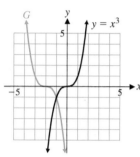

Figure 9 **Combined transformations**

Piecewise-Defined Functions

Earlier we noted that the absolute value of a real number x can be defined as

$$|x| = \begin{cases} -x & \text{if } x < 0 \\ x & \text{if } x \geq 0 \end{cases}$$

Notice that this function is defined by different rules for different parts of its domain. Functions whose definitions involve more than one rule are called **piecewise-defined functions**. Graphing one of these functions involves graphing each rule over the appropriate portion of the domain (Fig. 10). In Figure 10C, notice that an open dot is used to show that the point $(0, -2)$ is not part of the graph and a solid dot is used to show that $(0, 2)$ is part of the graph.

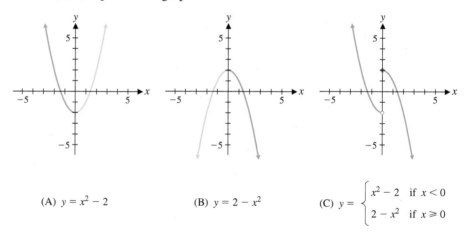

(A) $y = x^2 - 2$ (B) $y = 2 - x^2$ (C) $y = \begin{cases} x^2 - 2 & \text{if } x < 0 \\ 2 - x^2 & \text{if } x \geq 0 \end{cases}$

Figure 10 **Graphing a piecewise-defined function**

EXAMPLE 6 Graphing Piecewise-Defined Functions Graph the piecewise-defined function

$$g(x) = \begin{cases} x + 1 & \text{if } 0 \leq x < 2 \\ 0.5x & \text{if } x \geq 2 \end{cases}$$

SOLUTION If $0 \leq x < 2$, then the first rule applies and the graph of g lies on the line $y = x + 1$ (a vertical shift of the identity function $y = x$). If $x = 0$, then $(0, 1)$ lies on $y = x + 1$; we plot $(0, 1)$ with a solid dot (Fig. 11) because $g(0) = 1$. If $x = 2$, then $(2, 3)$ lies on $y = x + 1$; we plot $(2, 3)$ with an open dot because $g(2) \neq 3$. The line segment from $(0, 1)$ to $(2, 3)$ is the graph of g for $0 \leq x < 2$. If $x \geq 2$, then the second rule applies and the graph of g lies on the line $y = 0.5x$ (a vertical shrink of the identity function $y = x$). If $x = 2$, then $(2, 1)$ lies on the line $y = 0.5x$; we plot $(2, 1)$ with a solid dot because $g(2) = 1$. The portion of $y = 0.5x$ that starts at $(2, 1)$ and extends to the right is the graph of g for $x \geq 2$.

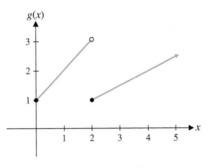

Figure 11

Matched Problem 6 Graph the piecewise-defined function

$$h(x) = \begin{cases} -2x + 4 & \text{if } 0 \leq x \leq 2 \\ x - 1 & \text{if } x > 2 \end{cases}$$

As the next example illustrates, piecewise-defined functions occur naturally in many applications.

EXAMPLE 7 Natural Gas Rates Easton Utilities uses the rates shown in Table 1 to compute the monthly cost of natural gas for each customer. Write a piecewise definition for the cost of consuming x CCF (cubic hundred feet) of natural gas and graph the function.

Table 1 **Charges per Month**

$0.7866 per CCF for the first 5 CCF
$0.4601 per CCF for the next 35 CCF
$0.2508 per CCF for all over 40 CCF

SOLUTION If $C(x)$ is the cost, in dollars, of using x CCF of natural gas in one month, then the first line of Table 1 implies that

$$C(x) = 0.7866x \quad \text{if } 0 \leq x \leq 5$$

Note that $C(5) = 3.933$ is the cost of 5 CCF. If $5 < x \leq 40$, then $x - 5$ represents the amount of gas that cost $0.4601 per CCF, $0.4601(x - 5)$ represents the cost of this gas, and the total cost is

$$C(x) = 3.933 + 0.4601(x - 5)$$

If $x > 40$, then

$$C(x) = 20.0365 + 0.2508(x - 40)$$

where $20.0365 = C(40)$, the cost of the first 40 CCF. Combining all these equations, we have the following piecewise definition for $C(x)$:

$$C(x) = \begin{cases} 0.7866x & \text{if } 0 \leq x \leq 5 \\ 3.933 + 0.4601(x - 5) & \text{if } 5 < x \leq 40 \\ 20.0365 + 0.2508(x - 40) & \text{if } x > 40 \end{cases}$$

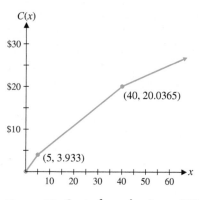

Figure 12 Cost of purchasing *x* CCF of natural gas

To graph *C*, first note that each rule in the definition of *C* represents a transformation of the identity function $f(x) = x$. Graphing each transformation over the indicated interval produces the graph of *C* shown in Figure 12.

Matched Problem 7 Trussville Utilities uses the rates shown in Table 2 to compute the monthly cost of natural gas for residential customers. Write a piecewise definition for the cost of consuming *x* CCF of natural gas and graph the function.

Table 2 **Charges per Month**

$0.7675 per CCF for the first 50 CCF
$0.6400 per CCF for the next 150 CCF
$0.6130 per CCF for all over 200 CCF

Exercises 1.2

In Problems 1–8, find the domain and range of function.

1. $f(x) = 5x - 10$

2. $f(x) = -4x + 12$

3. $f(x) = 15 - \sqrt{x}$

4. $f(x) = 3 + \sqrt{x}$

5. $f(x) = 2|x| + 7$

6. $f(x) = -5|x| + 2$

7. $f(x) = \sqrt[3]{x} + 100$

8. $f(x) = 20 - 10\sqrt[3]{x}$

In Problems 9–24, graph each of the functions using the graphs of functions f and g below.

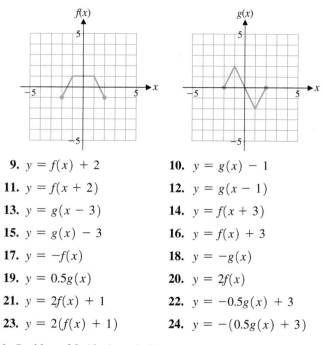

9. $y = f(x) + 2$

10. $y = g(x) - 1$

11. $y = f(x + 2)$

12. $y = g(x - 1)$

13. $y = g(x - 3)$

14. $y = f(x + 3)$

15. $y = g(x) - 3$

16. $y = f(x) + 3$

17. $y = -f(x)$

18. $y = -g(x)$

19. $y = 0.5g(x)$

20. $y = 2f(x)$

21. $y = 2f(x) + 1$

22. $y = -0.5g(x) + 3$

23. $y = 2(f(x) + 1)$

24. $y = -(0.5g(x) + 3)$

In Problems 25–32, describe how the graph of each function is related to the graph of one of the six basic functions in Figure 1 on page 19. Sketch a graph of each function.

25. $g(x) = -|x + 3|$

26. $h(x) = -|x - 5|$

27. $f(x) = (x - 4)^2 - 3$

28. $m(x) = (x + 3)^2 + 4$

29. $f(x) = 7 - \sqrt{x}$

30. $g(x) = -6 + \sqrt[3]{x}$

31. $h(x) = -3|x|$

32. $m(x) = -0.4x^2$

Each graph in Problems 33–40 is the result of applying a sequence of transformations to the graph of one of the six basic functions in Figure 1 on page 19. Identify the basic function and describe the transformation verbally. Write an equation for the given graph.

33.

34.

35.

36.

37.

38.

39.   **40.**

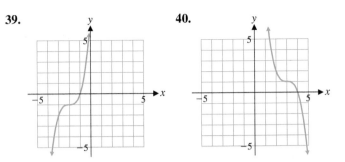

In Problems 41–46, the graph of the function g is formed by applying the indicated sequence of transformations to the given function f. Find an equation for the function g and graph g using $-5 \le x \le 5$ and $-5 \le y \le 5$.

41. The graph of $f(x) = \sqrt{x}$ is shifted 2 units to the right and 3 units down.

42. The graph of $f(x) = \sqrt[3]{x}$ is shifted 3 units to the left and 2 units up.

43. The graph of $f(x) = |x|$ is reflected in the x axis and shifted to the left 3 units.

44. The graph of $f(x) = |x|$ is reflected in the x axis and shifted to the right 1 unit.

45. The graph of $f(x) = x^3$ is reflected in the x axis and shifted 2 units to the right and down 1 unit.

46. The graph of $f(x) = x^2$ is reflected in the x axis and shifted to the left 2 units and up 4 units.

Graph each function in Problems 47–52.

47. $f(x) = \begin{cases} 2 - 2x & \text{if } x < 2 \\ x - 2 & \text{if } x \ge 2 \end{cases}$

48. $g(x) = \begin{cases} x + 1 & \text{if } x < -1 \\ 2 + 2x & \text{if } x \ge -1 \end{cases}$

49. $h(x) = \begin{cases} 5 + 0.5x & \text{if } 0 \le x \le 10 \\ -10 + 2x & \text{if } x > 10 \end{cases}$

50. $h(x) = \begin{cases} 10 + 2x & \text{if } 0 \le x \le 20 \\ 40 + 0.5x & \text{if } x > 20 \end{cases}$

51. $h(x) = \begin{cases} 2x & \text{if } 0 \le x \le 20 \\ x + 20 & \text{if } 20 < x \le 40 \\ 0.5x + 40 & \text{if } x > 40 \end{cases}$

52. $h(x) = \begin{cases} 4x + 20 & \text{if } 0 \le x \le 20 \\ 2x + 60 & \text{if } 20 < x \le 100 \\ -x + 360 & \text{if } x > 100 \end{cases}$

Each of the graphs in Problems 53–58 involves a reflection in the x axis and/or a vertical stretch or shrink of one of the basic functions in Figure 1 on page 19. Identify the basic function, and describe the transformation verbally. Write an equation for the given graph.

53.   **54.**

55.   **56.**

57.   **58.**

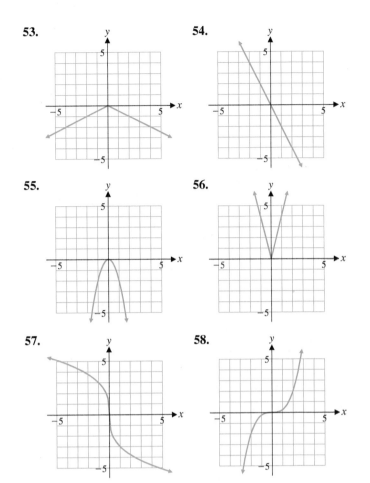

Changing the order in a sequence of transformations may change the final result. Investigate each pair of transformations in Problems 59–64 to determine if reversing their order can produce a different result. Support your conclusions with specific examples and/or mathematical arguments. (The graph of $y = f(-x)$ is the reflection of $y = f(x)$ in the y axis.)

59. Vertical shift; horizontal shift

60. Vertical shift; reflection in y axis

61. Vertical shift; reflection in x axis

62. Vertical shift; vertical stretch

63. Horizontal shift; reflection in y axis

64. Horizontal shift; vertical shrink

Applications

65. *Price–demand.* A retail chain sells DVD players. The retail price $p(x)$ (in dollars) and the weekly demand x for a particular model are related by

$$p(x) = 115 - 4\sqrt{x} \qquad 9 \le x \le 289$$

(A) Describe how the graph of function p can be obtained from the graph of one of the basic functions in Figure 1 on page 19.

(B) Sketch a graph of function p using part (A) as an aid.

66. Price–supply. The manufacturers of the DVD players in Problem 65 are willing to supply x players at a price of $p(x)$ as given by the equation

$$p(x) = 4\sqrt{x} \qquad 9 \leq x \leq 289$$

(A) Describe how the graph of function p can be obtained from the graph of one of the basic functions in Figure 1 on page 19.

(B) Sketch a graph of function p using part (A) as an aid.

67. Hospital costs. Using statistical methods, the financial department of a hospital arrived at the cost equation

$$C(x) = 0.00048(x - 500)^3 + 60,000 \quad 100 \leq x \leq 1,000$$

where $C(x)$ is the cost in dollars for handling x cases per month.

(A) Describe how the graph of function C can be obtained from the graph of one of the basic functions in Figure 1 on page 19.

(B) Sketch a graph of function C using part (A) and a graphing calculator as aids.

68. Price–demand. A company manufactures and sells in-line skates. Its financial department has established the price–demand function

$$p(x) - 190 - 0.013(x - 10)^2 \quad 10 \leq x < 100$$

where $p(x)$ is the price at which x thousand pairs of in-line skates can be sold.

(A) Describe how the graph of function p can be obtained from the graph of one of the basic functions in Figure 1 on page 19.

(B) Sketch a graph of function p using part (A) and a graphing calculator as aids.

69. Electricity rates. Table 3 shows the electricity rates charged by Monroe Utilities in the summer months. The base is a fixed monthly charge, independent of the kWh (kilowatt-hours) used during the month.

(A) Write a piecewise definition of the monthly charge $S(x)$ for a customer who uses x kWh in a summer month.

(B) Graph $S(x)$.

Table 3 **Summer (July–October)**

Base charge, $8.50
First 700 kWh or less at 0.0650/kWh
Over 700 kWh at 0.0900/kWh

70. Electricity rates. Table 4 shows the electricity rates charged by Monroe Utilities in the winter months.

(A) Write a piecewise definition of the monthly charge $W(x)$ for a customer who uses x kWh in a winter month.

Table 4 **Winter (November–June)**

Base charge, $8.50
First 700 kWh or less at 0.0650/kWh
Over 700 kWh at 0.0530/kWh

(B) Graph $W(x)$.

71. State income tax. Table 5 shows a recent state income tax schedule for married couples filing a joint return in Kansas.

(A) Write a piecewise definition for the tax due $T(x)$ on an income of x dollars.

(B) Graph $T(x)$.

(C) Find the tax due on a taxable income of $40,000. Of $70,000.

Table 5 **Kansas State Income Tax**

SCHEDULE I—MARRIED FILING JOINT

If taxable income is

Over	But Not Over	Tax Due Is
$0	$30,000	3.50% of taxable income
$30,000	$60,000	$1,050 plus 6.25% of excess over $30,000
$60,000		$2,925 plus 6.45% of excess over $60,000

72. State income tax. Table 6 shows a recent state income tax schedule for individuals filing a return in Kansas.

Table 6 **Kansas State Income Tax**

SCHEDULE II—SINGLE, HEAD OF HOUSEHOLD, OR MARRIED FILING SEPARATE

If taxable income is

Over	But Not Over	Tax Due Is
$0	$15,000	3.50% of taxable income
$15,000	$30,000	$525 plus 6.25% of excess over $15,000
$30,000		$1,462.50 plus 6.45% of excess over $30,000

(A) Write a piecewise definition for the tax due $T(x)$ on an income of x dollars.

(B) Graph $T(x)$.

(C) Find the tax due on a taxable income of $20,000. Of $35,000.

(D) Would it be better for a married couple in Kansas with two equal incomes to file jointly or separately? Discuss.

73. Human weight. A good approximation of the normal weight of a person 60 inches or taller but not taller than 80 inches is given by $w(x) = 5.5x - 220$, where x is height in inches and $w(x)$ is weight in pounds.

(A) Describe how the graph of function w can be obtained from the graph of one of the basic functions in Figure 1, page 19.

(B) Sketch a graph of function w using part (A) as an aid.

74. Herpetology. The average weight of a particular species of snake is given by $w(x) = 463x^3$, $0.2 \le x \le 0.8$, where x is length in meters and $w(x)$ is weight in grams.

✎ (A) Describe how the graph of function w can be obtained from the graph of one of the basic functions in Figure 1, page 19.

(B) Sketch a graph of function w using part (A) as an aid.

75. Safety research. Under ideal conditions, if a person driving a vehicle slams on the brakes and skids to a stop, the speed of the vehicle $v(x)$ (in miles per hour) is given approximately by $v(x) = C\sqrt{x}$, where x is the length of skid marks (in feet) and C is a constant that depends on the road conditions and the weight of the vehicle. For a particular vehicle, $v(x) = 7.08\sqrt{x}$ and $4 \le x \le 144$.

✎ (A) Describe how the graph of function v can be obtained from the graph of one of the basic functions in Figure 1, page 19.

(B) Sketch a graph of function v using part (A) as an aid.

76. Learning. A production analyst has found that on average it takes a new person $T(x)$ minutes to perform a particular assembly operation after x performances of the operation, where $T(x) = 10 - \sqrt[3]{x}$, $0 \le x \le 125$.

✎ (A) Describe how the graph of function T can be obtained from the graph of one of the basic functions in Figure 1, page 19.

(B) Sketch a graph of function T using part (A) as an aid.

Answers to Matched Problems

1. (A) $f(729) = 729$, $h(729) = 531,441$,
$m(729) = 387,420,489$, $n(729) = 27$, $p(729) = 9$,
$g(729) = 729$

(B) $f(-5.25) = -5.25$, $h(-5.25) = 27.5625$,
$m(-5.25) = -144.7031$, $n(-5.25)$ is not a real number,
$p(-5.25) = -1.7380$, $g(-5.25) = 5.25$

2. (A) The graph of $y = \sqrt{x} + 5$ is the same as the graph of $y = \sqrt{x}$ shifted upward 5 units, and the graph of $y = \sqrt{x} - 4$ is the same as the graph of $y = \sqrt{x}$ shifted downward 4 units. The figure confirms these conclusions.

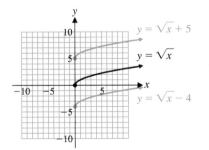

(B) The graph of $y = \sqrt{x + 5}$ is the same as the graph of $y = \sqrt{x}$ shifted to the left 5 units, and the graph of $y = \sqrt{x - 4}$ is the same as the graph of $y = \sqrt{x}$ shifted to the right 4 units. The figure confirms these conclusions.

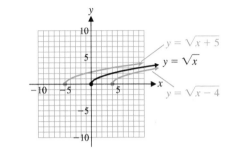

3. $H(x) = \sqrt[3]{x + 3}$, $G(x) = \sqrt[3]{x - 2}$, $M(x) = \sqrt[3]{x} + 2$, $N(x) = \sqrt[3]{x} - 3$

4. (A) The graph of $y = 2x$ is a vertical stretch of the graph of $y = x$, and the graph of $y = 0.5x$ is a vertical shrink of the graph of $y = x$. The figure confirms these conclusions.

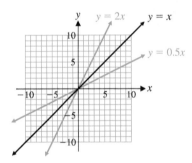

(B) The graph of $y = -0.5x$ is a vertical shrink and a reflection in the x axis of the graph of $y = x$. The figure confirms this conclusion.

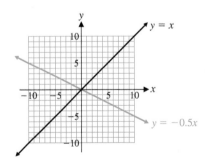

5. The graph of function G is a reflection in the x axis and a horizontal translation of 2 units to the left of the graph of $y = x^3$. An equation for G is $G(x) = -(x + 2)^3$.

6.

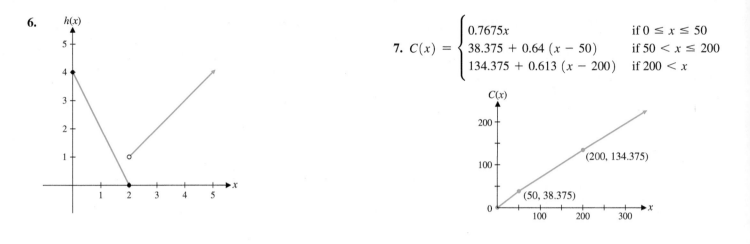

7. $C(x) = \begin{cases} 0.7675x & \text{if } 0 \le x \le 50 \\ 38.375 + 0.64\,(x - 50) & \text{if } 50 < x \le 200 \\ 134.375 + 0.613\,(x - 200) & \text{if } 200 < x \end{cases}$

1.3 Linear and Quadratic Functions

- Linear Functions, Equations, and Inequalities
- Quadratic Functions, Equations, and Inequalities
- Properties of Quadratic Functions and Their Graphs
- Applications
- Linear and Quadratic Regression

Mathematical modeling is the process of using mathematics to solve real-world problems. This process can be broken down into three steps (Fig. 1):

Step 1 *Construct* **mathematical model** (that is, a mathematics problem that, when solved, will provide information about the real-world problem).

Step 2 *Solve* the mathematical model.

Step 3 *Interpret* the solution to the mathematical model in terms of the original real-world problem.

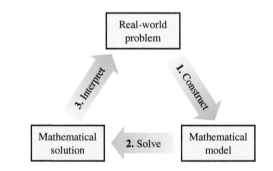

Figure 1

In more complex problems, this cycle may have to be repeated several times to obtain the required information about the real-world problem. In this section, we will show how linear functions and quadratic functions can be used to construct mathematical models of real-world problems.

Linear Functions, Equations, and Inequalities

Linear equations in two variables have (straight) lines as their graphs.

DEFINITION Linear Equations in Two Variables

A **linear equation in two variables** is an equation that can be written in the **standard form**

$$Ax + By = C$$

where A, B, and C are constants (A and B not both 0), and x and y are variables.

THEOREM 1   Graph of a Linear Equation in Two Variables

The graph of any equation of the form

$$Ax + By = C \quad (A \text{ and } B \text{ not both } O) \tag{1}$$

is a line, and any line in a Cartesian coordinate system is the graph of an equation of this form.

If $B = 0$ and $A \neq 0$, then equation (1) can be written as $x = \frac{C}{A}$ and its graph is a vertical line. If $B \neq 0$, then $-A/B$ is the *slope* of the line (see Problems 57–58 in Exercises 1.3).

DEFINITION   Slope of a Line

If (x_1, y_1) and (x_2, y_2) are two points on a line with $x_1 \neq x_2$, then the **slope** of the line is

$$m = \frac{y_2 - y_1}{x_2 - x_1}$$

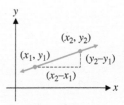

The slope measures the steepness of a line. The vertical change $y_2 - y_1$ is often called the **rise**, and the horizontal change is often called the **run**. The slope may be positive, negative, zero, or undefined (see Table 1).

Table 1 **Geometric Interpretation of Slope**

Line	Rising as x moves from left to right	Falling as x moves from left to right	Horizontal	Vertical
Slope	Positive	Negative	0	Not defined
Example				

If $B \neq 0$ in the standard form of the equation of a line, then solving for y gives the **slope-intercept form** $y = mx + b$, where m is the slope and b is the y intercept.* If a line has slope m and passes through the point (x_1, y_1), then $y - y_1 = m(x - x_1)$ is the **point-slope** form of the equation of the line. The various forms of the equation of a line are summarized in Table 2.

Table 2 **Equations of a Line**

Standard form	$Ax + By = C$	A and B not both 0
Slope-intercept form	$y = mx + b$	Slope: m; y intercept: b
Point-slope form	$y - y_1 = m(x - x_1)$	Slope: m; point: (x_1, y_1)
Horizontal line	$y = b$	Slope: 0
Vertical line	$x = a$	Slope: undefined

---

*If a line passes through the points $(a, 0)$ and $(0, b)$, then a is called the **x intercept** and b is called the **y intercept**. It is common practice to refer to either a or $(a, 0)$ as the x intercept, and either b or $(0, b)$ as the y intercept.

EXAMPLE 1 Equations of lines   A line has slope 4 and passes through the point $(3, 8)$. Find an equation of the line in point-slope form, slope-intercept form, and standard form.

SOLUTION Let $m = 4$ and $(x_1, y_1) = (3, 8)$. Substitute into the point-slope form $y - y_1 = m(x - x_1)$:

Point-slope form:	$y - 8 = 4(x - 3)$	Add 8 to both sides.
	$y = 4(x - 3) + 8$	Simplify.
Slope-intercept form:	$y = 4x - 4$	Subtract 4x from both sides.
Standard form:	$-4x + y = -4$	

Matched Problem 1 ⌋ A line has slope -3 and passes through the point $(-2, 10)$. Find an equation of the line in point-slope form, slope-intercept form, and standard form.

DEFINITION Linear Function

If m and b are real numbers with $m \neq 0$, then the function

$$f(x) = mx + b$$

is a **linear function**.

So the linear function $f(x) = mx + b$ is the function that is specified by the linear equation $y = mx + b$.

EXAMPLE 2 Graphing a Linear Function

(A) Use intercepts to graph the equation $3x - 4y = 12$.

* (B) Use a graphing calculator to graph the function $f(x)$ that is specified by $3x - 4y = 12$, and to find its x and y intercepts.

(C) Solve the inequality $f(x) \geq 0$.

SOLUTION

(A) To find the y intercept, let $x = 0$ and solve for y. To find the x intercept, let $y = 0$ and solve for x. It is a good idea to find a third point on the line as a check point.

x	y	
0	−3	y intercept
4	0	x intercept
8	3	Check point

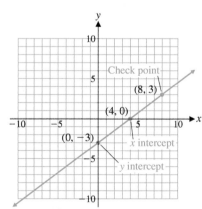

---

*The icon in the margin is used throughout the book to identify optional graphing calculator activities that are intended to give additional insight. We used a Texas Instruments graphing calculator from the TI-83/84 family to produce the graphing calculator screens in this book. You may need to consult the manual for your calculator for the details necessary to carry out these activities.

(B) To find $f(x)$, we solve $3x - 4y = 12$ for y.

$$3x - 4y = 12 \qquad \text{Add } -3x \text{ to both sides.}$$
$$-4y = -3x + 12 \qquad \text{Divide both sides by } -4.$$
$$y = \frac{-3x + 12}{-4} \qquad \text{Simplify.}$$
$$y = f(x) = \frac{3}{4}x - 3 \tag{2}$$

Now we enter the right side of equation (2) in a calculator (Fig. 2A), enter values for the window variables (Fig 2B), and graph the line (Fig. 2C). (The numerals to the left and right of the screen in Figure 2C are Xmin and Xmax, respectively. Similarly, the numerals below and above the screen are Ymin and Ymax.)

(A)   (B)   (C)

Figure 2 **Graphing a line on a graphing calculator**

Next we use two calculator commands to find the intercepts: TRACE (Fig. 3A) and ZERO (Fig. 3B).

(A)   (B)

Figure 3 **Using TRACE and ZERO on a graphing calculator**

(C) $f(x) \geq 0$ if the graph of $f(x) = \frac{3}{4}x - 3$ in the figures in parts (A) or (B) is on or above the x axis. This occurs if $x \geq 4$, so the solution of the inequality, in interval notation,* is $[4, \infty)$.

Matched Problem 2

(A) Use intercepts to graph the equation $4x - 3y = 12$.

(B) Use a graphing calculator to graph the function $f(x)$ that is specified by $4x - 3y = 12$, and to find its x and y intercepts.

(C) Solve the inequality $f(x) \geq 0$.

---

*We use standard **interval notation** (see Table 3). The numbers a and b in Table 3 are called the **endpoints** of the interval. An interval is **closed** if it contains its endpoints and **open** if it does not contain any of its endpoints. The symbol ∞ (read "infinity") is not a number, and is not considered to be an endpoint. The notation $[b, \infty)$ simply denotes the interval that starts at b and continues indefinitely to the right. We never write $[b, \infty]$. The interval $(-\infty, \infty)$ is the entire real line.

Table 3 Interval Notation

Interval Notation	Inequality Notation	Line Graph
$[a, b]$	$a \leq x \leq b$	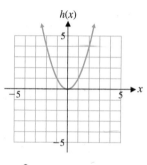
$[a, b)$	$a \leq x < b$	
$(a, b]$	$a < x \leq b$	
(a, b)	$a < x < b$	
$(-\infty, a]$	$x \leq a$	
$(-\infty, a)$	$x < a$	
$[b, \infty)$	$x \geq b$	
(b, ∞)	$x > b$	

Quadratic Functions, Equations, and Inequalities

One of the basic elementary functions of Section 1.2 is the square function $h(x) = x^2$. Its graph is the parabola shown in Figure 4. It is an example of a *quadratic function*.

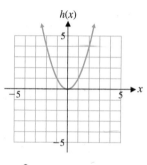

Figure 4 **Square function $h(x) = x^2$**

DEFINITION Quadratic Functions

If a, b, and c are real numbers with $a \neq 0$, then the function

$$f(x) = ax^2 + bx + c \quad \text{Standard form}$$

is a **quadratic function** and its graph is a **parabola**.

The domain of any quadratic function is the set of all real numbers. We will discuss methods for determining the range of a quadratic function later in this section. Typical graphs of quadratic functions are shown in Figure 5.

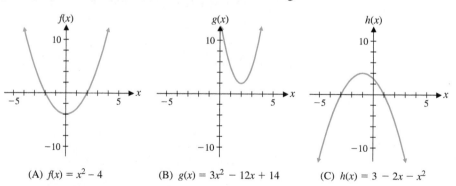

(A) $f(x) = x^2 - 4$ (B) $g(x) = 3x^2 - 12x + 14$ (C) $h(x) = 3 - 2x - x^2$

Figure 5 **Graphs of quadratic functions**

CONCEPTUAL INSIGHT

An x intercept of a function is also called a **zero** of the function. The x intercepts of a quadratic function can be found by solving the quadratic equation $y = ax^2 + bx + c = 0$ for x, $a \neq 0$. Several methods for solving quadratic equations are discussed in Appendix A, Section A.7. The most popular of these is the **quadratic formula**.

If $ax^2 + bx + c = 0$, $a \neq 0$, then

$$x = \frac{-b \pm \sqrt{b^2 - 4ac}}{2a}, \text{ provided } b^2 - 4ac \geq 0$$

EXAMPLE 3   Intercepts, Equations, and Inequalities

(A) Sketch a graph of $f(x) = -x^2 + 5x + 3$ in a rectangular coordinate system.

(B) Find x and y intercepts algebraically to four decimal places.

(C) Graph $f(x) = -x^2 + 5x + 3$ in a standard viewing window.

(D) Find the x and y intercepts to four decimal places using TRACE and ZERO on your graphing calculator.

(E) Solve the quadratic inequality $-x^2 + 5x + 3 \geq 0$ graphically to four decimal places using the results of parts (A) and (B) or (C) and (D).

(F) Solve the equation $-x^2 + 5x + 3 = 4$ graphically to four decimal places using INTERSECT on your graphing calculator.

SOLUTION

(A) Hand-sketching a graph of f:

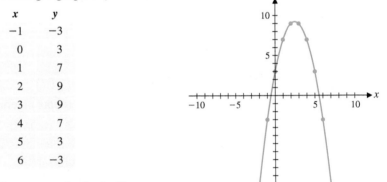

x	y
-1	-3
0	3
1	7
2	9
3	9
4	7
5	3
6	-3

(B) Finding intercepts algebraically:

y intercept: $f(0) = -(0)^2 + 5(0) + 3 = 3$

x intercepts: $f(x) = 0$

$$-x^2 + 5x + 3 = 0 \qquad \text{Quadratic equation}$$

$$x = \frac{-b \pm \sqrt{b^2 - 4ac}}{2a} \qquad \text{Quadratic formula (see Appendix A.7)}$$

$$x = \frac{-(5) \pm \sqrt{5^2 - 4(-1)(3)}}{2(-1)}$$

$$= \frac{-5 \pm \sqrt{37}}{-2} = -0.5414 \quad \text{or} \quad 5.5414$$

(C) Graphing in a graphing calculator:

(D) Finding intercepts graphically using a graphing calculator:

x intercept: −0.5414   x intercept: 0.5414   y intercept: 3

(E) Solving $-x^2 + 5x + 3 \geq 0$ graphically: The quadratic inequality

$$-x^2 + 5x + 3 \geq 0$$

holds for those values of x for which the graph of $f(x) = -x^2 + 5x + 3$ in the figures in parts (A) and (C) is at or above the x axis. This happens for x between the two x intercepts [found in part (B) or (D)], including the two x intercepts. The solution set for the quadratic inequality is $-0.5414 \leq x \leq 5.5414$ or, in interval notation, $[-0.5414, 5.5414]$.

(F) Solving the equation $-x^2 + 5x + 3 = 4$ using a graphing calculator:

$-x^2 + 5x + 3 = 4$ at $x = 0.2087$ $-x^2 + 5x + 3 = 4$ at $x = 4.7913$

Matched Problem 3

(A) Sketch a graph of $g(x) = 2x^2 - 5x - 5$ in a rectangular coordinate system.

(B) Find x and y intercepts algebraically to four decimal places.

(C) Graph $g(x) = 2x^2 - 5x - 5$ in a standard viewing window.

(D) Find the x and y intercepts to four decimal places using TRACE and the ZERO command on your graphing calculator.

(E) Solve $2x^2 - 5x - 5 \geq 0$ graphically to four decimal places using the results of parts (A) and (B) or (C) and (D).

(F) Solve the equation $2x^2 - 5x - 5 = -3$ graphically to four decimal places using INTERSECT on your graphing calculator.

Explore and Discuss 1   How many x intercepts can the graph of a quadratic function have? How many y intercepts? Explain your reasoning.

Properties of Quadratic Functions and Their Graphs

Many useful properties of the quadratic function can be uncovered by transforming

$$f(x) = ax^2 + bx + c \qquad a \neq 0$$

into the **vertex form**

$$f(x) = a(x - h)^2 + k$$

The process of *completing the square* (see Appendix A.7) is central to the transformation. We illustrate the process through a specific example and then generalize the results.

Consider the quadratic function given by

$$f(x) = -2x^2 + 16x - 24 \qquad (3)$$

We use completing the square to transform this function into vertex form:

$$
\begin{aligned}
f(x) &= -2x^2 + 16x - 24 \\
&= -2(x^2 - 8x) - 24 \\
&= -2(x^2 - 8x + \,?\,) - 24 \\[6pt]
&= -2(x^2 - 8x + 16) - 24 + 32 \\[6pt]
&= -2(x - 4)^2 + 8
\end{aligned}
$$

Factor the coefficient of x^2 out of the first two terms.

Add 16 to complete the square inside the parentheses. Because of the -2 outside the parentheses, we have actually added -32, so we must add 32 to the outside.

The transformation is complete and can be checked by multiplying out.

Therefore,

$$f(x) = -2(x - 4)^2 + 8 \qquad (4)$$

If $x = 4$, then $-2(x - 4)^2 = 0$ and $f(4) = 8$. For any other value of x, the negative number $-2(x - 4)^2$ is added to 8, making it smaller. Therefore,

$$f(4) = 8$$

is the *maximum value* of $f(x)$ for all x. Furthermore, if we choose any two x values that are the same distance from 4, we will obtain the same function value. For example, $x = 3$ and $x = 5$ are each one unit from $x = 4$ and their function values are

$$
\begin{aligned}
f(3) &= -2(3 - 4)^2 + 8 = 6 \\
f(5) &= -2(5 - 4)^2 + 8 = 6
\end{aligned}
$$

Therefore, the vertical line $x = 4$ is a line of symmetry. That is, if the graph of equation (3) is drawn on a piece of paper and the paper is folded along the line $x = 4$, then the two sides of the parabola will match exactly. All these results are illustrated by graphing equations (3) and (4) and the line $x = 4$ simultaneously in the same coordinate system (Fig. 6).

From the preceding discussion, we see that as x moves from left to right, $f(x)$ is increasing on $(-\infty, 4]$, and decreasing on $[4, \infty)$, and that $f(x)$ can assume no value greater than 8. Thus,

$$\text{Range of } f: \quad y \le 8 \quad \text{or} \quad (-\infty, 8]$$

In general, the graph of a quadratic function is a parabola with line of symmetry parallel to the vertical axis. The lowest or highest point on the parabola, whichever exists, is called the **vertex**. The maximum or minimum value of a quadratic function always occurs at the vertex of the parabola. The line of symmetry through the vertex is called the **axis** of the parabola. In the example above, $x = 4$ is the axis of the parabola and $(4, 8)$ is its vertex.

Figure 6 **Graph of a quadratic function**

CONCEPTUAL INSIGHT

Applying the graph transformation properties discussed in Section 1.2 to the transformed equation,

$$f(x) = -2x^2 + 16x - 24$$
$$= -2(x - 4)^2 + 8$$

we see that the graph of $f(x) = -2x^2 + 16x - 24$ is the graph of $h(x) = x^2$ vertically stretched by a factor of 2, reflected in the x axis, and shifted to the right 4 units and up 8 units, as shown in Figure 7.

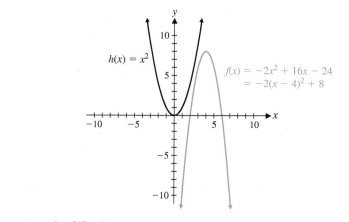

Figure 7 **Graph of f is the graph of h transformed**

Note the important results we have obtained from the vertex form of the quadratic function f:

- The vertex of the parabola
- The axis of the parabola
- The maximum value of $f(x)$
- The range of the function f
- The relationship between the graph of $h(x) = x^2$ and the graph of $f(x) = -2x^2 + 16x - 24$

The preceding discussion is generalized to all quadratic functions in the following summary:

SUMMARY   Properties of a Quadratic Function and Its Graph
Given a quadratic function and the vertex form obtained by completing the square

$$f(x) = ax^2 + bx + c \qquad a \neq 0 \qquad \text{Standard form}$$
$$= a(x - h)^2 + k \qquad\qquad \text{Vertex form}$$

we summarize general properties as follows:

1. The graph of f is a parabola:

2. Vertex: (h, k) (parabola increases on one side of the vertex and decreases on the other)
3. Axis (of symmetry): $x = h$ (parallel to y axis)
4. $f(h) = k$ is the minimum if $a > 0$ and the maximum if $a < 0$
5. Domain: All real numbers. Range: $(-\infty, k]$ if $a < 0$ or $[k, \infty)$ if $a > 0$
6. The graph of f is the graph of $g(x) = ax^2$ translated horizontally h units and vertically k units.

EXAMPLE 4   Analyzing a Quadratic Function Given the quadratic function

$$f(x) = 0.5x^2 - 6x + 21$$

(A) Find the vertex form for f.

(B) Find the vertex and the maximum or minimum. State the range of f.

(C) Describe how the graph of function f can be obtained from the graph of $h(x) = x^2$ using transformations.

(D) Sketch a graph of function f in a rectangular coordinate system.

(E) Graph function f using a suitable viewing window.

(F) Find the vertex and the maximum or minimum using the appropriate graphing calculator command.

SOLUTION

(A) Complete the square to find the vertex form:

$$\begin{aligned}
f(x) &= 0.5x^2 - 6x + 21 \\
&= 0.5(x^2 - 12x + \ ?) + 21 \\
&= 0.5(x^2 - 12x + 36) + 21 - 18 \\
&= 0.5(x - 6)^2 + 3
\end{aligned}$$

(B) From the vertex form, we see that $h = 6$ and $k = 3$. Thus, vertex: $(6, 3)$; minimum: $f(6) = 3$; range: $y \geq 3$ or $[3, \infty)$.

(C) The graph of $f(x) = 0.5(x - 6)^2 + 3$ is the same as the graph of $h(x) = x^2$ vertically shrunk by a factor of 0.5, and shifted to the right 6 units and up 3 units.

(D) Graph in a rectangular coordinate system:

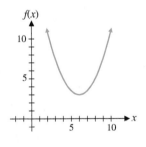

(E) Graph in a graphing calculator:

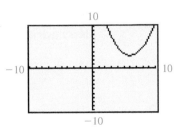

(F) Find the vertex and minimum using the *minimum* command:

Vertex: $(6, 3)$; minimum: $f(6) = 3$

Matched Problem 4 Given the quadratic function $f(x) = -0.25x^2 - 2x + 2$

(A) Find the vertex form for f.

(B) Find the vertex and the maximum or minimum. State the range of f.

(C) Describe how the graph of function f can be obtained from the graph of $h(x) = x^2$ using transformations.

(D) Sketch a graph of function f in a rectangular coordinate system.

(E) Graph function f using a suitable viewing window.

(F) Find the vertex and the maximum or minimum using the appropriate graphing calculator command.

Applications

In a free competitive market, the price of a product is determined by the relationship between supply and demand. If there is a surplus—that is, the supply is greater than the demand—the price tends to come down. If there is a shortage—that is, the demand is greater than the supply—the price tends to go up. The price tends to move toward an equilibrium price at which the supply and demand are equal. Example 5 introduces the basic concepts.

EXAMPLE 5 Supply and Demand At a price of $9.00 per box of oranges, the supply is 320,000 boxes and the demand is 200,000 boxes. At a price of $8.50 per box, the supply is 270,000 boxes and the demand is 300,000 boxes.

(A) Find a price–supply equation of the form $p = mx + b$, where p is the price in dollars and x is the corresponding supply in thousands of boxes.

(B) Find a price–demand equation of the form $p = mx + b$, where p is the price in dollars and x is the corresponding demand in thousands of boxes.

(C) Graph the price–supply and price–demand equations in the same coordinate system and find their point of intersection.

SOLUTION

(A) To find a price–supply equation of the form $p = mx + b$, we must find two points of the form (x, p) that are on the supply line. From the given supply data, $(320, 9)$ and $(270, 8.5)$ are two such points. First, find the slope of the line:

$$m = \frac{9 - 8.5}{320 - 270} = \frac{0.5}{50} = 0.01$$

Now use the point-slope form to find the equation of the line:

$$p - p_1 = m(x - x_1) \qquad (x_1, p_1) = (320, 9)$$
$$p - 9 = 0.01(x - 320)$$
$$p - 9 = 0.01x - 3.2$$
$$p = 0.01x + 5.8 \qquad \text{Price–supply equation}$$

(B) From the given demand data, (200, 9) and (300, 8.5) are two points on the demand line.

$$m = \frac{8.5 - 9}{300 - 200} = \frac{-0.5}{100} = -0.005$$

$$p - p_1 = m(x - x_1)$$
$$p - 9 = -0.005(x - 200) \quad (x_1, p_1) = (200, 9)$$
$$p - 9 = -0.005x + 1$$
$$p = -0.005x + 10 \qquad \text{Price–demand equation}$$

(C) From part (A), we plot the points (320, 9) and (270, 8.5) and then draw line through them. We do the same with the points (200, 9) and (300, 8.5) from part (B) (Fig. 8). (Note that we restricted the axes to intervals that contain these data points.) To find the intersection point of the two lines, we equate the right-hand sides of the price–supply and price–demand equations and solve for x:

$$\text{Price–supply} \quad \text{Price–demand}$$
$$0.01x + 5.8 = -0.005x + 10$$
$$0.015x = 4.2$$
$$x = 280$$

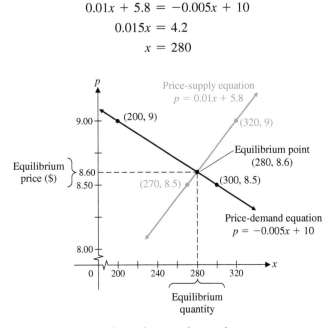

Figure 8 **Graphs of price–supply and price–demand equations**

Now use the price–supply equation to find p when $x = 280$:

$$p = 0.01x + 5.8$$
$$p = 0.01(280) + 5.8 = 8.6$$

As a check, we use the price–demand equation to find p when $x = 280$:

$$p = -0.005x + 10$$
$$p = -0.005(280) + 10 = 8.6$$

The lines intersect at (280, 8.6). The intersection point of the price–supply and price–demand equations is called the **equilibrium point**, and its coordinates are the **equilibrium quantity** (280) and the **equilibrium price** ($8.60). These terms are illustrated in Figure 8. The intersection point can also be found by using the **intersect** command on a graphing calculator (Fig. 9). To summarize, the price of a box of oranges tends toward the equilibrium price of $8.60, at which the supply and demand are both equal to 280,000 boxes.

Figure 9 **Finding an intersection point**

Matched Problem 5 At a price of $12.59 per box of grapefruit, the supply is 595,000 boxes and the demand is 650,000 boxes. At a price of $13.19 per box, the supply is 695,000 boxes and the demand is 590,000 boxes. Assume that the relationship between price and supply is linear and that the relationship between price and demand is linear.

(A) Find a price–supply equation of the form $p = mx + b$.

(B) Find a price–demand equation of the form $p = mx + b$.

(C) Find the equilibrium point.

EXAMPLE 6   Maximum Revenue This is a continuation of Example 7 in Section 1.1. Recall that the financial department in the company that produces a digital camera arrived at the following price–demand function and the corresponding revenue function:

$$p(x) = 94.8 - 5x \qquad \text{Price–demand function}$$
$$R(x) = xp(x) = x(94.8 - 5x) \qquad \text{Revenue function}$$

where $p(x)$ is the wholesale price per camera at which x million cameras can be sold and $R(x)$ is the corresponding revenue (in millions of dollars). Both functions have domain $1 \le x \le 15$.

(A) Find the value of x to the nearest thousand cameras that will generate the maximum revenue. What is the maximum revenue to the nearest thousand dollars? Solve the problem algebraically by completing the square.

(B) What is the wholesale price per camera (to the nearest dollar) that generates the maximum revenue?

(C) Graph the revenue function using an appropriate viewing window.

(D) Find the value of x to the nearest thousand cameras that will generate the maximum revenue. What is the maximum revenue to the nearest thousand dollars? Solve the problem graphically using the **maximum** command.

SOLUTION

(A) Algebraic solution:

$$R(x) = x(94.8 - 5x)$$
$$= -5x^2 + 94.8x$$
$$= -5(x^2 - 18.96x + \ ?)$$
$$= -5(x^2 - 18.96x + 89.8704) + 449.352$$
$$= -5(x - 9.48)^2 + 449.352$$

The maximum revenue of 449.352 million dollars ($449,352,000) occurs when $x = 9.480$ million cameras (9,480,000 cameras).

(B) Finding the wholesale price per camera: Use the price–demand function for an output of 9.480 million cameras:

$$p(x) = 94.8 - 5x$$
$$p(9.480) = 94.8 - 5(9.480)$$
$$= \$47 \text{ per camera}$$

(C) Graph on a graphing calculator:

(D) Graphical solution using a graphing calculator:

The manufacture and sale of 9.480 million cameras (9,480,000 cameras) will generate a maximum revenue of 449.352 million dollars ($449,352,000).

Matched Problem 6 The financial department in Example 6, using statistical and analytical techniques (see Matched Problem 7 in Section 1.1), arrived at the cost function

$$C(x) = 156 + 19.7x \quad \text{Cost function}$$

where $C(x)$ is the cost (in millions of dollars) for manufacturing and selling x million cameras.

(A) Using the revenue function from Example 6 and the preceding cost function, write an equation for the profit function.

(B) Find the value of x to the nearest thousand cameras that will generate the maximum profit. What is the maximum profit to the nearest thousand dollars? Solve the problem algebraically by completing the square.

(C) What is the wholesale price per camera (to the nearest dollar) that generates the maximum profit?

(D) Graph the profit function using an appropriate viewing window.

(E) Find the output to the nearest thousand cameras that will generate the maximum profit. What is the maximum profit to the nearest thousand dollars? Solve the problem graphically using the **maximum** command.

Linear and Quadratic Regression

Price–demand and price–supply equations (see Example 5), or cost functions (see Example 6), can be obtained from data using **regression analysis**. **Linear regression** produces the linear function (line) that is the **best fit*** for a data set; **quadratic regression** produces the quadratic function (parabola) that is the best fit for a data set; and so on. Examples 7 and 8 illustrate how a graphing calculator can be used to produce a **scatter plot**, that is, a graph of the points in a data set, and to find a linear or quadratic regression model.

EXAMPLE 7 Diamond Prices Table 4 gives diamond prices for round-shaped diamonds. Use linear regression to find the best linear model of the form $y = ax + b$ for the price y (in dollars) of a diamond as a function of its weight x (in carats).

Table 4 **Round-Shaped Diamond Prices**

Weight (carats)	Price
0.5	$2,790
0.6	$3,191
0.7	$3,694
0.8	$4,154
0.9	$5,018
1.0	$5,898

Source: www.tradeshop.com

*The definition of "best fit" is given in Section 7.5, where calculus is used to justify regression methods.

SOLUTION Enter the data in a graphing calculator (Fig. 10A) and find the linear regression equation (Fig. 10B). The data set and the model, that is, the line $y = 6{,}137.4x - 478.9$, are graphed in Figure 10C.

Table 5 **Emerald-Shaped Diamond Prices**

Weight (carats)	Price
0.5	$1,677
0.6	$2,353
0.7	$2,718
0.8	$3,218
0.9	$3,982
1.0	$4,510

Source: www.tradeshop.com

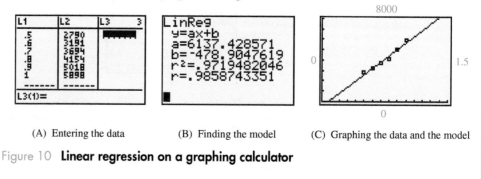

(A) Entering the data   (B) Finding the model   (C) Graphing the data and the model

Figure 10 **Linear regression on a graphing calculator**

Matched Problem 7 ⌋ Prices for emerald-shaped diamonds are given in Table 5. Repeat Example 7 for this data set.

A visual inspection of the plot of a data set might indicate that a parabola would be a better model of the data than a straight line. In that case, we would use quadratic, rather than linear, regression.

EXAMPLE 8   Outboard Motors Table 6 gives performance data for a boat powered by an Evinrude outboard motor. Use quadratic regression to find the best model of the form $y = ax^2 + bx + c$ for fuel consumption y (in miles per gallon) as a function of speed x (in miles per hour). Estimate the fuel consumption (to one decimal place) at a speed of 12 miles per hour.

Table 6

rpm	mph	mpg
2,500	10.3	4.1
3,000	18.3	5.6
3,500	24.6	6.6
4,000	29.1	6.4
4,500	33.0	6.1
5,000	36.0	5.4
5,400	38.9	4.9

SOLUTION Enter the data in a graphing calculator (Fig. 11A) and find the quadratic regression equation (Fig. 11B). The data set and the regression equation are graphed in Figure 11C. Using TRACE, we see that the estimated fuel consumption at a speed of 12 mph is 4.5 mpg.

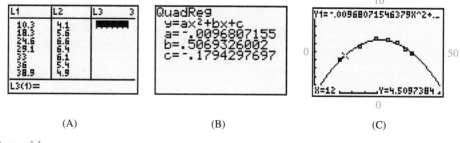

(A)   (B)   (C)

Figure 11

Matched Problem 8 ⌋ Refer to Table 6. Use quadratic regression to find the best model of the form $y = ax^2 + bx + c$ for boat speed y (in miles per hour) as a function of engine speed x (in revolutions per minute). Estimate the boat speed (in miles per hour, to one decimal place) at an engine speed of 3,400 rpm.

Exercises 1.3

In Problems 1–4, sketch a graph of each equation in a rectangular coordinate system.

1. $y = 2x - 3$

2. $y = \dfrac{x}{2} + 1$

3. $2x + 3y = 12$

4. $8x - 3y = 24$

In Problems 5–8, find the slope and y intercept of the graph of each equation.

5. $y = 5x - 7$

6. $y = 3x + 2$

7. $y = -\dfrac{5}{2}x - 9$

8. $y = -\dfrac{10}{3}x + 4$

In Problems 9–12, write an equation of the line with the indicated slope and y intercept.

9. Slope $= 2$
   y intercept $= 1$

10. Slope $= 1$
   y intercept $= 5$

11. Slope $= -\dfrac{1}{3}$
   y intercept $= 6$

12. Slope $= \dfrac{6}{7}$
   y intercept $= -\dfrac{9}{2}$

In Problems 13–16, use the graph of each line to find the x intercept, y intercept, and slope. Write the slope-intercept form of the equation of line.

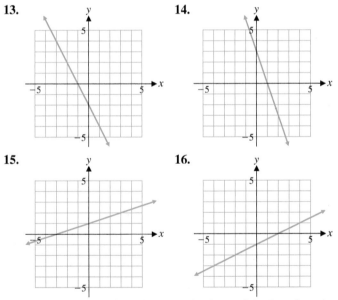

13.

14.

15.

16.

17. Match each equation with a graph of one of the functions f, g, m, or n in the figure.

(A) $y = -(x + 2)^2 + 1$

(B) $y = (x - 2)^2 - 1$

(C) $y = (x + 2)^2 - 1$

(D) $y = -(x - 2)^2 + 1$

18. Match each equation with a graph of one of the functions f, g, m, or n in the figure.

(A) $y = (x - 3)^2 - 4$

(B) $y = -(x + 3)^2 + 4$

(C) $y = -(x - 3)^2 + 4$

(D) $y = (x + 3)^2 - 4$

For the functions indicated in Problems 19–22, find each of the following to the nearest integer by referring to the graphs for Problems 17 and 18.

(A) Intercepts

(B) Vertex

(C) Maximum or minimum

(D) Range

19. Function n in the figure for Problem 17

20. Function m in the figure for Problem 18

21. Function f in the figure for Problem 17

22. Function g in the figure for Problem 18

In Problems 23–26, find each of the following:

(A) Intercepts

(B) Vertex

(C) Maximum or minimum

(D) Range

23. $f(x) = -(x - 3)^2 + 2$

24. $g(x) = -(x + 2)^2 + 3$

25. $m(x) = (x + 1)^2 - 2$

26. $n(x) = (x - 4)^2 - 3$

In Problems 27–34,

(A) Find the slope of the line that passes through the given points.

(B) Find the point-slope form of the equation of the line.

(C) Find the slope-intercept form of the equation of the line.

(D) Find the standard form of the equation of the line.

27. $(2, 5)$ and $(5, 7)$

28. $(1, 2)$ and $(3, 5)$

29. $(-2, -1)$ and $(2, -6)$

30. $(2, 3)$ and $(-3, 7)$

31. $(5, 3)$ and $(5, -3)$

32. $(1, 4)$ and $(0, 4)$

33. $(-2, 5)$ and $(3, 5)$

34. $(2, 0)$ and $(2, -3)$

In Problems 35–40, find the vertex form for each quadratic function. Then find each of the following:

(A) Intercepts

(B) Vertex

(C) Maximum or minimum

(D) Range

35. $f(x) = x^2 - 8x + 12$

36. $g(x) = x^2 - 6x + 5$

37. $r(x) = -4x^2 + 16x - 15$

38. $s(x) = -4x^2 - 8x - 3$

39. $u(x) = 0.5x^2 - 2x + 5$

40. $v(x) = 0.5x^2 + 4x + 10$

In Problems 41–48, use interval notation to write the solution set of the inequality.

41. $2x + 7 < 0$

42. $6x - 13 > 0$

43. $-5x + 3 \geq 6$

44. $-4x - 21 \leq 1$

45. $x^2 - 10x > 0$

46. $x^2 + 16x \leq 0$

47. $x^2 + 20x + 50 \leq 0$

48. $x^2 - 4x + 5 > 0$

49. Graph $y = 25x + 200, x \geq 0$.

50. Graph $y = 40x + 160, x \geq 0$.

51. (A) Graph $y = 1.2x - 4.2$ in a rectangular coordinate system.

   (B) Find the x and y intercepts algebraically to one decimal place.

   (C) Graph $y = 1.2x - 4.2$ in a graphing calculator.

   (D) Find the x and y intercepts to one decimal place using TRACE and the zero command.

52. (A) Graph $y = -0.8x + 5.2$ in a rectangular coordinate system.

   (B) Find the x and y intercepts algebraically to one decimal place.

   (C) Graph $y = -0.8x + 5.2$ in a graphing calculator.

   (D) Find the x and y intercepts to one decimal place using TRACE and the zero command.

   (E) Using the results of parts (A) and (B), or (C) and (D), find the solution set for the linear inequality

$$-0.8x + 5.2 < 0$$

53. Let $f(x) = 0.3x^2 - x - 8$. Solve each equation graphically to two decimal places.

   (A) $f(x) = 4$ (B) $f(x) = -1$ (C) $f(x) = -9$

54. Let $g(x) = -0.6x^2 + 3x + 4$. Solve each equation graphically to two decimal places.

   (A) $g(x) = -2$ (B) $g(x) = 5$ (C) $g(x) = 8$

55. Let $f(x) = 125x - 6x^2$. Find the maximum value of f to four decimal places graphically.

56. Let $f(x) = 100x - 7x^2 - 10$. Find the maximum value of f to four decimal places graphically.

57. If $B \neq 0$, $Ax_1 + By_1 = C$, and $Ax_2 + By_2 = C$, show that the slope of the line through (x_1, y_1) and (x_2, y_2) is equal to $-\dfrac{A}{B}$.

58. If $B \neq 0$ and (x_1, y_1), (x_2, y_2), and (x_3, y_3) are all solutions of $Ax + By = C$, show that the slope of the line through (x_1, y_1) and (x_2, y_2) is equal to the slope of the line through (x_1, y_1) and (x_3, y_3).

Applications

59. Underwater pressure. At sea level, the weight of the atmosphere exerts a pressure of 14.7 pounds per square inch, commonly referred to as 1 **atmosphere of pressure**. As an object descends in water, pressure P and depth d are linearly related. In salt water, the pressure at a depth of 33 ft is 2 atms, or 29.4 pounds per square inch.

   (A) Find a linear model that relates pressure P (in pounds per square inch) to depth d (in feet).

   (B) Interpret the slope of the model.

   (C) Find the pressure at a depth of 50 ft.

   (D) Find the depth at which the pressure is 4 atms.

60. Underwater pressure. Refer to Problem 59. In fresh water, the pressure at a depth of 34 ft is 2 atms, or 29.4 pounds per square inch.

   (A) Find a linear model that relates pressure P (in pounds per square inch) to depth d (in feet).

   (B) Interpret the slope of the model.

   (C) Find the pressure at a depth of 50 ft.

   (D) Find the depth at which the pressure is 4 atms.

61. Rate of descent—Parachutes. At low altitudes, the altitude of a parachutist and time in the air are linearly related. A jump at 2,880 ft using the U.S. Army's T-10 parachute system lasts 120 secs.

   (A) Find a linear model relating altitude a (in feet) and time in the air t (in seconds).

   (B) Find the rate of descent for a T-10 system.

   (C) Find the speed of the parachutist at landing.

62. Rate of descent—Parachutes. The U.S Army is considering a new parachute, the Advanced Tactical Parachute System (ATPS). A jump at 2,880 ft using the ATPS system lasts 180 secs.

   (A) Find a linear model relating altitude a (in feet) and time in the air t (in seconds).

   (B) Find the rate of descent for an ATPS system parachute.

   (C) Find the speed of the parachutist at landing.

63. Cost analysis. A plant can manufacture 80 golf clubs per day for a total daily cost of $7,647 and 100 golf clubs per day for a total daily cost of $9,147.

   (A) Assuming that daily cost and production are linearly related, find the total daily cost of producing x golf clubs.

(B) Graph the total daily cost for $0 \leq x \leq 200$.

(C) Interpret the slope and y intercept of this cost equation.

64. Cost analysis. A plant can manufacture 50 tennis rackets per day for a total daily cost of $3,855 and 60 tennis rackets per day for a total daily cost of $4,245.

(A) Assuming that daily cost and production are linearly related, find the total daily cost of producing x tennis rackets.

(B) Graph the total daily cost for $0 \leq x \leq 100$.

(C) Interpret the slope and y intercept of this cost equation.

65. Business—Depreciation. A farmer buys a new tractor for $157,000 and assumes that it will have a trade-in value of $82,000 after 10 years. The farmer uses a constant rate of depreciation (commonly called **straight-line depreciation—** one of several methods permitted by the IRS) to determine the annual value of the tractor.

(A) Find a linear model for the depreciated value V of the tractor t years after it was purchased.

(B) What is the depreciated value of the tractor after 6 years?

(C) When will the depreciated value fall below $70,000?

(D) Graph V for $0 \leq t \leq 20$ and illustrate the answers from parts (B) and (C) on the graph.

66. Business—Depreciation. A charter fishing company buys a new boat for $224,000 and assumes that it will have a trade-in value of $115,200 after 16 years.

(A) Find a linear model for the depreciated value V of the boat t years after it was purchased.

(B) What is the depreciated value of the boat after 10 years?

(C) When will the depreciated value fall below $100,000?

(D) Graph V for $0 \leq t \leq 30$ and illustrate the answers from (B) and (C) on the graph.

67. Flight conditions. In stable air, the air temperature drops about 3.6°F for each 1,000-foot rise in altitude. (*Source: Federal Aviation Administration*)

(A) If the temperature at sea level is 70°F, write a linear equation that expresses temperature T in terms of altitude A in thousands of feet.

(B) At what altitude is the temperature 34°F?

68. Flight navigation. The airspeed indicator on some aircraft is affected by the changes in atmospheric pressure at different altitudes. A pilot can estimate the true airspeed by observing the indicated airspeed and adding to it about 1.6% for every 1,000 feet of altitude. (*Source: Megginson Technologies Ltd.*)

(A) A pilot maintains a constant reading of 200 miles per hour on the airspeed indicator as the aircraft climbs from sea level to an altitude of 10,000 feet. Write a linear equation that expresses true airspeed T (in miles per hour) in terms of altitude A (in thousands of feet).

(B) What would be the true airspeed of the aircraft at 6,500 feet?

69. Supply and demand. At a price of $2.28 per bushel, the supply of barley is 7,500 million bushels and the demand is 7,900 million bushels. At a price of $2.37 per bushel, the supply is 7,900 million bushels and the demand is 7,800 million bushels.

(A) Find a price–supply equation of the form $p = mx + b$.

(B) Find a price–demand equation of the form $p = mx + b$.

(C) Find the equilibrium point.

(D) Graph the price–supply equation, price–demand equation, and equilibrium point in the same coordinate system.

70. Supply and demand. At a price of $1.94 per bushel, the supply of corn is 9,800 million bushels and the demand is 9,300 million bushels. At a price of $1.82 per bushel, the supply is 9,400 million bushels and the demand is 9,500 million bushels.

(A) Find a price–supply equation of the form $p = mx + b$.

(B) Find a price–demand equation of the form $p = mx + b$.

(C) Find the equilibrium point.

(D) Graph the price–supply equation, price–demand equation, and equilibrium point in the same coordinate system.

71. Licensed drivers. The table contains the state population and the number of licensed drivers in the state (both in millions) for the states with population under 1 million in 2010. The regression model for this data is

$$y = 0.75x$$

where x is the state population and y is the number of licensed drivers in the state.

Licensed Drivers in 2010

State	Population	Licensed Drivers
Alaska	0.71	0.52
Delaware	0.90	0.70
Montana	0.99	0.74
North Dakota	0.67	0.48
South Dakota	0.81	0.60
Vermont	0.63	0.51
Wyoming	0.56	0.42

Source: Bureau of Transportation Statistics

(A) Draw a scatter plot of the data and a graph of the model on the same axes.

(B) If the population of Idaho in 2010 was about 1.6 million, use the model to estimate the number of licensed drivers in Idaho in 2010 to the nearest thousand.

(C) If the number of licensed drivers in Rhode Island in 2006 was about 0.75 million, use the model to estimate the population of Rhode Island in 2010 to the nearest thousand.

72. Licensed drivers. The table contains the state population and the number of licensed drivers in the state (both in millions) for the states with population over 10 million in 2010. The regression model for this data is

$$y = 0.63x + 0.31$$

where x is the state population and y is the number of licensed drivers in the state.

Licensed Drivers in 2010

State	Population	Licensed Drivers
California	37	24
Florida	19	14
Illinois	13	8
New York	19	11
Ohio	12	8
Pennsylvania	13	9
Texas	25	15

Source: Bureau of Transportation Statistics

(A) Draw a scatter plot of the data and a graph of the model on the same axes.

(B) If the population of Minnesota in 2010 was about 5.3 million, use the model to estimate the number of licensed drivers in Minnesota in 2010 to the nearest thousand.

(C) If the number of licensed drivers in Wisconsin in 2010 was about 4.1 million, use the model to estimate the population of Wisconsin in 2010 to the nearest thousand.

73. Tire mileage. An automobile tire manufacturer collected the data in the table relating tire pressure x (in pounds per square inch) and mileage (in thousands of miles):

x	Mileage
28	45
30	52
32	55
34	51
36	47

A mathematical model for the data is given by

$$f(x) = -0.518x^2 + 33.3x - 481$$

(A) Complete the following table. Round values of $f(x)$ to one decimal place.

x	Mileage	$f(x)$
28	45	
30	52	
32	55	
34	51	
36	47	

(B) Sketch the graph of f and the mileage data in the same coordinate system.

(C) Use values of the modeling function rounded to two decimal places to estimate the mileage for a tire pressure of 31 lb/sq in. and for 35 lb/sq in.

(D) Write a brief description of the relationship between tire pressure and mileage.

74. Automobile production. The table shows the retail market share of passenger cars from Ford Motor Company as a percentage of the U.S. market.

Year	Market Share
1980	17.2%
1985	18.8%
1990	20.0%
1995	20.7%
2000	20.2%
2005	17.4%
2010	16.4%

A mathematical model for this data is given by

$$f(x) = -0.0169x^2 + 0.47x + 17.1$$

where $x = 0$ corresponds to 1980.

(A) Complete the following table. Round values of $f(x)$ to one decimal place.

x	Market Share	$f(x)$
0	17.2	
5	18.8	
10	20.0	
15	20.7	
20	20.2	
25	17.4	
30	16.4	

(B) Sketch the graph of f and the market share data in the same coordinate system.

(C) Use values of the modeling function f to estimate Ford's market share in 2020 and in 2025.

(D) Write a brief description of Ford's market share from 1980 to 2010.

75. Tire mileage. Using quadratic regression on a graphing calculator, show that the quadratic function that best fits the data on tire mileage in Problem 73 is

$$f(x) = -0.518x^2 + 33.3x - 481$$

76. Automobile production. Using quadratic regression on a graphing calculator, show that the quadratic function that best fits the data on market share in Problem 74 is

$$f(x) = -0.0169x^2 + 0.47x + 17.1$$

77. Revenue. The marketing research department for a company that manufactures and sells memory chips for microcomputers established the following price–demand and revenue functions:

$$p(x) = 75 - 3x \qquad \text{Price–demand function}$$
$$R(x) = xp(x) = x(75 - 3x) \quad \text{Revenue function}$$

where $p(x)$ is the wholesale price in dollars at which x million chips can be sold, and $R(x)$ is in millions of dollars. Both functions have domain $1 \leq x \leq 20$.

(A) Sketch a graph of the revenue function in a rectangular coordinate system.

(B) Find the value of x that will produce the maximum revenue. What is the maximum revenue?

(C) What is the wholesale price per chip that produces the maximum revenue?

78. Revenue. The marketing research department for a company that manufactures and sells notebook computers established the following price–demand and revenue functions:

$$p(x) = 2{,}000 - 60x \qquad \text{Price–demand function}$$
$$R(x) = xp(x) \qquad\qquad \text{Revenue function}$$
$$ = x(2{,}000 - 60x)$$

where $p(x)$ is the wholesale price in dollars at which x thousand computers can be sold, and $R(x)$ is in thousands of dollars. Both functions have domain $1 \leq x \leq 25$.

(A) Sketch a graph of the revenue function in a rectangular coordinate system.

(B) Find the value of x that will produce the maximum revenue. What is the maximum revenue to the nearest thousand dollars?

(C) What is the wholesale price per computer (to the nearest dollar) that produces the maximum revenue?

79. Forestry. The figure contains a scatter plot of 100 data points for black spruce trees and the linear regression model for this data.

(A) Interpret the slope of the model.

(B) What is the effect of a 1-in. increase in the diameter at breast height (Dbh)?

(C) Estimate the height of a black spruce with a Dbh of 15 in. Round your answer to the nearest foot.

(D) Estimate the Dbh of a black spruce that is 25 ft tall. Round your answer to the nearest inch.

black spruce
Source: Lakehead University

80. Forestry. The figure contains a scatter plot of 100 data points for black walnut trees and the linear regression model for this data.

(A) Interpret the slope of the model.

(B) What is the effect of a 1-in. increase in Dbh?

(C) Estimate the height of a black walnut with a Dbh of 12 in. Round your answer to the nearest foot.

(D) Estimate the Dbh of a black walnut that is 25 ft tall. Round your answer to the nearest inch.

black walnut
Source: Kagen Research

81. Cable television. The table shows the increase in both price and revenue for cable television in the United States. The figure shows a scatter plot and a linear regression model for the average monthly price data in the table.

(A) Interpret the slope of the model.

(B) Use the model to predict the average monthly price (to the nearest dollar) in 2024.

Table for 81 and 82 Cable Television Price and Revenue

Year	Average Monthly Price (dollars)	Annual Total Revenue (billions of dollars)
2000	30.37	36.43
2002	34.71	47.99
2004	38.14	58.59
2006	41.17	71.89
2008	44.28	85.23
2010	47.89	93.37

Source: SNL Kagan

82. Cable television. The figure shows a scatter plot and a linear regression model for the annual revenue data in the table.

(A) Interpret the slope of the model.

(B) Use the model to predict the annual revenue (to the nearest billion dollars) in 2024.

Problems 83 and 84 require a graphing calculator or a computer that can calculate the linear regression line for a given data set.

83. Olympic Games. Find a linear regression model for the men's 100-meter freestyle data given in the table, where x is years since 1990 and y is winning time (in seconds). Do the same for the women's 100-meter freestyle data. (Round regression coefficients to three decimal places.) Do these models indicate that the women will eventually catch up with the men?

Table for 83 and 84 Winning Times in Olympic Swimming Events

	100-Meter Freestyle		200-Meter Backstroke	
	Men	Women	Men	Women
1992	49.02	54.65	1:58.47	2:07.06
1996	48.74	54.50	1:58.54	2:07.83
2000	48.30	53.83	1:56.76	2:08.16
2004	48.17	53.84	1:54.76	2:09.16
2008	47.21	53.12	1:53.94	2:05.24
2012	47.52	53.00	1:53.41	2:04.06

Source: www.infoplease.com

84. Olympic Games. Find a linear regression model for the men's 200-meter backstroke data given in the table, where x is years since 1990 and y is winning time (in seconds). Do the same for the women's 200-meter backstroke data. (Round regression coefficients to three decimal places.) Do these models indicate that the women will eventually catch up with the men?

85. Outboard motors. The table gives performance data for a boat powered by an Evinrude outboard motor. Find a quadratic regression model ($y = ax^2 + bx + c$) for boat speed y (in miles per hour) as a function of engine speed (in revolutions per minute). Estimate the boat speed at an engine speed of 3,100 revolutions per minute.

Table for 85 and 86

rpm	mph	mpg
1,500	4.5	8.2
2,000	5.7	6.9
2,500	7.8	4.8
3,000	9.6	4.1
3,500	13.4	3.7

86. Outboard motors. The table gives performance data for a boat powered by an Evinrude outboard motor. Find a quadratic regression model ($y = ax^2 + bx + c$) for fuel consumption y (in miles per gallon) as a function of engine speed (in revolutions per minute). Estimate the fuel consumption at an engine speed of 2,300 revolutions per minute.

Answers to Matched Problems

1. $y - 10 = -3(x + 2)$; $y = -3x + 4$; $3x + y = 4$

2. (A)

(B) y intercept $= -4$, x intercept $= 3$

(C) $[3, \infty)$

3. (A)

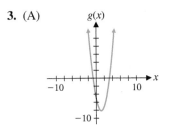

(B) x intercepts: -0.7656, 3.2656; y intercept: -5

(C)

(D) x intercepts: -0.7656, 3.2656; y intercept: -5

(E) $x \leq -0.7656$ or $x \geq 3.2656$; or $(-\infty, -0.7656]$ or $[3.2656, \infty)$

(F) $x = -0.3508$, 2.8508

4. (A) $f(x) = -0.25(x + 4)^2 + 6$.

(B) Vertex: $(-4, 6)$; maximum: $f(-4) = 6$; range: $y \leq 6$ or $(-\infty, 6]$

(C) The graph of $f(x) = -0.25(x + 4)^2 + 6$ is the same as the graph of $h(x) = x^2$ vertically shrunk by a factor of 0.25, reflected in the x axis, and shifted 4 units to the left and 6 units up.

(D)

(E)

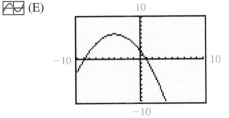

(F) Vertex: $(-4, 6)$; maximum: $f(-4) = 6$

5. (A) $p = 0.006x + 9.02$

(B) $p = -0.01x + 19.09$

(C) $(629, 12.80)$

6. (A) $P(x) = R(x) - C(x) = -5x^2 + 75.1x - 156$

(B) $P(x) = R(x) - C(x) = -5(x - 7.51)^2 + 126.0005$; the manufacture and sale of 7,510,000 million cameras will produce a maximum profit of $126,001,000.

(C) $p(7.510) = \$57$

(D)

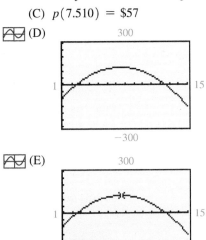

(E)

The manufacture and sale of 7,510,000 million cameras will produce a maximum profit of $126,001,000. (Notice that maximum profit does not occur at the same value of x where maximum revenue occurs.)

7. $y = 5,586x - 1,113$

8.

22.9 mph

1.4   Polynomial and Rational Functions

- Polynomial Functions
- Regression Polynomials
- Rational Functions
- Applications

Linear and quadratic functions are special cases of the more general class of *polynomial functions*. Polynomial functions are a special case of an even larger class of functions, the *rational functions*. We will describe the basic features of the graphs of polynomial and rational functions. We will use these functions to solve real-world problems where linear or quadratic models are inadequate; for example, to determine the relationship between length and weight of a species of fish, or to model the training of new employees.

Polynomial Functions

A linear function has the form $f(x) = mx + b$ (where $m \neq 0$) and is a polynomial function of degree 1. A quadratic function has the form $f(x) = ax^2 + bx + c$ (where $a \neq 0$) and is a polynomial function of degree 2. Here is the general definition of a polynomial function.

DEFINITION   Polynomial Function

A **polynomial function** is a function that can be written in the form

$$f(x) = a_n x^n + a_{n-1} x^{n-1} + \cdots + a_1 x + a_0$$

for n a nonnegative integer, called the **degree** of the polynomial. The coefficients $a_0, a_1, \ldots, a_n$ are real numbers with $a_n \neq 0$. The **domain** of a polynomial function is the set of all real numbers.

Figure 1 shows graphs of representative polynomial functions of degrees 1 through 6. The figure, which also appears on the inside back cover, suggests some general properties of graphs of polynomial functions.

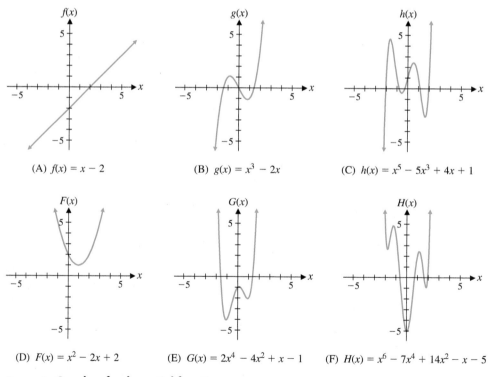

(A) $f(x) = x - 2$ (B) $g(x) = x^3 - 2x$ (C) $h(x) = x^5 - 5x^3 + 4x + 1$

(D) $F(x) = x^2 - 2x + 2$ (E) $G(x) = 2x^4 - 4x^2 + x - 1$ (F) $H(x) = x^6 - 7x^4 + 14x^2 - x - 5$

Figure 1   **Graphs of polynomial functions**

Notice that the odd-degree polynomial graphs start negative, end positive, and cross the x axis at least once. The even-degree polynomial graphs start positive, end positive, and may not cross the x axis at all. In all cases in Figure 1, the **leading coefficient**—that is, the coefficient of the highest-degree term—was chosen positive. If any leading coefficient had been chosen negative, then we would have a similar graph but reflected in the x axis.

A polynomial of degree n can have, at most, n linear factors. Therefore, the graph of a polynomial function of positive degree n can intersect the x axis at most n times. Note from Figure 1 that a polynomial of degree n may intersect the x axis fewer than n times. An x intercept of a function is also called a **zero*** or **root** of the function.

The graph of a polynomial function is **continuous**, with no holes or breaks. That is, the graph can be drawn without removing a pen from the paper. Also, the graph of a polynomial has no sharp corners. Figure 2 shows the graphs of two functions— one that is not continuous, and the other that is continuous but with a sharp corner. Neither function is a polynomial.

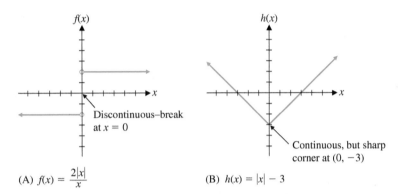

Discontinuous–break at $x = 0$

Continuous, but sharp corner at $(0, -3)$

(A) $f(x) = \dfrac{2|x|}{x}$

(B) $h(x) = |x| - 3$

Figure 2 **Discontinuous and sharp-corner functions**

Regression Polynomials

In Section 1.3, we saw that regression techniques can be used to fit a straight line to a set of data. Linear functions are not the only ones that can be applied in this manner. Most graphing calculators have the ability to fit a variety of curves to a given set of data. We will discuss polynomial regression models in this section and other types of regression models in later sections.

EXAMPLE 1   Estimating the Weight of a Fish Using the length of a fish to estimate its weight is of interest to both scientists and sport anglers. The data in Table 1 give the average weights of lake trout for certain lengths. Use the data and regression techniques to find a polynomial model that can be used to estimate the weight of a lake trout for any length. Estimate (to the nearest ounce) the weights of lake trout of lengths 39, 40, 41, 42, and 43 inches, respectively.

Table 1 **Lake Trout**

Length (in.)	Weight (oz)	Length (in.)	Weight (oz)
x	y	x	y
10	5	30	152
14	12	34	226
18	26	38	326
22	56	44	536
26	96		

---

*Only real numbers can be x intercepts. Functions may have complex zeros that are not real numbers, but such zeros, which are not x intercepts, will not be discussed in this book.

SOLUTION The graph of the data in Table 1 (Fig. 3A) indicates that a linear regression model would not be appropriate in this case. And, in fact, we would not expect a linear relationship between length and weight. Instead, it is more likely that the weight would be related to the cube of the length. We use a cubic regression polynomial to model the data (Fig. 3B). (Consult your manual for the details of calculating regression polynomials on your graphing utility.) Figure 3C adds the graph of the polynomial model to the graph of the data. The graph in Figure 3C shows that this cubic polynomial does provide a good fit for the data. (We will have more to say about the choice of functions and the accuracy of the fit provided by regression analysis later in the book.) Figure 3D shows the estimated weights for the lengths requested.

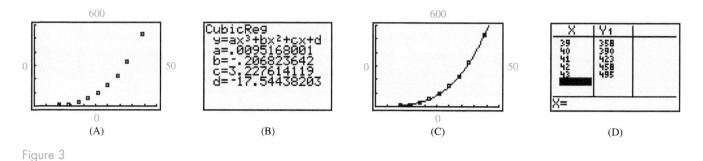

Figure 3

Matched Problem 1 The data in Table 2 give the average weights of pike for certain lengths. Use a cubic regression polynomial to model the data. Estimate (to the nearest ounce) the weights of pike of lengths 39, 40, 41, 42, and 43 inches, respectively.

Table 2 **Pike**

Length (in.)	Weight (oz)	Length (in.)	Weight (oz)
x	y	x	y
10	5	30	108
14	12	34	154
18	26	38	210
22	44	44	326
26	72	52	522

Rational Functions

Just as rational numbers are defined in terms of quotients of integers, *rational functions* are defined in terms of quotients of polynomials. The following equations specify rational functions:

$$f(x) = \frac{1}{x} \quad g(x) = \frac{x-2}{x^2-x-6} \quad h(x) = \frac{x^3-8}{x}$$

$$p(x) = 3x^2 - 5x \quad q(x) = 7 \quad r(x) = 0$$

DEFINITION Rational Function

A **rational function** is any function that can be written in the form

$$f(x) = \frac{n(x)}{d(x)} \quad d(x) \neq 0$$

where $n(x)$ and $d(x)$ are polynomials. The **domain** is the set of all real numbers such that $d(x) \neq 0$.

Figure 4 shows the graphs of representative rational functions. Note, for example, that in Figure 4A the line $x = 2$ is a *vertical asymptote* for the function. The graph of f gets closer to this line as x gets closer to 2. The line $y = 1$ in Figure 4A is a *horizontal asymptote* for the function. The graph of f gets closer to this line as x increases or decreases without bound.

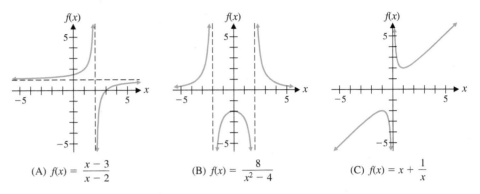

(A) $f(x) = \dfrac{x-3}{x-2}$ (B) $f(x) = \dfrac{8}{x^2-4}$ (C) $f(x) = x + \dfrac{1}{x}$

Figure 4 **Graphs of rational functions**

The number of vertical asymptotes of a rational function $f(x) = n(x)/d(x)$ is at most equal to the degree of $d(x)$. A rational function has at most one horizontal asymptote (note that the graph in Fig. 4C does not have a horizontal asymptote). Moreover, the graph of a rational function approaches the horizontal asymptote (when one exists) both as x increases and decreases without bound.

> **EXAMPLE 2**   Graphing Rational Functions **Given the rational function**
>
> $$f(x) = \frac{3x}{x^2 - 4}$$
>
> (A) Find the domain.
> (B) Find the x and y intercepts.
> (C) Find the equations of all vertical asymptotes.
> (D) If there is a horizontal asymptote, find its equation.
> (E) Using the information from (A)–(D) and additional points as necessary, sketch a graph of f.

SOLUTION

(A) $x^2 - 4 = (x - 2)(x + 2)$, so the denominator is 0 if $x = -2$ or $x = 2$. Therefore the domain is the set of all real numbers except -2 and 2.

(B) *x intercepts:* $f(x) = 0$ only if $3x = 0$, or $x = 0$. So the only x intercept is 0.
  y intercept:

$$f(0) = \frac{3 \cdot 0}{0^2 - 4} = \frac{0}{-4} = 0$$

So the y intercept is 0.

(C) Consider individually the values of x for which the denominator is 0, namely, 2 and -2, found in part (A).

  (i) If $x = 2$, the numerator is 6, and the denominator is 0, so $f(2)$ is undefined. But for numbers just to the right of 2 (like 2.1, 2.01, 2.001), the numerator is close to 6, and the denominator is a positive number close to 0, so the fraction $f(x)$ is large and positive. For numbers just to the left of 2 (like 1.9, 1.99, 1.999), the numerator is close to 6, and the denominator is a negative number close to 0, so the fraction $f(x)$ is large (in absolute value) and negative. Therefore, the line $x = 2$ is a vertical asymptote, and $f(x)$ is positive to the right of the asymptote, and negative to the left.

(ii) If $x = -2$, the numerator is -6, and the denominator is 0, so $f(2)$ is undefined. But for numbers just to the right of -2 (like -1.9, -1.99, -1.999), the numerator is close to -6, and the denominator is a negative number close to 0, so the fraction $f(x)$ is large and positive. For numbers just to the left of -2 (like -2.1, -2.01, -2.001), the numerator is close to -6, and the denominator is a positive number close to 0, so the fraction $f(x)$ is large (in absolute value) and negative. Therefore, the line $x = -2$ is a vertical asymptote, and $f(x)$ is positive to the right of the asymptote and negative to the left.

(D) Rewrite $f(x)$ by dividing each term in the numerator and denominator by the highest power of x in $f(x)$.

$$f(x) = \frac{3x}{x^2 - 4} = \frac{\dfrac{3x}{x^2}}{\dfrac{x^2}{x^2} - \dfrac{4}{x^2}} = \frac{\dfrac{3}{x}}{1 - \dfrac{4}{x^2}}$$

As x increases or decreases without bound, the numerator tends to 0 and the denominator tends to 1; so, $f(x)$ tends to 0. The line $y = 0$ is a horizontal asymptote.

(E) Use the information from parts (A)–(D) and plot additional points as necessary to complete the graph, as shown in Figure 5.

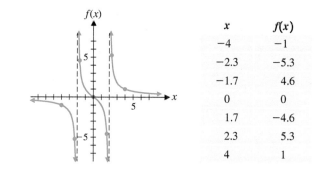

x	$f(x)$
-4	-1
-2.3	-5.3
-1.7	4.6
0	0
1.7	-4.6
2.3	5.3
4	1

Figure 5

Matched Problem 2 Given the rational function $g(x) = \dfrac{3x + 3}{x^2 - 9}$

(A) Find the domain.

(B) Find the x and y intercepts.

(C) Find the equations of all vertical asymptotes.

(D) If there is a horizontal asymptote, find its equation.

(E) Using the information from parts (A)–(D) and additional points as necessary, sketch a graph of g.

CONCEPTUAL INSIGHT

Consider the rational function

$$g(x) = \frac{3x^2 - 12x}{x^3 - 4x^2 - 4x + 16} = \frac{3x(x - 4)}{(x^2 - 4)(x - 4)}$$

The numerator and denominator of g have a common zero, $x = 4$. If $x \neq 4$, then we can cancel the factor $x - 4$ from the numerator and denominator, leaving the function $f(x)$ of Example 2. So the graph of g (Fig. 6) is identical to the graph of f (Fig. 5), except that the graph of g has an open dot at $(4, 1)$, indicating that 4 is not in the domain of g. In particular, f and g have the same asymptotes. Note that the line $x = 4$ is *not* a vertical asymptote of g, even though 4 is a zero of its denominator.

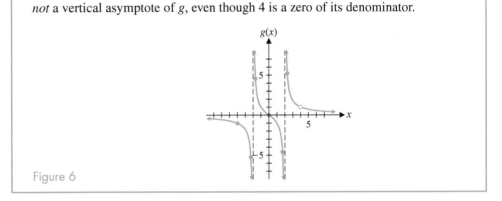

Figure 6

Graphing rational functions is aided by locating vertical and horizontal asymptotes first, if they exist. The following general procedure is suggested by Example 2 and the Conceptual Insight above.

PROCEDURE   Vertical and Horizontal Asymptotes of Rational Functions

Consider the rational function

$$f(x) = \frac{n(x)}{d(x)}$$

where $n(x)$ and $d(x)$ are polynomials.

Vertical asymptotes:

Case 1. Suppose $n(x)$ and $d(x)$ have no real zero in common. If c is a real number such that $d(c) = 0$, then the line $x = c$ is a vertical asymptote of the graph of f.

Case 2. If $n(x)$ and $d(x)$ have one or more real zeros in common, cancel common linear factors, and apply Case 1 to the reduced function. (The reduced function has the same asymptotes as f.)

Horizontal asymptote:

Case 1. If degree $n(x) <$ degree $d(x)$, then $y = 0$ is the horizontal asymptote.

Case 2. If degree $n(x) =$ degree $d(x)$, then $y = a/b$ is the horizontal asymptote, where a is the leading coefficient of $n(x)$, and b is the leading coefficient of $d(x)$.

Case 3. If degree $n(x) >$ degree $d(x)$, there is no horizontal asymptote.

Example 2 illustrates Case 1 of the procedure for horizontal asymptotes. Cases 2 and 3 are illustrated in Example 3 and Matched Problem 3.

EXAMPLE 3   Finding Asymptotes Find the vertical and horizontal asymptotes of the rational function

$$f(x) = \frac{3x^2 + 3x - 6}{2x^2 - 2}$$

SOLUTION   Vertical asymptotes   We factor the numerator $n(x)$ and the denominator $d(x)$:

$$n(x) = 3(x^2 + x - 2) = 3(x - 1)(x + 2)$$
$$d(x) = 2(x^2 - 1) = 2(x - 1)(x + 1)$$

The reduced function is

$$\frac{3(x + 2)}{2(x + 1)}$$

which, by the procedure, has the vertical asymptote $x = -1$. Therefore, $x = -1$ is the only vertical asymptote of f.

Horizontal asymptote   Both $n(x)$ and $d(x)$ have degree 2 (Case 2 of the procedure for horizontal asymptotes). The leading coefficient of the numerator $n(x)$ is 3, and the leading coefficient of the denominator $d(x)$ is 2. So $y = 3/2$ is the horizontal asymptote.

Matched Problem 3   Find the vertical and horizontal asymptotes of the rational function

$$f(x) = \frac{x^3 - 4x}{x^2 + 5x}$$

Explore and Discuss 1   A function f is **bounded** if the entire graph of f lies between two horizontal lines. The only polynomials that are bounded are the constant functions, but there are many rational functions that are bounded. Give an example of a bounded rational function, with domain the set of all real numbers, that is not a constant function.

Applications

Rational functions occur naturally in many types of applications.

EXAMPLE 4   *Employee Training*   A company that manufactures computers has established that, on the average, a new employee can assemble $N(t)$ components per day after t days of on-the-job training, as given by

$$N(t) = \frac{50t}{t + 4} \quad t \ge 0$$

Sketch a graph of $N, 0 \le t \le 100$, including any vertical or horizontal asymptotes. What does $N(t)$ approach as t increases without bound?

SOLUTION   *Vertical asymptotes*   None for $t \ge 0$

Horizontal asymptote

$$N(t) = \frac{50t}{t + 4} = \frac{50}{1 + \dfrac{4}{t}}$$

$N(t)$ approaches 50 (the leading coefficient of $50t$ divided by the leading coefficient of $t + 4$) as t increases without bound. So $y = 50$ is a horizontal asymptote.

Sketch of graph   The graph is shown in the margin.

$N(t)$ approaches 50 as t increases without bound. It appears that 50 components per day would be the upper limit that an employee would be expected to assemble.

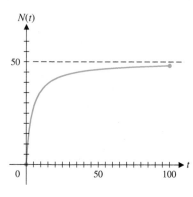

Matched Problem 4   Repeat Example 4 for $N(t) = \dfrac{25t + 5}{t + 5} \quad t \ge 0$.

Exercises 1.4

In Problems 1–10, for each polynomial function find the following:

(A) Degree of the polynomial

(B) All x intercepts

(C) The y intercept

1. $f(x) = 50 - 5x$

2. $f(x) = 72 + 12x$

3. $f(x) = x^4(x - 1)$

4. $f(x) = x^3(x + 5)$

5. $f(x) = x^2 + 3x + 2$

6. $f(x) = x^2 - 4x - 5$

7. $f(x) = (x^2 - 1)(x^2 - 9)$

8. $f(x) = (x^2 - 4)(x^3 + 27)$

9. $f(x) = (2x + 3)^4(x - 5)^5$

10. $f(x) = (x + 3)^2(8x - 4)^6$

Each graph in Problems 11–18 is the graph of a polynomial function. Answer the following questions for each graph:

(A) What is the minimum degree of a polynomial function that could have the graph?

(B) Is the leading coefficient of the polynomial negative or positive?

17.

18.

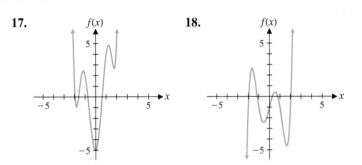

19. What is the maximum number of x intercepts that a polynomial of degree 10 can have?

20. What is the maximum number of x intercepts that a polynomial of degree 7 can have?

21. What is the minimum number of x intercepts that a polynomial of degree 9 can have? Explain.

22. What is the minimum number of x intercepts that a polynomial of degree 6 can have? Explain.

For each rational function in Problems 23–28,

(A) Find the intercepts for the graph.

(B) Determine the domain.

(C) Find any vertical or horizontal asymptotes for the graph.

(D) Sketch any asymptotes as dashed lines. Then sketch a graph of $y = f(x)$.

(E) Graph $y = f(x)$ in a standard viewing window using a graphing calculator.

23. $f(x) = \dfrac{x + 2}{x - 2}$

24. $f(x) = \dfrac{x - 3}{x + 3}$

25. $f(x) = \dfrac{3x}{x + 2}$

26. $f(x) = \dfrac{2x}{x - 3}$

27. $f(x) = \dfrac{4 - 2x}{x - 4}$

28. $f(x) = \dfrac{3 - 3x}{x - 2}$

29. Compare the graph of $y = 2x^4$ to the graph of $y = 2x^4 - 5x^2 + x + 2$ in the following two viewing windows:

(A) $-5 \le x \le 5, -5 \le y \le 5$

(B) $-5 \le x \le 5, -500 \le y \le 500$

30. Compare the graph of $y = x^3$ to the graph of $y = x^3 - 2x + 2$ in the following two viewing windows:

(A) $-5 \le x \le 5, -5 \le y \le 5$

(B) $-5 \le x \le 5, -500 \le y \le 500$

31. Compare the graph of $y = -x^5$ to the graph of $y = -x^5 + 4x^3 - 4x + 1$ in the following two viewing windows:

(A) $-5 \le x \le 5, -5 \le y \le 5$

(B) $-5 \le x \le 5, -500 \le y \le 500$

32. Compare the graph of $y = -x^5$ to the graph of 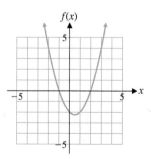 $y = -x^5 + 5x^3 - 5x + 2$ in the following two viewing windows:

(A) $-5 \leq x \leq 5, -5 \leq y \leq 5$

(B) $-5 \leq x \leq 5, -500 \leq y \leq 500$

In Problems 33–40, find the equation of any horizontal asymptote.

33. $f(x) = \dfrac{5x^3 + 2x - 3}{6x^3 - 7x + 1}$

34. $f(x) = \dfrac{6x^4 - x^3 + 2}{4x^4 + 10x + 5}$

35. $f(x) = \dfrac{1 - 5x + x^2}{2 + 3x + 4x^2}$

36. $f(x) = \dfrac{8 - x^3}{1 + 2x^3}$

37. $f(x) = \dfrac{x^4 + 2x^2 + 1}{1 - x^5}$

38. $f(x) = \dfrac{3 + 5x}{x^2 + x + 3}$

39. $f(x) = \dfrac{x^2 + 6x + 1}{x - 5}$

40. $f(x) = \dfrac{x^2 + x^4 + 1}{x^3 + 2x - 4}$

In Problems 41–46, find the equations of any vertical asymptotes.

41. $f(x) = \dfrac{x^2 + 1}{(x^2 - 1)(x^2 - 9)}$

42. $f(x) = \dfrac{2x + 5}{(x^2 - 4)(x^2 - 16)}$

43. $f(x) = \dfrac{x^2 - x - 6}{x^2 - 3x - 10}$

44. $f(x) = \dfrac{x^2 - 8x + 7}{x^2 + 7x - 8}$

45. $f(x) = \dfrac{x^2 + 3x}{x^3 - 36x}$

46. $f(x) = \dfrac{x^2 + x - 2}{x^3 - 3x^2 + 2x}$

For each rational function in Problems 47–52,

(A) *Find any intercepts for the graph.*

(B) *Find any vertical and horizontal asymptotes for the graph.*

(C) *Sketch any asymptotes as dashed lines. Then sketch a graph of f.*

(D) *Graph the function in a standard viewing window using a graphing calculator.*

47. $f(x) = \dfrac{2x^2}{x^2 - x - 6}$

48. $f(x) = \dfrac{3x^2}{x^2 + x - 6}$

49. $f(x) = \dfrac{6 - 2x^2}{x^2 - 9}$

50. $f(x) = \dfrac{3 - 3x^2}{x^2 - 4}$

51. $f(x) = \dfrac{-4x + 24}{x^2 + x - 6}$

52. $f(x) = \dfrac{5x - 10}{x^2 + x - 12}$

53. Write an equation for the lowest-degree polynomial function with the graph and intercepts shown in the figure.

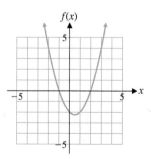

54. Write an equation for the lowest-degree polynomial function with the graph and intercepts shown in the figure.

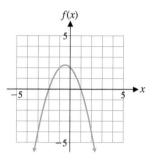

55. Write an equation for the lowest-degree polynomial function with the graph and intercepts shown in the figure.

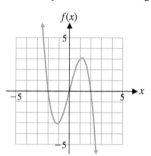

56. Write an equation for the lowest-degree polynomial function with the graph and intercepts shown in the figure.

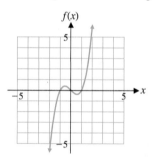

Applications

57. Average cost. A company manufacturing snowboards has fixed costs of $200 per day and total costs of $3,800 per day at a daily output of 20 boards.

(A) Assuming that the total cost per day, $C(x)$, is linearly related to the total output per day, x, write an equation for the cost function.

(B) The average cost per board for an output of x boards is given by $\overline{C}(x) = C(x)/x$. Find the average cost function.

(C) Sketch a graph of the average cost function, including any asymptotes, for $1 \leq x \leq 30$.

(D) What does the average cost per board tend to as production increases?

58. Average cost. A company manufacturing surfboards has fixed costs of $300 per day and total costs of $5,100 per day at a daily output of 20 boards.

(A) Assuming that the total cost per day, $C(x)$, is linearly related to the total output per day, x, write an equation for the cost function.

(B) The average cost per board for an output of x boards is given by $\overline{C}(x) = C(x)/x$. Find the average cost function.

(C) Sketch a graph of the average cost function, including any asymptotes, for $1 \leq x \leq 30$.

(D) What does the average cost per board tend to as production increases?

59. Replacement time. An office copier has an initial price of $2,500. A service contract costs $200 for the first year and increases $50 per year thereafter. It can be shown that the total cost of the copier after n years is given by

$$C(n) = 2,500 + 175n + 25n^2$$

The average cost per year for n years is given by $\overline{C}(n) = C(n)/n$.

(A) Find the rational function $\overline{C}$.

(B) Sketch a graph of $\overline{C}$ for $2 \leq n \leq 20$.

(C) When is the average cost per year at a minimum, and what is the minimum average annual cost? [*Hint:* Refer to the sketch in part (B) and evaluate $\overline{C}(n)$ at appropriate integer values until a minimum value is found.] The time when the average cost is minimum is frequently referred to as the **replacement time** for the piece of equipment.

(D) Graph the average cost function $\overline{C}$ on a graphing calculator and use an appropriate command to find when the average annual cost is at a minimum.

60. Minimum average cost. Financial analysts in a company that manufactures DVD players arrived at the following daily cost equation for manufacturing x DVD players per day:

$$C(x) = x^2 + 2x + 2,000$$

The average cost per unit at a production level of x players per day is $\overline{C}(x) = C(x)/x$.

(A) Find the rational function $\overline{C}$.

(B) Sketch a graph of $\overline{C}$ for $5 \leq x \leq 150$.

(C) For what daily production level (to the nearest integer) is the average cost per unit at a minimum, and what is the minimum average cost per player (to the nearest cent)? [*Hint:* Refer to the sketch in part (B) and evaluate $\overline{C}(x)$ at appropriate integer values until a minimum value is found.]

(D) Graph the average cost function $\overline{C}$ on a graphing calculator and use an appropriate command to find the daily production level (to the nearest integer) at which the average cost per player is at a minimum. What is the minimum average cost to the nearest cent?

61. Minimum average cost. A consulting firm, using statistical methods, provided a veterinary clinic with the cost equation

$$C(x) = 0.00048(x - 500)^3 + 60,000$$

$$100 \leq x \leq 1,000$$

where $C(x)$ is the cost in dollars for handling x cases per month. The average cost per case is given by $\overline{C}(x) = C(x)/x$.

(A) Write the equation for the average cost function $\overline{C}$.

(B) Graph $\overline{C}$ on a graphing calculator.

(C) Use an appropriate command to find the monthly caseload for the minimum average cost per case. What is the minimum average cost per case?

62. Minimum average cost. The financial department of a hospital, using statistical methods, arrived at the cost equation

$$C(x) = 20x^3 - 360x^2 + 2,300x - 1,000$$

$$1 \leq x \leq 12$$

where $C(x)$ is the cost in thousands of dollars for handling x thousand cases per month. The average cost per case is given by $\overline{C}(x) = C(x)/x$.

(A) Write the equation for the average cost function $\overline{C}$.

(B) Graph $\overline{C}$ on a graphing calculator.

(C) Use an appropriate command to find the monthly caseload for the minimum average cost per case. What is the minimum average cost per case to the nearest dollar?

63. Diet. Table 3 shows the per capita consumption of ice cream and eggs in the United States for selected years since 1980.

(A) Let x represent the number of years since 1980 and find a cubic regression polynomial for the per capita consumption of ice cream.

(B) Use the polynomial model from part (A) to estimate (to the nearest tenth of a pound) the per capita consumption of ice cream in 2025.

Table 3 **Per Capita Consumption of Ice Cream and Eggs**

Year	Ice Cream (pounds)	Eggs (number)
1980	17.5	266
1985	18.1	251
1990	15.8	231
1995	15.5	229
2000	16.5	247
2005	14.4	252
2010	13.3	242

Source: U.S. Department of Agriculture

64. Diet. Refer to Table 3.

(A) Let x represent the number of years since 1980 and find a cubic regression polynomial for the per capita consumption of eggs.

(B) Use the polynomial model from part (A) to estimate (to the nearest integer) the per capita consumption of eggs in 2022.

65. Physiology. In a study on the speed of muscle contraction in frogs under various loads, researchers W. O. Fenns and J. Marsh found that the speed of contraction decreases with increasing loads. In particular, they found that the relationship between speed of contraction v (in centimeters per second) and load x (in grams) is given approximately by

$$v(x) = \frac{26 + 0.06x}{x} \qquad x \geq 5$$

(A) What does $v(x)$ approach as x increases?

(B) Sketch a graph of function v.

66. Learning theory. In 1917, L. L. Thurstone, a pioneer in quantitative learning theory, proposed the rational function

$$f(x) = \frac{a(x + c)}{(x + c) + b}$$

to model the number of successful acts per unit time that a person could accomplish after x practice sessions. Suppose that for a particular person enrolled in a typing class,

$$f(x) = \frac{55(x + 1)}{(x + 8)} \quad x \geq 0$$

where $f(x)$ is the number of words per minute the person is able to type after x weeks of lessons.

(A) What does $f(x)$ approach as x increases?

(B) Sketch a graph of function f, including any vertical or horizontal asymptotes.

67. Marriage. Table 4 shows the marriage and divorce rates per 1,000 population for selected years since 1960.

(A) Let x represent the number of years since 1960 and find a cubic regression polynomial for the marriage rate.

(B) Use the polynomial model from part (A) to estimate the marriage rate (to one decimal place) for 2025.

Table 4 **Marriages and Divorces (per 1,000 population)**

Date	Marriages	Divorces
1960	8.5	2.2
1970	10.6	3.5
1980	10.6	5.2
1990	9.8	4.7
2000	8.5	4.1
2010	6.8	3.6

Source: National Center for Health Statistics

68. Divorce. Refer to Table 4.

(A) Let x represent the number of years since 1950 and find a cubic regression polynomial for the divorce rate.

(B) Use the polynomial model from part (A) to estimate the divorce rate (to one decimal place) for 2025.

Answers to Matched Problems

1.

2. (A) Domain: all real numbers except -3 and 3

   (B) x intercept: -1; y intercept: $-\frac{1}{3}$

   (C) Vertical asymptotes: $x = -3$ and $x = 3$;

   (D) Horizontal asymptote: $y = 0$

   (E)

3. Vertical asymptote: $x = -5$

   Horizontal asymptote: none

4. No vertical asymptotes for $t \geq 0$; $y = 25$ is a horizontal asymptote. $N(t)$ approaches 25 as t increases without bound. It appears that 25 components per day would be the upper limit that an employee would be expected to assemble.

1.5   Exponential Functions

- Exponential Functions
- Base e Exponential Functions
- Growth and Decay Applications
- Compound Interest

This section introduces an important class of functions called *exponential functions*. These functions are used extensively in modeling and solving a wide variety of real-world problems, including growth of money at compound interest, growth of populations, radioactive decay and learning associated with the mastery of such devices as a new computer or an assembly process in a manufacturing plant.

Exponential Functions

We start by noting that

$$f(x) = 2^x \quad \text{and} \quad g(x) = x^2$$

are not the same function. Whether a variable appears as an exponent with a constant base or as a base with a constant exponent makes a big difference. The function g is a quadratic function, which we have already discussed. The function f is a new type of function called an *exponential function*. In general,

DEFINITION Exponential Function

The equation

$$f(x) = b^x \quad b > 0, b \neq 1$$

defines an **exponential function** for each different constant b, called the **base**. The **domain** of f is the set of all real numbers, and the **range** of f is the set of all positive real numbers.

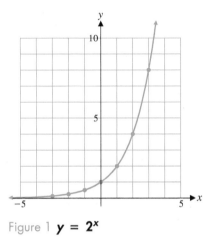

Figure 1 $y = 2^x$

We require the base b to be positive to avoid imaginary numbers such as $(-2)^{1/2} = \sqrt{-2} = i\sqrt{2}$. We exclude $b = 1$ as a base, since $f(x) = 1^x = 1$ is a constant function, which we have already considered.

When asked to hand-sketch graphs of equations such as $y = 2^x$ or $y = 2^{-x}$, many students do not hesitate. [*Note:* $2^{-x} = 1/2^x = (1/2)^x$.] They make tables by assigning integers to x, plot the resulting points, and then join these points with a smooth curve as in Figure 1. The only catch is that we have not defined 2^x for all real numbers. From Appendix A, Section A.6, we know what 2^5, 2^{-3}, $2^{2/3}$, $2^{-3/5}$, $2^{1.4}$, and $2^{-3.14}$ mean (that is, 2^p, where p is a rational number), but what does

$$2^{\sqrt{2}}$$

mean? The question is not easy to answer at this time. In fact, a precise definition of $2^{\sqrt{2}}$ must wait for more advanced courses, where it is shown that

$$2^x$$

names a positive real number for x any real number, and that the graph of $y = 2^x$ is as indicated in Figure 1.

It is useful to compare the graphs of $y = 2^x$ and $y = 2^{-x}$ by plotting both on the same set of coordinate axes, as shown in Figure 2A. The graph of

$$f(x) = b^x \quad b > 1 \text{ (Fig.2B)}$$

looks very much like the graph of $y = 2^x$, and the graph of

$$f(x) = b^x \quad 0 < b < 1 \text{ (Fig.2B)}$$

looks very much like the graph of $y = 2^{-x}$. Note that in both cases the x axis is a horizontal asymptote for the graphs.

The graphs in Figure 2 suggest the following general properties of exponential functions, which we state without proof:

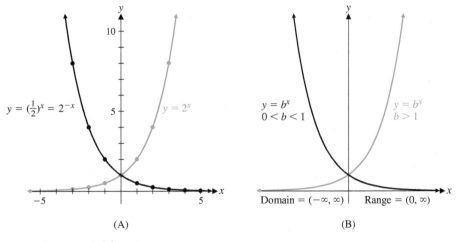

(A)

(B)

Figure 2 **Exponential functions**

THEOREM 1   Basic Properties of the Graph of $f(x) = b^x$, $b > 0$, $b \neq 1$

1. All graphs will pass through the point $(0,1)$. $b^0 = 1$ for any permissible base b.
2. All graphs are continuous curves, with no holes or jumps.
3. The x axis is a horizontal asymptote.
4. If $b > 1$, then b^x increases as x increases.
5. If $0 < b < 1$, then b^x decreases as x increases.

CONCEPTUAL INSIGHT

Recall that the graph of a rational function has at most one horizontal asymptote and that it approaches the horizontal asymptote (if one exists) both as $x \to \infty$ *and* as $x \to -\infty$ (see Section 1.4). The graph of an exponential function, on the other hand, approaches its horizontal asymptote as $x \to \infty$ *or* as $x \to -\infty$, but not both. In particular, there is no rational function that has the same graph as an exponential function.

The use of a calculator with the key $\boxed{y^x}$, or its equivalent, makes the graphing of exponential functions almost routine. Example 1 illustrates the process.

EXAMPLE 1   Graphing Exponential Functions   Sketch a graph of $y = \left(\frac{1}{2}\right)4^x$, $-2 \leq x \leq 2$.

SOLUTION   Use a calculator to create the table of values shown. Plot these points, and then join them with a smooth curve as in Figure 3.

x	y
-2	0.031
-1	0.125
0	0.50
1	2.00
2	8.00

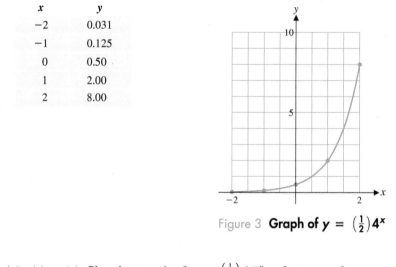

Figure 3 **Graph of $y = \left(\frac{1}{2}\right)4^x$**

Matched Problem 1   Sketch a graph of $y = \left(\frac{1}{2}\right)4^{-x}$, $-2 \leq x \leq 2$.

Exponential functions, whose domains include irrational numbers, obey the familiar laws of exponents discussed in Appendix A, Section A.6 for rational exponents. We summarize these exponent laws here and add two other important and useful properties.

THEOREM 2   Properties of Exponential Functions

For a and b positive, $a \neq 1$, $b \neq 1$, and x and y real,

1. Exponent laws:

$$a^x a^y = a^{x+y} \qquad \frac{a^x}{a^y} = a^{x-y}$$

$$\frac{4^{2y}}{4^{5y}} = 4^{2y-5y} = 4^{-3y}$$

$$(a^x)^y = a^{xy} \quad (ab)^x = a^x b^x \quad \left(\frac{a}{b}\right)^x = \frac{a^x}{b^x}$$

2. $a^x = a^y$ if and only if $x = y$

If $7^{5t+1} = 7^{3t-3}$, then
$5t + 1 = 3t - 3$, and $t = -2$.

3. For $x \neq 0$,

$a^x = b^x$ if and only if $a = b$

If $a^5 = 2^5$, then $a = 2$.

Base e Exponential Functions

Of all the possible bases b we can use for the exponential function $y = b^x$, which ones are the most useful? If you look at the keys on a calculator, you will probably see $\boxed{10^x}$ and $\boxed{e^x}$. It is clear why base 10 would be important, because our number system is a base 10 system. But what is e, and why is it included as a base? It turns out that base e is used more frequently than all other bases combined. The reason for this is that certain formulas and the results of certain processes found in calculus and more advanced mathematics take on their simplest form if this base is used. This is why you will see e used extensively in expressions and formulas that model real-world phenomena. In fact, its use is so prevalent that you will often hear people refer to $y = e^x$ as *the* exponential function.

The base e is an irrational number and, like π, it cannot be represented exactly by any finite decimal or fraction. However, e can be approximated as closely as we like by evaluating the expression

$$\left(1 + \frac{1}{x}\right)^x \tag{1}$$

for sufficiently large values of x. What happens to the value of expression (1) as x increases without bound? Think about this for a moment before proceeding. Maybe you guessed that the value approaches 1, because

$$1 + \frac{1}{x}$$

approaches 1, and 1 raised to any power is 1. Let us see if this reasoning is correct by actually calculating the value of the expression for larger and larger values of x. Table 1 summarizes the results.

Table 1

x	$\left(1 + \dfrac{1}{x}\right)^x$
1	2
10	2.593 74...
100	2.704 81...
1,000	2.716 92...
10,000	2.718 14...
100,000	2.718 27...
1,000,000	2.718 28...

Interestingly, the value of expression (1) is never close to 1 but seems to be approaching a number close to 2.7183. In fact, as x increases without bound, the value of expression (1) approaches an irrational number that we call e. The irrational number e to 12 decimal places is

$$e = 2.718\ 281\ 828\ 459$$

Compare this value of e with the value of e^1 from a calculator.

DEFINITION Exponential Function with Base e

Exponential function with base e and base $1/e$, respectively, are defined by

$$y = e^x \quad \text{and} \quad y = e^{-x}$$

Domain: $(-\infty, \infty)$

Range: $(0, \infty)$

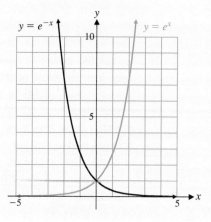

Explore and Discuss 1   Graph the functions $f(x) = e^x$, $g(x) = 2^x$, and $h(x) = 3^x$ on the same set of coordinate axes. At which values of x do the graphs intersect? For positive values of x, which of the three graphs lies above the other two? Below the other two? How does your answer change for negative values of x?

Growth and Decay Applications

Functions of the form $y = ce^{kt}$, where c and k are constants and the independent variable t represents time, are often used to model population growth and radioactive decay. Note that if $t = 0$, then $y = c$. So the constant c represents the initial population (or initial amount). The constant k is called the **relative growth rate** and has the following interpretation: Suppose that $y = ce^{kt}$ models the population of a country, where y is the number of persons and t is time in years. If the relative growth rate is $k = 0.02$, then at any time t, the population is growing at a rate of $0.02\,y$ persons (that is, 2% of the population) per year.

We say that **population is growing continuously at relative growth rate k** to mean that the population y is given by the model $y = ce^{kt}$.

EXAMPLE 2   Exponential Growth   Cholera, an intestinal disease, is caused by a cholera bacterium that multiplies exponentially. The number of bacteria grows continuously at relative growth rate 1.386, that is,

$$N = N_0 e^{1.386t}$$

Figure 4

where N is the number of bacteria present after t hours and N_0 is the number of bacteria present at the start $(t = 0)$. If we start with 25 bacteria, how many bacteria (to the nearest unit) will be present

(A) In 0.6 hour?   (B) In 3.5 hours?

SOLUTION   Substituting $N_0 = 25$ into the preceding equation, we obtain

$$N = 25e^{1.386t} \quad \text{The graph is shown in Figure 4.}$$

(A) Solve for N when $t = 0.6$:

$$N = 25e^{1.386(0.6)} \quad \text{Use a calculator.}$$
$$= 57 \text{ bacteria}$$

(B) Solve for N when $t = 3.5$:

$$N = 25e^{1.386(3.5)} \quad \text{Use a calculator.}$$
$$= 3,197 \text{ bacteria}$$

Matched Problem 2   Refer to the exponential growth model for cholera in Example 2. If we start with 55 bacteria, how many bacteria (to the nearest unit) will be present

(A) In 0.85 hour?   (B) In 7.25 hours?

EXAMPLE 3   Exponential Decay   Cosmic-ray bombardment of the atmosphere produces neutrons, which in turn react with nitrogen to produce radioactive carbon-14 (^{14}C). Radioactive ^{14}C enters all living tissues through carbon dioxide, which is first absorbed by plants. As long as a plant or animal is alive, ^{14}C is maintained in the living organism at a constant level. Once the organism dies, however, ^{14}C decays according to the equation

$$A = A_0 e^{-0.000124t}$$

where A is the amount present after t years and A_0 is the amount present at time $t = 0$.

(A) If 500 milligrams of ^{14}C is present in a sample from a skull at the time of death, how many milligrams will be present in the sample in 15,000 years? Compute the answer to two decimal places.

(B) The **half-life** of ^{14}C is the time t at which the amount present is one-half the amount at time $t = 0$. Use Figure 5 to estimate the half-life of ^{14}C.

SOLUTION   Substituting $A_0 = 500$ in the decay equation, we have

$$A = 500e^{-0.000124t} \quad \text{See the graph in Figure 5.}$$

(A) Solve for A when $t = 15,000$:

$$A = 500e^{-0.000124(15,000)} \quad \text{Use a calculator.}$$
$$= 77.84 \text{ milligrams}$$

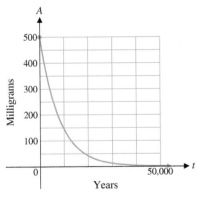

Figure 5

(B) Refer to Figure 5, and estimate the time t at which the amount A has fallen to 250 milligrams: $t \approx 6,000$ years. (Finding the intersection of $y_1 = 500e^{-0.000124x}$ and $y_2 = 250$ on a graphing calculator gives a better estimate: $t \approx 5,590$ years.)

Matched Problem 3   Refer to the exponential decay model in Example 3. How many milligrams of ^{14}C would have to be present at the beginning in order to have 25 milligrams present after 18,000 years? Compute the answer to the nearest milligram.

If you buy a new car, it is likely to depreciate in value by several thousand dollars during the first year you own it. You would expect the value of the car to decrease in each subsequent year, but not by as much as in the previous year. If you drive the car long enough, its resale value will get close to zero. An exponential decay function will often be a good model of depreciation; a linear or quadratic function would not be suitable (why?). We can use **exponential regression** on a graphing calculator to find the function of the form $y = ab^x$ that best fits a data set.

EXAMPLE 4 Depreciation Table 2 gives the market value of a hybrid sedan (in dollars) x years after its purchase. Find an exponential regression model of the form $y = ab^x$ for this data set. Estimate the purchase price of the hybrid. Estimate the value of the hybrid 10 years after its purchase. Round answers to the nearest dollar.

Table 2

x	Value ($)
1	12,575
2	9,455
3	8,115
4	6,845
5	5,225
6	4,485

SOLUTION Enter the data into a graphing calculator (Fig. 6A) and find the exponential regression equation (Fig. 6B). The estimated purchase price is $y_1(0) = \$14{,}910$. The data set and the regression equation are graphed in Figure 6C. Using TRACE, we see that the estimated value after 10 years is $1,959.

(A)   (B)   (C)

Figure 6

Matched Problem 4 Table 3 gives the market value of a midsize sedan (in dollars) x years after its purchase. Find an exponential regression model of the form $y = ab^x$ for this data set. Estimate the purchase price of the sedan. Estimate the value of the sedan 10 years after its purchase. Round answers to the nearest dollar.

Table 3

x	Value ($)
1	23,125
2	19,050
3	15,625
4	11,875
5	9,450
6	7,125

Compound Interest

The fee paid to use another's money is called **interest**. It is usually computed as a percent (called **interest rate**) of the principal over a given period of time. If, at the end of a payment period, the interest due is reinvested at the same rate, then the interest earned as well as the principal will earn interest during the next payment period. Interest paid on interest reinvested is called **compound interest** and may be calculated using the following compound interest formula:

If a **principal P (present value)** is invested at an annual **rate r** (expressed as a decimal) compounded m times a year, then the **amount A (future value)** in the account at the end of t years is given by

$$A = P\left(1 + \frac{r}{m}\right)^{mt} \qquad \text{Compound interest formula}$$

For given r and m, the amount A is equal to the principal P multiplied by the exponential function b^t, where $b = (1 + r/m)^m$.

EXAMPLE 5 Compound Growth   If $1,000 is invested in an account paying 10% compounded monthly, how much will be in the account at the end of 10 years? Compute the answer to the nearest cent.

SOLUTION We use the compound interest formula as follows:

$$A = P\left(1 + \frac{r}{m}\right)^{mt}$$

$$= 1,000\left(1 + \frac{0.10}{12}\right)^{(12)(10)} \qquad \text{Use a calculator.}$$

$$= \$2,707.04$$

The graph of

$$A = 1,000\left(1 + \frac{0.10}{12}\right)^{12t}$$

for $0 \le t \le 20$ is shown in Figure 7.

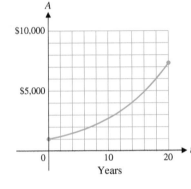

A

$10,000

$5,000

0   10   20 t

Years

Figure 7

Matched Problem 5   If you deposit $5,000 in an account paying 9% compounded daily, how much will you have in the account in 5 years? Compute the answer to the nearest cent.

Explore and Discuss 2   Suppose that $1,000 is deposited in a savings account at an annual rate of 5%. Guess the amount in the account at the end of 1 year if interest is compounded (1) quarterly, (2) monthly, (3) daily, (4) hourly. Use the compound interest formula to compute the amounts at the end of 1 year to the nearest cent. Discuss the accuracy of your initial guesses.

Explore and Discuss 2 suggests that if $1,000 were deposited in a savings account at an annual interest rate of 5%, then the amount at the end of 1 year would be less than $1,051.28, even if interest were compounded every minute or every second. The limiting value, approximately $1,051.271 096, is said to be the amount in the account if interest were compounded continuously.

If a principal, P, is invested at an annual rate, r, and compounded continuously, then the amount in the account at the end of t years is given by

$$A = Pe^{rt} \qquad \text{Continuous compound interest formula}$$

where the constant $e \approx 2.718\ 28$ is the base of the exponential function.

EXAMPLE 6 Continuous Compound Interest   If $1,000 is invested in an account paying 10% compounded continuously, how much will be in the account at the end of 10 years? Compute the answer to the nearest cent.

SOLUTION We use the continuous compound interest formula:

$$A = Pe^{rt} = 1000e^{0.10(10)} = 1000e = \$2{,}718.28$$

Compare with the answer to Example 5.

Matched Problem 6 If you deposit $5,000 in an account paying 9% compounded continuously, how much will you have in the account in 5 years? Compute the answer to the nearest cent.

The formulas for compound interest and continuous compound interest are summarized below for convenient reference.

SUMMARY

Compound Interest: $A = P\left(1 + \dfrac{r}{m}\right)^{mt}$

Continuous Compound Interest: $A = Pe^{rt}$

where A = amount (future value) at the end of t years
     P = principal (present value)
     r = annual rate (expressed as a decimal)
     m = number of compounding periods per year
     t = time in years

Exercises 1.5

1. Match each equation with the graph of f, g, h, or k in the figure.

(A) $y = 2^x$ (B) $y = (0.2)^x$

(C) $y = 4^x$ (D) $y = \left(\frac{1}{3}\right)^x$

2. Match each equation with the graph of f, g, h, or k in the figure.

(A) $y = \left(\frac{1}{4}\right)^x$ (B) $y = (0.5)^x$

(C) $y = 5^x$ (D) $y = 3^x$

Graph each function in Problems 3–10 over the indicated interval.

3. $y = 5^x$; $[-2, 2]$ **4.** $y = 3^x$; $[-3, 3]$

5. $y = \left(\frac{1}{5}\right)^x = 5^{-x}$; $[-2, 2]$ **6.** $y = \left(\frac{1}{3}\right)^x = 3^{-x}$; $[-3, 3]$

7. $f(x) = -5^x$; $[-2, 2]$ **8.** $g(x) = -3^{-x}$; $[-3, 3]$

9. $y = -e^{-x}$; $[-3, 3]$ **10.** $y = -e^x$; $[-3, 3]$

In Problems 11–18, describe verbally the transformations that can be used to obtain the graph of g from the graph of f (see Section 1.2).

11. $g(x) = -2^x$; $f(x) = 2^x$

12. $g(x) = 2^{x-2}$; $f(x) = 2^x$

13. $g(x) = 3^{x+1}$; $f(x) = 3^x$

14. $g(x) = -3^x$; $f(x) = 3^x$

15. $g(x) = e^x + 1$; $f(x) = e^x$

16. $g(x) = e^x - 2$; $f(x) = e^x$

17. $g(x) = 2e^{-(x+2)}$; $f(x) = e^{-x}$

18. $g(x) = 0.5e^{-(x-1)}$; $f(x) = e^{-x}$

19. Use the graph of f shown in the figure to sketch the graph of each of the following.

(A) $y = f(x) - 1$ (B) $y = f(x + 2)$

(C) $y = 3f(x) - 2$ (D) $y = 2 - f(x - 3)$

Figure for 19 and 20

20. Use the graph of f shown in the figure to sketch the graph of each of the following.

(A) $y = f(x) + 2$ (B) $y = f(x - 3)$

(C) $y = 2f(x) - 4$ (D) $y = 4 - f(x + 2)$

In Problems 21–26, graph each function over the indicated interval.

21. $f(t) = 2^{t/10}$; $[-30, 30]$ **22.** $G(t) = 3^{t/100}$; $[-200, 200]$

23. $y = -3 + e^{1+x}$; $[-4, 2]$ **24.** $y = 2 + e^{x-2}$; $[-1, 5]$

25. $y = e^{|x|}$; $[-3, 3]$ **26.** $y = e^{-|x|}$; $[-3, 3]$

27. Find all real numbers a such that $a^2 = a^{-2}$. Explain why this does not violate the second exponential function property in Theorem 2 on page 65.

28. Find real numbers a and b such that $a \neq b$ but $a^4 = b^4$. Explain why this does not violate the third exponential function property in Theorem 2 on page 65.

Solve each equation in Problems 29–34 for x.

29. $10^{2-3x} = 10^{5x-6}$ **30.** $5^{3x} = 5^{4x-2}$

31. $4^{5x-x^2} = 4^{-6}$ **32.** $7^{x^2} = 7^{2x+3}$

33. $5^3 = (x+2)^3$ **34.** $(1-x)^5 = (2x-1)^5$

In Problems 35–42, solve each equation for x. (Remember: $e^x \neq 0$ and $e^{-x} \neq 0$ for all values of x).

35. $xe^{-x} + 7e^{-x} = 0$ **36.** $10xe^x - 5e^x = 0$

37. $2x^2e^x - 8e^x = 0$ **38.** $x^2e^{-x} - 9e^{-x} = 0$

39. $e^{4x} - e = 0$ **40.** $e^{4x} + e = 0$

41. $e^{3x-1} + e = 0$ **42.** $e^{3x-1} - e = 0$

Graph each function in Problems 43–46 over the indicated interval.

43. $h(x) = x(2^x)$; $[-5, 0]$ **44.** $m(x) = x(3^{-x})$; $[0, 3]$

45. $N = \dfrac{100}{1 + e^{-t}}$; $[0, 5]$ **46.** $N = \dfrac{200}{1 + 3e^{-t}}$; $[0, 5]$

Applications

In all problems involving days, a 365-day year is assumed.

47. Continuous compound interest. Find the value of an investment of $10,000 in 12 years if it earns an annual rate of 3.95% compounded continuously.

48. Continuous compound interest. Find the value of an investment of $24,000 in 7 years if it earns an annual rate of 4.35% compounded continuously.

49. Compound growth. Suppose that $2,500 is invested at 7% compounded quarterly. How much money will be in the account in

(A) $\frac{3}{4}$ year? (B) 15 years?

Compute answers to the nearest cent.

50. Compound growth. Suppose that $4,000 is invested at 6% compounded weekly. How much money will be in the account in

(A) $\frac{1}{2}$ year? (B) 10 years?

Compute answers to the nearest cent.

51. Finance. A person wishes to have $15,000 cash for a new car 5 years from now. How much should be placed in an account now, if the account pays 6.75% compounded weekly? Compute the answer to the nearest dollar.

52. Finance. A couple just had a baby. How much should they invest now at 5.5% compounded daily in order to have $40,000 for the child's education 17 years from now? Compute the answer to the nearest dollar.

53. Money growth. BanxQuote operates a network of websites providing real-time market data from leading financial providers. The following rates for 12-month certificates of deposit were taken from the websites:

(A) Stonebridge Bank, 0.95% compounded monthly

(B) DeepGreen Bank, 0.80% compounded daily

(C) Provident Bank, 0.85% compounded quarterly

Compute the value of $10,000 invested in each account at the end of 1 year.

54. Money growth. Refer to Problem 53. The following rates for 60-month certificates of deposit were also taken from BanxQuote websites:

(A) Oriental Bank & Trust, 1.35% compounded quarterly

(B) BMW Bank of North America, 1.30% compounded monthly

(C) BankFirst Corporation, 1.25% compounded daily

Compute the value of $10,000 invested in each account at the end of 5 years.

55. Advertising. A company is trying to introduce a new product to as many people as possible through television advertising in a large metropolitan area with 2 million possible viewers. A model for the number of people N (in millions) who are aware of the product after t days of advertising was found to be

$$N = 2(1 - e^{-0.037t})$$

Graph this function for $0 \leq t \leq 50$. What value does N approach as t increases without bound?

56. Learning curve. People assigned to assemble circuit boards for a computer manufacturing company undergo on-the-job training. From past experience, the learning curve for the average employee is given by

$$N = 40(1 - e^{-0.12t})$$

where N is the number of boards assembled per day after t days of training. Graph this function for $0 \le t \le 30$. What is the maximum number of boards an average employee can be expected to produce in 1 day?

57. Sports salaries. Table 4 shows the average salaries for players in Major League Baseball (MLB) and the National Basketball Association (NBA) in selected years since 1990.

(A) Let x represent the number of years since 1990 and find an exponential regression model $(y = ab^x)$ for the average salary in MLB. Use the model to estimate the average salary (to the nearest thousand dollars) in 2022.

(B) The average salary in MLB in 2000 was 1.984 million. How does this compare with the value given by the model of part (A)?

Table 4 **Average Salary (thousand $)**

Year	MLB	NBA
1990	589	750
1993	1,062	1,300
1996	1,101	2,000
1999	1,724	2,400
2002	2,300	4,500
2005	2,633	5,000
2008	3,155	5,585
2011	3,298	4,755

58. Sports salaries. Refer to Table 4.

(A) Let x represent the number of years since 1990 and find an exponential regression model $(y = ab^x)$ for the average salary in the NBA. Use the model to estimate the average salary (to the nearest thousand dollars) in 2022.

(B) The average salary in the NBA in 1997 was $2.2 million. How does this compare with the value given by the model of part (A)?

59. Marine biology. Marine life depends on the microscopic plant life that exists in the photic zone, a zone that goes to a depth where only 1% of surface light remains. In some waters with a great deal of sediment, the photic zone may go down only 15 to 20 feet. In some murky harbors, the intensity of light d feet below the surface is given approximately by

$$I = I_0 e^{-0.23d}$$

What percentage of the surface light will reach a depth of

(A) 10 feet?   (B) 20 feet?

60. Marine biology. Refer to Problem 59. Light intensity I relative to depth d (in feet) for one of the clearest bodies of water in the world, the Sargasso Sea, can be approximated by

$$I = I_0 e^{-0.00942d}$$

where I_0 is the intensity of light at the surface. What percentage of the surface light will reach a depth of

(A) 50 feet?   (B) 100 feet?

61. World population growth. From the dawn of humanity to 1830, world population grew to one billion people. In 100 more years (by 1930) it grew to two billion, and 3 billion more were added in only 60 years (by 1990). In 2013, the estimated world population was 7.1 billion with a relative growth rate of 1.1%.

(A) Write an equation that models the world population growth, letting 2013 be year 0.

(B) Based on the model, what is the expected world population (to the nearest hundred million) in 2025? In 2035?

62. Population growth in Ethiopia. In 2012, the estimated population in Ethiopia was 94 million people with a relative growth rate of 3.2%.

(A) Write an equation that models the population growth in Ethiopia, letting 2012 be year 0.

(B) Based on the model, what is the expected population in Ethiopia (to the nearest million) in 2025? In 2035?

63. Internet growth. The number of Internet hosts grew very rapidly from 1994 to 2012 (Table 5).

(A) Let x represent the number of years since 1994. Find an exponential regression model $(y = ab^x)$ for this data set and estimate the number of hosts in 2022 (to the nearest million).

(B) Discuss the implications of this model if the number of Internet hosts continues to grow at this rate.

Table 5 **Internet Hosts (millions)**

Year	Hosts
1994	2.4
1997	16.1
2000	72.4
2003	171.6
2006	394.0
2009	625.2
2012	888.2

Source: Internet Software Consortium

64. Life expectancy. Table 6 shows the life expectancy (in years) at birth for residents of the United States from 1970 to 2010. Let x represent years since 1970. Find an exponential regression model for this data and use it to estimate the life expectancy for a person born in 2025.

Table 6

Year of Birth	Life Expectancy
1970	70.8
1975	72.6
1980	73.7
1985	74.7
1990	75.4
1995	75.9
2000	76.9
2005	77.7
2010	78.2

1.

2. (A) 179 bacteria   (B) 1,271,659 bacteria

3. 233 mg

4. Purchase price: $30,363; value after 10 yr: $2,864

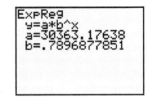

5. $7,841.13

6. $7,841.56

1.6 Logarithmic Functions

- Inverse Functions
- Logarithmic Functions
- Properties of Logarithmic Functions
- Calculator Evaluation of Logarithms
- Applications

Find the exponential function keys $\boxed{10^x}$ and $\boxed{e^x}$ on your calculator. Close to these keys you will find the $\boxed{\text{LOG}}$ and $\boxed{\text{LN}}$ keys. The latter two keys represent *logarithmic functions,* and each is closely related to its nearby exponential function. In fact, the exponential function and the corresponding logarithmic function are said to be *inverses* of each other. In this section we will develop the concept of inverse functions and use it to define a logarithmic function as the inverse of an exponential function. We will then investigate basic properties of logarithmic functions, use a calculator to evaluate them for particular values of x, and apply them to real-world problems.

Logarithmic functions are used in modeling and solving many types of problems. For example, the decibel scale is a logarithmic scale used to measure sound intensity, and the Richter scale is a logarithmic scale used to measure the force of an earthquake. An important business application has to do with finding the time it takes money to double if it is invested at a certain rate compounded a given number of times a year or compounded continuously. This requires the solution of an exponential equation, and logarithms play a central role in the process.

Inverse Functions

Look at the graphs of $f(x) = \dfrac{x}{2}$ and $g(x) = \dfrac{|x|}{2}$ in Figure 1:

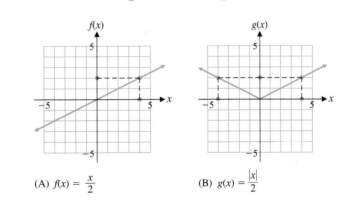

(A) $f(x) = \dfrac{x}{2}$ (B) $g(x) = \dfrac{|x|}{2}$

Figure 1

Because both f and g are functions, each domain value corresponds to exactly one range value. For which function does each range value correspond to exactly one domain value? This is the case only for function f. Note that for function f, the range value 2 corresponds to the domain value 4. For function g the range value 2 corresponds to both -4 and 4. Function f is said to be *one-to-one*.

DEFINITION   One-to-One Functions

A function f is said to be **one-to-one** if each range value corresponds to exactly one domain value.

It can be shown that any continuous function that is either increasing* or decreasing for all domain values is one-to-one. If a continuous function increases for some domain values and decreases for others, then it cannot be one-to-one. Figure 1 shows an example of each case.

Explore and Discuss 1

Graph $f(x) = 2^x$ and $g(x) = x^2$. For a range value of 4, what are the corresponding domain values for each function? Which of the two functions is one-to-one? Explain why.

Starting with a one-to-one function f, we can obtain a new function called the *inverse* of f.

DEFINITION   Inverse of a Function

If f is a one-to-one function, then the **inverse** of f is the function formed by interchanging the independent and dependent variables for f. Thus, if (a, b) is a point on the graph of f, then (b, a) is a point on the graph of the inverse of f.

Note: If f is not one-to-one, then f **does not have an inverse**.

In this course, we are interested in the inverses of exponential functions, called *logarithmic functions*.

Logarithmic Functions

If we start with the exponential function f defined by

$$y = 2^x \tag{1}$$

and interchange the variables, we obtain the inverse of f:

$$x = 2^y \tag{2}$$

We call the inverse the **logarithmic function with base 2**, and write

$$y = \log_2 x \quad \text{if and only if} \quad x = 2^y$$

We can graph $y = \log_2 x$ by graphing $x = 2^y$ since they are equivalent. Any ordered pair of numbers on the graph of the exponential function will be on the graph of the logarithmic function if we interchange the order of the components. For example, $(3, 8)$ satisfies equation (1) and $(8, 3)$ satisfies equation (2). The graphs of $y = 2^x$ and $y = \log_2 x$ are shown in Figure 2. Note that if we fold the paper along the dashed line $y = x$ in Figure 2, the two graphs match exactly. The line $y = x$ is a line of symmetry for the two graphs.

---

*Formally, we say that the function f is **increasing** on an interval (a, b) if $f(x_2) > f(x_1)$ whenever $a < x_1 < x_2 < b$; and f is **decreasing** on (a, b) if $f(x_2) < f(x_1)$ whenever $a < x_1 < x_2 < b$.

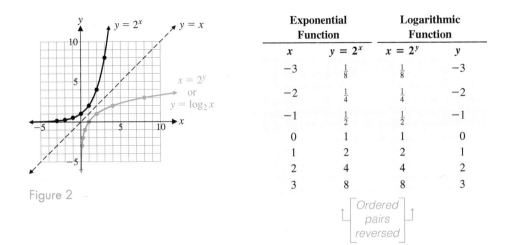

Figure 2

Exponential Function		Logarithmic Function	
x	$y = 2^x$	$x = 2^y$	y
-3	$\frac{1}{8}$	$\frac{1}{8}$	-3
-2	$\frac{1}{4}$	$\frac{1}{4}$	-2
-1	$\frac{1}{2}$	$\frac{1}{2}$	-1
0	1	1	0
1	2	2	1
2	4	4	2
3	8	8	3

Ordered pairs reversed

In general, since the graphs of all exponential functions of the form $f(x) = b^x$, $b \neq 1, b > 0$, are either increasing or decreasing, exponential functions have inverses.

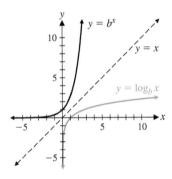

Figure 3

DEFINITION Logarithmic Functions

The inverse of an exponential function is called a **logarithmic function**. For $b > 0$ and $b \neq 1$,

Logarithmic form   Exponential form

$$y = \log_b x \qquad \text{is equivalent to} \qquad x = b^y$$

The **log to the base b of x** is the exponent to which b must be raised to obtain x. [*Remember:* A logarithm is an exponent.] The **domain** of the logarithmic function is the set of all positive real numbers, which is also the range of the corresponding exponential function; and the **range** of the logarithmic function is the set of all real numbers, which is also the domain of the corresponding exponential function. Typical graphs of an exponential function and its inverse, a logarithmic function, are shown in Figure 3.

CONCEPTUAL INSIGHT

Because the domain of a logarithmic function consists of the positive real numbers, the entire graph of a logarithmic function lies to the right of the y axis. In contrast, the graphs of polynomial and exponential functions intersect every vertical line, and the graphs of rational functions intersect all but a finite number of vertical lines.

The following examples involve converting logarithmic forms to equivalent exponential forms, and vice versa.

EXAMPLE 1 Logarithmic–Exponential Conversions Change each logarithmic form to an equivalent exponential form:

(A) $\log_5 25 = 2$ (B) $\log_9 3 = \frac{1}{2}$ (C) $\log_2\left(\frac{1}{4}\right) = -2$

SOLUTION

(A) $\log_5 25 = 2$ is equivalent to $25 = 5^2$

(B) $\log_9 3 = \frac{1}{2}$ is equivalent to $3 = 9^{1/2}$

(C) $\log_2\left(\frac{1}{4}\right) = -2$ is equivalent to $\frac{1}{4} = 2^{-2}$

Matched Problem 1 Change each logarithmic form to an equivalent exponential form:

(A) $\log_3 9 = 2$ (B) $\log_4 2 = \frac{1}{2}$ (C) $\log_3\left(\frac{1}{9}\right) = -2$

EXAMPLE 2 Exponential–Logarithmic Conversions Change each exponential form to an equivalent logarithmic form:

(A) $64 = 4^3$ (B) $6 = \sqrt{36}$ (C) $\frac{1}{8} = 2^{-3}$

SOLUTION

(A) $64 = 4^3$ is equivalent to $\log_4 64 = 3$

(B) $6 = \sqrt{36}$ is equivalent to $\log_{36} 6 = \frac{1}{2}$

(C) $\frac{1}{8} = 2^{-3}$ is equivalent to $\log_2\left(\frac{1}{8}\right) = -3$

Matched Problem 2 Change each exponential form to an equivalent logarithmic form:

(A) $49 = 7^2$ (B) $3 = \sqrt{9}$ (C) $\frac{1}{3} = 3^{-1}$

To gain a deeper understanding of logarithmic functions and their relationship to exponential functions, we consider a few problems where we want to find x, b, or y in $y = \log_b x$, given the other two values. All values are chosen so that the problems can be solved exactly without a calculator.

EXAMPLE 3 Solutions of the Equation $y = \log_b x$ Find y, b, or x, as indicated.

(A) Find y: $y = \log_4 16$ (B) Find x: $\log_2 x = -3$

(C) Find b: $\log_b 100 = 2$

SOLUTION

(A) $y = \log_4 16$ is equivalent to $16 = 4^y$. So,

$$y = 2$$

(B) $\log_2 x = -3$ is equivalent to $x = 2^{-3}$. So,

$$x = \frac{1}{2^3} = \frac{1}{8}$$

(C) $\log_b 100 = 2$ is equivalent to $100 = b^2$. So,

$$b = 10 \quad \text{Recall that } b \text{ cannot be negative.}$$

Matched Problem 3 Find y, b, or x, as indicated.

(A) Find y: $y = \log_9 27$ (B) Find x: $\log_3 x = -1$

(C) Find b: $\log_b 1{,}000 = 3$

Properties of Logarithmic Functions

The properties of exponential functions (Section 1.5) lead to properties of logarithmic functions. For example, consider the exponential property $b^x b^y = b^{x+y}$. Let $M = b^x$, $N = b^y$. Then

$$\log_b MN = \log_b(b^x b^y) = \log_b b^{x+y} = x + y = \log_b M + \log_b N$$

So $\log_b MN = \log_b M + \log_b N$, that is, the logarithm of a product is the sum of the logarithms. Similarly, the logarithm of a quotient is the difference of the logarithms. These properties are among the eight useful properties of logarithms that are listed in Theorem 1.

THEOREM 1   Properties of Logarithmic Functions

If b, M, and N are positive real numbers, $b \neq 1$, and p and x are real numbers, then

1. $\log_b 1 = 0$
2. $\log_b b = 1$
3. $\log_b b^x = x$
4. $b^{\log_b x} = x, \quad x > 0$

5. $\log_b MN = \log_b M + \log_b N$
6. $\log_b \dfrac{M}{N} = \log_b M - \log_b N$
7. $\log_b M^p = p \log_b M$
8. $\log_b M = \log_b N$ if and only if $M = N$

EXAMPLE 4   Using Logarithmic Properties

(A) $\log_b \dfrac{wx}{yz}$ $\quad\begin{aligned} &= \log_b wx - \log_b yz \\ &= \log_b w + \log_b x - (\log_b y + \log_b z) \\ &= \log_b w + \log_b x - \log_b y - \log_b z \end{aligned}$

(B) $\log_b (wx)^{3/5}$ $\quad = \frac{3}{5} \log_b wx \; = \frac{3}{5}(\log_b w + \log_b x)$

(C) $e^{x \log_e b} = e^{\log_e b^x} = b^x$

(D) $\dfrac{\log_e x}{\log_e b} = \dfrac{\log_e (b^{\log_b x})}{\log_e b} = \dfrac{(\log_b x)(\log_e b)}{\log_e b} = \log_b x$

Matched Problem 4   Write in simpler forms, as in Example 4.

(A) $\log_b \dfrac{R}{ST}$
(B) $\log_b \left(\dfrac{R}{S}\right)^{2/3}$
(C) $2^{u \log_2 b}$
(D) $\dfrac{\log_2 x}{\log_2 b}$

The following examples and problems will give you additional practice in using basic logarithmic properties.

EXAMPLE 5   Solving Logarithmic Equations   Find x so that

$$\tfrac{3}{2}\log_b 4 - \tfrac{2}{3}\log_b 8 + \log_b 2 = \log_b x$$

SOLUTION

$$\tfrac{3}{2}\log_b 4 - \tfrac{2}{3}\log_b 8 + \log_b 2 = \log_b x$$

$$\log_b 4^{3/2} - \log_b 8^{2/3} + \log_b 2 = \log_b x \quad \text{Property 7}$$

$$\log_b 8 - \log_b 4 + \log_b 2 = \log_b x$$

$$\log_b \dfrac{8 \cdot 2}{4} = \log_b x \quad \text{Properties 5 and 6}$$

$$\log_b 4 = \log_b x$$

$$x = 4 \quad \text{Property 8}$$

Matched Problem 5   Find x so that $3 \log_b 2 + \tfrac{1}{2}\log_b 25 - \log_b 20 = \log_b x$.

EXAMPLE 6   Solving Logarithmic Equations   Solve: $\log_{10} x + \log_{10}(x + 1) = \log_{10} 6$.

SOLUTION

$$\log_{10} x + \log_{10}(x + 1) = \log_{10} 6$$

$$\log_{10}[x(x + 1)] = \log_{10} 6 \quad \text{Property 5}$$

$$x(x + 1) = 6 \quad \text{Property 8}$$

$$x^2 + x - 6 = 0 \quad \text{Solve by factoring.}$$

$$(x + 3)(x - 2) = 0$$

$$x = -3, 2$$

We must exclude $x = -3$, since the domain of the function $\log_{10} x$ is $(0, \infty)$; so $x = 2$ is the only solution.

Matched Problem 6 Solve: $\log_3 x + \log_3(x - 3) = \log_3 10$.

Calculator Evaluation of Logarithms

Of all possible logarithmic bases, e and 10 are used almost exclusively. Before we can use logarithms in certain practical problems, we need to be able to approximate the logarithm of any positive number either to base 10 or to base e. And conversely, if we are given the logarithm of a number to base 10 or base e, we need to be able to approximate the number. Historically, tables were used for this purpose, but now calculators make computations faster and far more accurate.

Common logarithms are logarithms with base 10. **Natural logarithms** are logarithms with base e. Most calculators have a key labeled "log" (or "LOG") and a key labeled "ln" (or "LN"). The former represents a common (base 10) logarithm and the latter a natural (base e) logarithm. In fact, "log" and "ln" are both used extensively in mathematical literature, and whenever you see either used in this book without a base indicated, they will be interpreted as follows:

Common logarithm: $\log x$ means $\log_{10} x$
Natural logarithm: $\ln x$ means $\log_e x$

Finding the common or natural logarithm using a calculator is very easy. On some calculators, you simply enter a number from the domain of the function and press $\boxed{\text{LOG}}$ or $\boxed{\text{LN}}$. On other calculators, you press either $\boxed{\text{LOG}}$ or $\boxed{\text{LN}}$, enter a number from the domain, and then press $\boxed{\text{ENTER}}$. Check the user's manual for your calculator.

EXAMPLE 7 Calculator Evaluation of Logarithms Use a calculator to evaluate each to six decimal places:

(A) $\log 3,184$ (B) $\ln 0.000\ 349$ (C) $\log(-3.24)$

SOLUTION

(A) $\log 3,184 = 3.502\ 973$
(B) $\ln 0.000\ 349 = -7.960\ 439$
(C) $\log(-3.24) = $ Error*   −3.24 is not in the domain of the log function.

Matched Problem 7 Use a calculator to evaluate each to six decimal places:

(A) $\log 0.013\ 529$ (B) $\ln 28.693\ 28$ (C) $\ln(-0.438)$

Given the logarithm of a number, how do you find the number? We make direct use of the logarithmic-exponential relationships, which follow from the definition of logarithmic function given at the beginning of this section.

$\log x = y$ is equivalent to $x = 10^y$
$\ln x = y$ is equivalent to $x = e^y$

EXAMPLE 8 Solving $\log_b x = y$ for x Find x to four decimal places, given the indicated logarithm:

(A) $\log x = -2.315$ (B) $\ln x = 2.386$

SOLUTION

(A) $\log x = -2.315$ Change to equivalent exponential form.
   $x = 10^{-2.315}$ Evaluate with a calculator.
   $= 0.0048$

---

*Some calculators use a more advanced definition of logarithms involving complex numbers and will display an ordered pair of real numbers as the value of $\log(-3.24)$. You should interpret such a result as an indication that the number entered is not in the domain of the logarithm function as we have defined it.

(B) $\ln x = 2.386$ Change to equivalent exponential form.

$x = e^{2.386}$ Evaluate with a calculator.

$= 10.8699$

Matched Problem 8 Find x to four decimal places, given the indicated logarithm:

(A) $\ln x = -5.062$ (B) $\log x = 2.0821$

We can use logarithms to solve exponential equations.

EXAMPLE 9 Solving Exponential Equations Solve for x to four decimal places:

(A) $10^x = 2$ (B) $e^x = 3$ (C) $3^x = 4$

SOLUTION

(A) $10^x = 2$ Take common logarithms of both sides.

$\log 10^x = \log 2$ Property 3

$x = \log 2$ Use a calculator.

$= 0.3010$ To four decimal places

(B) $e^x = 3$ Take natural logarithms of both sides.

$\ln e^x = \ln 3$ Property 3

$x = \ln 3$ Use a calculator.

$= 1.0986$ To four decimal places

(C) $3^x = 4$ Take either natural or common logarithms of both sides. (We choose common logarithms.)

$\log 3^x = \log 4$ Property 7

$x \log 3 = \log 4$ Solve for x.

$x = \dfrac{\log 4}{\log 3}$ Use a calculator.

$= 1.2619$ To four decimal places

Matched Problem 9 Solve for x to four decimal places:

(A) $10^x = 7$ (B) $e^x = 6$ (C) $4^x = 5$

  Exponential equations can also be solved graphically by graphing both sides of an equation and finding the points of intersection. Figure 4 illustrates this approach for the equations in Example 9.

(A) $y_1 = 10^x$ (B) $y_1 = e^x$ (C) $y_1 = 3^x$
     $y_2 = 2$ $y_2 = 3$ $y_2 = 4$

Figure 4 **Graphical solution of exponential equations**

Explore and Discuss 2   Discuss how you could find $y = \log_5 38.25$ using either natural or common logarithms on a calculator. [*Hint:* Start by rewriting the equation in exponential form.]

Remark—In the usual notation for natural logarithms, the simplifications of Example 4, parts (C) and (D) on page 77, become

$$e^{x \ln b} = b^x \quad \text{and} \quad \frac{\ln x}{\ln b} = \log_b x$$

With these formulas, we can change an exponential function with base b, or a logarithmic function with base b, to expressions involving exponential or logarithmic functions, respectively, to the base e. Such **change-of-base formulas** are useful in calculus.

Applications

A convenient and easily understood way of comparing different investments is to use their **doubling times**—the length of time it takes the value of an investment to double. Logarithm properties, as you will see in Example 10, provide us with just the right tool for solving some doubling-time problems.

EXAMPLE 10   Doubling Time for an Investment How long (to the next whole year) will it take money to double if it is invested at 20% compounded annually?

SOLUTION We use the compound interest formula discussed in Section 1.5:

$$A = P\left(1 + \frac{r}{m}\right)^{mt} \quad \text{Compound interest}$$

The problem is to find t, given $r = 0.20$, $m = 1$, and $A = 2P$; that is,

$$2P = P(1 + 0.2)^t$$

$$2 = 1.2^t \qquad \text{Solve for } t \text{ by taking the natural or}$$
$$1.2^t = 2 \qquad \text{common logarithm of both sides (we choose}$$
$$\ln 1.2^t = \ln 2 \qquad \text{the natural logarithm).}$$
$$t \ln 1.2 = \ln 2 \qquad \text{Property 7}$$
$$t = \frac{\ln 2}{\ln 1.2} \qquad \text{Use a calculator.}$$
$$\approx 3.8 \text{ years} \qquad [\textit{Note: } (\ln 2)/(\ln 1.2) \neq \ln 2 - \ln 1.2]$$
$$\approx 4 \text{ years} \qquad \text{To the next whole year}$$

When interest is paid at the end of 3 years, the money will not be doubled; when paid at the end of 4 years, the money will be slightly more than doubled.

Example 10 can also be solved graphically by graphing both sides of the equation $2 = 1.2^t$, and finding the intersection point (Fig. 5).

Figure 5 $y_1 = 1.2^x$, $y_2 = 2$

Matched Problem 10   How long (to the next whole year) will it take money to triple if it is invested at 13% compounded annually?

It is interesting and instructive to graph the doubling times for various rates compounded annually. We proceed as follows:

$$A = P(1 + r)^t$$
$$2P = P(1 + r)^t$$
$$2 = (1 + r)^t$$
$$(1 + r)^t = 2$$
$$\ln(1 + r)^t = \ln 2$$
$$t \ln(1 + r) = \ln 2$$
$$t = \frac{\ln 2}{\ln(1 + r)}$$

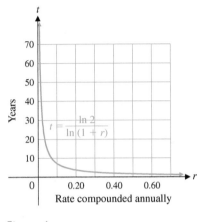

Figure 6

Figure 6 shows the graph of this equation (doubling time in years) for interest rates compounded annually from 1 to 70% (expressed as decimals). Note the dramatic change in doubling time as rates change from 1 to 20% (from 0.01 to 0.20).

Among increasing functions, the logarithmic functions (with bases $b > 1$) increase much more slowly for large values of x than either exponential or polynomial functions. When a visual inspection of the plot of a data set indicates a slowly increasing function, a logarithmic function often provides a good model. We use **logarithmic regression** on a graphing calculator to find the function of the form $y = a + b \ln x$ that best fits the data.

EXAMPLE 11   Home Ownership Rates The U.S. Census Bureau published the data in Table 1 on home ownership rates. Let x represent time in years with $x = 0$ representing 1900. Use logarithmic regression to find the best model of the form $y = a + b \ln x$ for the home ownership rate y as a function of time x. Use the model to predict the home ownership rate in the United States in 2025 (to the nearest tenth of a percent).

Table 1 **Home Ownership Rates**

Year	Rate (%)
1950	55.0
1960	61.9
1970	62.9
1980	64.4
1990	64.2
2000	67.4
2010	66.9

SOLUTION Enter the data in a graphing calculator (Fig. 7A) and find the logarithmic regression equation (Fig. 7B). The data set and the regression equation are graphed in Figure 7C. Using TRACE, we predict that the home ownership rate in 2025 would be 69.8%.

(A)   (B)   (C)

Figure 7

Matched Problem 11 Refer to Example 11. Use the model to predict the home ownership rate in the United States in 2030 (to the nearest tenth of a percent).

⚠️ **CAUTION** Note that in Example 11 we let $x = 0$ represent 1900. If we let $x = 0$ represent 1940, for example, we would obtain a different logarithmic regression equation. We would *not* let $x = 0$ represent 1950 (the first year in Table 1) or any later year, because logarithmic functions are undefined at 0.   ▲

Exercises 1.6

For Problems 1–6, rewrite in equivalent exponential form.

1. $\log_3 27 = 3$

2. $\log_2 32 = 5$

3. $\log_{10} 1 = 0$

4. $\log_e 1 = 0$

5. $\log_4 8 = \frac{3}{2}$

6. $\log_9 27 = \frac{3}{2}$

For Problems 7–12, rewrite in equivalent logarithmic form.

7. $49 = 7^2$

8. $36 = 6^2$

9. $8 = 4^{3/2}$

10. $9 = 27^{2/3}$

11. $A = b^u$

12. $M = b^x$

In Problems 13–20, evaluate the expression without using a calculator.

13. $\log_{10} 100$

14. $\log_{10} 100,000$

15. $\log_2 16$

16. $\log_3 \frac{1}{3}$

17. $\log_5 \frac{1}{25}$

18. $\log_4 1$

19. $\ln \frac{1}{e^4}$

20. $\ln e^{-5}$

For Problems 21–26, write in terms simpler forms, as in Example 4.

21. $\log_b \frac{P}{Q}$

22. $\log_b FG$

23. $\log_b L^5$

24. $\log_b w^{15}$

25. $3^{p \log_3 q}$

26. $\frac{\log_3 P}{\log_3 R}$

For Problems 27–34, find x, y, or b without a calculator.

27. $\log_3 x = 2$

28. $\log_2 x = 2$

29. $\log_7 49 = y$

30. $\log_3 27 = y$

31. $\log_b 10^{-4} = -4$

32. $\log_b e^{-2} = -2$

33. $\log_4 x = \frac{1}{2}$

34. $\log_{25} x = \frac{1}{2}$

✏️ *In Problems 35–42, discuss the validity of each statement. If the statement is always true, explain why. If not, give a counterexample.*

35. Every polynomial function is one-to-one.

36. Every polynomial function of odd degree is one-to-one.

37. If g is the inverse of a function f, then g is one-to-one.

38. The graph of a one-to-one function intersects each vertical line exactly once.

39. The inverse of $f(x) = 2x$ is $g(x) = x/2$.

40. The inverse of $f(x) = x^2$ is $g(x) = \sqrt{x}$.

41. If f is one-to-one, then the domain of f is equal to the range of f.

42. If g is the inverse of a function f, then f is the inverse of g.

Find x in Problems 43–50.

43. $\log_b x = \frac{2}{3}\log_b 8 + \frac{1}{2}\log_b 9 - \log_b 6$

44. $\log_b x = \frac{2}{3}\log_b 27 + 2\log_b 2 - \log_b 3$

45. $\log_b x = \frac{3}{2}\log_b 4 - \frac{2}{3}\log_b 8 + 2\log_b 2$

46. $\log_b x = 3\log_b 2 + \frac{1}{2}\log_b 25 - \log_b 20$

47. $\log_b x + \log_b (x - 4) = \log_b 21$

48. $\log_b(x + 2) + \log_b x = \log_b 24$

49. $\log_{10}(x - 1) - \log_{10}(x + 1) = 1$

50. $\log_{10}(x + 6) - \log_{10}(x - 3) = 1$

Graph Problems 51 and 52 by converting to exponential form first.

51. $y = \log_2 (x - 2)$

52. $y = \log_3 (x + 2)$

✏️ **53.** Explain how the graph of the equation in Problem 51 can be obtained from the graph of $y = \log_2 x$ using a simple transformation (see Section 1.2).

✏️ **54.** Explain how the graph of the equation in Problem 52 can be obtained from the graph of $y = \log_3 x$ using a simple transformation (see Section 1.2).

55. What are the domain and range of the function defined by $y = 1 + \ln(x + 1)$?

56. What are the domain and range of the function defined by $y = \log (x - 1) - 1$?

For Problems 57 and 58, evaluate to five decimal places using a calculator.

57. (A) $\log 3{,}527.2$

(B) $\log 0.006\,913\,2$

(C) $\ln 277.63$

(D) $\ln 0.040\,883$

58. (A) log 72.604   (B) log 0.033 041

(C) ln 40,257   (D) ln 0.005 926 3

For Problems 59 and 60, find x to four decimal places.

59. (A) $\log x = 1.1285$ (B) $\log x = -2.0497$

(C) $\ln x = 2.7763$ (D) $\ln x = -1.8879$

60. (A) $\log x = 2.0832$ (B) $\log x = -1.1577$

(C) $\ln x = 3.1336$ (D) $\ln x = -4.3281$

For Problems 61–66, solve each equation to four decimal places.

61. $10^x = 12$ **62.** $10^x = 153$

63. $e^x = 4.304$ **64.** $e^x = 0.3059$

65. $1.005^{12t} = 3$ **66.** $1.02^{4t} = 2$

Graph Problems 67–74 using a calculator and point-by-point plotting. Indicate increasing and decreasing intervals.

67. $y = \ln x$ **68.** $y = -\ln x$

69. $y = |\ln x|$ **70.** $y = \ln|x|$

71. $y = 2\ln(x + 2)$ **72.** $y = 2\ln x + 2$

73. $y = 4\ln x - 3$ **74.** $y = 4\ln(x - 3)$

75. Explain why the logarithm of 1 for any permissible base is 0.

76. Explain why 1 is not a suitable logarithmic base.

77. Let $p(x) = \ln x$, $q(x) = \sqrt{x}$, and $r(x) = x$. Use a graphing calculator to draw graphs of all three functions in the same viewing window for $1 \le x \le 16$. Discuss what it means for one function to be larger than another on an interval, and then order the three functions from largest to smallest for $1 < x \le 16$.

78. Let $p(x) = \log x$, $q(x) = \sqrt[3]{x}$, and $r(x) = x$. Use a graphing calculator to draw graphs of all three functions in the same viewing window for $1 \le x \le 16$. Discuss what it means for one function to be smaller than another on an interval, and then order the three functions from smallest to largest for $1 < x \le 16$.

Applications

79. Doubling time. In its first 10 years the Gabelli Growth Fund produced an average annual return of 21.36%. Assume that money invested in this fund continues to earn 21.36% compounded annually. How long (to the nearest year) will it take money invested in this fund to double?

80. Doubling time. In its first 10 years the Janus Flexible Income Fund produced an average annual return of 9.58%. Assume that money invested in this fund continues to earn 9.58% compounded annually. How long (to the nearest year) will it take money invested in this fund to double?

81. Investing. How many years (to two decimal places) will it take $1,000 to grow to $1,800 if it is invested at 6% compounded quarterly? Compounded daily?

82. Investing. How many years (to two decimal places) will it take $5,000 to grow to $7,500 if it is invested at 8% compounded semiannually? Compounded monthly?

83. Continuous compound interest. How many years (to two decimal places) will it take an investment of $35,000 to grow to $50,000 if it is invested at 4.75% compounded continuously?

84. Continuous compound interest. How many years (to two decimal places) will it take an investment of $17,000 to grow to $41,000 if it is invested at 2.95% compounded continuously?

85. Supply and demand. A cordless screwdriver is sold through a national chain of discount stores. A marketing company established price–demand and price–supply tables (Tables 2 and 3), where x is the number of screwdrivers people are willing to buy and the store is willing to sell each month at a price of p dollars per screwdriver.

(A) Find a logarithmic regression model $(y = a + b\ln x)$ for the data in Table 2. Estimate the demand (to the nearest unit) at a price level of $50.

Table 2 **Price–Demand**

x	$p = D(x)$ ($)
1,000	91
2,000	73
3,000	64
4,000	56
5,000	53

(B) Find a logarithmic regression model $(y = a + b\ln x)$ for the data in Table 3. Estimate the supply (to the nearest unit) at a price level of $50.

Table 3 **Price–Supply**

x	$p = S(x)$ ($)
1,000	9
2,000	26
3,000	34
4,000	38
5,000	41

(C) Does a price level of $50 represent a stable condition, or is the price likely to increase or decrease? Explain.

86. Equilibrium point. Use the models constructed in Problem 85 to find the equilibrium point. Write the equilibrium price to the nearest cent and the equilibrium quantity to the nearest unit.

87. Sound intensity: decibels. Because of the extraordinary range of sensitivity of the human ear (a range of over 1,000 million millions to 1), it is helpful to use a logarithmic scale, rather than an absolute scale, to measure sound intensity over this range. The unit of measure is called the *decibel,* after the inventor of the telephone, Alexander Graham Bell. If we let N be the number of decibels, I the power of the sound in question (in watts per square centimeter), and I_0 the power of sound just below the threshold of hearing (approximately 10^{-16} watt per square centimeter), then

$$I = I_0 10^{N/10}$$

Show that this formula can be written in the form

$$N = 10 \log \frac{I}{I_0}$$

88. Sound intensity: decibels. Use the formula in Problem 87 (with $I_0 = 10^{-16}$ W/cm^2) to find the decibel ratings of the following sounds:

(A) Whisper: 10^{-13} W/cm^2

(B) Normal conversation: 3.16×10^{-10} W/cm^2

(C) Heavy traffic: 10^{-8} W/cm^2

(D) Jet plane with afterburner: 10^{-1} W/cm^2

89. Agriculture. Table 4 shows the yield (in bushels per acre) and the total production (in millions of bushels) for corn in the United States for selected years since 1950. Let x

Table 4 **United States Corn Production**

Year	x	Yield (bushels per acre)	Total Production (million bushels)
1950	50	38	2,782
1960	60	56	3,479
1970	70	81	4,802
1980	80	98	6,867
1990	90	116	7,802
2000	100	140	10,192
2010	110	153	12,447

represent years since 1900. Find a logarithmic regression model $(y = a + b \ln x)$ for the yield. Estimate (to the nearest bushel per acre) the yield in 2024.

90. Agriculture. Refer to Table 4. Find a logarithmic regression model $(y = a + b \ln x)$ for the total production. Estimate (to the nearest million) the production in 2024.

91. World population. If the world population is now 7.1 billion people and if it continues to grow at an annual rate of 1.1% compounded continuously, how long (to the nearest year) would it take before there is only 1 square yard of land per person? (The Earth contains approximately 1.68×10^{14} square yards of land.)

92. Archaeology: carbon-14 dating. The radioactive carbon-14 (^{14}C) in an organism at the time of its death decays according to the equation

$$A = A_0 e^{-0.000124t}$$

where t is time in years and A_0 is the amount of ^{14}C present at time $t = 0$. (See Example 3 in Section 1.5.) Estimate the age of a skull uncovered in an archaeological site if 10% of the original amount of ^{14}C is still present. [*Hint:* Find t such that $A = 0.1A_0$.]

Answers to Matched Problems

1. (A) $9 = 3^2$ (B) $2 = 4^{1/2}$ (C) $\frac{1}{9} = 3^{-2}$

2. (A) $\log_7 49 = 2$ (B) $\log_9 3 = \frac{1}{2}$ (C) $\log_3 \left(\frac{1}{3}\right) = -1$

3. (A) $y = \frac{3}{2}$ (B) $x = \frac{1}{3}$ (C) $b = 10$

4. (A) $\log_b R - \log_b S - \log_b T$ (B) $\frac{2}{3}(\log_b R - \log_b S)$
    (C) b^u (D) $\log_b x$

5. $x = 2$ 6. $x = 5$

7. (A) $-1.868\,734$ (B) $3.356\,663$ (C) Not defined

8. (A) 0.0063 (B) 120.8092

9. (A) 0.8451 (B) 1.7918 (C) 1.1610

10. 9 yr   11. 70.3%

Chapter 1   Summary and Review

Important Terms, Symbols, and Concepts

1.1 Functions

EXAMPLES

- A **Cartesian or rectangular coordinate system** is formed by the intersection of a horizontal real number line, usually called the *x* **axis**, and a vertical real number line, usually called the *y* **axis**, at their origins. The axes determine a plane and divide this plane into four **quadrants**. Each point in the plane corresponds to its **coordinates**—an ordered pair (a, b) determined by passing horizontal and vertical lines through the point. The **abscissa** or *x* **coordinate** a is the coordinate of the intersection of the vertical line and the *x* axis, and the **ordinate** or *y* **coordinate** b is the coordinate of the intersection of the horizontal line and the *y* axis. The point with coordinates $(0, 0)$ is called the **origin**.

- **Point-by-point plotting** may be used to **sketch the graph** of an equation in two variables: Plot enough points from its **solution set** in a rectangular cordinate system so that the total graph is apparent and then connect these points with a smooth curve.

Ex. 1, p. 4

- A **function** is a correspondence between two sets of elements such that to each element in the first set there corresponds one and only one element in the second set. The first set is called the **domain** and the set of corresponding elements in the second set is called the **range**.

- If x is a placeholder for the elements in the domain of a function, then x is called the **independent variable** or the **input**. If y is a placeholder for the elements in the range, then y is called the **dependent variable** or the **output**.

- If in an equation in two variables we get exactly one output for each input, then the equation specifies a function. The graph of such a function is just the graph of the specifying equation. If we get more than one output for a given input, then the equation does not specify a function.

Ex. 2, p. 7

- The **vertical-line test** can be used to determine whether or not an equation in two variables specifies a function (Theorem 1, p. 8).

- The functions specified by equations of the form $y = mx + b$, where $m \neq 0$, are called **linear functions**. Functions specified by equations of the form $y = b$ are called **constant functions**.

- If a function is specified by an equation and the domain is not indicated, we agree to assume that the domain is the set of all inputs that produce outputs that are real numbers.

Ex. 3, p. 8
Ex. 5, p. 10

- The symbol $f(x)$ represents the element in the range of f that corresponds to the element x of the domain.

Ex. 4, p. 9
Ex. 6, p. 11

- **Break-even** and **profit–loss** analysis use a cost function C and a revenue function R to determine when a company will have a loss $(R < C)$, will break even $(R = C)$, or will have a profit $(R > C)$. Typical **cost**, **revenue**, **profit**, and **price–demand functions** are given on page 11.

Ex. 7, p. 12

1.2 Elementary Functions: Graphs and Transformations

- The graphs of **six basic elementary functions** (the identity function, the square and cube functions, the square root and cube root functions, and the absolute value function) are shown on page 19.

Ex. 1, p. 18

- Performing an operation on a function produces a **transformation** of the graph of the function. The basic graph transformations, **vertical and horizontal translations** (shifts), **reflection in the x axis**, and **vertical stretches and shrinks**, are summarized on pages 21 and 23.

Ex. 2, p. 20
Ex. 3, p. 21
Ex. 4, p. 22

- A **piecewise-defined function** is a function whose definition uses different rules for different parts of its domain.

Ex. 5, p. 24
Ex. 6, p. 24
Ex. 7, p. 25

1.3 Linear and Quadratic Functions

- A **mathematical model** is a mathematics problem that, when solved, will provide information about a real-world problem.

- A **linear equation in two variables** is an equation that can be written in the **standard form** $Ax + By = C$, where A, B, and C are constants (A and B are not both zero), and x and y are variables.

- The graph of a linear equation in two variables is a line, and every line in a Cartesian coordinate system is the graph of an equation of the form $Ax + By = C$.

Ex. 2, p. 32

- If (x_1, y_1) and (x_2, y_2) are two points on a line with $x_1 \neq x_2$, then the **slope** of the line is $m = \dfrac{y_2 - y_1}{x_2 - x_1}$.

- The **point-slope form** of the line with slope m that passes through the point (x_1, y_1) is $y - y_1 = m(x - x_1)$.

Ex. 1, p. 32

- The **slope-intercept form** of the line with slope m that has y intercept b is $y = mx + b$.

- The graph of the equation $x = a$ is a **vertical line**, and the graph of $y = b$ is a **horizontal line**.

- A function of the form $f(x) = mx + b$, where $m \neq 0$, is a **linear function**.

- A function of the form $f(x) = ax^2 + bx + c$, where $a \neq 0$, is a **quadratic function** in **standard form**, and its graph is a **parabola**.

Ex. 3, p. 35

1.3 Linear and Quadratic Functions (*Continued*)

- Completing the square in the standard form of a quadratic function produces the **vertex form**

$$f(x) = a(x - h)^2 + k \quad \text{Vertex form}$$

Ex. 4, p. 39
Ex. 6, p. 42

- From the vertex form of a quadratic function, we can read off the vertex, axis of symmetry, maximum or minimum, and range, and can easily sketch the graph (p. 38).

- In a competitive market, the intersection of the supply equation and the demand equation is called the **equilibrium point**, the corresponding price is called the **equilibrium price**, and the common value of supply and demand is called the **equilibrium quantity**.

Ex. 5, p. 40

- A graph of the points in a data set is called a **scatter plot**. **Linear regression** can be used to find the linear function (line) that is the best fit for a data set. **Quadratic regression** can be used to find the quadratic function (parabola) that is the best fit.

Ex. 7, p. 43
Ex. 8, p. 44

1.4 Polynomial and Rational Functions

- A **polynomial function** is a function that can be written in the form

$$f(x) = a_n x^n + a_{n-1} x^{n-1} + \cdots + a_1 x + a_0$$

for n a nonnegative integer called the **degree** of the polynomial. The coefficients $a_0, a_1, \ldots, a_n$ are real numbers with **leading coefficient** $a_n \neq 0$. The **domain** of a polynomial function is the set of all real numbers. Graphs of representative polynomial functions are shown on page 52 and inside the front cover.

- The graph of a polynomial function of degree n can intersect the x axis at most n times. An x intercept is also called a **zero** or **root**.

- The graph of a polynomial function has no sharp corners and is **continuous**, that is, it has no holes or breaks.

- **Polynomial regression** produces a polynomial of specified degree that best fits a data set.

Ex. 1, p. 53

- A **rational function** is any function that can be written in the form

$$f(x) = \frac{n(x)}{d(x)} \qquad d(x) \neq 0$$

where $n(x)$ and $d(x)$ are polynomials. The **domain** is the set of all real numbers such that $d(x) \neq 0$. Graphs of representative rational functions are shown on page 55 and inside the front cover.

- Unlike polynomial functions, a rational function can have vertical asymptotes [but not more than the degree of the denominator $d(x)$] and at most one horizontal asymptote.

Ex. 2, p. 55

- A procedure for finding the vertical and horizontal asymptotes of a rational function is given on page 57.

Ex. 3, p. 57

1.5 Exponential Functions

- An **exponential function** is a function of the form

$$f(x) = b^x$$

where $b \neq 1$ is a positive constant called the **base**. The **domain** of f is the set of all real numbers, and the **range** is the set of positive real numbers.

- The graph of an exponential function is continuous, passes through $(0, 1)$, and has the x axis as a horizontal asymptote. If $b > 1$, then b^x increases as x increases; if $0 < b < 1$, then b^x decreases as x increases (Theorem 1, p. 64).

Ex. 1, p. 64

- Exponential functions obey the familiar laws of exponents and satisfy additional properties (Theorem 2, p. 65).

- The base that is used most frequently in mathematics is the irrational number $e \approx 2.7183$.

Ex. 2, p. 66

- Exponential functions can be used to model population growth and radioactive decay.

Ex. 3, p. 67

- **Exponential regression** on a graphing calculator produces the function of the form $y = ab^x$ that best fits a data set.

Ex. 4, p. 68

- Exponential functions are used in computations of **compound interest** and **continuous compound interest**:

$$A = P\left(1 + \frac{r}{m}\right)^{mt} \qquad \text{Compound interest}$$

$$A = Pe^{rt} \qquad \text{Continuous compound interest}$$

(see summary on p. 70).

1.6 Logarithmic Functions

- A function is said to be **one-to-one** if each range value corresponds to exactly one domain value.

- The **inverse** of a one-to-one function f is the function formed by interchanging the independent and dependent variables of f. That is, (a, b) is a point on the graph of f if and only if (b, a) is a point on the graph of the inverse of f. A function that is not one-to-one does not have an inverse.

- The inverse of the exponential function with base b is called the **logarithmic function with base b**, denoted $y = \log_b x$. The **domain** of $\log_b x$ is the set of all positive real numbers (which is the range of b^x), and the range of $\log_b x$ is the set of all real numbers (which is the domain of b^x).

- Because $\log_b x$ is the inverse of the function b^x,

Logarithmic form		Exponential form
$y = \log_b x$	is equivalent to	$x = b^y$

- Properties of logarithmic functions can be obtained from corresponding properties of exponential functions (Theorem 1, p. 77).

- Logarithms to the base 10 are called **common logarithms**, often denoted simply by log x. Logarithms to the base e are called **natural logarithms**, often denoted by ln x.

- Logarithms can be used to find an investment's **doubling time**—the length of time it takes for the value of an investment to double.

- **Logarithmic regression** on a graphing calculator produces the function of the form $y = a + b \ln x$ that best fits a data set.

Review Exercises

Work through all the problems in this chapter review and check your answers in the back of the book. Answers to all review problems are there along with section numbers in italics to indicate where each type of problem is discussed. Where weaknesses show up, review appropriate sections in the text.

In Problems 1–3, use point-by-point plotting to sketch the graph of each equation.

1. $y = 5 - x^2$

2. $x^2 = y^2$

3. $y^2 = 4x^2$

4. Indicate whether each graph specifies a function:

(A)

(B)

(C)

(D)

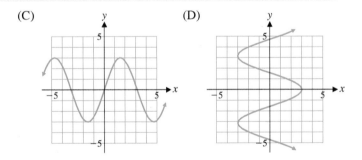

5. For $f(x) = 2x - 1$ and $g(x) = x^2 - 2x$, find:

(A) $f(-2) + g(-1)$ (B) $f(0) \cdot g(4)$

(C) $\dfrac{g(2)}{f(3)}$ (D) $\dfrac{f(3)}{g(2)}$

6. Sketch a graph of $3x + 2y = 9$.

7. Write an equation of a line with x intercept 6 and y intercept 4. Write the final answer in the form $Ax + By = C$.

8. Sketch a graph of $2x - 3y = 18$. What are the intercepts and slope of the line?

9. Write an equation in the form $y = mx + b$ for a line with slope $-\dfrac{2}{3}$ and y intercept 6.

10. Write the equations of the vertical line and the horizontal line that pass through $(-6, 5)$.

11. Write the equation of a line through each indicated point with the indicated slope. Write the final answer in the form $y = mx + b$.

   (A) $m = -\dfrac{2}{3}; (-3, 2)$ (B) $m = 0; (3, 3)$

12. Write the equation of the line through the two indicated points. Write the final answer in the form $Ax + By = C$.

   (A) $(-3, 5), (1, -1)$ (B) $(-1, 5), (4, 5)$

   (C) $(-2, 7), (-2, -2)$

13. Write in logarithmic form using base e: $u = e^v$.

14. Write in logarithmic form using base 10: $x = 10^y$.

15. Write in exponential form using base e: $\ln M = N$.

16. Write in exponential form using base 10: $\log u = v$.

Solve Problems 17–19 for x exactly without using a calculator.

17. $\log_3 x = 2$ **18.** $\log_x 36 = 2$

19. $\log_2 16 = x$

Solve problems 20–23 for x to three decimal places.

20. $10^x = 143.7$ **21.** $e^x = 503,000$

22. $\log x = 3.105$ **23.** $\ln x = -1.147$

24. Use the graph of function f in the figure to determine (to the nearest integer) x or y as indicated.

   (A) $y = f(0)$ (B) $4 = f(x)$

   (C) $y = f(3)$ (D) $3 = f(x)$

   (E) $y = f(-6)$ (F) $-1 = f(x)$

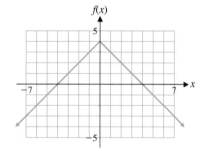

25. Sketch a graph of each of the functions in parts (A)–(D) using the graph of function f in the figure below.

   (A) $y = -f(x)$ (B) $y = f(x) + 4$

   (C) $y = f(x - 2)$ (D) $y = -f(x + 3) - 3$

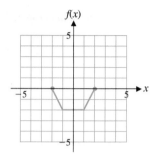

26. Complete the square and find the vertex form for the quadratic function

$$f(x) = -x^2 + 4x$$

Then write a brief description of the relationship between the graph of f and the graph of $y = x^2$.

27. Match each equation with a graph of one of the functions f, g, m, or n in the figure.

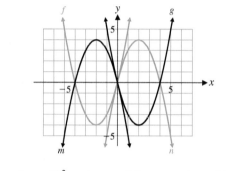

   (A) $y = (x - 2)^2 - 4$ (B) $y = -(x + 2)^2 + 4$

   (C) $y = -(x - 2)^2 + 4$ (D) $y = (x + 2)^2 - 4$

28. Referring to the graph of function f in the figure for Problem 27 and using known properties of quadratic functions, find each of the following to the nearest integer:

   (A) Intercepts   (B) Vertex

   (C) Maximum or minimum   (D) Range

In Problems 29–32, each equation specifies a function. Determine whether the function is linear, quadratic, constant, or none of these.

29. $y = 4 - x + 3x^2$ **30.** $y = \dfrac{1 + 5x}{6}$

31. $y = \dfrac{7 - 4x}{2x}$ **32.** $y = 8x + 2(10 - 4x)$

Solve Problems 33–36 for x exactly without using a calculator.

33. $\log(x + 5) = \log(2x - 3)$ **34.** $2 \ln(x - 1) = \ln(x^2 - 5)$

35. $2x^2 e^x = 3xe^x$ **36.** $\log_{1/3} 9 = x$

Solve Problems 37–40 for x to four decimal places.

37. $35 = 7(3^x)$ **38.** $0.01 = e^{-0.05x}$

39. $8,000 = 4,000(1.08^x)$ **40.** $5^{2x-3} = 7.08$

41. Find the domain of each function:

   (A) $f(x) = \dfrac{2x - 5}{x^2 - x - 6}$ (B) $g(x) = \dfrac{3x}{\sqrt{5 - x}}$

42. Find the vertex form for $f(x) = 4x^2 + 4x - 3$ and then find the intercepts, the vertex, the maximum or minimum, and the range.

43. Let $f(x) = e^x - 1$ and $g(x) = \ln(x + 2)$. Find all points of intersection for the graphs of f and g. Round answers to two decimal places.

In Problems 44 and 45, use point-by-point plotting to sketch the graph of each function.

44. $f(x) = \dfrac{50}{x^2 + 1}$ **45.** $f(x) = \dfrac{-66}{2 + x^2}$

In Problems 46–49, if $f(x) = 5x + 1$, find and simplify.

46. $f(f(0))$ **47.** $f(f(-1))$

48. $f(2x - 1)$ **49.** $f(4 - x)$

50. Let $f(x) = 3 - 2x$. Find

(A) $f(2)$ (B) $f(2 + h)$

(C) $f(2 + h) - f(2)$ (D) $\dfrac{f(2 + h) - f(2)}{h}, h \neq 0$

51. Explain how the graph of $m(x) = -|x - 4|$ is related to the graph of $y = |x|$.

52. Explain how the graph of $g(x) = 0.3x^3 + 3$ is related to the graph of $y = x^3$.

In Problems 53–55, find the equation of any horizontal asymptote.

53. $f(x) = \dfrac{5x + 4}{x^2 - 3x + 1}$ **54.** $f(x) = \dfrac{3x^2 + 2x - 1}{4x^2 - 5x + 3}$

55. $f(x) = \dfrac{x^2 + 4}{100x + 1}$

In Problems 56 and 57, find the equations of any vertical asymptotes.

56. $f(x) = \dfrac{x^2 + 100}{x^2 - 100}$ **57.** $f(x) = \dfrac{x^2 + 3x}{x^2 + 2x}$

In Problems 58–60, discuss the validity of each statement. If the statement is always true, explain why. If not, give a counter example.

58. Every polynomial function is a rational function.

59. Every rational function is a polynomial function.

60. The graph of every rational function has at least one vertical asymptote.

61. There exists a rational function that has both a vertical and horizontal asymptote.

62. Sketch the graph of f for $x \geq 0$.

$$f(x) = \begin{cases} 9 + 0.3x & \text{if } 0 \leq x \leq 20 \\ 5 + 0.2x & \text{if } x > 20 \end{cases}$$

63. Sketch the graph of g for $x \geq 0$.

$$g(x) = \begin{cases} 0.5x + 5 & \text{if } 0 \leq x \leq 10 \\ 1.2x - 2 & \text{if } 10 < x \leq 30 \\ 2x - 26 & \text{if } x > 30 \end{cases}$$

64. Write an equation for the graph shown in the form $y = a(x - h)^2 + k$, where a is either -1 or $+1$ and h and k are integers.

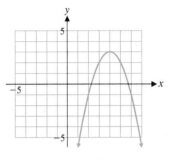

65. Given $f(x) = -0.4x^2 + 3.2x + 1.2$, find the following algebraically (to one decimal place) without referring to a graph:

(A) Intercepts   (B) Vertex

(C) Maximum or minimum   (D) Range

66. Graph $f(x) = -0.4x^2 + 3.2x + 1.2$ in a graphing calculator and find the following (to one decimal place) using TRACE and appropriate commands:

(A) Intercepts   (B) Vertex

(C) Maximum or minimum   (D) Range

67. Noting that $\pi = 3.141\,592\,654\ldots$ and $\sqrt{2} = 1.414\,213\,562\ldots$ explain why the calculator results shown here are obvious. Discuss similar connections between the natural logarithmic function and the exponential function with base e.

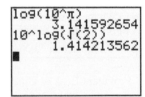

Solve Problems 68–71 exactly without using a calculator.

68. $\log x - \log 3 = \log 4 - \log(x + 4)$

69. $\ln(2x - 2) - \ln(x - 1) = \ln x$

70. $\ln(x + 3) - \ln x = 2 \ln 2$

71. $\log 3x^2 = 2 + \log 9x$

72. Write $\ln y = -5t + \ln c$ in an exponential form free of logarithms. Then solve for y in terms of the remaining variables.

73. Explain why 1 cannot be used as a logarithmic base.

74. The following graph is the result of applying a sequence of transformations to the graph of $y = \sqrt[3]{x}$. Describe the transformations and write an equation for the graph.

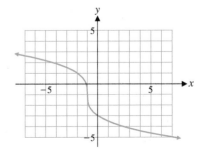

75. Given $G(x) = 0.3x^2 + 1.2x - 6.9$, find the following algebraically (to one decimal place) without the use of a graph:

(A) Intercepts   (B) Vertex

(C) Maximum or minimum   (D) Range

76. Graph $G(x) = 0.3x^2 + 1.2x - 6.9$ in a standard viewing window. Then find each of the following (to one decimal place) using appropriate commands.

(A) Intercepts   (B) Vertex

(C) Maximum or minimum   (D) Range

Applications

In all problems involving days, a 365-day year is assumed.

77. Electricity rates. The table shows the electricity rates charged by Easton Utilities in the summer months.

(A) Write a piecewise definition of the monthly charge $S(x)$ (in dollars) for a customer who uses x kWh in a summer month.

(B) Graph $S(x)$.

Energy Charge (June–September)
$3.00 for the first 20 kWh or less
5.70¢ per kWh for the next 180 kWh
3.46¢ per kWh for the next 800 kWh
2.17¢ per kWh for all over 1,000 kWh

78. Money growth. Provident Bank of Cincinnati, Ohio, offered a certificate of deposit that paid 1.25% compounded quarterly. If a $5,000 CD earns this rate for 5 years, how much will it be worth?

79. Money growth. Capital One Bank of Glen Allen, Virginia, offered a certificate of deposit that paid 1.05% compounded daily. If a $5,000 CD earns this rate for 5 years, how much will it be worth?

80. Money growth. How long will it take for money invested at 6.59% compounded monthly to triple?

81. Money growth. How long will it take for money invested at 7.39% compounded continuously to double?

82. Sports medicine. A simple rule of thumb for determining your maximum safe heart rate (in beats per minute) is to subtract your age from 220. While exercising, you should maintain a heart rate between 60% and 85% of your maximum safe rate.

(A) Find a linear model for the minimum heart rate m that a person of age x years should maintain while exercising.

(B) Find a linear model for the maximum heart rate M that a person of age x years should maintain while exercising.

(C) What range of heartbeats should you maintain while exercising if you are 20 years old?

(D) What range of heartbeats should you maintain while exercising if you are 50 years old?

83. Linear depreciation. A bulldozer was purchased by a construction company for $224,000 and has a depreciated value of $100,000 after 8 years. If the value is depreciated linearly from $224,000 to $100,000,

(A) Find the linear equation that relates value V (in dollars) to time t (in years).

(B) What would be the depreciated value after 12 years?

84. High school dropout rates. The table gives U.S. high school dropout rates as percentages for selected years since 1980. A linear regression model for the data is

$$r = -0.198t + 14.2$$

where t represents years since 1980 and r is the dropout rate expressed as a percentage.

High School Dropout Rates (%)

1980	1985	1990	1995	2000	2005	2010
14.1	12.6	12.1	12.0	10.9	9.4	7.4

(A) Interpret the slope of the model.

(B) Draw a scatter plot of the data and the model in the same coordinate system.

(C) Use the model to predict the first year for which the dropout rate is less than 5%.

85. Consumer Price Index. The U.S. Consumer Price Index (CPI) in recent years is given in the table. A scatter plot of the data and linear regression line are shown in the figure, where x represents years since 2000.

Consumer Price Index (1982–1984 = 100)

Year	CPI
2000	172.2
2002	179.9
2004	188.9
2006	198.3
2008	211.1
2010	218.1

Source: U.S. Bureau of Labor Statistics

(A) Interpret the slope of the model.

(B) Predict the CPI in 2024.

86. Construction. A construction company has 840 feet of chain-link fence that is used to enclose storage areas for equipment and materials at construction sites. The supervisor wants to set up two identical rectangular storage areas sharing a common fence (see the figure).

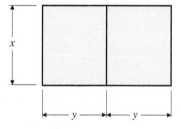

Assuming that all fencing is used,

(A) Express the total area $A(x)$ enclosed by both pens as a function of x.

(B) From physical considerations, what is the domain of the function A?

(C) Graph function A in a rectangular coordinate system.

(D) Use the graph to discuss the number and approximate locations of values of x that would produce storage areas with a combined area of 25,000 square feet.

(E) Approximate graphically (to the nearest foot) the values of x that would produce storage areas with a combined area of 25,000 square feet.

(F) Determine algebraically the dimensions of the storage areas that have the maximum total combined area. What is the maximum area?

87. Equilibrium point. A company is planning to introduce a 10-piece set of nonstick cookware. A marketing company established price–demand and price–supply tables for selected prices (Tables 1 and 2), where x is the number of cookware sets people are willing to buy and the company is willing to sell each month at a price of p dollars per set.

Table 1 **Price–Demand**

x	$p = D(x)(\$)$
985	330
2,145	225
2,950	170
4,225	105
5,100	50

Table 2 **Price–Supply**

x	$p = S(x)(\$)$
985	30
2,145	75
2,950	110
4,225	155
5,100	190

(A) Find a quadratic regression model for the data in Table 1. Estimate the demand at a price level of $180.

(B) Find a linear regression model for the data in Table 2. Estimate the supply at a price level of $180.

(C) Does a price level of $180 represent a stable condition, or is the price likely to increase or decrease? Explain.

(D) Use the models in parts (A) and (B) to find the equilibrium point. Write the equilibrium price to the nearest cent and the equilibrium quantity to the nearest unit.

88. Crime statistics. According to data published by the FBI, the crime index in the United States has shown a downward trend since the early 1990s (see table).

Crime Index

Year	Crimes per 100,000 Inhabitants
1987	5,550
1992	5,660
1997	4,930
2002	4,125
2007	3,749
2009	3,466

(A) Find a cubic regression model for the crime index if $x = 0$ represents 1987.

(B) Use the cubic regression model to predict the crime index in 2022.

89. Medicine. One leukemic cell injected into a healthy mouse will divide into 2 cells in about $\frac{1}{2}$ day. At the end of the day these 2 cells will divide into 4. This doubling continues until 1 billion cells are formed; then the animal dies with leukemic cells in every part of the body.

(A) Write an equation that will give the number N of leukemic cells at the end of t days.

(B) When, to the nearest day, will the mouse die?

90. Marine biology. The intensity of light entering water is reduced according to the exponential equation

$$I = I_0 e^{-kd}$$

where I is the intensity d feet below the surface, I_0 is the intensity at the surface, and k is the coefficient of extinction. Measurements in the Sargasso Sea have indicated that half of the surface light reaches a depth of 73.6 feet. Find k (to five decimal places), and find the depth (to the nearest foot) at which 1% of the surface light remains.

91. Agriculture. The number of dairy cows on farms in the United States is shown in the table for selected years since 1950. Let 1940 be year 0.

Dairy Cows on Farms in the United States

Year	Dairy Cows (thousands)
1950	23,853
1960	19,527
1970	12,091
1980	10,758
1990	10,015
2000	9,190
2010	9,117

(A) Find a logarithmic regression model $(y = a + b \ln x)$ for the data. Estimate (to the nearest thousand) the number of dairy cows in 2023.

(B) Explain why it is not a good idea to let 1950 be year 0.

92. Population growth. The population of some countries has a relative growth rate of 3% (or more) per year. At this rate, how many years (to the nearest tenth of a year) will it take a population to double?

93. Medicare. The annual expenditures for Medicare (in billions of dollars) by the U.S. government for selected years since 1980 are shown in the table. Let x represent years since 1980.

Medicare Expenditures

Year	Billion $
1980	37
1985	72
1990	111
1995	181
2000	197
2005	299
2010	452

(A) Find an exponential regression model $(y = ab^x)$ for the data. Estimate (to the nearest billion) the annual expenditures in 2022.

(B) When will the annual expenditures reach two trillion dollars?

PART 2

CALCULUS

2

Limits and the Derivative

Introduction

How do algebra and calculus differ? The two words *static* and *dynamic* probably come as close as any to expressing the difference between the two disciplines. In algebra, we solve equations for a particular value of a variable—a static notion. In calculus, we are interested in how a change in one variable affects another variable—a dynamic notion.

Isaac Newton (1642–1727) of England and Gottfried Wilhelm von Leibniz (1646–1716) of Germany developed calculus independently to solve problems concerning motion. Today calculus is used not just in the physical sciences, but also in business, economics, life sciences, and social sciences—any discipline that seeks to understand dynamic phenomena.

In Chapter 2 we introduce the *derivative*, one of the two key concepts of calculus. The second, the *integral*, is the subject of Chapter 5. Both key concepts depend on the notion of *limit*, which is explained in Sections 2.1 and 2.2. We consider many applications of limits and derivatives. See, for example, Problems 89 and 90 in Section 2.2 on the concentration of a drug in the bloodstream.

2.1   Introduction to Limits

Basic to the study of calculus is the concept of a *limit*. This concept helps us to describe, in a precise way, the behavior of $f(x)$ when x is close, but not equal, to a particular value c. In this section, we develop an intuitive and informal approach to evaluating limits.

Functions and Graphs: Brief Review

The graph of the function $y = f(x) = x + 2$ is the graph of the set of all ordered pairs $(x, f(x))$. For example, if $x = 2$, then $f(2) = 4$ and $(2, f(2)) = (2, 4)$ is a point on the graph of f. Figure 1 shows $(-1, f(-1))$, $(1, f(1))$, and $(2, f(2))$ plotted on the graph of f. Notice that the domain values -1, 1, and 2 are associated with the x axis and the range values $f(-1) = 1$, $f(1) = 3$, and $f(2) = 4$ are associated with the y axis.

Given x, it is sometimes useful to read $f(x)$ directly from the graph of f. Example 1 reviews this process.

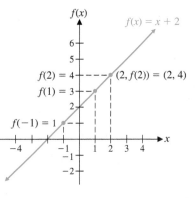

Figure 1

EXAMPLE 1   Finding Values of a Function from Its Graph   Complete the following table, using the given graph of the function g.

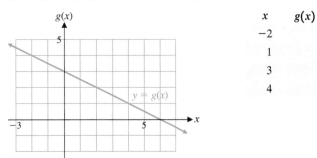

x	$g(x)$
-2	
1	
3	
4	

SOLUTION   To determine $g(x)$, proceed vertically from the x value on the x axis to the graph of g and then horizontally to the corresponding y value $g(x)$ on the y axis (as indicated by the dashed lines).

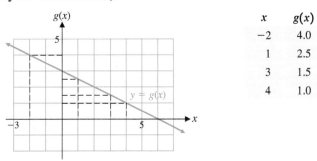

x	$g(x)$
-2	4.0
1	2.5
3	1.5
4	1.0

Matched Problem 1) Complete the following table, using the given graph of the function h.

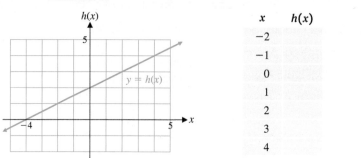

x	$h(x)$
-2	
-1	
0	
1	
2	
3	
4	

Limits: A Graphical Approach

We introduce the important concept of a *limit* through an example, which leads to an intuitive definition of the concept.

EXAMPLE 2   Analyzing a Limit   Let $f(x) = x + 2$. Discuss the behavior of the values of $f(x)$ when x is close to 2.

SOLUTION We begin by drawing a graph of f that includes the domain value $x = 2$ (Fig. 2).

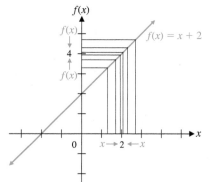

Figure 2

In Figure 2, we are using a static drawing to describe a dynamic process. This requires careful interpretation. The thin vertical lines in Figure 2 represent values of x that are close to 2. The corresponding horizontal lines identify the value of $f(x)$ associated with each value of x. [Example 1 dealt with the relationship between x and $f(x)$ on a graph.] The graph in Figure 2 indicates that as the values of x get closer and closer to 2 on either side of 2, the corresponding values of $f(x)$ get closer and closer to 4. Symbolically, we write

$$\lim_{x \to 2} f(x) = 4$$

This equation is read as "The limit of $f(x)$ as x approaches 2 is 4." Note that $f(2) = 4$. That is, the value of the function at 2 and the limit of the function as x approaches 2 are the same. This relationship can be expressed as

$$\lim_{x \to 2} f(x) = f(2) = 4$$

Graphically, this means that there is no hole or break in the graph of f at $x = 2$.

Matched Problem 2) Let $f(x) = x + 1$. Discuss the behavior of the values of $f(x)$ when x is close to 1.

We now present an informal definition of the important concept of a limit. A precise definition is not needed for our discussion, but one is given in a footnote.*

DEFINITION Limit
We write
$$\lim_{x \to c} f(x) = L \quad \text{or} \quad f(x) \to L \quad \text{as} \quad x \to c$$
if the functional value $f(x)$ is close to the single real number L whenever x is close, but not equal, to c (on either side of c).

Note: The existence of a limit at c has nothing to do with the value of the function at c. In fact, c may not even be in the domain of f. However, the function must be defined on both sides of c.

The next example involves the **absolute value function**:

$$f(x) = |x| = \begin{cases} -x & \text{if } x < 0 \\ x & \text{if } x \geq 0 \end{cases} \quad \begin{array}{l} f(-2) = |-2| = -(-2) = 2 \\ f(3) \;\;= |3| = 3 \end{array}$$

The graph of f is shown in Figure 3.

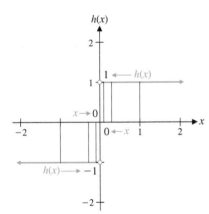

Figure 3 $f(x) = |x|$

Figure 4

EXAMPLE 3 Analyzing a limit Let $h(x) = |x|/x$. Explore the behavior of $h(x)$ for x near, but not equal, to 0. Find $\lim_{x \to 0} h(x)$ if it exists.

SOLUTION The function h is defined for all real numbers except 0 [$h(0) = |0|/0$ is undefined]. For example,

$$h(-2) = \frac{|-2|}{-2} = \frac{2}{-2} = -1$$

Note that if x is any negative number, then $h(x) = -1$ (if $x < 0$, then the numerator $|x|$ is positive but the denominator x is negative, so $h(x) = |x|/x = -1$). If x is any positive number, then $h(x) = 1$ (if $x > 0$, then the numerator $|x|$ is equal to the denominator x, so $h(x) = |x|/x = 1$). Figure 4 illustrates the behavior of $h(x)$ for x near 0. Note that the absence of a solid dot on the vertical axis indicates that h is not defined when $x = 0$.

When x is near 0 (on either side of 0), is $h(x)$ near one specific number? The answer is "No," because $h(x)$ is -1 for $x < 0$ and 1 for $x > 0$. Consequently, we say that

$$\lim_{x \to 0} \frac{|x|}{x} \quad \text{does not exist}$$

Neither $h(x)$ nor the limit of $h(x)$ exists at $x = 0$. However, the limit from the left and the limit from the right both exist at 0, but they are not equal.

Matched Problem 3 Graph
$$h(x) = \frac{x - 2}{|x - 2|}$$
and find $\lim_{x \to 2} h(x)$ if it exists.

In Example 3, we see that the values of the function $h(x)$ approach two different numbers, depending on the direction of approach, and it is natural to refer to these values as "the limit from the left" and "the limit from the right." These experiences suggest that the notion of **one-sided limits** will be very useful in discussing basic limit concepts.

*To make the informal definition of *limit* precise, we must make the word *close* more precise. This is done as follows: We write $\lim_{x \to c} f(x) = L$ if, for each $e > 0$, there exists a $d > 0$ such that $|f(x) - L| < e$ whenever $0 < |x - c| < d$. This definition is used to establish particular limits and to prove many useful properties of limits that will be helpful in finding particular limits.

DEFINITION   One-Sided Limits

We write

$$\lim_{x\to c^-} f(x) = K \qquad x \to c^- \text{ is read "}x\text{ approaches } c \text{ from the left" and means } x \to c \text{ and } x < c.$$

and call K the **limit from the left** or the **left-hand limit** if $f(x)$ is close to K whenever x is close to, but to the left of, c on the real number line. We write

$$\lim_{x\to c^+} f(x) = L \qquad x \to c^+ \text{ is read "}x\text{ approaches } c \text{ from the right" and means } x \to c \text{ and } x > c.$$

and call L the **limit from the right** or the **right-hand limit** if $f(x)$ is close to L whenever x is close to, but to the right of, c on the real number line.

If no direction is specified in a limit statement, we will always assume that the limit is **two-sided** or **unrestricted**. Theorem 1 states an important relationship between one-sided limits and unrestricted limits.

THEOREM 1   On the Existence of a Limit

For a (two-sided) limit to exist, the limit from the left and the limit from the right must exist and be equal. That is,

$$\lim_{x\to c} f(x) = L \text{ if and only if } \lim_{x\to c^-} f(x) = \lim_{x\to c^+} f(x) = L$$

In Example 3,

$$\lim_{x\to 0^-} \frac{|x|}{x} = -1 \qquad \text{and} \qquad \lim_{x\to 0^+} \frac{|x|}{x} = 1$$

Since the left- and right-hand limits are *not* the same,

$$\lim_{x\to 0} \frac{|x|}{x} \text{ does not exist}$$

EXAMPLE 4   Analyzing Limits Graphically   Given the graph of the function f in Figure 5, discuss the behavior of $f(x)$ for x near (A) -1, (B) 1, and (C) 2.

SOLUTION

(A) Since we have only a graph to work with, we use vertical and horizontal lines to relate the values of x and the corresponding values of $f(x)$. For any x near -1 on either side of -1, we see that the corresponding value of $f(x)$, determined by a horizontal line, is close to 1.

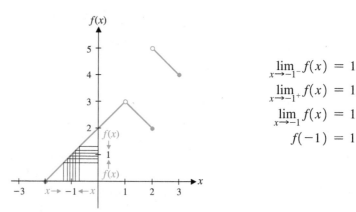

$$\lim_{x\to -1^-} f(x) = 1$$

$$\lim_{x\to -1^+} f(x) = 1$$

$$\lim_{x\to -1} f(x) = 1$$

$$f(-1) = 1$$

Figure 5

(B) Again, for any x near, but not equal to, 1, the vertical and horizontal lines indicate that the corresponding value of $f(x)$ is close to 3. The open dot at $(1, 3)$, together with the absence of a solid dot anywhere on the vertical line through $x = 1$, indicates that $f(1)$ is not defined.

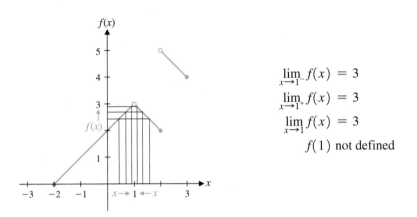

$$\lim_{x \to 1^-} f(x) = 3$$

$$\lim_{x \to 1^+} f(x) = 3$$

$$\lim_{x \to 1} f(x) = 3$$

$f(1)$ not defined

(C) The abrupt break in the graph at $x = 2$ indicates that the behavior of the graph near $x = 2$ is more complicated than in the two preceding cases. If x is close to 2 on the left side of 2, the corresponding horizontal line intersects the y axis at a point close to 2. If x is close to 2 on the right side of 2, the corresponding horizontal line intersects the y axis at a point close to 5. This is a case where the one-sided limits are different.

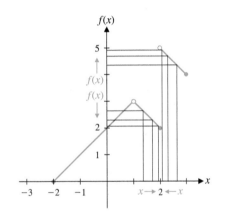

$$\lim_{x \to 2^-} f(x) = 2$$

$$\lim_{x \to 2^+} f(x) = 5$$

$$\lim_{x \to 2} f(x) \text{ does not exist}$$

$$f(2) = 2$$

Matched Problem 4 Given the graph of the function f shown in Figure 6, discuss the following, as we did in Example 4:

(A) Behavior of $f(x)$ for x near 0

(B) Behavior of $f(x)$ for x near 1

(C) Behavior of $f(x)$ for x near 3

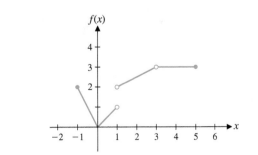

Figure 6

> **CONCEPTUAL INSIGHT**
>
> In Example 4B, note that $\lim_{x \to 1} f(x)$ exists even though f is not defined at $x = 1$ and the graph has a hole at $x = 1$. In general, the value of a function at $x = c$ has no effect on the limit of the function as x approaches c.

Limits: An Algebraic Approach

Graphs are very useful tools for investigating limits, especially if something unusual happens at the point in question. However, many of the limits encountered in calculus are routine and can be evaluated quickly with a little algebraic simplification, some intuition, and basic properties of limits. The following list of properties of limits forms the basis for this approach:

THEOREM 2 Properties of Limits

Let f and g be two functions, and assume that

$$\lim_{x \to c} f(x) = L \qquad \lim_{x \to c} g(x) = M$$

where L and M are real numbers (both limits exist). Then

1. $\lim_{x \to c} k = k$ for any constant k
2. $\lim_{x \to c} x = c$
3. $\lim_{x \to c} [f(x) + g(x)] = \lim_{x \to c} f(x) + \lim_{x \to c} g(x) = L + M$
4. $\lim_{x \to c} [f(x) - g(x)] = \lim_{x \to c} f(x) - \lim_{x \to c} g(x) = L - M$
5. $\lim_{x \to c} kf(x) = k \lim_{x \to c} f(x) = kL$ for any constant k
6. $\lim_{x \to c} [f(x) \cdot g(x)] = [\lim_{x \to c} f(x)][\lim_{x \to c} g(x)] = LM$
7. $\lim_{x \to c} \dfrac{f(x)}{g(x)} = \dfrac{\lim\limits_{x \to c} f(x)}{\lim\limits_{x \to c} g(x)} = \dfrac{L}{M}$ if $M \neq 0$
8. $\lim_{x \to c} \sqrt[n]{f(x)} = \sqrt[n]{\lim_{x \to c} f(x)} = \sqrt[n]{L}$ $L > 0$ for n even

Each property in Theorem 2 is also valid if $x \to c$ is replaced everywhere by $x \to c^-$ or replaced everywhere by $x \to c^+$.

Explore and Discuss 1   The properties listed in Theorem 2 can be paraphrased in brief verbal statements. For example, property 3 simply states that *the limit of a sum is equal to the sum of the limits.* Write brief verbal statements for the remaining properties in Theorem 2.

EXAMPLE 5   Using Limit Properties   Find $\lim_{x \to 3} (x^2 - 4x)$.

SOLUTION

$$
\begin{aligned}
\lim_{x \to 3} (x^2 - 4x) &= \lim_{x \to 3} x^2 - \lim_{x \to 3} 4x && \text{Property 4} \\
&= \left(\lim_{x \to 3} x \right) \cdot \left(\lim_{x \to 3} x \right) - 4 \lim_{x \to 3} x && \text{Properties 5 and 6} \\
&= \left(\lim_{x \to 3} x \right)^2 - 4 \lim_{x \to 3} x && \text{Definition of exponent} \\
&= 3^2 - 4 \cdot 3 = -3
\end{aligned}
$$

So, omitting the steps in the dashed boxes,

$$\lim_{x \to 3} (x^2 - 4x) = 3^2 - 4 \cdot 3 = -3$$

Matched Problem 5 Find $\lim_{x \to -2} (x^2 + 5x)$.

If $f(x) = x^2 - 4$ and c is any real number, then, just as in Example 5

$$\lim_{x \to c} f(x) = \lim_{x \to c} (x^2 - 4x) = c^2 - 4c = f(c)$$

So the limit can be found easily by evaluating the function f at c.

This simple method for finding limits is very useful, because there are many functions that satisfy the property

$$\lim_{x \to c} f(x) = f(c) \tag{1}$$

Any polynomial function

$$f(x) = a_n x^n + a_{n-1} x^{n-1} + \cdots + a_0$$

satisfies (1) for any real number c. Also, any rational function

$$r(x) = \frac{n(x)}{d(x)}$$

where $n(x)$ and $d(x)$ are polynomials, satisfies (1) provided c is a real number for which $d(c) \neq 0$.

THEOREM 3 Limits of Polynomial and Rational Functions

1. $\lim_{x \to c} f(x) = f(c)$ for f any polynomial function.

2. $\lim_{x \to c} r(x) = r(c)$ for r any rational function with a nonzero denominator at $x = c$.

If Theorem 3 is applicable, the limit is easy to find: *Simply evaluate the function at c.*

EXAMPLE 6 Evaluating Limits Find each limit.

(A) $\lim_{x \to 2} (x^3 - 5x - 1)$ (B) $\lim_{x \to -1} \sqrt{2x^2 + 3}$ (C) $\lim_{x \to 4} \frac{2x}{3x + 1}$

SOLUTION

(A) $\lim_{x \to 2} (x^3 - 5x - 1) = 2^3 - 5 \cdot 2 - 1 = -3$ Theorem 3

(B) $\lim_{x \to -1} \sqrt{2x^2 + 3} = \sqrt{\lim_{x \to -1} (2x^2 + 3)}$ Property 8

$$= \sqrt{2(-1)^2 + 3}$$ Theorem 3

$$= \sqrt{5}$$

(C) $\lim_{x \to 4} \frac{2x}{3x + 1} = \frac{2 \cdot 4}{3 \cdot 4 + 1}$ Theorem 3

$$= \frac{8}{13}$$

Matched Problem 6 Find each limit.

(A) $\lim_{x \to -1} (x^4 - 2x + 3)$ (B) $\lim_{x \to 2} \sqrt{3x^2 - 6}$ (C) $\lim_{x \to -2} \frac{x^2}{x^2 + 1}$

EXAMPLE 7 Evaluating Limits Let

$$f(x) = \begin{cases} x^2 + 1 & \text{if } x < 2 \\ x - 1 & \text{if } x > 2 \end{cases}$$

Find:

(A) $\lim\limits_{x \to 2^-} f(x)$ (B) $\lim\limits_{x \to 2^+} f(x)$ (C) $\lim\limits_{x \to 2} f(x)$ (D) $f(2)$

SOLUTION

(A) $\lim\limits_{x \to 2^-} f(x) = \lim\limits_{x \to 2^-} (x^2 + 1)$ If $x < 2$, $f(x) = x^2 + 1$.

$\qquad\qquad = 2^2 + 1 = 5$

(B) $\lim\limits_{x \to 2^+} f(x) = \lim\limits_{x \to 2^+} (x - 1)$ If $x > 2$, $f(x) = x - 1$.

$\qquad\qquad = 2 - 1 = 1$

(C) Since the one-sided limits are not equal, $\lim\limits_{x \to 2} f(x)$ does not exist.

(D) Because the definition of f does not assign a value to f for $x = 2$, only for $x < 2$ and $x > 2$, $f(2)$ does not exist.

Matched Problem 7 Let

$$f(x) = \begin{cases} 2x + 3 & \text{if } x < 5 \\ -x + 12 & \text{if } x > 5 \end{cases}$$

Find:

(A) $\lim\limits_{x \to 5^-} f(x)$ (B) $\lim\limits_{x \to 5^+} f(x)$ (C) $\lim\limits_{x \to 5} f(x)$ (D) $f(5)$

It is important to note that there are restrictions on some of the limit properties. In particular, if

$$\lim_{x \to c} f(x) = 0 \quad \text{and} \quad \lim_{x \to c} g(x) = 0, \quad \text{then finding} \lim_{x \to c} \frac{f(x)}{g(x)}$$

may present some difficulties, since limit property 7 (the limit of a quotient) does not apply when $\lim\limits_{x \to c} g(x) = 0$. The next example illustrates some techniques that can be useful in this situation.

EXAMPLE 8 Evaluating Limits Find each limit.

(A) $\lim\limits_{x \to 2} \dfrac{x^2 - 4}{x - 2}$

(B) $\lim\limits_{x \to -1} \dfrac{x|x + 1|}{x + 1}$

SOLUTION

(A) Note that $\lim\limits_{x \to 2} x^2 - 4 = 2^2 - 4 = 0$ and $\lim\limits_{x \to 2} x - 2 = 2 - 2 = 0$. Algebraic simplification is often useful in such a case when the numerator and denominator both have limit 0.

$$\lim_{x \to 2} \frac{x^2 - 4}{x - 2} = \lim_{x \to 2} \frac{(x - 2)(x + 2)}{x - 2} = \lim_{x \to 2} (x + 2) = 4$$

(B) One-sided limits are helpful for limits involving the absolute value function.

$$\lim_{x \to -1^+} \frac{x|x + 1|}{x + 1} = \lim_{x \to -1^+} (x) = -1 \quad \text{If } x > -1, \text{ then } \frac{|x + 1|}{x + 1} = 1.$$

$$\lim_{x \to -1^-} \frac{x|x + 1|}{x + 1} = \lim_{x \to -1^-} (-x) = 1 \quad \text{If } x < -1, \text{ then } \frac{|x + 1|}{x + 1} = -1.$$

Since the limit from the left and the limit from the right are not the same, we conclude that

$$\lim_{x \to -1} \frac{x|x + 1|}{x + 1} \quad \text{does not exist}$$

Matched Problem 8 Find each limit.

(A) $\lim\limits_{x \to -3} \dfrac{x^2 + 4x + 3}{x + 3}$

(B) $\lim\limits_{x \to 4} \dfrac{x^2 - 16}{|x - 4|}$

CONCEPTUAL INSIGHT

In the solution to Example 8A we used the following algebraic identity:

$$\frac{x^2 - 4}{x - 2} = \frac{(x - 2)(x + 2)}{x - 2} = x + 2, \quad x \neq 2$$

The restriction $x \neq 2$ is necessary here because the first two expressions are not defined at $x = 2$. Why didn't we include this restriction in the solution? When x approaches 2 in a limit problem, it is assumed that x is close, but not equal, to 2. It is important that you understand that both of the following statements are valid:

$$\lim_{x \to 2} \frac{x^2 - 4}{x - 2} = \lim_{x \to 2} (x + 2) \quad \text{and} \quad \frac{x^2 - 4}{x - 2} = x + 2, \quad x \neq 2$$

Limits like those in Example 8 occur so frequently in calculus that they are given a special name.

DEFINITION Indeterminate Form

If $\lim\limits_{x \to c} f(x) = 0$ and $\lim\limits_{x \to c} g(x) = 0$, then $\lim\limits_{x \to c} \dfrac{f(x)}{g(x)}$ is said to be **indeterminate**, or, more specifically, a **0/0 indeterminate form**.

The term *indeterminate* is used because the limit of an indeterminate form may or may not exist (see Example 8A and 8B).

⚠ CAUTION The expression 0/0 does not represent a real number and should never be used as the value of a limit. If a limit is a 0/0 indeterminate form, further investigation is always required to determine whether the limit exists and to find its value if it does exist. ▲

If the denominator of a quotient approaches 0 and the numerator approaches a nonzero number, then the limit of the quotient is not an indeterminate form. In fact, in this case the limit of the quotient does not exist.

THEOREM 4 Limit of a Quotient

If $\lim\limits_{x \to c} f(x) = L, L \neq 0$, and $\lim\limits_{x \to c} g(x) = 0$,

then

$$\lim_{x \to c} \frac{f(x)}{g(x)} \qquad \text{does not exist}$$

EXAMPLE 9 Indeterminate Forms Is the limit expression a 0/0 indeterminate form? Find the limit or explain why the limit does not exist.

(A) $\lim\limits_{x \to 1} \dfrac{x - 1}{x^2 + 1}$

(B) $\lim\limits_{x \to 1} \dfrac{x - 1}{x^2 - 1}$

(C) $\lim\limits_{x \to 1} \dfrac{x + 1}{x^2 - 1}$

SOLUTION

(A) $\lim\limits_{x\to 1} (x - 1) = 0$ but $\lim\limits_{x\to 1} (x^2 + 1) = 2$. So no, the limit expression is not a $0/0$ indeterminate form. By property 7 of Theorem 2,

$$\lim_{x\to 1} \frac{x - 1}{x^2 + 1} = \frac{0}{2} = 0$$

(B) $\lim\limits_{x\to 1} (x - 1) = 0$ and $\lim\limits_{x\to 1} (x^2 - 1) = 0$. So yes, the limit expression is a $0/0$ indeterminate form. We factor $x^2 - 1$ to simplify the limit expression and find the limit:

$$\lim_{x\to 1} \frac{x - 1}{x^2 - 1} = \lim_{x\to 1} \frac{x - 1}{(x - 1)(x + 1)} = \lim_{x\to 1} \frac{1}{x + 1} = \frac{1}{2}$$

(C) $\lim\limits_{x\to 1} (x + 1) = 2$ and $\lim\limits_{x\to 1} (x^2 - 1) = 0$. So no, the limit expression is not a $0/0$ indeterminate form. By Theorem 4,

$$\lim_{x\to 1} \frac{x + 1}{x^2 - 1} \quad \text{does not exist}$$

Matched Problem 9 Is the limit expression a $0/0$ indeterminate form? Find the limit or explain why the limit does not exist.

(A) $\lim\limits_{x\to 3} \dfrac{x + 1}{x + 3}$ (B) $\lim\limits_{x\to 3} \dfrac{x - 3}{x^2 + 9}$ (C) $\lim\limits_{x\to 3} \dfrac{x^2 - 9}{x - 3}$

Limits of Difference Quotients

Let the function f be defined in an open interval containing the number a. One of the most important limits in calculus is the limit of the **difference quotient**,

$$\lim_{h\to 0} \frac{f(a + h) - f(a)}{h} \tag{2}$$

If

$$\lim_{h\to 0} [f(a + h) - f(a)] = 0$$

as it often does, then limit (2) is an indeterminate form.

EXAMPLE 10 Limit of a Difference Quotient Find the following limit for $f(x) = 4x - 5$:

$$\lim_{h\to 0} \frac{f(3 + h) - f(3)}{h}$$

SOLUTION

$$\lim_{h\to 0} \frac{f(3 + h) - f(3)}{h} = \lim_{h\to 0} \frac{[4(\mathbf{3 + h}) - 5] - [4(\mathbf{3}) - 5]}{h}$$

Since this is a 0/0 indeterminate form and property 7 in Theorem 2 does not apply, we proceed with algebraic simplification.

$$= \lim_{h\to 0} \frac{12 + 4h - 5 - 12 + 5}{h}$$

$$= \lim_{h\to 0} \frac{4h}{h} = \lim_{h\to 0} 4 = 4$$

Matched Problem 10 Find the following limit for $f(x) = 7 - 2x$:

$$\lim_{h\to 0} \frac{f(4 + h) - f(4)}{h}.$$

Explore and Discuss 2   If $f(x) = \dfrac{1}{x}$, explain why $\displaystyle\lim_{h\to 0} \dfrac{f(3+h) - f(3)}{h} = -\dfrac{1}{9}$.

Exercises 2.1

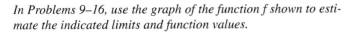

Skills Warm-up Exercises

W

In Problems 1–8, factor each polynomial into the product of first-degree factors with integer coefficients. (If necessary, review Section A.3).

1. $x^2 - 81$

2. $x^2 - 64$

3. $x^2 - 4x - 21$

4. $x^2 + 5x - 36$

5. $x^3 - 7x^2 + 12x$

6. $x^3 + 15x^2 + 50x$

7. $6x^2 - x - 1$

8. $20x^2 + 11x - 3$

In Problems 9–16, use the graph of the function f shown to estimate the indicated limits and function values.

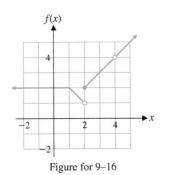

Figure for 9–16

9. $f(-0.5)$

10. $f(-1.5)$

11. $f(1.75)$

12. $f(1.25)$

13. (A) $\displaystyle\lim_{x\to 0^-} f(x)$ (B) $\displaystyle\lim_{x\to 0^+} f(x)$

   (C) $\displaystyle\lim_{x\to 0} f(x)$ (D) $f(0)$

14. (A) $\displaystyle\lim_{x\to 1^-} f(x)$ (B) $\displaystyle\lim_{x\to 1^+} f(x)$

   (C) $\displaystyle\lim_{x\to 1} f(x)$ (D) $f(1)$

15. (A) $\displaystyle\lim_{x\to 2^-} f(x)$ (B) $\displaystyle\lim_{x\to 2^+} f(x)$

   (C) $\displaystyle\lim_{x\to 2} f(x)$ (D) $f(2)$

✎ (E) Is it possible to redefine $f(2)$ so that $\displaystyle\lim_{x\to 2} f(x) = f(2)$? Explain.

16. (A) $\displaystyle\lim_{x\to 4^-} f(x)$ (B) $\displaystyle\lim_{x\to 4^+} f(x)$

   (C) $\displaystyle\lim_{x\to 4} f(x)$ (D) $f(4)$

✎ (E) Is it possible to define $f(4)$ so that $\displaystyle\lim_{x\to 4} f(x) = f(4)$? Explain.

In Problems 17–24, use the graph of the function g shown to estimate the indicated limits and function values.

Figure for 17–24

17. $g(1.9)$ 18. $g(0.1)$

19. $g(3.5)$ 20. $g(2.5)$

21. (A) $\displaystyle\lim_{x\to 1^-} g(x)$ (B) $\displaystyle\lim_{x\to 1^+} g(x)$

   (C) $\displaystyle\lim_{x\to 1} g(x)$ (D) $g(1)$

✎ (E) Is it possible to define $g(1)$ so that $\displaystyle\lim_{x\to 1} g(x) = g(1)$? Explain.

22. (A) $\displaystyle\lim_{x\to 2^-} g(x)$ (B) $\displaystyle\lim_{x\to 2^+} g(x)$

   (C) $\displaystyle\lim_{x\to 2} g(x)$ (D) $g(2)$

23. (A) $\displaystyle\lim_{x\to 3^-} g(x)$ (B) $\displaystyle\lim_{x\to 3^+} g(x)$

   (C) $\displaystyle\lim_{x\to 3} g(x)$ (D) $g(3)$

✎ (E) Is it possible to redefine $g(3)$ so that $\displaystyle\lim_{x\to 3} g(x) = g(3)$? Explain.

24. (A) $\displaystyle\lim_{x\to 4^-} g(x)$ (B) $\displaystyle\lim_{x\to 4^+} g(x)$

   (C) $\displaystyle\lim_{x\to 4} g(x)$ (D) $g(4)$

In Problems 25–28, use the graph of the function f shown to estimate the indicated limits and function values.

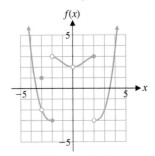

Figure for 25–28

25. (A) $\lim\limits_{x\to -3^+} f(x)$ (B) $\lim\limits_{x\to -3^-} f(x)$

    (C) $\lim\limits_{x\to -3} f(x)$ (D) $f(-3)$

  (E) Is it possible to redefine $f(-3)$ so that $\lim\limits_{x\to -3} f(x) = f(-3)$? Explain.

26. (A) $\lim\limits_{x\to -2^+} f(x)$ (B) $\lim\limits_{x\to -2^-} f(x)$

    (C) $\lim\limits_{x\to -2} f(x)$ (D) $f(-2)$

  (E) Is it possible to redefine $f(-2)$ so that $\lim\limits_{x\to -2} f(x) = f(-2)$? Explain.

27. (A) $\lim\limits_{x\to 0^+} f(x)$ (B) $\lim\limits_{x\to 0^-} f(x)$

    (C) $\lim\limits_{x\to 0} f(x)$ (D) $f(0)$

  (E) Is it possible to define $f(0)$ so that $\lim\limits_{x\to 0} f(x) = f(0)$? Explain.

28. (A) $\lim\limits_{x\to 2^+} f(x)$ (B) $\lim\limits_{x\to 2^-} f(x)$

    (C) $\lim\limits_{x\to 2} f(x)$ (D) $f(2)$

  (E) Is it possible to redefine $f(2)$ so that $\lim\limits_{x\to 2} f(x) = f(2)$? Explain.

In Problems 29–38, find each limit if it exists.

29. $\lim\limits_{x\to 3} 4x$ **30.** $\lim\limits_{x\to -2} 3x$

31. $\lim\limits_{x\to -4} (x+5)$ **32.** $\lim\limits_{x\to 5} (x-3)$

33. $\lim\limits_{x\to 2} x(x-4)$ **34.** $\lim\limits_{x\to -1} x(x+3)$

35. $\lim\limits_{x\to -3} \dfrac{x}{x+5}$ **36.** $\lim\limits_{x\to 4} \dfrac{x-2}{x}$

37. $\lim\limits_{x\to 1} \sqrt{5x+4}$ **38.** $\lim\limits_{x\to 0} \sqrt{16-7x}$

Given that $\lim_{x\to 1} f(x) = -5$ and $\lim_{x\to 1} g(x) = 4$, find the indicated limits in Problems 39–46.

39. $\lim\limits_{x\to 1} (-3)f(x)$ **40.** $\lim\limits_{x\to 1} 2g(x)$

41. $\lim\limits_{x\to 1} [2f(x)+g(x)]$ **42.** $\lim\limits_{x\to 1} [g(x)-3f(x)]$

43. $\lim\limits_{x\to 1} \dfrac{2-f(x)}{x+g(x)}$ **44.** $\lim\limits_{x\to 1} \dfrac{3-f(x)}{1-4g(x)}$

45. $\lim\limits_{x\to 1} \sqrt{g(x)-f(x)}$ **46.** $\lim\limits_{x\to 1} \sqrt[3]{2x+2f(x)}$

In Problems 47–50, sketch a possible graph of a function that satisfies the given conditions.

47. $f(0)=1$; $\lim\limits_{x\to 0^-} f(x)=3$; $\lim\limits_{x\to 0^+} f(x)=1$

48. $f(1)=-2$; $\lim\limits_{x\to 1^-} f(x)=2$; $\lim\limits_{x\to 1^+} f(x)=-2$

49. $f(-2)=2$; $\lim\limits_{x\to -2^-} f(x)=1$; $\lim\limits_{x\to -2^+} f(x)=1$

50. $f(0)=-1$; $\lim\limits_{x\to 0^-} f(x)=2$; $\lim\limits_{x\to 0^+} f(x)=2$

In Problems 51–66, find each indicated quantity if it exists.

51. Let $f(x) = \begin{cases} 1-x^2 & \text{if } x \le 0 \\ 1+x^2 & \text{if } x > 0 \end{cases}$. Find

    (A) $\lim\limits_{x\to 0^+} f(x)$ (B) $\lim\limits_{x\to 0^-} f(x)$

    (C) $\lim\limits_{x\to 0} f(x)$ (D) $f(0)$

52. Let $f(x) = \begin{cases} 2+x & \text{if } x \le 0 \\ 2-x & \text{if } x > 0 \end{cases}$. Find

    (A) $\lim\limits_{x\to 0^+} f(x)$ (B) $\lim\limits_{x\to 0^-} f(x)$

    (C) $\lim\limits_{x\to 0} f(x)$ (D) $f(0)$

53. Let $f(x) = \begin{cases} x^2 & \text{if } x < 1 \\ 2x & \text{if } x > 1 \end{cases}$. Find

    (A) $\lim\limits_{x\to 1^+} f(x)$ (B) $\lim\limits_{x\to 1^-} f(x)$

    (C) $\lim\limits_{x\to 1} f(x)$ (D) $f(1)$

54. Let $f(x) = \begin{cases} x+3 & \text{if } x < -2 \\ \sqrt{x+2} & \text{if } x > -2 \end{cases}$. Find

    (A) $\lim\limits_{x\to -2^+} f(x)$ (B) $\lim\limits_{x\to -2^-} f(x)$

    (C) $\lim\limits_{x\to -2} f(x)$ (D) $f(-2)$

55. Let $f(x) = \begin{cases} \dfrac{x^2-9}{x+3} & \text{if } x < 0 \\ \dfrac{x^2-9}{x-3} & \text{if } x > 0 \end{cases}$. Find

    (A) $\lim\limits_{x\to -3} f(x)$ (B) $\lim\limits_{x\to 0} f(x)$

    (C) $\lim\limits_{x\to 3} f(x)$

56. Let $f(x) = \begin{cases} \dfrac{x}{x+3} & \text{if } x < 0 \\ \dfrac{x}{x-3} & \text{if } x > 0 \end{cases}$. Find

    (A) $\lim\limits_{x\to -3} f(x)$ (B) $\lim\limits_{x\to 0} f(x)$

    (C) $\lim\limits_{x\to 3} f(x)$

57. Let $f(x) = \dfrac{|x-1|}{x-1}$. Find

    (A) $\lim\limits_{x\to 1^+} f(x)$ (B) $\lim\limits_{x\to 1^-} f(x)$

    (C) $\lim\limits_{x\to 1} f(x)$ (D) $f(1)$

58. Let $f(x) = \dfrac{x-3}{|x-3|}$. Find

    (A) $\lim\limits_{x\to 3^+} f(x)$ (B) $\lim\limits_{x\to 3^-} f(x)$

    (C) $\lim\limits_{x\to 3} f(x)$ (D) $f(3)$

59. Let $f(x) = \dfrac{x-2}{x^2-2x}$. Find

    (A) $\lim\limits_{x\to 0} f(x)$ (B) $\lim\limits_{x\to 2} f(x)$

    (C) $\lim\limits_{x\to 4} f(x)$

60. Let $f(x) = \dfrac{x+3}{x^2+3x}$. Find

    (A) $\lim\limits_{x\to -3} f(x)$ (B) $\lim\limits_{x\to 0} f(x)$

    (C) $\lim\limits_{x\to 3} f(x)$

61. Let $f(x) = \dfrac{x^2-x-6}{x+2}$. Find

    (A) $\lim\limits_{x\to -2} f(x)$ (B) $\lim\limits_{x\to 0} f(x)$

    (C) $\lim\limits_{x\to 3} f(x)$

62. Let $f(x) = \dfrac{x^2+x-6}{x+3}$. Find

    (A) $\lim\limits_{x\to -3} f(x)$ (B) $\lim\limits_{x\to 0} f(x)$

    (C) $\lim\limits_{x\to 2} f(x)$

63. Let $f(x) = \dfrac{(x+2)^2}{x^2 - 4}$. Find

(A) $\lim\limits_{x \to -2} f(x)$ (B) $\lim\limits_{x \to 0} f(x)$

(C) $\lim\limits_{x \to 2} f(x)$

64. Let $f(x) = \dfrac{x^2 - 1}{(x+1)^2}$. Find

(A) $\lim\limits_{x \to -1} f(x)$ (B) $\lim\limits_{x \to 0} f(x)$

(C) $\lim\limits_{x \to 1} f(x)$

65. Let $f(x) = \dfrac{2x^2 - 3x - 2}{x^2 + x - 6}$. Find

(A) $\lim\limits_{x \to 2} f(x)$ (B) $\lim\limits_{x \to 0} f(x)$

(C) $\lim\limits_{x \to 1} f(x)$

66. Let $f(x) = \dfrac{3x^2 + 2x - 1}{x^2 + 3x + 2}$. Find

(A) $\lim\limits_{x \to -3} f(x)$ (B) $\lim\limits_{x \to -1} f(x)$

(C) $\lim\limits_{x \to 2} f(x)$

✎ In Problems 67–72, discuss the validity of each statement. If the statement is always true, explain why. If not, give a counterexample.

67. If $\lim\limits_{x \to 1} f(x) = 0$ and $\lim\limits_{x \to 1} g(x) = 0$, then $\lim\limits_{x \to 1} \dfrac{f(x)}{g(x)} = 0$.

68. If $\lim\limits_{x \to 1} f(x) = 1$ and $\lim\limits_{x \to 1} g(x) = 1$, then $\lim\limits_{x \to 1} \dfrac{f(x)}{g(x)} = 1$.

69. If f is a polynomial, then, as x approaches 0, the right-hand limit exists and is equal to the left-hand limit.

70. If f is a rational function, then, as x approaches 0, the right-hand limit exists and is equal to the left-hand limit.

71. If f is a function such that $\lim\limits_{x \to 0} f(x)$ exists, then $f(0)$ exists.

72. If f is a function such that $f(0)$ exists, then $\lim\limits_{x \to 0} f(x)$ exists.

In Problems 73–80, is the limit expression a 0/0 indeterminate form? Find the limit or explain why the limit does not exist.

73. $\lim\limits_{x \to 7} \dfrac{(x-7)^2}{x^2 - 4x - 21}$

74. $\lim\limits_{x \to 2} \dfrac{x-5}{x+2}$

75. $\lim\limits_{x \to 4} \dfrac{x^2 + 4}{(x+4)^2}$

76. $\lim\limits_{x \to 9} \dfrac{x^2 - 5x - 36}{x - 9}$

77. $\lim\limits_{x \to -6} \dfrac{x^2 + 36}{x + 6}$

78. $\lim\limits_{x \to 10} \dfrac{x^2 - 15x + 50}{(x - 10)^2}$

79. $\lim\limits_{x \to 8} \dfrac{x-8}{x^2 - 64}$

80. $\lim\limits_{x \to -3} \dfrac{x+3}{x-3}$

Compute the following limit for each function in Problems 81–88.

$$\lim\limits_{h \to 0} \dfrac{f(2+h) - f(2)}{h}$$

81. $f(x) = 3x + 1$

82. $f(x) = 5x - 1$

83. $f(x) = x^2 + 1$

84. $f(x) = x^2 - 2$

85. $f(x) = -7x + 9$

86. $f(x) = -4x + 13$

87. $f(x) = |x + 1|$ 88. $f(x) = -3|x|$

89. Let f be defined by
$$f(x) = \begin{cases} 1 + mx & \text{if } x \le 1 \\ 4 - mx & \text{if } x > 1 \end{cases}$$
where m is a constant.

(A) Graph f for $m = 1$, and find
$$\lim\limits_{x \to 1^-} f(x) \quad \text{and} \quad \lim\limits_{x \to 1^+} f(x)$$

(B) Graph f for $m = 2$, and find
$$\lim\limits_{x \to 1^-} f(x) \quad \text{and} \quad \lim\limits_{x \to 1^+} f(x)$$

(C) Find m so that
$$\lim\limits_{x \to 1^-} f(x) = \lim\limits_{x \to 1^+} f(x)$$
and graph f for this value of m.

✎ (D) Write a brief verbal description of each graph. How does the graph in part (C) differ from the graphs in parts (A) and (B)?

90. Let f be defined by
$$f(x) = \begin{cases} -3m + 0.5x & \text{if } x \le 2 \\ 3m - x & \text{if } x > 2 \end{cases}$$
where m is a constant.

(A) Graph f for $m = 0$, and find
$$\lim\limits_{x \to 2^-} f(x) \quad \text{and} \quad \lim\limits_{x \to 2^-} f(x)$$

(B) Graph f for $m = 1$, and find
$$\lim\limits_{x \to 2^-} f(x) \quad \text{and} \quad \lim\limits_{x \to 2^+} f(x)$$

(C) Find m so that
$$\lim\limits_{x \to 2^-} f(x) = \lim\limits_{x \to 2^+} f(x)$$
and graph f for this value of m.

✎ (D) Write a brief verbal description of each graph. How does the graph in part (C) differ from the graphs in parts (A) and (B)?

Applications

91. **Telephone rates.** A long-distance telephone service charges $0.99 for the first 20 minutes or less of a call and $0.07 per minute thereafter.

(A) Write a piecewise definition of the charge $F(x)$ for a long-distance call lasting x minutes.

(B) Graph $F(x)$ for $0 < x \le 40$.

(C) Find $\lim\limits_{x \to 20^-} F(x)$, $\lim\limits_{x \to 20^+} F(x)$, and $\lim\limits_{x \to 20} F(x)$, whichever exist.

92. **Telephone rates.** A second long-distance telephone service charges $0.09 per minute for calls lasting 10 minutes or more and $0.18 per minute for calls lasting less than 10 minutes.

(A) Write a piecewise definition of the charge $G(x)$ for a long-distance call lasting x minutes.

(B) Graph $G(x)$ for $0 < x \le 40$.

(C) Find $\lim\limits_{x \to 10^-} G(x)$, $\lim\limits_{x \to 10^+} G(x)$, and $\lim\limits_{x \to 10} G(x)$, whichever exist.

93. Telephone rates. Refer to Problems 91 and 92. Write a brief verbal comparison of the two services described for calls lasting 20 minutes or less.

94. Telephone rates. Refer to Problems 91 and 92. Write a brief verbal comparison of the two services described for calls lasting more than 20 minutes.

A company sells custom embroidered apparel and promotional products. Table 1 shows the volume discounts offered by the company, where x is the volume of a purchase in dollars. Problems 95 and 96 deal with two different interpretations of this discount method.

Table 1 **Volume Discount (Excluding Tax)**

Volume (x)	Discount Amount
$300 \le x < $1,000	3%
$1,000 \le x < $3,000	5%
$3,000 \le x < $5,000	7%
$5,000 \le x$	10%

95. Volume discount. Assume that the volume discounts in Table 1 apply to the entire purchase. That is, if the volume x satisfies $300 \le x < $1,000, then the entire purchase is discounted 3%. If the volume x satisfies $1,000 \le x < $3,000, the entire purchase is discounted 5%, and so on.

  (A) If x is the volume of a purchase before the discount is applied, then write a piecewise definition for the discounted price $D(x)$ of this purchase.

  (B) Use one-sided limits to investigate the limit of $D(x)$ as x approaches $1,000. As x approaches $3,000.

96. Volume discount. Assume that the volume discounts in Table 1 apply only to that portion of the volume in each interval. That is, the discounted price for a $4,000 purchase would be computed as follows:

$$300 + 0.97(700) + 0.95(2,000) + 0.93(1,000) = 3,809$$

  (A) If x is the volume of a purchase before the discount is applied, then write a piecewise definition for the discounted price $P(x)$ of this purchase.

  (B) Use one-sided limits to investigate the limit of $P(x)$ as x approaches $1,000. As x approaches $3,000.

  (C) Compare this discount method with the one in Problem 95. Does one always produce a lower price than the other? Discuss.

97. Pollution A state charges polluters an annual fee of $20 per ton for each ton of pollutant emitted into the atmosphere, up to a maximum of 4,000 tons. No fees are charged for emissions beyond the 4,000-ton limit. Write a piecewise definition of the fees $F(x)$ charged for the emission of x tons of pollutant in a year. What is the limit of $F(x)$ as x approaches 4,000 tons? As x approaches 8,000 tons?

98. Pollution Refer to Problem 97. The average fee per ton of pollution is given by $A(x) = F(x)/x$. Write a piecewise definition of $A(x)$. What is the limit of $A(x)$ as x approaches 4,000 tons? As x approaches 8,000 tons?

99. Voter turnout. Statisticians often use piecewise-defined functions to predict outcomes of elections. For the following functions f and g, find the limit of each function as x approaches 5 and as x approaches 10.

$$f(x) = \begin{cases} 0 & \text{if } x \le 5 \\ 0.8 - 0.08x & \text{if } 5 < x < 10 \\ 0 & \text{if } 10 \le x \end{cases}$$

$$g(x) = \begin{cases} 0 & \text{if } x \le 5 \\ 0.8x - 0.04x^2 - 3 & \text{if } 5 < x < 10 \\ 1 & \text{if } 10 \le x \end{cases}$$

Answers to Matched Problems

1.

x	-2	-1	0	1	2	3	4
$h(x)$	1.0	1.5	2.0	2.5	3.0	3.5	4.0

2. $\lim\limits_{x \to 1} f(x) = 2$

3.

$$\lim\limits_{x \to 2} \frac{x-2}{|x-2|} \text{ does not exist}$$

4. (A) $\lim\limits_{x \to 0^-} f(x) = 0$ (B) $\lim\limits_{x \to 1^-} f(x) = 1$

  $\lim\limits_{x \to 0^+} f(x) = 0$ $\lim\limits_{x \to 1^+} f(x) = 2$

  $\lim\limits_{x \to 0} f(x) = 0$ $\lim\limits_{x \to 1} f(x)$ does not exist

  $f(0) = 0$ $f(1)$ not defined

  (C) $\lim\limits_{x \to 3^-} f(x) = 3$

  $\lim\limits_{x \to 3^+} f(x) = 3$

  $\lim\limits_{x \to 3} f(x) = 3$ $f(3)$ not defined

5. -6

6. (A) 6

  (B) $\sqrt{6}$

  (C) $\frac{4}{5}$

7. (A) 13

  (B) 7

  (C) Does not exist

  (D) Not defined

8. (A) -2

  (B) Does not exist

9. (A) No; $\dfrac{2}{3}$

  (B) No; 0

  (C) Yes; 6

10. -2

2.2 Infinite Limits and Limits at Infinity

- Infinite Limits
- Locating Vertical Asymptotes
- Limits at Infinity
- Finding Horizontal Asymptotes

In this section, we consider two new types of limits: infinite limits and limits at infinity. Infinite limits and vertical asymptotes are used to describe the behavior of functions that are unbounded near $x = a$. Limits at infinity and horizontal asymptotes are used to describe the behavior of functions as x assumes arbitrarily large positive values or arbitrarily large negative values. Although we will include graphs to illustrate basic concepts, we postpone a discussion of graphing techniques until Chapter 4.

Infinite Limits

The graph of $f(x) = \dfrac{1}{x - 1}$ (Fig. 1) indicates that

$$\lim_{x \to 1^+} \frac{1}{x - 1}$$

does not exist. There does not exist a real number L that the values of $f(x)$ approach as x approaches 1 from the right. Instead, as x approaches 1 from the right, the values of $f(x)$ are positive and become larger and larger; that is, $f(x)$ increases without bound (Table 1). We express this behavior symbolically as

$$\lim_{x \to 1^+} \frac{1}{x - 1} = \infty \quad \text{or} \quad f(x) = \frac{1}{x - 1} \to \infty \quad \text{as} \quad x \to 1^+ \tag{1}$$

Since ∞ is a not a real number, *the limit in (1) does not exist*. We are using the symbol ∞ to describe the manner in which the limit fails to exist, and we call this situation an **infinite limit**. If x approaches 1 from the left, the values of $f(x)$ are negative and become larger and larger in absolute value; that is, $f(x)$ decreases through negative values without bound (Table 2). We express this behavior symbolically as

$$\lim_{x \to 1^-} \frac{1}{x - 1} = -\infty \quad \text{or} \quad f(x) = \frac{1}{x - 1} \to -\infty \quad \text{as} \quad x \to 1^- \tag{2}$$

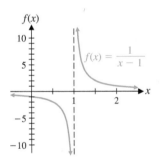

Figure 1

Table 1

x	$f(x) = \dfrac{1}{x - 1}$
1.1	10
1.01	100
1.001	1,000
1.0001	10,000
1.00001	100,000
1.000001	1,000,000

Table 2

x	$f(x) = \dfrac{1}{x - 1}$
0.9	−10
0.99	−100
0.999	−1,000
0.9999	−10,000
0.99999	−100,000
0.999999	−1,000,000

The one-sided limits in (1) and (2) describe the behavior of the graph as $x \to 1$ (Fig. 1). Does the two-sided limit of $f(x)$ as $x \to 1$ exist? No, because neither of the one-sided limits exists. Also, there is no reasonable way to use the symbol ∞ to describe the behavior of $f(x)$ as $x \to 1$ on both sides of 1. We say that

$$\lim_{x \to 1} \frac{1}{x - 1} \quad \text{does not exist}$$

Explore and Discuss 1

Let $g(x) = \dfrac{1}{(x - 1)^2}$.

Construct tables for $g(x)$ as $x \to 1^+$ and as $x \to 1^-$. Use these tables and infinite limits to discuss the behavior of $g(x)$ near $x = 1$.

We used the dashed vertical line $x = 1$ in Figure 1 to illustrate the infinite limits as x approaches 1 from the right and from the left. We call this line a *vertical asymptote*.

DEFINITION   Infinite Limits and Vertical Asymptotes

The vertical line $x = a$ is a **vertical asymptote** for the graph of $y = f(x)$ if

$$f(x) \to \infty \quad \text{or} \quad f(x) \to -\infty \quad \text{as} \quad x \to a^+ \quad \text{or} \quad x \to a^-$$

[That is, if $f(x)$ either increases or decreases without bound as x approaches a from the right or from the left].

Locating Vertical Asymptotes

How do we locate vertical asymptotes? If f is a polynomial function, then $\lim\limits_{x \to a} f(x)$ is equal to the real number $f(a)$ [Theorem 3, Section 2.1]. So *a polynomial function has no vertical asymptotes*. Similarly (again by Theorem 3, Section 2.1), *a vertical asymptote of a rational function can occur only at a zero of its denominator*. Theorem 1 provides a simple procedure for locating the vertical asymptotes of a rational function.

THEOREM 1   Locating Vertical Asymptotes of Rational Functions

If $f(x) = n(x)/d(x)$ is a rational function, $d(c) = 0$ and $n(c) \neq 0$, then the line $x = c$ is a vertical asymptote of the graph of f.

If $f(x) = n(x)/d(x)$ and both $n(c) = 0$ and $d(c) = 0$, then the limit of $f(x)$ as x approaches c involves an indeterminate form and Theorem 1 does not apply:

$$\lim_{x \to c} f(x) = \lim_{x \to c} \frac{n(x)}{d(x)} \quad \frac{0}{0} \text{ indeterminate form}$$

Algebraic simplification is often useful in this situation.

EXAMPLE 1   Locating Vertical Asymptotes   Let $f(x) = \dfrac{x^2 + x - 2}{x^2 - 1}$.

Describe the behavior of f at each zero of the denominator. Use ∞ and $-\infty$ when appropriate. Identify all vertical asymptotes.

SOLUTION   Let $n(x) = x^2 + x - 2$ and $d(x) = x^2 - 1$. Factoring the denominator, we see that

$$d(x) = x^2 - 1 = (x - 1)(x + 1)$$

has two zeros: $x = -1$ and $x = 1$.

First, we consider $x = -1$. Since $d(-1) = 0$ and $n(-1) = -2 \neq 0$, Theorem 1 tells us that the line $x = -1$ is a vertical asymptote. So at least one of the one-sided limits at $x = -1$ must be either ∞ or $-\infty$. Examining tables of values of f for x near -1 or a graph on a graphing calculator will show which is the case. From Tables 3 and 4, we see that

$$\lim_{x \to -1^-} \frac{x^2 + x - 2}{x^2 - 1} = -\infty \quad \text{and} \quad \lim_{x \to -1^+} \frac{x^2 + x - 2}{x^2 - 1} = \infty$$

Table 3

x	$f(x) = \dfrac{x^2 + x - 2}{x^2 - 1}$
-1.1	-9
-1.01	-99
-1.001	-999
-1.0001	$-9,999$
-1.00001	$-99,999$

Table 4

x	$f(x) = \dfrac{x^2 + x - 2}{x^2 - 1}$
-0.9	11
-0.99	101
-0.999	$1,001$
-0.9999	$10,001$
-0.99999	$100,001$

Now we consider the other zero of $d(x)$, $x = 1$. This time $n(1) = 0$ and Theorem 1 does not apply. We use algebraic simplification to investigate the behavior of the function at $x = 1$:

$$\lim_{x \to 1} f(x) = \lim_{x \to 1} \frac{x^2 + x - 2}{x^2 - 1} \qquad \frac{0}{0} \text{ indeterminate form}$$

$$= \lim_{x \to 1} \frac{(x-1)(x+2)}{(x-1)(x+1)}$$

$$= \lim_{x \to 1} \frac{x + 2}{x + 1} \qquad \text{Reduced to lowest terms (see Appendix A.4)}$$

$$= \frac{3}{2}$$

Since the limit exists as x approaches 1, f does not have a vertical asymptote at $x = 1$. The graph of f (Fig. 2) shows the behavior at the vertical asymptote $x = -1$ and also at $x = 1$.

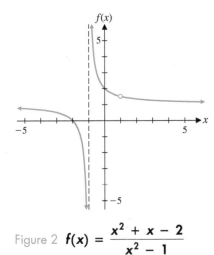

Figure 2 $f(x) = \dfrac{x^2 + x - 2}{x^2 - 1}$

Matched Problem 1 Let $f(x) = \dfrac{x - 3}{x^2 - 4x + 3}$.

Describe the behavior of f at each zero of the denominator. Use ∞ and $-\infty$ when appropriate. Identify all vertical asymptotes.

EXAMPLE 2 Locating Vertical Asymptotes Let $f(x) = \dfrac{x^2 + 20}{5(x - 2)^2}$.

Describe the behavior of f at each zero of the denominator. Use ∞ and $-\infty$ when appropriate. Identify all vertical asymptotes.

SOLUTION Let $n(x) = x^2 + 20$ and $d(x) = 5(x - 2)^2$. The only zero of $d(x)$ is $x = 2$. Since $n(2) = 24 \neq 0$, f has a vertical asymptote at $x = 2$ (Theorem 1). Tables 5 and 6 show that $f(x) \to \infty$ as $x \to 2$ from either side, and we have

$$\lim_{x \to 2^+} \frac{x^2 + 20}{5(x - 2)^2} = \infty \quad \text{and} \quad \lim_{x \to 2^-} \frac{x^2 + 20}{5(x - 2)^2} = \infty$$

Table 5

x	$f(x) = \dfrac{x^2 + 20}{5(x - 2)^2}$
2.1	488.2
2.01	$48,080.02$
2.001	$4,800,800.2$

Table 6

x	$f(x) = \dfrac{x^2 + 20}{5(x - 2)^2}$
1.9	472.2
1.99	$47,920.02$
1.999	$4,799,200.2$

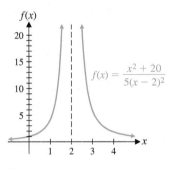

$$f(x) = \frac{x^2 + 20}{5(x - 2)^2}$$

Figure 3

The denominator d has no other zeros, so f does not have any other vertical asymptotes. The graph of f (Fig. 3) shows the behavior at the vertical asymptote $x = 2$. Because the left- and right-hand limits are both infinite, we write

$$\lim_{x \to 2} \frac{x^2 + 20}{5(x - 2)^2} = \infty$$

Matched Problem 2   Let $f(x) = \dfrac{x - 1}{(x + 3)^2}$.

Describe the behavior of f at each zero of the denominator. Use ∞ and $-\infty$ when appropriate. Identify all vertical asymptotes.

CONCEPTUAL INSIGHT

When is it correct to say that a limit does not exist, and when is it correct to use $\pm\infty$? It depends on the situation. Table 7 lists the infinite limits that we discussed in Examples 1 and 2.

Table 7

Right-Hand Limit	Left-Hand Limit	Two-Sided Limit
$\lim\limits_{x \to -1^+} \dfrac{x^2 + x - 2}{x^2 - 1} = \infty$	$\lim\limits_{x \to -1^-} \dfrac{x^2 + x - 2}{x^2 - 1} = -\infty$	$\lim\limits_{x \to -1} \dfrac{x^2 + x - 2}{x^2 - 1}$ does not exist
$\lim\limits_{x \to 2^+} \dfrac{x^2 + 20}{5(x - 2)^2} = \infty$	$\lim\limits_{x \to 2^-} \dfrac{x^2 + 20}{5(x - 2)^2} = \infty$	$\lim\limits_{x \to 2} \dfrac{x^2 + 20}{5(x - 2)^2} = \infty$

The instructions in Examples 1 and 2 said that we should use infinite limits to describe the behavior at vertical asymptotes. If we had been asked to *evaluate* the limits, with no mention of ∞ or asymptotes, then the correct answer would be that **all of these limits do not exist**. Remember, ∞ is a symbol used to describe the behavior of functions at vertical asymptotes.

Limits at Infinity

The symbol ∞ can also be used to indicate that an independent variable is increasing or decreasing without bound. We write $x \to \infty$ to indicate that x is increasing without bound through positive values and $x \to -\infty$ to indicate that x is decreasing without bound through negative values. We begin by considering power functions of the form x^p and $1/x^p$ where p is a positive real number.

If p is a positive real number, then x^p increases as x increases. There is no upper bound on the values of x^p. We indicate this behavior by writing

$$\lim_{x \to \infty} x^p = \infty \quad \text{or} \quad x^p \to \infty \quad \text{as} \quad x \to \infty$$

Since the reciprocals of very large numbers are very small numbers, it follows that $1/x^p$ approaches 0 as x increases without bound. We indicate this behavior by writing

$$\lim_{x \to \infty} \frac{1}{x^p} = 0 \quad \text{or} \quad \frac{1}{x^p} \to 0 \quad \text{as} \quad x \to \infty$$

Figure 4 illustrates the preceding behavior for $f(x) = x^2$ and $g(x) = 1/x^2$, and we write

$$\lim_{x \to \infty} f(x) = \infty \quad \text{and} \quad \lim_{x \to \infty} g(x) = 0$$

Limits of power forms as x decreases without bound behave in a similar manner, with two important differences. First, if x is negative, then x^p is not defined for all values of p. For example, $x^{1/2} = \sqrt{x}$ is not defined for negative values of x. Second,

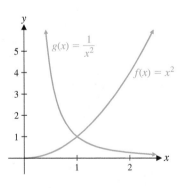

$$g(x) = \frac{1}{x^2}$$

$$f(x) = x^2$$

Figure 4

if x^p is defined, then it may approach ∞ or $-\infty$, depending on the value of p. For example,

$$\lim_{x \to -\infty} x^2 = \infty \quad \text{but} \quad \lim_{x \to -\infty} x^3 = -\infty$$

For the function g in Figure 4, the line $y = 0$ (the x axis) is called a *horizontal asymptote*. In general, a line $y = b$ is a **horizontal asymptote** of the graph of $y = f(x)$ if $f(x)$ approaches b as either x increases without bound or x decreases without bound. Symbolically, $y = b$ is a horizontal asymptote if either

$$\lim_{x \to -\infty} f(x) = b \quad \text{or} \quad \lim_{x \to \infty} f(x) = b$$

In the first case, the graph of f will be close to the horizontal line $y = b$ for large (in absolute value) negative x. In the second case, the graph will be close to the horizontal line $y = b$ for large positive x. Figure 5 shows the graph of a function with two horizontal asymptotes: $y = 1$ and $y = -1$.

Theorem 2 summarizes the various possibilities for limits of power functions as x increases or decreases without bound.

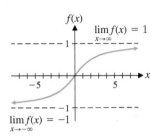

Figure 5

THEOREM 2   Limits of Power Functions at Infinity

If p is a positive real number and k is any real number except 0, then

1. $\displaystyle\lim_{x \to -\infty} \frac{k}{x^p} = 0$ **2.** $\displaystyle\lim_{x \to \infty} \frac{k}{x^p} = 0$

3. $\displaystyle\lim_{x \to -\infty} kx^p = \pm\infty$ **4.** $\displaystyle\lim_{x \to \infty} kx^p = \pm\infty$

provided that x^p is a real number for negative values of x. The limits in 3 and 4 will be either $-\infty$ or ∞, depending on k and p.

How can we use Theorem 2 to evaluate limits at infinity? It turns out that the limit properties listed in Theorem 2, Section 2.1, are also valid if we replace the statement $x \to c$ with $x \to \infty$ or $x \to -\infty$.

EXAMPLE 3 Limit of a Polynomial Function at Infinity Let $p(x) = 2x^3 - x^2 - 7x + 3$. Find the limit of $p(x)$ as x approaches ∞ and as x approaches $-\infty$.

SOLUTION Since limits of power functions of the form $1/x^p$ approach 0 as x approaches ∞ or $-\infty$, it is convenient to work with these reciprocal forms whenever possible. If we factor out the term involving the highest power of x, then we can write $p(x)$ as

$$p(x) = 2x^3\left(1 - \frac{1}{2x} - \frac{7}{2x^2} + \frac{3}{2x^3}\right)$$

Using Theorem 2 above and Theorem 2 in Section 2.1, we write

$$\lim_{x \to \infty}\left(1 - \frac{1}{2x} - \frac{7}{2x^2} + \frac{3}{2x^3}\right) = 1 - 0 - 0 + 0 = 1$$

For large values of x,

$$\left(1 - \frac{1}{2x} - \frac{7}{2x^2} + \frac{3}{2x^3}\right) \approx 1$$

and

$$p(x) = 2x^3\left(1 - \frac{1}{2x} - \frac{7}{2x^2} + \frac{3}{2x^3}\right) \approx 2x^3$$

Since $2x^3 \to \infty$ as $x \to \infty$, it follows that

$$\lim_{x \to \infty} p(x) = \lim_{x \to \infty} 2x^3 = \infty$$

Similarly, $2x^3 \to -\infty$ as $x \to -\infty$ implies that

$$\lim_{x \to -\infty} p(x) = \lim_{x \to -\infty} 2x^3 = -\infty$$

So the behavior of $p(x)$ for large values is the same as the behavior of the highest-degree term, $2x^3$.

Matched Problem 3 Let $p(x) = -4x^4 + 2x^3 + 3x$. Find the limit of $p(x)$ as x approaches ∞ and as x approaches $-\infty$.

The term with highest degree in a polynomial is called the **leading term**. In the solution to Example 3, the limits at infinity of $p(x) = 2x^3 - x^2 - 7x + 3$ were the same as the limits of the leading term $2x^3$. Theorem 3 states that this is true for any polynomial of degree greater than or equal to 1.

THEOREM 3   Limits of Polynomial Functions at Infinity

If

$$p(x) = a_n x^n + a_{n-1} x^{n-1} + \cdots + a_1 x + a_0, a_n \neq 0, n \geq 1$$

then

$$\lim_{x \to \infty} p(x) = \lim_{x \to \infty} a_n x^n = \pm\infty$$

and

$$\lim_{x \to -\infty} p(x) = \lim_{x \to -\infty} a_n x^n = \pm\infty$$

Each limit will be either $-\infty$ or ∞, depending on a_n and n.

A polynomial of degree 0 is a constant function $p(x) = a_0$, and its limit as x approaches ∞ or $-\infty$ is the number a_0. For any polynomial of degree 1 or greater, Theorem 3 states that the limit as x approaches ∞ or $-\infty$ cannot be equal to a number. This means that **polynomials of degree 1 or greater never have horizontal asymptotes**.

A pair of limit expressions of the form

$$\lim_{x \to \infty} f(x) = A, \quad \lim_{x \to -\infty} f(x) = B$$

where A and B are ∞, $-\infty$, or real numbers, describes the **end behavior** of the function f. The first of the two limit expressions describes the **right end behavior** and the second describes the **left end behavior**. By Theorem 3, the end behavior of any nonconstant polynomial function is described by a pair of infinite limits.

EXAMPLE 4   End Behavior of a Polynomial   Give a pair of limit expressions that describe the end behavior of each polynomial.

(A) $p(x) = 3x^3 - 500x^2$ 　　　　　 (B) $p(x) = 3x^3 - 500x^4$

SOLUTION

(A) By Theorem 3,

$$\lim_{x \to \infty} (3x^3 - 500x^2) = \lim_{x \to \infty} 3x^3 = \infty \qquad \text{Right end behavior}$$

and

$$\lim_{x \to -\infty} (3x^3 - 500x^2) = \lim_{x \to -\infty} 3x^3 = -\infty \qquad \text{Left end behavior}$$

(B) By Theorem 3,

$$\lim_{x \to \infty} (3x^3 - 500x^4) = \lim_{x \to \infty} (-500x^4) = -\infty \qquad \text{Right end behavior}$$

and

$$\lim_{x \to -\infty} (3x^3 - 500x^4) = \lim_{x \to -\infty} (-500x^4) = -\infty \qquad \text{Left end behavior}$$

Matched Problem 4 ⌋ Give a pair of limit expressions that describe the end behavior of each polynomial.

(A) $p(x) = 300x^2 - 4x^5$ (B) $p(x) = 300x^6 - 4x^5$

Finding Horizontal Asymptotes

Since a rational function is the ratio of two polynomials, it is not surprising that reciprocals of powers of x can be used to analyze limits of rational functions at infinity. For example, consider the rational function

$$f(x) = \frac{3x^2 - 5x + 9}{2x^2 + 7}$$

Factoring the highest-degree term out of the numerator and the highest-degree term out of the denominator, we write

$$f(x) = \frac{3x^2}{2x^2} \cdot \frac{1 - \dfrac{5}{3x} + \dfrac{3}{x^2}}{1 + \dfrac{7}{2x^2}}$$

$$\lim_{x \to \infty} f(x) = \lim_{x \to \infty} \frac{3x^2}{2x^2} \cdot \lim_{x \to \infty} \frac{1 - \dfrac{5}{3x} + \dfrac{3}{x^2}}{1 + \dfrac{7}{2x^2}} = \frac{3}{2} \cdot \frac{1 - 0 + 0}{1 + 0} = \frac{3}{2}$$

The behavior of this rational function as x approaches infinity is determined by the ratio of the highest-degree term in the numerator ($3x^2$) to the highest-degree term in the denominator ($2x^2$). Theorem 2 can be used to generalize this result to any rational function. Theorem 4 lists the three possible outcomes.

THEOREM 4 Limits of Rational Functions at Infinity and Horizontal Asymptotes of Rational Functions

(A) If $f(x) = \dfrac{a_m x^m + a_{m-1} x^{m-1} + \cdots + a_1 x + a_0}{b_n x^n + b_{n-1} x^{n-1} + \cdots + b_1 x + b_0}$, $a_m \neq 0, b_n \neq 0$

then $\displaystyle\lim_{x \to \infty} f(x) = \lim_{x \to \infty} \frac{a_m x^m}{b_n x^n}$ and $\displaystyle\lim_{x \to -\infty} f(x) = \lim_{x \to -\infty} \frac{a_m x^m}{b_n x^n}$

(B) There are three possible cases for these limits:

  1. If $m < n$, then $\displaystyle\lim_{x \to \infty} f(x) = \lim_{x \to -\infty} f(x) = 0$, and the line $y = 0$ (the x axis) is a horizontal asymptote of $f(x)$.

  2. If $m = n$, then $\displaystyle\lim_{x \to \infty} f(x) = \lim_{x \to -\infty} f(x) = \frac{a_m}{b_n}$, and the line $y = \frac{a_m}{b_n}$ is a horizontal asymptote of $f(x)$.

  3. If $m > n$, then each limit will be ∞ or $-\infty$, depending on $m, n, a_m,$ and b_n, and $f(x)$ does not have a horizontal asymptote.

Notice that in cases 1 and 2 of Theorem 4, the limit is the same if x approaches ∞ or $-\infty$. So, **a rational function can have at most one horizontal asymptote** (see Fig. 6).

Figure 6 $f(x) = \dfrac{3x^2 - 5x + 9}{2x^2 + 7}$

CONCEPTUAL INSIGHT

The graph of f in Figure 6 dispels the misconception that the graph of a function cannot cross a horizontal asymptote. Horizontal asymptotes give us information about the graph of a function only as $x \to \infty$ and $x \to -\infty$, not at any specific value of x.

EXAMPLE 5 Finding Horizontal Asymptotes Find all horizontal asymptotes, if any, of each function.

(A) $f(x) = \dfrac{5x^3 - 2x^2 + 1}{4x^3 + 2x - 7}$

(B) $f(x) = \dfrac{3x^4 - x^2 + 1}{8x^6 - 10}$

(C) $f(x) = \dfrac{2x^5 - x^3 - 1}{6x^3 + 2x^2 - 7}$

SOLUTION We will make use of part A of Theorem 4.

(A) $\displaystyle \lim_{x \to \infty} f(x) = \lim_{x \to \infty} \frac{5x^3 - 2x^2 + 1}{4x^3 + 2x - 7} = \lim_{x \to \infty} \frac{5x^3}{4x^3} = \frac{5}{4}$

The line $y = 5/4$ is a horizontal asymptote of $f(x)$.

(B) $\displaystyle \lim_{x \to \infty} f(x) = \lim_{x \to \infty} \frac{3x^4 - x^2 + 1}{8x^6 - 10} = \lim_{x \to \infty} \frac{3x^4}{8x^6} = \lim_{x \to \infty} \frac{3}{8x^2} = 0$

The line $y = 0$ (the x axis) is a horizontal asymptote of $f(x)$.

(C) $\displaystyle \lim_{x \to \infty} f(x) = \lim_{x \to \infty} \frac{2x^5 - x^3 - 1}{6x^3 + 2x^2 - 7} = \lim_{x \to \infty} \frac{2x^5}{6x^3} = \lim_{x \to \infty} \frac{x^2}{3} = \infty$

The function $f(x)$ has no horizontal asymptotes.

Matched Problem 5 Find all horizontal asymptotes, if any, of each function.

(A) $f(x) = \dfrac{4x^3 - 5x + 8}{2x^4 - 7}$

(B) $f(x) = \dfrac{5x^6 + 3x}{2x^5 - x - 5}$

(C) $f(x) = \dfrac{2x^3 - x + 7}{4x^3 + 3x^2 - 100}$

An accurate sketch of the graph of a rational function requires knowledge of both vertical and horizontal asymptotes. As we mentioned earlier, we are postponing a detailed discussion of graphing techniques until Section 4.4.

EXAMPLE 6 Find all vertical and horizontal asymptotes of the function
$$f(x) = \frac{2x^2 - 5}{x^2 + 5x + 4}$$

SOLUTION Let $n(x) = 2x^2 - 5$ and $d(x) = x^2 + 5x + 4 = (x + 1)(x + 4)$. The denominator $d(x) = 0$ at $x = -1$ and $x = -4$. Since the numerator $n(x)$ is not zero at these values of x [$n(-1) = -3$ and $n(-4) = 27$], by Theorem 1 there are two vertical asymptotes of f: the line $x = -1$ and the line $x = -4$. Since

$$\lim_{x \to \infty} f(x) = \lim_{x \to \infty} \frac{2x^2 - 5}{x^2 + 5x + 4} = \lim_{x \to \infty} \frac{2x^2}{x^2} = 2$$

the horizontal asymptote is the line $y = 2$ (Theorem 3).

Matched Problem 6 Find all vertical and horizontal asymptotes of the function
$$f(x) = \frac{x^2 - 9}{x^2 - 4}.$$

Exercises 2.2

Skills Warm-up Exercises

W | In Problems 1–8, find an equation of the form $Ax + By = C$ for the given line. (If necessary, review Section 1.3).

1. The horizontal line through $(0, 4)$

2. The vertical line through $(5, 0)$

3. The vertical line through $(-6, 3)$

4. The horizontal line through $(7, 1)$

5. The line through $(-2, 9)$ that has slope 2

6. The line through $(8, -4)$ that has slope -3

7. The line through $(9, 0)$ and $(0, 7)$

8. The line through $(-1, 20)$ and $(1, 30)$

Problems 9–16 refer to the following graph of $y = f(x)$.

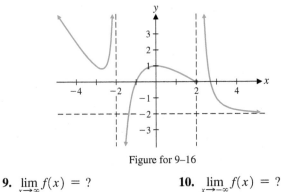

Figure for 9–16

9. $\lim_{x \to \infty} f(x) = ?$

10. $\lim_{x \to -\infty} f(x) = ?$

11. $\lim_{x \to -2^+} f(x) = ?$

12. $\lim_{x \to -2^-} f(x) = ?$

13. $\lim_{x \to 2^-} f(x) = ?$

14. $\lim_{x \to 2^+} f(x) = ?$

15. $\lim_{x \to 2^-} f(x) = ?$

16. $\lim_{x \to 2} f(x) = ?$

In Problems 17–24, find each limit. Use $-\infty$ and ∞ when appropriate.

17. $f(x) = \dfrac{x}{x - 5}$

(A) $\lim_{x \to 5^-} f(x)$ 　(B) $\lim_{x \to 5^+} f(x)$ 　(C) $\lim_{x \to 5} f(x)$

18. $f(x) = \dfrac{x^2}{x + 3}$

(A) $\lim_{x \to -3^-} f(x)$ 　(B) $\lim_{x \to -3^+} f(x)$ 　(C) $\lim_{x \to -3} f(x)$

19. $f(x) = \dfrac{2x - 4}{(x - 4)^2}$

(A) $\lim_{x \to 4^-} f(x)$ 　(B) $\lim_{x \to 4^+} f(x)$ 　(C) $\lim_{x \to 4} f(x)$

20. $f(x) = \dfrac{2x + 2}{(x + 2)^2}$

(A) $\lim_{x \to -2^-} f(x)$ 　(B) $\lim_{x \to -2^+} f(x)$ 　(C) $\lim_{x \to -2} f(x)$

21. $f(x) = \dfrac{x^2 + x - 2}{x - 1}$

(A) $\lim_{x \to 1^-} f(x)$ 　(B) $\lim_{x \to 1^+} f(x)$ 　(C) $\lim_{x \to 1} f(x)$

22. $f(x) = \dfrac{x^2 + x + 2}{x - 1}$

(A) $\lim_{x \to 1^-} f(x)$ 　(B) $\lim_{x \to 1^+} f(x)$ 　(C) $\lim_{x \to 1} f(x)$

23. $f(x) = \dfrac{x^2 - 3x + 2}{x + 2}$

(A) $\lim_{x \to -2^-} f(x)$ 　(B) $\lim_{x \to -2^+} f(x)$ 　(C) $\lim_{x \to -2} f(x)$

24. $f(x) = \dfrac{x^2 + x - 2}{x + 2}$

(A) $\lim_{x \to -2^-} f(x)$ 　(B) $\lim_{x \to -2^+} f(x)$ 　(C) $\lim_{x \to -2} f(x)$

In Problems 25–32, find (A) the leading term of the polynomial, (B) the limit as x approaches ∞, and (C) the limit as x approaches −∞.

25. $p(x) = 15 + 3x^2 - 5x^3$

26. $p(x) = 10 - x^6 + 7x^3$

27. $p(x) = 9x^2 - 6x^4 + 7x$

28. $p(x) = -x^5 + 2x^3 + 9x$

29. $p(x) = x^2 + 7x + 12$

30. $p(x) = 5x + x^3 - 8x^2$

31. $p(x) = x^4 + 2x^5 - 11x$

32. $p(x) = 1 + 4x^2 + 4x^4$

In Problems 33–42, use −∞ or ∞ where appropriate to describe the behavior at each zero of the denominator and identify all vertical asymptotes.

33. $f(x) = \dfrac{1}{x + 3}$

34. $g(x) = \dfrac{x}{4 - x}$

35. $h(x) = \dfrac{x^2 + 4}{x^2 - 4}$

36. $k(x) = \dfrac{x^2 - 9}{x^2 + 9}$

37. $F(x) = \dfrac{x^2 - 4}{x^2 + 4}$

38. $G(x) = \dfrac{x^2 + 9}{9 - x^2}$

39. $H(x) = \dfrac{x^2 - 2x - 3}{x^2 - 4x + 3}$

40. $K(x) - \dfrac{x^2 + 2x - 3}{x^2 - 4x + 3}$

41. $T(x) = \dfrac{8x - 16}{x^4 - 8x^3 + 16x^2}$

42. $S(x) = \dfrac{6x + 9}{x^4 + 6x^3 + 9x^2}$

In Problems 43–50, find each function value and limit. Use −∞ or ∞ where appropriate.

43. $f(x) = \dfrac{4x + 7}{5x - 9}$

    (A) $f(10)$ (B) $f(100)$ (C) $\lim\limits_{x \to \infty} f(x)$

44. $f(x) = \dfrac{2 - 3x^3}{7 + 4x^3}$

    (A) $f(5)$ (B) $f(10)$ (C) $\lim\limits_{x \to \infty} f(x)$

45. $f(x) = \dfrac{5x^2 + 11}{7x - 2}$

    (A) $f(20)$ (B) $f(50)$ (C) $\lim\limits_{x \to \infty} f(x)$

46. $f(x) = \dfrac{5x + 11}{7x^3 - 2}$

    (A) $f(-8)$ (B) $f(-16)$ (C) $\lim\limits_{x \to -\infty} f(x)$

47. $f(x) = \dfrac{7x^4 - 14x^2}{6x^5 + 3}$

    (A) $f(-6)$ (B) $f(-12)$ (C) $\lim\limits_{x \to -\infty} f(x)$

48. $f(x) = \dfrac{4x^7 - 8x}{6x^4 + 9x^2}$

    (A) $f(-3)$ (B) $f(-6)$ (C) $\lim\limits_{x \to -\infty} f(x)$

49. $f(x) = \dfrac{10 - 7x^3}{4 + x^3}$

    (A) $f(-10)$ (B) $f(-20)$ (C) $\lim\limits_{x \to -\infty} f(x)$

50. $f(x) = \dfrac{3 + x}{5 + 4x}$

    (A) $f(-50)$ (B) $f(-100)$ (C) $\lim\limits_{x \to -\infty} f(x)$

In Problems 51–64, find all horizontal and vertical asymptotes.

51. $f(x) = \dfrac{2x}{x + 2}$

52. $f(x) = \dfrac{3x + 2}{x - 4}$

53. $f(x) = \dfrac{x^2 + 1}{x^2 - 1}$

54. $f(x) = \dfrac{x^2 - 1}{x^2 + 2}$

55. $f(x) = \dfrac{x^3}{x^2 + 6}$

56. $f(x) = \dfrac{x}{x^2 - 4}$

57. $f(x) = \dfrac{x}{x^2 + 4}$

58. $f(x) = \dfrac{x^2 + 9}{x}$

59. $f(x) = \dfrac{x^2}{x - 3}$

60. $f(x) = \dfrac{x + 5}{x^2}$

61. $f(x) = \dfrac{2x^2 + 3x - 2}{x^2 - x - 2}$

62. $f(x) = \dfrac{2x^2 + 7x + 12}{2x^2 + 5x - 12}$

63. $f(x) = \dfrac{2x^2 - 5x + 2}{x^2 - x - 2}$

64. $f(x) = \dfrac{x^2 - x - 12}{2x^2 + 5x - 12}$

In Problems 65–68, give a limit expression that describes the right end behavior of the function.

65. $f(x) = \dfrac{x + 3}{x^2 - 5}$

66. $f(x) = \dfrac{3 + 4x + x^2}{5 - x}$

67. $f(x) = \dfrac{x^2 - 5}{x + 3}$

68. $f(x) = \dfrac{4x + 1}{5x - 7}$

In Problems 69–72, give a limit expression that describes the left end behavior of the function.

69. $f(x) = \dfrac{5 - 2x^2}{1 + 8x^2}$

70. $f(x) = \dfrac{2x + 3}{x^2 - 1}$

71. $f(x) = \dfrac{x^2 + 4x}{3x + 2}$

72. $f(x) = \dfrac{6 - x^4}{1 + 2x}$

In Problems 73–76, give a pair of limit expressions that describe the end behavior of the function.

73. $f(x) = x^3 - 3x + 1$

74. $f(x) = 4 - 5x - x^3$

75. $f(x) = \dfrac{2 + 5x}{1 - x}$

76. $f(x) = \dfrac{9x^2 + 6x + 1}{4x^2 + 4x + 1}$

In Problems 77–82, discuss the validity of each statement. If the statement is always true, explain why. If not, give a counterexample.

77. A rational function has at least one vertical asymptote.

78. A rational function has at most one vertical asymptote.

79. A rational function has at least one horizontal asymptote.

80. A rational function has at most one horizontal asymptote.

81. A polynomial function of degree ≥ 1 has neither horizontal nor vertical asymptotes.

82. The graph of a rational function cannot cross a horizontal asymptote.

83. Theorem 3 states that

$$\lim_{x \to \infty} (a_n x^n + a_{n-1}x^{n-1} + \cdots + a_0) = \pm\infty.$$

What conditions must n and a_n satisfy for the limit to be ∞? For the limit to be $-\infty$?

84. Theorem 3 also states that

$$\lim_{x \to -\infty} (a_n x^n + a_{n-1}x^{n-1} + \cdots + a_0) = \pm\infty.$$

What conditions must n and a_n satisfy for the limit to be ∞? For the limit to be $-\infty$?

Applications

85. Average cost. A company manufacturing snowboards has fixed costs of $200 per day and total costs of $3,800 per day for a daily output of 20 boards.

(A) Assuming that the total cost per day $C(x)$ is linearly related to the total output per day x, write an equation for the cost function.

(B) The average cost per board for an output of x boards is given by $\overline{C}(x) = C(x)/x$. Find the average cost function.

(C) Sketch a graph of the average cost function, including any asymptotes, for $1 \le x \le 30$.

(D) What does the average cost per board tend to as production increases?

86. Average cost. A company manufacturing surfboards has fixed costs of $300 per day and total costs of $5,100 per day for a daily output of 20 boards.

(A) Assuming that the total cost per day $C(x)$ is linearly related to the total output per day x, write an equation for the cost function.

(B) The average cost per board for an output of x boards is given by $\overline{C}(x) = C(x)/x$. Find the average cost function.

(C) Sketch a graph of the average cost function, including any asymptotes, for $1 \le x \le 30$.

(D) What does the average cost per board tend to as production increases?

87. Energy costs. Most appliance manufacturers produce conventional and energy-efficient models. The energy-efficient models are more expensive to make but cheaper to operate. The costs of purchasing and operating a 23-cubic-foot refrigerator of each type are given in Table 8. These costs do not include maintenance charges or changes in electricity prices.

Table 8 **23-ft³ Refrigerators**

	Energy-Efficient Model	Conventional Model
Initial cost	$950	$900
Total volume	23 ft³	23 ft³
Annual cost of electricity	$56	$66

(A) Express the total cost $C_e(x)$ and the average cost $\overline{C}_e(x) = C_e(x)/x$ of purchasing and operating an energy-efficient model for x years.

(B) Express the total cost $C_c(x)$ and the average cost $\overline{C}_c(x) = C_c(x)/x$ of purchasing and operating a conventional model for x years.

(C) Are the total costs for an energy-efficient model and for a conventional model ever the same? If so, when?

(D) Are the average costs for an energy-efficient model and for a conventional model ever the same? If so, when?

(E) Find the limit of each average cost function as $x \to \infty$ and discuss the implications of the results.

88. Energy costs. Most appliance manufacturers produce conventional and energy-efficient models. The energy-efficient models are more expensive to make but cheaper to operate. The costs of purchasing and operating a 36,000-Btu central air conditioner of each type are given in Table 9. These costs do not include maintenance charges or changes in electricity prices.

Table 9 **36,000 Btu Central Air Conditioner**

	Energy-Efficient Model	Conventional Model
Initial cost	$4,000	$2,700
Total capacity	36,000 Btu	36,000 Btu
Annual cost of electricity	$932	$1,332

(A) Express the total cost $C_e(x)$ and the average cost $\overline{C}_e(x) = C_e(x)/x$ of purchasing and operating an energy-efficient model for x years.

(B) Express the total cost $C_c(x)$ and the average cost $\overline{C}_c(x) = C_c(x)/x$ of purchasing and operating a conventional model for x years.

(C) Are the total costs for an energy-efficient model and for a conventional model ever the same? If so, when?

(D) Are the average costs for an energy-efficient model and for a conventional model ever the same? If so, when?

(E) Find the limit of each average cost function as $x \to \infty$ and discuss the implications of the results.

89. Drug concentration. A drug is administered to a patient through an injection. The drug concentration (in milligrams/milliliter) in the bloodstream t hours after the injection is given by $C(t) = \dfrac{5t^2(t + 50)}{t^3 + 100}$. Find and interpret $\lim\limits_{t \to \infty} C(t)$.

90. Drug concentration. A drug is administered to a patient through an IV drip. The drug concentration (in milligrams/milliliter) in the bloodstream t hours after the drip was started is given by $C(t) = \dfrac{5t(t + 50)}{t^3 + 100}$. Find and interpret $\lim\limits_{t \to \infty} C(t)$.

91. Pollution. In Silicon Valley, a number of computer-related manufacturing firms were contaminating underground water supplies with toxic chemicals stored in leaking underground containers. A water quality control agency ordered the companies to take immediate corrective action and contribute to a monetary pool for the testing and cleanup of the underground contamination. Suppose that the monetary pool (in millions of dollars) for the testing and cleanup is given by

$$P(x) = \frac{2x}{1 - x} \qquad 0 \le x < 1$$

where x is the percentage (expressed as a decimal) of the total contaminant removed.

(A) How much must be in the pool to remove 90% of the contaminant?

(B) How much must be in the pool to remove 95% of the contaminant?

(C) Find $\lim\limits_{x \to 1^-} P(x)$ and discuss the implications of this limit.

92. Employee training. A company producing computer components has established that, on average, a new employee can assemble $N(t)$ components per day after t days of on-the-job training, as given by

$$N(t) = \frac{100t}{t + 9} \qquad t \ge 0$$

(A) How many components per day can a new employee assemble after 6 days of on-the-job training?

(B) How many days of on-the-job training will a new employee need to reach the level of 70 components per day?

(C) Find $\lim\limits_{t \to \infty} N(t)$ and discuss the implications of this limit.

93. Biochemistry. In 1913, biochemists Leonor Michaelis and Maude Menten proposed the rational function model (see figure)

$$v(s) = \frac{V_{\max}\, s}{K_M + s}$$

for the velocity of the enzymatic reaction v, where s is the substrate concentration. The constants $V_{\max}$ and K_M are determined from experimental data.

(A) Show that $\lim\limits_{s \to \infty} v(s) = V_{\max}$.

(B) Show that $v(K_M) = \dfrac{V_{\max}}{2}$.

(C) Table 10* lists data for the substrate saccharose treated with an enzyme.

   Plot the points in Table 10 on graph paper and estimate $V_{\max}$ to the nearest integer. To estimate K_M, add the horizontal line $v = \dfrac{V_{\max}}{2}$ to your graph, connect successive points on the graph with straight-line segments, and

Table 10	
s	**v**
5.2	0.866
10.4	1.466
20.8	2.114
41.6	2.666
83.3	3.236
167	3.636
333	3.636

estimate the value of s (to the nearest multiple of 10) that satisfies $v(s) = \dfrac{V_{\max}}{2}$.

(D) Use the constants $V_{\max}$ and K_M from part (C) to form a Michaelis–Menten function for the data in Table 10.

(E) Use the function from part (D) to estimate the velocity of the enzyme reaction when the saccharose is 15 and to estimate the saccharose when the velocity is 3.

94. Biochemistry. Table 11* lists data for the substrate sucrose treated with the enzyme invertase. We want to model these data with a Michaelis–Menten function.

Table 11	
s	**v**
2.92	18.2
5.84	26.5
8.76	31.1
11.7	33
14.6	34.9
17.5	37.2
23.4	37.1

(A) Plot the points in Table 11 on graph paper and estimate $V_{\max}$ to the nearest integer. To estimate K_M, add the horizontal line $v = \dfrac{V_{\max}}{2}$ to your graph, connect successive points on the graph with straight-line segments, and estimate the value of s (to the nearest integer) that satisfies $v(s) = \dfrac{V_{\max}}{2}$.

(B) Use the constants $V_{\max}$ and K_M from part (A) to form a Michaelis–Menten function for the data in Table 11.

(C) Use the function from part (B) to estimate the velocity of the enzyme reaction when the sucrose is 9 and to estimate the sucrose when the velocity is 32.

95. Physics. The coefficient of thermal expansion (CTE) is a measure of the expansion of an object subjected to extreme temperatures. To model this coefficient, we use a Michaelis–Menten function of the form

$$C(T) = \frac{C_{\max}\, T}{M + T} \qquad \text{(Problem 93)}$$

where C = CTE, T is temperature in K (degrees Kelvin), and $C_{\max}$ and M are constants. Table 12† lists the coefficients of thermal expansion for nickel and for copper at various temperatures.

---

*Michaelis and Menten (1913) *Biochem. Z.* 49, 333–369.

*Institute of Chemistry, Macedonia.
†National Physical Laboratory

Table 12 **Coefficients of Thermal Expansion**

T (K)	Nickel	Copper
100	6.6	10.3
200	11.3	15.2
293	13.4	16.5
500	15.3	18.3
800	16.8	20.3
1,100	17.8	23.7

(A) Plot the points in columns 1 and 2 of Table 12 on graph paper and estimate C_{max} to the nearest integer. To estimate M, add the horizontal line CTE $= \dfrac{C_{max}}{2}$ to your graph, connect successive points on the graph with straight-line segments, and estimate the value of T (to the nearest multiple of fifty) that satisfies $C(T) = \dfrac{C_{max}}{2}$.

(B) Use the constants $\dfrac{C_{max}}{2}$ and M from part (A) to form a Michaelis–Menten function for the CTE of nickel.

(C) Use the function from part (B) to estimate the CTE of nickel at 600 K and to estimate the temperature when the CTE of nickel is 12.

96. Physics. Repeat Problem 95 for the CTE of copper (column 3 of Table 12).

Answers to Matched Problems

1. Vertical asymptote: $x = 1$; $\lim\limits_{x \to 1^+} f(x) = \infty$, $\lim\limits_{x \to 1^-} f(x) = -\infty$ $\lim\limits_{x \to 3} f(x) = 1/2$ so f does not have a vertical asymptote at $x = 3$

2. Vertical asymptote: $x = -3$; $\lim\limits_{x \to -3^+} f(x) = \lim\limits_{x \to -3^-} f(x) = -\infty$

3. $\lim\limits_{x \to \infty} p(x) = \lim\limits_{x \to -\infty} p(x) = -\infty$

4. (A) $\lim\limits_{x \to \infty} p(x) = -\infty$, $\lim\limits_{x \to -\infty} p(x) = \infty$
(B) $\lim\limits_{x \to \infty} p(x) = \infty$, $\lim\limits_{x \to -\infty} p(x) = \infty$

5. (A) $y = 0$ (B) No horizontal asymptotes
(C) $y = 1/2$

6. Vertical asymptotes: $x = -2$, $x = 2$; horizontal asymptote: $y = 1$

2.3 Continuity

- Continuity
- Continuity Properties
- Solving Inequalities Using Continuity Properties

Theorem 3 in Section 2.1 states that if f is a polynomial function or a rational function with a nonzero denominator at $x = c$, then

$$\lim_{x \to c} f(x) = f(c) \qquad (1)$$

Functions that satisfy equation (1) are said to be *continuous* at $x = c$. A firm understanding of continuous functions is essential for sketching and analyzing graphs. We will also see that continuity properties provide a simple and efficient method for solving inequalities—a tool that we will use extensively in later sections.

Continuity

Compare the graphs shown in Figure 1. Notice that two of the graphs are broken; that is, they cannot be drawn without lifting a pen off the paper. Informally, a function is *continuous over an interval* if its graph over the interval can be drawn without removing a pen from the paper. A function whose graph is broken (disconnected) at $x = c$ is said to be *discontinuous* at $x = c$. Function f (Fig. 1A) is continuous for all x. Function g (Fig. 1B) is discontinuous at $x = 2$ but is continuous over any interval that does not include 2. Function h (Fig. 1C) is discontinuous at $x = 0$ but is continuous over any interval that does not include 0.

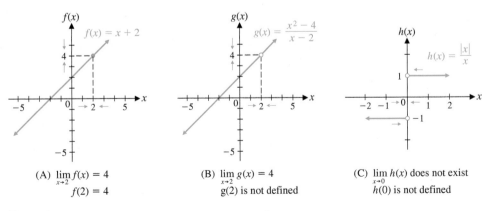

(A) $\lim\limits_{x \to 2} f(x) = 4$
$f(2) = 4$

(B) $\lim\limits_{x \to 2} g(x) = 4$
$g(2)$ is not defined

(C) $\lim\limits_{x \to 0} h(x)$ does not exist
$h(0)$ is not defined

Figure 1

Most graphs of natural phenomena are continuous, whereas many graphs in business and economics applications have discontinuities. Figure 2A illustrates temperature variation over a 24-hour period—a continuous phenomenon. Figure 2B illustrates warehouse inventory over a 1-week period—a discontinuous phenomenon.

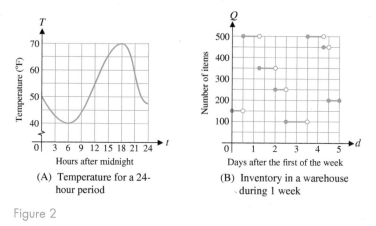

(A) Temperature for a 24-hour period

(B) Inventory in a warehouse during 1 week

Figure 2

Explore and Discuss 1   (A) Write a brief verbal description of the temperature variation illustrated in Figure 2A, including estimates of the high and low temperatures during the period shown and the times at which they occurred.

(B) Write a brief verbal description of the changes in inventory illustrated in Figure 2B, including estimates of the changes in inventory and the times at which those changes occurred.

The preceding discussion leads to the following formal definition of continuity:

DEFINITION   Continuity
A function f is **continuous at the point $x = c$ if**

1. $\lim_{x \to c} f(x)$ exists   **2.** $f(c)$ exists   **3.** $\lim_{x \to c} f(x) = f(c)$

A function is **continuous on the open interval* (a, b)** if it is continuous at each point on the interval.

*See Table 3 in section 1.3 for a review of interval notation.

If one or more of the three conditions in the definition fails, then the function is **discontinuous** at $x = c$.

EXAMPLE 1   Continuity of a Function Defined by a Graph   Use the definition of continuity to discuss the continuity of the function whose graph is shown in Figure 3.

Figure 3

SOLUTION We begin by identifying the points of discontinuity. Examining the graph, we see breaks or holes at $x = -4, -2, 1,$ and 3. Now we must determine which conditions in the definition of continuity are not satisfied at each of these points. In each case, we find the value of the function and the limit of the function at the point in question.

Discontinuity at $x = -4$:

$$\lim_{x \to -4^-} f(x) = 2 \qquad \text{Since the one-sided limits are different,}$$
$$\lim_{x \to -4^+} f(x) = 3 \qquad \text{the limit does not exist (Section 2.1).}$$
$$\lim_{x \to -4} f(x) \text{ does not exist}$$
$$f(-4) = 3$$

So, f is not continuous at $x = -4$ because condition 1 is not satisfied.

Discontinuity at $x = -2$:

$$\lim_{x \to -2^-} f(x) = 5 \qquad \text{The hole at } (-2, 5) \text{ indicates that 5 is not the value of } f$$
$$\lim_{x \to -2^+} f(x) = 5 \qquad \text{at } -2. \text{ Since there is no solid dot elsewhere on the}$$
$$\lim_{x \to -2} f(x) = 5 \qquad \text{vertical line } x = -2, f(-2) \text{ is not defined.}$$
$$f(-2) \text{ does not exist}$$

So even though the limit as x approaches -2 exists, f is not continuous at $x = -2$ because condition 2 is not satisfied.

Discontinuity at $x = 1$:

$$\lim_{x \to 1^-} f(x) = 4$$
$$\lim_{x \to 1^+} f(x) = 1$$
$$\lim_{x \to 1} f(x) \text{ does not exist}$$
$$f(1) \text{ does not exist}$$

This time, f is not continuous at $x = 1$ because neither of conditions 1 and 2 is satisfied.

Discontinuity at $x = 3$:

$$\lim_{x \to 3^-} f(x) = 3 \qquad \text{The solid dot at } (3, 1) \text{ indicates that } f(3) = 1.$$
$$\lim_{x \to 3^+} f(x) = 3$$
$$\lim_{x \to 3} f(x) = 3$$
$$f(3) = 1$$

Conditions 1 and 2 are satisfied, but f is not continuous at $x = 3$ because condition 3 is not satisfied.

Having identified and discussed all points of discontinuity, we can now conclude that f is continuous except at $x = -4, -2, 1,$ and 3.

CONCEPTUAL INSIGHT

Rather than list the points where a function is discontinuous, sometimes it is useful to state the intervals on which the function is continuous. Using the set operation **union,** denoted by $\cup$, we can express the set of points where the function in Example 1 is continuous as follows:

$$(-\infty, -4) \cup (-4, -2) \cup (-2, 1) \cup (1, 3) \cup (3, \infty)$$

Matched Problem 1 | Use the definition of continuity to discuss the continuity of the function whose graph is shown in Figure 4.

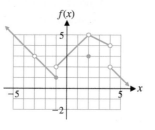

$f(x)$

Figure 4

For functions defined by equations, it is important to be able to locate points of discontinuity by examining the equation.

EXAMPLE 2 Continuity of Functions Defined by Equations Using the definition of continuity, discuss the continuity of each function at the indicated point(s).

(A) $f(x) = x + 2$ at $x = 2$

(B) $g(x) = \dfrac{x^2 - 4}{x - 2}$ at $x = 2$

(C) $h(x) = \dfrac{|x|}{x}$ at $x = 0$ and at $x = 1$

SOLUTION

(A) f is continuous at $x = 2$, since

$$\lim_{x \to 2} f(x) = 4 = f(2) \quad \text{See Figure 1A.}$$

(B) g is not continuous at $x = 2$, since $g(2) = 0/0$ is not defined (see Fig. 1B).

(C) h is not continuous at $x = 0$, since $h(0) = |0|/0$ is not defined; also, $\lim_{x \to 0} h(x)$ does not exist.

h is continuous at $x = 1$, since

$$\lim_{x \to 1} \frac{|x|}{x} = 1 = h(1) \quad \text{See Figure 1C.}$$

Matched Problem 2 | Using the definition of continuity, discuss the continuity of each function at the indicated point(s).

(A) $f(x) = x + 1$ at $x = 1$

(B) $g(x) = \dfrac{x^2 - 1}{x - 1}$ at $x = 1$

(C) $h(x) = \dfrac{x - 2}{|x - 2|}$ at $x = 2$ and at $x = 0$

We can also talk about one-sided continuity, just as we talked about one-sided limits. For example, a function is said to be **continuous on the right** at $x = c$ if $\lim_{x \to c^+} f(x) = f(c)$ and **continuous on the left** at $x = c$ if $\lim_{x \to c^-} f(x) = f(c)$. A function is **continuous on the closed interval [a, b]** if it is continuous on the open interval (a, b) and is continuous both on the right at a and on the left at b.

Figure 5A illustrates a function that is continuous on the closed interval $[-1, 1]$. Figure 5B illustrates a function that is continuous on the half-closed interval $[0, \infty)$.

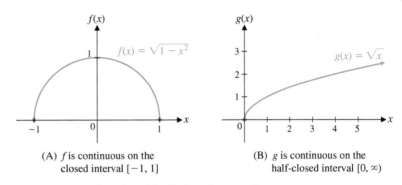

(A) f is continuous on the
closed interval $[-1, 1]$

(B) g is continuous on the
half-closed interval $[0, \infty)$

Figure 5 **Continuity on closed and half-closed intervals**

Continuity Properties

Functions have some useful **general continuity properties**:

> If two functions are continuous on the same interval, then their sum, difference, product, and quotient are continuous on the same interval except for values of x that make a denominator 0.

These properties, along with Theorem 1, enable us to determine intervals of continuity for some important classes of functions without having to look at their graphs or use the three conditions in the definition.

THEOREM 1   Continuity Properties of Some Specific Functions

(A) A constant function $f(x) = k$, where k is a constant, is continuous for all x.
  $f(x) = 7$ is continuous for all x.

(B) For n a positive integer, $f(x) = x^n$ is continuous for all x.
  $f(x) = x^5$ is continuous for all x.

(C) A polynomial function is continuous for all x.
  $2x^3 - 3x^2 + x - 5$ is continuous for all x.

(D) A rational function is continuous for all x except those values that make a denominator 0.
  $\dfrac{x^2 + 1}{x - 1}$ is continuous for all x except $x = 1$, a value that makes the denominator 0.

(E) For n an odd positive integer greater than 1, $\sqrt[n]{f(x)}$ is continuous wherever $f(x)$ is continuous.
  $\sqrt[3]{x^2}$ is continuous for all x.

(F) For n an even positive integer, $\sqrt[n]{f(x)}$ is continuous wherever $f(x)$ is continuous and nonnegative.
  $\sqrt[4]{x}$ is continuous on the interval $[0, \infty)$.

Parts (C) and (D) of Theorem 1 are the same as Theorem 3 in Section 2.1. They are repeated here to emphasize their importance.

EXAMPLE 3   Using Continuity Properties   Using Theorem 1 and the general properties of continuity, determine where each function is continuous.

(A) $f(x) = x^2 - 2x + 1$

(B) $f(x) = \dfrac{x}{(x + 2)(x - 3)}$

(C) $f(x) = \sqrt[3]{x^2 - 4}$

(D) $f(x) = \sqrt{x - 2}$

SOLUTION

(A) Since f is a polynomial function, f is continuous for all x.

(B) Since f is a rational function, f is continuous for all x except -2 and 3 (values that make the denominator 0).

(C) The polynomial function $x^2 - 4$ is continuous for all x. Since $n = 3$ is odd, f is continuous for all x.

(D) The polynomial function $x - 2$ is continuous for all x and nonnegative for $x \geq 2$. Since $n = 2$ is even, f is continuous for $x \geq 2$, or on the interval $[2, \infty)$.

Matched Problem 3) Using Theorem 1 and the general properties of continuity, determine where each function is continuous.

(A) $f(x) = x^4 + 2x^2 + 1$ (B) $f(x) = \dfrac{x^2}{(x + 1)(x - 4)}$

(C) $f(x) = \sqrt{x - 4}$ (D) $f(x) = \sqrt[3]{x^3 + 1}$

Solving Inequalities Using Continuity Properties

One of the basic tools for analyzing graphs in calculus is a special line graph called a *sign chart*. We will make extensive use of this type of chart in later sections. In the discussion that follows, we use continuity properties to develop a simple and efficient procedure for constructing sign charts.

Suppose that a function f is continuous over the interval $(1, 8)$ and $f(x) \neq 0$ for any x in $(1, 8)$. Suppose also that $f(2) = 5$, a positive number. Is it possible for $f(x)$ to be negative for any x in the interval $(1, 8)$? The answer is "no." If $f(7)$ were -3, for example, as shown in Figure 6, then how would it be possible to join the points $(2, 5)$ and $(7, -3)$ with the graph of a continuous function without crossing the x axis between 1 and 8 at least once? [Crossing the x axis would violate our assumption that $f(x) \neq 0$ for any x in $(1, 8)$.] We conclude that $f(x)$ must be positive for all x in $(1, 8)$. If $f(2)$ were negative, then, using the same type of reasoning, $f(x)$ would have to be negative over the entire interval $(1, 8)$.

In general, **if f is continuous and $f(x) \neq 0$ on the interval (a, b), then $f(x)$ cannot change sign on (a, b).** This is the essence of Theorem 2.

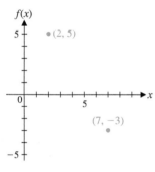

$f(x)$

• $(2, 5)$

$(7, -3)$
•

Figure 6

THEOREM 2   Sign Properties on an Interval (a, b)

If f is continuous on (a, b) and $f(x) \neq 0$ for all x in (a, b), then either $f(x) > 0$ for all x in (a, b) or $f(x) < 0$ for all x in (a, b).

Theorem 2 provides the basis for an effective method of solving many types of inequalities. Example 4 illustrates the process.

EXAMPLE 4   Solving an Inequality   Solve $\dfrac{x + 1}{x - 2} > 0$.

SOLUTION   We start by using the left side of the inequality to form the function f.

$$f(x) = \frac{x + 1}{x - 2}$$

The denominator is equal to 0 if $x = 2$, and the numerator is equal to 0 if $x = -1$. So the rational function f is discontinuous at $x = 2$, and $f(x) = 0$ for $x = -1$ (a fraction is 0 when the numerator is 0 and the denominator is not 0). We plot

Figure 7

Test Numbers

x	$f(x)$
-2	$\frac{1}{4}$ (+)
0	$-\frac{1}{2}$ (−)
3	4 (+)

$x = 2$ and $x = -1$, which we call *partition numbers,* on a real number line (Fig. 7). (Note that the dot at 2 is open because the function is not defined at $x = 2$.) The partition numbers 2 and -1 determine three open intervals: $(-\infty, -1), (-1, 2),$ and $(2, \infty)$. The function f is continuous and nonzero on each of these intervals. From Theorem 2, we know that $f(x)$ does not change sign on any of these intervals. We can find the sign of $f(x)$ on each of the intervals by selecting a **test number** in each interval and evaluating $f(x)$ at that number. Since any number in each subinterval will do, we choose test numbers that are easy to evaluate: $-2, 0,$ and 3. The table in the margin shows the results.

The sign of $f(x)$ at each test number is the same as the sign of $f(x)$ over the interval containing that test number. Using this information, we construct a **sign chart** for $f(x)$ as shown in Figure 8.

Figure 8

From the sign chart, we can easily write the solution of the given nonlinear inequality:

$$f(x) > 0 \quad \text{for} \quad \begin{array}{ll} x < -1 \quad \text{or} \quad x > 2 & \text{Inequality notation} \\ (-\infty, -1) \cup (2, \infty) & \text{Interval notation} \end{array}$$

Matched Problem 4   Solve $\dfrac{x^2 - 1}{x - 3} < 0$.

Most of the inequalities we encounter will involve strict inequalities ($>$ or $<$). If it is necessary to solve inequalities of the form $\geq$ or $\leq$, we simply include the endpoint x of any interval if f is defined at x and $f(x)$ satisfies the given inequality. For example, from the sign chart in Figure 8, the solution of the inequality

$$\frac{x + 1}{x - 2} \geq 0 \quad \text{is} \quad \begin{array}{ll} x \leq -1 \quad \text{or} \quad x > 2 & \text{Inequality notation} \\ (-\infty, -1] \cup (2, \infty) & \text{Interval notation} \end{array}$$

Example 4 illustrates a general procedure for constructing sign charts.

DEFINITION

A real number x is a **partition number** for a function f if f is discontinuous at x or $f(x) = 0$.

Suppose that p_1 and p_2 are consecutive partition numbers for f, that is, there are no partition numbers in the open interval (p_1, p_2). Then f is continuous on (p_1, p_2) [since there are no points of discontinuity in that interval], so f does not change sign on (p_1, p_2) [since $f(x) \neq 0$ for x in that interval]. In other words, **partition numbers determine open intervals on which f does not change sign.** By using a test number from each interval, we can construct a sign chart for f on the real number line. It is then easy to solve the inequality $f(x) < 0$ or the inequality $f(x) > 0$.

We summarize the procedure for constructing sign charts in the following box.

> **PROCEDURE Constructing Sign Charts**
>
> Given a function f,
>
> Step 1 Find all partition numbers of f:
>
> (A) Find all numbers x such that f is discontinuous at x. (Rational functions are discontinuous at values of x that make a denominator 0.)
>
> (B) Find all numbers x such that $f(x) = 0$. (For a rational function, this occurs where the numerator is 0 and the denominator is not 0.)
>
> Step 2 Plot the numbers found in step 1 on a real number line, dividing the number line into intervals.
>
> Step 3 Select a test number in each open interval determined in step 2 and evaluate $f(x)$ at each test number to determine whether $f(x)$ is positive $(+)$ or negative $(-)$ in each interval.
>
> Step 4 Construct a sign chart, using the real number line in step 2. This will show the sign of $f(x)$ on each open interval.

There is an alternative to step 3 in the procedure for constructing sign charts that may save time if the function $f(x)$ is written in factored form. The key is to determine the sign of each factor in the numerator and denominator of $f(x)$. We will illustrate with Example 4. The partition numbers -1 and 2 divide the x axis into three open intervals. If $x > 2$, then both the numerator and denominator are positive, so $f(x) > 0$. If $-1 < x < 2$, then the numerator is positive but the denominator is negative, so $f(x) < 0$. If $x < -1$, then both the numerator and denominator are negative, so $f(x) > 0$. Of course both approaches, the test number approach and the sign of factors approach, give the same sign chart.

Exercises 2.3

Skills Warm-up Exercises

W

In Problems 1–8, use interval notation to specify the given interval. (If necessary, review Table 3 in Section 1.3).

1. The set of all real numbers from -3 to 5, including -3 and 5

2. The set of all real numbers from -8 to -4, excluding -8 but including -4

3. $\{x\,|-10 < x < 100\}$ **4.** $\{x\,|\,0.1 \le x \le 0.3\}$

5. $\{x\,|\,x^2 > 25\}$ **6.** $\{x\,|\,x^2 \ge 16\}$

7. $\{x\,|\,x \le -1 \text{ or } x > 2\}$

8. $\{x\,|\,x < 6 \text{ or } x \ge 9\}$

In Problems 9–14, sketch a possible graph of a function that satisfies the given conditions at $x = 1$ and discuss the continuity of f at $x = 1$.

9. $f(1) = 2$ and $\lim\limits_{x \to 1} f(x) = 2$

10. $f(1) = -2$ and $\lim\limits_{x \to 1} f(x) = 2$

11. $f(1) = 2$ and $\lim\limits_{x \to 1} f(x) = -2$

12. $f(1) = -2$ and $\lim\limits_{x \to 1} f(x) = -2$

13. $f(1) = -2$, $\lim\limits_{x \to 1^-} f(x) = 2$, and $\lim\limits_{x \to 1^+} f(x) = -2$

14. $f(1) = 2$, $\lim\limits_{x \to 1^-} f(x) = 2$, and $\lim\limits_{x \to 1^+} f(x) = -2$

Problems 15–22 refer to the function f shown in the figure. Use the graph to estimate the indicated function values and limits.

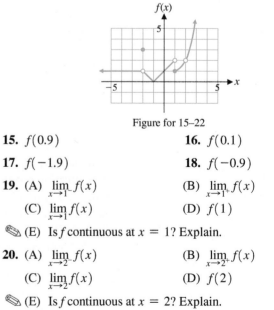

Figure for 15–22

15. $f(0.9)$ **16.** $f(0.1)$

17. $f(-1.9)$ **18.** $f(-0.9)$

19. (A) $\lim\limits_{x \to 1^-} f(x)$ (B) $\lim\limits_{x \to 1^+} f(x)$

(C) $\lim\limits_{x \to 1} f(x)$ (D) $f(1)$

✎ (E) Is f continuous at $x = 1$? Explain.

20. (A) $\lim\limits_{x \to 2^-} f(x)$ (B) $\lim\limits_{x \to 2^+} f(x)$

(C) $\lim\limits_{x \to 2} f(x)$ (D) $f(2)$

✎ (E) Is f continuous at $x = 2$? Explain.

21. (A) $\lim_{x \to -2^-} f(x)$ (B) $\lim_{x \to -2^+} f(x)$

     (C) $\lim_{x \to -2} f(x)$ (D) $f(-2)$

✎ (E) Is f continuous at $x = -2$? Explain.

22. (A) $\lim_{x \to -1^-} f(x)$ (B) $\lim_{x \to -1^+} f(x)$

     (C) $\lim_{x \to -1} f(x)$ (D) $f(-1)$

✎ (E) Is f continuous at $x = -1$? Explain.

Problems 23–30 refer to the function g shown in the figure. Use the graph to estimate the indicated function values and limits.

Figure for 23–30

23. $g(-3.1)$ **24.** $g(-2.1)$

25. $g(1.9)$ **26.** $g(-1.9)$

27. (A) $\lim_{x \to -3^-} g(x)$ (B) $\lim_{x \to -3^+} g(x)$

     (C) $\lim_{x \to -3} g(x)$ (D) $g(-3)$

✎ (E) Is g continuous at $x = -3$? Explain.

28. (A) $\lim_{x \to -2^-} g(x)$ (B) $\lim_{x \to -2^+} g(x)$

     (C) $\lim_{x \to -2} g(x)$ (D) $g(-2)$

✎ (E) Is g continuous at $x = -2$? Explain.

29. (A) $\lim_{x \to 2^-} g(x)$ (B) $\lim_{x \to 2^+} g(x)$

     (C) $\lim_{x \to 2} g(x)$ (D) $g(2)$

✎ (E) Is g continuous at $x = 2$? Explain.

30. (A) $\lim_{x \to 4^-} g(x)$ (B) $\lim_{x \to 4^+} g(x)$

     (C) $\lim_{x \to 4} g(x)$ (D) $g(4)$

✎ (E) Is g continuous at $x = 4$? Explain.

Use Theorem 1 to determine where each function in Problems 31–40 is continuous.

31. $f(x) = 3x - 4$ **32.** $h(x) = 4 - 2x$

33. $g(x) = \dfrac{3x}{x + 2}$ **34.** $k(x) = \dfrac{2x}{x - 4}$

35. $m(x) = \dfrac{x + 1}{x^2 + 3x - 4}$ **36.** $n(x) = \dfrac{x - 2}{x^2 - 2x - 3}$

37. $F(x) = \dfrac{2x}{x^2 + 9}$ **38.** $G(x) = \dfrac{1 - x^2}{x^2 + 1}$

39. $M(x) = \dfrac{x - 1}{4x^2 - 9}$ **40.** $N(x) = \dfrac{x^2 + 4}{4 - 25x^2}$

In Problems 41–46, find all partition numbers of the function.

41. $f(x) = \dfrac{3x + 8}{x - 4}$ **42.** $f(x) = \dfrac{2x + 7}{5x - 1}$

43. $f(x) = \dfrac{1 - x^2}{1 + x^2}$ **44.** $f(x) = \dfrac{x^2 + 4}{x^2 - 9}$

45. $f(x) = \dfrac{x^2 + 4x - 45}{x^2 + 6x}$ **46.** $f(x) = \dfrac{x^3 + x}{x^2 - x - 42}$

In Problems 47–54, use a sign chart to solve each inequality. Express answers in inequality and interval notation.

47. $x^2 - x - 12 < 0$ **48.** $x^2 - 2x - 8 < 0$

49. $x^2 + 21 > 10x$ **50.** $x^2 + 7x > -10$

51. $x^3 < 4x$ **52.** $x^4 - 9x^2 > 0$

53. $\dfrac{x^2 + 5x}{x - 3} > 0$ **54.** $\dfrac{x - 4}{x^2 + 2x} < 0$

55. Use the graph of f to determine where

     (A) $f(x) > 0$ (B) $f(x) < 0$

     Express answers in interval notation.

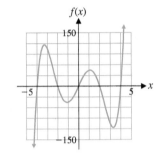

56. Use the graph of g to determine where

     (A) $g(x) > 0$ (B) $g(x) < 0$

     Express answers in interval notation.

📉 *In Problems 57–60, use a graphing calculator to approximate the partition numbers of each function f(x) to four decimal places. Then solve the following inequalities:*

     (A) $f(x) > 0$ (B) $f(x) < 0$

Express answers in interval notation.

57. $f(x) = x^4 - 6x^2 + 3x + 5$

58. $f(x) = x^4 - 4x^2 - 2x + 2$

59. $f(x) = \dfrac{3 + 6x - x^3}{x^2 - 1}$ **60.** $f(x) = \dfrac{x^3 - 5x + 1}{x^2 - 1}$

Use Theorem 1 to determine where each function in Problems 61–68 is continuous. Express the answer in interval notation.

61. $\sqrt{x - 6}$ **62.** $\sqrt{7 - x}$

63. $\sqrt[3]{5 - x}$ **64.** $\sqrt[3]{x - 8}$

65. $\sqrt{x^2 - 9}$ **66.** $\sqrt{4 - x^2}$

67. $\sqrt{x^2 + 1}$ **68.** $\sqrt[3]{x^2 + 2}$

In Problems 69–74, graph f, locate all points of discontinuity, and discuss the behavior of f at these points.

69. $f(x) = \begin{cases} 1 + x & \text{if } x < 1 \\ 5 - x & \text{if } x \geq 1 \end{cases}$

70. $f(x) = \begin{cases} x^2 & \text{if } x \leq 1 \\ 2x & \text{if } x > 1 \end{cases}$

71. $f(x) = \begin{cases} 1 + x & \text{if } x \leq 2 \\ 5 - x & \text{if } x > 2 \end{cases}$

72. $f(x) = \begin{cases} x^2 & \text{if } x \leq 2 \\ 2x & \text{if } x > 2 \end{cases}$

73. $f(x) = \begin{cases} -x & \text{if } x < 0 \\ 1 & \text{if } x = 0 \\ x & \text{if } x > 0 \end{cases}$

74. $f(x) = \begin{cases} 1 & \text{if } x < 0 \\ 0 & \text{if } x = 0 \\ 1 + x & \text{if } x > 0 \end{cases}$

*Problems 75 and 76 refer to the **greatest integer function**, which is denoted by $[\![x]\!]$ and is defined as*

$$[\![x]\!] = \text{greatest integer} \leq x$$

For example,

$$[\![-3.6]\!] = \text{greatest integer} \leq -3.6 = -4$$

$$[\![2]\!] = \text{greatest integer} \leq 2 = 2$$

$$[\![2.5]\!] = \text{greatest integer} \leq 2.5 = 2$$

The graph of $f(x) = [\![x]\!]$ is shown. There, we can see that

$$[\![x]\!] = -2 \quad for \quad -2 \leq x < -1$$

$$[\![x]\!] = -1 \quad for \quad -1 \leq x < 0$$

$$[\![x]\!] = 0 \quad for \quad 0 \leq x < 1$$

$$[\![x]\!] = 1 \quad for \quad 1 \leq x < 2$$

$$[\![x]\!] = 2 \quad for \quad 2 \leq x < 3$$

and so on.

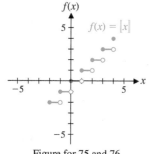

Figure for 75 and 76

75. (A) Is f continuous from the right at $x = 0$?

(B) Is f continuous from the left at $x = 0$?

(C) Is f continuous on the open interval $(0, 1)$?

(D) Is f continuous on the closed interval $[0, 1]$?

(E) Is f continuous on the half-closed interval $[0, 1)$?

76. (A) Is f continuous from the right at $x = 2$?

(B) Is f continuous from the left at $x = 2$?

(C) Is f continuous on the open interval $(1, 2)$?

(D) Is f continuous on the closed interval $[1, 2]$?

(E) Is f continuous on the half-closed interval $[1, 2)$?

In Problems 77–82, discuss the validity of each statement. If the statement is always true, explain why. If not, give a counterexample.

77. A polynomial function is continuous for all real numbers.

78. A rational function is continuous for all but finitely many real numbers.

79. If f is a function that is continuous at $x = 0$ and $x = 2$, then f is continuous at $x = 1$.

80. If f is a function that is continuous on the open interval $(0, 2)$, then f is continuous at $x = 1$.

81. If f is a function that has no partition numbers in the interval (a, b), then f is continuous on (a, b).

82. The greatest integer function (see Problem 75) is a rational function.

In Problems 83–86, sketch a possible graph of a function f that is continuous for all real numbers and satisfies the given conditions. Find the x intercepts of f.

83. $f(x) < 0$ on $(-\infty, -5)$ and $(2, \infty)$; $f(x) > 0$ on $(-5, 2)$

84. $f(x) > 0$ on $(-\infty, -4)$ and $(3, \infty)$; $f(x) < 0$ on $(-4, 3)$

85. $f(x) < 0$ on $(-\infty, -6)$ and $(-1, 4)$; $f(x) > 0$ on $(-6, -1)$ and $(4, \infty)$

86. $f(x) > 0$ on $(-\infty, -3)$ and $(2, 7)$; $f(x) < 0$ on $(-3, 2)$ and $(7, \infty)$

87. The function $f(x) = 2/(1 - x)$ satisfies $f(0) = 2$ and $f(2) = -2$. Is f equal to 0 anywhere on the interval $(-1, 3)$? Does this contradict Theorem 2? Explain.

88. The function $f(x) = 6/(x - 4)$ satisfies $f(2) = -3$ and $f(7) = 2$. Is f equal to 0 anywhere on the interval $(0, 9)$? Does this contradict Theorem 2? Explain.

Applications

89. *Postal rates.* First-class postage in 2009 was $0.44 for the first ounce (or any fraction thereof) and $0.17 for each additional ounce (or fraction thereof) up to a maximum weight of 3.5 ounces.

(A) Write a piecewise definition of the first-class postage $P(x)$ for a letter weighing x ounces.

(B) Graph $P(x)$ for $0 < x \leq 3.5$.

(C) Is $P(x)$ continuous at $x = 2.5$? At $x = 3$? Explain.

90. Telephone rates. A long-distance telephone service charges $0.07 for the first minute (or any fraction thereof) and $0.05 for each additional minute (or fraction thereof).

   (A) Write a piecewise definition of the charge $R(x)$ for a long-distance call lasting x minutes.

   (B) Graph $R(x)$ for $0 < x \le 6$.

   (C) Is $R(x)$ continuous at $x = 3.5$? At $x = 3$? Explain.

91. Postal rates. Discuss the differences between the function $Q(x) = 0.44 + 0.17[\![x]\!]$ and the function $P(x)$ defined in Problem 89.

92. Telephone rates. Discuss the differences between the function $S(x) = 0.07 + 0.05[\![x]\!]$ and the function $R(x)$ defined in Problem 90.

93. Natural-gas rates. Table 1 shows the rates for natural gas charged by the Middle Tennessee Natural Gas Utility District during summer months. The base charge is a fixed monthly charge, independent of the amount of gas used per month.

Table 1 **Summer (May–September)**

Base charge	$5.00
First 50 therms	0.63 per therm
Over 50 therms	0.45 per therm

   (A) Write a piecewise definition of the monthly charge $S(x)$ for a customer who uses x therms* in a summer month.

   (B) Graph $S(x)$.

   (C) Is $S(x)$ continuous at $x = 50$? Explain.

94. Natural-gas rates. Table 2 shows the rates for natural gas charged by the Middle Tennessee Natural Gas Utility District during winter months. The base charge is a fixed monthly charge, independent of the amount of gas used per month.

Table 2 **Winter (October– April)**

Base charge	$5.00
First 5 therms	0.69 per therm
Next 45 therms	0.65 per therm
Over 50 therms	0.63 per therm

---

*A British thermal unit (Btu) is the amount of heat required to raise the temperature of 1 pound of water 1 degree Fahrenheit, and a therm is 100,000 Btu.

(A) Write a piecewise definition of the monthly charge $S(x)$ for a customer who uses x therms in a winter month.

(B) Graph $S(x)$.

(C) Is $S(x)$ continuous at $x = 5$? At $x = 50$? Explain.

95. Income. A personal-computer salesperson receives a base salary of $1,000 per month and a commission of 5% of all sales over $10,000 during the month. If the monthly sales are $20,000 or more, then the salesperson is given an additional $500 bonus. Let $E(s)$ represent the person's earnings per month as a function of the monthly sales s.

   (A) Graph $E(s)$ for $0 \le s \le 30,000$.

   (B) Find $\lim_{s \to 10,000} E(s)$ and $E(10,000)$.

   (C) Find $\lim_{s \to 20,000} E(s)$ and $E(20,000)$.

   (D) Is E continuous at $s = 10,000$? At $s = 20,000$?

96. Equipment rental. An office equipment rental and leasing company rents copiers for $10 per day (and any fraction thereof) or for $50 per 7-day week. Let $C(x)$ be the cost of renting a copier for x days.

   (A) Graph $C(x)$ for $0 \le x \le 10$.

   (B) Find $\lim_{x \to 4.5} C(x)$ and $C(4.5)$.

   (C) Find $\lim_{x \to 8} C(x)$ and $C(8)$.

   (D) Is C continuous at $x = 4.5$? At $x = 8$?

97. Animal supply. A medical laboratory raises its own rabbits. The number of rabbits $N(t)$ available at any time t depends on the number of births and deaths. When a birth or death occurs, the function N generally has a discontinuity, as shown in the figure.

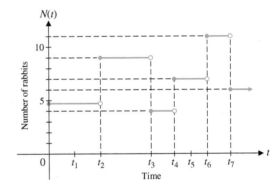

   (A) Where is the function N discontinuous?

   (B) $\lim_{t \to t_5} N(t) = ?$; $N(t_5) = ?$

   (C) $\lim_{t \to t_3} N(t) = ?$; $N(t_3) = ?$

98. Learning. The graph shown represents the history of a person learning the material on limits and continuity in this book. At time t_2, the student's mind goes blank during a quiz. At time t_4, the instructor explains a concept particularly well, then suddenly a big jump in understanding takes place.

   (A) Where is the function p discontinuous?

   (B) $\lim_{t \to t_1} p(t) = ?$; $p(t_1) = ?$

(C) $\lim_{t \to t_2} p(t) = ?;\quad p(t_2) = ?$

(D) $\lim_{t \to t_4} p(t) = ?;\quad p(t_4) = ?$

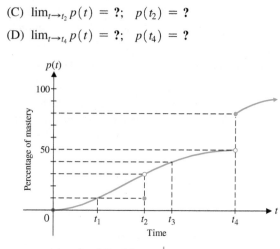

Answers to Matched Problems

1. f is not continuous at $x = -3, -1, 2,$ and 4.

   $x = -3:\ \lim\limits_{x \to -3} f(x) = 3,\ \text{but} f(-3) \text{ does not exist}$

   $x = -1: f(-1) = 1,\ \text{but} \lim\limits_{x \to -1} f(x) \text{ does not exist}$

$x = 2:\ \lim\limits_{x \to 2} f(x) = 5,\ \text{but} f(2) = 3$

$x = 4:\ \lim\limits_{x \to 4} f(x) \text{ does not exist, and} f(4) \text{ does not exist}$

2. (A) f is continuous at $x = 1$, since $\lim\limits_{x \to 1} f(x) = 2 = f(1)$.

   (B) g is not continuous at $x = 1$, since $g(1)$ is not defined.

   (C) h is not continuous at $x = 2$ for two reasons: $h(2)$ does not exist and $\lim\limits_{x \to 2} h(x)$ does not exist.

   h is continuous at $x = 0$, since $\lim\limits_{x \to 0} h(x) = -1 = h(0)$.

3. (A) Since f is a polynomial function, f is continuous for all x.

   (B) Since f is a rational function, f is continuous for all x except -1 and 4 (values that make the denominator 0).

   (C) The polynomial function $x - 4$ is continuous for all x and nonnegative for $x \geq 4$. Since $n = 2$ is even, f is continuous for $x \geq 4$, or on the interval $[4, \infty)$.

   (D) The polynomial function $x^3 + 1$ is continuous for all x. Since $n = 3$ is odd, f is continuous for all x.

4. $-\infty < x < -1$ or $1 < x < 3$; $(-\infty, -1) \cup (1, 3)$

2.4 The Derivative

- Rate of Change
- Slope of the Tangent Line
- The Derivative
- Nonexistence of the Derivative

We will now make use of the limit concepts developed in Sections 2.1, 2.2, and 2.3 to solve the two important problems illustrated in Figure 1. The solution of each of these apparently unrelated problems involves a common concept called the *derivative*.

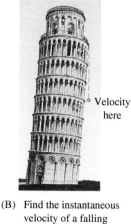

(A) Find the equation of the tangent line at (x_1, y_1) given $y = f(x)$

(B) Find the instantaneous velocity of a falling object

Figure 1 **Two basic problems of calculus**

Rate of Change

If you pass mile marker 120 on the interstate highway at 9 a.m. and mile marker 250 at 11 a.m., then the *average rate of change* of distance with respect to time, also known as *average velocity*, is

$$\frac{250 - 120}{11 - 9} = \frac{130}{2} = 65 \text{ miles per hour}$$

Of course your speedometer reading, that is, the *instantaneous rate of change*, or *instantaneous velocity*, might well have been 75 mph at some moment between 9 a.m. and 11 a.m.

We will define the concepts of average rate of change and instantaneous rate of change more generally, and will apply them in situations that are unrelated to velocity.

DEFINITION Average Rate of Change

For $y = f(x)$, the **average rate of change from** $x = a$ **to** $x = a + h$ is

$$\frac{f(a + h) - f(a)}{(a + h) - a} = \frac{f(a + h) - f(a)}{h} \qquad h \neq 0 \qquad (1)$$

Note that the numerator and denominator in (1) are differences, so (1) is a **difference quotient** (see Section 1.1).

EXAMPLE 1 Revenue Analysis The revenue (in dollars) from the sale of x plastic planter boxes is given by

$$R(x) = 20x - 0.02x^2 \qquad 0 \leq x \leq 1,000$$

and is graphed in Figure 2.

(A) What is the change in revenue if production is changed from 100 planters to 400 planters?

(B) What is the average rate of change in revenue for this change in production?

SOLUTION

(A) The change in revenue is given by

$$R(400) - R(100) = 20(400) - 0.02(400)^2 - [20(100) - 0.02(100)^2]$$
$$= 4,800 - 1,800 = \$3,000$$

Increasing production from 100 planters to 400 planters will increase revenue by $3,000.

(B) To find the average rate of change in revenue, we divide the change in revenue by the change in production:

$$\frac{R(400) - R(100)}{400 - 100} = \frac{3,000}{300} = \$10$$

The average rate of change in revenue is $10 per planter when production is increased from 100 to 400 planters.

Matched Problem 1 Refer to the revenue function in Example 1.

(A) What is the change in revenue if production is changed from 600 planters to 800 planters?

(B) What is the average rate of change in revenue for this change in production?

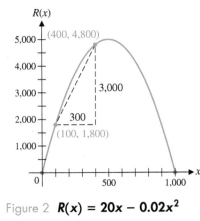

Figure 2 $R(x) = 20x - 0.02x^2$

EXAMPLE 2 Velocity A small steel ball dropped from a tower will fall a distance of y feet in x seconds, as given approximately by the formula

$$y = f(x) = 16x^2$$

Figure 3 shows the position of the ball on a coordinate line (positive direction down) at the end of 0, 1, 2, and 3 seconds.

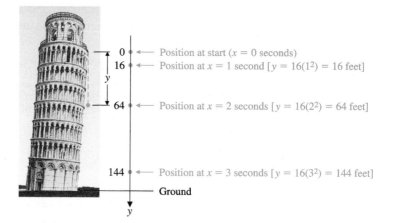

0 ← Position at start ($x = 0$ seconds)

16 ← Position at $x = 1$ second [$y = 16(1^2) = 16$ feet]

64 ← Position at $x = 2$ seconds [$y = 16(2^2) = 64$ feet]

144 ← Position at $x = 3$ seconds [$y = 16(3^2) = 144$ feet]

Ground

Figure 3 **Note: Positive y direction is down.**

(A) Find the average velocity from $x = 2$ seconds to $x = 3$ seconds.

(B) Find and simplify the average velocity from $x = 2$ seconds to $x = 2 + h$ seconds, $h \neq 0$.

(C) Find the limit of the expression from part (B) as $h \to 0$ if that limit exists.

(D) Discuss possible interpretations of the limit from part (C).

SOLUTION

(A) Recall the formula $d = rt$, which can be written in the form

$$r = \frac{d}{t} = \frac{\text{Distance covered}}{\text{Elapsed time}} = \text{Average velocity}$$

For example, if a person drives from San Francisco to Los Angeles (a distance of about 420 miles) in 7 hours, then the average velocity is

$$r = \frac{d}{t} = \frac{420}{7} = 60 \text{ miles per hour}$$

Sometimes the person will be traveling faster and sometimes slower, but the average velocity is 60 miles per hour. In our present problem, the average velocity of the steel ball from $x = 2$ seconds to $x = 3$ seconds is

$$
\begin{aligned}
\text{Average velocity} &= \frac{\text{Distance covered}}{\text{Elapsed time}} \\
&= \frac{f(3) - f(2)}{3 - 2} \\
&= \frac{16(3)^2 - 16(2)^2}{1} = 80 \text{ feet per second}
\end{aligned}
$$

We see that if $y = f(x)$ is the position of the falling ball, then the average velocity is simply the average rate of change of $f(x)$ with respect to time x.

(B) Proceeding as in part (A), we have

$$
\begin{aligned}
\text{Average velocity} &= \frac{\text{Distance covered}}{\text{Elapsed time}} \\
&= \frac{f(2 + h) - f(2)}{h} \qquad \text{Difference quotient} \\
&= \frac{16(2 + h)^2 - 16(2)^2}{h} \qquad \text{Simplify this O/O indeterminate form.}
\end{aligned}
$$

$$= \frac{64 + 64h + 16h^2 - 64}{h}$$

$$= \frac{h(64 + 16h)}{h} = 64 + 16h \qquad h \neq 0$$

Notice that if $h = 1$, the average velocity is 80 feet per second, which is the result in part (A).

(C) The limit of the average velocity expression from part (B) as $h \to 0$ is

$$\lim_{h \to 0} \frac{f(2 + h) - f(2)}{h} = \lim_{h \to 0} (64 + 16h)$$

$$= 64 \text{ feet per second}$$

(D) The average velocity over smaller and smaller time intervals approaches 64 feet per second. This limit can be interpreted as the velocity of the ball at the *instant* that the ball has been falling for exactly 2 seconds. Therefore, 64 feet per second is referred to as the **instantaneous velocity** at $x = 2$ seconds, and we have solved one of the basic problems of calculus (see Fig. 1B).

Matched Problem 2 For the falling steel ball in Example 2, find

(A) The average velocity from $x = 1$ second to $x = 2$ seconds

(B) The average velocity (in simplified form) from $x = 1$ second to $x = 1 + h$ seconds, $h \neq 0$

(C) The instantaneous velocity at $x = 1$ second

The ideas in Example 2 can be applied to the average rate of change of any function.

DEFINITION Instantaneous Rate of Change

For $y = f(x)$, the **instantaneous rate of change at $x = a$** is

$$\lim_{h \to 0} \frac{f(a + h) - f(a)}{h} \tag{2}$$

if the limit exists.

The adjective *instantaneous* is often omitted with the understanding that the phrase **rate of change** always refers to the instantaneous rate of change and not the average rate of change. Similarly, **velocity** always refers to the instantaneous rate of change of distance with respect to time.

Slope of the Tangent Line

So far, our interpretations of the difference quotient have been numerical in nature. Now we want to consider a geometric interpretation.

In geometry, a line that intersects a circle in two points is called a *secant line*, and a line that intersects a circle in exactly one point is called a *tangent line* (Fig. 4, page 136). If the point Q in Figure 4 is moved closer and closer to the point P, then the angle between the secant line PQ and the tangent line at P gets smaller and smaller. We will generalize the geometric concepts of secant line and tangent line of a circle and will use them to study graphs of functions.

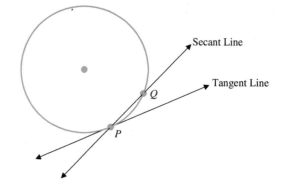

Figure 4 **Secant line and tangent line of a circle**

A line through two points on the graph of a function is called a **secant line**. If $(a, f(a))$ and $(a + h, f(a + h))$ are two points on the graph of $y = f(x)$, then we can use the slope formula from Section 1.3 to find the slope of the secant line through these points (Fig. 5).

Slope of secant line $= \dfrac{y_2 - y_1}{x_2 - x_1} = \dfrac{f(a + h) - f(a)}{(a + h) - a}$

$$= \frac{f(a + h) - f(a)}{h} \qquad \text{Difference quotient}$$

The difference quotient can be interpreted as both the average rate of change and the slope of the secant line.

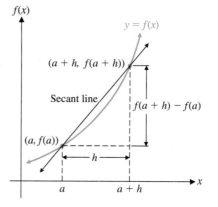

Figure 5 **Secant line**

EXAMPLE 3   Slope of a Secant Line   Given $f(x) = x^2$,

(A) Find the slope of the secant line for $a = 1$ and $h = 2$ and 1, respectively. Graph $y = f(x)$ and the two secant lines.

(B) Find and simplify the slope of the secant line for $a = 1$ and h any nonzero number.

(C) Find the limit of the expression in part (B).

(D) Discuss possible interpretations of the limit in part (C).

SOLUTION

(A) For $a = 1$ and $h = 2$, the secant line goes through $(1, f(1)) = (1, 1)$ and $(3, f(3)) = (3, 9)$, and its slope is

$$\frac{f(1 + 2) - f(1)}{2} = \frac{3^2 - 1^2}{2} = 4$$

Figure 6 **Secant lines**

Figure 7 **Tangent line**

For $a = 1$ and $h = 1$, the secant line goes through $(1, f(1)) = (1, 1)$ and $(2, f(2)) = (2, 4)$, and its slope is

$$\frac{f(1 + 1) - f(1)}{1} = \frac{2^2 - 1^2}{1} = 3$$

The graphs of $y = f(x)$ and the two secant lines are shown in Figure 6.

(B) For $a = 1$ and h any nonzero number, the secant line goes through $(1, f(1)) = (1, 1)$ and $(1 + h, f(1 + h)) = (1 + h, (1 + h)^2)$, and its slope is

$$\frac{f(1 + h) - f(1)}{h} = \frac{(1 + h)^2 - 1^2}{h} \qquad \text{Square the binomial.}$$

$$= \frac{1 + 2h + h^2 - 1}{h} \qquad \text{Combine like terms and factor the numerator.}$$

$$= \frac{h(2 + h)}{h} \qquad \text{Cancel.}$$

$$= 2 + h \qquad h \neq 0$$

(C) The limit of the secant line slope from part (B) is

$$\lim_{h \to 0} \frac{f(1 + h) - f(1)}{h} = \lim_{h \to 0} (2 + h)$$

$$= 2$$

(D) In part (C), we saw that the limit of the slopes of the secant lines through the point $(1, f(1))$ is 2. If we graph the line through $(1, f(1))$ with slope 2 (Fig. 7), then this line is the limit of the secant lines. The slope obtained from the limit of slopes of secant lines is called the *slope of the graph* at $x = 1$. The line through the point $(1, f(1))$ with this slope is called the *tangent line*. We have solved another basic problem of calculus (see Fig. 1A on page 132).

Matched Problem 3 ⟩ Given $f(x) = x^2$,

(A) Find the slope of the secant line for $a = 2$ and $h = 2$ and 1, respectively.

(B) Find and simplify the slope of the secant line for $a = 2$ and h any nonzero number.

(C) Find the limit of the expression in part (B).

(D) Find the slope of the graph and the slope of the tangent line at $a = 2$.

The ideas introduced in the preceding example are summarized next:

DEFINITION   Slope of a Graph and Tangent Line
Given $y = f(x)$, the **slope of the graph** at the point $(a, f(a))$ is given by

$$\lim_{h \to 0} \frac{f(a + h) - f(a)}{h} \qquad (3)$$

provided the limit exists. In this case, the **tangent line** to the graph is the line through $(a, f(a))$ with slope given by (3).

CONCEPTUAL **INSIGHT**

If the function f is continuous at a, then

$$\lim_{h \to 0} f(a + h) = f(a)$$

and limit (3) will be a $0/0$ indeterminate form. As we saw in Examples 2 and 3, evaluating this type of limit typically involves algebraic simplification.

The Derivative

We have seen that the limit of a difference quotient can be interpreted as a rate of change, as a velocity, or as the slope of a tangent line. In addition, this limit provides solutions to the two basic problems stated at the beginning of this section. We are now ready to introduce some terms that refer to that limit. To follow customary practice, we use x in place of a and think of the difference quotient

$$\frac{f(x + h) - f(x)}{h}$$

as a function of h, with x held fixed as h tends to 0.

DEFINITION   The Derivative

For $y = f(x)$, we define the **derivative of f at x**, denoted $f'(x)$, by

$$f'(x) = \lim_{h \to 0} \frac{f(x + h) - f(x)}{h} \quad \text{if the limit exists}$$

If $f'(x)$ exists for each x in the open interval (a, b), then f is said to be **differentiable** over (a, b).

(Differentiability from the left or from the right is defined by using $h \to 0^-$ or $h \to 0^+$, respectively, in place of $h \to 0$ in the preceding definition.)

The process of finding the derivative of a function is called **differentiation**. The derivative of a function is obtained by **differentiating** the function.

SUMMARY   Interpretations of the Derivative

The derivative of a function f is a new function f'. The domain of f' is a subset of the domain of f. The derivative has various applications and interpretations, including the following:

1. *Slope of the tangent line.* For each x in the domain of f', $f'(x)$ is the slope of the line tangent to the graph of f at the point $(x, f(x))$.
2. *Instantaneous rate of change.* For each x in the domain of f', $f'(x)$ is the instantaneous rate of change of $y = f(x)$ with respect to x.
3. *Velocity.* If $f(x)$ is the position of a moving object at time x, then $v = f'(x)$ is the velocity of the object at that time.

Example 4 illustrates the **four-step process** that we use to find derivatives in this section. In subsequent sections, we develop rules for finding derivatives that do not involve limits. However, it is important that you master the limit process in order to fully comprehend and appreciate the various applications we will consider.

EXAMPLE 4   Finding a Derivative Find $f'(x)$, the derivative of f at x, for $f(x) = 4x - x^2$.

SOLUTION   To find $f'(x)$, we use a four-step process.

Step 1   Find $f(x + h)$.

$$\begin{aligned} f(x + h) &= 4(x + h) - (x + h)^2 \\ &= 4x + 4h - x^2 - 2xh - h^2 \end{aligned}$$

Step 2   Find $f(x + h) - f(x)$.

$$\begin{aligned} f(x + h) - f(x) &= 4x + 4h - x^2 - 2xh - h^2 - (4x - x^2) \\ &= 4h - 2xh - h^2 \end{aligned}$$

Step 3 Find $\dfrac{f(x+h)-f(x)}{h}$.

$$\frac{f(x+h)-f(x)}{h}=\frac{4h-2xh-h^2}{h}=\frac{h(4-2x-h)}{h}$$

$$=4-2x-h,\quad h\neq 0$$

Step 4 Find $f'(x)=\lim\limits_{h\to 0}\dfrac{f(x+h)-f(x)}{h}$.

$$f'(x)=\lim\limits_{h\to 0}\frac{f(x+h)-f(x)}{h}=\lim\limits_{h\to 0}(4-2x-h)=4-2x$$

So if $f(x)=4x-x^2$, then $f'(x)=4-2x$. The function f' is a new function derived from the function f.

Matched Problem 4 Find $f'(x)$, the derivative of f at x, for $f(x)=8x-2x^2$.

The four-step process used in Example 4 is summarized as follows for easy reference:

PROCEDURE The four-step process for finding the derivative of a function f:

Step 1 Find $f(x+h)$.

Step 2 Find $f(x+h)-f(x)$.

Step 3 Find $\dfrac{f(x+h)-f(x)}{h}$.

Step 4 Find $\lim\limits_{h\to 0}\dfrac{f(x+h)-f(x)}{h}$.

EXAMPLE 5 Finding Tangent Line Slopes In Example 4, we started with the function $f(x)=4x-x^2$ and found the derivative of f at x to be $f'(x)=4-2x$. So the slope of a line tangent to the graph of f at any point $(x, f(x))$ on the graph is

$$m=f'(x)=4-2x$$

(A) Find the slope of the graph of f at $x=0$, $x=2$, and $x=3$.

(B) Graph $y=f(x)=4x-x^2$ and use the slopes found in part (A) to make a rough sketch of the lines tangent to the graph at $x=0$, $x=2$, and $x=3$.

SOLUTION

(A) Using $f'(x)=4-2x$, we have

$$f'(0)=4-2(0)=4\qquad\text{Slope at }x=0$$
$$f'(2)=4-2(2)=0\qquad\text{Slope at }x=2$$
$$f'(3)=4-2(3)=-2\qquad\text{Slope at }x=3$$

Matched Problem 5 In Matched Problem 4, we started with the function $f(x) = 8x - 2x^2$. Using the derivative found there,

(A) Find the slope of the graph of f at $x = 1$, $x = 2$, and $x = 4$.

(B) Graph $y = f(x) = 8x - 2x^2$, and use the slopes from part (A) to make a rough sketch of the lines tangent to the graph at $x = 1$, $x = 2$, and $x = 4$.

Explore and Discuss 1 In Example 4, we found that the derivative of $f(x) = 4x - x^2$ is $f'(x) = 4 - 2x$. In Example 5, we graphed $f(x)$ and several tangent lines.

(A) Graph f and f' on the same set of axes.

(B) The graph of f' is a straight line. Is it a tangent line for the graph of f? Explain.

(C) Find the x intercept for the graph of f'. What is the slope of the line tangent to the graph of f for this value of x? Write a verbal description of the relationship between the slopes of the tangent lines of a function and the x intercepts of the derivative of the function.

EXAMPLE 6 Finding a Derivative Find $f'(x)$, the derivative of f at x, for $f(x) = \dfrac{1}{x}$.

SOLUTION

Step 1 Find $f(x + h)$.

$$f(x + h) = \frac{1}{x + h}$$

Step 2 Find $f(x + h) - f(x)$.

$$f(x + h) - f(x) = \frac{1}{x + h} - \frac{1}{x} \qquad \text{Add fractions. (Section A.4)}$$

$$= \frac{x - (x + h)}{x(x + h)} \qquad \text{Simplify.}$$

$$= \frac{-h}{x(x + h)}$$

Step 3 Find $\dfrac{f(x + h) - f(x)}{h}$

$$\frac{f(x + h) - f(x)}{h} = \frac{\dfrac{-h}{x(x + h)}}{h} \qquad \text{Simplify.}$$

$$= \frac{-1}{x(x + h)} \qquad h \neq 0$$

Step 4 Find $\displaystyle\lim_{h \to 0} \dfrac{f(x + h) - f(x)}{h}$.

$$\lim_{h \to 0} \frac{f(x + h) - f(x)}{h} = \lim_{h \to 0} \frac{-1}{x(x + h)}$$

$$= \frac{-1}{x^2} \qquad x \neq 0$$

So the derivative of $f(x) = \dfrac{1}{x}$ is $f'(x) = \dfrac{-1}{x^2}$, a new function. The domain of f is the set of all nonzero real numbers. The domain of f' is also the set of all nonzero real numbers.

Matched Problem 6 Find $f'(x)$ for $f(x) = \dfrac{1}{x + 2}$.

EXAMPLE 7 Finding a Derivative Find $f'(x)$, the derivative of f at x, for $f(x) = \sqrt{x} + 2$.

SOLUTION We use the four-step process to find $f'(x)$.

Step 1 Find $f(x + h)$.

$$f(x + h) = \sqrt{x + h} + 2$$

Step 2 Find $f(x + h) - f(x)$.

$$f(x + h) - f(x) = \sqrt{x + h} + 2 - (\sqrt{x} + 2) \quad \text{Combine like terms.}$$
$$= \sqrt{x + h} - \sqrt{x}$$

Step 3 Find $\dfrac{f(x + h) - f(x)}{h}$.

$$\frac{f(x + h) - f(x)}{h} = \frac{\sqrt{x + h} - \sqrt{x}}{h}$$

We rationalize the numerator (Appendix A, Section A.6) to change the form of this fraction.

$$= \frac{\sqrt{x + h} - \sqrt{x}}{h} \cdot \frac{\sqrt{x + h} + \sqrt{x}}{\sqrt{x + h} + \sqrt{x}}$$

$$= \frac{x + h - x}{h(\sqrt{x + h} + \sqrt{x})}$$

Combine like terms.

$$= \frac{h}{h(\sqrt{x + h} + \sqrt{x})}$$

Cancel.

$$= \frac{1}{\sqrt{x + h} + \sqrt{x}} \quad h \neq 0$$

Step 4 Find $f'(x) = \lim\limits_{h \to 0} \dfrac{f(x + h) - f(x)}{h}$.

$$\lim_{h \to 0} \frac{f(x + h) - f(x)}{h} = \lim_{h \to 0} \frac{1}{\sqrt{x + h} + \sqrt{x}}$$

$$= \frac{1}{\sqrt{x} + \sqrt{x}} = \frac{1}{2\sqrt{x}} \quad x > 0$$

So the derivative of $f(x) = \sqrt{x} + 2$ is $f'(x) = 1/(2\sqrt{x})$, a new function. The domain of f is $[0, \infty)$. Since $f'(0)$ is not defined, the domain of f' is $(0, \infty)$, a subset of the domain of f.

Matched Problem 7 Find $f'(x)$ for $f(x) = \sqrt{x} + 4$.

EXAMPLE 8 Sales Analysis A company's total sales (in millions of dollars) t months from now are given by $S(t) = \sqrt{t} + 2$. Find and interpret $S(25)$ and $S'(25)$. Use these results to estimate the total sales after 26 months and after 27 months.

SOLUTION The total sales function S has the same form as the function f in Example 7. Only the letters used to represent the function and the independent variable have been changed. It follows that S' and f' also have the same form:

$$S(t) = \sqrt{t} + 2 \qquad f(x) = \sqrt{x} + 2$$

$$S'(t) = \frac{1}{2\sqrt{t}} \qquad f'(x) = \frac{1}{2\sqrt{x}}$$

Evaluating S and S' at $t = 25$, we have

$$S(25) = \sqrt{25} + 2 = 7 \qquad S'(25) = \frac{1}{2\sqrt{25}} = 0.1$$

So 25 months from now, the total sales will be $7 million and will be increasing at the rate of $0.1 million ($100,000) per month. If this instantaneous rate of change of sales remained constant, the sales would grow to $7.1 million after 26 months, $7.2 million after 27 months, and so on. Even though $S'(t)$ is not a constant function in this case, these values provide useful estimates of the total sales.

Matched Problem 8 A company's total sales (in millions of dollars) t months from now are given by $S(t) = \sqrt{t + 4}$. Find and interpret $S(12)$ and $S'(12)$. Use these results to estimate the total sales after 13 months and after 14 months. (Use the derivative found in Matched Problem 7.)

In Example 8, we can compare the estimates of total sales by using the derivative with the corresponding exact values of $S(t)$:

Exact values	Estimated values

$$S(26) = \sqrt{26} + 2 = 7.099\ldots \approx 7.1$$
$$S(27) = \sqrt{27} + 2 = 7.196\ldots \approx 7.2$$

For this function, the estimated values provide very good approximations to the exact values of $S(t)$. For other functions, the approximation might not be as accurate.

Using the instantaneous rate of change of a function at a point to estimate values of the function at nearby points is an important application of the derivative.

Nonexistence of the Derivative

The existence of a derivative at $x = a$ depends on the existence of a limit at $x = a$, that is, on the existence of

$$f'(a) = \lim_{h \to 0} \frac{f(a + h) - f(a)}{h} \tag{4}$$

If the limit does not exist at $x = a$, we say that the function f is **nondifferentiable at** $x = a$, or $f'(a)$ **does not exist.**

Explore and Discuss 2 Let $f(x) = |x - 1|$.

(A) Graph f.

(B) Complete the following table:

h	-0.1	-0.01	-0.001	$\to 0 \leftarrow$	0.001	0.01	0.1
$\dfrac{f(1 + h) - f(1)}{h}$	?	?	?	$\to ? \leftarrow$	?	?	?

(C) Find the following limit if it exists:

$$\lim_{h \to 0} \frac{f(1 + h) - f(1)}{h}$$

(D) Use the results of parts (A)–(C) to discuss the existence of $f'(1)$.

(E) Repeat parts (A)–(D) for $\sqrt[3]{x - 1}$.

How can we recognize the points on the graph of f where $f'(a)$ does not exist? It is impossible to describe all the ways that the limit of a difference quotient can fail to exist. However, we can illustrate some common situations where $f'(a)$ fails to exist (see Fig. 8):

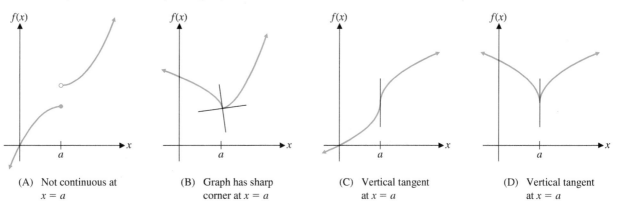

(A) Not continuous at $x = a$

(B) Graph has sharp corner at $x = a$

(C) Vertical tangent at $x = a$

(D) Vertical tangent at $x = a$

Figure 8 **The function f is nondifferentiable at x = a.**

1. If the graph of f has a hole or a break at $x = a$, then $f'(a)$ does not exist (Fig. 8A).
2. If the graph of f has a sharp corner at $x = a$, then $f'(a)$ does not exist, and the graph has no tangent line at $x = a$ (Fig. 8B). (In Fig. 8B, the left- and right-hand derivatives exist but are not equal.)
3. If the graph of f has a vertical tangent line at $x = a$, then $f'(a)$ does not exist (Fig. 8C and D).

Exercises 2.4

Skills Warm-up Exercises

W *In Problems 1–4, find the slope of the line through the given points. Write the slope as a reduced fraction, and also give its decimal form. (If necessary, review Section 1.3).*

1. $(2, 7)$ and $(6, 16)$

2. $(-1, 11)$ and $(1, 8)$

3. $(10, 14)$ and $(0, 68)$

4. $(-12, -3)$ and $(4, 3)$

In Problems 5–8, write the expression in the form $a + b\sqrt{n}$ where a and b are reduced fractions and n is an integer. (If necessary, review Section A.6).

5. $\dfrac{1}{\sqrt{3}}$

6. $\dfrac{2}{\sqrt{5}}$

7. $\dfrac{5}{3 + \sqrt{7}}$

8. $\dfrac{1 - \sqrt{2}}{5 + \sqrt{2}}$

In Problems 9 and 10, find the indicated quantity for $y = f(x) = 5 - x^2$ and interpret that quantity in terms of the following graph.

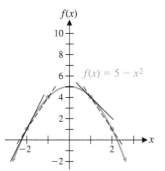

9. (A) $\dfrac{f(2) - f(1)}{2 - 1}$ (B) $\dfrac{f(1 + h) - f(1)}{h}$

(C) $\lim\limits_{h \to 0} \dfrac{f(1 + h) - f(1)}{h}$

10. (A) $\dfrac{f(-1) - f(-2)}{-1 - (-2)}$ (B) $\dfrac{f(-2 + h) - f(-2)}{h}$

(C) $\lim\limits_{h \to 0} \dfrac{f(-2 + h) - f(-2)}{h}$

11. Find the indicated quantities for $f(x) = 3x^2$.

(A) The slope of the secant line through the points $(1, f(1))$ and $(4, f(4))$ on the graph of $y = f(x)$.

(B) The slope of the secant line through the points $(1, f(1))$ and $(1 + h, f(1 + h))$, $h \neq 0$. Simplify your answer.

(C) The slope of the graph at $(1, f(1))$.

12. Find the indicated quantities for $f(x) = 3x^2$.

(A) The slope of the secant line through the points $(2, f(2))$ and $(5, f(5))$ on the graph of $y = f(x)$.

(B) The slope of the secant line through the points $(2, f(2))$ and $(2 + h, f(2 + h))$, $h \neq 0$. Simplify your answer.

(C) The slope of the graph at $(2, f(2))$.

13. Two hours after the start of a 100-kilometer bicycle race, a cyclist passes the 80-kilometer mark while riding at a velocity of 45 kilometers per hour.

(A) Find the cyclist's average velocity during the first two hours of the race.

(B) Let $f(x)$ represent the distance traveled (in kilometers) from the start of the race $(x = 0)$ to time x (in hours). Find the slope of the secant line through the points $(0, f(0))$ and $(2, f(2))$ on the graph of $y = f(x)$.

(C) Find the equation of the tangent line to the graph of $y = f(x)$ at the point $(2, f(2))$.

14. Four hours after the start of a 600-mile auto race, a driver's velocity is 150 miles per hour as she completes the 352nd lap on a 1.5-mile track.

(A) Find the driver's average velocity during the first four hours of the race.

(B) Let $f(x)$ represent the distance traveled (in miles) from the start of the race $(x = 0)$ to time x (in hours). Find the slope of the secant line through the points $(0, f(0))$ and $(4, f(4))$ on the graph of $y = f(x)$.

(C) Find the equation of the tangent line to the graph of $y = f(x)$ at the point $(4, f(4))$.

15. For $f(x) = \frac{1}{1 + x^2}$, the slope of the graph of $y = f(x)$ is known to be $-\frac{1}{2}$ at the point with x coordinate 1. Find the equation of the tangent line at that point.

16. For $f(x) = \frac{1}{1 + x^2}$, the slope of the graph of $y = f(x)$ is known to be -0.16 at the point with x coordinate 2. Find the equation of the tangent line at that point.

17. For $f(x) = x^4$, the instantaneous rate of change is known to be -32 at $x = -2$. Find the equation of the tangent line to the graph of $y = f(x)$ at the point with x coordinate -2.

18. For $f(x) = x^4$, the instantaneous rate of change is known to be -4 at $x = -1$. Find the equation of the tangent line to the graph of $y = f(x)$ at the point with x coordinate -1.

In Problems 19–42, use the four-step process to find $f'(x)$ and then find $f'(1), f'(2),$ and $f'(3)$.

19. $f(x) = -5$

20. $f(x) = 9$

21. $f(x) = 3x - 7$

22. $f(x) = 4 - 6x$

23. $f(x) = 2 - 3x^2$

24. $f(x) = 2x^2 + 8$

25. $f(x) = x^2 + 6x - 10$

26. $f(x) = x^2 + 4x + 7$

27. $f(x) = 2x^2 - 7x + 3$

28. $f(x) = 2x^2 + 5x + 1$

29. $f(x) = -x^2 + 4x - 9$

30. $f(x) = -x^2 + 9x - 2$

31. $f(x) = 2x^3 + 1$

32. $f(x) = -2x^3 + 5$

33. $f(x) = 4 + \frac{4}{x}$

34. $f(x) = \frac{6}{x} - 2$

35. $f(x) = 5 + 3\sqrt{x}$

36. $f(x) = 3 - 7\sqrt{x}$

37. $f(x) = 10\sqrt{x} + 5$

38. $f(x) = 16\sqrt{x} + 9$

39. $f(x) = \dfrac{1}{x - 4}$

40. $f(x) = \dfrac{1}{x + 4}$

41. $f(x) = \dfrac{x}{x + 1}$

42. $f(x) = \dfrac{x}{x + 2}$

Problems 43 and 44 refer to the graph of $y = f(x) = x^2 + x$ shown.

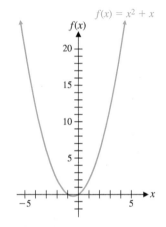

43. (A) Find the slope of the secant line joining $(1, f(1))$ and $(3, f(3))$.

(B) Find the slope of the secant line joining $(1, f(1))$ and $(1 + h, f(1 + h))$.

(C) Find the slope of the tangent line at $(1, f(1))$.

(D) Find the equation of the tangent line at $(1, f(1))$.

44. (A) Find the slope of the secant line joining $(2, f(2))$ and $(4, f(4))$.

(B) Find the slope of the secant line joining $(2, f(2))$ and $(2 + h, f(2 + h))$.

(C) Find the slope of the tangent line at $(2, f(2))$.

(D) Find the equation of the tangent line at $(2, f(2))$.

In Problems 45 and 46, suppose an object moves along the y axis so that its location is $y = f(x) = x^2 + x$ at time x (y is in meters and x is in seconds). Find

45. (A) The average velocity (the average rate of change of y with respect to x) for x changing from 1 to 3 seconds

(B) The average velocity for x changing from 1 to $1 + h$ seconds

(C) The instantaneous velocity at $x = 1$ second

46. (A) The average velocity (the average rate of change of y with respect to x) for x changing from 2 to 4 seconds

(B) The average velocity for x changing from 2 to $2 + h$ seconds

(C) The instantaneous velocity at $x = 2$ seconds

Problems 47–54, refer to the function F in the graph shown. Use the graph to determine whether F'(x) exists at each indicated value of x.

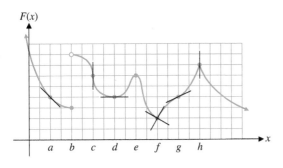

47. $x = a$ **48.** $x = b$

49. $x = c$ **50.** $x = d$

51. $x = e$ **52.** $x = f$

53. $x = g$ **54.** $x = h$

55. Given $f(x) = x^2 - 4x$,

   (A) Find $f'(x)$.

   (B) Find the slopes of the lines tangent to the graph of f at $x = 0, 2$, and 4.

   (C) Graph f and sketch in the tangent lines at $x = 0, 2$, and 4.

56. Given $f(x) = x^2 + 2x$,

   (A) Find $f'(x)$.

   (B) Find the slopes of the lines tangent to the graph of f at $x = -2, -1$, and 1.

   (C) Graph f and sketch in the tangent lines at $x = -2, -1$, and 1.

57. If an object moves along a line so that it is at $y = f(x) = 4x^2 - 2x$ at time x (in seconds), find the instantaneous velocity function $v = f'(x)$ and find the velocity at times $x = 1, 3$, and 5 seconds (y is measured in feet).

58. Repeat Problem 57 with $f(x) = 8x^2 - 4x$.

59. Let $f(x) = x^2$, $g(x) = x^2 - 1$, and $h(x) = x^2 + 2$.

   (A) How are the graphs of these functions related? How would you expect the derivatives of these functions to be related?

   (B) Use the four-step process to find the derivative of $m(x) = x^2 + C$, where C is any real constant.

60. Let $f(x) = -x^2$, $g(x) = -x^2 - 1$, and $h(x) = -x^2 + 2$.

   (A) How are the graphs of these functions related? How would you expect the derivatives of these functions to be related?

   (B) Use the four-step process to find the derivative of $m(x) = -x^2 + C$, where C is any real constant.

In Problems 61–66, discuss the validity of each statement. If the statement is always true, explain why. If not, give a counterexample.

61. If $f(x) = C$ is a constant function, then $f'(x) = 0$.

62. If $f(x) = mx + b$ is a linear function, then $f'(x) = m$.

63. If a function f is continuous on the interval (a, b), then f is differentiable on (a, b).

64. If a function f is differentiable on the interval (a, b), then f is continuous on (a, b).

65. The average rate of change of a function f from $x = a$ to $x = a + h$ is less than the instantaneous rate of change at $x = a + \dfrac{h}{2}$.

66. If the graph of f has a sharp corner at $x = a$, then f is not continuous at $x = a$.

In Problems 67–70, sketch the graph of f and determine where f is nondifferentiable.

67. $f(x) = \begin{cases} 2x & \text{if } x < 1 \\ 2 & \text{if } x \geq 1 \end{cases}$ **68.** $f(x) = \begin{cases} 2x & \text{if } x < 2 \\ 6 - x & \text{if } x \geq 2 \end{cases}$

69. $f(x) = \begin{cases} x^2 + 1 & \text{if } x < 0 \\ 1 & \text{if } x \geq 0 \end{cases}$

70. $f(x) = \begin{cases} 2 - x^2 & \text{if } x \leq 0 \\ 2 & \text{if } x > 0 \end{cases}$

In Problems 71–76, determine whether f is differentiable at $x = 0$ by considering

$$\lim_{h \to 0} \frac{f(0 + h) - f(0)}{h}$$

71. $f(x) = |x|$ **72.** $f(x) = 1 - |x|$

73. $f(x) = x^{1/3}$ **74.** $f(x) = x^{2/3}$

75. $f(x) = \sqrt{1 - x^2}$ **76.** $f(x) = \sqrt{1 + x^2}$

77. A ball dropped from a balloon falls $y = 16x^2$ feet in x seconds. If the balloon is 576 feet above the ground when the ball is dropped, when does the ball hit the ground? What is the velocity of the ball at the instant it hits the ground?

78. Repeat Problem 77 if the balloon is 1,024 feet above the ground when the ball is dropped.

Applications

79. *Revenue.* The revenue (in dollars) from the sale of x infant car seats is given by

$$R(x) = 60x - 0.025x^2 \qquad 0 \leq x \leq 2,400$$

   (A) Find the average change in revenue if production is changed from 1,000 car seats to 1,050 car seats.

   (B) Use the four-step process to find $R'(x)$.

   (C) Find the revenue and the instantaneous rate of change of revenue at a production level of 1,000 car seats, and write a brief verbal interpretation of these results.

80. Profit. The profit (in dollars) from the sale of x infant car seats is given by

$$P(x) = 45x - 0.025x^2 - 5,000 \qquad 0 \le x \le 2,400$$

(A) Find the average change in profit if production is changed from 800 car seats to 850 car seats.

(B) Use the four-step process to find $P'(x)$.

(C) Find the profit and the instantaneous rate of change of profit at a production level of 800 car seats, and write a brief verbal interpretation of these results.

81. Sales analysis. A company's total sales (in millions of dollars) t months from now are given by

$$S(t) = 2\sqrt{t} + 10$$

(A) Use the four-step process to find $S'(t)$.

(B) Find $S(15)$ and $S'(15)$. Write a brief verbal interpretation of these results.

(C) Use the results in part (B) to estimate the total sales after 16 months and after 17 months.

82. Sales analysis. A company's total sales (in millions of dollars) t months from now are given by

$$S(t) = 2\sqrt{t} + 6$$

(A) Use the four-step process to find $S'(t)$.

(B) Find $S(10)$ and $S'(10)$. Write a brief verbal interpretation of these results.

(C) Use the results in part (B) to estimate the total sales after 11 months and after 12 months.

83. Mineral consumption. The U.S. consumption of tungsten (in metric tons) is given approximately by

$$p(t) = 138t^2 + 1,072t + 14,917$$

where t is time in years and $t = 0$ corresponds to 2010.

(A) Use the four-step process to find $p'(t)$.

(B) Find the annual consumption in 2020 and the instantaneous rate of change of consumption in 2020, and write a brief verbal interpretation of these results.

84. Mineral consumption. The U.S. consumption of refined copper (in thousands of metric tons) is given approximately by

$$p(t) = 48t^2 - 37t + 1,698$$

where t is time in years and $t = 0$ corresponds to 2010.

(A) Use the four-step process to find $p'(t)$.

(B) Find the annual consumption in 2022 and the instantaneous rate of change of consumption in 2022, and write a brief verbal interpretation of these results.

85. Electricity consumption. Table 1 gives the retail sales of electricity (in billions of kilowatt-hours) for the residential and commercial sectors in the United States. (*Source:* Energy Information Administration)

Table 1 Electricity Sales

Year	Residential	Commercial
2000	1,192	1,055
2002	1,265	1,104
2004	1,292	1,230
2006	1,352	1,300
2008	1,379	1,336
2010	1,446	1,330

(A) Let x represent time (in years) with $x = 0$ corresponding to 2000, and let y represent the corresponding residential sales. Enter the appropriate data set in a graphing calculator and find a quadratic regression equation for the data.

(B) If $y = R(x)$ denotes the regression equation found in part (A), find $R(20)$ and $R'(20)$, and write a brief verbal interpretation of these results. Round answers to the nearest tenth of a billion.

86. Electricity consumption. Refer to the data in Table 1.

(A) Let x represent time (in years) with $x = 0$ corresponding to 2000, and let y represent the corresponding commercial sales. Enter the appropriate data set in a graphing calculator and find a quadratic regression equation for the data.

(B) If $y = C(x)$ denotes the regression equation found in part (A), find $C(20)$ and $C'(20)$, and write a brief verbal interpretation of these results. Round answers to the nearest tenth of a billion.

87. Air pollution. The ozone level (in parts per billion) on a summer day in a metropolitan area is given by

$$P(t) = 80 + 12t - t^2$$

where t is time in hours and $t = 0$ corresponds to 9 A.M.

(A) Use the four-step process to find $P'(t)$.

(B) Find $P(3)$ and $P'(3)$. Write a brief verbal interpretation of these results.

88. Medicine. The body temperature (in degrees Fahrenheit) of a patient t hours after taking a fever-reducing drug is given by

$$F(t) = 98 + \frac{4}{t + 1}$$

(A) Use the four-step process to find $F'(t)$.

(B) Find $F(3)$ and $F'(3)$. Write a brief verbal interpretation of these results.

Answers to Matched Problems

1. (A) $-\$1,600$ (B) $-\$8$ per planter
2. (A) 48 ft/s   (B) $32 + 16h$
   (C) 32 ft/s
3. (A) 6, 5   (B) $4 + h$
   (C) 4   (D) Both are 4
4. $f'(x) = 8 - 4x$

5. (A) $f'(1) = 4, f'(2) = 0, f'(4) = -8$

(B) $f(x)$

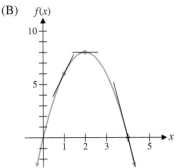

6. $f'(x) = -1/(x + 2)^2, x \neq -2$

7. $f'(x) = 1/(2\sqrt{x + 4}), x \geq -4$

8. $S(12) = 4, S'(12) = 0.125$; 12 months from now, the total sales will be \$4 million and will be increasing at the rate of \$0.125 million (\$125,000) per month. The estimated total sales are \$4.125 million after 13 months and \$4.25 million after 14 months.

2.5 Basic Differentiation Properties

- Constant Function Rule
- Power Rule
- Constant Multiple Property
- Sum and Difference Properties
- Applications

In Section 2.4, we defined the derivative of f at x as

$$f'(x) = \lim_{h \to 0} \frac{f(x + h) - f(x)}{h}$$

if the limit exists, and we used this definition and a four-step process to find the derivatives of several functions. Now we want to develop some rules of differentiation. These rules will enable us to find the derivative of many functions without using the four-step process.

Before exploring these rules, we list some symbols that are often used to represent derivatives.

NOTATION The Derivative
If $y = f(x)$, then

$$f'(x) \qquad y' \qquad \frac{dy}{dx}$$

all represent the derivative of f at x.

Each of these derivative symbols has its particular advantage in certain situations. All of them will become familiar to you after a little experience.

Constant Function Rule

If $f(x) = C$ is a constant function, then the four-step process can be used to show that $f'(x) = 0$. Therefore,

The derivative of any constant function is 0.

THEOREM 1 Constant Function Rule
If $y = f(x) = C$, then

$$f'(x) = 0$$

Also, $y' = 0$ and $dy/dx = 0$.

Note: When we write $C' = 0$ or $\dfrac{d}{dx} C = 0$, we mean that $y' = \dfrac{dy}{dx} = 0$ when $y = C$.

CONCEPTUAL INSIGHT

The graph of $f(x) = C$ is a horizontal line with slope 0 (Fig. 1), so we would expect that $f'(x) = 0$.

Figure 1

EXAMPLE 1   Differentiating Constant Functions

(A) If $f(x) = 3$,   then $f'(x) = 0$.   (B) If $y = -1.4$,   then $y' = 0$.

(C) If $y = \pi$,   then $\dfrac{dy}{dx} = 0$.   (D) $\dfrac{d}{dx} 23 = 0$

Matched Problem 1   Find

(A) $f'(x)$ for $f(x) = -24$ (B) y' for $y = 12$

(C) $\dfrac{dy}{dx}$ for $y = -\sqrt{7}$ (D) $\dfrac{d}{dx}(-\pi)$

Power Rule

A function of the form $f(x) = x^k$, where k is a real number, is called a **power function**. The following elementary functions are examples of power functions:

$$f(x) = x \qquad h(x) = x^2 \qquad m(x) = x^3 \tag{1}$$
$$n(x) = \sqrt{x} \qquad p(x) = \sqrt[3]{x}$$

Explore and Discuss 1   (A) It is clear that the functions f, h, and m in (1) are power functions. Explain why the functions n and p are also power functions.

(B) The domain of a power function depends on the power. Discuss the domain of each of the following power functions:

$$r(x) = x^4 \qquad s(x) = x^{-4} \qquad t(x) = x^{1/4}$$
$$u(x) = x^{-1/4} \qquad v(x) = x^{1/5} \qquad w(x) = x^{-1/5}$$

The definition of the derivative and the four-step process introduced in Section 2.4 can be used to find the derivatives of many power functions. For example, it can be shown that

$$\begin{aligned} \text{If} \quad & f(x) = x^2, \quad \text{then} \quad f'(x) = 2x. \\ \text{If} \quad & f(x) = x^3, \quad \text{then} \quad f'(x) = 3x^2. \\ \text{If} \quad & f(x) = x^4, \quad \text{then} \quad f'(x) = 4x^3. \\ \text{If} \quad & f(x) = x^5, \quad \text{then} \quad f'(x) = 5x^4. \end{aligned}$$

Notice the pattern in these derivatives. In each case, the power in f becomes the coefficient in f' and the power in f' is 1 less than the power in f. In general, for any positive integer n,

$$\text{If} \quad f(x) = x^n, \quad \text{then} \quad f'(x) = nx^{n-1}. \quad (2)$$

In fact, more advanced techniques can be used to show that (2) holds for *any* real number n. We will assume this general result for the remainder of the book.

THEOREM 2 Power Rule

If $y = f(x) = x^n$, where n is a real number, then

$$f'(x) = nx^{n-1}$$

Also, $y' = nx^{n-1}$ and $dy/dx = nx^{n-1}$.

EXAMPLE 2 Differentiating Power Functions

(A) If $f(x) = x^5$, then $f'(x) = 5x^{5-1} = 5x^4$.

(B) If $y = x^{25}$, then $y' = 25x^{25-1} = 25x^{24}$.

(C) If $y = t^{-3}$, then $\dfrac{dy}{dt} = -3t^{-3-1} = -3t^{-4} = -\dfrac{3}{t^4}$.

(D) $\dfrac{d}{dx}x^{5/3} = \dfrac{5}{3}x^{(5/3)-1} = \dfrac{5}{3}x^{2/3}$.

Matched Problem 2 Find

(A) $f'(x)$ for $f(x) = x^6$

(B) y' for $y = x^{30}$

(C) $\dfrac{dy}{dt}$ for $y = t^{-2}$

(D) $\dfrac{d}{dx}x^{3/2}$

In some cases, properties of exponents must be used to rewrite an expression before the power rule is applied.

EXAMPLE 3 Differentiating Power Functions

(A) If $f(x) = 1/x^4$, we can write $f(x) = x^{-4}$ and

$$f'(x) = -4x^{-4-1} = -4x^{-5}, \quad \text{or} \quad \frac{-4}{x^5}$$

(B) If $y = \sqrt{u}$, we can write $y = u^{1/2}$ and

$$y' = \frac{1}{2}u^{(1/2)-1} = \frac{1}{2}u^{-1/2}, \quad \text{or} \quad \frac{1}{2\sqrt{u}}$$

(C) $\dfrac{d}{dx}\dfrac{1}{\sqrt[3]{x}} = \dfrac{d}{dx}x^{-1/3} = -\dfrac{1}{3}x^{(-1/3)-1} = -\dfrac{1}{3}x^{-4/3}$, or $\dfrac{-1}{3\sqrt[3]{x^4}}$

Matched Problem 3 Find

(A) $f'(x)$ for $f(x) = \dfrac{1}{x}$

(B) y' for $y = \sqrt[3]{u^2}$

(C) $\dfrac{d}{dx}\dfrac{1}{\sqrt{x}}$

Constant Multiple Property

Let $f(x) = ku(x)$, where k is a constant and u is differentiable at x. Using the four-step process, we have the following:

Step 1 $f(x + h) = ku(x + h)$

Step 2 $f(x + h) - f(x) = ku(x + h) - ku(x) = k[u(x + h) - u(x)]$

Step 3 $\dfrac{f(x + h) - f(x)}{h} = \dfrac{k[u(x + h) - u(x)]}{h} = k\left[\dfrac{u(x + h) - u(x)}{h}\right]$

Step 4 $f'(x) = \lim\limits_{h \to 0} \dfrac{f(x + h) - f(x)}{h}$

$\qquad\qquad = \lim\limits_{h \to 0} k\left[\dfrac{u(x + h) - u(x)}{h}\right]$ $\lim\limits_{x \to c} kg(x) = k \lim\limits_{x \to c} g(x)$

$\qquad\qquad = k \lim\limits_{h \to 0} \left[\dfrac{u(x + h) - u(x)}{h}\right]$ Definition of $u'(x)$

$\qquad\qquad = ku'(x)$

Therefore,

> The derivative of a constant times a differentiable function is the constant times the derivative of the function.

THEOREM 3 Constant Multiple Property

If $y = f(x) = ku(x)$, then

$$f'(x) = ku'(x)$$

Also,

$$y' = ku' \qquad \dfrac{dy}{dx} = k\dfrac{du}{dx}$$

EXAMPLE 4 Differentiating a Constant Times a Function

(A) If $f(x) = 3x^2$, then $f'(x) = 3 \cdot 2x^{2-1} = 6x$.

(B) If $y = \dfrac{t^3}{6} = \dfrac{1}{6}t^3$, then $\dfrac{dy}{dt} = \dfrac{1}{6} \cdot 3t^{3-1} = \dfrac{1}{2}t^2$.

(C) If $y = \dfrac{1}{2x^4} = \dfrac{1}{2}x^{-4}$, then $y' = \dfrac{1}{2}(-4x^{-4-1}) = -2x^{-5}$, or $\dfrac{-2}{x^5}$.

(D) $\dfrac{d}{dx}\dfrac{0.4}{\sqrt{x^3}} = \dfrac{d}{dx}\dfrac{0.4}{x^{3/2}} = \dfrac{d}{dx}0.4x^{-3/2} = 0.4\left[-\dfrac{3}{2}x^{(-3/2)-1}\right]$

$\qquad\qquad\qquad\qquad\qquad\qquad\qquad = -0.6x^{-5/2},$ or $-\dfrac{0.6}{\sqrt{x^5}}$

Matched Problem 4 Find

(A) $f'(x)$ for $f(x) = 4x^5$

(B) $\dfrac{dy}{dt}$ for $y = \dfrac{t^4}{12}$

(C) y' for $y = \dfrac{1}{3x^3}$

(D) $\dfrac{d}{dx}\dfrac{0.9}{\sqrt[3]{x}}$

Sum and Difference Properties

Let $f(x) = u(x) + v(x)$, where $u'(x)$ and $v'(x)$ exist. Using the four-step process (see Problems 87 and 88 in Exercises 2.5):

$$f'(x) = u'(x) + v'(x)$$

Therefore,

> The derivative of the sum of two differentiable functions is the sum of the derivatives of the functions.

Similarly, we can show that

> The derivative of the difference of two differentiable functions is the difference of the derivatives of the functions.

Together, we have the **sum and difference property** for differentiation:

THEOREM 4 Sum and Difference Property
If $y = f(x) = u(x) \pm v(x)$, then

$$f'(x) = u'(x) \pm v'(x)$$

Also,

$$y' = u' \pm v' \qquad \frac{dy}{dx} = \frac{du}{dx} \pm \frac{dv}{dx}$$

Note: This rule generalizes to the sum and difference of any given number of functions.

With Theorems 1 through 4, we can compute the derivatives of all polynomials and a variety of other functions.

EXAMPLE 5 Differentiating Sums and Differences

(A) If $f(x) = 3x^2 + 2x$,   then
$$f'(x) = (3x^2)' + (2x)' = 3(2x) + 2(1) = 6x + 2$$

(B) If $y = 4 + 2x^3 - 3x^{-1}$,   then
$$y' = (4)' + (2x^3)' - (3x^{-1})' = 0 + 2(3x^2) - 3(-1)x^{-2} = 6x^2 + 3x^{-2}$$

(C) If $y = \sqrt[3]{w} - 3w$,   then
$$\frac{dy}{dw} = \frac{d}{dw}w^{1/3} - \frac{d}{dw}3w = \frac{1}{3}w^{-2/3} - 3 = \frac{1}{3w^{2/3}} - 3$$

(D) $\dfrac{d}{dx}\left(\dfrac{5}{3x^2} - \dfrac{2}{x^4} + \dfrac{x^3}{9}\right) = \dfrac{d}{dx}\dfrac{5}{3}x^{-2} - \dfrac{d}{dx}2x^{-4} + \dfrac{d}{dx}\dfrac{1}{9}x^3$

$$= \frac{5}{3}(-2)x^{-3} - 2(-4)x^{-5} + \frac{1}{9}\cdot 3x^2$$

$$= -\frac{10}{3x^3} + \frac{8}{x^5} + \frac{1}{3}x^2$$

Matched Problem 5 Find

(A) $f'(x)$ for $f(x) = 3x^4 - 2x^3 + x^2 - 5x + 7$

(B) y' for $y = 3 - 7x^{-2}$

(C) $\dfrac{dy}{dv}$ for $y = 5v^3 - \sqrt[4]{v}$

(D) $\dfrac{d}{dx}\left(-\dfrac{3}{4x} + \dfrac{4}{x^3} - \dfrac{x^4}{8}\right)$

Some algebraic rewriting of a function is sometimes required before we can apply the rules for differentiation.

EXAMPLE 6 Rewrite before Differentiating Find the derivative of

$$f(x) = \frac{1 + x^2}{x^4}.$$

SOLUTION It is helpful to rewrite $f(x) = \frac{1 + x^2}{x^4}$, expressing $f(x)$ as the sum of terms, each of which can be differentiated by applying the power rule.

$$f(x) = \frac{1 + x^2}{x^4} \qquad \text{Write as a sum of two terms}$$

$$= \frac{1}{x^4} + \frac{x^2}{x^4} \qquad \text{Write each term as a power of } x$$

$$= x^{-4} + x^{-2}$$

Note that we have rewritten $f(x)$, but we have not used any rules of differentiation. Now, however, we can apply those rules to find the derivative:

$$f'(x) = -4x^{-5} - 2x^{-3}$$

Matched Problem 6 Find the derivative of $f(x) = \dfrac{5 - 3x + 4x^2}{x}$.

Applications

EXAMPLE 7 Instantaneous Velocity An object moves along the y axis (marked in feet) so that its position at time x (in seconds) is

$$f(x) = x^3 - 6x^2 + 9x$$

(A) Find the instantaneous velocity function v.
(B) Find the velocity at $x = 2$ and $x = 5$ seconds.
(C) Find the time(s) when the velocity is 0.

SOLUTION
(A) $v = f'(x) = (x^3)' - (6x^2)' + (9x)' = 3x^2 - 12x + 9$
(B) $f'(2) = 3(2)^2 - 12(2) + 9 = -3$ feet per second
   $f'(5) = 3(5)^2 - 12(5) + 9 = 24$ feet per second
(C) $v = f'(x) = 3x^2 - 12x + 9 = 0$ Factor 3 out of each term.
   $3(x^2 - 4x + 3) = 0$ Factor the quadratic term.
   $3(x - 1)(x - 3) = 0$ Use the zero property.
   $x = 1, 3$

So, $v = 0$ at $x = 1$ and $x = 3$ seconds.

Matched Problem 7 Repeat Example 7 for $f(x) = x^3 - 15x^2 + 72x$.

EXAMPLE 8 Tangents Let $f(x) = x^4 - 6x^2 + 10$.

(A) Find $f'(x)$.
(B) Find the equation of the tangent line at $x = 1$.
(C) Find the values of x where the tangent line is horizontal.

SOLUTION

(A) $f'(x) \boxed{= (x^4)' - (6x^2)' + (10)'}$

$= 4x^3 - 12x$

(B) $y - y_1 = m(x - x_1)$ $y_1 = f(x_1) = f(1) = (1)^4 - 6(1)^2 + 10 = 5$

$y - 5 = -8(x - 1)$ $m = f'(x_1) = f'(1) = 4(1)^3 - 12(1) = -8$

$y = -8x + 13$ Tangent line at $x = 1$

(C) Since a horizontal line has 0 slope, we must solve $f'(x) = 0$ for x:

$$f'(x) = 4x^3 - 12x = 0 \qquad \text{Factor } 4x \text{ out of each term.}$$

$$4x(x^2 - 3) = 0 \qquad \text{Factor the difference of two squares.}$$

$$4x(x + \sqrt{3})(x - \sqrt{3}) = 0 \qquad \text{Use the zero property.}$$

$$x = 0, -\sqrt{3}, \sqrt{3}$$

Matched Problem 8] Repeat Example 8 for $f(x) = x^4 - 8x^3 + 7$.

Exercises 2.5

Skills Warm-up Exercises

W   *In Problems 1–8, write the expression in the form x^n. (If necessary, review Section A.6).*

1. $\sqrt{x}$ **2.** $\sqrt[3]{x}$ **3.** $\dfrac{1}{x^5}$ **4.** $\dfrac{1}{x}$

5. $(x^4)^3$ **6.** $\dfrac{1}{(x^5)^2}$ **7.** $\dfrac{1}{\sqrt[4]{x}}$ **8.** $\dfrac{1}{\sqrt[5]{x}}$

Find the indicated derivatives in Problems 9–26.

9. $f'(x)$ for $f(x) = 7$ **10.** $\dfrac{d}{dx} 3$

11. $\dfrac{dy}{dx}$ for $y = x^9$ **12.** y' for $y = x^6$

13. $\dfrac{d}{dx} x^3$ **14.** $g'(x)$ for $g(x) = x^5$

15. y' for $y = x^{-4}$ **16.** $\dfrac{dy}{dx}$ for $y = x^{-8}$

17. $g'(x)$ for $g(x) = x^{8/3}$ **18.** $f'(x)$ for $f(x) = x^{9/2}$

19. $\dfrac{dy}{dx}$ for $y = \dfrac{1}{x^{10}}$ **20.** y' for $y = \dfrac{1}{x^{12}}$

21. $f'(x)$ for $f(x) = 5x^2$ **22.** $\dfrac{d}{dx}(-2x^3)$

23. y' for $y = 0.4x^7$

24. $f'(x)$ for $f(x) = 0.8x^4$

25. $\dfrac{d}{dx}\left(\dfrac{x^3}{18}\right)$ **26.** $\dfrac{dy}{dx}$ for $y = \dfrac{x^5}{25}$

Problems 27–32 refer to functions f and g that satisfy $f'(2) = 3$ and $g'(2) = -1$. In each problem, find $h'(2)$ for the indicated function h.

27. $h(x) = 4f(x)$ **28.** $h(x) = 5g(x)$

29. $h(x) = f(x) + g(x)$ **30.** $h(x) = g(x) - f(x)$

31. $h(x) = 2f(x) - 3g(x) + 7$

32. $h(x) = -4f(x) + 5g(x) - 9$

Find the indicated derivatives in Problems 33–56.

33. $\dfrac{d}{dx}(2x - 5)$ **34.** $\dfrac{d}{dx}(-4x + 9)$

35. $f'(t)$ if $f(t) = 2t^2 - 3t + 1$

36. $\dfrac{dy}{dt}$ if $y = 2 + 5t - 8t^3$

37. y' for $y = 5x^{-2} + 9x^{-1}$

38. $g'(x)$ if $g(x) = 5x^{-7} - 2x^{-4}$

39. $\dfrac{d}{du}(5u^{0.3} - 4u^{2.2})$

40. $\dfrac{d}{du}(2u^{4.5} - 3.1u + 13.2)$

41. $h'(t)$ if $h(t) = 2.1 + 0.5t - 1.1t^3$

42. $F'(t)$ if $F(t) = 0.2t^3 - 3.1t + 13.2$

43. y' if $y = \dfrac{2}{5x^4}$

44. w' if $w = \dfrac{7}{5u^2}$

45. $\dfrac{d}{dx}\left(\dfrac{3x^2}{2} - \dfrac{7}{5x^2}\right)$

46. $\dfrac{d}{dx}\left(\dfrac{5x^3}{4} - \dfrac{2}{5x^3}\right)$

47. $G'(w)$ if $G(w) = \dfrac{5}{9w^4} + 5\sqrt[3]{w}$

48. $H'(w)$ if $H(w) = \dfrac{5}{w^6} - 2\sqrt{w}$

49. $\dfrac{d}{du}(3u^{2/3} - 5u^{1/3})$

50. $\dfrac{d}{du}(8u^{3/4} + 4u^{-1/4})$

51. $h'(t)$ if $h(t) = \dfrac{3}{t^{3/5}} - \dfrac{6}{t^{1/2}}$

52. $F'(t)$ if $F(t) = \dfrac{5}{t^{1/5}} - \dfrac{8}{t^{3/2}}$

53. y' if $y = \dfrac{1}{\sqrt[3]{x}}$

54. w' if $w = \dfrac{10}{\sqrt[5]{u}}$

55. $\dfrac{d}{dx}\left(\dfrac{1.2}{\sqrt{x}} - 3.2x^{-2} + x\right)$

56. $\dfrac{d}{dx}\left(2.8x^{-3} - \dfrac{0.6}{\sqrt[3]{x^2}} + 7\right)$

For Problems 57–60, find

(A) *$f'(x)$*

(B) *The slope of the graph of f at $x = 2$ and $x = 4$*

(C) *The equations of the tangent lines at $x = 2$ and $x = 4$*

(D) *The value(s) of x where the tangent line is horizontal*

57. $f(x) = 6x - x^2$ **58.** $f(x) = 2x^2 + 8x$

59. $f(x) = 3x^4 - 6x^2 - 7$ **60.** $f(x) = x^4 - 32x^2 + 10$

If an object moves along the y axis (marked in feet) so that its position at time x (in seconds) is given by the indicated functions in Problems 61–64, find

(A) *The instantaneous velocity function $v = f'(x)$*

(B) *The velocity when $x = 0$ and $x = 3$ seconds*

(C) *The time(s) when $v = 0$*

61. $f(x) = 176x - 16x^2$ **62.** $f(x) = 80x - 10x^2$

63. $f(x) = x^3 - 9x^2 + 15x$ **64.** $f(x) = x^3 - 9x^2 + 24x$

Problems 65–72 require the use of a graphing calculator. For each problem, find $f'(x)$ and approximate (to four decimal places) the value(s) of x where the graph of f has a horizontal tangent line.

65. $f(x) = x^2 - 3x - 4\sqrt{x}$

66. $f(x) = x^2 + x - 10\sqrt{x}$

67. $f(x) = 3\sqrt[3]{x^4} - 1.5x^2 - 3x$

68. $f(x) = 3\sqrt[3]{x^4} - 2x^2 + 4x$

69. $f(x) = 0.05x^4 + 0.1x^3 - 1.5x^2 - 1.6x + 3$

70. $f(x) = 0.02x^4 - 0.06x^3 - 0.78x^2 + 0.94x + 2.2$

71. $f(x) = 0.2x^4 - 3.12x^3 + 16.25x^2 - 28.25x + 7.5$

72. $f(x) = 0.25x^4 - 2.6x^3 + 8.1x^2 - 10x + 9$

73. Let $f(x) = ax^2 + bx + c, a \neq 0$. Recall that the graph of $y = f(x)$ is a parabola. Use the derivative $f'(x)$ to derive a formula for the x coordinate of the vertex of this parabola.

74. Now that you know how to find derivatives, explain why it is no longer necessary for you to memorize the formula for the x coordinate of the vertex of a parabola.

75. Give an example of a cubic polynomial function that has

(A) No horizontal tangents

(B) One horizontal tangent

(C) Two horizontal tangents

76. Can a cubic polynomial function have more than two horizontal tangents? Explain.

Find the indicated derivatives in Problems 77–82.

77. $f'(x)$ if $f(x) = (2x - 1)^2$

78. y' if $y = (2x - 5)^2$

79. $\dfrac{d}{dx}\dfrac{10x + 20}{x}$

80. $\dfrac{dy}{dx}$ if $y = \dfrac{x^2 + 25}{x^2}$

81. $\dfrac{dy}{dx}$ if $y = \dfrac{3x - 4}{12x^2}$

82. $f'(x)$ if $f(x) = \dfrac{2x^5 - 4x^3 + 2x}{x^3}$

In Problems 83–86, discuss the validity of each statement. If the statement is always true, explain why. If not, give a counterexample.

83. The derivative of a product is the product of the derivatives.

84. The derivative of a quotient is the quotient of the derivatives.

85. The derivative of a constant is 0.

86. The derivative of a constant times a function is 0.

87. Let $f(x) = u(x) + v(x)$, where $u'(x)$ and $v'(x)$ exist. Use the four-step process to show that $f'(x) = u'(x) + v'(x)$.

88. Let $f(x) = u(x) - v(x)$, where $u'(x)$ and $v'(x)$ exist. Use the four-step process to show that $f'(x) = u'(x) - v'(x)$.

Applications

89. Sales analysis. A company's total sales (in millions of dollars) t months from now are given by

$$S(t) = 0.03t^3 + 0.5t^2 + 2t + 3$$

(A) Find $S'(t)$.

(B) Find $S(5)$ and $S'(5)$ (to two decimal places). Write a brief verbal interpretation of these results.

(C) Find $S(10)$ and $S'(10)$ (to two decimal places). Write a brief verbal interpretation of these results.

90. Sales analysis. A company's total sales (in millions of dollars) t months from now are given by

$$S(t) = 0.015t^4 + 0.4t^3 + 3.4t^2 + 10t - 3$$

(A) Find $S'(t)$.

(B) Find $S(4)$ and $S'(4)$ (to two decimal places). Write a brief verbal interpretation of these results.

(C) Find $S(8)$ and $S'(8)$ (to two decimal places). Write a brief verbal interpretation of these results.

91. Advertising. A marine manufacturer will sell $N(x)$ power boats after spending $\$x$ thousand on advertising, as given by

$$N(x) = 1,000 - \frac{3,780}{x} \qquad 5 \le x \le 30$$

(see figure).

(A) Find $N'(x)$.

(B) Find $N'(10)$ and $N'(20)$. Write a brief verbal interpretation of these results.

92. Price–demand equation. Suppose that, in a given gourmet food store, people are willing to buy x pounds of chocolate candy per day at $\$p$ per quarter pound, as given by the price–demand equation

$$x = 10 + \frac{180}{p} \qquad 2 \le p \le 10$$

This function is graphed in the figure. Find the demand and the instantaneous rate of change of demand with respect to price when the price is $5. Write a brief verbal interpretation of these results.

93. College enrollment. The percentages of male high-school graduates who enrolled in college are given in the second column of Table 1.

Table 1 **College enrollment percentages**

Year	Male	Female
1970	41.0	25.5
1980	33.5	30.3
1990	40.0	38.3
2000	40.8	45.6
2010	45.9	50.5

(A) Let x represent time (in years) since 1970, and let y represent the corresponding percentage of male high-school graduates who enrolled in college. Enter the data in a graphing calculator and find a cubic regression equation for the data.

(B) If $y = M(x)$ denotes the regression equation found in part (A), find $M(50)$ and $M'(50)$ (to the nearest tenth), and write a brief verbal interpretation of these results.

94. College enrollment. The percentages of female high-school graduates who enrolled in college are given in the third column of Table 1.

(A) Let x represent time (in years) since 1970, and let y represent the corresponding percentage of female high-school graduates who enrolled in college. Enter the data in a graphing calculator and find a cubic regression equation for the data.

(B) If $y = F(x)$ denotes the regression equation found in part (A), find $F(50)$ and $F'(50)$ (to the nearest tenth), and write a brief verbal interpretation of these results.

95. Medicine. A person x inches tall has a pulse rate of y beats per minute, as given approximately by

$$y = 590x^{-1/2} \qquad 30 \le x \le 75$$

What is the instantaneous rate of change of pulse rate at the

(A) 36-inch level?

(B) 64-inch level?

96. Ecology. A coal-burning electrical generating plant emits sulfur dioxide into the surrounding air. The concentration $C(x)$, in parts per million, is given approximately by

$$C(x) = \frac{0.1}{x^2}$$

where x is the distance from the plant in miles. Find the instantaneous rate of change of concentration at

(A) $x = 1$ mile

(B) $x = 2$ miles

97. Learning. Suppose that a person learns y items in x hours, as given by

$$y = 50\sqrt{x} \qquad 0 \le x \le 9$$

(see figure). Find the rate of learning at the end of

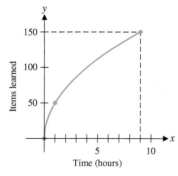

Time (hours)

(A) 1 hour

(B) 9 hours

98. Learning. If a person learns y items in x hours, as given by

$$y = 21\sqrt[3]{x^2} \qquad 0 \le x \le 8$$

find the rate of learning at the end of

(A) 1 hour

(B) 8 hours

Answers to Matched Problems

1. All are 0.

2. (A) $6x^5$ (B) $30x^{29}$

   (C) $-2t^{-3} = -2/t^3$ (D) $\frac{3}{2}x^{1/2}$

3. (A) $-x^{-2}$, or $-1/x^2$ (B) $\frac{2}{3}u^{-1/3}$, or $2/(3\sqrt[3]{u})$

   (C) $-\frac{1}{2}x^{-3/2}$, or $-1/(2\sqrt{x^3})$

4. (A) $20x^4$ (B) $t^3/3$

   (C) $-x^{-4}$, or $-1/x^4$ (D) $-0.3x^{-4/3}$, or $-0.3/\sqrt[3]{x^4}$

5. (A) $12x^3 - 6x^2 + 2x - 5$ (B) $14x^{-3}$, or $14/x^3$

   (C) $15v^2 - \frac{1}{4}v^{-3/4}$, or $15v^2 - 1/(4v^{3/4})$

   (D) $3/(4x^2) - (12/x^4) - (x^3/2)$

6. $f'(x) = -5x^{-2} + 4$

7. (A) $v = 3x^2 - 30x + 72$

   (B) $f'(2) = 24$ ft/s; $f'(5) = -3$ ft/s

   (C) $x = 4$ and $x = 6$ seconds

8. (A) $f'(x) = 4x^3 - 24x^2$ (B) $y = -20x + 20$

   (C) $x = 0$ and $x = 6$

2.6 Differentials

- Increments
- Differentials
- Approximations Using Differentials

In this section, we introduce increments and differentials. Increments are useful and they provide an alternative notation for defining the derivative. Differentials are often easier to compute than increments and can be used to approximate increments.

Increments

In Section 2.4, we defined the derivative of f at x as the limit of the difference quotient

$$f'(x) = \lim_{h \to 0} \frac{f(x + h) - f(x)}{h}$$

We considered various interpretations of this limit, including slope, velocity, and instantaneous rate of change. Increment notation enables us to interpret the numerator and denominator of the difference quotient separately.

Given $y = f(x) = x^3$, if x changes from 2 to 2.1, then y will change from $y = f(2) = 2^3 = 8$ to $y = f(2.1) = 2.1^3 = 9.261$. The change in x is called the *increment in x* and is denoted by Δx (read as "delta x").* Similarly, the change in y is called the *increment in y* and is denoted by Δy. In terms of the given example, we write

$$\Delta x = 2.1 - 2 = 0.1 \quad \text{Change in } x$$
$$\Delta y = f(2.1) - f(2) \quad f(x) = x^3$$
$$= 2.1^3 - 2^3 \quad \text{Use a calculator.}$$
$$= 9.261 - 8$$
$$= 1.261 \quad \text{Corresponding change in } y$$

> **CONCEPTUAL INSIGHT**
>
> The symbol Δx does not represent the product of Δ and x but is the symbol for a single quantity: the *change in x*. Likewise, the symbol Δy represents a single quantity: the *change in y*.

---

*Δ is the uppercase Greek letter delta.

DEFINITION Increments

For $y = f(x)$, $\quad \Delta x = x_2 - x_1$, $\quad$ so $\quad x_2 = x_1 + \Delta x$, and

$$\begin{aligned} \Delta y &= y_2 - y_1 \\ &= f(x_2) - f(x_1) \\ &= f(x_1 + \Delta x) - f(x_1) \end{aligned}$$

Δy represents the change in y corresponding to a change Δx in x.
Δx can be either positive or negative.

[**Note:** Δy depends on the function f, the input x_1, and the increment Δx.]

EXAMPLE 1 Increments Given the function $y = f(x) = \dfrac{x^2}{2}$,

(A) Find Δx, Δy, and $\Delta y / \Delta x$ for $x_1 = 1$ and $x_2 = 2$.

(B) Find $\dfrac{f(x_1 + \Delta x) - f(x_1)}{\Delta x}$ for $x_1 = 1$ and $\Delta x = 2$.

SOLUTION

(A) $\Delta x = x_2 - x_1 = 2 - 1 = 1$

$$\begin{aligned} \Delta y &= f(x_2) - f(x_1) \\ &= f(2) - f(1) = \frac{4}{2} - \frac{1}{2} = \frac{3}{2} \end{aligned}$$

$$\frac{\Delta y}{\Delta x} = \frac{f(x_2) - f(x_1)}{x_2 - x_1} = \frac{\frac{3}{2}}{1} = \frac{3}{2}$$

(B) $\dfrac{f(x_1 + \Delta x) - f(x_1)}{\Delta x} = \dfrac{f(1 + 2) - f(1)}{2}$

$$= \frac{f(3) - f(1)}{2} = \frac{\frac{9}{2} - \frac{1}{2}}{2} = \frac{4}{2} = 2$$

Matched Problem 1 Given the function $y = f(x) = x^2 + 1$,

(A) Find Δx, Δy, and $\Delta y / \Delta x$ for $x_1 = 2$ and $x_2 = 3$.

(B) Find $\dfrac{f(x_1 + \Delta x) - f(x_1)}{\Delta x}$ for $x_1 = 1$ and $\Delta x = 2$.

In Example 1, we observe another notation for the difference quotient

$$\frac{f(x + h) - f(x)}{h} \tag{1}$$

It is common to refer to h, the change in x, as Δx. Then the difference quotient (1) takes on the form

$$\frac{f(x + \Delta x) - f(x)}{\Delta x} \qquad \text{or} \qquad \frac{\Delta y}{\Delta x} \qquad \Delta y = f(x + \Delta x) - f(x)$$

and the derivative is defined by

$$f'(x) = \lim_{\Delta x \to 0} \frac{f(x + \Delta x) - f(x)}{\Delta x}$$

or

$$f'(x) = \lim_{\Delta x \to 0} \frac{\Delta y}{\Delta x} \qquad (2)$$

if the limit exists.

Explore and Discuss 1   Suppose that $y = f(x)$ defines a function whose domain is the set of all real numbers. If every increment Δy is equal to 0, then what is the range of f?

Differentials

Assume that the limit in equation (2) exists. Then, for small Δx, the difference quotient $\Delta y / \Delta x$ provides a good approximation for $f'(x)$. Also, $f'(x)$ provides a good approximation for $\Delta y / \Delta x$. We write

$$\frac{\Delta y}{\Delta x} \approx f'(x) \qquad \Delta x \text{ is small, but } \neq 0 \qquad (3)$$

Multiplying both sides of (3) by Δx gives us

$$\Delta y \approx f'(x) \, \Delta x \qquad \Delta x \text{ is small, but } \neq 0 \qquad (4)$$

From equation (4), we see that $f'(x) \Delta x$ provides a good approximation for Δy when Δx is small.

Because of the practical and theoretical importance of $f'(x) \, \Delta x$, we give it the special name **differential** and represent it with the special symbol dy or df:

$$dy = f'(x) \, \Delta x \qquad \text{or} \qquad df = f'(x) \, \Delta x$$

For example,

$$d(2x^3) = (2x^3)' \, \Delta x = 6x^2 \, \Delta x$$
$$d(x) = (x)' \, \Delta x = 1 \, \Delta x = \Delta x$$

In the second example, we usually drop the parentheses in $d(x)$ and simply write

$$dx = \Delta x$$

In summary, we have the following:

DEFINITION   Differentials

If $y = f(x)$ defines a differentiable function, then the **differential dy, or df**, is defined as the product of $f'(x)$ and dx, where $dx = \Delta x$. Symbolically,

$$dy = f'(x) \, dx, \qquad \text{or} \qquad df = f'(x) \, dx$$

where

$$dx = \Delta x$$

Note: The differential dy (or df) is actually a function involving two independent variables, x and dx. A change in either one or both will affect dy (or df).

EXAMPLE 2 Differentials Find dy for $f(x) = x^2 + 3x$. Evaluate dy for

(A) $x = 2$ and $dx = 0.1$

(B) $x = 3$ and $dx = 0.1$

(C) $x = 1$ and $dx = 0.02$

SOLUTION

$dy = f'(x)\, dx$

$\quad = (2x + 3)\, dx$

(A) When $x = 2$ and $dx = 0.1$, $\qquad$ (B) When $x = 3$ and $dx = 0.1$,

$\qquad dy = \big[2(2) + 3\big]0.1 = 0.7$ $\qquad\qquad dy = \big[2(3) + 3\big]0.1 = 0.9$

(C) When $x = 1$ and $dx = 0.02$,

$\qquad dy = \big[2(1) + 3\big]0.02 = 0.1$

Matched Problem 2 Find dy for $f(x) = \sqrt{x} + 3$. Evaluate dy for

(A) $x = 4$ and $dx = 0.1$

(B) $x = 9$ and $dx = 0.12$

(C) $x = 1$ and $dx = 0.01$

We now have two interpretations of the symbol dy/dx. Referring to the function $y = f(x) = x^2 + 3x$ in Example 2 with $x = 2$ and $dx = 0.1$, we have

$$\frac{dy}{dx} = f'(2) = 7 \quad \text{Derivative}$$

and

$$\frac{dy}{dx} = \frac{0.7}{0.1} = 7 \quad \text{Ratio of differentials}$$

Approximations Using Differentials

Earlier, we noted that for small Δx,

$$\frac{\Delta y}{\Delta x} \approx f'(x) \quad \text{and} \quad \Delta y \approx f'(x)\,\Delta x$$

Also, since

$$dy = f'(x)\, dx$$

it follows that

$$\Delta y \approx dy$$

and dy can be used to approximate Δy.

To interpret this result geometrically, we need to recall a basic property of the slope. The vertical change in a line is equal to the product of the slope and the horizontal change, as shown in Figure 1 on page 160.

Now consider the line tangent to the graph of $y = f(x)$, as shown in Figure 2 on page 160. Since $f'(x)$ is the slope of the tangent line and dx is the horizontal change in the tangent line, it follows that the vertical change in the tangent line is given by $dy = f'(x)\, dx$, as indicated in Figure 2.

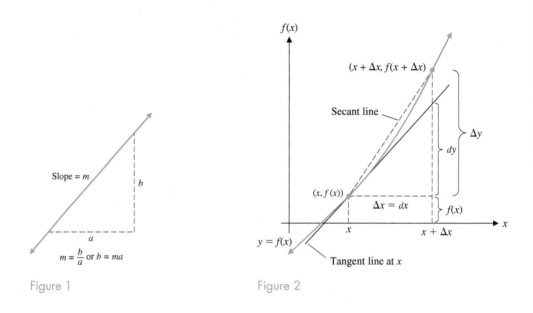

Figure 1

Figure 2

EXAMPLE 3   Comparing Increments and Differentials   Let $y = f(x) = 6x - x^2$.
(A) Find Δy and dy when $x = 2$.
(B) Compare Δy and dy from part (A) for $\Delta x = 0.1, 0.2$, and 0.3.

SOLUTION
(A) $\Delta y = f(2 + \Delta x) - f(2)$
$\qquad = 6(2 + \Delta x) - (2 + \Delta x)^2 - (6 \cdot 2 - 2^2)$ Remove parentheses.
$\qquad = 12 + 6\Delta x - 4 - 4\Delta x - \Delta x^2 - 12 + 4$ Collect like terms.
$\qquad = 2\Delta x - \Delta x^2$

Since $f'(x) = 6 - 2x, f'(2) = 2$, and $dx = \Delta x, dy = f'(2) \, dx = 2\Delta x$
(B) Table 1 compares the values of Δx and dy for the indicated values of Δx.

Table 1

Δx	Δy	dy
0.1	0.19	0.2
0.2	0.36	0.4
0.3	0.51	0.6

Matched Problem 3   Repeat Example 3 for $x = 4$ and $\Delta x = dx = -0.1, -0.2$,
and -0.3.

EXAMPLE 4   Cost–Revenue   A company manufactures and sells x transistor
radios per week. If the weekly cost and revenue equations are

$$C(x) = 5,000 + 2x \qquad R(x) = 10x - \frac{x^2}{1,000} \qquad 0 \le x \le 8,000$$

then use differentials to approximate the changes in revenue and profit if production is increased from 2,000 to 2,010 units per week.

SOLUTION   We will approximate ΔR and ΔP with dR and dP, respectively, using
$x = 2,000$ and $dx = 2,010 - 2,000 = 10$.

$$R(x) = 10x - \frac{x^2}{1,000}$$

$$P(x) = R(x) - C(x) = 10x - \frac{x^2}{1,000} - 5,000 - 2x$$

$$= 8x - \frac{x^2}{1,000} - 5,000$$

$$dR = R'(x)\,dx$$

$$dP = P'(x)\,dx$$

$$= \left(10 - \frac{x}{500}\right)dx$$

$$= \left(8 - \frac{x}{500}\right)dx$$

$$= \left(10 - \frac{2,000}{500}\right)10$$

$$= \left(8 - \frac{2,000}{500}\right)10$$

$$= \$60 \text{ per week}$$

$$= \$40 \text{ per week}$$

Matched Problem 4 Repeat Example 4 with production increasing from 6,000 to 6,010.

Comparing the results in Example 4 and Matched Problem 4, we see that an increase in production results in a revenue and profit increase at the 2,000 production level but a revenue and profit loss at the 6,000 production level.

Exercises 2.6

Skills Warm-up Exercises

W In Problems 1–4, let $f(x) = 0.1x + 3$ and find the given values without using a calculator. (If necessary, review Section 1.1.)

1. $f(0)$; $f(0.1)$

2. $f(7)$; $f(7.1)$

3. $f(-2)$; $f(-2.01)$

4. $f(-10)$; $f(-10.01)$

In Problems 5–8, let $g(x) = x^2$ and find the given values without using a calculator.

5. $g(0)$; $g(0.1)$

6. $g(1)$; $g(1.1)$

7. $g(10)$; $g(10.1)$

8. $g(5)$; $g(4.9)$

In Problems 9–14, find the indicated quantities for $y = f(x) = 3x^2$.

9. Δx, Δy, and $\Delta y/\Delta x$; given $x_1 = 1$ and $x_2 = 4$

10. Δx, Δy, and $\Delta y/\Delta x$; given $x_1 = 2$ and $x_2 = 5$

11. $\dfrac{f(x_1 + \Delta x) - f(x_1)}{\Delta x}$; given $x_1 = 1$ and $\Delta x = 2$

12. $\dfrac{f(x_1 + \Delta x) - f(x_1)}{\Delta x}$; given $x_1 = 2$ and $\Delta x = 1$

13. $\Delta y/\Delta x$; given $x_1 = 1$ and $x_2 = 3$

14. $\Delta y/\Delta x$; given $x_1 = 2$ and $x_2 = 3$

In Problems 15–20, find dy for each function.

15. $y = 30 + 12x^2 - x^3$

16. $y = 200x - \dfrac{x^2}{30}$

17. $y = x^2\left(1 - \dfrac{x}{9}\right)$

18. $y = x^3(60 - x)$

19. $y = \dfrac{590}{\sqrt{x}}$

20. $y = 52\sqrt{x}$

In Problems 21 and 22, find the indicated quantities for $y = f(x) = 3x^2$.

21. (A) $\dfrac{f(2 + \Delta x) - f(2)}{\Delta x}$ (simplify)

(B) What does the quantity in part (A) approach as Δx approaches 0?

22. (A) $\dfrac{f(3 + \Delta x) - f(3)}{\Delta x}$ (simplify)

(B) What does the quantity in part (A) approach as Δx approaches 0?

In Problems 23–26, find dy for each function.

23. $y = (2x + 1)^2$

24. $y = (3x + 5)^2$

25. $y = \dfrac{x^2 + 9}{x}$

26. $y = \dfrac{(x - 1)^2}{x^2}$

In Problems 27–30, evaluate dy and Δy for each function for the indicated values.

27. $y = f(x) = x^2 - 3x + 2$; $x = 5$, $dx = \Delta x = 0.2$

28. $y = f(x) = 30 + 12x^2 - x^3$; $x = 2$, $dx = \Delta x = 0.1$

29. $y = f(x) = 75\left(1 - \dfrac{2}{x}\right)$; $x = 5$, $dx = \Delta x = -0.5$

30. $y = f(x) = 100\left(x - \dfrac{4}{x^2}\right)$; $x = 2$, $dx = \Delta x = -0.1$

31. A cube with 10-inch sides is covered with a coat of fiberglass 0.2 inch thick. Use differentials to estimate the volume of the fiberglass shell.

32. A sphere with a radius of 5 centimeters is coated with ice 0.1 centimeter thick. Use differentials to estimate the volume of the ice. $\left[\text{Recall that } V = \frac{4}{3}\pi r^3.\right]$

In Problems 33–36,

(A) Find Δy and dy for the function f at the indicated value of x.

(B) Graph Δy and dy from part (A) as functions of Δx.

(C) Compare the values of Δy and dy from part (A) at the indicated values of Δx.

33. $f(x) = x^2 + 2x + 3; x = -0.5, \Delta x = dx = 0.1, 0.2, 0.3$

34. $f(x) = x^2 + 2x + 3; x = -2, \Delta x = dx = -0.1, -0.2, -0.3$

35. $f(x) = x^3 - 2x^2; x = 1, \Delta x = dx = 0.05, 0.10, 0.15$

36. $f(x) = x^3 - 2x^2; x = 2, \Delta x = dx = -0.05, -0.10, -0.15$

In Problems 37–40, discuss the validity of each statement. If the statement is always true, explain why. If not, give a counterexample.

37. If the graph of the function $y = f(x)$ is a line, then the functions Δy and dy (of the independent variable $\Delta x = dx$) for $f(x)$ at $x = 3$ are identical.

38. If the graph of the function $y = f(x)$ is a parabola, then the functions Δy and dy (of the independent variable $\Delta x = dx$) for $f(x)$ at $x = 0$ are identical.

39. Suppose that $y = f(x)$ defines a differentiable function whose domain is the set of all real numbers. If every differential dy at $x = 2$ is equal to 0, then $f(x)$ is a constant function.

40. Suppose that $y = f(x)$ defines a function whose domain is the set of all real numbers. If every increment at $x = 2$ is equal to 0, then $f(x)$ is a constant function.

41. Find dy if $y = (1 - 2x)\sqrt[3]{x^2}$.

42. Find dy if $y = (2x^2 - 4)\sqrt{x}$.

43. Find dy and Δy for $y = 52\sqrt{x}, x = 4$, and $\Delta x = dx = 0.3$.

44. Find dy and Δy for $y = 590/\sqrt{x}, x = 64$, and $\Delta x = dx = 1$.

Applications

Use differential approximations in the following problems.

45. Advertising. A company will sell N units of a product after spending $\$x$ thousand in advertising, as given by

$$N = 60x - x^2 \qquad 5 \le x \le 30$$

Approximately what increase in sales will result by increasing the advertising budget from $10,000 to $11,000? From $20,000 to $21,000?

46. Price–demand. Suppose that the daily demand (in pounds) for chocolate candy at $\$x$ per pound is given by

$$D = 1,000 - 40x^2 \qquad 1 \le x \le 5$$

If the price is increased from $3.00 per pound to $3.20 per pound, what is the approximate change in demand?

47. Average cost. For a company that manufactures tennis rackets, the average cost per racket $\overline{C}$ is

$$\overline{C} = \frac{400}{x} + 5 + \frac{1}{2}x \qquad x \ge 1$$

where x is the number of rackets produced per hour. What will the approximate change in average cost per racket be if production is increased from 20 per hour to 25 per hour? From 40 per hour to 45 per hour?

48. Revenue and profit. A company manufactures and sells x televisions per month. If the cost and revenue equations are

$$C(x) = 72,000 + 60x$$

$$R(x) = 200x - \frac{x^2}{30} \qquad 0 \le x \le 6,000$$

what will the approximate changes in revenue and profit be if production is increased from 1,500 to 1,510? From 4,500 to 4,510?

49. Pulse rate. The average pulse rate y (in beats per minute) of a healthy person x inches tall is given approximately by

$$y = \frac{590}{\sqrt{x}} \qquad 30 \le x \le 75$$

Approximately how will the pulse rate change for a change in height from 36 to 37 inches? From 64 to 65 inches?

50. Measurement. An egg of a particular bird is nearly spherical. If the radius to the inside of the shell is 5 millimeters and the radius to the outside of the shell is 5.3 millimeters, approximately what is the volume of the shell? [Remember that $V = \frac{4}{3}\pi r^3$.]

51. Medicine. A drug is given to a patient to dilate her arteries. If the radius of an artery is increased from 2 to 2.1 millimeters, approximately how much is the cross-sectional area increased? [Assume that the cross section of the artery is circular; that is, $A = \pi r^2$.]

52. Drug sensitivity. One hour after x milligrams of a particular drug are given to a person, the change in body temperature T (in degrees Fahrenheit) is given by

$$T = x^2\left(1 - \frac{x}{9}\right) \qquad 0 \le x \le 6$$

Approximate the changes in body temperature produced by the following changes in drug dosages:

(A) From 2 to 2.1 milligrams

(B) From 3 to 3.1 milligrams

(C) From 4 to 4.1 milligrams

53. Learning. A particular person learning to type has an achievement record given approximately by

$$N = 75\left(1 - \frac{2}{t}\right) \qquad 3 \le t \le 20$$

where N is the number of words per minute typed after t weeks of practice. What is the approximate improvement from 5 to 5.5 weeks of practice?

54. Learning. If a person learns y items in x hours, as given approximately by

$$y = 52\sqrt{x} \qquad 0 \leq x \leq 9$$

what is the approximate increase in the number of items learned when x changes from 1 to 1.1 hours? From 4 to 4.1 hours?

55. Politics. In a new city, the voting population (in thousands) is given by

$$N(t) = 30 + 12t^2 - t^3 \qquad 0 \leq t \leq 8$$

where t is time in years. Find the approximate change in votes for the following changes in time:

(A) From 1 to 1.1 years

(B) From 4 to 4.1 years

(C) From 7 to 7.1 years

Answers to Matched Problems

1. (A) $\Delta x = 1, \Delta y = 5, \Delta y / \Delta x = 5$ (B) 4

2. $dy = \dfrac{1}{2\sqrt{x}}\,dx$

   (A) 0.025   (B) 0.02   (C) 0.005

3. (A) $\Delta y = -2\Delta x - \Delta x^2; dy = -2\Delta x$

   (B)

Δx	Δy	dy
-0.1	0.19	0.2
-0.2	0.36	0.4
-0.3	0.51	0.6

4. $dR = -\$20/\text{wk}; dP = -\$40/\text{wk}$

2.7 Marginal Analysis in Business and Economics

- Marginal Cost, Revenue, and Profit
- Application
- Marginal Average Cost, Revenue, and Profit

Marginal Cost, Revenue, and Profit

One important application of calculus to business and economics involves *marginal analysis*. In economics, the word *marginal* refers to a rate of change—that is, to a derivative. Thus, if $C(x)$ is the total cost of producing x items, then $C'(x)$ is called the *marginal cost* and represents the instantaneous rate of change of total cost with respect to the number of items produced. Similarly, the *marginal revenue* is the derivative of the total revenue function, and the *marginal profit* is the derivative of the total profit function.

DEFINITION Marginal Cost, Revenue, and Profit
If x is the number of units of a product produced in some time interval, then

$$\text{total cost} = C(x)$$
$$\textbf{marginal cost} = C'(x)$$
$$\text{total revenue} = R(x)$$
$$\textbf{marginal revenue} = R'(x)$$
$$\text{total profit} = P(x) = R(x) - C(x)$$
$$\textbf{marginal profit} = P'(x) = R'(x) - C'(x)$$
$$= (\text{marginal revenue}) - (\text{marginal cost})$$

Marginal cost (or revenue or profit) is the instantaneous rate of change of cost (or revenue or profit) relative to production at a given production level.

To begin our discussion, we consider a cost function $C(x)$. It is important to remember that $C(x)$ represents the *total* cost of producing x items, not the cost of producing a *single* item. To find the cost of producing a single item, we use the difference of two successive values of $C(x)$:

$$\text{Total cost of producing } x + 1 \text{ items} = C(x + 1)$$
$$\text{Total cost of producing } x \text{ items} = C(x)$$
$$\text{Exact cost of producing the } (x + 1)\text{st item} = C(x + 1) - C(x)$$

EXAMPLE 1   Cost Analysis A company manufactures fuel tanks for cars. The total weekly cost (in dollars) of producing x tanks is given by

$$C(x) = 10,000 + 90x - 0.05x^2$$

(A) Find the marginal cost function.

(B) Find the marginal cost at a production level of 500 tanks per week.

(C) Interpret the results of part (B).

(D) Find the exact cost of producing the 501st item.

SOLUTION

(A) $C'(x) = 90 - 0.1x$

(B) $C'(500) = 90 - 0.1(500) = \$40$ Marginal cost

(C) At a production level of 500 tanks per week, the total production costs are increasing at the rate of $40 per tank.

(D)
$$C(501) = 10,000 + 90(501) - 0.05(501)^2$$
$$= \$42,539.95 \quad \text{Total cost of producing 501 tanks per week}$$
$$C(500) = 10,000 + 90(500) - 0.05(500)^2$$
$$= \$42,500.00 \quad \text{Total cost of producing 500 tanks per week}$$
$$C(501) - C(500) = 42,539.95 - 42,500.00$$
$$= \$39.95 \quad \text{Exact cost of producing the 501st tank}$$

Matched Problem 1 A company manufactures automatic transmissions for cars. The total weekly cost (in dollars) of producing x transmissions is given by

$$C(x) = 50,000 + 600x - 0.75x^2$$

(A) Find the marginal cost function.

(B) Find the marginal cost at a production level of 200 transmissions per week.

(C) Interpret the results of part (B).

(D) Find the exact cost of producing the 201st transmission.

In Example 1, we found that the cost of the 501st tank and the marginal cost at a production level of 500 tanks differ by only a nickel. Increments and differentials will help us understand the relationship between marginal cost and the cost of a single item. If $C(x)$ is any total cost function, then

$$C'(x) \approx \frac{C(x + \Delta x) - C(x)}{\Delta x} \qquad \text{See Section 2.6}$$
$$C'(x) \approx C(x + 1) - C(x) \qquad \Delta x = 1$$

We see that the marginal cost $C'(x)$ approximates $C(x + 1) - C(x)$, the exact cost of producing the $(x + 1)$st item. These observations are summarized next and are illustrated in Figure 1.

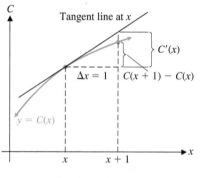

Figure 1 $C'(x) \approx C(x + 1) - C(x)$

THEOREM 1 Marginal Cost and Exact Cost

If $C(x)$ is the total cost of producing x items, then the marginal cost function approximates the exact cost of producing the $(x + 1)$st item:

Marginal cost   Exact cost

$$C'(x) \approx C(x + 1) - C(x)$$

Similar statements can be made for total revenue functions and total profit functions.

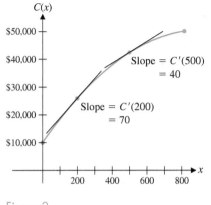

Figure 2
$C(x) = 10,000 + 90x - 0.05x^2$

Theorem 1 states that the marginal cost at a given production level x approximates the cost of producing the $(x + 1)$st, or *next,* item. In practice, the marginal cost is used more frequently than the exact cost. One reason for this is that the marginal cost is easily visualized when one is examining the graph of the total cost function. Figure 2 shows the graph of the cost function discussed in Example 1, with tangent lines added at $x = 200$ and $x = 500$. The graph clearly shows that as production increases, the slope of the tangent line decreases. Thus, the cost of producing the next tank also decreases, a desirable characteristic of a total cost function. We will have much more to say about graphical analysis in Chapter 4.

EXAMPLE 2 Exact Cost and Marginal Cost The total cost of producing x bicycles is given by the cost function

$$C(x) = 10,000 + 150x - 0.2x^2$$

(A) Find the exact cost of producing the 121st bicycle.

(B) Use marginal cost to approximate the cost of producing the 121st bicycle.

SOLUTION

(A) The cost of producing 121 bicycles is

$$C(121) = 10,000 + 150(121) - 0.2(121)^2 = \$25,221.80$$

and the cost of producing 120 bicycles is

$$C(120) = 10,000 + 150(120) - 0.2(120)^2 = \$25,120.00$$

So the exact cost of producing the 121st bicycle is

$$C(121) - C(120) = \$25,221.80 - 25,120.00 = \$101.80$$

(B) By Theorem 1, the marginal cost function $C'(x)$, evaluated at $x = 120$, approximates the cost of producing the 121st bicycle:

$$C'(x) = 150 - 0.4x$$
$$C'(120) = 150 - 0.4(120) = \$102.00$$

Note that the marginal cost, $102.00, at a production level of 120 bicycles, is a good approximation to the exact cost, $101.80, of producing the 121st bicycle.

Matched Problem 2 For the cost function $C(x)$ in Example 2

(A) Find the exact cost of producing the 141st bicycle.

(B) Use marginal cost to approximate the cost of producing the 141st bicycle.

Application

Now we discuss how price, demand, revenue, cost, and profit are tied together in typical applications. Although either price or demand can be used as the independent variable in a price–demand equation, it is common to use demand as the independent variable when marginal revenue, cost, and profit are also involved.

EXAMPLE 3 Production Strategy A company's market research department recommends the manufacture and marketing of a new headphone set for MP3 players. After suitable test marketing, the research department presents the following **price–demand equation:**

$$x = 10,000 - 1,000p \quad x \text{ is demand at price } p. \tag{1}$$

In the price–demand equation (1), the demand x is given as a function of price p. By solving (1) for p (add $1,000p$ to both sides of the equation, subtract x from both sides, and divide both sides by 1,000), we obtain equation (2), in which the price p is given as a function of demand x:

$$p = 10 - 0.001x \qquad (2)$$

where x is the number of headphones that retailers are likely to buy at $\$p$ per set.

The financial department provides the **cost function**

$$C(x) = 7,000 + 2x \qquad (3)$$

where $\$7,000$ is the estimate of fixed costs (tooling and overhead) and $\$2$ is the estimate of variable costs per headphone set (materials, labor, marketing, transportation, storage, etc.).

(A) Find the domain of the function defined by the price–demand equation (2).

(B) Find and interpret the marginal cost function $C'(x)$.

(C) Find the revenue function as a function of x and find its domain.

(D) Find the marginal revenue at $x = 2,000$, $5,000$, and $7,000$. Interpret these results.

(E) Graph the cost function and the revenue function in the same coordinate system. Find the intersection points of these two graphs and interpret the results.

(F) Find the profit function and its domain and sketch the graph of the function.

(G) Find the marginal profit at $x = 1,000$, $4,000$, and $6,000$. Interpret these results.

SOLUTION

(A) Since price p and demand x must be nonnegative, we have $x \geq 0$ and

$$p = 10 - 0.001x \geq 0$$
$$10 \geq 0.001x$$
$$10,000 \geq x$$

Thus, the permissible values of x are $0 \leq x \leq 10,000$.

(B) The marginal cost is $C'(x) = 2$. Since this is a constant, it costs an additional $\$2$ to produce one more headphone set at any production level.

(C) The **revenue** is the amount of money R received by the company for manufacturing and selling x headphone sets at $\$p$ per set and is given by

$$R = (\text{number of headphone sets sold})(\text{price per headphone set}) = xp$$

In general, the revenue R can be expressed as a function of p using equation (1) or as a function of x using equation (2). As we mentioned earlier, when using marginal functions, we will always use the number of items x as the independent variable. Thus, the **revenue function** is

$$R(x) = xp = x(10 - 0.001x) \quad \text{Using equation (2)} \qquad (4)$$
$$= 10x - 0.001x^2$$

Since equation (2) is defined only for $0 \leq x \leq 10,000$, it follows that the domain of the revenue function is $0 \leq x \leq 10,000$.

(D) The **marginal revenue** is

$$R'(x) = 10 - 0.002x$$

For production levels of $x = 2,000$, $5,000$, and $7,000$, we have

$$R'(2,000) = 6 \qquad R'(5,000) = 0 \qquad R'(7,000) = -4$$

This means that at production levels of 2,000, 5,000, and 7,000, the respective approximate changes in revenue per unit change in production are $\$6$, $\$0$, and $-\$4$. That is, at the 2,000 output level, revenue increases as production increases; at the 5,000 output level, revenue does not change with a "small" change in production; and at the 7,000 output level, revenue decreases with an increase in production.

(E) Graphing $R(x)$ and $C(x)$ in the same coordinate system results in Figure 3 on page 168. The intersection points are called the **break-even points**, because revenue equals cost at these production levels. The company neither makes nor loses money, but just breaks even. The break-even points are obtained as follows:

$$C(x) = R(x)$$
$$7,000 + 2x = 10x - 0.001x^2$$
$$0.001x^2 - 8x + 7,000 = 0 \quad \text{Solve by the quadratic formula}$$
$$x^2 - 8,000x + 7,000,000 = 0 \quad \text{(see Appendix A.7).}$$
$$x = \frac{8,000 \pm \sqrt{8,000^2 - 4(7,000,000)}}{2}$$
$$= \frac{8,000 \pm \sqrt{36,000,000}}{2}$$
$$= \frac{8,000 \pm 6,000}{2}$$
$$= 1,000, \quad 7,000$$
$$R(1,000) = 10(1,000) - 0.001(1,000)^2 = 9,000$$
$$C(1,000) = 7,000 + 2(1,000) = 9,000$$
$$R(7,000) = 10(7,000) - 0.001(7,000)^2 = 21,000$$
$$C(7,000) = 7,000 + 2(7,000) = 21,000$$

The break-even points are (1,000, 9,000) and (7,000, 21,000), as shown in Figure 3. Further examination of the figure shows that cost is greater than revenue for production levels between 0 and 1,000 and also between 7,000 and 10,000. Consequently, the company incurs a loss at these levels. By contrast, for production levels between 1,000 and 7,000, revenue is greater than cost, and the company makes a profit.

(F) The **profit function** is

$$P(x) = R(x) - C(x)$$
$$= (10x - 0.001x^2) - (7,000 + 2x)$$
$$= -0.001x^2 + 8x - 7,000$$

The domain of the cost function is $x \geq 0$, and the domain of the revenue function is $0 \leq x \leq 10,000$. The domain of the profit function is the set of x values for which both functions are defined—that is, $0 \leq x \leq 10,000$. The graph of the profit function is shown in Figure 4 on page 168. Notice that the x coordinates of the break-even points in Figure 3 are the x intercepts of the profit function. Furthermore, the intervals on which cost is greater than revenue and on which revenue is greater than cost correspond, respectively, to the intervals on which profit is negative and on which profit is positive.

(G) The **marginal profit** is

$$P'(x) = -0.002x + 8$$

For production levels of 1,000, 4,000, and 6,000, we have

$$P'(1,000) = 6 \qquad P'(4,000) = 0 \qquad P'(6,000) = -4$$

This means that at production levels of 1,000, 4,000, and 6,000, the respective approximate changes in profit per unit change in production are $6, $0, and −$4. That is, at the 1,000 output level, profit will be increased if production is increased; at the 4,000 output level, profit does not change for "small" changes in production;

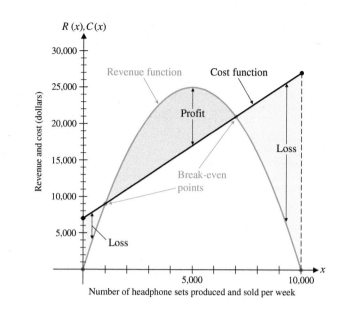

Figure 3

and at the 6,000 output level, profits will decrease if production is increased. It seems that the best production level to produce a maximum profit is 4,000.

Example 3 requires careful study since a number of important ideas in economics and calculus are involved. In the next chapter, we will develop a systematic procedure for finding the production level (and, using the demand equation, the selling price) that will maximize profit.

Matched Problem 3   Refer to the revenue and profit functions in Example 3.

(A) Find $R'(3,000)$ and $R'(6,000)$. Interpret the results.

(B) Find $P'(2,000)$ and $P'(7,000)$. Interpret the results.

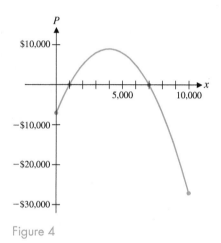

Figure 4

Marginal Average Cost, Revenue, and Profit

Sometimes it is desirable to carry out marginal analysis relative to **average cost (cost per unit), average revenue (revenue per unit),** and **average profit (profit per unit).**

DEFINITION   Marginal Average Cost, Revenue, and Profit

If x is the number of units of a product produced in some time interval, then

Cost per unit: average cost = $\overline{C}(x) = \dfrac{C(x)}{x}$

marginal average cost = $\overline{C}'(x) = \dfrac{d}{dx}\overline{C}(x)$

Revenue per unit: average revenue = $\overline{R}(x) = \dfrac{R(x)}{x}$

marginal average revenue = $\overline{R}'(x) = \dfrac{d}{dx}\overline{R}(x)$

Profit per unit: average profit = $\overline{P}(x) = \dfrac{P(x)}{x}$

marginal average profit = $\overline{P}'(x) = \dfrac{d}{dx}\overline{P}(x)$

EXAMPLE 4   Cost Analysis   A small machine shop manufactures drill bits used in the petroleum industry. The manager estimates that the total daily cost (in dollars) of producing x bits is

$$C(x) = 1{,}000 + 25x - 0.1x^2$$

(A) Find $\overline{C}(x)$ and $\overline{C}'(x)$.

(B) Find $\overline{C}(10)$ and $\overline{C}'(10)$. Interpret these quantities.

(C) Use the results in part (B) to estimate the average cost per bit at a production level of 11 bits per day.

SOLUTION

(A) $\overline{C}(x) = \dfrac{C(x)}{x} = \dfrac{1{,}000 + 25x - 0.1x^2}{x}$

$\qquad = \dfrac{1{,}000}{x} + 25 - 0.1x$ $\qquad\qquad$ Average cost function

$\overline{C}'(x) = \dfrac{d}{dx}\overline{C}(x) = -\dfrac{1{,}000}{x^2} - 0.1$ $\qquad$ Marginal average cost function

(B) $\overline{C}(10) = \dfrac{1{,}000}{10} + 25 - 0.1(10) = \$124$

$\overline{C}'(10) = -\dfrac{1{,}000}{10^2} - 0.1 = -\$10.10$

At a production level of 10 bits per day, the average cost of producing a bit is $124. This cost is decreasing at the rate of $10.10 per bit.

(C)   If production is increased by 1 bit, then the average cost per bit will decrease by approximately $10.10. So, the average cost per bit at a production level of 11 bits per day is approximately $124 - \$10.10 = \$113.90$.

Matched Problem 4   Consider the cost function for the production of headphone sets from Example 3: $\qquad C(x) = 7{,}000 + 2x$

(A) Find $\overline{C}(x)$ and $\overline{C}'(x)$.

(B) Find $\overline{C}(100)$ and $\overline{C}'(100)$. Interpret these quantities.

(C) Use the results in part (B) to estimate the average cost per headphone set at a production level of 101 headphone sets.

Explore and Discuss 1   A student produced the following solution to Matched Problem 4:

$$C(x) = 7{,}000 + 2x \qquad \text{Cost}$$
$$C'(x) = 2 \qquad\qquad\qquad \text{Marginal cost}$$
$$\dfrac{C'(x)}{x} = \dfrac{2}{x} \qquad\qquad \text{"Average" of the marginal cost}$$

Explain why the last function is not the same as the marginal average cost function.

⚠ **CAUTION**

1. The marginal average cost function is computed by first finding the average cost function and then finding its derivative. As Explore and Discuss 1 illustrates, reversing the order of these two steps produces a different function that does not have any useful economic interpretations.

2. Recall that the marginal cost function has two interpretations: the usual interpretation of any derivative as an instantaneous rate of change and the special interpretation as an approximation to the exact cost of the $(x + 1)$st item. This special interpretation does not apply to the marginal average cost function. Referring to Example 4, we would be incorrect to interpret $\overline{C}'(10) = -\$10.10$ to mean that the average cost of the next bit is approximately $-\$10.10$. In fact, the phrase "average cost of the next bit" does not even make sense. Averaging is a concept applied to a collection of items, not to a single item.

These remarks also apply to revenue and profit functions.   ▲

Exercises 2.7

Skills Warm-up Exercises

W   *In Problems 1–8, let $C(x) = 10,000 + 150x - 0.2x^2$ be the total cost in dollars of producing x bicycles. (If necessary, review Section 1–1).*

1. Find the total cost of producing 99 bicycles.

2. Find the total cost of producing 100 bicycles.

3. Find the cost of producing the 100th bicycle.

4. Find the total cost of producing 199 bicycles.

5. Find the total cost of producing 200 bicycles.

6. Find the cost of producing the 200th bicycle.

7. Find the average cost per bicycle of producing 100 bicycles.

8. Find the average cost per bicycle of producing 200 bicycles.

In Problems 9–12, find the marginal cost function.

9. $C(x) = 175 + 0.8x$ 10. $C(x) = 4,500 + 9.5x$

11. $C(x) = 210 + 4.6x - 0.01x^2$

12. $C(x) = 790 + 13x - 0.2x^2$

In Problems 13–16, find the marginal revenue function.

13. $R(x) = 4x - 0.01x^2$ 14. $R(x) = 36x - 0.03x^2$

15. $R(x) = x(12 - 0.04x)$ 16. $R(x) = x(25 - 0.05x)$

In Problems 17–20, find the marginal profit function if the cost and revenue, respectively, are those in the indicated problems.

17. Problem 9 and Problem 13

18. Problem 10 and Problem 14

19. Problem 11 and Problem 15

20. Problem 12 and Problem 16

In Problems 21–28, find the indicated function if cost and revenue are given by $C(x) = 145 + 1.1x$ and $R(x) = 5x - 0.02x^2$, respectively.

21. Average cost function

22. Average revenue function

23. Marginal average cost function

24. Marginal average revenue function

25. Profit function

26. Marginal profit function

27. Average profit function

28. Marginal average profit function

In Problems 29–32, discuss the validity of each statement. If the statement is always true, explain why. If not, give a counterexample.

29. If a cost function is linear, then the marginal cost is a constant.

30. If a price–demand equation is linear, then the marginal revenue function is linear.

31. Marginal profit is equal to marginal cost minus marginal revenue.

32. Marginal average cost is equal to average marginal cost.

Applications

33. Cost analysis. The total cost (in dollars) of producing x food processors is

$$C(x) = 2,000 + 50x - 0.5x^2$$

(A) Find the exact cost of producing the 21st food processor.

(B) Use marginal cost to approximate the cost of producing the 21st food processor.

34. Cost analysis. The total cost (in dollars) of producing x electric guitars is

$$C(x) = 1,000 + 100x - 0.25x^2$$

(A) Find the exact cost of producing the 51st guitar.

(B) Use marginal cost to approximate the cost of producing the 51st guitar.

35. Cost analysis. The total cost (in dollars) of manufacturing x auto body frames is

$$C(x) = 60,000 + 300x$$

(A) Find the average cost per unit if 500 frames are produced.

(B) Find the marginal average cost at a production level of 500 units and interpret the results.

(C) Use the results from parts (A) and (B) to estimate the average cost per frame if 501 frames are produced.

36. Cost analysis. The total cost (in dollars) of printing x dictionaries is

$$C(x) = 20,000 + 10x$$

(A) Find the average cost per unit if 1,000 dictionaries are produced.

(B) Find the marginal average cost at a production level of 1,000 units and interpret the results.

(C) Use the results from parts (A) and (B) to estimate the average cost per dictionary if 1,001 dictionaries are produced.

37. Profit analysis. The total profit (in dollars) from the sale of x skateboards is

$$P(x) = 30x - 0.3x^2 - 250 \qquad 0 \le x \le 100$$

(A) Find the exact profit from the sale of the 26th skateboard.

(B) Use marginal profit to approximate the profit from the sale of the 26th skateboard.

38. Profit analysis. The total profit (in dollars) from the sale of x calendars is

$$P(x) = 22x - 0.2x^2 - 400 \qquad 0 \le x \le 100$$

(A) Find the exact profit from the sale of the 41st calendar.

(B) Use the marginal profit to approximate the profit from the sale of the 41st calendar.

39. Profit analysis. The total profit (in dollars) from the sale of x DVDs is

$$P(x) = 5x - 0.005x^2 - 450 \qquad 0 \le x \le 1,000$$

Evaluate the marginal profit at the given values of x, and interpret the results.

(A) $x = 450$ (B) $x = 750$

40. Profit analysis. The total profit (in dollars) from the sale of x cameras is

$$P(x) = 12x - 0.02x^2 - 1,000 \qquad 0 \le x \le 600$$

Evaluate the marginal profit at the given values of x, and interpret the results.

(A) $x = 200$ (B) $x = 350$

41. Profit analysis. The total profit (in dollars) from the sale of x lawn mowers is

$$P(x) = 30x - 0.03x^2 - 750 \qquad 0 \le x \le 1,000$$

(A) Find the average profit per mower if 50 mowers are produced.

(B) Find the marginal average profit at a production level of 50 mowers and interpret the results.

(C) Use the results from parts (A) and (B) to estimate the average profit per mower if 51 mowers are produced.

42. Profit analysis. The total profit (in dollars) from the sale of x gas grills is

$$P(x) = 20x - 0.02x^2 - 320 \qquad 0 \le x \le 1,000$$

(A) Find the average profit per grill if 40 grills are produced.

(B) Find the marginal average profit at a production level of 40 grills and interpret the results.

(C) Use the results from parts (A) and (B) to estimate the average profit per grill if 41 grills are produced.

43. Revenue analysis. The price p (in dollars) and the demand x for a brand of running shoes are related by the equation

$$x = 4,000 - 40p$$

(A) Express the price p in terms of the demand x, and find the domain of this function.

(B) Find the revenue $R(x)$ from the sale of x pairs of running shoes. What is the domain of R?

(C) Find the marginal revenue at a production level of 1,600 pairs and interpret the results.

(D) Find the marginal revenue at a production level of 2,500 pairs, and interpret the results.

44. Revenue analysis. The price p (in dollars) and the demand x for a particular steam iron are related by the equation

$$x = 1,000 - 20p$$

(A) Express the price p in terms of the demand x, and find the domain of this function.

(B) Find the revenue $R(x)$ from the sale of x steam irons. What is the domain of R?

(C) Find the marginal revenue at a production level of 400 steam irons and interpret the results.

(D) Find the marginal revenue at a production level of 650 steam irons and interpret the results.

45. Revenue, cost, and profit. The price–demand equation and the cost function for the production of table saws are given, respectively, by

$$x = 6,000 - 30p \qquad \text{and} \qquad C(x) = 72,000 + 60x$$

where x is the number of saws that can be sold at a price of $\$p$ per saw and $C(x)$ is the total cost (in dollars) of producing x saws.

(A) Express the price p as a function of the demand x, and find the domain of this function.

(B) Find the marginal cost.

(C) Find the revenue function and state its domain.

(D) Find the marginal revenue.

(E) Find $R'(1,500)$ and $R'(4,500)$ and interpret these quantities.

(F) Graph the cost function and the revenue function on the same coordinate system for $0 \leq x \leq 6,000$. Find the break-even points, and indicate regions of loss and profit.

(G) Find the profit function in terms of x.

(H) Find the marginal profit.

(I) Find $P'(1,500)$ and $P'(3,000)$ and interpret these quantities.

46. Revenue, cost, and profit. The price–demand equation and the cost function for the production of HDTVs are given, respectively, by

$$x = 9,000 - 30p \quad \text{and} \quad C(x) = 150,000 + 30x$$

where x is the number of HDTVs that can be sold at a price of $\$p$ per TV and $C(x)$ is the total cost (in dollars) of producing x TVs.

(A) Express the price p as a function of the demand x, and find the domain of this function.

(B) Find the marginal cost.

(C) Find the revenue function and state its domain.

(D) Find the marginal revenue.

(E) Find $R'(3,000)$ and $R'(6,000)$ and interpret these quantities.

(F) Graph the cost function and the revenue function on the same coordinate system for $0 \leq x \leq 9,000$. Find the break-even points and indicate regions of loss and profit.

(G) Find the profit function in terms of x.

(H) Find the marginal profit.

(I) Find $P'(1,500)$ and $P'(4,500)$ and interpret these quantities.

47. Revenue, cost, and profit. A company is planning to manufacture and market a new two-slice electric toaster. After conducting extensive market surveys, the research department provides the following estimates: a weekly demand of 200 toasters at a price of $16 per toaster and a weekly demand of 300 toasters at a price of $14 per toaster. The financial department estimates that weekly fixed costs will be $1,400 and variable costs (cost per unit) will be $4.

(A) Assume that the relationship between price p and demand x is linear. Use the research department's estimates to express p as a function of x and find the domain of this function.

(B) Find the revenue function in terms of x and state its domain.

(C) Assume that the cost function is linear. Use the financial department's estimates to express the cost function in terms of x.

(D) Graph the cost function and revenue function on the same coordinate system for $0 \leq x \leq 1,000$. Find the break-even points and indicate regions of loss and profit.

(E) Find the profit function in terms of x.

(F) Evaluate the marginal profit at $x = 250$ and $x = 475$ and interpret the results.

48. Revenue, cost, and profit. The company in Problem 47 is also planning to manufacture and market a four-slice toaster. For this toaster, the research department's estimates are a weekly demand of 300 toasters at a price of $25 per toaster and a weekly demand of 400 toasters at a price of $20. The financial department's estimates are fixed weekly costs of $5,000 and variable costs of $5 per toaster.

(A) Assume that the relationship between price p and demand x is linear. Use the research department's estimates to express p as a function of x, and find the domain of this function.

(B) Find the revenue function in terms of x and state its domain.

(C) Assume that the cost function is linear. Use the financial department's estimates to express the cost function in terms of x.

(D) Graph the cost function and revenue function on the same coordinate system for $0 \leq x \leq 800$. Find the break-even points and indicate regions of loss and profit.

(E) Find the profit function in terms of x.

(F) Evaluate the marginal profit at $x = 325$ and $x = 425$ and interpret the results.

49. Revenue, cost, and profit. The total cost and the total revenue (in dollars) for the production and sale of x ski jackets are given, respectively, by

$$C(x) = 24x + 21,900 \quad \text{and} \quad R(x) = 200x - 0.2x^2$$
$$0 \leq x \leq 1,000$$

(A) Find the value of x where the graph of $R(x)$ has a horizontal tangent line.

(B) Find the profit function $P(x)$.

(C) Find the value of x where the graph of $P(x)$ has a horizontal tangent line.

(D) Graph $C(x)$, $R(x)$, and $P(x)$ on the same coordinate system for $0 \leq x \leq 1,000$. Find the break-even points. Find the x intercepts of the graph of $P(x)$.

50. Revenue, cost, and profit. The total cost and the total revenue (in dollars) for the production and sale of x hair dryers are given, respectively, by

$$C(x) = 5x + 2,340 \quad \text{and} \quad R(x) = 40x - 0.1x^2$$
$$0 \leq x \leq 400$$

(A) Find the value of x where the graph of $R(x)$ has a horizontal tangent line.

(B) Find the profit function $P(x)$.

(C) Find the value of x where the graph of $P(x)$ has a horizontal tangent line.

(D) Graph $C(x)$, $R(x)$, and $P(x)$ on the same coordinate system for $0 \leq x \leq 400$. Find the break-even points. Find the x intercepts of the graph of $P(x)$.

51. Break-even analysis. The price–demand equation and the cost function for the production of garden hoses are given, respectively, by

$$p = 20 - \sqrt{x} \quad \text{and} \quad C(x) = 500 + 2x$$

where x is the number of garden hoses that can be sold at a price of $\$p$ per unit and $C(x)$ is the total cost (in dollars) of producing x garden hoses.

(A) Express the revenue function in terms of x.

(B) Graph the cost function and revenue function in the same viewing window for $0 \leq x \leq 400$. Use approximation techniques to find the break-even points correct to the nearest unit.

52. Break-even analysis. The price–demand equation and the cost function for the production of handwoven silk scarves are given, respectively, by

$$p = 60 - 2\sqrt{x} \quad \text{and} \quad C(x) = 3,000 + 5x$$

where x is the number of scarves that can be sold at a price of $\$p$ per unit and $C(x)$ is the total cost (in dollars) of producing x scarves.

(A) Express the revenue function in terms of x.

(B) Graph the cost function and the revenue function in the same viewing window for $0 \leq x \leq 900$. Use approximation techniques to find the break-even points correct to the nearest unit.

53. Break-even analysis. Table 1 contains price–demand and total cost data for the production of projectors, where p is the wholesale price (in dollars) of a projector for an annual demand of x projectors and C is the total cost (in dollars) of producing x projectors.

Table 1

x	$p(\$)$	$C(\$)$
3,190	581	1,130,000
4,570	405	1,241,000
5,740	181	1,410,000
7,330	85	1,620,000

(A) Find a quadratic regression equation for the price–demand data, using x as the independent variable.

(B) Find a linear regression equation for the cost data, using x as the independent variable. Use this equation to estimate the fixed costs and variable costs per projector. Round answers to the nearest dollar.

(C) Find the break-even points. Round answers to the nearest integer.

(D) Find the price range for which the company will make a profit. Round answers to the nearest dollar.

54. Break-even analysis. Table 2 contains price–demand and total cost data for the production of treadmills, where p is the wholesale price (in dollars) of a treadmill for an annual demand of x treadmills and C is the total cost (in dollars) of producing x treadmills.

Table 2

x	$p(\$)$	$C(\$)$
2,910	1,435	3,650,000
3,415	1,280	3,870,000
4,645	1,125	4,190,000
5,330	910	4,380,000

(A) Find a linear regression equation for the price–demand data, using x as the independent variable.

(B) Find a linear regression equation for the cost data, using x as the independent variable. Use this equation to estimate the fixed costs and variable costs per treadmill. Round answers to the nearest dollar.

(C) Find the break-even points. Round answers to the nearest integer.

(D) Find the price range for which the company will make a profit. Round answers to the nearest dollar.

Answers to Matched Problems

1. (A) $C'(x) = 600 - 1.5x$

(B) $C'(200) = 300$.

(C) At a production level of 200 transmissions, total costs are increasing at the rate of $300 per transmission.

(D) $C(201) - C(200) = \$299.25$

2. (A) $93.80   (B) $94.00

3. (A) $R'(3,000) = 4$. At a production level of 3,000, a unit increase in production will increase revenue by approximately $4.
$R'(6,000) = -2$. At a production level of 6,000, a unit increase in production will decrease revenue by approximately $2.

(B) $P'(2,000) = 4$. At a production level of 2,000, a unit increase in production will increase profit by approximately $4.
$P'(7,000) = -6$. At a production level of 7,000, a unit increase in production will decrease profit by approximately $6.

4. (A) $\overline{C}(x) = \dfrac{7,000}{x} + 2$; $\overline{C}'(x) = -\dfrac{7,000}{x^2}$

(B) $\overline{C}(100) = \$72$; $\overline{C}'(100) = -\$0.70$. At a production level of 100 headphone sets, the average cost per headphone set is $72. This average cost is decreasing at a rate of $0.70 per headphone set.

(C) Approx. $71.30.

Chapter 2   Summary and Review

Important Terms, Symbols, and Concepts

2.1 Introduction to Limits

- The graph of the function $y = f(x)$ is the graph of the set of all ordered pairs $(x, f(x))$.

- The limit of the function $y = f(x)$ as x approaches c is L, written as $\lim_{x \to c} f(x) = L$, if the functional value $f(x)$ is close to the single real number L whenever x is close, but not equal, to c (on either side of c).

- The limit of the function $y = f(x)$ as x approaches c from the left is K, written as $\lim_{x \to c^-} f(x) = K$, if $f(x)$ is close to K whenever x is close to, but to the left of, c on the real-number line.

- The limit of the function $y = f(x)$ as x approaches c from the right is L, written as $\lim_{x \to c^+} f(x) = L$, if $f(x)$ is close to L whenever x is close to, but to the right of, c on the real-number line.

- The limit of the difference quotient $[f(a + h) - f(a)]/h$ is often a $0/0$ indeterminate form. Algebraic simplification is often required to evaluate this type of limit.

2.2 Infinite Limits and Limits at Infinity

- If $f(x)$ increases or decreases without bound as x approaches a from either side of a, then the line $x = a$ is a **vertical asymptote** of the graph of $y = f(x)$.

- If $f(x)$ gets close to L as x increases without bound or decreases without bound, then L is called the limit of f at ∞ or $-\infty$.

- The **end behavior** of a function is described by its limits at infinity.

- If $f(x)$ approaches L as $x \to \infty$ or as $x \to -\infty$, then the line $y = L$ is a **horizontal asymptote** of the graph of $y = f(x)$. Polynomial functions never have horizontal asymptotes. A rational function can have at most one.

2.3 Continuity

- Intuitively, the graph of a continuous function can be drawn without lifting a pen off the paper. By definition, a function f is **continuous at c** if

   1. $\lim_{x \to c} f(x)$ exists,   **2.** $f(c)$ exists, and   **3.** $\lim_{x \to c} f(x) = f(c)$

- Continuity properties are useful for determining where a function is continuous and where it is discontinuous.

- Continuity properties are also useful for solving inequalities.

2.4 The Derivative

- Given a function $y = f(x)$, the **average rate of change** is the ratio of the change in y to the change in x.

- The **instantaneous rate of change** is the limit of the average rate of change as the change in x approaches 0.

- The slope of the secant line through two points on the graph of a function $y = f(x)$ is the ratio of the change in y to the change in x. The **slope of the graph** at the point $(a, f(a))$ is the limit of the slope of the secant line through the points $(a, f(a))$ and $(a + h, f(a + h))$ as h approaches 0, provided the limit exists. In this case, the **tangent line** to the graph is the line through $(a, f(a))$ with slope equal to the limit.

- The **derivative of $y = f(x)$ at x**, denoted $f'(x)$, is the limit of the difference quotient $[f(x + h) - f(x)]/h$ as $h \to 0$ (if the limit exists).

- The four-step process is used to find derivatives.

- If the limit of the difference quotient does not exist at $x = a$, then f is **nondifferentiable at a** and $f'(a)$ does not exist.

2.5 Basic Differentiation Properties

- The derivative of a constant function is 0.
- For any real number n, the derivative of $f(x) = x^n$ is nx^{n-1}.
- If f is a differentiable function, then the derivative of $kf(x)$ is $kf'(x)$.
- The derivative of the sum or difference of two differentiable functions is the sum or difference of the derivatives of the functions.

2.6 Differentials

- Given the function $y = f(x)$, the change in x is also called the **increment of x** and is denoted as Δx. The corresponding change in y is called the **increment of y** and is given by $\Delta y = f(x + \Delta x) - f(x)$.
- If $y = f(x)$ is differentiable at x, then the **differential of x** is $dx = \Delta x$ and the **differential of y** $= f(x)$ is $dy = f'(x)dx$, or $df = f'(x)dx$. In this context, x and dx are both independent variables.

2.7 Marginal Analysis in Business and Economics

- If $y = C(x)$ is the total cost of producing x items, then $y = C'(x)$ is the **marginal cost** and $C(x + 1) - C(x)$ is the exact cost of producing item $x + 1$. Furthermore, $C'(x) \approx C(x + 1) - C(x)$. Similar statements can be made regarding total revenue and total profit functions.
- If $y = C(x)$ is the total cost of producing x items, then the **average cost**, or cost per unit, is $\overline{C}(x) = \dfrac{C(x)}{x}$ and the **marginal average cost** is $\overline{C}'(x) = \dfrac{d}{dx}\overline{C}(x)$. Similar statements can be made regarding total revenue and total profit functions.

Review Exercises

Work through all the problems in this chapter review, and check your answers in the back of the book. Answers to all review problems are there, along with section numbers in italics to indicate where each type of problem is discussed. Where weaknesses show up, review appropriate sections of the text.

Many of the problems in this exercise set ask you to find a derivative. Most of the answers to these problems contain both an unsimplified form and a simplified form of the derivative. When checking your work, first check that you applied the rules correctly, and then check that you performed the algebraic simplification correctly.

1. Find the indicated quantities for $y = f(x) = 2x^2 + 5$:

(A) The change in y if x changes from 1 to 3

(B) The average rate of change of y with respect to x if x changes from 1 to 3

(C) The slope of the secant line through the points $(1, f(1))$ and $(3, f(3))$ on the graph of $y = f(x)$

(D) The instantaneous rate of change of y with respect to x at $x = 1$

(E) The slope of the line tangent to the graph of $y = f(x)$ at $x = 1$

(F) $f'(1)$

2. Use the four-step process to find $f'(x)$ for $f(x) = -3x + 2$.

3. If $\lim\limits_{x \to 1} f(x) = 2$ and $\lim\limits_{x \to 1} g(x) = 4$, find

(A) $\lim\limits_{x \to 1}(5f(x) + 3g(x))$ (B) $\lim\limits_{x \to 1}[f(x)g(x)]$

(C) $\lim\limits_{x \to 1}\dfrac{g(x)}{f(x)}$ (D) $\lim\limits_{x \to 1}[5 + 2x - 3g(x)]$

In Problems 4–10, use the graph of f to estimate the indicated limits and function values.

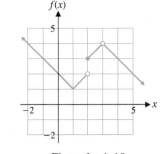

Figure for 4–10

4. $f(1.5)$ **5.** $f(2.5)$ **6.** $f(2.75)$ **7.** $f(3.25)$

8. (A) $\lim\limits_{x \to 1^-} f(x)$ (B) $\lim\limits_{x \to 1^+} f(x)$

    (C) $\lim\limits_{x \to 1} f(x)$ (D) $f(1)$

9. (A) $\lim\limits_{x \to 2^-} f(x)$ (B) $\lim\limits_{x \to 2^+} f(x)$

    (C) $\lim\limits_{x \to 2} f(x)$ (D) $f(2)$

10. (A) $\lim\limits_{x \to 3^-} f(x)$ (B) $\lim\limits_{x \to 3^+} f(x)$

    (C) $\lim\limits_{x \to 3} f(x)$ (D) $f(3)$

In Problems 11–13, use the graph of the function f shown in the figure to answer each question.

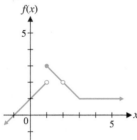

Figure for 11–13

11. (A) $\lim_{x \to 1} f(x) = ?$ (B) $f(1) = ?$

(C) Is f continuous at $x = 1$?

12. (A) $\lim_{x \to 2} f(x) = ?$ (B) $f(2) = ?$

(C) Is f continuous at $x = 2$?

13. (A) $\lim_{x \to 3} f(x) = ?$ (B) $f(3) = ?$

(C) Is f continuous at $x = 3$?

In Problems 14–23, refer to the following graph of $y = f(x)$:

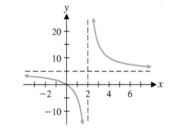

Figure for 14–23

14. $\lim_{x \to \infty} f(x) = ?$ **15.** $\lim_{x \to -\infty} f(x) = ?$

16. $\lim_{x \to 2^+} f(x) = ?$ **17.** $\lim_{x \to 2^-} f(x) = ?$

18. $\lim_{x \to 0^-} f(x) = ?$ **19.** $\lim_{x \to 0^+} f(x) = ?$

20. $\lim_{x \to 0} f(x) = ?$

21. Identify any vertical asymptotes.

22. Identify any horizontal asymptotes.

23. Where is $y = f(x)$ discontinuous?

24. Use the four-step process to find $f'(x)$ for $f(x) = 5x^2$.

25. If $f(5) = 4, f'(5) = -1, g(5) = 2$, and $g'(5) = -3$, then find $h'(5)$ for each of the following functions:

(A) $h(x) = 3f(x)$

(B) $h(x) = -2g(x)$

(C) $h(x) = 2f(x) + 5$

(D) $h(x) = -g(x) - 1$

(E) $h(x) = 2f(x) + 3g(x)$

In Problems 26–31, find $f'(x)$ and simplify.

26. $f(x) = \frac{1}{3}x^3 - 5x^2 + 1$ **27.** $f(x) = 2x^{1/2} - 3x$

28. $f(x) = 5$ **29.** $f(x) = \frac{3}{2x} + \frac{5x^3}{4}$

30. $f(x) = \frac{0.5}{x^4} + 0.25x^4$

31. $f(x) = (3x^3 - 2)(x + 1)$ (*Hint:* Multiply and then differentiate.)

In Problems 32–35, find the indicated quantities for $y = f(x) = x^2 + x$.

32. $\Delta x, \Delta y$, and $\Delta y / \Delta x$ for $x_1 = 1$ and $x_2 = 3$.

33. $[f(x_1 + \Delta x) - f(x_1)] / \Delta x$ for $x_1 = 1$ and $\Delta x = 2$.

34. dy for $x_1 = 1$ and $x_2 = 3$.

35. Δy and dy for $x = 1, \Delta x = dx = 0.2$.

Problems 36–38 refer to the function.

$$f(x) = \begin{cases} x^2 & \text{if } 0 \le x < 2 \\ 8 - x & \text{if } x \ge 2 \end{cases}$$

which is graphed in the figure.

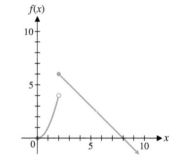

Figure for 36–38

36. (A) $\lim_{x \to 2^-} f(x) = ?$ (B) $\lim_{x \to 2^+} f(x) = ?$

(C) $\lim_{x \to 2} f(x) = ?$ (D) $f(2) = ?$

(E) Is f continuous at $x = 2$?

37. (A) $\lim_{x \to 5^-} f(x) = ?$ (B) $\lim_{x \to 5^+} f(x) = ?$

(C) $\lim_{x \to 5} f(x) = ?$ (D) $f(5) = ?$

(E) Is f continuous at $x = 5$?

38. Solve each inequality. Express answers in interval notation.

(A) $f(x) < 0$ (B) $f(x) \ge 0$

In Problems 39–41, solve each inequality. Express the answer in interval notation. Use a graphing calculator in Problem 41 to approximate partition numbers to four decimal places.

39. $x^2 - x < 12$ **40.** $\frac{x - 5}{x^2 + 3x} > 0$

41. $x^3 + x^2 - 4x - 2 > 0$

42. Let $f(x) = 0.5x^2 - 5$.

(A) Find the slope of the secant line through $(2, f(2))$ and $(4, f(4))$.

(B) Find the slope of the secant line through $(2, f(2))$ and $(2 + h, f(2 + h)), h \ne 0$.

(C) Find the slope of the tangent line at $x = 2$.

In Problems 43–46, find the indicated derivative and simplify.

43. $\frac{dy}{dx}$ for $y = \frac{1}{3}x^{-3} - 5x^{-2} + 1$

44. y' for $y = \dfrac{3\sqrt{x}}{2} + \dfrac{5}{3\sqrt{x}}$

45. $g'(x)$ for $g(x) = 1.8\sqrt[3]{x} + \dfrac{0.9}{\sqrt[3]{x}}$

46. $\dfrac{dy}{dx}$ for $y = \dfrac{2x^3 - 3}{5x^3}$

47. For $y = f(x) = x^2 + 4$, find

    (A) The slope of the graph at $x = 1$

    (B) The equation of the tangent line at $x = 1$ in the form $y = mx + b$

In Problems 48 and 49, find the value(s) of x where the tangent line is horizontal.

48. $f(x) = 10x - x^2$

49. $f(x) = x^3 + 3x^2 - 45x - 135$

In Problems 50 and 51, approximate (to four decimal places) the value(s) of x where the graph of f has a horizontal tangent line.

50. $f(x) = x^4 - 2x^3 - 5x^2 + 7x$

51. $f(x) = x^5 - 10x^3 - 5x + 10$

52. If an object moves along the y axis (scale in feet) so that it is at $y = f(x) = 8x^2 - 4x + 1$ at time x (in seconds), find

    (A) The instantaneous velocity function

    (B) The velocity at time $x = 3$ seconds

53. An object moves along the y axis (scale in feet) so that at time x (in seconds) it is at $y = f(x) = -5x^2 + 16x + 3$. Find

    (A) The instantaneous velocity function

    (B) The time(s) when the velocity is 0

54. Let $f(x) = x^3$, $g(x) = (x - 4)^3$, and $h(x) = (x + 3)^3$.

    (A) How are the graphs of f, g, and h related? Illustrate your conclusion by graphing f, g, and h on the same coordinate axes.

    (B) How would you expect the graphs of the derivatives of these functions to be related? Illustrate your conclusion by graphing f', g', and h' on the same coordinate axes.

In Problems 55–59, determine where f is continuous. Express the answer in interval notation.

55. $f(x) = x^2 - 4$

56. $f(x) = \dfrac{x + 1}{x - 2}$

57. $f(x) = \dfrac{x + 4}{x^2 + 3x - 4}$

58. $f(x) = \sqrt[3]{4 - x^2}$

59. $f(x) = \sqrt{4 - x^2}$

In Problems 60–69, evaluate the indicated limits if they exist.

60. Let $f(x) = \dfrac{2x}{x^2 - 3x}$. Find

    (A) $\lim\limits_{x \to 1} f(x)$ (B) $\lim\limits_{x \to 3} f(x)$ (C) $\lim\limits_{x \to 0} f(x)$

61. Let $f(x) = \dfrac{x + 1}{(3 - x)^2}$. Find

    (A) $\lim\limits_{x \to 1} f(x)$ (B) $\lim\limits_{x \to -1} f(x)$ (C) $\lim\limits_{x \to 3} f(x)$

62. Let $f(x) = \dfrac{|x - 4|}{x - 4}$. Find

    (A) $\lim\limits_{x \to 4^-} f(x)$ (B) $\lim\limits_{x \to 4^+} f(x)$ (C) $\lim\limits_{x \to 4} f(x)$

63. Let $f(x) = \dfrac{x - 3}{9 - x^2}$. Find

    (A) $\lim\limits_{x \to 3} f(x)$ (B) $\lim\limits_{x \to -3} f(x)$ (C) $\lim\limits_{x \to 0} f(x)$

64. Let $f(x) = \dfrac{x^2 - x - 2}{x^2 - 7x + 10}$. Find

    (A) $\lim\limits_{x \to -1} f(x)$ (B) $\lim\limits_{x \to 2} f(x)$ (C) $\lim\limits_{x \to 5} f(x)$

65. Let $f(x) = \dfrac{2x}{3x - 6}$. Find

    (A) $\lim\limits_{x \to \infty} f(x)$ (B) $\lim\limits_{x \to -\infty} f(x)$ (C) $\lim\limits_{x \to 2} f(x)$

66. Let $f(x) = \dfrac{2x^3}{3(x - 2)^2}$. Find

    (A) $\lim\limits_{x \to \infty} f(x)$ (B) $\lim\limits_{x \to -\infty} f(x)$ (C) $\lim\limits_{x \to 2} f(x)$

67. Let $f(x) = \dfrac{2x}{3(x - 2)^3}$. Find

    (A) $\lim\limits_{x \to \infty} f(x)$ (B) $\lim\limits_{x \to -\infty} f(x)$ (C) $\lim\limits_{x \to 2} f(x)$

68. $\lim\limits_{h \to 0} \dfrac{f(2 + h) - f(2)}{h}$ for $f(x) = x^2 + 4$

69. $\lim\limits_{h \to 0} \dfrac{f(x + h) - f(x)}{h}$ for $f(x) = \dfrac{1}{x + 2}$

In Problems 70 and 71, use the definition of the derivative and the four-step process to find $f'(x)$.

70. $f(x) = x^2 - x$ **71.** $f(x) = \sqrt{x} - 3$

Problems 72–77 refer to the function f in the figure. Determine whether f is differentiable at the indicated value of x.

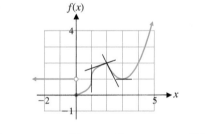

$f(x)$

72. $x = -1$ **73.** $x = 0$ **74.** $x = 1$

75. $x = 2$ **76.** $x = 3$ **77.** $x = 4$

In Problems 78–82, find all horizontal and vertical asymptotes.

78. $f(x) = \dfrac{5x}{x - 7}$ **79.** $f(x) = \dfrac{-2x + 5}{(x - 4)^2}$

80. $f(x) = \dfrac{x^2 + 9}{x - 3}$ **81.** $f(x) = \dfrac{x^2 - 9}{x^2 + x - 2}$

82. $f(x) = \dfrac{x^3 - 1}{x^3 - x^2 - x + 1}$

83. The domain of the power function $f(x) = x^{1/5}$ is the set of all real numbers. Find the domain of the derivative $f'(x)$. Discuss the nature of the graph of $y = f(x)$ for any x values excluded from the domain of $f'(x)$.

84. Let f be defined by

$$f(x) = \begin{cases} x^2 - m & \text{if } x \le 1 \\ -x^2 + m & \text{if } x > 1 \end{cases}$$

where m is a constant.

(A) Graph f for $m = 0$, and find

$$\lim_{x \to 1^-} f(x) \quad \text{and} \quad \lim_{x \to 1^+} f(x)$$

(B) Graph f for $m = 2$, and find

$$\lim_{x \to 1^-} f(x) \quad \text{and} \quad \lim_{x \to 1^+} f(x)$$

(C) Find m so that

$$\lim_{x \to 1^-} f(x) = \lim_{x \to 1^+} f(x)$$

and graph f for this value of m.

(D) Write a brief verbal description of each graph. How does the graph in part (C) differ from the graphs in parts (A) and (B)?

85. Let $f(x) = 1 - |x - 1|, 0 \le x \le 2$ (see the figure).

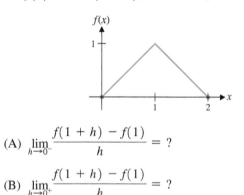

(A) $\displaystyle\lim_{h \to 0^-} \dfrac{f(1 + h) - f(1)}{h} = ?$

(B) $\displaystyle\lim_{h \to 0^+} \dfrac{f(1 + h) - f(1)}{h} = ?$

(C) $\displaystyle\lim_{h \to 0} \dfrac{f(1 + h) - f(1)}{h} = ?$

(D) Does $f'(1)$ exist?

Applications

86. Natural-gas rates. Table 1 shows the winter rates for natural gas charged by the Bay State Gas Company. The base charge is a fixed monthly charge, independent of the amount of gas used per month.

Table 1 **Natural Gas Rates**

Base charge	$7.47
First 90 therms	$0.4000 per therm
All usage over 90 therms	$0.2076 per therm

(A) Write a piecewise definition of the monthly charge $S(x)$ for a customer who uses x therms in a winter month.

(B) Graph $S(x)$.

(C) Is $S(x)$ continuous at $x = 90$? Explain.

87. Cost analysis. The total cost (in dollars) of producing x HDTVs is

$$C(x) = 10{,}000 + 200x - 0.1x^2$$

(A) Find the exact cost of producing the 101st TV.

(B) Use the marginal cost to approximate the cost of producing the 101st TV.

88. Cost analysis. The total cost (in dollars) of producing x bicycles is

$$C(x) = 5{,}000 + 40x + 0.05x^2$$

(A) Find the total cost and the marginal cost at a production level of 100 bicycles and interpret the results.

(B) Find the average cost and the marginal average cost at a production level of 100 bicycles and interpret the results.

89. Cost analysis. The total cost (in dollars) of producing x laser printers per week is shown in the figure. Which is greater, the approximate cost of producing the 201st printer or the approximate cost of producing the 601st printer? Does this graph represent a manufacturing process that is becoming more efficient or less efficient as production levels increase? Explain.

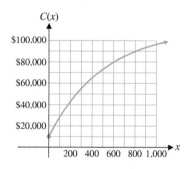

90. Cost analysis. Let

$$p = 25 - 0.01x \quad \text{and} \quad C(x) = 2x + 9{,}000$$
$$0 \le x \le 2{,}500$$

be the price–demand equation and cost function, respectively, for the manufacture of umbrellas.

(A) Find the marginal cost, average cost, and marginal average cost functions.

(B) Express the revenue in terms of x, and find the marginal revenue, average revenue, and marginal average revenue functions.

(C) Find the profit, marginal profit, average profit, and marginal average profit functions.

(D) Find the break-even point(s).

(E) Evaluate the marginal profit at $x = 1{,}000, 1{,}150$, and $1{,}400$, and interpret the results.

(F) Graph $R = R(x)$ and $C = C(x)$ on the same coordinate system, and locate regions of profit and loss.

91. Employee training. A company producing computer components has established that, on average, a new employee can assemble $N(t)$ components per day after t days of on-the-job training, as given by

$$N(t) = \frac{40t - 80}{t}, t \geq 2$$

(A) Find the average rate of change of $N(t)$ from 2 days to 5 days.

(B) Find the instantaneous rate of change of $N(t)$ at 2 days.

92. Sales analysis. The total number of swimming pools, N (in thousands), sold during a year is given by

$$N(t) = 2t + \frac{1}{3}t^{3/2}$$

where t is the number of months since the beginning of the year. Find $N(9)$ and $N'(9)$, and interpret these quantities.

93. Natural-gas consumption. The data in Table 2 give the U.S. consumption of natural gas in trillions of cubic feet.

Table 2

Year	Natural-Gas Consumption
1960	12.0
1970	21.1
1980	19.9
1990	18.7
2000	21.9
2010	24.1

(A) Let x represent time (in years), with $x = 0$ corresponding to 1960, and let y represent the corresponding U.S. consumption of natural gas. Enter the data set in a graphing calculator and find a cubic regression equation for the data.

(B) If $y = N(x)$ denotes the regression equation found in part (A), find $N(60)$ and $N'(60)$, and write a brief verbal interpretation of these results.

94. Break-even analysis. Table 3 contains price–demand and total cost data from a bakery for the production of kringles (a Danish pastry), where p is the price (in dollars) of a kringle for a daily demand of x kringles and C is the total cost (in dollars) of producing x kringles.

Table 3

x	$p(\$)$	$C(\$)$
125	9	740
140	8	785
170	7	850
200	6	900

(A) Find a linear regression equation for the price–demand data, using x as the independent variable.

(B) Find a linear regression equation for the cost data, using x as the independent variable. Use this equation to estimate the fixed costs and variable costs per kringle.

(C) Find the break-even points.

(D) Find the price range for which the bakery will make a profit.

95. Pollution. A sewage treatment plant uses a pipeline that extends 1 mile toward the center of a large lake. The concentration of effluent $C(x)$ in parts per million, x meters from the end of the pipe is given approximately by

$$C(x) = \frac{500}{x^2}, x \geq 1$$

What is the instantaneous rate of change of concentration at 10 meters? At 100 meters?

96. Medicine. The body temperature (in degrees Fahrenheit) of a patient t hours after taking a fever-reducing drug is given by

$$F(t) = 0.16t^2 - 1.6t + 102$$

Find $F(4)$ and $F'(4)$. Write a brief verbal interpretation of these quantities.

97. Learning. If a person learns N items in t hours, as given by

$$N(t) = 20\sqrt{t}$$

find the rate of learning after

(A) 1 hour   (B) 4 hours

98. Physics: The coefficient of thermal expansion (CTE) is a measure of the expansion of an object subjected to extreme temperatures. We want to use a Michaelis–Menten function of the form

$$C(T) = \frac{C_{max}T}{M + T}$$

where $C = $ CTE, T is temperature in K (degrees Kelvin), and C_{max} and M are constants. Table 4 lists the coefficients of thermal expansion for titanium at various temperatures.

Table 4 **Coefficients of Thermal Expansion**

$T(K)$	Titanium
100	4.5
200	7.4
293	8.6
500	9.9
800	11.1
1100	11.7

(A) Plot the points in columns 1 and 2 of Table 4 on graph paper and estimate C_{max} to the nearest integer. To estimate M, add the horizontal line CTE $= \frac{C_{max}}{2}$ to your graph, connect successive points on the graph with straight-line segments, and estimate the value of T (to the nearest multiple of fifty) that satisfies

$$C(T) = \frac{C_{max}}{2}.$$

(B) Use the constants $\frac{C_{max}}{2}$ and M from part (A) to form a Michaelis–Menten function for the CTE of titanium.

(C) Use the function from part (B) to estimate the CTE of titanium at 600 K and to estimate the temperature when the CTE of titanium is 10.

3 Additional Derivative Topics

Introduction

In this chapter, we develop techniques for finding derivatives of a wide variety of functions, including exponential and logarithmic functions. There are straightforward procedures—the product rule, quotient rule, and chain rule—for writing down the derivative of any function that is the product, quotient, or composite of functions whose derivatives are known. With the ability to calculate derivatives easily, we consider a wealth of applications involving rates of change. For example, we apply the derivative to study population growth, radioactive decay, elasticity of demand, and environmental crises (see Problem 39 in Section 3.6 or Problem 87 in Section 3.7). Before starting this chapter, you may find it helpful to review the basic properties of exponential and logarithmic functions in Sections 1.5 and 1.6.

3.1   The Constant *e* and Continuous Compound Interest

- The Constant *e*
- Continuous Compound Interest

In Chapter 1, both the exponential function with base *e* and continuous compound interest were introduced informally. Now, with an understanding of limit concepts, we can give precise definitions of *e* and continuous compound interest.

The Constant *e*

The irrational number *e* is a particularly suitable base for both exponential and logarithmic functions. The reasons for choosing this number as a base will become clear as we develop differentiation formulas for the exponential function e^x and the natural logarithmic function $\ln x$.

In precalculus treatments (Chapter 1), the number *e* is defined informally as the irrational number that can be approximated by the expression $[1 + (1/n)]^n$ for *n* sufficiently large. Now we will use the limit concept to formally define *e* as either of the following two limits. [*Note:* If $s = 1/n$, then as $n \to \infty$, $s \to 0$.]

DEFINITION   The Number *e*

$$e = \lim_{n \to \infty} \left(1 + \frac{1}{n} \right)^n \qquad \text{or, alternatively,} \qquad e = \lim_{s \to 0} (1 + s)^{1/s}$$

Both limits are equal to $e = 2.718\ 281\ 828\ 459 \ldots$

Proof that the indicated limits exist and represent an irrational number between 2 and 3 is not easy and is omitted.

CONCEPTUAL INSIGHT

The two limits used to define *e* are unlike any we have encountered so far. Some people reason (incorrectly) that both limits are 1, since $1 + s \to 1$ as $s \to 0$ and 1 to any power is 1. An ordinary scientific calculator with a y^x key can convince you otherwise. Consider the following table of values for *s* and $f(s) = (1 + s)^{1/s}$ and Figure 1 for *s* close to 0. Compute the table values with a calculator yourself, and try several values of *s* even closer to 0. Note that the function is discontinuous at $s = 0$.

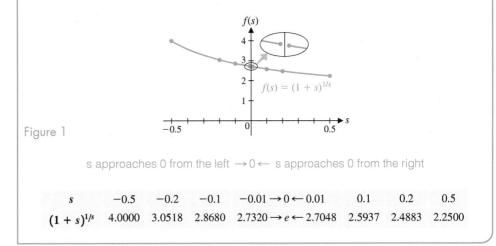

Figure 1

s approaches 0 from the left $\to 0 \leftarrow$ s approaches 0 from the right

s	-0.5	-0.2	-0.1	$-0.01 \to 0 \leftarrow 0.01$	0.1	0.2	0.5
$(1+s)^{1/s}$	4.0000	3.0518	2.8680	$2.7320 \to e \leftarrow 2.7048$	2.5937	2.4883	2.2500

Continuous Compound Interest

Now we can see how *e* appears quite naturally in the important application of compound interest. Let us start with simple interest, move on to compound interest, and then proceed on to continuous compound interest.

On one hand, if a principal P is borrowed at an annual rate r,* then after t years at simple interest, the borrower will owe the lender an amount A given by

$$A = P + Prt = P(1 + rt) \quad \text{Simple interest} \tag{1}$$

On the other hand, if interest is compounded m times a year, then the borrower will owe the lender an amount A given by

$$A = P\left(1 + \frac{r}{m}\right)^{mt} \quad \text{Compound interest} \tag{2}$$

where r/m is the interest rate per compounding period and mt is the number of compounding periods. Suppose that P, r, and t in equation (2) are held fixed and m is increased. Will the amount A increase without bound, or will it tend to approach some limiting value?

Let us perform a calculator experiment before we attack the general limit problem. If $P = \$100$, $r = 0.06$, and $t = 2$ years, then

$$A = 100\left(1 + \frac{0.06}{m}\right)^{2m}$$

We compute A for several values of m in Table 1. The biggest gain appears in the first step, then the gains slow down as m increases. The amount A appears to approach $\$112.75$ as m gets larger and larger.

Table 1

Compounding Frequency	m	$A = 100\left(1 + \dfrac{0.06}{m}\right)^{2m}$
Annually	1	\$112.3600
Semiannually	2	112.5509
Quarterly	4	112.6493
Monthly	12	112.7160
Weekly	52	112.7419
Daily	365	112.7486
Hourly	8,760	112.7496

Keeping P, r, and t fixed in equation (2), we compute the following limit and observe an interesting and useful result:

$$\lim_{m \to \infty} P\left(1 + \frac{r}{m}\right)^{mt} = P \lim_{m \to \infty} \left(1 + \frac{r}{m}\right)^{(m/r)rt} \quad \text{Insert } r/r \text{ in the exponent and let } s = r/m. \text{ Note that } m \to \infty \text{ implies } s \to 0.$$

$$= P \lim_{s \to 0} [(1 + s)^{1/s}]^{rt} \quad \text{Use a limit property.}^\dagger$$

$$= P[\lim_{s \to 0} (1 + s)^{1/s}]^{rt} \quad \lim_{s \to 0} (1 + s)^{1/s} = e$$

$$= Pe^{rt}$$

The resulting formula is called the **continuous compound interest formula**, a widely used formula in business and economics.

THEOREM 1 Continuous Compound Interest Formula

If a principal P is invested at an annual rate r (expressed as a decimal) compounded continuously, then the amount A in the account at the end of t years is given by

$$A = Pe^{rt}$$

---

*If r is the interest rate written as a decimal, then $100r\%$ is the rate in percent. For example, if $r = 0.12$, then $100r\% = 100(0.12)\% = 12\%$. The expressions 0.12 and 12% are equivalent. Unless stated otherwise, all formulas in this book use r in decimal form.
†The following new limit property is used: If $\lim_{x \to c} f(x)$ exists, then $\lim_{x \to c} [f(x)]^p = [\lim_{x \to c} f(x)]^p$, provided that the last expression names a real number.

EXAMPLE 1 Computing Continuously Compounded Interest If $100 is invested at 6% compounded continuously,* what amount will be in the account after 2 years? How much interest will be earned?

SOLUTION
$$A = Pe^{rt}$$
$$= 100e^{(0.06)(2)} \quad \text{6\% is equivalent to } r = 0.06.$$
$$\approx \$112.7497$$

Compare this result with the values calculated in Table 1. The interest earned is $112.7497 − $100 = $12.7497.

Matched Problem 1 What amount (to the nearest cent) will be in an account after 5 years if $100 is invested at an annual nominal rate of 8% compounded annually? Semiannually? Continuously?

EXAMPLE 2 Graphing the Growth of an Investment Union Savings Bank offers a 5-year certificate of deposit (CD) that earns 5.75% compounded continuously. If $1,000 is invested in one of these CDs, graph the amount in the account as a function of time for a period of 5 years.

SOLUTION We want to graph

$$A = 1,000e^{0.0575t} \quad 0 \le t \le 5$$

Using a calculator, we construct a table of values (Table 2). Then we graph the points from the table and join the points with a smooth curve (Fig. 2).

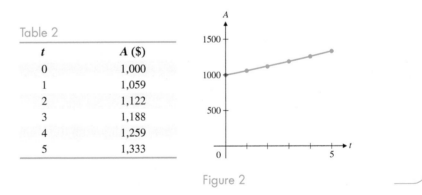

Table 2

t	A ($)
0	1,000
1	1,059
2	1,122
3	1,188
4	1,259
5	1,333

Figure 2

CONCEPTUAL INSIGHT

Depending on the domain, the graph of an exponential function can appear to be linear. Table 2 shows that the graph in Figure 2 is *not* linear. The slope determined by the first two points (for $t = 0$ and $t = 1$) is 59 but the slope determined by the first and third points (for $t = 0$ and $t = 2$) is 61. For a linear graph, the slope determined by any two points is constant.

Matched Problem 2 If $5,000 is invested in a Union Savings Bank 4-year CD that earns 5.61% compounded continuously, graph the amount in the account as a function of time for a period of 4 years.

---

*Following common usage, we will often write "at 6% compounded continuously," understanding that this means "at an annual rate of 6% compounded continuously."

EXAMPLE 3 Computing Growth Time How long will it take an investment of $5,000 to grow to $8,000 if it is invested at 5% compounded continuously?

SOLUTION Starting with the continous compound interest formula $A = Pe^{rt}$, we must solve for t:

$$A = Pe^{rt}$$
$$8,000 = 5,000e^{0.05t} \quad \text{Divide both sides by 5,000 and}$$
$$e^{0.05t} = 1.6 \quad \text{reverse the equation.}$$
$$\ln e^{0.05t} = \ln 1.6 \quad \text{Take the natural logarithm of both}$$
$$0.05t = \ln 1.6 \quad \text{sides—recall that } \log_b b^x = x.$$
$$t = \frac{\ln 1.6}{0.05}$$
$$t \approx 9.4 \text{ years}$$

Figure 3 shows an alternative method for solving Example 3 on a graphing calculator.

Figure 3

$$y_1 = 5,000e^{0.05x}$$
$$y_2 = 8,000$$

Matched Problem 3 How long will it take an investment of $10,000 to grow to $15,000 if it is invested at 9% compounded continuously?

EXAMPLE 4 Computing Doubling Time How long will it take money to double if it is invested at 6.5% compounded continuously?

SOLUTION Starting with the continuous compound interest formula $A = Pe^{rt}$, we solve for t, given $A = 2P$ and $R = 0.065$:

$$2P = Pe^{0.065t} \quad \text{Divide both sides by } P \text{ and reverse the equation.}$$
$$e^{0.065t} = 2 \quad \text{Take the natural logarithm of both sides.}$$
$$\ln e^{0.065t} = \ln 2$$
$$0.065t = \ln 2$$
$$t = \frac{\ln 2}{0.065}$$
$$t \approx 10.66 \text{ years}$$

Matched Problem 4 How long will it take money to triple if it is invested at 5.5% compounded continuously?

Explore and Discuss 1 You are considering three options for investing $10,000: at 7% compounded annually, at 6% compounded monthly, and at 5% compounded continuously.

(A) Which option would be the best for investing $10,000 for 8 years?

(B) How long would you need to invest your money for the third option to be the best?

Exercises 3.1

Skills Warm-up Exercise

In Problems 1–8, solve for the variable to two decimal places. (If necessary, review Section 1.5).

1. $A = 1,200e^{0.04(5)}$

2. $A = 3,000e^{0.07(10)}$

3. $9827.30 = Pe^{0.025(3)}$

4. $50,000 = Pe^{0.054(7)}$

5. $6,000 = 5,000e^{0.0325t}$

6. $10,0000 = 7,500e^{0.085t}$

7. $956 = 900e^{1.5r}$

8. $4,840 = 3,750e^{4.25r}$

Use a calculator to evaluate A to the nearest cent in Problems 9 and 10.

9. $A = \$1,000e^{0.1t}$ for $t = 2, 5,$ and 8

10. $A = \$5,000e^{0.08t}$ for $t = 1, 4,$ and 10

11. If \$6,000 is invested at 10% compounded continuously, graph the amount in the account as a function of time for a period of 8 years.

12. If \$4,000 is invested at 8% compounded continuously, graph the amount in the account as a function of time for a period of 6 years.

In Problems 13–18, solve for t or r to two decimal places.

13. $2 = e^{0.06t}$

14. $2 = e^{0.03t}$

15. $3 = e^{0.1r}$

16. $3 = e^{0.25t}$

17. $2 = e^{5r}$

18. $3 = e^{10r}$

In Problems 19 and 20, use a calculator to complete each table to five decimal places.

19.

n	$[1 + (1/n)]^n$
10	2.593 74
100	
1,000	
10,000	
100,000	
1,000,000	
10,000,000	
↓	↓
∞	$e = 2.718\,281\,828\,459\ldots$

20.

s	$(1 + s)^{1/s}$
0.01	2.704 81
−0.01	
0.001	
−0.001	
0.000 1	
−0.000 1	
0.000 01	
−0.000 01	
↓	↓
0	$e = 2.718\,281\,828\,459\ldots$

21. Use a calculator and a table of values to investigate

$$\lim_{n \to \infty} (1 + n)^{1/n}$$

Do you think this limit exists? If so, what do you think it is?

22. Use a calculator and a table of values to investigate

$$\lim_{s \to 0^+} \left(1 + \frac{1}{s}\right)^s$$

Do you think this limit exists? If so, what do you think it is?

23. It can be shown that the number e satisfies the inequality

$$\left(1 + \frac{1}{n}\right)^n < e < \left(1 + \frac{1}{n}\right)^{n+1} \qquad n \geq 1$$

Illustrate this condition by graphing

$$y_1 = (1 + 1/n)^n$$
$$y_2 = 2.718\,281\,828 \approx e$$
$$y_3 = (1 + 1/n)^{n+1}$$

in the same viewing window, for $1 \leq n \leq 20$.

24. It can be shown that

$$e^s = \lim_{n \to \infty} \left(1 + \frac{s}{n}\right)^n$$

for any real number s. Illustrate this equation graphically for $s = 2$ by graphing

$$y_1 = (1 + 2/n)^n$$
$$y_2 = 7.389\,056\,099 \approx e^2$$

in the same viewing window, for $1 \leq n \leq 50$.

Applications

25. Continuous compound interest. Provident Bank offers a 10-year CD that earns 2.15% compounded continuously.

(A) If \$10,000 is invested in this CD, how much will it be worth in 10 years?

(B) How long will it take for the account to be worth \$18,000?

26. Continuous compound interest. Provident Bank also offers a 3-year CD that earns 1.64% compounded continuously.

(A) If \$10,000 is invested in this CD, how much will it be worth in 3 years?

(B) How long will it take for the account to be worth \$11,000?

27. Present value. A note will pay \$20,000 at maturity 10 years from now. How much should you be willing to pay for the note now if money is worth 5.2% compounded continuously?

28. Present value. A note will pay $50,000 at maturity 5 years from now. How much should you be willing to pay for the note now if money is worth 6.4% compounded continuously?

29. Continuous compound interest. An investor bought stock for $20,000. Five years later, the stock was sold for $30,000. If interest is compounded continuously, what annual nominal rate of interest did the original $20,000 investment earn?

30. Continuous compound interest. A family paid $99,000 cash for a house. Fifteen years later, the house was sold for $195,000. If interest is compounded continuously, what annual nominal rate of interest did the original $99,000 investment earn?

31. Present value. Solving $A = Pe^{rt}$ for P, we obtain

$$P = Ae^{-rt}$$

which is the present value of the amount A due in t years if money earns interest at an annual nominal rate r compounded continuously.

(A) Graph $P = 10,000e^{-0.08t}$, $0 \le t \le 50$.

(B) $\lim\limits_{t \to \infty} 10,000e^{-0.08t} = $? [Guess, using part (A).]

[*Conclusion:* The longer the time until the amount A is due, the smaller is its present value, as we would expect.]

32. Present value. Referring to Problem 31, in how many years will the $10,000 be due in order for its present value to be $5,000?

33. Doubling time. How long will it take money to double if it is invested at 4% compounded continuously?

34. Doubling time. How long will it take money to double if it is invested at 5% compounded continuously?

35. Doubling rate. At what nominal rate compounded continuously must money be invested to double in 8 years?

36. Doubling rate. At what nominal rate compounded continuously must money be invested to double in 10 years?

37. Growth time. A man with $20,000 to invest decides to diversify his investments by placing $10,000 in an account that earns 7.2% compounded continuously and $10,000 in an account that earns 8.4% compounded annually. Use graphical approximation methods to determine how long it will take for his total investment in the two accounts to grow to $35,000.

38. Growth time. A woman invests $5,000 in an account that earns 8.8% compounded continuously and $7,000 in an account that earns 9.6% compounded annually. Use graphical approximation methods to determine how long it will take for her total investment in the two accounts to grow to $20,000.

39. Doubling times

(A) Show that the doubling time t (in years) at an annual rate r compounded continuously is given by

$$t = \frac{\ln 2}{r}$$

(B) Graph the doubling-time equation from part (A) for $0.02 \le r \le 0.30$. Is this restriction on r reasonable? Explain.

(C) Determine the doubling times (in years, to two decimal places) for $r = 5\%, 10\%, 15\%, 20\%, 25\%,$ and 30%.

40. Doubling rates

(A) Show that the rate r that doubles an investment at continuously compounded interest in t years is given by

$$r = \frac{\ln 2}{t}$$

(B) Graph the doubling-rate equation from part (A) for $1 \le t \le 20$. Is this restriction on t reasonable? Explain.

(C) Determine the doubling rates for $t = 2, 4, 6, 8, 10,$ and 12 years.

41. Radioactive decay. A mathematical model for the decay of radioactive substances is given by

$$Q = Q_0 e^{rt}$$

where

$$Q_0 = \text{amount of the substance at time } t = 0$$
$$r = \text{continuous compound rate of decay}$$
$$t = \text{time in years}$$
$$Q = \text{amount of the substance at time } t$$

If the continuous compound rate of decay of radium per year is $r = -0.000\,433\,2$, how long will it take a certain amount of radium to decay to half the original amount? (This period is the *half-life* of the substance.)

42. Radioactive decay. The continuous compound rate of decay of carbon-14 per year is $r = -0.000\,123\,8$. How long will it take a certain amount of carbon-14 to decay to half the original amount? (Use the radioactive decay model in Problem 41.)

43. Radioactive decay. A cesium isotope has a half-life of 30 years. What is the continuous compound rate of decay? (Use the radioactive decay model in Problem 41.)

44. Radioactive decay. A strontium isotope has a half-life of 90 years. What is the continuous compound rate of decay? (Use the radioactive decay model in Problem 41.)

45. World population. A mathematical model for world population growth over short intervals is given by

$$P = P_0 e^{rt}$$

where

$$P_0 = \text{population at time } t = 0$$
$$r = \text{continuous compound rate of growth}$$
$$t = \text{time in years}$$
$$P = \text{population at time } t$$

How long will it take world population to double if it continues to grow at its current continuous compound rate of 1.3% per year?

46. U.S. population. How long will it take for the U.S. population to double if it continues to grow at a rate of 0.975% per year?

47. Population growth. Some underdeveloped nations have population doubling times of 50 years. At what continuous compound rate is the population growing? (Use the population growth model in Problem 45.)

48. Population growth. Some developed nations have population doubling times of 200 years. At what continuous compound rate is the population growing? (Use the population growth model in Problem 45.)

Answers to Matched Problems

1. $146.93; $148.02; $149.18

2. $A = 5,000e^{0.0561t}$

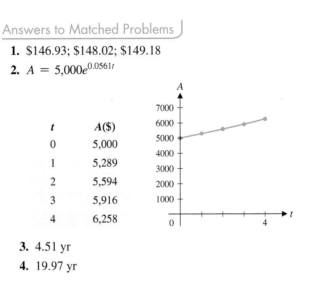

t	$A(\$)$
0	5,000
1	5,289
2	5,594
3	5,916
4	6,258

3. 4.51 yr

4. 19.97 yr

3.2 Derivatives of Exponential and Logarithmic Functions

- The Derivative of e^x
- The Derivative of ln x
- Other Logarithmic and Exponential Functions
- Exponential and Logarithmic Models

In this section, we find formulas for the derivatives of logarithmic and exponential functions. A review of Sections 1.5 and 1.6 may prove helpful. In particular, recall that $f(x) = e^x$ is the exponential function with base $e \approx 2.718$, and the inverse of the function e^x is the natural logarithm function ln x. More generally, if b is a positive real number, $b \neq 1$, then the exponential function b^x with base b, and the logarithmic function $\log_b x$ with base b, are inverses of each other.

The Derivative of e^x

In the process of finding the derivative of e^x, we use (without proof) the fact that

$$\lim_{h \to 0} \frac{e^h - 1}{h} = 1 \tag{1}$$

Explore and Discuss 1   Complete Table 1.

Table 1

h	−0.1	−0.01	−0.001	→ 0 ←	0.001	0.01	0.1
$\dfrac{e^h - 1}{h}$							

Do your calculations make it reasonable to conclude that

$$\lim_{h \to 0} \frac{e^h - 1}{h} = 1?$$

Discuss.

We now apply the four-step process (Section 2.4) to the exponential function $f(x) = e^x$.

Step 1 Find $f(x + h)$.

$$f(x + h) = e^{x+h} = e^x e^h \qquad \text{See Section 1.4.}$$

Step 2 Find $f(x + h) - f(x)$.

$$f(x + h) - f(x) = e^x e^h - e^x \qquad \text{Factor out } e^x.$$
$$= e^x(e^h - 1)$$

Step 3 Find $\dfrac{f(x + h) - f(x)}{h}$.

$$\frac{f(x + h) - f(x)}{h} = \frac{e^x(e^h - 1)}{h} = e^x\left(\frac{e^h - 1}{h}\right)$$

Step 4 Find $f'(x) = \lim\limits_{h \to 0} \dfrac{f(x + h) - f(x)}{h}$.

$$f'(x) = \lim_{h \to 0} \frac{f(x + h) - f(x)}{h}$$
$$= \lim_{h \to 0} e^x\left(\frac{e^h - 1}{h}\right)$$
$$= e^x \lim_{h \to 0}\left(\frac{e^h - 1}{h}\right) \qquad \text{Use the limit in (1).}$$
$$= e^x \cdot 1 = e^x$$

Therefore,

$$\frac{d}{dx}e^x = e^x \qquad \text{The derivative of the exponential function is the exponential function.}$$

EXAMPLE 1 Finding Derivatives Find $f'(x)$ for

(A) $f(x) = 5e^x - 3x^4 + 9x + 16$ (B) $f(x) = -7x^e + 2e^x + e^2$

SOLUTIONS

(A) $f'(x) = 5e^x - 12x^3 + 9$ (B) $f'(x) = -7ex^{e-1} + 2e^x$

Remember that e is a real number, so the power rule (Section 2.5) is used to find the derivative of x^e. The derivative of the exponential function e^x, however, is e^x. Note that $e^2 \approx 7.389$ is a constant, so its derivative is 0.

Matched Problem 1 Find $f'(x)$ for

(A) $f(x) = 4e^x + 8x^2 + 7x - 14$ (B) $f(x) = x^7 - x^5 + e^3 - x + e^x$

⚠ **CAUTION**

$$\frac{d}{dx}e^x \neq xe^{x-1} \qquad \frac{d}{dx}e^x = e^x$$

The power rule cannot be used to differentiate the exponential function. The power rule applies to exponential forms x^n, where the exponent is a constant and the base is a variable. In the exponential form e^x, the base is a constant and the exponent is a variable. ▲

The Derivative of ln x

We summarize some important facts about logarithmic functions from Section 1.6:

SUMMARY

Recall that the inverse of an exponential function is called a **logarithmic function**. For $b > 0$ and $b \neq 1$,

Logarithmic form		Exponential form
$y = \log_b x$	is equivalent to	$x = b^y$
Domain: $(0, \infty)$		Domain: $(-\infty, \infty)$
Range: $(-\infty, \infty)$		Range: $(0, \infty)$

The graphs of $y = \log_b x$ and $y = b^x$ are symmetric with respect to the line $y = x$. (See Figure 1.)

Figure 1

Of all the possible bases for logarithmic functions, the two most widely used are

$$\log x = \log_{10} x \quad \text{Common logarithm (base 10)}$$

$$\ln x = \log_e x \quad \text{Natural logarithm (base } e)$$

We are now ready to use the definition of the derivative and the four-step process discussed in Section 2.4 to find a formula for the derivative of $\ln x$. Later we will extend this formula to include $\log_b x$ for any base b.

Let $f(x) = \ln x, x > 0$.

Step 1 Find $f(x + h)$.

$$f(x + h) = \ln(x + h) \quad \ln(x + h) \text{ cannot be simplified.}$$

Step 2 Find $f(x + h) - f(x)$.

$$f(x + h) - f(x) = \ln(x + h) - \ln x \quad \text{Use } \ln A - \ln B = \ln \frac{A}{B}.$$

$$= \ln \frac{x + h}{x}$$

Step 3 Find $\dfrac{f(x + h) - f(x)}{h}$.

$$\frac{f(x + h) - f(x)}{h} = \frac{\ln(x + h) - \ln x}{h}$$

$$= \frac{1}{h} \ln \frac{x + h}{x} \quad \text{Multiply by } 1 = x/x \text{ to change form.}$$

$$= \frac{x}{x} \cdot \frac{1}{h} \ln \frac{x + h}{x}$$

$$= \frac{1}{x} \left[\frac{x}{h} \ln\left(1 + \frac{h}{x} \right) \right] \quad \text{Use } p \ln A = \ln A^p.$$

$$= \frac{1}{x} \ln\left(1 + \frac{h}{x} \right)^{x/h}$$

Step 4 Find $f'(x) = \lim\limits_{h \to 0} \dfrac{f(x+h) - f(x)}{h}$.

$$
\begin{aligned}
f'(x) &= \lim_{h \to 0} \frac{f(x+h) - f(x)}{h} \\
&= \lim_{h \to 0} \left[\frac{1}{x} \ln\left(1 + \frac{h}{x}\right)^{x/h} \right] && \text{Let } s = h/x. \text{ Note that } h \to 0 \text{ implies } s \to 0. \\
&= \frac{1}{x} \lim_{s \to 0} \left[\ln(1 + s)^{1/s} \right] && \text{Use a new limit property.}^* \\
&= \frac{1}{x} \ln\left[\lim_{s \to 0} (1 + s)^{1/s} \right] && \text{Use the definition of } e. \\
&= \frac{1}{x} \ln e && \ln e = \log_e e = 1 \\
&= \frac{1}{x}
\end{aligned}
$$

Therefore,

$$
\frac{d}{dx} \ln x = \frac{1}{x} \quad (x > 0)
$$

CONCEPTUAL INSIGHT

In finding the derivative of ln x, we used the following properties of logarithms:

$$
\ln \frac{A}{B} = \ln A - \ln B \qquad \ln A^p = p \ln A
$$

We also noted that there is no property that simplifies $\ln(A + B)$. (See Theorem 1 in Section 1.6 for a list of properties of logarithms.)

EXAMPLE 2 Finding Derivatives Find y' for

(A) $y = 3e^x + 5 \ln x$ (B) $y = x^4 - \ln x^4$

SOLUTIONS

(A) $y' = 3e^x + \dfrac{5}{x}$

(B) Before taking the derivative, we use a property of logarithms (see Theorem 1, Section 1.6) to rewrite y.

$$
\begin{aligned}
y &= x^4 - \ln x^4 && \text{Use } \ln M^p = p \ln M. \\
y &= x^4 - 4 \ln x && \text{Now take the derivative of both sides.} \\
y' &= 4x^3 - \frac{4}{x}
\end{aligned}
$$

Matched Problem 2 Find y' for

(A) $y = 10x^3 - 100 \ln x$ (B) $y = \ln x^5 + e^x - \ln e^2$

Other Logarithmic and Exponential Functions

In most applications involving logarithmic or exponential functions, the number e is the preferred base. However, in some situations it is convenient to use a base other than e. Derivatives of $y = \log_b x$ and $y = b^x$ can be obtained by expressing these functions in terms of the natural logarithmic and exponential functions.

---

*The following new limit property is used: If $\lim_{x \to c} f(x)$ exists and is positive, then $\lim_{x \to c} [\ln f(x)] = \ln[\lim_{x \to c} f(x)]$.

We begin by finding a relationship between $\log_b x$ and $\ln x$ for any base b such that $b > 0$ and $b \neq 1$.

$$y = \log_b x \qquad \text{Change to exponential form.}$$
$$b^y = x \qquad \text{Take the natural logarithm of both sides.}$$
$$\ln b^y = \ln x \qquad \text{Recall that } \ln b^y = y \ln b.$$
$$y \ln b = \ln x \qquad \text{Solve for } y.$$
$$y = \frac{1}{\ln b} \ln x$$

Therefore,

$$\log_b x = \frac{1}{\ln b} \ln x \qquad \text{Change-of-base formula for logarithms*} \qquad (2)$$

Similarly, we can find a relationship between b^x and e^x for any base b such that $b > 0, b \neq 1$.

$$y = b^x \qquad \text{Take the natural logarithm of both sides.}$$
$$\ln y = \ln b^x \qquad \text{Recall that } \ln b^x = x \ln b.$$
$$\ln y = x \ln b \qquad \text{Take the exponential function of both sides.}$$
$$y = e^{x \ln b}$$

Therefore,

$$b^x = e^{x \ln b} \qquad \text{Change-of-base formula for exponential functions} \qquad (3)$$

Differentiating both sides of equation (2) gives

$$\frac{d}{dx} \log_b x = \frac{1}{\ln b} \frac{d}{dx} \ln x = \frac{1}{\ln b} \left(\frac{1}{x} \right) \quad (x > 0)$$

It can be shown that the derivative of the function e^{cx}, where c is a constant, is the function ce^{cx} (see Problems 61–62 in Exercise 3.2 or the more general results of Section 3.4). Therefore, differentiating both sides of equation (3), we have

$$\frac{d}{dx} b^x = e^{x \ln b} \ln b = b^x \ln b$$

For convenience, we list the derivative formulas for exponential and logarithmic functions:

Derivatives of Exponential and Logarithmic Functions
For $b > 0, b \neq 1$,

$$\frac{d}{dx} e^x = e^x \qquad \frac{d}{dx} b^x = b^x \ln b$$

For $b > 0, b \neq 1$, and $x > 0$,

$$\frac{d}{dx} \ln x = \frac{1}{x} \qquad \frac{d}{dx} \log_b x = \frac{1}{\ln b} \left(\frac{1}{x} \right)$$

EXAMPLE 3 Finding Derivatives Find $g'(x)$ for

(A) $g(x) = 2^x - 3^x$

(B) $g(x) = \log_4 x^5$

---

*Equation (2) is a special case of the **general change-of-base formula** for logarithms (which can be derived in the same way): $\log_b x = (\log_a x)/(\log_a b)$.

SOLUTIONS

(A) $g'(x) = 2^x \ln 2 - 3^x \ln 3$

(B) First, use a property of logarithms to rewrite $g(x)$.

$$g(x) = \log_4 x^5 \qquad \text{Use } \log_b M^p = p \log_b M.$$
$$g(x) = 5 \log_4 x \qquad \text{Take the derivative of both sides.}$$
$$g'(x) = \frac{5}{\ln 4}\left(\frac{1}{x}\right)$$

Matched Problem 3 Find $g'(x)$ for

(A) $g(x) = x^{10} + 10^x$ 　　　　　　 (B) $g(x) = \log_2 x - 6 \log_5 x$

Explore and Discuss 2 (A) The graphs of $f(x) = \log_2 x$ and $g(x) = \log_4 x$ are shown in Figure 2. Which graph belongs to which function?

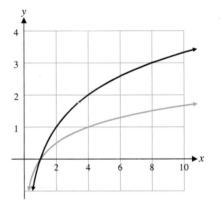

Figure 2

(B) Sketch graphs of $f'(x)$ and $g'(x)$.

(C) The function $f(x)$ is related to $g(x)$ in the same way that $f'(x)$ is related to $g'(x)$. What is that relationship?

Exponential and Logarithmic Models

EXAMPLE 4 Price–Demand Model An Internet store sells Australian wool blankets. If the store sells x blankets at a price of $\$p$ per blanket, then the price–demand equation is $p = 350(0.999)^x$. Find the rate of change of price with respect to demand when the demand is 800 blankets and interpret the result.

SOLUTION

$$\frac{dp}{dx} = 350(0.999)^x \ln 0.999$$

If $x = 800$, then

$$\frac{dp}{dx} = 350(0.999)^{800} \ln 0.999 \approx -0.157, \text{ or } -\$0.16$$

When the demand is 800 blankets, the price is decreasing by $0.16 per blanket.

Matched Problem 4 The store in Example 4 also sells a reversible fleece blanket. If the price–demand equation for reversible fleece blankets is $p = 200(0.998)^x$, find the rate of change of price with respect to demand when the demand is 400 blankets and interpret the result.

EXAMPLE 5 Continuous Compound Interest An investment of $1,000 earns interest at an annual rate of 4% compounded continuously.

(A) Find the instantaneous rate of change of the amount in the account after 2 years.

(B) Find the instantaneous rate of change of the amount in the account at the time the amount is equal to $2,000.

SOLUTION

(A) The amount $A(t)$ at time t (in years) is given by $A(t) = 1,000e^{0.04t}$. Note that $A(t) = 1,000b^t$, where $b = e^{0.04}$. The instantaneous rate of change is the derivative $A'(t)$, which we find by using the formula for the derivative of the exponential function with base b:

$$A'(t) = 1,000b^t \ln b = 1,000e^{0.04t}(0.04) = 40e^{0.04t}$$

After 2 years, $A'(2) = 40e^{0.04(2)} = \$43.33$ per year.

(B) From the calculation of the derivative in part (A), we note that $A'(t) = (0.04)1,000e^{0.04t} = 0.04A(t)$. In other words, the instantaneous rate of change of the amount is always equal to 4% of the amount. So if the amount is $2,000, then the instantaneous rate of change is $(0.04)\$2,000 = \$80$ per year.

Matched Problem 5 An investment of $5,000 earns interest at an annual rate of 6% compounded continuously.

(A) Find the instantaneous rate of change of the amount in the account after 3 years.

(B) Find the instantaneous rate of change of the amount in the account at the time the amount is equal to $8,000.

EXAMPLE 6 Cable TV Subscribers A statistician used data from the U.S. Census Bureau to construct the model

$$S(t) = 11 \ln t + 29$$

where $S(t)$ is the number of cable TV subscribers (in millions) in year ($t = 0$ corresponds to 1980). Use this model to estimate the number of cable TV subscribers in 2020 and the rate of change of the number of subscribers in 2020. Round both to the nearest tenth of a million. Interpret these results.

SOLUTION Since 2020 corresponds to $t = 40$, we must find $S(40)$ and $S'(40)$.

$$S(40) = 11 \ln 40 + 29 = 69.6 \text{ million}$$

$$S'(t) = 11\frac{1}{t} = \frac{11}{t}$$

$$S'(40) = \frac{11}{40} = 0.3 \text{ million}$$

In 2020 there will be approximately 69.6 million subscribers, and this number is growing at the rate of 0.3 million subscribers per year.

Matched Problem 6 A model for a newspaper's circulation is

$$C(t) = 83 - 9 \ln t$$

where $C(t)$ is the circulation (in thousands) in year t ($t = 0$ corresponds to 1980). Use this model to estimate the circulation and the rate of change of circulation in 2020. Round both to the nearest hundred. Interpret these results.

CONCEPTUAL INSIGHT

On most graphing calculators, exponential regression produces a function of the form $y = a \cdot b^x$. Formula (3) on page 191 allows you to change the base b (chosen by the graphing calculator) to the more familiar base e:

$$y = a \cdot b^x = a \cdot e^{x \ln b}$$

On most graphing calculators, logarithmic regression produces a function of the form $y = a + b \ln x$. Formula (2) on page 191 allows you to write the function in terms of logarithms to any base d that you may prefer:

$$y = a + b \ln x = a + b(\ln d) \log_d x$$

Exercises 3.2

W | Skills Warm-up Exercises

In Problems 1–8, solve for the variable without using a calculator. (If necessary, review Section 1.6).

1. $y = \log_2 128$ **2.** $y = \ln e^5$

3. $\log_3 x = 4$ **4.** $\log_5 x = -2$

5. $\log_b 64 = 2$ **6.** $\log_b 5 = \dfrac{1}{3}$

7. $y = \ln \sqrt{e}$ **8.** $y = \ln (\ln e)$

In Problems 9–26, find $f'(x)$.

9. $f(x) = 5e^x + 3x + 1$ **10.** $f(x) = -7e^x - 2x + 5$

11. $f(x) = -2 \ln x + x^2 - 4$ **12.** $f(x) = 6 \ln x - x^3 + 2$

13. $f(x) = x^3 - 6e^x$ **14.** $f(x) = 9e^x + 2x^2$

15. $f(x) = e^x + x - \ln x$ **16.** $f(x) = \ln x + 2e^x - 3x^2$

17. $f(x) = \ln x^3$ **18.** $f(x) = \ln x^8$

19. $f(x) = 5x - \ln x^5$ **20.** $f(x) = 4 + \ln x^9$

21. $f(x) = \ln x^2 + 4e^x$ **22.** $f(x) = \ln x^{10} + 2 \ln x$

23. $f(x) = e^x + x^e$ **24.** $f(x) = 3x^e - 2e^x$

25. $f(x) = xx^e$ **26.** $f(x) = ee^x$

In Problems 27–34, find the equation of the line tangent to the graph of f at the indicated value of x.

27. $f(x) = 3 + \ln x; x = 1$ **28.** $f(x) = 2 \ln x; x = 1$

29. $f(x) = 3e^x; x = 0$ **30.** $f(x) = e^x + 1; x = 0$

31. $f(x) = \ln x^3; x = e$ **32.** $f(x) = 1 + \ln x^4; x = e$

33. $f(x) = 2 + e^x; x = 1$ **34.** $f(x) = 5e^x; x = 1$

35. A student claims that the line tangent to the graph of $f(x) = e^x$ at $x = 3$ passes through the point $(2, 0)$ (see the figure). Is she correct? Will the line tangent at $x = 4$ pass through $(3, 0)$? Explain.

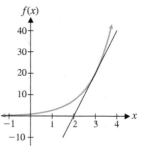

36. Refer to Problem 35. Does the line tangent to the graph of $f(x) = e^x$ at $x = 1$ pass through the origin? Are there any other lines tangent to the graph of f that pass through the origin? Explain.

37. A student claims that the line tangent to the graph of $g(x) = \ln x$ at $x = 3$ passes through the origin (see the figure). Is he correct? Will the line tangent at $x = 4$ pass through the origin? Explain.

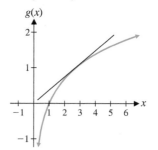

38. Refer to Problem 37. Does the line tangent to the graph of $f(x) = \ln x$ at $x = e$ pass through the origin? Are there any other lines tangent to the graph of f that pass through the origin? Explain.

In Problems 39–42, first use appropriate properties of logarithms to rewrite $f(x)$, and then find $f'(x)$.

39. $f(x) = 10x + \ln 10x$ **40.** $f(x) = 2 + 3 \ln \dfrac{1}{x}$

41. $f(x) = \ln \dfrac{4}{x^3}$ **42.** $f(x) = x + 5 \ln 6x$

In Problems 43–54, find $\dfrac{dy}{dx}$ for the indicated function y.

43. $y = \log_2 x$

44. $y = 3 \log_5 x$

45. $y = 3^x$

46. $y = 4^x$

47. $y = 2x - \log x$

48. $y = \log x + 4x^2 + 1$

49. $y = 10 + x + 10^x$

50. $y = x^5 - 5^x$

51. $y = 3 \ln x + 2 \log_3 x$

52. $y = -\log_2 x + 10 \ln x$

53. $y = 2^x + e^2$

54. $y = e^3 - 3^x$

In Problems 55–60, use graphical approximation methods to find the points of intersection of $f(x)$ and $g(x)$ (to two decimal places).

55. $f(x) = e^x$; $g(x) = x^4$

[Note that there are three points of intersection and that e^x is greater than x^4 for large values of x.]

56. $f(x) = e^x$; $g(x) = x^5$

[Note that there are two points of intersection and that e^x is greater than x^5 for large values of x.]

57. $f(x) = (\ln x)^2$; $g(x) = x$

58. $f(x) = (\ln x)^3$; $g(x) = x$

59. $f(x) = \ln x$; $g(x) = x^{1/5}$

60. $f(x) = \ln x$; $g(x) = x^{1/4}$

61. Explain why $\lim\limits_{h \to 0} \dfrac{e^{ch} - 1}{h} = c$.

62. Use the result of Problem 61 and the four-step process to show that if $f(x) = e^{cx}$, then $f'(x) = ce^{cx}$.

Applications

63. Salvage value. The estimated salvage value S (in dollars) of a company airplane after t years is given by

$$S(t) = 300{,}000(0.9)^t$$

What is the rate of depreciation (in dollars per year) after 1 year? 5 years? 10 years?

64. Resale value. The estimated resale value R (in dollars) of a company car after t years is given by

$$R(t) = 20{,}000(0.86)^t$$

What is the rate of depreciation (in dollars per year) after 1 year? 2 years? 3 years?

65. Bacterial growth. A single cholera bacterium divides every 0.5 hour to produce two complete cholera bacteria. If we start with a colony of 5,000 bacteria, then after t hours, there will be

$$A(t) = 5{,}000 \cdot 2^{2t} = 5{,}000 \cdot 4^t$$

bacteria. Find $A'(t), A'(1)$, and $A'(5)$, and interpret the results.

66. Bacterial growth. Repeat Problem 65 for a starting colony of 1,000 bacteria such that a single bacterium divides every 0.25 hour.

67. Blood pressure. An experiment was set up to find a relationship between weight and systolic blood pressure in children. Using hospital records for 5,000 children, the experimenters found that the systolic blood pressure was given approximately by

$$P(x) = 17.5(1 + \ln x) \qquad 10 \le x \le 100$$

where $P(x)$ is measured in millimeters of mercury and x is measured in pounds. What is the rate of change of blood pressure with respect to weight at the 40-pound weight level? At the 90-pound weight level?

68. Blood pressure. Refer to Problem 67. Find the weight (to the nearest pound) at which the rate of change of blood pressure with respect to weight is 0.3 millimeter of mercury per pound.

69. Psychology: stimulus/response. In psychology, the Weber–Fechner law for the response to a stimulus is

$$R = k \ln \frac{S}{S_0}$$

where R is the response, S is the stimulus, and S_0 is the lowest level of stimulus that can be detected. Find dR/dS.

70. Psychology: learning. A mathematical model for the average of a group of people learning to type is given by

$$N(t) = 10 + 6 \ln t \qquad t \ge 1$$

where $N(t)$ is the number of words per minute typed after t hours of instruction and practice (2 hours per day, 5 days per week). What is the rate of learning after 10 hours of instruction and practice? After 100 hours?

71. Continuous Compound Interest. An investment of $10,000 earns interest at an annual rate of 7.5% compounded continuously.

(A) Find the instantaneous rate of change of the amount in the account after 1 year.

(B) Find the instantaneous rate of change of the amount in the account at the time the amount is equal to $12,500.

72. Continuous Compound Interest. An investment of $25,000 earns interest at an annual rate of 8.4% compounded continuously.

(A) Find the instantaneous rate of change of the amount in the account after 2 years.

(B) Find the instantaneous rate of change of the amount in the account at the time the amount is equal to $30,000.

Answers to Matched Problems

1. (A) $4e^x + 16x + 7$ (B) $7x^6 - 5x^4 - 1 + e^x$

2. (A) $30x^2 - \dfrac{100}{x}$ (B) $\dfrac{5}{x} + e^x$

3. (A) $10x^9 + 10^x \ln 10$ (B) $\left(\dfrac{1}{\ln 2} - \dfrac{6}{\ln 5} \right) \dfrac{1}{x}$

4. The price is decreasing at the rate of $0.18 per blanket.

5. (A) $359.17 per year   (B) $480 per year

6. The circulation in 2020 is approximately 49,800 and is decreasing at the rate of 200 per year.

3.3 Derivatives of Products and Quotients

- Derivatives of Products
- Derivatives of Quotients

The derivative properties discussed in Section 2.5 add substantially to our ability to compute and apply derivatives to many practical problems. In this and the next two sections, we add a few more properties that will increase this ability even further.

Derivatives of Products

In Section 2.5, we found that the derivative of a sum is the sum of the derivatives. Is the derivative of a product the product of the derivatives?

Explore and Discuss 1 Let $F(x) = x^2$, $S(x) = x^3$, and $f(x) = F(x)S(x) = x^5$. Which of the following is $f'(x)$?

(A) $F'(x)S'(x)$ (B) $F(x)S'(x)$

(C) $F'(x)S(x)$ (D) $F(x)S'(x) + F'(x)S(x)$

Comparing the various expressions computed in Explore and Discuss 1, we see that the derivative of a product is not the product of the derivatives.

Using the definition of the derivative and the four-step process, we can show that

The derivative of the product of two functions is the first times the derivative of the second, plus the second times the derivative of the first.

This **product rule** is expressed more compactly in Theorem 1, with notation chosen to aid memorization (F for "first", S for "second").

THEOREM 1 Product Rule

If
$$y = f(x) = F(x)S(x)$$
and if $F'(x)$ and $S'(x)$ exist, then
$$f'(x) = F(x)S'(x) + S(x)F'(x)$$
Using simplified notation,

$$y' = FS' + SF' \quad\quad \text{or} \quad\quad \frac{dy}{dx} = F\frac{dS}{dx} + S\frac{dF}{dx}$$

EXAMPLE 1 Differentiating a Product Use two different methods to find $f'(x)$ for

$$f(x) = 2x^2(3x^4 - 2).$$

SOLUTION

Method 1. Use the product rule with $F(x) = 2x^2$ and $S(x) = 3x^4 - 2$:

$$f'(x) = 2x^2(3x^4 - 2)' + (3x^4 - 2)(2x^2)' \quad \text{First times derivative of}$$
$$= 2x^2(12x^3) + (3x^4 - 2)(4x) \quad \text{second, plus second times}$$
$$= 24x^5 + 12x^5 - 8x \quad \text{derivative of first}$$
$$= 36x^5 - 8x$$

Method 2. Multiply first; then find the derivative:

$$f(x) = 2x^2(3x^4 - 2) = 6x^6 - 4x^2$$
$$f'(x) = 36x^5 - 8x$$

Matched Problem 1) Use two different methods to find $f'(x)$ for
$$f(x) = 3x^3(2x^2 - 3x + 1).$$

Some products we encounter can be differentiated by either method illustrated in Example 1. In other situations, the product rule *must* be used. Unless instructed otherwise, you should use the product rule to differentiate all products in this section in order to gain experience with this important differentiation rule.

EXAMPLE 2 Tangent Lines Let $f(x) = (2x - 9)(x^2 + 6)$.
(A) Find the equation of the line tangent to the graph of $f(x)$ at $x = 3$.
(B) Find the value(s) of x where the tangent line is horizontal.

SOLUTION
(A) First, find $f'(x)$:
$$f'(x) = (2x - 9)(x^2 + 6)' + (x^2 + 6)(2x - 9)'$$
$$= (2x - 9)(2x) + (x^2 + 6)(2)$$

Then, find $f(3)$ and $f'(3)$:
$$f(3) = [2(3) - 9](3^2 + 6) = (-3)(15) = -45$$
$$f'(3) = [2(3) - 9]2(3) + (3^2 + 6)(2) = -18 + 30 = 12$$

Now, find the equation of the tangent line at $x = 3$:
$$y - y_1 = m(x - x_1) \quad y_1 = f(x_1) = f(3) = -45$$
$$y - (-45) = 12(x - 3) \quad m = f'(x_1) = f'(3) = 12$$
$$y = 12x - 81 \quad \text{Tangent line at } x = 3$$

(B) The tangent line is horizontal at any value of x such that $f'(x) = 0$, so
$$f'(x) = (2x - 9)2x + (x^2 + 6)2 = 0$$
$$6x^2 - 18x + 12 = 0$$
$$x^2 - 3x + 2 = 0$$
$$(x - 1)(x - 2) = 0$$
$$x = 1, 2$$

The tangent line is horizontal at $x = 1$ and at $x = 2$.

Matched Problem 2) Repeat Example 2 for $f(x) = (2x + 9)(x^2 - 12)$.

CONCEPTUAL INSIGHT

As Example 2 illustrates, the way we write $f'(x)$ depends on what we want to do. If we are interested only in evaluating $f'(x)$ at specified values of x, then the form in part (A) is sufficient. However, if we want to solve $f'(x) = 0$, we must multiply and collect like terms, as we did in part (B).

EXAMPLE 3 Finding Derivatives Find $f'(x)$ for
(A) $f(x) = 2x^3e^x$ 　　　　　　　　　　　　　(B) $f(x) = 6x^4 \ln x$

SOLUTIONS

(A) $f'(x) = 2x^3(e^x)' + e^x(2x^3)'$

$= 2x^3 e^x + e^x(6x^2)$

$= 2x^2 e^x(x + 3)$

(B) $f'(x) = 6x^4 (\ln x)' + (\ln x) (6x^4)'$

$= 6x^4 \dfrac{1}{x} + (\ln x)(24x^3)$

$= 6x^3 + 24x^3 \ln x$

$= 6x^3 (1 + 4 \ln x)$

Matched Problem 3⌋ Find $f'(x)$ for

(A) $f(x) = 5x^8 e^x$

(B) $f(x) = x^7 \ln x$

Derivatives of Quotients

The derivative of a quotient of two functions is not the quotient of the derivatives of the two functions.

Explore and Discuss 2   Let $T(x) = x^5, B(x) = x^2$, and

$$f(x) = \frac{T(x)}{B(x)} = \frac{x^5}{x^2} = x^3$$

Which of the following is $f'(x)$?

(A) $\dfrac{T'(x)}{B'(x)}$

(B) $\dfrac{T'(x)B(x)}{[B(x)]^2}$

(C) $\dfrac{T(x)B'(x)}{[B(x)]^2}$

(D) $\dfrac{T'(x)B(x)}{[B(x)]^2} - \dfrac{T(x)B'(x)}{[B(x)]^2} = \dfrac{B(x)T'(x) - T(x)B'(x)}{[B(x)]^2}$

The expressions in Explore and Discuss 2 suggest that the derivative of a quotient leads to a more complicated quotient than expected.

If $T(x)$ and $B(x)$ are any two differentiable functions and

$$f(x) = \frac{T(x)}{B(x)}$$

then

$$f'(x) = \frac{B(x)T'(x) - T(x)B'(x)}{[B(x)]^2}$$

Therefore,

The derivative of the quotient of two functions is the denominator times the derivative of the numerator, minus the numerator times the derivative of the denominator, divided by the denominator squared.

This **quotient rule** is expressed more compactly in Theorem 2, with notation chosen to aid memorization (*T* for "top", *B* for "bottom").

THEOREM 2 Quotient Rule

If

$$y = f(x) = \frac{T(x)}{B(x)}$$

and if $T'(x)$ and $B'(x)$ exist, then

$$f'(x) = \frac{B(x)T'(x) - T(x)B'(x)}{[B(x)]^2}$$

Using simplified notation,

$$y' = \frac{BT' - TB'}{B^2} \qquad \text{or} \qquad \frac{dy}{dx} = \frac{B\dfrac{dT}{dx} - T\dfrac{dB}{dx}}{B^2}$$

EXAMPLE 4 Differentiating Quotients

(A) If $f(x) = \dfrac{x^2}{2x - 1}$, find $f'(x)$. (B) If $y = \dfrac{t^2 - t}{t^3 + 1}$, find y'.

(C) Find $\dfrac{d}{dx} \dfrac{x^2 - 3}{x^2}$ by using the quotient rule and also by splitting the fraction into two fractions.

SOLUTION

(A) Use the quotient rule with $T(x) = x^2$ and $B(x) = 2x - 1$;

$$f'(x) = \frac{(2x - 1)(x^2)' - x^2(2x - 1)'}{(2x - 1)^2}$$

The denominator times the derivative of the numerator, minus the numerator times the derivative of the denominator, divided by the square of the denominator

$$= \frac{(2x - 1)(2x) - x^2(2)}{(2x - 1)^2}$$

$$= \frac{4x^2 - 2x - 2x^2}{(2x - 1)^2}$$

$$= \frac{2x^2 - 2x}{(2x - 1)^2}$$

(B) $$y' = \frac{(t^3 + 1)(t^2 - t)' - (t^2 - t)(t^3 + 1)'}{(t^3 + 1)^2}$$

$$= \frac{(t^3 + 1)(2t - 1) - (t^2 - t)(3t^2)}{(t^3 + 1)^2}$$

$$= \frac{2t^4 - t^3 + 2t - 1 - 3t^4 + 3t^3}{(t^3 + 1)^2}$$

$$= \frac{-t^4 + 2t^3 + 2t - 1}{(t^3 + 1)^2}$$

(C) Method 1. Use the quotient rule:

$$\frac{d}{dx} \frac{x^2 - 3}{x^2} = \frac{x^2 \dfrac{d}{dx}(x^2 - 3) - (x^2 - 3)\dfrac{d}{dx}x^2}{(x^2)^2}$$

$$= \frac{x^2(2x) - (x^2 - 3)2x}{x^4}$$

$$= \frac{2x^3 - 2x^3 + 6x}{x^4} = \frac{6x}{x^4} = \frac{6}{x^3}$$

Method 2. Split into two fractions:

$$\frac{x^2 - 3}{x^2} = \frac{x^2}{x^2} - \frac{3}{x^2} = 1 - 3x^{-2}$$

$$\frac{d}{dx}(1 - 3x^{-2}) = 0 - 3(-2)x^{-3} = \frac{6}{x^3}$$

Comparing methods 1 and 2, we see that it often pays to change an expression algebraically before choosing a differentiation formula.

Matched Problem 4 Find

(A) $f'(x)$ for $f(x) = \dfrac{2x}{x^2 + 3}$

(B) y' for $y = \dfrac{t^3 - 3t}{t^2 - 4}$

(C) $\dfrac{d}{dx} \dfrac{2 + x^3}{x^3}$ in two ways

EXAMPLE 5   Finding Derivatives   Find $f'(x)$ for

(A) $f(x) = \dfrac{3e^x}{1 + e^x}$

(B) $f(x) = \dfrac{\ln x}{2x + 5}$

SOLUTIONS

(A) $f'(x) = \dfrac{(1 + e^x)(3e^x)' - 3e^x(1 + e^x)'}{(1 + e^x)^2}$

$= \dfrac{(1 + e^x)3e^x - 3e^x e^x}{(1 + e^x)^2}$

$= \dfrac{3e^x}{(1 + e^x)^2}$

(B) $f'(x) = \dfrac{(2x + 5)(\ln x)' - (\ln x)(2x + 5)'}{(2x + 5)^2}$

$= \dfrac{(2x + 5) \cdot \dfrac{1}{x} - (\ln x)(2)}{(2x + 5)^2}$ Multiply by $\dfrac{x}{x}$

$= \dfrac{2x + 5 - 2x \ln x}{x(2x + 5)^2}$

Matched Problem 5 Find $f'(x)$ for

(A) $f(x) = \dfrac{x^3}{e^x + 2}$

(B) $f(x) = \dfrac{4x}{1 + \ln x}$

EXAMPLE 6   Sales Analysis   The total sales S (in thousands of games) of a video game t months after the game is introduced are given by

$$S(t) = \dfrac{125t^2}{t^2 + 100}$$

(A) Find $S'(t)$.

(B) Find $S(10)$ and $S'(10)$. Write a brief interpretation of these results.

(C) Use the results from part (B) to estimate the total sales after 11 months.

SOLUTION

(A) $S'(t) = \dfrac{(t^2 + 100)(125t^2)' - 125t^2(t^2 + 100)'}{(t^2 + 100)^2}$

$= \dfrac{(t^2 + 100)(250t) - 125t^2(2t)}{(t^2 + 100)^2}$

$= \dfrac{250t^3 + 25{,}000t - 250t^3}{(t^2 + 100)^2}$

$= \dfrac{25{,}000t}{(t^2 + 100)^2}$

(B) $S(10) = \dfrac{125(10)^2}{10^2 + 100} = 62.5$ and $S'(10) = \dfrac{25,000(10)}{(10^2 + 100)^2} = 6.25.$

Total sales after 10 months are 62,500 games, and sales are increasing at the rate of 6,250 games per month.

(C) Total sales will increase by approximately 6,250 games during the next month, so the estimated total sales after 11 months are $62,500 + 6,250 = 68,750$ games.

Matched Problem 6 Refer to Example 6. Suppose that the total sales S (in thousands of games) t months after the game is introduced are given by

$$S(t) = \dfrac{150t}{t + 3}$$

(A) Find $S'(t)$.

(B) Find $S(12)$ and $S'(12)$. Write a brief interpretation of these results.

(C) Use the results from part (B) to estimate the total sales after 13 months.

Exercises 3.3

Skills Warm-up Exercises

W *In Problems 1–4, find functions $F(x)$ and $S(x)$, neither a constant function, such that the given function $f(x)$ is equal to the product $F(x)S(x)$. (If necessary, review Section A.2).*

1. $f(x) = 5x^3 - 4x^3 \ln\ x$

2. $f(x) = 6e^x + 2x^2e^x + 3x^4e^x$

3. $f(x) = x^3e^x + 2x^3 + 3e^x + 6$

4. $f(x) = 20 + 5\ \ln\ x + 4x^2 + x^2\ \ln\ x$

In Problems 5–8, find functions $T(x)$ and $B(x)$, neither a constant function, such that the given function $f(x)$ is equal to the quotient $T(x)/B(x)$. (If necessary, review Section A.2).

5. $f(x) = 9x^2e^{-5x}$ 6. $f(x) = 8x^{-2}\ \ln\ x$

7. $f(x) = \dfrac{3}{x^2} + \dfrac{e^x}{x^4}$ 8. $f(x) = \dfrac{1}{x} + \dfrac{2}{x^2} + \dfrac{4}{x^3}$

Answers to most of the following problems in this exercise set contain both an unsimplified form and a simplified form of the derivative. When checking your work, first check that you applied the rules correctly and then check that you performed the algebraic simplification correctly. Unless instructed otherwise, when differentiating a product, use the product rule rather than performing the multiplication first.

In Problems 9–34, find $f'(x)$ and simplify.

9. $f(x) = 2x^3(x^2 - 2)$ 10. $f(x) = 5x^2(x^3 + 2)$

11. $f(x) = (x - 3)(2x - 1)$

12. $f(x) = (3x + 2)(4x - 5)$

13. $f(x) = \dfrac{x}{x - 3}$ 14. $f(x) = \dfrac{3x}{2x + 1}$

15. $f(x) = \dfrac{2x + 3}{x - 2}$ 16. $f(x) = \dfrac{3x - 4}{2x + 3}$

17. $f(x) = 3xe^x$ 18. $f(x) = x^2e^x$

19. $f(x) = x^3\ \ln\ x$ 20. $f(x) = 5x\ \ln\ x$

21. $f(x) = (x^2 + 1)(2x - 3)$

22. $f(x) = (3x + 5)(x^2 - 3)$

23. $f(x) = (0.4x + 2)(0.5x - 5)$

24. $f(x) = (0.5x - 4)(0.2x + 1)$

25. $f(x) = \dfrac{x^2 + 1}{2x - 3}$ 26. $f(x) = \dfrac{3x + 5}{x^2 - 3}$

27. $f(x) = (x^2 + 2)(x^2 - 3)$

28. $f(x) = (x^2 - 4)(x^2 + 5)$

29. $f(x) = \dfrac{x^2 + 2}{x^2 - 3}$ 30. $f(x) = \dfrac{x^2 - 4}{x^2 + 5}$

31. $f(x) = \dfrac{e^x}{x^2 + 1}$ 32. $f(x) = \dfrac{1 - e^x}{1 + e^x}$

33. $f(x) = \dfrac{\ln\ x}{1 + x}$ 34. $f(x) = \dfrac{2x}{1 + \ln\ x}$

In Problems 35–46, find $h'(x)$, where $f(x)$ is an unspecified differentiable function.

35. $h(x) = xf(x)$ 36. $h(x) = x^2f(x)$

37. $h(x) = x^3f(x)$ 38. $h(x) = \dfrac{f(x)}{x}$

39. $h(x) = \dfrac{f(x)}{x^2}$ 40. $h(x) = \dfrac{f(x)}{x^3}$

41. $h(x) = \dfrac{x}{f(x)}$ 42. $h(x) = \dfrac{x^2}{f(x)}$

43. $h(x) = e^x f(x)$

44. $h(x) = \dfrac{e^x}{f(x)}$

45. $h(x) = \dfrac{\ln x}{f(x)}$

46. $h(x) = \dfrac{f(x)}{\ln x}$

In Problems 47–56, find the indicated derivatives and simplify.

47. $f'(x)$ for $f(x) = (2x + 1)(x^2 - 3x)$

48. y' for $y = (x^3 + 2x^2)(3x - 1)$

49. $\dfrac{dy}{dt}$ for $y = (2.5t - t^2)(4t + 1.4)$

50. $\dfrac{d}{dt}[(3 - 0.4t^3)(0.5t^2 - 2t)]$

51. y' for $y = \dfrac{5x - 3}{x^2 + 2x}$

52. $f'(x)$ for $f(x) = \dfrac{3x^2}{2x - 1}$

53. $\dfrac{d}{dw}\dfrac{w^2 - 3w + 1}{w^2 - 1}$

54. $\dfrac{dy}{dw}$ for $y = \dfrac{w^4 - w^3}{3w - 1}$

55. y' for $y = (1 + x - x^2)e^x$

56. $\dfrac{dy}{dt}$ for $y - (1 + e^t)\ln t$

In Problems 57–60:

(A) *Find $f'(x)$ using the quotient rule, and*

(B) *Explain how $f'(x)$ can be found easily without using the quotient rule.*

57. $f(x) = \dfrac{1}{x}$

58. $f(x) = \dfrac{-1}{x^2}$

59. $f(x) = \dfrac{-3}{x^4}$

60. $f(x) = \dfrac{2}{x^3}$

In Problems 61–66, find $f'(x)$ and find the equation of the line tangent to the graph of f at $x = 2$.

61. $f(x) = (1 + 3x)(5 - 2x)$

62. $f(x) = (7 - 3x)(1 + 2x)$

63. $f(x) = \dfrac{x - 8}{3x - 4}$

64. $f(x) = \dfrac{2x - 5}{2x - 3}$

65. $f(x) = \dfrac{x}{2^x}$

66. $f(x) = (x - 2)\ln x$

In Problems 67–70, find $f'(x)$ and find the value(s) of x where $f'(x) = 0$.

67. $f(x) = (2x - 15)(x^2 + 18)$

68. $f(x) = (2x - 3)(x^2 - 6)$

69. $f(x) = \dfrac{x}{x^2 + 1}$

70. $f(x) = \dfrac{x}{x^2 + 9}$

In Problems 71–74, find $f'(x)$ in two ways: (1) using the product or quotient rule and (2) simplifying first.

71. $f(x) = x^3(x^4 - 1)$

72. $f(x) = x^4(x^3 - 1)$

73. $f(x) = \dfrac{x^3 + 9}{x^3}$

74. $f(x) = \dfrac{x^4 + 4}{x^4}$

In Problems 75–92, find each indicated derivative and simplify.

75. $f(w) = (w + 1)2^w$

76. $g(w) = (w - 5)\log_3 w$

77. $\dfrac{dy}{dx}$ for $y = 9x^{1/3}(x^3 + 5)$

78. $\dfrac{d}{dx}[(4x^{1/2} - 1)(3x^{1/3} + 2)]$

79. y' for $y = \dfrac{\log_2 x}{1 + x^2}$

80. $\dfrac{dy}{dx}$ for $y = \dfrac{10^x}{1 + x^4}$

81. $f'(x)$ for $f(x) = \dfrac{6^3\sqrt{x}}{x^2 - 3}$

82. y' for $y = \dfrac{2\sqrt{x}}{x^2 - 3x + 1}$

83. $g'(t)$ if $g(t) = \dfrac{0.2t}{3t^2 - 1}$

84. $h'(t)$ if $h(t) = \dfrac{-0.05t^2}{2t + 1}$

85. $\dfrac{d}{dx}[4x \log x^5]$

86. $\dfrac{d}{dt}[10^t \log t]$

87. $\dfrac{d}{dx}\dfrac{x^3 - 2x^2}{\sqrt[3]{x^2}}$

88. $\dfrac{dy}{dx}$ for $y = \dfrac{x^2 - 3x + 1}{\sqrt[4]{x}}$

89. $f'(x)$ for $f(x) = \dfrac{(2x^2 - 1)(x^2 + 3)}{x^2 + 1}$

90. y' for $y = \dfrac{2x - 1}{(x^3 + 2)(x^2 - 3)}$

91. $\dfrac{dy}{dt}$ for $y = \dfrac{t \ln t}{e^t}$

92. $\dfrac{dy}{du}$ for $y = \dfrac{u^2 e^u}{1 + \ln u}$

Applications

93. Sales analysis. The total sales S (in thousands of DVDs) of a DVD are given by

$$S(t) = \dfrac{90t^2}{t^2 + 50}$$

where t is the number of months since the release of the DVD.

(A) Find $S'(t)$.

(B) Find $S(10)$ and $S'(10)$. Write a brief interpretation of these results.

(C) Use the results from part (B) to estimate the total sales after 11 months.

94. Sales analysis. A communications company has installed a new cable television system in a city. The total number N (in thousands) of subscribers t months after the installation of the system is given by

$$N(t) = \frac{180t}{t + 4}$$

(A) Find $N'(t)$.

(B) Find $N(16)$ and $N'(16)$. Write a brief interpretation of these results.

(C) Use the results from part (B) to estimate the total number of subscribers after 17 months.

95. Price–demand equation. According to economic theory, the demand x for a quantity in a free market decreases as the price p increases (see the figure). Suppose that the number x of DVD players people are willing to buy per week from a retail chain at a price of $\$p$ is given by

$$x = \frac{4,000}{0.1p + 1} \qquad 10 \leq p \leq 70$$

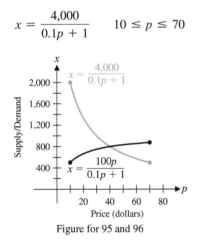

Figure for 95 and 96

(A) Find dx/dp.

(B) Find the demand and the instantaneous rate of change of demand with respect to price when the price is $40. Write a brief interpretation of these results.

(C) Use the results from part (B) to estimate the demand if the price is increased to $41.

96. Price–supply equation. According to economic theory, the supply x of a quantity in a free market increases as the price p increases (see the figure). Suppose that the number x of DVD players a retail chain is willing to sell per week at a price of $\$p$ is given by

$$x = \frac{100p}{0.1p + 1} \qquad 10 \leq p \leq 70$$

(A) Find dx/dp.

(B) Find the supply and the instantaneous rate of change of supply with respect to price when the price is $40. Write a brief verbal interpretation of these results.

(C) Use the results from part (B) to estimate the supply if the price is increased to $41.

97. Medicine. A drug is injected into a patient's bloodstream through her right arm. The drug concentration (in milligrams per cubic centimeter) in the bloodstream of the left arm t hours after the injection is given by

$$C(t) = \frac{0.14t}{t^2 + 1}$$

(A) Find $C'(t)$.

(B) Find $C'(0.5)$ and $C'(3)$, and interpret the results.

98. Drug sensitivity. One hour after a dose of x milligrams of a particular drug is administered to a person, the change in body temperature $T(x)$, in degrees Fahrenheit, is given approximately by

$$T(x) = x^2\left(1 - \frac{x}{9}\right) \qquad 0 \leq x \leq 7$$

The rate $T'(x)$ at which T changes with respect to the size of the dosage x is called the *sensitivity* of the body to the dosage.

(A) Use the product rule to find $T'(x)$.

(B) Find $T'(1)$, $T'(3)$, and $T'(6)$.

Answers to Matched Problems

1. $30x^4 - 36x^3 + 9x^2$

2. (A) $y = 84x - 297$ (B) $x = -4, x = 1$

3. (A) $5x^8e^x + e^x(40x^7) = 5x^7(x + 8)e^x$

(B) $x^7 \cdot \dfrac{1}{x} + \ln x\,(7x^6) = x^6(1 + 7\ln x)$

4. (A) $\dfrac{(x^2 + 3)2 - (2x)(2x)}{(x^2 + 3)^2} = \dfrac{6 - 2x^2}{(x^2 + 3)^2}$

(B) $\dfrac{(t^2 - 4)(3t^2 - 3) - (t^3 - 3t)(2t)}{(t^2 - 4)^2} = \dfrac{t^4 - 9t^2 + 12}{(t^2 - 4)^2}$

(C) $-\dfrac{6}{x^4}$

5. (A) $\dfrac{(e^x + 2)\,3x^2 - x^3e^x}{(e^x + 2)^2}$

(B) $\dfrac{(1 + \ln x)4 - 4x\,\dfrac{1}{x}}{(1 + \ln x)^2} = \dfrac{4\ln x}{(1 + \ln x)^2}$

6. (A) $S'(t) = \dfrac{450}{(t + 3)^2}$

(B) $S(12) = 120$; $S'(12) = 2$. After 12 months, the total sales are 120,000 games, and sales are increasing at the rate of 2,000 games per month.

(C) 122,000 games

3.4 The Chain Rule

- Composite Functions
- General Power Rule
- The Chain Rule

The word *chain* in the name "chain rule" comes from the fact that a function formed by composition involves a chain of functions—that is, a function of a function. The *chain rule* enables us to compute the derivative of a composite function in terms of the derivatives of the functions making up the composite. In this section, we review composite functions, introduce the chain rule by means of a special case known as the *general power rule,* and then discuss the chain rule itself.

Composite Functions

The function $m(x) = (x^2 + 4)^3$ is a combination of a quadratic function and a cubic function. To see this more clearly, let

$$y = f(u) = u^3 \quad \text{and} \quad u = g(x) = x^2 + 4$$

We can express y as a function of x:

$$y = f(u) = f[g(x)] = [x^2 + 4]^3 = m(x)$$

The function m is the *composite* of the two functions f and g.

DEFINITION   Composite Functions
A function m is a **composite** of functions f and g if

$$m(x) = f[g(x)]$$

The domain of m is the set of all numbers x such that x is in the domain of g, and $g(x)$ is in the domain of f.

The composite m of functions f and g is pictured in Figure 1. The domain of m is the shaded subset of the domain of g (Fig. 1); it consists of all numbers x such that x is in the domain of g and $g(x)$ is in the domain of f. Note that the functions f and g play different roles. The function g, which is on the *inside* or *interior* of the square brackets in $f[g(x)]$, is applied first to x. Then function f, which appears on the *outside* or *exterior* of the square brackets, is applied to $g(x)$, provided $g(x)$ is in the domain of f. Because f and g play different roles, the composite of f and g is usually a different function than the composite of g and f, as illustrated by Example 1.

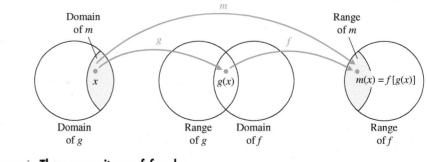

Domain of *m*   Range of *m*

x $g(x)$ $m(x) = f[g(x)]$

Domain of *g*   Range of *g*   Domain of *f*   Range of *f*

Figure 1 **The composite *m* of *f* and *g***

EXAMPLE 1 Composite Functions Let $f(u) = e^u$ and $g(x) = -3x$. Find $f[g(x)]$ and $g[f(u)]$.

SOLUTION

$$f[g(x)] = f(-3x) = e^{-3x}$$
$$g[f(u)] = g(e^u) = -3e^u$$

Matched Problem 1 Let $f(u) = 2u$ and $g(x) = e^x$. Find $f[g(x)]$ and $g[f(u)]$.

EXAMPLE 2 Composite Functions Write each function as a composite of two simpler functions.

(A) $y = 100e^{0.04x}$ (B) $y = \sqrt{4 - x^2}$

SOLUTION

(A) Let

$$y = f(u) = 100e^u$$
$$u = g(x) = 0.04x$$

Check: $y = f[g(x)] = f(0.04x) = 100e^{0.04x}$

(B) Let

$$y = f(u) = \sqrt{u}$$
$$u = g(x) = 4 - x^2$$

Check: $y = f[g(x)] = f(4 - x^2) = \sqrt{4 - x^2}$

Matched Problem 2 Write each function as a composite of two simpler functions.

(A) $y = 50e^{-2x}$ (B) $y = \sqrt[3]{1 + x^3}$

CONCEPTUAL INSIGHT

There can be more than one way to express a function as a composite of simpler functions. Choosing $y = f(u) = 100u$ and $u = g(x) = e^{0.04x}$ in Example 2A produces the same result:

$$y = f[g(x)] = 100g(x) = 100e^{0.04x}$$

Since we will be using composition as a means to an end (finding a derivative), usually it will not matter which functions you choose for the composition.

General Power Rule

We have already made extensive use of the power rule,

$$\frac{d}{dx}x^n = nx^{n-1} \tag{1}$$

Can we apply rule (1) to find the derivative of the composite function $m(x) = p[u(x)] = [u(x)]^n$, where p is the power function $p(u) = u^n$ and $u(x)$ is a differentiable function? In other words, is rule (1) valid if x is replaced by $u(x)$?

Explore and Discuss 1 Let $u(x) = 2x^2$ and $m(x) = [u(x)]^3 = 8x^6$. Which of the following is $m'(x)$?
(A) $3[u(x)]^2$ (B) $3[u'(x)]^2$ (C) $3[u(x)]^2u'(x)$

The calculations in Explore and Discuss 1 show that we cannot find the derivative of $[u(x)]^n$ simply by replacing x with $u(x)$ in equation (1).

How can we find a formula for the derivative of $[u(x)]^n$, where $u(x)$ is an arbitrary differentiable function? Let's begin by considering the derivatives of $[u(x)]^2$ and $[u(x)]^3$ to see if a general pattern emerges. Since $[u(x)]^2 = u(x)u(x)$, we use the product rule to write

$$\frac{d}{dx}[u(x)]^2 = \frac{d}{dx}[u(x)u(x)]$$

$$= u(x)u'(x) + u(x)u'(x)$$

$$= 2u(x)u'(x) \qquad (2)$$

Because $[u(x)]^3 = [u(x)]^2 u(x)$, we use the product rule and the result in equation (2) to write

$$\frac{d}{dx}[u(x)]^3 = \frac{d}{dx}\{[u(x)]^2 u(x)\}$$ Use equation (2) to substitute for

$$= [u(x)]^2 \frac{d}{dx}u(x) + u(x)\frac{d}{dx}[u(x)]^2 \qquad \frac{d}{dx}[u(x)]^2.$$

$$= [u(x)]^2 u'(x) + u(x)[2u(x)u'(x)]$$

$$= 3[u(x)]^2 u'(x)$$

Continuing in this fashion, we can show that

$$\frac{d}{dx}[u(x)]^n = n[u(x)]^{n-1}u'(x) \qquad n \text{ a positive integer} \qquad (3)$$

Using more advanced techniques, we can establish formula (3) for all real numbers n, obtaining the **general power rule**.

THEOREM 1 General Power Rule

If $u(x)$ is a differentiable function, n is any real number, and

$$y = f(x) = [u(x)]^n$$

then

$$f'(x) = n[u(x)]^{n-1}u'(x)$$

Using simplified notation,

$$y' = nu^{n-1}u' \qquad \text{or} \qquad \frac{d}{dx}u^n = nu^{n-1}\frac{du}{dx} \qquad \text{where } u = u(x)$$

EXAMPLE 3   Using the General Power Rule   Find the indicated derivatives:

(A) $f'(x)$ if $f(x) = (3x + 1)^4$

(B) y' if $y = (x^3 + 4)^7$

(C) $\dfrac{d}{dt}\dfrac{1}{(t^2 + t + 4)^3}$

(D) $\dfrac{dh}{dw}$ if $h(w) = \sqrt{3 - w}$

SOLUTION

(A) $f(x) = (3x + 1)^4$ Let $u = 3x + 1, n = 4.$

$$f'(x) = 4(3x + 1)^3(3x + 1)' \qquad nu^{n-1}\frac{du}{dx}$$

$$= 4(3x + 1)^3 \, 3 \qquad\qquad \frac{du}{dx} = 3$$

$$= 12(3x + 1)^3$$

(B) $y = (x^3 + 4)^7$ Let $u = (x^3 + 4), n = 7.$

$$y' = 7(x^3 + 4)^6(x^3 + 4)' \qquad nu^{n-1}\frac{du}{dx}$$

$$= 7(x^3 + 4)^6 \, 3x^2 \qquad\qquad \frac{du}{dx} = 3x^2$$

$$= 21x^2(x^3 + 4)^6$$

(C) $\dfrac{d}{dt}\dfrac{1}{(t^2 + t + 4)^3}$

$$= \frac{d}{dt}(t^2 + t + 4)^{-3} \qquad\qquad \text{Let } u = t^2 + t + 4, n = -3.$$

$$= -3(t^2 + t + 4)^{-4}(t^2 + t + 4)' \qquad nu^{n-1}\frac{du}{dt}$$

$$= -3(t^2 + t + 4)^{-4}(2t + 1) \qquad\qquad \frac{du}{dt} = 2t + 1$$

$$= \frac{-3(2t + 1)}{(t^2 + t + 4)^4}$$

(D) $h(w) = \sqrt{3 - w} = (3 - w)^{1/2}$ Let $u = 3 - w, n = \dfrac{1}{2}.$

$$\frac{dh}{dw} = \frac{1}{2}(3 - w)^{-1/2}(3 - w)' \qquad nu^{n-1}\frac{du}{dw}$$

$$= \frac{1}{2}(3 - w)^{-1/2}(-1) \qquad\qquad \frac{du}{dw} = -1$$

$$= -\frac{1}{2(3 - w)^{1/2}} \qquad \text{or} \qquad -\frac{1}{2\sqrt{3 - w}}$$

Matched Problem 3   Find the indicated derivatives:

(A) $h'(x)$ if $h(x) = (5x + 2)^3$

(B) y' if $y = (x^4 - 5)^5$

(C) $\dfrac{d}{dt}\dfrac{1}{(t^2 + 4)^2}$

(D) $\dfrac{dg}{dw}$ if $g(w) = \sqrt{4 - w}$

    Notice that we used two steps to differentiate each function in Example 3. First, we applied the general power rule, and then we found du/dx. As you gain experience with the general power rule, you may want to combine these two steps. If you do this, be certain to multiply by du/dx. For example,

$$\frac{d}{dx}(x^5 + 1)^4 = 4(x^5 + 1)^3 5x^4 \qquad \text{Correct}$$

$$\frac{d}{dx}(x^5 + 1)^4 \neq 4(x^5 + 1)^3 \qquad du/dx = 5x^4 \text{ is missing}$$

CONCEPTUAL INSIGHT

If we let $u(x) = x$, then $du/dx = 1$, and the general power rule reduces to the (ordinary) power rule discussed in Section 2.5. Compare the following:

$$\frac{d}{dx}x^n = nx^{n-1} \qquad \text{Yes—power rule}$$

$$\frac{d}{dx}u^n = nu^{n-1}\frac{du}{dx} \qquad \text{Yes—general power rule}$$

$$\frac{d}{dx}u^n \neq nu^{n-1} \qquad \text{Unless } u(x) = x + k, \text{ so that } du/dx = 1$$

The Chain Rule

We have used the general power rule to find derivatives of composite functions of the form $f[g(x)]$, where $f(u) = u^n$ is a power function. But what if f is not a power function? Then a more general rule, the *chain rule*, enables us to compute the derivatives of many composite functions of the form $f[g(x)]$.

Suppose that

$$y = m(x) = f[g(x)]$$

is a composite of f and g, where

$$y = f(u) \qquad \text{and} \qquad u = g(x)$$

To express the derivative dy/dx in terms of the derivatives of f and g, we use the definition of a derivative (see Section 2.4).

$$m'(x) = \lim_{h \to 0}\frac{m(x+h) - m(x)}{h} \qquad \begin{array}{l}\text{Substitute } m(x+h) = f[g(x+h)] \\ \text{and } m(x) = f[g(x)].\end{array}$$

$$= \lim_{h \to 0}\frac{f[g(x+h)] - f[g(x)]}{h} \qquad \text{Multiply by } 1 = \frac{g(x+h) - g(x)}{g(x+h) - g(x)}.$$

$$= \lim_{h \to 0}\left[\frac{f[g(x+h)] - f[g(x)]}{h} \cdot \frac{g(x+h) - g(x)}{g(x+h) - g(x)}\right]$$

$$= \lim_{h \to 0}\left[\frac{f[g(x+h)] - f[g(x)]}{g(x+h) - g(x)} \cdot \frac{g(x+h) - g(x)}{h}\right] \qquad (4)$$

We recognize the second factor in equation (4) as the difference quotient for $g(x)$. To interpret the first factor as the difference quotient for $f(u)$, we let $k = g(x+h) - g(x)$. Since $u = g(x)$, we write

$$u + k = g(x) + g(x+h) - g(x) = g(x+h)$$

Substituting in equation (4), we have

$$m'(x) = \lim_{h \to 0}\left[\frac{f(u+k) - f(u)}{k} \cdot \frac{g(x+h) - g(x)}{h}\right] \qquad (5)$$

If we assume that $k = [g(x+h) - g(x)] \to 0$ as $h \to 0$, we can find the limit of each difference quotient in equation (5):

$$m'(x) = \left[\lim_{k \to 0}\frac{f(u+k) - f(u)}{k}\right]\left[\lim_{h \to 0}\frac{g(x+h) - g(x)}{h}\right]$$

$$= f'(u)g'(x)$$

$$= f'[g(x)]g'(x)$$

Therefore, referring to f and g in the composite function $f[g(x)]$ as the exterior function and interior function, respectively,

The derivative of the composite of two functions is the derivative of the exterior, evaluated at the interior, times the derivative of the interior.

This **chain rule** is expressed more compactly in Theorem 2, with notation chosen to aid memorization (E for "exterior", I for "interior").

THEOREM 2 Chain Rule

If $m(x) = E[I(x)]$ is a composite function, then

$$m'(x) = E'[I(x)]I'(x)$$

provided that $E'[I(x)]$ and $I'(x)$ exist.
Equivalently,   if $y = E(u)$ and $u = I(x)$, then

$$\frac{dy}{dx} = \frac{dy}{du}\frac{du}{dx}$$

provided that $\dfrac{dy}{du}$ and $\dfrac{du}{dx}$ exist.

EXAMPLE 4   Using the Chain Rule   Find the derivative $m'(x)$ of the composite function $m(x)$.

(A) $m(x) = (3x^2 + 1)^{3/2}$ (B) $m(x) = e^{2x^3+5}$ (C) $m(x) = \ln(x^2 - 4x + 2)$

SOLUTION

(A) The function m is the composite of $E(u) = u^{3/2}$ and $I(x) = 3x^2 + 1$. Then
   $E'(u) = \frac{3}{2}u^{1/2}$ and $I'(x) = 6x$, so by the chain rule,
   $m'(x) = \frac{3}{2}(3x^2 + 1)^{1/2}(6x) = 9x(3x^2 + 1)^{1/2}$.

(B) The function m is the composite of $E(u) = e^u$ and $I(x) = 2x^3 + 5$. Then
   $E'(u) = e^u$ and $I'(x) = 6x^2$, so by the chain rule,
   $m'(x) = e^{2x^3+5}(6x^2) = 6x^2 e^{2x^3+5}$.

(C) The function m is the composite of $E(u) = \ln u$ and $I(x) = x^2 - 4x + 2$.
   Then $E'(u) = \frac{1}{u}$ and $I'(x) = 2x - 4$, so by the chain rule,
   $m'(x) = \frac{1}{x^2 - 4x + 2}(2x - 4) = \frac{2x - 4}{x^2 - 4x + 2}$.

Matched Problem 4)   Find the derivative $m'(x)$ of the composite function $m(x)$.
(A) $m(x) = (2x^3 + 4)^{-5}$ (B) $m(x) = e^{3x^4+6}$ (C) $m(x) = \ln(x^2 + 9x + 4)$

Explore and Discuss 2   Let $m(x) = f[g(x)]$. Use the chain rule and Figures 2 and 3 to find

(A) $f(4)$ (B) $g(6)$ (C) $m(6)$
(D) $f'(4)$ (E) $g'(6)$ (F) $m'(6)$

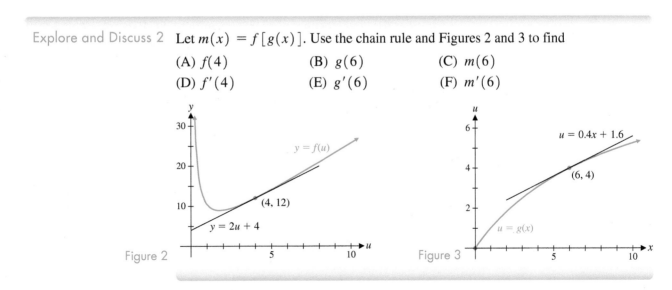

Figure 2   Figure 3

The chain rule can be extended to compositions of three or more functions. For example, if $y = f(w)$, $w = g(u)$, and $u = h(x)$, then

$$\frac{dy}{dx} = \frac{dy}{dw}\frac{dw}{du}\frac{du}{dx}$$

EXAMPLE 5   Using the Chain Rule   For $y = h(x) = e^{1+(\ln x)^2}$, find dy/dx.

SOLUTION   Note that h is of the form $y = e^w$, where $w = 1 + u^2$ and $u = \ln x$.

$$\frac{dy}{dx} = \frac{dy}{dw}\frac{dw}{du}\frac{du}{dx}$$

$$= e^w(2u)\left(\frac{1}{x}\right)$$

$$= e^{1+u^2}(2u)\left(\frac{1}{x}\right) \qquad \text{Since } w = 1 + u^2$$

$$= e^{1+(\ln x)^2}(2\ln x)\left(\frac{1}{x}\right) \qquad \text{Since } u = \ln x$$

$$= \frac{2}{x}(\ln x)e^{1+(\ln x)^2}$$

Matched Problem 5   For $y = h(x) = [\ln(1 + e^x)]^3$, find dy/dx.

The chain rule generalizes basic derivative rules. We list three general derivative rules here for convenient reference [the first, equation (6), is the general power rule of Theorem 1].

General Derivative Rules

$$\frac{d}{dx}[f(x)]^n = n[f(x)]^{n-1}f'(x) \tag{6}$$

$$\frac{d}{dx}\ln[f(x)] = \frac{1}{f(x)}f'(x) \tag{7}$$

$$\frac{d}{dx}e^{f(x)} = e^{f(x)}f'(x) \tag{8}$$

Unless directed otherwise, you now have a choice between the chain rule and the general derivative rules. However, practicing with the chain rule will help prepare you for concepts that appear later in the text. Examples 4 and 5 illustrate the chain rule method, and the next example illustrates the general derivative rules method.

EXAMPLE 6   Using General Derivative Rules

(A) $\dfrac{d}{dx}e^{2x} = e^{2x}\dfrac{d}{dx}2x$ Using equation (8)

$\qquad = e^{2x}(2) = 2e^{2x}$

(B) $\dfrac{d}{dx}\ln(x^2 + 9) = \dfrac{1}{x^2 + 9}\dfrac{d}{dx}(x^2 + 9)$ Using equation (7)

$\qquad = \dfrac{1}{x^2 + 9}2x = \dfrac{2x}{x^2 + 9}$

(C) $\dfrac{d}{dx}(1 + e^{x^2})^3 = 3(1 + e^{x^2})^2 \dfrac{d}{dx}(1 + e^{x^2})$ Using equation (6)

$= 3(1 + e^{x^2})^2 e^{x^2} \dfrac{d}{dx} x^2$ Using equation (8)

$= 3(1 + e^{x^2})^2 e^{x^2}(2x)$

$= 6xe^{x^2}(1 + e^{x^2})^2$

Matched Problem 6 Find

(A) $\dfrac{d}{dx} \ln(x^3 + 2x)$ (B) $\dfrac{d}{dx} e^{3x^2+2}$ (C) $\dfrac{d}{dx}(2 + e^{-x^2})^4$

Exercises 3.4

For many of the problems in this exercise set, the answers in the back of the book include both an unsimplified form and a simplified form. When checking your work, first check that you applied the rules correctly, and then check that you performed the algebraic simplification correctly.

Skills Warm-up Exercises

W   In Problems 1–4, find f [g(x)]. (If necessary, review Section 1.1).

1. $f(u) = 3u + 5; g(x) = x^3$

2. $f(u) = u^2 + u; g(x) = 2x - 7$

3. $f(u) = 2u + \ln u; g(x) = x^2 e^x$

4. $f(u) = 4ue^u; g(x) = x^3 + 1$

A In Problems 5–8, find functions E(u) and I(x) so that y = E[I(x)].

5. $y = \ln(x^3 - 6x + 10)$ 6. $y = (2x - 9)^8$

7. $y = \sqrt{x^2 + 4}$ 8. $y = e^{2x} + 3e^x - 10$

In Problems 9–16, replace ? with an expression that will make the indicated equation valid.

9. $\dfrac{d}{dx}(3x + 4)^4 = 4(3x + 4)^3$ ____?____

10. $\dfrac{d}{dx}(5 - 2x)^6 = 6(5 - 2x)^5$ ____?____

11. $\dfrac{d}{dx}(4 - 2x^2)^3 = 3(4 - 2x^2)^2$ ____?____

12. $\dfrac{d}{dx}(3x^2 + 7)^5 = 5(3x^2 + 7)^4$ ____?____

13. $\dfrac{d}{dx}e^{x^2+1} = e^{x^2+1}$ ____?____

14. $\dfrac{d}{dx}e^{4x-2} = e^{4x-2}$ ____?____

15. $\dfrac{d}{dx}\ln(x^4 + 1) = \dfrac{1}{x^4 + 1}$ ____?____

16. $\dfrac{d}{dx}\ln(x - x^3) = \dfrac{1}{x - x^3}$ ____?____

In Problems 17–38, find f'(x) and simplify.

17. $f(x) = (5 - 2x)^4$ 18. $f(x) = (9 - 5x)^2$

19. $f(x) = (4 + 0.2x)^5$ 20. $f(x) = (6 - 0.5x)^4$

21. $f(x) = (3x^2 + 5)^5$ 22. $f(x) = (5x^2 - 3)^6$

23. $f(x) = 5e^x$ 24. $f(x) = 10 - 4e^x$

25. $f(x) = e^{5x}$ 26. $f(x) = 6e^{-2x}$

27. $f(x) = 3e^{-6x}$ 28. $f(x) = e^{x^2 + 3x + 1}$

29. $f(x) = (2x - 5)^{1/2}$ 30. $f(x) = (4x + 3)^{1/2}$

31. $f(x) = (x^4 + 1)^{-2}$ 32. $f(x) = (x^5 + 2)^{-3}$

33. $f(x) = 4 - 2\ln x$ 34. $f(x) = 8\ln x$

35. $f(x) = 3\ln(1 + x^2)$

36. $f(x) = 2\ln(x^2 - 3x + 4)$

37. $f(x) = (1 + \ln x)^3$

38. $f(x) = (x - 2\ln x)^4$

In Problems 39–44, find f'(x) and the equation of the line tangent to the graph of f at the indicated value of x. Find the value(s) of x where the tangent line is horizontal.

39. $f(x) = (2x - 1)^3$;   x = 1

40. $f(x) = (3x - 1)^4$;   x = 1

41. $f(x) = (4x - 3)^{1/2}$;   x = 3

42. $f(x) = (2x + 8)^{1/2}$;   x = 4

43. $f(x) = 5e^{x^2 - 4x + 1}$;   x = 0

44. $f(x) = \ln(1 - x^2 + 2x^4)$;   x = 1

In Problems 45–60, find the indicated derivative and simplify.

45. y' if $y = 3(x^2 - 2)^4$

46. y' if $y = 2(x^3 + 6)^5$

47. $\dfrac{d}{dt}2(t^2 + 3t)^{-3}$

48. $\dfrac{d}{dt} 3(t^3 + t^2)^{-2}$

49. $\dfrac{dh}{dw}$ if $h(w) = \sqrt{w^2 + 8}$

50. $\dfrac{dg}{dw}$ if $g(w) = \sqrt[3]{3w - 7}$

51. $g'(x)$ if $g(x) = 4xe^{3x}$

52. $h'(x)$ if $h(x) = \dfrac{e^{2x}}{x^2 + 9}$

53. $\dfrac{d}{dx} \dfrac{\ln(1 + x)}{x^3}$

54. $\dfrac{d}{dx} [x^4 \ln(1 + x^4)]$

55. $F'(t)$ if $F(t) = (e^{t^2+1})^3$

56. $G'(t)$ if $G(t) = (1 - e^{2t})^2$

57. y' if $y = \ln(x^2 + 3)^{3/2}$

58. y' if $y = [\ln(x^2 + 3)]^{3/2}$

59. $\dfrac{d}{dw} \dfrac{1}{(w^3 + 4)^5}$

60. $\dfrac{d}{dw} \dfrac{1}{(w^2 - 2)^6}$

In Problems 61–66, find $f'(x)$ and find the equation of the line tangent to the graph of f at the indicated value of x.

61. $f(x) = x(4 - x)^3; \quad x = 2$

62. $f(x) = x^2(1 - x)^4; \quad x = 2$

63. $f(x) = \dfrac{x}{(2x - 5)^3}; \quad x = 3$

64. $f(x) = \dfrac{x^4}{(3x - 8)^2}; \quad x = 4$

65. $f(x) = \sqrt{\ln x}; \quad x = e$ $f(e) = \sqrt{\ln e}$

66. $f(x) = e^{\sqrt{x}}; \quad x = 1$

In Problems 67–72, find $f'(x)$ and find the value(s) of x where the tangent line is horizontal.

67. $f(x) = x^2(x - 5)^3$

68. $f(x) = x^3(x - 7)^4$

69. $f(x) = \dfrac{x}{(2x + 5)^2}$

70. $f(x) = \dfrac{x - 1}{(x - 3)^3}$

71. $f(x) = \sqrt{x^2 - 8x + 20}$

72. $f(x) = \sqrt{x^2 + 4x + 5}$

73. A student reasons that the functions $f(x) = \ln[5(x^2 + 3)^4]$ and $g(x) = 4\ln(x^2 + 3)$ must have the same derivative since he has entered $f(x)$, $g(x)$, $f'(x)$, and $g'(x)$ into a graphing calculator, but only three graphs appear (see the figure). Is his reasoning correct? Are $f'(x)$ and $g'(x)$ the same function? Explain.

(A)   (B)

Figure for 73

74. A student reasons that the functions $f(x) = (x + 1) \ln(x + 1) - x$ and $g(x) = (x + 1)^{1/3}$ must have the same derivative since she has entered $f(x)$, $g(x)$, $f'(x)$, and $g'(x)$ into a graphing calculator, but only three graphs appear (see the figure). Is her reasoning correct? Are $f'(x)$ and $g'(x)$ the same function? Explain.

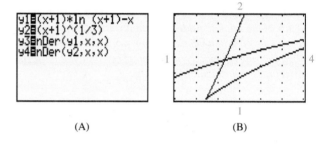

(A)   (B)

In Problems 75–78, give the domain of f, the domain of g, and the domain of m, where $m(x) = f[g(x)]$.

75. $f(u) = \ln u; g(x) = 4 - x^2$

76. $f(u) = \ln u; g(x) = 2x + 10$

77. $f(u) = \dfrac{1}{u^2 - 1}; g(x) = \ln x$

78. $f(u) = \dfrac{1}{u}; g(x) = x^2 - 9$

In Problems 79–90, find each derivative and simplify.

79. $\dfrac{d}{dx}[3x(x^2 + 1)^3]$

80. $\dfrac{d}{dx}[2x^2(x^3 - 3)^4]$

81. $\dfrac{d}{dx} \dfrac{(x^3 - 7)^4}{2x^3}$

82. $\dfrac{d}{dx} \dfrac{3x^2}{(x^2 + 5)^3}$

83. $\dfrac{d}{dx} \log_2(3x^2 - 1)$

84. $\dfrac{d}{dx} \log(x^3 - 1)$

85. $\dfrac{d}{dx} 10^{x^2+x}$

86. $\dfrac{d}{dx} 8^{1-2x^2}$

87. $\dfrac{d}{dx} \log_3(4x^3 + 5x + 7)$

88. $\dfrac{d}{dx} \log_5(5^{x^2-1})$

89. $\dfrac{d}{dx} 2^{x^3-x^2+4x+1}$

90. $\dfrac{d}{dx} 10^{\ln x}$

Applications

91. *Cost function.* The total cost (in hundreds of dollars) of producing x cell phones per day is

$$C(x) = 10 + \sqrt{2x + 16} \qquad 0 \le x \le 50$$

(see the figure).

Figure for 91

(A) Find $C'(x)$.

(B) Find $C'(24)$ and $C'(42)$. Interpret the results.

92. *Cost function.* The total cost (in hundreds of dollars) of producing x cameras per week is

$$C(x) = 6 + \sqrt{4x + 4} \qquad 0 \le x \le 30$$

(A) Find $C'(x)$.

(B) Find $C'(15)$ and $C'(24)$. Interpret the results.

93. *Price–supply equation.* The number x of bicycle helmets a retail chain is willing to sell per week at a price of $\$p$ is given by

$$x = 80\sqrt{p + 25} - 400 \qquad 20 \le p \le 100$$

(see the figure).

(A) Find dx/dp.

(B) Find the supply and the instantaneous rate of change of supply with respect to price when the price is $75. Write a brief interpretation of these results.

Figure for 93 and 94

94. *Price–demand equation.* The number x of bicycle helmets people are willing to buy per week from a retail chain at a price of $\$p$ is given by

$$x = 1{,}000 - 60\sqrt{p + 25} \qquad 20 \le p \le 100$$

(see the figure).

(A) Find dx/dp.

(B) Find the demand and the instantaneous rate of change of demand with respect to price when the price is $75. Write a brief interpretation of these results.

95. *Drug concentration.* The drug concentration in the bloodstream t hours after injection is given approximately by

$$C(t) = 4.35e^{-t} \qquad 0 \le t \le 5$$

where $C(t)$ is concentration in milligrams per milliliter.

(A) What is the rate of change of concentration after 1 hour? After 4 hours?

(B) Graph C.

96. *Water pollution.* The use of iodine crystals is a popular way of making small quantities of water safe to drink. Crystals placed in a 1-ounce bottle of water will dissolve until the solution is saturated. After saturation, half of the solution is poured into a quart container of water, and after about an hour, the water is usually safe to drink. The half-empty 1-ounce bottle is then refilled, to be used again in the same way. Suppose that the concentration of iodine in the 1-ounce bottle t minutes after the crystals are introduced can be approximated by

$$C(t) = 250(1 - e^{-t}) \qquad t \ge 0$$

where $C(t)$ is the concentration of iodine in micrograms per milliliter.

(A) What is the rate of change of the concentration after 1 minute? After 4 minutes?

(B) Graph C for $0 \le t \le 5$.

97. *Blood pressure and age.* A research group using hospital records developed the following mathematical model relating systolic blood pressure and age:

$$P(x) = 40 + 25 \ln(x + 1) \qquad 0 \le x \le 65$$

$P(x)$ is pressure, measured in millimeters of mercury, and x is age in years. What is the rate of change of pressure at the end of 10 years? At the end of 30 years? At the end of 60 years?

98. *Biology.* A yeast culture at room temperature (68°F) is placed in a refrigerator set at a constant temperature of 38°F. After t hours, the temperature T of the culture is given approximately by

$$T = 30e^{-0.58t} + 38 \qquad t \ge 0$$

What is the rate of change of temperature of the culture at the end of 1 hour? At the end of 4 hours?

Answers to Matched Problems

1. $f[g(x)] = 2e^x, \quad g[f(u)] = e^{2u}$

2. (A) $f(u) = 50e^u, \quad u = -2x$
   (B) $f(u) = \sqrt[3]{u}, \quad u = 1 + x^3$
   [*Note:* There are other correct answers.]

3. (A) $15(5x + 2)^2$ (B) $20x^3(x^4 - 5)^4$
   (C) $-4t/(t^2 + 4)^3$ (D) $-1/(2\sqrt{4 - w})$

4. (A) $m'(x) = -30x^2(2x^3 + 4)^{-6}$
   (B) $m'(x) = 12x^3 e^{3x^4 + 6}$ (C) $m'(x) = \dfrac{2x + 9}{x^2 + 9x + 4}$

5. $\dfrac{3e^x[\ln(1 + e^x)]^2}{1 + e^x}$

6. (A) $\dfrac{3x^2 + 2}{x^3 + 2x}$ (B) $6xe^{3x^2 + 2}$
   (C) $-8xe^{-x^2}(2 + e^{-x^2})^3$

3.5 Implicit Differentiation

Special Function Notation

The equation

$$y = 2 - 3x^2 \tag{1}$$

defines a function f with y as a dependent variable and x as an independent variable. Using function notation, we would write

$$y = f(x) \qquad \text{or} \qquad f(x) = 2 - 3x^2$$

In order to minimize the number of symbols, we will often write equation (1) in the form

$$y = 2 - 3x^2 = y(x)$$

where y is *both* a dependent variable and a function symbol. This is a convenient notation, and no harm is done as long as one is aware of the double role of y. Other examples are

$$x = 2t^2 - 3t + 1 = x(t)$$
$$z = \sqrt{u^2 - 3u} = z(u)$$
$$r = \frac{1}{(s^2 - 3s)^{2/3}} = r(s)$$

Until now, we have considered functions involving only one independent variable. There is no reason to stop there: The concept can be generalized to functions involving two or more independent variables, and this will be done in detail in Chapter 7. For now, we will "borrow" the notation for a function involving two independent variables. For example,

$$F(x, y) = x^2 - 2xy + 3y^2 - 5$$

specifies a function F involving two independent variables.

Implicit Differentiation

Consider the equation

$$3x^2 + y - 2 = 0 \tag{2}$$

and the equation obtained by solving equation (2) for y in terms of x,

$$y = 2 - 3x^2 \tag{3}$$

Both equations define the same function with x as the independent variable and y as the dependent variable. For equation (3), we write

$$y = f(x)$$

where

$$f(x) = 2 - 3x^2 \tag{4}$$

and we have an **explicit** (directly stated) rule that enables us to determine y for each value of x. On the other hand, the y in equation (2) is the same y as in equation (3), and equation (2) **implicitly** gives (implies, though does not directly express) y as a function of x. We say that equations (3) and (4) define the function f explicitly and equation (2) defines f implicitly.

Using an equation that defines a function implicitly to find the derivative of the function is called **implicit differentiation**. Let's differentiate equation (2) implicitly and equation (3) directly, and compare results.

Starting with

$$3x^2 + y - 2 = 0$$

we think of y as a function of x and write

$$3x^2 + y(x) - 2 = 0$$

Then we differentiate both sides with respect to x:

$$\frac{d}{dx}[(3x^2 + y(x) - 2)] = \frac{d}{dx}0$$ Since y is a function of x, but is not
explicitly given, we simply write

$$\frac{d}{dx}3x^2 + \frac{d}{dx}y(x) - \frac{d}{dx}2 = 0$$ $\frac{d}{dx}y(x) = y'$ to indicate its derivative.

$$6x + y' - 0 = 0$$

Now we solve for y':

$$y' = -6x$$

Note that we get the same result if we start with equation (3) and differentiate directly:

$$y = 2 - 3x^2$$
$$y' = -6x$$

Why are we interested in implicit differentiation? Why not solve for y in terms of x and differentiate directly? The answer is that there are many equations of the form

$$F(x, y) = 0 \qquad (5)$$

that are either difficult or impossible to solve for y explicitly in terms of x (try it for $x^2y^5 - 3xy + 5 = 0$ or for $e^y - y = 3x$, for example). But it can be shown that, under fairly general conditions on F, equation (5) will define one or more functions in which y is a dependent variable and x is an independent variable. To find y' under these conditions, we differentiate equation (5) implicitly.

Explore and Discuss 1   (A) How many tangent lines are there to the graph in Figure 1 when $x = 0$? When $x = 1$? When $x = 2$? When $x = 4$? When $x = 6$?

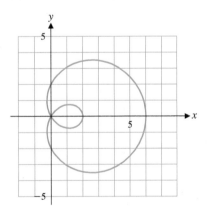

Figure 1

(B) Sketch the tangent lines referred to in part (A), and estimate each of their slopes.

(C) Explain why the graph in Figure 1 is not the graph of a function.

EXAMPLE 1   Differentiating Implicitly   Given

$$F(x, y) = x^2 + y^2 - 25 = 0 \qquad (6)$$

find y' and the slope of the graph at $x = 3$.

SOLUTION We start with the graph of $x^2 + y^2 - 25 = 0$ (a circle, as shown in Fig. 2) so that we can interpret our results geometrically. From the graph, it is clear that equation (6) does not define a function. But with a suitable restriction on the variables, equation (6) can define two or more functions. For example, the upper half and the lower half of the circle each define a function. On each half-circle, a point that corresponds to $x = 3$ is found by substituting $x = 3$ into equation (6) and solving for y:

$$x^2 + y^2 - 25 = 0$$
$$(3)^2 + y^2 = 25$$
$$y^2 = 16$$
$$y = \pm 4$$

The point $(3, 4)$ is on the upper half-circle, and the point $(3, -4)$ is on the lower half-circle. We will use these results in a moment. We now differentiate equation (6) implicitly, treating y as a function of x [i.e., $y = y(x)$]:

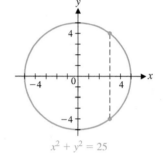

Figure 2

$x^2 + y^2 = 25$

$$x^2 + y^2 - 25 = 0$$
$$x^2 + [y(x)]^2 - 25 = 0$$
$$\frac{d}{dx}\{x^2 + [y(x)]^2 - 25\} = \frac{d}{dx}0$$
$$\frac{d}{dx}x^2 + \frac{d}{dx}[y(x)]^2 - \frac{d}{dx}25 = 0 \qquad \text{Use the chain rule.}$$
$$2x + 2[y(x)]^{2-1}y'(x) - 0 = 0$$
$$2x + 2yy' = 0 \qquad \text{Solve for } y' \text{ in terms of } x \text{ and } y.$$
$$y' = -\frac{2x}{2y}$$
$$y' = -\frac{x}{y} \qquad \text{Leave the answer in terms of } x \text{ and } y.$$

We have found y' without first solving $x^2 + y^2 - 25 = 0$ for y in terms of x. And by leaving y' in terms of x and y, we can use $y' = -x/y$ to find y' for *any* point on the graph of $x^2 + y^2 - 25 = 0$ (except where $y = 0$). In particular, for $x = 3$, we found that $(3, 4)$ and $(3, -4)$ are on the graph. The slope of the graph at $(3, 4)$ is

$$y'|_{(3, 4)} = -\tfrac{3}{4} \qquad \text{The slope of the graph at } (3, 4)$$

and the slope at $(3, -4)$ is

$$y'|_{(3, -4)} = -\tfrac{3}{-4} = \tfrac{3}{4} \qquad \text{The slope of the graph at } (3, -4)$$

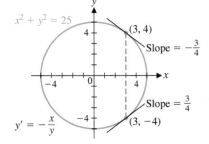

$x^2 + y^2 = 25$

(3, 4)

Slope $= -\frac{3}{4}$

Slope $= \frac{3}{4}$

(3, −4)

$y' = -\dfrac{x}{y}$

Figure 3

The symbol

$$y'\big|_{(a,\, b)}$$

is used to indicate that we are evaluating y' at $x = a$ and $y = b$.

The results are interpreted geometrically in Figure 3 on the original graph.

Matched Problem 1 Graph $x^2 + y^2 - 169 = 0$, find y' by implicit differentiation, and find the slope of the graph when $x = 5$.

CONCEPTUAL INSIGHT

When differentiating implicitly, the derivative of y^2 is $2yy'$, not just $2y$. This is because y represents a function of x, so the chain rule applies. Suppose, for example, that y represents the function $y = 5x + 4$. Then

$$(y^2)' = [(5x + 4)^2]' = 2(5x + 4) \cdot 5 = 2yy'$$

So, when differenting implicitly, the derivative of y is y', the derivative of y^2 is $2yy'$, the derivative of y^3 is $3y^2y'$, and so on.

EXAMPLE 2 Differentiating Implicitly Find the equation(s) of the tangent line(s) to the graph of

$$y - xy^2 + x^2 + 1 = 0 \qquad (7)$$

at the point(s) where $x = 1$.

SOLUTION We first find y when $x = 1$:

$$y - xy^2 + x^2 + 1 = 0$$
$$y - (1)y^2 + (1)^2 + 1 = 0$$
$$y - y^2 + 2 = 0$$
$$y^2 - y - 2 = 0$$
$$(y - 2)(y + 1) = 0$$
$$y = -1 \quad \text{or} \quad 2$$

So there are two points on the graph of (7) where $x = 1$, namely, $(1, -1)$ and $(1, 2)$. We next find the slope of the graph at these two points by differentiating equation (7) implicitly:

$$y - xy^2 + x^2 + 1 = 0 \qquad \text{Use the product rule and the}$$
$$\frac{d}{dx}y - \frac{d}{dx}xy^2 + \frac{d}{dx}x^2 + \frac{d}{dx}1 = \frac{d}{dx}0 \qquad \text{chain rule for } \frac{d}{dx}xy^2.$$
$$y' - (x \cdot 2yy' + y^2) + 2x = 0$$
$$y' - 2xyy' - y^2 + 2x = 0 \qquad \text{Solve for } y' \text{ by getting all}$$
$$y' - 2xyy' = y^2 - 2x \qquad \text{terms involving } y' \text{ on one side.}$$
$$(1 - 2xy)y' = y^2 - 2x \qquad \text{Factor out } y'.$$
$$y' = \frac{y^2 - 2x}{1 - 2xy}$$

Now find the slope at each point:

$$y'\big|_{(1,\,-1)} = \frac{(-1)^2 - 2(1)}{1 - 2(1)(-1)} = \frac{1 - 2}{1 + 2} = \frac{-1}{3} = -\frac{1}{3}$$

$$y'\big|_{(1,\,2)} = \frac{(2)^2 - 2(1)}{1 - 2(1)(2)} = \frac{4 - 2}{1 - 4} = \frac{2}{-3} = -\frac{2}{3}$$

Equation of tangent line at $(1, -1)$:

$$y - y_1 = m(x - x_1)$$
$$y + 1 = -\tfrac{1}{3}(x - 1)$$
$$y + 1 = -\tfrac{1}{3}x + \tfrac{1}{3}$$
$$y = -\tfrac{1}{3}x - \tfrac{2}{3}$$

Equation of tangent line at $(1, 2)$:

$$y - y_1 = m(x - x_1)$$
$$y - 2 = -\tfrac{2}{3}(x - 1)$$
$$y - 2 = -\tfrac{2}{3}x + \tfrac{2}{3}$$
$$y = -\tfrac{2}{3}x + \tfrac{8}{3}$$

Matched Problem 2 | Repeat Example 2 for $x^2 + y^2 - xy - 7 = 0$ at $x = 1$.

EXAMPLE 3 Differentiating Implicitly Find x' for $x = x(t)$ defined implicitly by

$$t \ln x = xe^t - 1$$

and evaluate x' at $(t, x) = (0, 1)$.

SOLUTION It is important to remember that x is the dependent variable and t is the independent variable. Therefore, we differentiate both sides of the equation with respect to t (using product and chain rules where appropriate) and then solve for x':

$$t \ln x = xe^t - 1 \qquad \text{Differentiate implicitly with respect to } t.$$

$$\frac{d}{dt}(t \ln x) = \frac{d}{dt}(xe^t) - \frac{d}{dt}1 \qquad \text{Use the product rule twice.}$$

$$t\frac{x'}{x} + \ln x = xe^t + e^t x' \qquad \text{Clear fractions.}$$

$$x \cdot t\frac{x'}{x} + x \cdot \ln x = x \cdot xe^t + x \cdot e^t x' \qquad x \neq 0$$

$$tx' + x \ln x = x^2 e^t + xe^t x' \qquad \text{Solve for } x'.$$

$$tx' - xe^t x' = x^2 e^t - x \ln x \qquad \text{Factor out } x'.$$

$$(t - xe^t)x' = x^2 e^t - x \ln x$$

$$x' = \frac{x^2 e^t - x \ln x}{t - xe^t}$$

Now we evaluate x' at $(t, x) = (0, 1)$, as requested:

$$x'|_{(0, 1)} = \frac{(1)^2 e^0 - 1 \ln 1}{0 - 1e^0}$$

$$= \frac{1}{-1} = -1$$

Matched Problem 3 | Find x' for $x = x(t)$ defined implicitly by

$$1 + x \ln t = te^x$$

and evaluate x' at $(t, x) = (1, 0)$.

Exercises 3.5

Skills Warm-up Exercises

W | In Problems 1–8, if it is possible to solve for y in terms of x, do so. If not, write "Impossible". (If necessary, review Section 1.1).

1. $3x + 2y - 20 = 0$

2. $-4x^2 + 3y + 12 = 0$

3. $\dfrac{x^2}{9} + \dfrac{y^2}{16} = 1$

4. $4y^2 - x^2 = 36$

5. $x^2 + xy + y^2 = 1$

6. $2 \ln y + y \ln x = 3x$

7. $5x + 3y = e^y$

8. $y^2 + e^x y + x^3 = 0$

In Problems 9–12, find y' in two ways:

(A) Differentiate the given equation implicitly and then solve for y'.

(B) Solve the given equation for y and then differentiate directly.

9. $3x + 5y + 9 = 0$

10. $-2x + 6y - 4 = 0$

11. $3x^2 - 4y - 18 = 0$ **12.** $2x^3 + 5y - 2 = 0$

In Problems 13–30, use implicit differentiation to find y' and evaluate y' at the indicated point.

13. $y - 5x^2 + 3 = 0;\ (1, 2)$

14. $5x^3 - y - 1 = 0;\ (1, 4)$

15. $x^2 - y^3 - 3 = 0;\ (2, 1)$

16. $y^2 + x^3 + 4 = 0;\ (-2, 2)$

17. $y^2 + 2y + 3x = 0;\ (-1, 1)$

18. $y^2 - y - 4x = 0;\ (0, 1)$

19. $xy - 6 = 0;\ (2, 3)$

20. $3xy - 2x - 2 = 0;\ (2, 1)$

21. $2xy + y + 2 = 0;\ (-1, 2)$

22. $2y + xy - 1 = 0;\ (-1, 1)$

23. $x^2y - 3x^2 - 4 = 0;\ (2, 4)$

24. $2x^3y - x^3 + 5 = 0;\ (-1, 3)$

25. $e^y = x^2 + y^2;\ (1, 0)$ **26.** $x^2 - y = 4e^y;\ (2, 0)$

27. $x^3 - y = \ln y;\ (1, 1)$ **28.** $\ln y = 2y^2 - x;\ (2, 1)$

29. $x \ln y + 2y = 2x^3;\ (1, 1)$ **30.** $xe^y - y = x^2 - 2;\ (2, 0)$

In Problems 31 and 32, find x' for $x = x(t)$ defined implicitly by the given equation. Evaluate x' at the indicated point.

31. $x^2 - t^2x + t^3 + 11 = 0;\ (-2, 1)$

32. $x^3 - tx^2 - 4 = 0;\ (-3, -2)$

Problems 33 and 34 refer to the equation and graph shown in the figure.

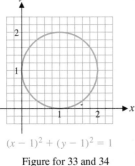

$(x - 1)^2 + (y - 1)^2 = 1$

Figure for 33 and 34

33. Use implicit differentiation to find the slopes of the tangent lines at the points on the graph where $x = 1.6$. Check your answers by visually estimating the slopes on the graph in the figure.

34. Find the slopes of the tangent lines at the points on the graph where $x = 0.2$. Check your answers by visually estimating the slopes on the graph in the figure.

In Problems 35–38, find the equation(s) of the tangent line(s) to the graphs of the indicated equations at the point(s) with the given value of x.

35. $xy - x - 4 = 0;\ x = 2$ **36.** $3x + xy + 1 = 0;\ x = -1$

37. $y^2 - xy - 6 = 0;\ x = 1$ **38.** $xy^2 - y - 2 = 0;\ x = 1$

39. If $xe^y = 1$, find y' in two ways, first by differentiating implicitly and then by solving for y explicitly in terms of x. Which method do you prefer? Explain.

40. Explain the difficulty that arises in solving $x^3 + y + xe^y = 1$ for y as an explicit function of x. Find the slope of the tangent line to the graph of the equation at the point $(0, 1)$.

In Problems 41–48, find y' and the slope of the tangent line to the graph of each equation at the indicated point.

41. $(1 + y)^3 + y = x + 7;\ (2, 1)$

42. $(y - 3)^4 - x = y;\ (-3, 4)$

43. $(x - 2y)^3 = 2y^2 - 3;\ (1, 1)$

44. $(2x - y)^4 - y^3 = 8;\ (-1, -2)$

45. $\sqrt{7 + y^2} - x^3 + 4 = 0;\ (2, 3)$

46. $6\sqrt{y^3 + 1} - 2x^{3/2} - 2 = 0;\ (4, 2)$

47. $\ln(xy) = y^2 - 1;\ (1, 1)$

48. $e^{xy} - 2x = y + 1;\ (0, 0)$

49. Find the equation(s) of the tangent line(s) at the point(s) on the graph of the equation

$$y^3 - xy - x^3 = 2$$

where $x = 1$. Round all approximate values to two decimal places.

50. Refer to the equation in Problem 49. Find the equation(s) of the tangent line(s) at the point(s) on the graph where $y = -1$. Round all approximate values to two decimal places.

Applications

For the demand equations in Problems 51–54, find the rate of change of p with respect to x by differentiating implicitly (x is the number of items that can be sold at a price of $\$p$).

51. $x = p^2 - 2p + 1{,}000$ **52.** $x = p^3 - 3p^2 + 200$

53. $x = \sqrt{10{,}000 - p^2}$ **54.** $x = \sqrt[3]{1{,}500 - p^3}$

55. **Biophysics.** In biophysics, the equation

$$(L + m)(V + n) = k$$

is called the *fundamental equation of muscle contraction*, where m, n, and k are constants and V is the velocity of the shortening of muscle fibers for a muscle subjected to a load L. Find dL/dV by implicit differentiation.

56. **Biophysics.** In Problem 55, find dV/dL by implicit differentiation.

57. **Speed of sound.** The speed of sound in air is given by the formula

$$v = k\sqrt{T}$$

where v is the velocity of sound, T is the temperature of the air, and k is a constant. Use implicit differentiation to find $\dfrac{dT}{dv}$.

58. Gravity. The equation

$$F = G\frac{m_1 m_2}{r^2}$$

is Newton's law of universal gravitation. G is a constant and F is the gravitational force between two objects having masses m_1 and m_2 that are a distance r from each other. Use implicit differentiation to find $\dfrac{dr}{dF}$. Assume that m_1 and m_2 are constant.

59. Speed of sound. Refer to Problem 57. Find $\dfrac{dv}{dT}$ and discuss the connection between $\dfrac{dv}{dT}$ and $\dfrac{dT}{dv}$.

60. Gravity. Refer to Problem 58. Find $\dfrac{dF}{dr}$ and discuss the connection between $\dfrac{dF}{dr}$ and $\dfrac{dr}{dF}$.

Answers to Matched Problems

1. $y' = -x/y$. When $x = 5$, $y = \pm 12$; thus, $y'|_{(5,12)} = -\frac{5}{12}$ and $y'|_{(5,-12)} = \frac{5}{12}$

2. $y' = \dfrac{y - 2x}{2y - x}$; $y = \frac{4}{5}x - \frac{14}{5}$, $y = \frac{1}{5}x + \frac{14}{5}$

3. $x' = \dfrac{te^x - x}{t \ln t - t^2 e^x}$; $x'|_{(1, 0)} = -1$

3.6 Related Rates

Union workers are concerned that the rate at which wages are increasing is lagging behind the rate of increase in the company's profits. An automobile dealer wants to predict how much an anticipated increase in interest rates will decrease his rate of sales. An investor is studying the connection between the rate of increase in the Dow Jones average and the rate of increase in the gross domestic product over the past 50 years.

In each of these situations, there are two quantities—wages and profits, for example—that are changing with respect to time. We would like to discover the precise relationship between the rates of increase (or decrease) of the two quantities. We begin our discussion of such *related rates* by considering familiar situations in which the two quantities are distances and the two rates are velocities.

EXAMPLE 1 Related Rates and Motion A 26-foot ladder is placed against a wall (Fig. 1). If the top of the ladder is sliding down the wall at 2 feet per second, at what rate is the bottom of the ladder moving away from the wall when the bottom of the ladder is 10 feet away from the wall?

SOLUTION Many people think that since the ladder is a constant length, the bottom of the ladder will move away from the wall at the rate that the top of the ladder is moving down the wall. This is not the case, however.

At any moment in time, let x be the distance of the bottom of the ladder from the wall and let y be the distance of the top of the ladder from the ground (see Fig. 1). Both x and y are changing with respect to time and can be thought of as functions of time; that is, $x = x(t)$ and $y = y(t)$. Furthermore, x and y are related by the Pythagorean relationship:

$$x^2 + y^2 = 26^2 \tag{1}$$

Differentiating equation (1) implicitly with respect to time t and using the chain rule where appropriate, we obtain

$$2x\frac{dx}{dt} + 2y\frac{dy}{dt} = 0 \tag{2}$$

The rates dx/dt and dy/dt are related by equation (2). This is a **related-rates problem**.

Our problem is to find dx/dt when $x = 10$ feet, given that $dy/dt = -2$ (y is decreasing at a constant rate of 2 feet per second). We have all the quantities we

26 ft

y

x

Figure 1

need in equation (2) to solve for dx/dt, except y. When $x = 10$, y can be found from equation (1):

$$10^2 + y^2 = 26^2$$
$$y = \sqrt{26^2 - 10^2} = 24 \text{ feet}$$

Substitute $dy/dt = -2$, $x = 10$, and $y = 24$ into (2). Then solve for dx/dt:

$$2(10)\frac{dx}{dt} + 2(24)(-2) = 0$$

$$\frac{dx}{dt} = \frac{-2(24)(-2)}{2(10)} = 4.8 \text{ feet per second}$$

The bottom of the ladder is moving away from the wall at a rate of 4.8 feet per second.

CONCEPTUAL INSIGHT

In the solution to Example 1, we used equation (1) in two ways: first, to find an equation relating dy/dt and dx/dt, and second, to find the value of y when $x = 10$. These steps must be done in this order. Substituting $x = 10$ and then differentiating does not produce any useful results:

$$x^2 + y^2 = 26^2 \quad \text{Substituting 10 for } x \text{ has the effect of}$$
$$100 + y^2 = 26^2 \quad \text{stopping the ladder.}$$
$$0 + 2yy' = 0 \quad \text{The rate of change of a stationary object}$$
$$y' = 0 \quad \text{is always 0, but that is not the rate of change of the moving ladder.}$$

Matched Problem 1   Again, a 26-foot ladder is placed against a wall (Fig. 1). If the bottom of the ladder is moving away from the wall at 3 feet per second, at what rate is the top moving down when the top of the ladder is 24 feet above ground?

Explore and Discuss 1

(A) For which values of x and y in Example 1 is dx/dt equal to 2 (i.e., the same rate that the ladder is sliding down the wall)?

(B) When is dx/dt greater than 2? Less than 2?

DEFINITION   Suggestions for Solving Related-Rates Problems

Step 1   Sketch a figure if helpful.

Step 2   Identify all relevant variables, including those whose rates are given and those whose rates are to be found.

Step 3   Express all given rates and rates to be found as derivatives.

Step 4   Find an equation connecting the variables identified in step 2.

Step 5   Implicitly differentiate the equation found in step 4, using the chain rule where appropriate, and substitute in all given values.

Step 6   Solve for the derivative that will give the unknown rate.

EXAMPLE 2   Related Rates and Motion   Suppose that two motorboats leave from the same point at the same time. If one travels north at 15 miles per hour and the other travels east at 20 miles per hour, how fast will the distance between them be changing after 2 hours?

Figure 2

SOLUTION First, draw a picture, as shown in Figure 2.

All variables, x, y, and z, are changing with time. They can be considered as functions of time: $x = x(t)$, $y = y(t)$, and $z = z(t)$, given implicitly. It now makes sense to find derivatives of each variable with respect to time. From the Pythagorean theorem,

$$z^2 = x^2 + y^2 \qquad (3)$$

We also know that

$$\frac{dx}{dt} = 20 \text{ miles per hour} \qquad \text{and} \qquad \frac{dy}{dt} = 15 \text{ miles per hour}$$

We want to find dz/dt at the end of 2 hours—that is, when $x = 40$ miles and $y = 30$ miles. To do this, we differentiate both sides of equation (3) with respect to t and solve for dz/dt:

$$2z\frac{dz}{dt} = 2x\frac{dx}{dt} + 2y\frac{dy}{dt} \qquad (4)$$

We have everything we need except z. From equation (3), when $x = 40$ and $y = 30$, we find z to be 50. Substituting the known quantities into equation (4), we obtain

$$2(50)\frac{dz}{dt} = 2(40)(20) + 2(30)(15)$$

$$\frac{dz}{dt} = 25 \text{ miles per hour}$$

The boats will be separating at a rate of 25 miles per hour.

Matched Problem 2   Repeat Example 2 for the same situation at the end of 3 hours.

EXAMPLE 3   Related Rates and Motion   Suppose that a point is moving along the graph of $x^2 + y^2 = 25$ (Fig. 3). When the point is at $(-3, 4)$, its x coordinate is increasing at the rate of 0.4 unit per second. How fast is the y coordinate changing at that moment?

SOLUTION Since both x and y are changing with respect to time, we can consider each as a function of time, namely,

$$x = x(t) \qquad \text{and} \qquad y = y(t)$$

but restricted so that

$$x^2 + y^2 = 25 \qquad (5)$$

We want to find dy/dt, given $x = -3$, $y = 4$, and $dx/dt = 0.4$. Implicitly differentiating both sides of equation (5) with respect to t, we have

$$x^2 + y^2 = 25$$

$$2x\frac{dx}{dt} + 2y\frac{dy}{dt} = 0 \qquad \text{Divide both sides by 2.}$$

$$x\frac{dx}{dt} + y\frac{dy}{dt} = 0 \qquad \begin{array}{l}\text{Substitute } x = -3, y = 4, \text{ and}\\ dx/dt = 0.4, \text{ and solve for } dy/dt.\end{array}$$

$$(-3)(0.4) + 4\frac{dy}{dt} = 0$$

$$\frac{dy}{dt} = 0.3 \text{ unit per second}$$

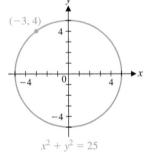

Figure 3

Matched Problem 3   A point is moving on the graph of $y^3 = x^2$. When the point is at $(-8, 4)$, its y coordinate is decreasing by 2 units per second. How fast is the x coordinate changing at that moment?

EXAMPLE 4 Related Rates and Business Suppose that for a company manufacturing flash drives, the cost, revenue, and profit equations are given by

$$C = 5{,}000 + 2x \qquad \text{Cost equation}$$
$$R = 10x - 0.001x^2 \qquad \text{Revenue equation}$$
$$P = R - C \qquad \text{Profit equation}$$

where the production output in 1 week is x flash drives. If production is increasing at the rate of 500 flash drives per week when production is 2,000 flash drives, find the rate of increase in

(A) Cost   (B) Revenue   (C) Profit

SOLUTION If production x is a function of time (it must be, since it is changing with respect to time), then C, R, and P must also be functions of time. These functions are given implicitly (rather than explicitly). Letting t represent time in weeks, we differentiate both sides of each of the preceding three equations with respect to t and then substitute $x = 2{,}000$ and $dx/dt = 500$ to find the desired rates.

(A) $C = 5{,}000 + 2x$ Think: $C = C(t)$ and $x = x(t)$.

$\dfrac{dC}{dt} = \dfrac{d}{dt}(5{,}000) + \dfrac{d}{dt}(2x)$ Differentiate both sides with respect to t.

$\dfrac{dC}{dt} = 0 + 2\dfrac{dx}{dt} = 2\dfrac{dx}{dt}$

Since $dx/dt = 500$ when $x = 2{,}000$,

$$\frac{dC}{dt} = 2(500) = \$1{,}000 \text{ per week}$$

Cost is increasing at a rate of $1,000 per week.

(B) $R = 10x - 0.001x^2$

$\dfrac{dR}{dt} = \dfrac{d}{dt}(10x) - \dfrac{d}{dt}0.001x^2$

$\dfrac{dR}{dt} = 10\dfrac{dx}{dt} - 0.002x\dfrac{dx}{dt}$

$\dfrac{dR}{dt} = (10 - 0.002x)\dfrac{dx}{dt}$

Since $dx/dt = 500$ when $x = 2{,}000$,

$$\frac{dR}{dt} = [10 - 0.002(2{,}000)](500) = \$3{,}000 \text{ per week}$$

Revenue is increasing at a rate of $3,000 per week.

(C) $P = R - C$

$\dfrac{dP}{dt} = \dfrac{dR}{dt} - \dfrac{dC}{dt}$ Results from parts (A) and (B)

$\qquad = \$3{,}000 - \$1{,}000$

$\qquad = \$2{,}000 \text{ per week}$

Profit is increasing at a rate of $2,000 per week.

Matched Problem 4 Repeat Example 4 for a production level of 6,000 flash drives per week.

Exercises 3.6

W *For Problems 1–8, review the geometric formulas in Appendix C, if necessary.*

1. A circular flower bed has an area of 300 square feet. Find its diameter to the nearest tenth of a foot.

2. A central pivot irrigation system covers a circle of radius 400 meters. Find the area of the circle to the nearest square meter.

3. The hypotenuse of a right triangle has length 50 meters, and another side has length 20 meters. Find the length of the third side to the nearest meter.

4. The legs of a right triangle have lengths 54 feet and 69 feet. Find the length of the hypotenuse to the nearest foot.

5. A person 69 inches tall stands 40 feet from the base of a streetlight. The streetlight casts a shadow of length 96 inches. How far above the ground is the streetlight?

6. The radius of a spherical balloon is 3 meters. Find its volume to the nearest tenth of a cubic meter.

7. A right circular cylinder and a sphere both have radius 12 feet. If the volume of the cylinder is twice the volume of the sphere, find the height of the cylinder.

8. The height of a right circular cylinder is twice its radius. If the volume is 1,000 cubic meters, find the radius and height to the nearest hundredth of a meter.

In Problems 9–14, assume that $x = x(t)$ and $y = y(t)$. Find the indicated rate, given the other information.

9. $y = x^2 + 2$; $dx/dt = 3$ when $x = 5$; find dy/dt

10. $y = x^3 - 3$; $dx/dt = -2$ when $x = 2$; find dy/dt

11. $x^2 + y^2 = 1$; $dy/dt = -4$ when $x = -0.6$ and $y = 0.8$; find dx/dt

12. $x^2 + y^2 = 4$; $dy/dt = 5$ when $x = 1.2$ and $y = -1.6$; find dx/dt

13. $x^2 + 3xy + y^2 = 11$; $dx/dt = 2$ when $x = 1$ and $y = 2$; find dy/dt

14. $x^2 - 2xy - y^2 = 7$; $dy/dt = -1$ when $x = 2$ and $y = -1$; find dx/dt

15. A point is moving on the graph of $xy = 36$. When the point is at $(4, 9)$, its x coordinate is increasing by 4 units per second. How fast is the y coordinate changing at that moment?

16. A point is moving on the graph of $4x^2 + 9y^2 = 36$. When the point is at $(3, 0)$, its y coordinate is decreasing by 2 units per second. How fast is its x coordinate changing at that moment?

17. A boat is being pulled toward a dock as shown in the figure. If the rope is being pulled in at 3 feet per second, how fast is the distance between the dock and the boat decreasing when it is 30 feet from the dock?

Figure for 17 and 18

18. Refer to Problem 17. Suppose that the distance between the boat and the dock is decreasing by 3.05 feet per second. How fast is the rope being pulled in when the boat is 10 feet from the dock?

19. A rock thrown into a still pond causes a circular ripple. If the radius of the ripple is increasing by 2 feet per second, how fast is the area changing when the radius is 10 feet?

20. Refer to Problem 19. How fast is the circumference of a circular ripple changing when the radius is 10 feet?

21. The radius of a spherical balloon is increasing at the rate of 3 centimeters per minute. How fast is the volume changing when the radius is 10 centimeters?

22. Refer to Problem 21. How fast is the surface area of the sphere increasing when the radius is 10 centimeters?

23. Boyle's law for enclosed gases states that if the volume is kept constant, the pressure P and temperature T are related by the equation

$$\frac{P}{T} = k$$

where k is a constant. If the temperature is increasing at 3 kelvins per hour, what is the rate of change of pressure when the temperature is 250 kelvins and the pressure is 500 pounds per square inch?

24. Boyle's law for enclosed gases states that if the temperature is kept constant, the pressure P and volume V of a gas are related by the equation

$$VP = k$$

where k is a constant. If the volume is decreasing by 5 cubic inches per second, what is the rate of change of pressure when the volume is 1,000 cubic inches and the pressure is 40 pounds per square inch?

25. A 10-foot ladder is placed against a vertical wall. Suppose that the bottom of the ladder slides away from the wall at a constant rate of 3 feet per second. How fast is the top of the ladder sliding down the wall when the bottom is 6 feet from the wall?

26. A weather balloon is rising vertically at the rate of 5 meters per second. An observer is standing on the ground 300 meters from where the balloon was released. At what rate is the distance between the observer and the balloon changing when the balloon is 400 meters high?

27. A streetlight is on top of a 20-foot pole. A person who is 5 feet tall walks away from the pole at the rate of 5 feet per second. At what rate is the tip of the person's shadow moving away from the pole when he is 20 feet from the pole?

28. Refer to Problem 27. At what rate is the person's shadow growing when he is 20 feet from the pole?

29. Helium is pumped into a spherical balloon at a constant rate of 4 cubic feet per second. How fast is the radius increasing after 1 minute? After 2 minutes? Is there any time at which the radius is increasing at a rate of 100 feet per second? Explain.

30. A point is moving along the x axis at a constant rate of 5 units per second. At which point is its distance from (0, 1) increasing at a rate of 2 units per second? At 4 units per second? At 5 units per second? At 10 units per second? Explain.

31. A point is moving on the graph of $y = e^x + x + 1$ in such a way that its x coordinate is always increasing at a rate of 3 units per second. How fast is the y coordinate changing when the point crosses the x axis?

32. A point is moving on the graph of $x^3 + y^2 = 1$ in such a way that its y coordinate is always increasing at a rate of 2 units per second. At which point(s) is the x coordinate increasing at a rate of 1 unit per second?

Applications

33. Cost, revenue, and profit rates. Suppose that for a company manufacturing calculators, the cost, revenue, and profit equations are given by

$$C = 90,000 + 30x \qquad R = 300x - \frac{x^2}{30}$$
$$P = R - C$$

where the production output in 1 week is x calculators. If production is increasing at a rate of 500 calculators per week when production output is 6,000 calculators, find the rate of increase (decrease) in

(A) Cost   (B) Revenue   (C) Profit

34. Cost, revenue, and profit rates. Repeat Problem 33 for

$$C = 72,000 + 60x \qquad R = 200x - \frac{x^2}{30}$$
$$P = R - C$$

where production is increasing at a rate of 500 calculators per week at a production level of 1,500 calculators.

35. Advertising. A retail store estimates that weekly sales s and weekly advertising costs x (both in dollars) are related by

$$s = 60,000 - 40,000e^{-0.0005x}$$

The current weekly advertising costs are $2,000, and these costs are increasing at the rate of $300 per week. Find the current rate of change of sales.

36. Advertising. Repeat Problem 35 for

$$s = 50,000 - 20,000e^{-0.0004x}$$

37. Price–demand. The price p (in dollars) and demand x for a product are related by

$$2x^2 + 5xp + 50p^2 = 80,000$$

(A) If the price is increasing at a rate of $2 per month when the price is $30, find the rate of change of the demand.

(B) If the demand is decreasing at a rate of 6 units per month when the demand is 150 units, find the rate of change of the price.

38. Price–demand. Repeat Problem 37 for

$$x^2 + 2xp + 25p^2 = 74,500$$

39. Pollution. An oil tanker aground on a reef is forming a circular oil slick about 0.1 foot thick (see the figure). To estimate the rate dV/dt (in cubic feet per minute) at which the oil is leaking from the tanker, it was found that the radius of the slick was increasing at 0.32 foot per minute ($dR/dt = 0.32$) when the radius R was 500 feet. Find dV/dt.

Tanker
R
Oil slick
$A = \pi R^2$
$V = 0.1 A$

40. Learning. A person who is new on an assembly line performs an operation in T minutes after x performances of the operation, as given by

$$T = 6\left(1 + \frac{1}{\sqrt{x}}\right)$$

If $dx/dt = 6$ operations per hours, where t is time in hours, find dT/dt after 36 performances of the operation.

Answers to Matched Problems

1. $dy/dt = -1.25$ ft/sec   **2.** $dz/dt = 25$ mi/hr
3. $dx/dt = 6$ units/sec
4. (A) $dC/dt = \$1,000/$wk   (B) $dR/dt = -\$1,000/$wk
(C) $dP/dt = -\$2,000/$wk

3.7 Elasticity of Demand

- Relative Rate of Change
- Elasticity of Demand

When will a price increase lead to an increase in revenue? To answer this question and study relationships among price, demand, and revenue, economists use the notion of *elasticity of demand*. In this section, we define the concepts of *relative rate of change*, *percentage rate of change*, and *elasticity of demand*.

Relative Rate of Change

Explore and Discuss 1 A broker is trying to sell you two stocks: Biotech and Comstat. The broker estimates that Biotech's price per share will increase $2 per year over the next several years, while Comstat's price per share will increase only $1 per year. Is this sufficient information for you to choose between the two stocks? What other information might you request from the broker to help you decide?

Interpreting rates of change is a fundamental application of calculus. In Explore and Discuss 1, Biotech's price per share is increasing at twice the rate of Comstat's, but that does not automatically make Biotech the better buy. The obvious information that is missing is the current price of each stock. If Biotech costs $100 a share and Comstat costs $25 a share, then which stock is the better buy? To answer this question, we introduce two new concepts: *relative rate of change* and *percentage rate of change*.

DEFINITION Relative and Percentage Rates of Change

The **relative rate of change** of a function $f(x)$ is $\dfrac{f'(x)}{f(x)}$, or equivalently, $\dfrac{d}{dx} \ln f(x)$.

The **percentage rate of change** is $100 \times \dfrac{f'(x)}{f(x)}$, or equivalently, $100 \times \dfrac{d}{dx} \ln f(x)$.

The alternative form for the relative rate of change, $\dfrac{d}{dx} \ln f(x)$, is called the **logarithmic derivative** of $f(x)$.

Note that

$$\frac{d}{dx} \ln f(x) = \frac{f'(x)}{f(x)}$$

by the chain rule. So the relative rate of change of a function $f(x)$ is its logarithmic derivative, and the percentage rate of change is 100 times the logarithmic derivative.

Returning to Explore and Discuss 1, the table shows the relative rate of change and percentage rate of change for Biotech and Comstat. We conclude that Comstat is the better buy.

	Relative rate of change	Percentage rate of change
Biotech	$\dfrac{2}{100} = 0.02$	2%
Comstat	$\dfrac{1}{25} = 0.04$	4%

EXAMPLE 1 Percentage Rate of Change Table 1 lists the GDP (gross domestic product expressed in billions of 2005 dollars) and U.S. population from 2000 to 2012. A model for the GDP is

$$f(t) = 209.5t + 11{,}361$$

where t is years since 2000. Find and graph the percentage rate of change of $f(t)$ for $0 \le t \le 12$.

Table 1

Year	Real GDP (billions of 2005 dollars)	Population (in millions)
2000	$11,226	282.2
2004	$12,264	292.9
2008	$13,312	304.1
2012	$13,670	313.9

SOLUTION If $p(t)$ is the percentage rate of change of $f(t)$, then

$$p(t) = 100 \times \frac{d}{dx} \ln{(209.5t + 11{,}361)}$$

$$= \frac{20{,}950}{209.5t + 11{,}361}$$

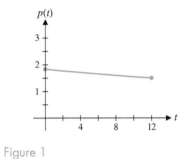

Figure 1

The graph of $p(t)$ is shown in Figure 1 (graphing details omitted). Notice that $p(t)$ is decreasing, even though the GDP is increasing.

Matched Problem 1 A model for the population data in Table 1 is

$$f(t) = 2.7t + 282$$

where t is years since 2000. Find and graph $p(t)$, the percentage rate of change of $f(t)$ for $0 \le t \le 12$.

CONCEPTUAL INSIGHT

If $10,000 is invested at an annual rate of 4.5% compounded continuously, what is the relative rate of change of the amount in the account? The answer is the logarithmic derivative of $A(t) = 10{,}000e^{0.045t}$, namely

$$\frac{d}{dx} \ln{(10{,}000e^{0.045t})} = \frac{10{,}000e^{0.045t}(0.045)}{10{,}000e^{0.045t}} = 0.045$$

So the relative rate of change of $A(t)$ is 0.045, and the percentage rate of change is just the annual interest rate, 4.5%.

Elasticity of Demand

Explore and Discuss 2 In both parts below, assume that increasing the price per unit by $1 will decrease the demand by 500 units. If your objective is to increase revenue, should you increase the price by $1 per unit?

(A) At the current price of $8.00 per baseball cap, there is a demand for 6,000 caps.

(B) At the current price of $12.00 per baseball cap, there is a demand for 4,000 caps.

In Explore and Discuss 2, the rate of change of demand with respect to price was assumed to be −500 units per dollar. But in one case, part (A), you should increase the price, and in the other, part (B), you should not. Economists use the concept of *elasticity of demand* to answer the question "When does an increase in price lead to an increase in revenue?"

DEFINITION   Elasticity of Demand
Let the price p and demand x for a product be related by a price–demand equation of the form $x = f(p)$. Then the **elasticity of demand at price p**, denoted by $E(p)$, is

$$E(p) = -\frac{\text{relative rate of change of demand}}{\text{relative rate of change of price}}$$

Using the definition of relative rate of change, we can find a formula for $E(p)$:

$$E(p) = -\frac{\text{relative rate of change of demand}}{\text{relative rate of change of price}} = -\frac{\dfrac{d}{dp}\ln f(p)}{\dfrac{d}{dp}\ln p}$$

$$= -\frac{\dfrac{f'(p)}{f(p)}}{\dfrac{1}{p}}$$

$$= -\frac{pf'(p)}{f(p)}$$

THEOREM 1   Elasticity of Demand
If price and demand are related by $x = f(p)$, then the elasticity of demand is given by

$$E(p) = -\frac{pf'(p)}{f(p)}$$

CONCEPTUAL INSIGHT

Since p and $f(p)$ are nonnegative and $f'(p)$ is negative (demand is usually a decreasing function of price), $E(p)$ is nonnegative. This is why elasticity of demand is defined as the negative of a ratio.

EXAMPLE 2   Elasticity of Demand   The price p and the demand x for a product are related by the price–demand equation

$$x + 500p = 10{,}000 \tag{1}$$

Find the elasticity of demand, $E(p)$, and interpret each of the following:
(A) $E(4)$ (B) $E(16)$ (C) $E(10)$

SOLUTION   To find $E(p)$, we first express the demand x as a function of the price p by solving (1) for x:

$$x = 10{,}000 - 500p$$
$$= 500(20 - p) \qquad \text{Demand as a function of price}$$

or

$$x = f(p) = 500(20 - p) \qquad 0 \le p \le 20 \tag{2}$$

Since x and p both represent nonnegative quantities, we must restrict p so that $0 \leq p \leq 20$. Note that the demand is a decreasing function of price. That is, a price increase results in lower demand, and a price decrease results in higher demand (see Figure 2).

Figure 2

$$E(p) = -\frac{pf'(p)}{f(p)} = -\frac{p(-500)}{500(20 - p)} = \frac{p}{20 - p}$$

In order to interpret values of $E(p)$, we must recall the definition of elasticity:

$$E(p) = -\frac{\text{relative rate of change of demand}}{\text{relative rate of change of price}}$$

or

$$-\left(\begin{array}{c}\text{relative rate of}\\\text{change of demand}\end{array}\right) \approx E(p)\left(\begin{array}{c}\text{relative rate of}\\\text{change of price}\end{array}\right)$$

(A) $E(4) = \frac{4}{16} = 0.25 < 1$. If the $4 price changes by 10%, then the demand will change by approximately $0.25(10\%) = 2.5\%$.

(B) $E(16) = \frac{16}{4} = 4 > 1$. If the $16 price changes by 10%, then the demand will change by approximately $4(10\%) = 40\%$.

(C) $E(10) = \frac{10}{10} = 1$. If the $10 price changes by 10%, then the demand will also change by approximately 10%.

Matched Problem 2   Find $E(p)$ for the price–demand equation

$$x = f(p) = 1,000(40 - p)$$

Find and interpret each of the following:

(A) $E(8)$ (B) $E(30)$ (C) $E(20)$

The three cases illustrated in the solution to Example 2 are referred to as **inelastic demand**, **elastic demand**, and **unit elasticity**, as indicated in Table 2.

Table 2

$E(p)$	Demand	Interpretation	Revenue
$0 < E(p) < 1$	Inelastic	Demand is not sensitive to changes in price, that is, percentage change in price produces a smaller percentage change in demand.	A price increase will increase revenue.
$E(p) > 1$	Elastic	Demand is sensitive to changes in price, that is, a percentage change in price produces a larger percentage change in demand.	A price increase will decrease revenue.
$E(p) = 1$	Unit	A percentage change in price produces the same percentage change in demand.	

To justify the connection between elasticity of demand and revenue as given in the fourth column of Table 2, we recall that revenue R is the demand x (number of items sold) multiplied by p (price per item). Assume that the price–demand equation is written in the form $x = f(p)$. Then

$$R(p) = xp = f(p)p \qquad \text{Use the product rule.}$$

$$R'(p) = f(p) \cdot 1 + pf'(p) \qquad \text{Multiply and divide by } f(p).$$

$$R'(p) = f(p) + pf'(p)\frac{f(p)}{f(p)} \qquad \text{Factor out } f(p).$$

$$R'(p) = f(p)\left[1 + \frac{pf'(p)}{f(p)}\right] \qquad \text{Use Theorem 1.}$$

$$R'(p) = f(p)[1 - E(p)]$$

Since $x = f(p) > 0$, it follows that $R'(p)$ and $1 - E(p)$ have the same sign. So if $E(p) < 1$, then $R'(p)$ is positive and revenue is increasing (Fig. 3). Similarly, if $E(p) > 1$, then $R'(p)$ is negative, and revenue is decreasing (Fig. 3).

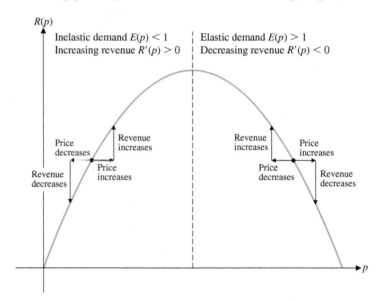

Figure 3 **Revenue and elasticity**

EXAMPLE 3   Elasticity and Revenue   A manufacturer of sunglasses currently sells one type for $15 a pair. The price p and the demand x for these glasses are related by

$$x = f(p) = 9{,}500 - 250p$$

If the current price is increased, will revenue increase or decrease?

SOLUTION
$$E(p) = -\frac{pf'(p)}{f(p)}$$

$$= -\frac{p(-250)}{9{,}500 - 250p}$$

$$= \frac{p}{38 - p}$$

$$E(15) = \frac{15}{23} \approx 0.65$$

At the $15 price level, demand is inelastic and a price increase will increase revenue.

Matched Problem 3   Repeat Example 3 if the current price for sunglasses is $21 a pair.

In summary, if demand is inelastic, then a price increase will increase revenue. But if demand is elastic, then a price increase will decrease revenue.

Exercises 3.7

W

Skills Warm-up Exercises

In Problems 1–8, use the given equation, which expresses price p as a function of demand x, to find a function $f(p)$ that expresses demand x as a function of price p. Give the domain of $f(p)$. (If necessary, review Section 1.6).

1. $p = 42 - 0.4x, 0 \le x \le 105$

2. $p = 125 - 0.02x, 0 \le x \le 6{,}250$

3. $p = 50 - 0.5x^2, 0 \le x \le 10$

4. $p = 180 - 0.8x^2, 0 \le x \le 15$

5. $p = 25e^{-x/20}, 0 \le x \le 20$

6. $p = 45 - e^{x/4}, 0 \le x \le 12$

7. $p = 80 - 10 \ln x, 1 \le x \le 30$

8. $p = \ln(500 - 5x), 0 \le x \le 90$

In Problems 9–14, find the relative rate of change of $f(x)$.

9. $f(x) = 35x - 0.4x^2$

10. $f(x) = 60x - 1.2x^2$

11. $f(x) = 7 + 4e^{-x}$

12. $f(x) = 15 - 3e^{-0.5x}$

13. $f(x) = 12 + 5 \ln x$

14. $f(x) = 25 - 2 \ln x$

In Problems 15–24, find the relative rate of change of $f(x)$ at the indicated value of x. Round to three decimal places.

15. $f(x) = 45; x = 100$

16. $f(x) = 580; x = 300$

17. $f(x) = 420 - 5x; x = 25$

18. $f(x) = 500 - 6x; x = 40$

19. $f(x) = 420 - 5x; x = 55$

20. $f(x) = 500 - 6x; x = 75$

21. $f(x) = 4x^2 - \ln x; x = 2$

22. $f(x) = 9x - 5 \ln x; x = 3$

23. $f(x) = 4x^2 - \ln x; x = 5$

24. $f(x) = 9x - 5 \ln x; x = 7$

In Problems 25–32, find the percentage rate of change of $f(x)$ at the indicated value of x. Round to the nearest tenth of a percent.

25. $f(x) = 225 + 65x; x = 5$

26. $f(x) = 75 + 110x; x = 4$

27. $f(x) = 225 + 65x; x = 15$

28. $f(x) = 75 + 110x; x = 16$

29. $f(x) = 5{,}100 - 3x^2; x = 35$

30. $f(x) = 3{,}000 - 8x^2; x = 12$

31. $f(x) = 5{,}100 - 3x^2; x = 41$

32. $f(x) = 3{,}000 - 8x^2; x = 18$

In Problems 33–38, use the price–demand equation to find $E(p)$, the elasticity of demand.

33. $x = f(p) = 25{,}000 - 450p$

34. $x = f(p) = 10{,}000 - 190p$

35. $x = f(p) = 4{,}800 - 4p^2$

36. $x = f(p) = 8{,}400 - 7p^2$

37. $x = f(p) = 98 - 0.6e^p$

38. $x = f(p) = 160 - 35 \ln p$

In Problems 39–46, find the logarithmic derivative.

39. $A(t) = 500e^{0.07t}$

40. $A(t) = 2{,}000e^{0.052t}$

41. $A(t) = 3{,}500e^{0.15t}$

42. $A(t) = 900e^{0.24t}$

43. $f(x) = xe^x$

44. $f(x) = x^2e^x$

45. $f(x) = \ln x$

46. $f(x) = x \ln x$

In Problems 47–50, use the price–demand equation to determine whether demand is elastic, is inelastic, or has unit elasticity at the indicated values of p.

47. $x = f(p) = 12{,}000 - 10p^2$

   (A) $p = 10$ (B) $p = 20$

   (C) $p = 30$

48. $x = f(p) = 1{,}875 - p^2$

   (A) $p = 15$ (B) $p = 25$

   (C) $p = 40$

49. $x = f(p) = 950 - 2p - 0.1p^2$

   (A) $p = 30$ (B) $p = 50$

   (C) $p = 70$

50. $x = f(p) = 875 - p - 0.05p^2$

   (A) $p = 50$ (B) $p = 70$

   (C) $p = 100$

51. Given the price–demand equation

$$p + 0.005x = 30$$

   (A) Express the demand x as a function of the price p.

   (B) Find the elasticity of demand, $E(p)$.

   (C) What is the elasticity of demand when $p = \$10$? If this price is increased by 10%, what is the approximate percentage change in demand?

   (D) What is the elasticity of demand when $p = \$25$? If this price is increased by 10%, what is the approximate percentage change in demand?

   (E) What is the elasticity of demand when $p = \$15$? If this price is increased by 10%, what is the approximate percentage change in demand?

52. Given the price–demand equation

$$p + 0.01x = 50$$

(A) Express the demand x as a function of the price p.

(B) Find the elasticity of demand, $E(p)$.

(C) What is the elasticity of demand when $p = \$10$? If this price is decreased by 5%, what is the approximate change in demand?

(D) What is the elasticity of demand when $p = \$45$? If this price is decreased by 5%, what is the approximate change in demand?

(E) What is the elasticity of demand when $p = \$25$? If this price is decreased by 5%, what is the approximate change in demand?

53. Given the price–demand equation

$$0.02x + p = 60$$

(A) Express the demand x as a function of the price p.

(B) Express the revenue R as a function of the price p.

(C) Find the elasticity of demand, $E(p)$.

(D) For which values of p is demand elastic? Inelastic?

(E) For which values of p is revenue increasing? Decreasing?

(F) If $p = \$10$ and the price is decreased, will revenue increase or decrease?

(G) If $p = \$40$ and the price is decreased, will revenue increase or decrease?

54. Repeat Problem 53 for the price–demand equation

$$0.025x + p = 50$$

In Problems 55–62, use the price–demand equation to find the values of p for which demand is elastic and the values for which demand is inelastic. Assume that price and demand are both positive.

55. $x = f(p) = 210 - 30p$ **56.** $x = f(p) = 480 - 8p$

57. $x = f(p) = 3{,}125 - 5p^2$ **58.** $x = f(p) = 2{,}400 - 6p^2$

59. $x = f(p) = \sqrt{144 - 2p}$ **60.** $x = f(p) = \sqrt{324 - 2p}$

61. $x = f(p) = \sqrt{2{,}500 - 2p^2}$

62. $x = f(p) = \sqrt{3{,}600 - 2p^2}$

In Problems 63–68, use the demand equation to find the revenue function. Sketch the graph of the revenue function, and indicate the regions of inelastic and elastic demand on the graph.

63. $x = f(p) = 20(10 - p)$ **64.** $x = f(p) = 10(16 - p)$

65. $x = f(p) = 40(p - 15)^2$ **66.** $x = f(p) = 10(p - 9)^2$

67. $x = f(p) = 30 - 10\sqrt{p}$ **68.** $x = f(p) = 30 - 5\sqrt{p}$

If a price–demand equation is solved for p, then price is expressed as $p = g(x)$ and x becomes the independent variable. In this case, it can be shown that the elasticity of demand is given by

$$E(x) = -\frac{g(x)}{xg'(x)}$$

In Problems 69–72, use the price–demand equation to find $E(x)$ at the indicated value of x.

69. $p = g(x) = 50 - 0.1x, x = 200$

70. $p = g(x) = 30 - 0.05x, x = 400$

71. $p = g(x) = 50 - 2\sqrt{x}, x = 400$

72. $p = g(x) = 20 - \sqrt{x}, x = 100$

In Problems 73–76, use the price–demand equation to find the values of x for which demand is elastic and for which demand is inelastic.

73. $p = g(x) = 180 - 0.3x$ **74.** $p = g(x) = 640 - 0.4x$

75. $p = g(x) = 90 - 0.1x^2$ **76.** $p = g(x) = 540 - 0.2x^2$

77. Find $E(p)$ for $x = f(p) = Ap^{-k}$, where A and k are positive constants.

78. Find $E(p)$ for $x = f(p) = Ae^{-kp}$, where A and k are positive constants.

Applications

79. Rate of change of cost. A fast-food restaurant can produce a hamburger for $2.50. If the restaurant's daily sales are increasing at the rate of 30 hamburgers per day, how fast is its daily cost for hamburgers increasing?

80. Rate of change of cost. The fast-food restaurant in Problem 79 can produce an order of fries for $0.80. If the restaurant's daily sales are increasing at the rate of 45 orders of fries per day, how fast is its daily cost for fries increasing?

81. Revenue and elasticity. The price–demand equation for hamburgers at a fast-food restaurant is

$$x + 400p = 3{,}000$$

Currently, the price of a hamburger is $3.00. If the price is increased by 10%, will revenue increase or decrease?

82. Revenue and elasticity. Refer to Problem 81. If the current price of a hamburger is $4.00, will a 10% price increase cause revenue to increase or decrease?

83. Revenue and elasticity. The price–demand equation for an order of fries at a fast-food restaurant is

$$x + 1{,}000p = 2{,}500$$

Currently, the price of an order of fries is $0.99. If the price is decreased by 10%, will revenue increase or decrease?

84. Revenue and elasticity. Refer to Problem 83. If the current price of an order of fries is $1.49; will a 10% price decrease cause revenue to increase or decrease?

85. Maximum revenue. Refer to Problem 81. What price will maximize the revenue from selling hamburgers?

86. Maximum revenue. Refer to Problem 83. What price will maximize the revenue from selling fries?

87. Population growth. A model for Canada's population (Table 3) is

$$f(t) = 0.31t + 18.5$$

where t is years since 1960. Find and graph the percentage rate of change of $f(t)$ for $0 \le t \le 50$.

Table 3 **Population**

Year	Canada (millions)	Mexico (millions)
1960	18	39
1970	22	53
1980	25	68
1990	28	85
2000	31	100
2010	34	112

88. Population growth. A model for Mexico's population (Table 3) is

$$f(t) = 1.49t + 38.8$$

where t is years since 1960. Find and graph the percentage rate of change of $f(t)$ for $0 \le t \le 50$.

89. Crime. A model for the number of robberies in the United States (Table 4) is

$$r(t) = 3.3 - 0.7 \ln t$$

where t is years since 1990. Find the relative rate of change for robberies in 2020.

Table 4 **Number of Victimizations per 1,000 Population**

	Robbery	Aggravated Assault
1995	2.21	4.18
2000	1.45	3.24
2005	1.41	2.91
2010	1.19	2.52

90. Crime. A model for the number of assaults in the United States (Table 4) is

$$a(t) = 6.0 - 1.2 \ln t$$

where t is years since 1990. Find the relative rate of change for assaults in 2020.

Answers to Matched Problems

1. $p(t) = \dfrac{270}{2.7t + 282}$

2. $E(p) = \dfrac{p}{40 - p}$

(A) $E(8) = 0.25$; demand is inelastic.

(B) $E(30) = 3$; demand is elastic.

(C) $E(20) = 1$; demand has unit elasticity.

3. $E(21) = \dfrac{21}{17} \approx 1.2$; demand is elastic. Increasing price will decrease revenue.

Chapter 3   Summary and Review

Important Terms, Symbols, and Concepts

3.1 The Constant e and Continuous Compound Interest

EXAMPLES

- The number e is defined as

$$\lim_{x \to \infty} \left(1 + \frac{1}{n}\right)^n = \lim_{x \to 0} (1 + s)^{1/s} = 2.718\ 281\ 828\ 459 \ldots$$

- If a principal P is invested at an annual rate r (expressed as a decimal) compounded continuously, then the amount A in the account at the end of t years is given by the **compound interest formula**

$$A = Pe^{rt}$$

Ex. 1, p. 183
Ex. 2, p. 183
Ex. 3, p. 184
Ex. 4, p. 184

3.2 Derivatives of Exponential and Logarithmic Functions

- For $b > 0, b \ne 1$,

$$\frac{d}{dx} e^x = e^x \qquad \frac{d}{dx} b^x = b^x \ln b$$

For $b > 0, b \ne 1$, and $x > 0$,

$$\frac{d}{dx} \ln x = \frac{1}{x} \qquad \frac{d}{dx} \log_b x = \frac{1}{\ln b} \frac{1}{x}$$

Ex. 1, p. 188
Ex. 2, p. 190
Ex. 3, p. 191
Ex. 4, p. 192
Ex. 5, p. 193

3.2 Derivatives of Exponential and Logarithmic Functions (*Continued*)

- The **change-of-base formulas** allow conversion from base e to any base b, $b > 0$, $b \neq 1$:

$$b^x = e^{x \ln b} \qquad \log_b x = \frac{\ln x}{\ln b}$$

3.3 Derivatives of Products and Quotients

- Product rule. If $y = f(x) = F(x)\,S(x)$, then $f'(x) = F(x)S'(x) + S(x)F'(x)$, provided that both $F'(x)$ and $S'(x)$ exist.

- Quotient rule. If $y = f(x) = \dfrac{T(x)}{B(x)}$, then $f'(x) = \dfrac{B(x)\,T'(x) - T(x)\,B'(x)}{[B(x)]^2}$ provided that both $T'(x)$ and $B'(x)$ exist.

3.4 The Chain Rule

- A function m is a **composite** of functions f and g if $m(x) = f[g(x)]$.
- The **chain rule** gives a formula for the derivative of the composite function $m(x) = E[I(x)]$:

$$m'(x) = E'[I(x)]I'(x)$$

- A special case of the chain rule is called the **general power rule**:

$$\frac{d}{dx}[f(x)]^n = n[f(x)]^{n-1}f'(x)$$

- Other special cases of the chain rule are the following **general derivative rules**:

$$\frac{d}{dx}\ln[f(x)] = \frac{1}{f(x)}f'(x)$$

$$\frac{d}{dx}e^{f(x)} = e^{f(x)}f'(x)$$

3.5 Implicit Differentiation

- If $y = y(x)$ is a function defined implicitly by the equation $F(x, y) = 0$, then we use **implicit differentiation** to find an equation in x, y, and y'.

3.6 Related Rates

- If x and y represent quantities that are changing with respect to time and are related by the equation $F(x, y) = 0$, then implicit differentiation produces an equation that relates x, y, dy/dt, and dx/dt. Problems of this type are called **related-rates problems**.
- Suggestions for solving related-rates problems are given on page 221.

3.7 Elasticity of Demand

- The **relative rate of change**, or the **logarithmic derivative**, of a function $f(x)$ is $f'(x)/f(x)$, and the **percentage rate of change** is $100 \times [f'(x)/f(x)]$.
- If price and demand are related by $x = f(p)$, then the **elasticity of demand** is given by

$$E(p) = -\frac{pf'(p)}{f(p)} = -\frac{\text{relative rate of change of demand}}{\text{relative rate of change of price}}$$

- **Demand is inelastic** if $0 < E(p) < 1$. (Demand is not sensitive to changes in price; a percentage change in price produces a smaller percentage change in demand.) **Demand is elastic** if $E(p) > 1$. (Demand is sensitive to changes in price; a percentage change in price produces a larger percentage change in demand.) **Demand has unit elasticity** if $E(p) = 1$. (A percentage change in price produces the same percentage change in demand.)
- If $R(p) = pf(p)$ is the revenue function, then $R'(p)$ and $[1 - E(p)]$ always have the same sign. If demand is inelastic, then a price increase will increase revenue. If demand is elastic, then a price increase will decrease revenue.

Review Exercises

Work through all the problems in this chapter review, and check your answers in the back of the book. Answers to all review problems are there, along with section numbers in italics to indicate where each type of problem is discussed. Where weaknesses show up, review appropriate sections of the text.

1. Use a calculator to evaluate $A = 2,000e^{0.09t}$ to the nearest cent for $t = 5, 10,$ and 20.

In Problems 2–4, find functions $E(u)$ and $I(x)$ so that $f(x) = E[I(x)]$.

2. $f(x) = (6x + 5)^{3/2}$ 3. $f(x) = \ln(x^2 + 4)$

4. $f(x) = e^{0.02x}$

In Problems 5–8, find the indicated derivative.

5. $\dfrac{d}{dx}(2 \ln x + 3e^x)$ 6. $\dfrac{d}{dx}e^{2x-3}$

7. y' for $y = \ln(2x + 7)$

8. $f'(x)$ for $f(x) = \ln(3 + e^x)$

9. Find y' for $y = y(x)$ defined implicity by the equation $2y^2 - 3x^3 - 5 = 0$, and evaluate at $(x, y) = (1, 2)$.

10. For $y = 3x^2 - 5$, where $x = x(t)$ and $y = y(t)$, find dy/dt if $dx/dt = 3$ when $x = 12$.

11. Given the demand equation $25p + x = 1,000$,

 (A) Express the demand x as a function of the price p.

 (B) Find the elasticity of demand, $E(p)$.

 (C) Find $E(15)$ and interpret.

 (D) Express the revenue function as a function of price p.

 (E) If $p = \$25$, what is the effect of a small price cut on revenue?

12. Find the slope of the line tangent to $y = 100e^{-0.1x}$ when $x = 0$.

13. Use a calculator and a table of values to investigate

$$\lim_{n \to \infty} \left(1 + \frac{2}{n}\right)^n$$

 Do you think the limit exists? If so, what do you think it is?

Find the indicated derivatives in Problems 14–19.

14. $\dfrac{d}{dz}\left[(\ln z)^7 + \ln z^7\right]$ 15. $\dfrac{d}{dx}(x^6 \ln x)$

16. $\dfrac{d}{dx}\dfrac{e^x}{x^6}$ 17. y' for $y = \ln(2x^3 - 3x)$

18. $f'(x)$ for $f(x) = e^{x^3 - x^2}$ 19. dy/dx for $y = e^{-2x} \ln 5x$

20. Find the equation of the line tangent to the graph of $y = f(x) = 1 + e^{-x}$ at $x = 0$. At $x = -1$.

21. Find y' for $y = y(x)$ defined implicitly by the equation $x^2 - 3xy + 4y^2 = 23$, and find the slope of the graph at $(-1, 2)$.

22. Find x' for $x = x(t)$ defined implicitly by $x^3 - 2t^2x + 8 = 0$, and evaluate at $(t, x) = (-2, 2)$.

23. Find y' for $y = y(x)$ defined implicitly by $x - y^2 = e^y$, and evaluate at $(1, 0)$.

24. Find y' for $y = y(x)$ defined implicitly by $\ln y = x^2 - y^2$, and evaluate at $(1, 1)$.

In Problems 25–27, find the logarithmic derivatives.

25. $A(t) = 400e^{0.049t}$ 26. $f(p) = 100 - 3p$

27. $f(x) = 1 + x^2$

28. A point is moving on the graph of $y^2 - 4x^2 = 12$ so that its x coordinate is decreasing by 2 units per second when $(x, y) = (1, 4)$. Find the rate of change of the y coordinate.

29. A 17-foot ladder is placed against a wall. If the foot of the ladder is pushed toward the wall at 0.5 foot per second, how fast is the top of the ladder rising when the foot is 8 feet from the wall?

30. Water is leaking onto a floor. The resulting circular pool has an area that is increasing at the rate of 24 square inches per minute. How fast is the radius R of the pool increasing when the radius is 12 inches?

31. Find the values of p for which demand is elastic and the values for which demand is inelastic if the price–demand equation is

$$x = f(p) = 20(p - 15)^2 \qquad 0 \le p \le 15$$

32. Graph the revenue function as a function of price p, and indicate the regions of inelastic and elastic demand if the price–demand equation is

$$x = f(p) = 5(20 - p) \qquad 0 \le p \le 20$$

33. Let $y = w^3$, $w = \ln u$, and $u = 4 - e^x$.

 (A) Express y in terms of x.

 (B) Use the chain rule to find dy/dx.

Find the indicated derivatives in Problems 34–36.

34. y' for $y = 5^{x^2 - 1}$ 35. $\dfrac{d}{dx}\log_5(x^2 - x)$

36. $\dfrac{d}{dx}\sqrt{\ln(x^2 + x)}$

37. Find y' for $y = y(x)$ defined implicitly by the equation $e^{xy} = x^2 + y + 1$, and evaluate at $(0, 0)$.

38. A rock thrown into a still pond causes a circular ripple. The radius is increasing at a constant rate of 3 feet per second. Show that the area does not increase at a constant rate. When is the rate of increase of the area the smallest? The largest? Explain.

39. A point moves along the graph of $y = x^3$ in such a way that its y coordinate is increasing at a constant rate of 5 units per second. Does the x coordinate ever increase at a faster rate than the y coordinate? Explain.

Applications

40. Doubling time. How long will it take money to double if it is invested at 5% interest compounded

(A) Annually?   (B) Continuously?

41. Continuous compound interest. If $100 is invested at 10% interest compounded continuously, then the amount (in dollars) at the end of t years is given by

$$A = 100e^{0.1t}$$

Find $A'(t), A'(1)$, and $A'(10)$.

42. Continuous compound interest. If $12,000 is invested in an account that earns 3.95% compounded continuously, find the instantaneous rate of change of the amount when the account is worth $25,000.

43. Marginal analysis. The price–demand equation for 14-cubic-foot refrigerators at an appliance store is

$$p(x) = 1,000e^{-0.02x}$$

where x is the monthly demand and p is the price in dollars. Find the marginal revenue equation.

44. Demand equation. Given the demand equation

$$x = \sqrt{5,000 - 2p^3}$$

find the rate of change of p with respect to x by implicit differentiation (x is the number of items that can be sold at a price of p per item).

45. Rate of change of revenue. A company is manufacturing kayaks and can sell all that it manufactures. The revenue (in dollars) is given by

$$R = 750x - \frac{x^2}{30}$$

where the production output in 1 day is x kayaks. If production is increasing at 3 kayaks per day when production is 40 kayaks per day, find the rate of increase in revenue.

46. Revenue and elasticity. The price–demand equation for home-delivered large pizzas is

$$p = 38.2 - 0.002x$$

where x is the number of pizzas delivered weekly. The current price of one pizza is $21. In order to generate additional revenue from the sale of large pizzas, would you recommend a price increase or a price decrease? Explain.

47. Average income. A model for the average income per household before taxes are paid is

$$f(t) = 1,700t + 20,500$$

where t is years since 1980. Find the relative rate of change of household income in 2015.

48. Drug concentration. The drug concentration in the bloodstream t hours after injection is given approximately by

$$C(t) = 5e^{-0.3t}$$

where $C(t)$ is concentration in milligrams per milliliter. What is the rate of change of concentration after 1 hour? After 5 hours?

49. Wound healing. A circular wound on an arm is healing at the rate of 45 square millimeters per day (the area of the wound is decreasing at this rate). How fast is the radius R of the wound decreasing when $R = 15$ millimeters?

50. Psychology: learning. In a computer assembly plant, a new employee, on the average, is able to assemble

$$N(t) = 10(1 - e^{-0.4t})$$

units after t days of on-the-job training.

(A) What is the rate of learning after 1 day? After 5 days?

(B) Find the number of days (to the nearest day) after which the rate of learning is less than 0.25 unit per day.

51. Learning. A new worker on the production line performs an operation in T minutes after x performances of the operation, as given by

$$T = 2\left(1 + \frac{1}{x^{3/2}}\right)$$

If, after performing the operation 9 times, the rate of improvement is $dx/dt = 3$ operations per hour, find the rate of improvement in time dT/dt in performing each operation.

4

Graphing and Optimization

Introduction

Since the derivative is associated with the slope of the graph of a function at a point, we might expect that it is also related to other properties of a graph. As we will see in this chapter, the derivative can tell us a great deal about the shape of the graph of a function. In particular, we will study methods for finding absolute maximum and minimum values. Manufacturing companies can use these methods to find production levels that will minimize cost or maximize profit, pharmacologists can use them to find levels of drug dosages that will produce maximum sensitivity, and advertisers can use them to determine the number of ads that will maximize the rate of change of sales (see, for example, Problem 93 in Section 4.2).

4.1   First Derivative and Graphs

- Increasing and Decreasing Functions
- Local Extrema
- First-Derivative Test
- Economics Applications

Increasing and Decreasing Functions

Sign charts will be used throughout this chapter. You may find it helpful to review the terminology and techniques for constructing sign charts in Section 2.3.

Explore and Discuss 1   Figure 1 shows the graph of $y = f(x)$ and a sign chart for $f'(x)$, where

$$f(x) = x^3 - 3x$$

and

$$f'(x) = 3x^2 - 3 = 3(x + 1)(x - 1)$$

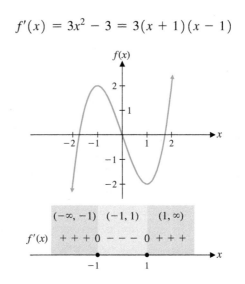

Figure 1

Discuss the relationship between the graph of f and the sign of $f'(x)$ over each interval on which $f'(x)$ has a constant sign. Also, describe the behavior of the graph of f at each partition number for f'.

As they are scanned from left to right, graphs of functions generally have rising and falling sections. If you scan the graph of $f(x) = x^3 - 3x$ in Figure 1 from left to right, you will observe the following:

- On the interval $(-\infty, -1)$, the graph of f is rising, $f(x)$ is increasing,* and tangent lines have positive slope $[f'(x) > 0]$.
- On the interval $(-1, 1)$, the graph of f is falling, $f(x)$ is decreasing, and tangent lines have negative slope $[f'(x) < 0]$.
- On the interval $(1, \infty)$, the graph of f is rising, $f(x)$ is increasing, and tangent lines have positive slope $[f'(x) > 0]$.
- At $x = -1$ and $x = 1$, the slope of the graph is 0 $[f'(x) = 0]$.

If $f'(x) > 0$ (is positive) on the interval (a, b) (Fig. 2), then $f(x)$ increases ($\nearrow$) and the graph of f rises as we move from left to right over the interval. If $f'(x) < 0$ (is negative) on an interval (a, b), then $f(x)$ decreases ($\searrow$) and the graph of f falls as we move from left to right over the interval. We summarize these important results in Theorem 1.

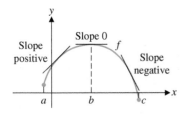

Figure 2

---

*Formally, we say that the function f is **increasing** on an interval (a, b) if $f(x_2) > f(x_1)$ whenever $a < x_1 < x_2 < b$, and f is **decreasing** on (a, b) if $f(x_2) < f(x_1)$ whenever $a < x_1 < x_2 < b$.

THEOREM 1 Increasing and Decreasing Functions

For the interval (a, b), if $f' > 0$, then f is increasing, and if $f' < 0$, then f is decreasing.

$f'(x)$	$f(x)$	Graph of f	Examples
+	Increases ↗	Rises ↗	
−	Decreases ↘	Falls ↘	

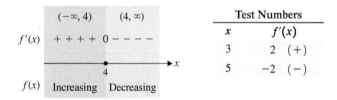

EXAMPLE 1 Finding Intervals on Which a Function Is Increasing or Decreasing

Given the function $f(x) = 8x - x^2$,

(A) Which values of x correspond to horizontal tangent lines?

(B) For which values of x is $f(x)$ increasing? Decreasing?

(C) Sketch a graph of f. Add any horizontal tangent lines.

SOLUTION

(A) $f'(x) = 8 - 2x = 0$

$$x = 4$$

So, a horizontal tangent line exists at $x = 4$ only.

(B) We will construct a sign chart for $f'(x)$ to determine which values of x make $f'(x) > 0$ and which values make $f'(x) < 0$. Recall from Section 2.3 that the partition numbers for a function are the numbers at which the function is 0 or discontinuous. When constructing a sign chart for $f'(x)$, we must locate all points where $f'(x) = 0$ or $f'(x)$ is discontinuous. From part (A), we know that $f'(x) = 8 - 2x = 0$ at $x = 4$. Since $f'(x) = 8 - 2x$ is a polynomial, it is continuous for all x. So, 4 is the only partition number for f'. We construct a sign chart for the intervals $(-\infty, 4)$ and $(4, \infty)$, using test numbers 3 and 5:

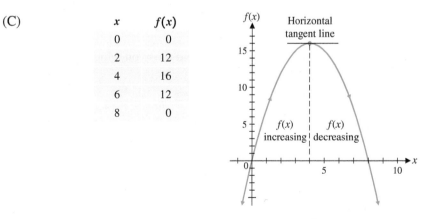

	Test Numbers
x	$f'(x)$
3	2 (+)
5	−2 (−)

Therefore, $f(x)$ is increasing on $(-\infty, 4)$ and decreasing on $(4, \infty)$.

(C)

x	$f(x)$
0	0
2	12
4	16
6	12
8	0

Matched Problem 1 Repeat Example 1 for $f(x) = x^2 - 6x + 10$.

As Example 1 illustrates, the construction of a sign chart will play an important role in using the derivative to analyze and sketch the graph of a function f. The partition numbers for f' are central to the construction of these sign charts and also to the analysis of the graph of $y = f(x)$. The partition numbers for f' that belong to the domain of f are called **critical numbers** of f.*

DEFINITION Critical Numbers
A real number x in the domain of f such that $f'(x) = 0$ or $f'(x)$ does not exist is called a **critical number** of f.

CONCEPTUAL INSIGHT

The critical numbers of f belong to the domain of f and are partition numbers for f'. But f' may have partition numbers that do not belong to the domain of f, so are not critical numbers of f.

If f is a polynomial, then both the partition numbers for f' and the critical numbers of f are the solutions of $f'(x) = 0$.

EXAMPLE 2 Partition Numbers for f' and Critical Numbers of f Find the critical numbers of f, the intervals on which f is increasing, and those on which f is decreasing, for $f(x) = 1 + x^3$.

SOLUTION Begin by finding the partition numbers for $f'(x)$ [since $f'(x) = 3x^2$ is continuous we just need to solve $f'(x) = 0$]

$$f'(x) = 3x^2 = 0 \quad \text{only if } x = 0$$

The partition number 0 for f' is in the domain of f, so 0 is the only critical number of f.

The sign chart for $f'(x) = 3x^2$ (partition number is 0) is

Figure 3

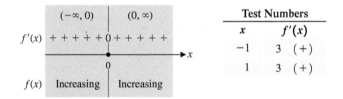

The sign chart indicates that $f(x)$ is increasing on $(-\infty, 0)$ and $(0, \infty)$. Since f is continuous at $x = 0$, it follows that $f(x)$ is increasing for all x. The graph of f is shown in Figure 3.

Matched Problem 2 Find the critical numbers of f, the intervals on which f is increasing, and those on which f is decreasing, for $f(x) = 1 - x^3$.

EXAMPLE 3 Partition Numbers for f' and Critical Numbers of f Find the critical numbers of f, the intervals on which f is increasing, and those on which f is decreasing, for $f(x) = (1 - x)^{1/3}$.

SOLUTION
$$f'(x) = -\frac{1}{3}(1 - x)^{-2/3} = \frac{-1}{3(1 - x)^{2/3}}$$

---

*We are assuming that $f'(c)$ does not exist at any point of discontinuity of f'. There do exist functions f such that f' is discontinuous at $x = c$, yet $f'(c)$ exists. However, we do not consider such functions in this book.

To find the partition numbers for f', we note that f' is continuous for all x, except for values of x for which the denominator is 0; that is, $f'(1)$ does not exist and f' is discontinuous at $x = 1$. Since the numerator of f' is the constant -1, $f'(x) \neq 0$ for any value of x. Thus, $x = 1$ is the only partition number for f'. Since 1 is in the domain of f, $x = 1$ is also the only critical number of f. When constructing the sign chart for f' we use the abbreviation ND to note the fact that $f'(x)$ is *not defined* at $x = 1$.

The sign chart for $f'(x) = -1/[3(1-x)^{2/3}]$ (partition number for f' is 1) is as follows:

	$(-\infty, 1)$	$(1, \infty)$
$f'(x)$	$- - - -$ ND $- - - -$	
$f(x)$	Decreasing	Decreasing

Test Numbers	
x	$f'(x)$
0	$-\frac{1}{3}$ $(-)$
2	$-\frac{1}{3}$ $(-)$

The sign chart indicates that f is decreasing on $(-\infty, 1)$ and $(1, \infty)$. Since f is continuous at $x = 1$, it follows that $f(x)$ is decreasing for all x. **A continuous function can be decreasing (or increasing) on an interval containing values of x where $f'(x)$ does not exist.** The graph of f is shown in Figure 4. Notice that the undefined derivative at $x = 1$ results in a vertical tangent line at $x = 1$. **A vertical tangent will occur at $x = c$ if f is continuous at $x = c$ and if $|f'(x)|$ becomes larger and larger as x approaches c.**

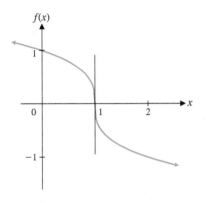

Figure 4

Matched Problem 3 Find the critical numbers of f, the intervals on which f is increasing, and those on which f is decreasing, for $f(x) = (1 + x)^{1/3}$.

EXAMPLE 4 Partition Numbers for f' and Critical Numbers of f Find the critical numbers of f, the intervals on which f is increasing, and those on which f is decreasing, for $f(x) = \dfrac{1}{x-2}$.

SOLUTION
$$f(x) = \frac{1}{x-2} = (x-2)^{-1}$$
$$f'(x) = -(x-2)^{-2} = \frac{-1}{(x-2)^2}$$

To find the partition numbers for f', note that $f'(x) \neq 0$ for any x and f' is not defined at $x = 2$. Thus, $x = 2$ is the only partition number for f'. However, $x = 2$ is *not* in the domain of f. Consequently, $x = 2$ is *not* a critical number of f. The function f has no critical numbers.

The sign chart for $f'(x) = -1/(x-2)^2$ (partition number for f' is 2) is as follows:

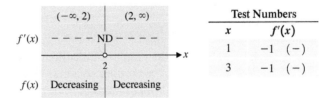

	$(-\infty, 2)$	$(2, \infty)$
$f'(x)$	$- - - -$ ND $- - - -$	
$f(x)$	Decreasing	Decreasing

Test Numbers	
x	$f'(x)$
1	-1 $(-)$
3	-1 $(-)$

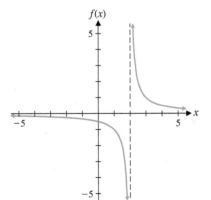

Figure 5

Therefore, f is decreasing on $(-\infty, 2)$ and $(2, \infty)$. The graph of f is shown in Figure 5.

Matched Problem 4 Find the critical numbers of f, the intervals on which f is increasing, and those on which f is decreasing, for $f(x) = \dfrac{1}{x}$.

EXAMPLE 5   Partition Numbers for f' and Critical Numbers of f Find the critical numbers of f, the intervals on which f is increasing, and those on which f is decreasing, for $f(x) = 8 \ln x - x^2$.

SOLUTION   The natural logarithm function $\ln x$ is defined on $(0, \infty)$, or $x > 0$, so $f(x)$ is defined only for $x > 0$.

$$f(x) = 8 \ln x - x^2, x > 0$$

$$f'(x) = \frac{8}{x} - 2x \qquad \text{Find a common denominator.}$$

$$= \frac{8}{x} - \frac{2x^2}{x} \qquad \text{Subtract numerators.}$$

$$= \frac{8 - 2x^2}{x} \qquad \text{Factor numerator.}$$

$$= \frac{2(2 - x)(2 + x)}{x}, \quad x > 0$$

The only partition number for f' that is positive, and therefore belongs to the domain of f, is 2. So 2 is the only critical number of f.

The sign chart for $f'(x) = \dfrac{2(2 - x)(2 + x)}{x}, x > 0$ (partition number for f' is 2), is as follows:

	$(0, 2)$	$(2, \infty)$		Test Numbers	
				x	$f'(x)$
$f'(x)$	$++++$ 0	$----$		1	6 $(+)$
	0	2		4	-6 $(-)$
$f(x)$	Increasing	Decreasing			

Therefore, f is increasing on $(0, 2)$ and decreasing on $(2, \infty)$. The graph of f is shown in Figure 6.

Matched Problem 5   Find the critical numbers of f, the intervals on which f is increasing, and those on which f is decreasing, for $f(x) = 5 \ln x - x$.

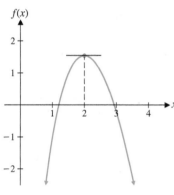

$f(x)$

Figure 6

CONCEPTUAL INSIGHT

Examples 4 and 5 illustrate two important ideas:

1. Do not assume that all partition numbers for the derivative f' are critical numbers of the function f. To be a critical number of f, a partition number for f' must also be in the domain of f.

2. The intervals on which a function f is increasing or decreasing must always be expressed in terms of open intervals that are subsets of the domain of f.

Local Extrema

When the graph of a continuous function changes from rising to falling, a high point, or *local maximum*, occurs. When the graph changes from falling to rising, a low point, or *local minimum*, occurs. In Figure 7, high points occur at c_3 and c_6, and low points occur at c_2 and c_4. In general, we call $f(c)$ a **local maximum** if there exists an interval (m, n) containing c such that

$$f(x) \leq f(c) \qquad \text{for all } x \text{ in } (m, n)$$

Note that this inequality need hold only for numbers x near c, which is why we use the term *local*. So the y coordinate of the high point $(c_3, f(c_3))$ in Figure 7 is a local maximum, as is the y coordinate of $(c_6, f(c_6))$.

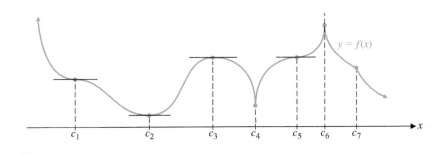

Figure 7

The value $f(c)$ is called a **local minimum** if there exists an interval (m, n) containing c such that

$$f(x) \geq f(c) \qquad \text{for all } x \text{ in } (m, n)$$

The value $f(c)$ is called a **local extremum** if it is either a local maximum or a local minimum. A point on a graph where a local extremum occurs is also called a **turning point**. In Figure 7 we see that local maxima occur at c_3 and c_6, local minima occur at c_2 and c_4, and all four values produce local extrema. Also, the local maximum $f(c_3)$ is not the largest y coordinate of points on the graph in Figure 7. Later in this chapter, we consider the problem of finding *absolute extrema*, the y coordinates of the highest and lowest points on a graph. For now, we are concerned only with locating *local* extrema.

EXAMPLE 6 Analyzing a Graph Use the graph of f in Figure 8 to find the intervals on which f is increasing, those on which f is decreasing, any local maxima, and any local minima.

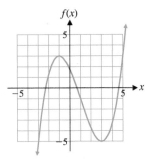

Figure 8

SOLUTION The function f is increasing (the graph is rising) on $(-\infty, -1)$ and on $(3, \infty)$ and is decreasing (the graph is falling) on $(-1, 3)$. Because the graph changes from rising to falling at $x = -1$, $f(-1) = 3$ is a local maximum. Because the graph changes from falling to rising at $x = 3$, $f(3) = -5$ is a local minimum.

Matched Problem 6 Use the graph of g in Figure 9 to find the intervals on which g is increasing, those on which g is decreasing, any local maxima, and any local minima.

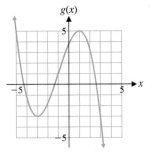

Figure 9

How can we locate local maxima and minima if we are given the equation of a function and not its graph? The key is to examine the critical numbers of the function. The local extrema of the function f in Figure 7 occur either at points where the derivative is 0 (c_2 and c_3) or at points where the derivative does not exist (c_4 and c_6). In other words, local extrema occur only at critical numbers of f.

THEOREM 2   Local Extrema and Critical Numbers

If $f(c)$ is a local extremum of the function f, then c is a critical number of f.

Theorem 2 states that a local extremum can occur only at a critical number, but it does not imply that every critical number produces a local extremum. In Figure 7, c_1 and c_5 are critical numbers (the slope is 0), but the function does not have a local maximum or local minimum at either of these numbers.

Our strategy for finding local extrema is now clear: We find all critical numbers of f and test each one to see if it produces a local maximum, a local minimum, or neither.

First-Derivative Test

If $f'(x)$ exists on both sides of a critical number c, the sign of $f'(x)$ can be used to determine whether the point $(c, f(c))$ is a local maximum, a local minimum, or neither. The various possibilities are summarized in the following box and are illustrated in Figure 10:

PROCEDURE   First-Derivative Test for Local Extrema

Let c be a critical number of f [$f(c)$ is defined and either $f'(c) = 0$ or $f'(c)$ is not defined]. Construct a sign chart for $f'(x)$ close to and on either side of c.

Sign Chart	$f(c)$
$f'(x)$ $---$ $+++$ m c n $f(x)$ Decreasing Increasing	$f(c)$ is a local minimum. If $f'(x)$ changes from negative to positive at c, then $f(c)$ is a local minimum.
$f'(x)$ $+++$ $---$ m c n $f(x)$ Increasing Decreasing	$f(c)$ is a local maximum. If $f'(x)$ changes from positive to negative at c, then $f(c)$ is a local maximum.
$f'(x)$ $+++$ $+++$ m c n $f(x)$ Increasing Increasing	$f(c)$ is not a local extremum. If $f'(x)$ does not change sign at c, then $f(c)$ is neither a local maximum nor a local minimum.
$f'(x)$ $---$ $---$ m c n $f(x)$ Decreasing Decreasing	$f(c)$ is not a local extremum. If $f'(x)$ does not change sign at c, then $f(c)$ is neither a local maximum nor a local minimum.

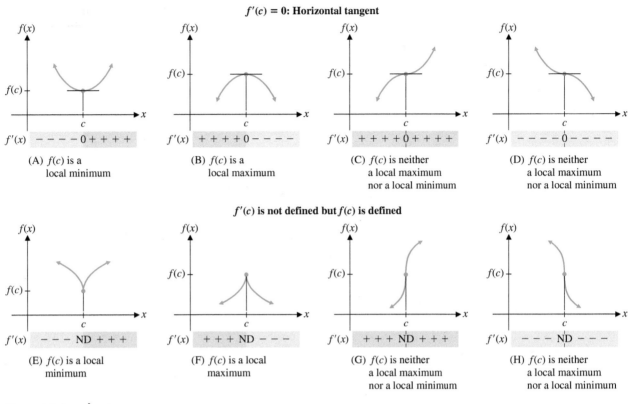

f'(c) = 0: Horizontal tangent

(A) f(c) is a
local minimum

(B) f(c) is a
local maximum

(C) f(c) is neither
a local maximum
nor a local minimum

(D) f(c) is neither
a local maximum
nor a local minimum

f'(c) is not defined but f(c) is defined

(E) f(c) is a local
minimum

(F) f(c) is a local
maximum

(G) f(c) is neither
a local maximum
nor a local minimum

(H) f(c) is neither
a local maximum
nor a local minimum

Figure 10 **Local extrema**

EXAMPLE 7 Locating Local Extrema Given $f(x) = x^3 - 6x^2 + 9x + 1$,

(A) Find the critical numbers of f.

(B) Find the local maxima and local minima of f.

(C) Sketch the graph of f.

SOLUTION

(A) Find all numbers x in the domain of f where $f'(x) = 0$ or $f'(x)$ does not exist.

$$f'(x) = 3x^2 - 12x + 9 = 0$$
$$3(x^2 - 4x + 3) = 0$$
$$3(x - 1)(x - 3) = 0$$
$$x = 1 \quad \text{or} \quad x = 3$$

$f'(x)$ exists for all x; the critical numbers of f are $x = 1$ and $x = 3$.

(B) The easiest way to apply the first-derivative test for local maxima and minima is to construct a sign chart for $f'(x)$ for all x. Partition numbers for $f'(x)$ are $x = 1$ and $x = 3$ (which also happen to be critical numbers of f).

Sign chart for $f'(x) = 3(x - 1)(x - 3)$:

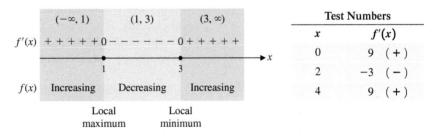

	Test Numbers	
x	$f'(x)$	
0	9	(+)
2	-3	(−)
4	9	(+)

The sign chart indicates that f increases on $(-\infty, 1)$, has a local maximum at $x = 1$, decreases on $(1, 3)$, has a local minimum at $x = 3$, and increases on $(3, \infty)$. These facts are summarized in the following table:

x	$f'(x)$	$f(x)$	Graph of f
$(-\infty, 1)$	$+$	Increasing	Rising
$x = 1$	0	Local maximum	Horizontal tangent
$(1, 3)$	$-$	Decreasing	Falling
$x = 3$	0	Local minimum	Horizontal tangent
$(3, \infty)$	$+$	Increasing	Rising

The local maximum is $f(1) = 5$; the local minimum is $f(3) = 1$.

(C) We sketch a graph of f, using the information from part (B) and point-by-point plotting.

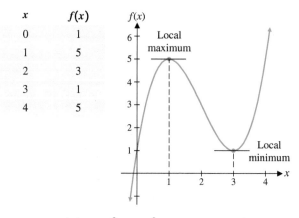

x	$f(x)$
0	1
1	5
2	3
3	1
4	5

Matched Problem 7 Given $f(x) = x^3 - 9x^2 + 24x - 10$,

(A) Find the critical numbers of f.

(B) Find the local maxima and local minima of f.

(C) Sketch a graph of f.

How can you tell if you have found all the local extrema of a function? In general, this can be a difficult question to answer. However, in the case of a polynomial function, there is an easily determined upper limit on the number of local extrema. Since the local extrema are the x intercepts of the derivative, this limit is a consequence of the number of x intercepts of a polynomial. The relevant information is summarized in the following theorem, which is stated without proof:

THEOREM 3   Intercepts and Local Extrema of Polynomial Functions

If $f(x) = a_n x^n + a_{n-1} x^{n-1} + \cdots + a_1 x + a_0, a_n \neq 0$, is a polynomial function of degree $n \geq 1$, then f has at most n x intercepts and at most $n - 1$ local extrema.

Theorem 3 does not guarantee that every nth-degree polynomial has exactly $n - 1$ local extrema; it says only that there can never be more than $n - 1$ local extrema. For example, the third-degree polynomial in Example 7 has two local extrema, while the third-degree polynomial in Example 2 does not have any.

Economics Applications

In addition to providing information for hand-sketching graphs, the derivative is an important tool for analyzing graphs and discussing the interplay between a function and its rate of change. The next two examples illustrate this process in the context of economics.

EXAMPLE 8   Agricultural Exports and Imports   Over the past few decades, the United States has exported more agricultural products than it has imported, maintaining a positive balance of trade in this area. However, the trade balance fluctuated considerably during that period. The graph in Figure 11 approximates the rate of change of the balance of trade over a 15-year period, where $B(t)$ is the balance of trade (in billions of dollars) and t is time (in years).

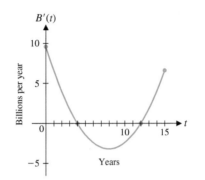

Figure 11 **Rate of change of the balance of trade**

(A) Write a brief description of the graph of $y = B(t)$, including a discussion of any local extrema.

(B) Sketch a possible graph of $y = B(t)$.

SOLUTION

(A) The graph of the derivative $y = B'(t)$ contains the same essential information as a sign chart. That is, we see that $B'(t)$ is positive on $(0, 4)$, 0 at $t = 4$, negative on $(4, 12)$, 0 at $t = 12$, and positive on $(12, 15)$. The trade balance increases for the first 4 years to a local maximum, decreases for the next 8 years to a local minimum, and then increases for the final 3 years.

(B) Without additional information concerning the actual values of $y = B(t)$, we cannot produce an accurate graph. However, we can sketch a possible graph that illustrates the important features, as shown in Figure 12. The absence of a scale on the vertical axis is a consequence of the lack of information about the values of $B(t)$.

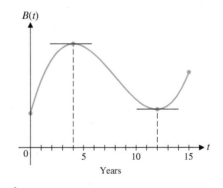

Figure 12 **Balance of trade**

Matched Problem 8   The graph in Figure 13 approximates the rate of change of the U.S. share of the total world production of motor vehicles over a 20-year period, where $S(t)$ is the U.S. share (as a percentage) and t is time (in years).

(A) Write a brief description of the graph of $y = S(t)$, including a discussion of any local extrema.

(B) Sketch a possible graph of $y = S(t)$.

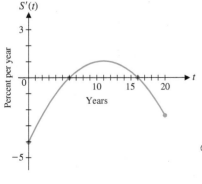

Figure 13

EXAMPLE 9   Revenue Analysis   The graph of the total revenue $R(x)$ (in dollars) from the sale of x bookcases is shown in Figure 14.

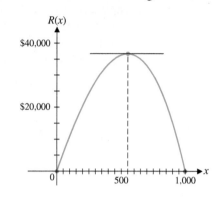

Figure 14 **Revenue**

(A) Write a brief description of the graph of the marginal revenue function $y = R'(x)$, including a discussion of any x intercepts.

(B) Sketch a possible graph of $y = R'(x)$.

SOLUTION

(A) The graph of $y = R(x)$ indicates that $R(x)$ increases on $(0, 550)$, has a local maximum at $x = 550$, and decreases on $(550, 1,000)$. Consequently, the marginal revenue function $R'(x)$ must be positive on $(0, 550)$, 0 at $x = 550$, and negative on $(550, 1,000)$.

(B) A possible graph of $y = R'(x)$ illustrating the information summarized in part (A) is shown in Figure 15.

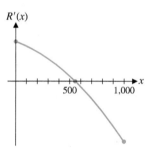

Figure 15 **Marginal revenue**

Matched Problem 9   The graph of the total revenue $R(x)$ (in dollars) from the sale of x desks is shown in Figure 16.

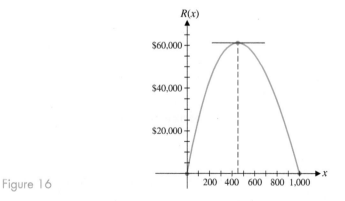

Figure 16

(A) Write a brief description of the graph of the marginal revenue function $y = R'(x)$, including a discussion of any x intercepts.

(B) Sketch a possible graph of $y = R'(x)$.

Comparing Examples 8 and 9, we see that we were able to obtain more information about the function from the graph of its derivative (Example 8) than we were when the process was reversed (Example 9). In the next section, we introduce some ideas that will help us obtain additional information about the derivative from the graph of the function.

Exercises 4.1

Skills Warm-up Exercises

W   *In Problems 1–8, inspect the graph of the function to determine whether it is increasing or decreasing on the given interval. (If necessary, review Section 1.2).*

1. $g(x) = |x|$ on $(-\infty, 0)$

2. $m(x) = x^3$ on $(0, \infty)$

3. $f(x) = x$ on $(-\infty, \infty)$

4. $k(x) = -x^2$ on $(0, \infty)$

5. $p(x) = \sqrt[3]{x}$ on $(-\infty, 0)$

6. $h(x) = x^2$ on $(-\infty, 0)$

7. $r(x) = 4 - \sqrt{x}$ on $(0, \infty)$

8. $g(x) = |x|$ on $(0, \infty)$

Problems 9–16, refer to the following graph of $y = f(x)$:

Figure for 9–16

9. Identify the intervals on which $f(x)$ is increasing.

10. Identify the intervals on which $f(x)$ is decreasing.

11. Identify the intervals on which $f'(x) < 0$.

12. Identify the intervals on which $f'(x) > 0$.

13. Identify the x coordinates of the points where $f'(x) = 0$.

14. Identify the x coordinates of the points where $f'(x)$ does not exist.

15. Identify the x coordinates of the points where $f(x)$ has a local maximum.

16. Identify the x coordinates of the points where $f(x)$ has a local minimum.

In Problems 17 and 18, $f(x)$ is continuous on $(-\infty, \infty)$ and has critical numbers at $x = a, b, c,$ and d. Use the sign chart for $f'(x)$ to determine whether f has a local maximum, a local minimum, or neither at each critical number.

17.

18.

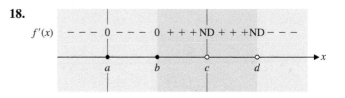

In Problems 19–26, give the local extrema of f and match the graph of f with one of the sign charts a–h in the figure on page 250.

19.

20.

21.

22.

23.

24.

25.

26.

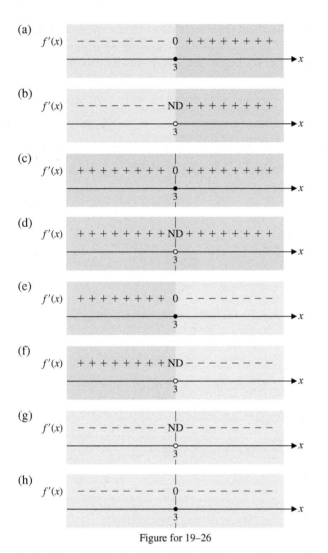

(a) $f'(x)$ $-\ -\ -\ -\ -\ -\ -\ 0\ +\ +\ +\ +\ +\ +\ +$ x
3

(b) $f'(x)$ $-\ -\ -\ -\ -\ -\ -\ ND\ +\ +\ +\ +\ +\ +\ +$ x
3

(c) $f'(x)$ $+\ +\ +\ +\ +\ +\ +\ 0\ +\ +\ +\ +\ +\ +\ +$ x
3

(d) $f'(x)$ $+\ +\ +\ +\ +\ +\ +\ ND\ +\ +\ +\ +\ +\ +\ +$ x
3

(e) $f'(x)$ $+\ +\ +\ +\ +\ +\ +\ 0\ -\ -\ -\ -\ -\ -\ -$ x
3

(f) $f'(x)$ $+\ +\ +\ +\ +\ +\ +\ ND\ -\ -\ -\ -\ -\ -\ -$ x
3

(g) $f'(x)$ $-\ -\ -\ -\ -\ -\ -\ ND\ -\ -\ -\ -\ -\ -\ -$ x
3

(h) $f'(x)$ $-\ -\ -\ -\ -\ -\ -\ 0\ -\ -\ -\ -\ -\ -\ -$ x
3

Figure for 19–26

In Problems 27–32, find (A) $f'(x)$, (B) the partition numbers for f', and (C) the critical numbers of f.

27. $f(x) = x^3 - 12x + 8$

28. $f(x) = x^3 - 27x + 30$

29. $f(x) = \dfrac{6}{x+2}$ **30.** $f(x) = \dfrac{5}{x-4}$

31. $f(x) = |x|$ **32.** $f(x) = |x+3|$

In Problems 33–46, find the intervals on which $f(x)$ is increasing, the intervals on which $f(x)$ is decreasing, and the local extrema.

33. $f(x) = 2x^2 - 4x$

34. $f(x) = -3x^2 - 12x$

35. $f(x) = -2x^2 - 16x - 25$

36. $f(x) = -3x^2 + 12x - 5$

37. $f(x) = x^3 + 4x - 5$

38. $f(x) = -x^3 - 4x + 8$

39. $f(x) = 2x^3 - 3x^2 - 36x$

40. $f(x) = -2x^3 + 3x^2 + 120x$

41. $f(x) = 3x^4 - 4x^3 + 5$

42. $f(x) = x^4 + 2x^3 + 5$

43. $f(x) = (x-1)e^{-x}$ **44.** $f(x) = x \ln x - x$

45. $f(x) = 4x^{1/3} - x^{2/3}$ **46.** $f(x) = (x^2 - 9)^{2/3}$

In Problems 47–52, use a graphing calculator to approximate the critical numbers of $f(x)$ to two decimal places. Find the intervals on which $f(x)$ is increasing, the intervals on which $f(x)$ is decreasing, and the local extrema.

47. $f(x) = x^4 - 4x^3 + 9x$ **48.** $f(x) = x^4 + 5x^3 - 15x$

49. $f(x) = x \ln x - (x-2)^3$ **50.** $f(x) = e^{-x} - 3x^2$

51. $f(x) = e^x - 2x^2$ **52.** $f(x) = \dfrac{\ln x}{x} - 5x + x^2$

In Problems 53–60, find the intervals on which $f(x)$ is increasing and the intervals on which $f(x)$ is decreasing. Then sketch the graph. Add horizontal tangent lines.

53. $f(x) = 4 + 8x - x^2$

54. $f(x) = 2x^2 - 8x + 9$

55. $f(x) = x^3 - 3x + 1$

56. $f(x) = x^3 - 12x + 2$

57. $f(x) = 10 - 12x + 6x^2 - x^3$

58. $f(x) = x^3 + 3x^2 + 3x$

59. $f(x) = x^4 - 18x^2$

60. $f(x) = -x^4 + 50x^2$

In Problems 61–68, $f(x)$ is continuous on $(-\infty, \infty)$. Use the given information to sketch the graph of f.

61.

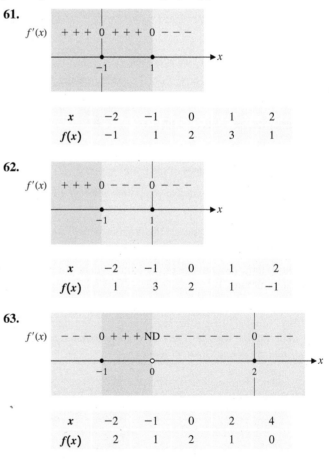

$f'(x)$ $+\ +\ +\ 0\ +\ +\ +\ 0\ -\ -\ -$ x
-1 1

x	-2	-1	0	1	2
$f(x)$	-1	1	2	3	1

62.

$f'(x)$ $+\ +\ +\ 0\ -\ -\ -\ 0\ -\ -\ -$ x
-1 1

x	-2	-1	0	1	2
$f(x)$	1	3	2	1	-1

63.

$f'(x)$ $-\ -\ -\ 0\ +\ +\ +\ ND\ -\ -\ -\ -\ -\ -\ -\ 0\ -\ -\ -$ x
-1 0 2

x	-2	-1	0	2	4
$f(x)$	2	1	2	1	0

64.

x	-2	-1	0	2	3
$f(x)$	-3	0	2	-1	0

65. $f(-2) = 4, f(0) = 0, f(2) = -4;$

$f'(-2) = 0, f'(0) = 0, f'(2) = 0;$

$f'(x) > 0$ on $(-\infty, -2)$ and $(2, \infty);$

$f'(x) < 0$ on $(-2, 0)$ and $(0, 2)$

66. $f(-2) = -1, f(0) = 0, f(2) = 1;$

$f'(-2) = 0, f'(2) = 0;$

$f'(x) > 0$ on $(-\infty, -2), (-2, 2),$ and $(2, \infty)$

67. $f(-1) = 2, f(0) = 0, f(1) = -2;$

$f'(-1) = 0, f'(1) = 0, f'(0)$ is not defined;

$f'(x) > 0$ on $(-\infty, -1)$ and $(1, \infty);$

$f'(x) < 0$ on $(-1, 0)$ and $(0, 1)$

68. $f(-1) = 2, f(0) = 0, f(1) = 2;$

$f'(-1) = 0, f'(1) = 0, f'(0)$ is not defined;

$f'(x) > 0$ on $(-\infty, -1)$ and $(0, 1);$

$f'(x) < 0$ on $(-1, 0)$ and $(1, \infty)$

Problems 69–74 involve functions f_1–f_6 and their derivatives, g_1–g_6. Use the graphs shown in figures (A) and (B) to match each function f_i with its derivative g_j.

69. f_1 **70.** f_2 **71.** f_3

72. f_4 **73.** f_5 **74.** f_6

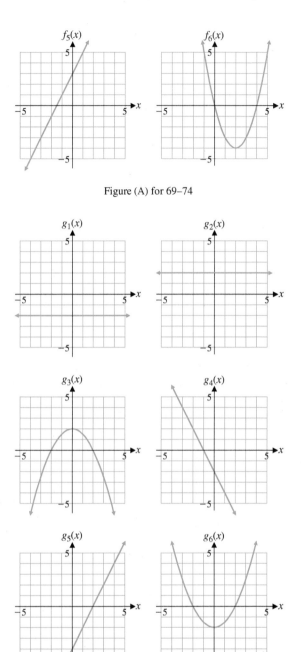

Figure (A) for 69–74

Figure (B) for 69–74

In Problems 75–80, use the given graph of $y = f'(x)$ to find the intervals on which f is increasing, the intervals on which f is decreasing, and the x coordinates of the local extrema of f. Sketch a possible graph of $y = f(x)$.

75.   **76.**

77.

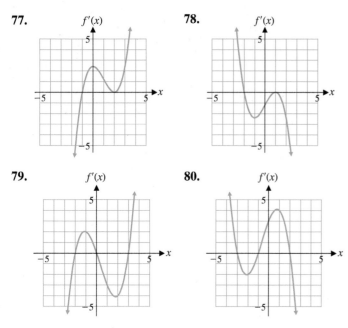

78.

79.

80.

In Problems 81–84, use the given graph of $y = f(x)$ to find the intervals on which $f'(x) > 0$, the intervals on which $f'(x) < 0$, and the values of x for which $f'(x) = 0$. Sketch a possible graph of $y = f'(x)$.

81.

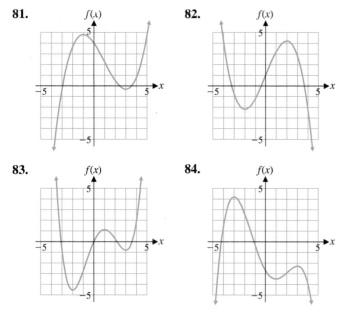

82.

83.

84.

In Problems 85–90, find the critical numbers, the intervals on which $f(x)$ is increasing, the intervals on which $f(x)$ is decreasing, and the local extrema. Do not graph.

85. $f(x) = x + \dfrac{4}{x}$

86. $f(x) = \dfrac{9}{x} + x$

87. $f(x) = 1 + \dfrac{1}{x} + \dfrac{1}{x^2}$

88. $f(x) = 3 - \dfrac{4}{x} - \dfrac{2}{x^2}$

89. $f(x) = \dfrac{x^2}{x - 2}$

90. $f(x) = \dfrac{x^2}{x + 1}$

Applications

91. Profit analysis. The graph of the total profit $P(x)$ (in dollars) from the sale of x cordless electric screwdrivers is shown in the figure.

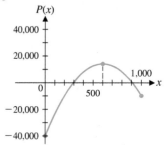

(A) Write a brief description of the graph of the marginal profit function $y = P'(x)$, including a discussion of any x intercepts.

(B) Sketch a possible graph of $y = P'(x)$.

92. Revenue analysis. The graph of the total revenue $R(x)$ (in dollars) from the sale of x cordless electric screwdrivers is shown in the figure.

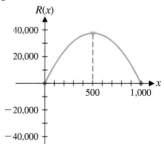

(A) Write a brief description of the graph of the marginal revenue function $y = R'(x)$, including a discussion of any x intercepts.

(B) Sketch a possible graph of $y = R'(x)$.

93. Price analysis. The figure approximates the rate of change of the price of bacon over a 70-month period, where $B(t)$ is the price of a pound of sliced bacon (in dollars) and t is time (in months).

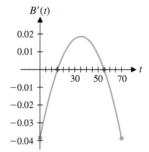

(A) Write a brief description of the graph of $y = B(t)$, including a discussion of any local extrema.

(B) Sketch a possible graph of $y = B(t)$.

94. Price analysis. The figure approximates the rate of change of the price of eggs over a 70-month period, where $E(t)$ is the price of a dozen eggs (in dollars) and t is time (in months).

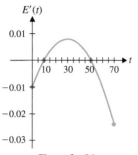

E'(t)

0.01

10 30 50 70 t

−0.01

−0.02

−0.03

Figure for 94

(A) Write a brief description of the graph of $y = E(t)$, including a discussion of any local extrema.

(B) Sketch a possible graph of $y = E(t)$.

95. Average cost. A manufacturer incurs the following costs in producing x water ski vests in one day, for $0 < x < 150$: fixed costs, \$320; unit production cost, \$20 per vest; equipment maintenance and repairs, $0.05x^2$ dollars. So, the cost of manufacturing x vests in one day is given by

$$C(x) = 0.05x^2 + 20x + 320 \qquad 0 < x < 150$$

(A) What is the average cost $\overline{C}(x)$ per vest if x vests are produced in one day?

(B) Find the critical numbers of $\overline{C}(x)$, the intervals on which the average cost per vest is decreasing, the intervals on which the average cost per vest is increasing, and the local extrema. Do not graph.

96. Average cost. A manufacturer incurs the following costs in producing x rain jackets in one day for $0 < x < 200$: fixed costs, \$450; unit production cost, \$30 per jacket; equipment maintenance and repairs, $0.08x^2$ dollars.

(A) What is the average cost $\overline{C}(x)$ per jacket if x jackets are produced in one day?

(B) Find the critical numbers of $\overline{C}(x)$, the intervals on which the average cost per jacket is decreasing, the intervals on which the average cost per jacket is increasing, and the local extrema. Do not graph.

97. Medicine. A drug is injected into the bloodstream of a patient through the right arm. The drug concentration in the bloodstream of the left arm t hours after the injection is approximated by

$$C(t) = \frac{0.28t}{t^2 + 4} \qquad 0 < t < 24$$

Find the critical numbers of $C(t)$, the intervals on which the drug concentration is increasing, the intervals on which the concentration of the drug is decreasing, and the local extrema. Do not graph.

98. Medicine. The concentration $C(t)$, in milligrams per cubic centimeter, of a particular drug in a patient's bloodstream is given by

$$C(t) = \frac{0.3t}{t^2 + 6t + 9} \qquad 0 < t < 12$$

where t is the number of hours after the drug is taken orally. Find the critical numbers of $C(t)$, the intervals on which

the drug concentration is increasing, the intervals on which the drug concentration is decreasing, and the local extrema. Do not graph.

Answers to Matched Problems

1. (A) Horizontal tangent line at $x = 3$.

(B) Decreasing on $(-\infty, 3)$; increasing on $(3, \infty)$

(C) $f(x)$

2. Partition number for f': $x = 0$; critical number of f: $x = 0$; decreasing for all x

3. Partition number for f': $x = -1$; critical number of f: $x = -1$; increasing for all x

4. Partition number for f': $x = 0$; no critical number of f; decreasing on $(-\infty, 0)$ and $(0, \infty)$

5. Partition number for f': $x = 5$; critical number of f: $x = 5$; increasing on $(0, 5)$; decreasing on $(5, \infty)$

6. Increasing on $(-3, 1)$; decreasing on $(-\infty, -3)$ and $(1, \infty)$; $f(1) = 5$ is a local maximum; $f(-3) = -3$ is a local minimum

7. (A) Critical numbers of f: $x = 2, x = 4$

(B) $f(2) = 10$ is a local maximum; $f(4) = 6$ is a local minimum

(C) $f(x)$

8. (A) The U.S. share of the world market decreases for 6 years to a local minimum, increases for the next 10 years to a local maximum, and then decreases for the final 4 years.

(B) $S(t)$

9. (A) The marginal revenue is positive on $(0, 450)$, 0 at $x = 450$, and negative on $(450, 1,000)$.

(B) $R'(x)$

4.2 Second Derivative and Graphs

- Using Concavity as a Graphing Tool
- Finding Inflection Points
- Analyzing Graphs
- Curve Sketching
- Point of Diminishing Returns

In Section 4.1, we saw that the derivative can be used to determine when a graph is rising or falling. Now we want to see what the *second derivative* (the derivative of the derivative) can tell us about the shape of a graph.

Using Concavity as a Graphing Tool

Consider the functions

$$f(x) = x^2 \quad \text{and} \quad g(x) = \sqrt{x}$$

for x in the interval $(0, \infty)$. Since

$$f'(x) = 2x > 0 \quad \text{for } 0 < x < \infty$$

and

$$g'(x) = \frac{1}{2\sqrt{x}} > 0 \quad \text{for } 0 < x < \infty$$

both functions are increasing on $(0, \infty)$.

Explore and Discuss 1 (A) Discuss the difference in the shapes of the graphs of f and g shown in Figure 1.

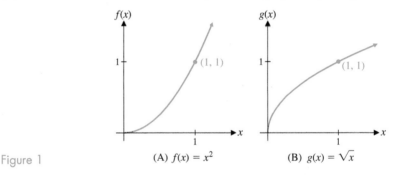

Figure 1   (A) $f(x) = x^2$ (B) $g(x) = \sqrt{x}$

(B) Complete the following table, and discuss the relationship between the values of the derivatives of f and g and the shapes of their graphs:

x	0.25	0.5	0.75	1
$f'(x)$				
$g'(x)$				

We use the term *concave upward* to describe a graph that opens upward and *concave downward* to describe a graph that opens downward. Thus, the graph of f in Figure 1A is concave upward, and the graph of g in Figure 1B is concave downward. Finding a mathematical formulation of concavity will help us sketch and analyze graphs.

We examine the slopes of f and g at various points on their graphs (see Fig. 2) and make two observations about each graph:

1. Looking at the graph of f in Figure 2A, we see that $f'(x)$ (the slope of the tangent line) is *increasing* and that the graph lies *above* each tangent line;

2. Looking at Figure 2B, we see that $g'(x)$ is *decreasing* and that the graph lies *below* each tangent line.

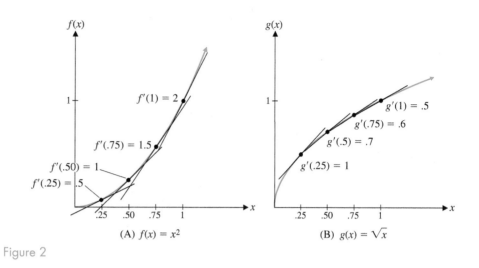

(A) $f(x) = x^2$ (B) $g(x) = \sqrt{x}$

Figure 2

DEFINITION   Concavity
The graph of a function f is **concave upward** on the interval (a, b) if $f'(x)$ is *increasing* on (a, b) and is **concave downward** on the interval (a, b) if $f'(x)$ is *decreasing* on (a, b).

Geometrically, the graph is concave upward on (a, b) if it lies above its tangent lines in (a, b) and is concave downward on (a, b) if it lies below its tangent lines in (a, b).

How can we determine when $f'(x)$ is increasing or decreasing? In Section 4.1, we used the derivative to determine when a function is increasing or decreasing. To determine when the function $f'(x)$ is increasing or decreasing, we use the derivative of $f'(x)$. The derivative of the derivative of a function is called the *second derivative* of the function. Various notations for the second derivative are given in the following box:

NOTATION   Second Derivative
For $y = f(x)$, the **second derivative** of f, provided that it exists, is

$$f''(x) = \frac{d}{dx} f'(x)$$

Other notations for $f''(x)$ are

$$\frac{d^2y}{dx^2} \quad \text{and} \quad y''$$

Returning to the functions f and g discussed at the beginning of this section, we have

$$f(x) = x^2 \qquad\qquad g(x) = \sqrt{x} = x^{1/2}$$

$$f'(x) = 2x \qquad\qquad g'(x) = \frac{1}{2}x^{-1/2} = \frac{1}{2\sqrt{x}}$$

$$f''(x) = \frac{d}{dx}2x = 2 \qquad g''(x) = \frac{d}{dx}\frac{1}{2}x^{-1/2} = -\frac{1}{4}x^{-3/2} = -\frac{1}{4\sqrt{x^3}}$$

For $x > 0$, we see that $f''(x) > 0$; so, $f'(x)$ is increasing, and the graph of f is concave upward (see Fig. 2A). For $x > 0$, we also see that $g''(x) < 0$; so, $g'(x)$ is decreasing, and the graph of g is concave downward (see Fig. 2B). These ideas are summarized in the following box:

SUMMARY Concavity
For the interval (a, b), if $f'' > 0$, then f is concave upward, and if $f'' < 0$, then f is concave downward.

$f''(x)$	$f'(x)$	Graph of $y = f(x)$	Examples
$+$	Increasing	Concave upward	
$-$	Decreasing	Concave downward	

CONCEPTUAL INSIGHT

Be careful not to confuse concavity with falling and rising. A graph that is concave upward on an interval may be falling, rising, or both falling and rising on that interval. A similar statement holds for a graph that is concave downward. See Figure 3.

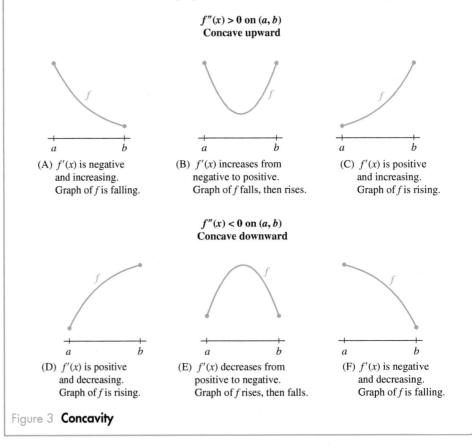

$f''(x) > 0$ on (a, b)
Concave upward

(A) $f'(x)$ is negative and increasing. Graph of f is falling.

(B) $f'(x)$ increases from negative to positive. Graph of f falls, then rises.

(C) $f'(x)$ is positive and increasing. Graph of f is rising.

$f''(x) < 0$ on (a, b)
Concave downward

(D) $f'(x)$ is positive and decreasing. Graph of f is rising.

(E) $f'(x)$ decreases from positive to negative. Graph of f rises, then falls.

(F) $f'(x)$ is negative and decreasing. Graph of f is falling.

Figure 3 **Concavity**

EXAMPLE 1   Concavity of Graphs   Determine the intervals on which the graph of each function is concave upward and the intervals on which it is concave downward. Sketch a graph of each function.

(A) $f(x) = e^x$

(B) $g(x) = \ln x$

(C) $h(x) = x^3$

SOLUTION

(A) $f(x) = e^x$

$f'(x) = e^x$

$f''(x) = e^x$

Since $f''(x) > 0$ on $(-\infty, \infty)$, the graph of $f(x) = e^x$ [Fig. 4(A)] is concave upward on $(-\infty, \infty)$.

(B) $g(x) = \ln x$

$g'(x) = \dfrac{1}{x}$

$g''(x) = -\dfrac{1}{x^2}$

The domain of $g(x) = \ln x$ is $(0, \infty)$ and $g''(x) < 0$ on this interval, so the graph of $g(x) = \ln x$ [Fig. 4(B)] is concave downward on $(0, \infty)$.

(C) $h(x) = x^3$

$h'(x) = 3x^2$

$h''(x) = 6x$

Since $h''(x) < 0$ when $x < 0$ and $h''(x) > 0$ when $x > 0$, the graph of $h(x) = x^3$ [Fig. 4(C)] is concave downward on $(-\infty, 0)$ and concave upward on $(0, \infty)$.

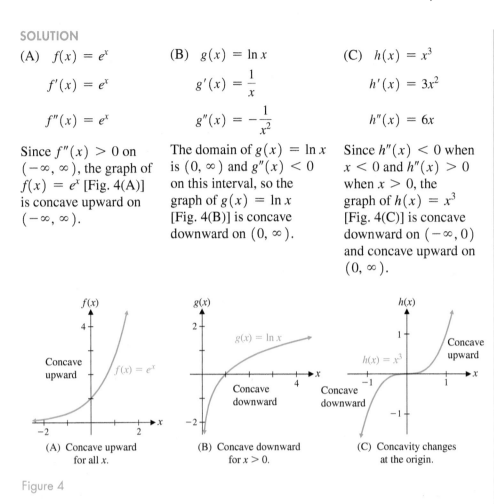

(A) Concave upward for all x.

(B) Concave downward for $x > 0$.

(C) Concavity changes at the origin.

Figure 4

Matched Problem 1⌋ Determine the intervals on which the graph of each function is concave upward and the intervals on which it is concave downward. Sketch a graph of each function.

(A) $f(x) = -e^{-x}$ (B) $g(x) = \ln\dfrac{1}{x}$ (C) $h(x) = x^{1/3}$

Refer to Example 1. The graphs of $f(x) = e^x$ and $g(x) = \ln x$ never change concavity. But the graph of $h(x) = x^3$ changes concavity at $(0, 0)$. This point is called an *inflection point*.

Finding Inflection Points

An **inflection point** is a point on the graph of a function where the concavity changes (from upward to downward or from downward to upward). For the concavity to change at a point, $f''(x)$ must change sign at that point. But in Section 2.2, we saw that the partition numbers identify the points where a function can change sign.

THEOREM 1   Inflection Points

If $(c, f(c))$ is an inflection point of f, then c is a partition number for f''.

Our strategy for finding inflection points is clear: We find all partition numbers c for f'' and ask

1. Does $f''(x)$ change sign at c?

2. Is c is in the domain of f?

If both answers are "yes", then $(c, f(c))$ is an inflection point of f. Figure 5 illustrates several typical cases.

If $f'(c)$ exists and $f''(x)$ changes sign at $x = c$, then the tangent line at an inflection point $(c, f(c))$ will always lie below the graph on the side that is concave upward and above the graph on the side that is concave downward (see Fig. 5A, B, and C).

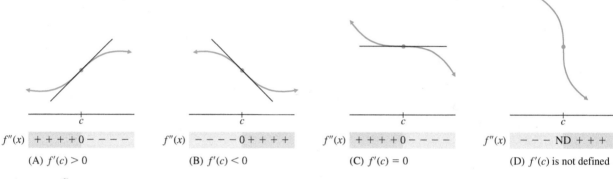

$f''(x)$ + + + + 0 − − − −	$f''(x)$ − − − − 0 + + + +	$f''(x)$ + + + + 0 − − − −	$f''(x)$ − − − ND + + +
(A) $f'(c) > 0$	(B) $f'(c) < 0$	(C) $f'(c) = 0$	(D) $f'(c)$ is not defined

Figure 5 **Inflection points**

EXAMPLE 2   Locating Inflection Points   Find the inflection point(s) of

$$f(x) = x^3 - 6x^2 + 9x + 1$$

SOLUTION   Since inflection points occur at values of x where $f''(x)$ changes sign, we construct a sign chart for $f''(x)$.

$$f(x) = x^3 - 6x^2 + 9x + 1$$
$$f'(x) = 3x^2 - 12x + 9$$
$$f''(x) = 6x - 12 = 6(x - 2)$$

The sign chart for $f''(x) = 6(x - 2)$ (partition number is 2) is as follows:

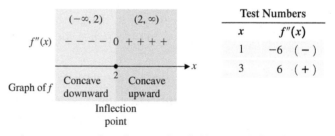

From the sign chart, we see that the graph of f has an inflection point at $x = 2$. That is, the point

$$(2, f(2)) = (2, 3) \quad f(2) = 2^3 - 6 \cdot 2^2 + 9 \cdot 2 + 1 = 3$$

is an inflection point on the graph of f.

Matched Problem 2   Find the inflection point(s) of

$$f(x) = x^3 - 9x^2 + 24x - 10$$

EXAMPLE 3 Locating Inflection Points Find the inflection point(s) of

$$f(x) = \ln(x^2 - 4x + 5)$$

SOLUTION First we find the domain of f. Since $\ln x$ is defined only for $x > 0$, f is defined only for

$$x^2 - 4x + 5 > 0 \quad \text{Complete the square (Section A.7).}$$
$$(x - 2)^2 + 1 > 0 \quad \text{True for all } x.$$

So the domain of f is $(-\infty, \infty)$. Now we find $f''(x)$ and construct a sign chart for it.

$$f(x) = \ln(x^2 - 4x + 5)$$

$$f'(x) = \frac{2x - 4}{x^2 - 4x + 5}$$

$$f''(x) = \frac{(x^2 - 4x + 5)(2x - 4)' - (2x - 4)(x^2 - 4x + 5)'}{(x^2 - 4x + 5)^2}$$

$$= \frac{(x^2 - 4x + 5)2 - (2x - 4)(2x - 4)}{(x^2 - 4x + 5)^2}$$

$$= \frac{2x^2 - 8x + 10 - 4x^2 + 16x - 16}{(x^2 - 4x + 5)^2}$$

$$= \frac{-2x^2 + 8x - 6}{(x^2 - 4x + 5)^2}$$

$$= \frac{-2(x - 1)(x - 3)}{(x^2 - 4x + 5)^2}$$

The partition numbers for $f''(x)$ are $x = 1$ and $x = 3$.
Sign chart for $f''(x)$:

	Test Numbers	
	x	$f''(x)$
	0	$-\dfrac{6}{25}$ (−)
	2	2 (+)
	4	$-\dfrac{6}{25}$ (−)

$(-\infty, 1)$ $(1, 3)$ $(3, \infty)$

$f''(x)$ $- - - -$ 0 $+ + + +$ 0 $- - - -$

1   3

Concave   Concave   Concave
downward upward   downward

Inflection Inflection
point   point

The sign chart shows that the graph of f has inflection points at $x = 1$ and $x = 3$.

Since $f(1) = \ln 2$ and $f(3) = \ln 2$, the inflection points are $(1, \ln 2)$ and $(3, \ln 2)$.

Matched Problem 3 Find the inflection point(s) of

$$f(x) = \ln(x^2 - 2x + 5)$$

CONCEPTUAL INSIGHT

It is important to remember that the partition numbers for f'' are only *candidates* for inflection points. The function f must be defined at $x = c$, and the second derivative must change sign at $x = c$ in order for the graph to have an inflection point at $x = c$. For example, consider

$$f(x) = x^4 \qquad g(x) = \frac{1}{x}$$

$$f'(x) = 4x^3 \qquad g'(x) = -\frac{1}{x^2}$$

$$f''(x) = 12x^2 \qquad g''(x) = \frac{2}{x^3}$$

In each case, $x = 0$ is a partition number for the second derivative, but neither the graph of $f(x)$ nor the graph of $g(x)$ has an inflection point at $x = 0$. Function f does not have an inflection point at $x = 0$ because $f''(x)$ does not change sign at $x = 0$ (see Fig. 6A). Function g does not have an inflection point at $x = 0$ because $g(0)$ is not defined (see Fig. 6B).

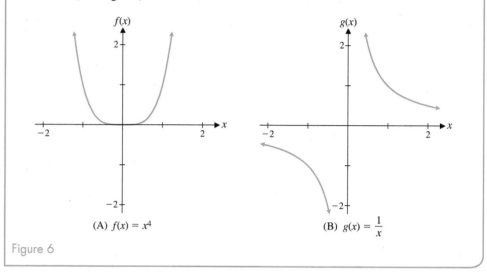

(A) $f(x) = x^4$ (B) $g(x) = \dfrac{1}{x}$

Figure 6

Analyzing Graphs

In the next example, we combine increasing/decreasing properties with concavity properties to analyze the graph of a function.

EXAMPLE 4   Analyzing a Graph   Figure 7 shows the graph of the derivative of a function f. Use this graph to discuss the graph of f. Include a sketch of a possible graph of f.

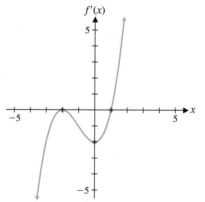

Figure 7

SOLUTION The sign of the derivative determines where the original function is increasing and decreasing, and the increasing/decreasing properties of the derivative determine the concavity of the original function. The relevant information obtained from the graph of f' is summarized in Table 1, and a possible graph of f is shown in Figure 8.

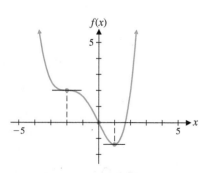

$f(x)$

Figure 8

Table 1

x	$f'(x)$ (Fig. 7)	$f(x)$ (Fig. 8)
$-\infty < x < -2$	Negative and increasing	Decreasing and concave upward
$x = -2$	Local maximum	Inflection point
$-2 < x < 0$	Negative and decreasing	Decreasing and concave downward
$x = 0$	Local minimum	Inflection point
$0 < x < 1$	Negative and increasing	Decreasing and concave upward
$x = 1$	x intercept	Local minimum
$1 < x < \infty$	Positive and increasing	Increasing and concave upward

Matched Problem 4 Figure 9 shows the graph of the derivative of a function f. Use this graph to discuss the graph of f. Include a sketch of a possible graph of f.

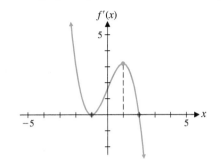

Figure 9

Curve Sketching

Graphing calculators and computers produce the graph of a function by plotting many points. However, key points on a plot many be difficult to identify. Using information gained from the function $f(x)$ and its derivatives, and plotting the key points—intercepts, local extrema, and inflection points—we can sketch by hand a very good representation of the graph of $f(x)$. This graphing process is called **curve sketching**.

PROCEDURE Graphing Strategy (First Version)*

Step 1 *Analyze $f(x)$.* Find the domain and the intercepts. The x intercepts are the solutions of $f(x) = 0$, and the y intercept is $f(0)$.

Step 2 *Analyze $f'(x)$.* Find the partition numbers for f' and the critical numbers of f. Construct a sign chart for $f'(x)$, determine the intervals on which f is increasing and decreasing, and find the local maxima and minima of f.

Step 3 *Analyze $f''(x)$.* Find the partition numbers for $f''(x)$. Construct a sign chart for $f''(x)$, determine the intervals on which the graph of f is concave upward and concave downward, and find the inflection points of f.

Step 4 *Sketch the graph of f.* Locate intercepts, local maxima and minima, and inflection points. Sketch in what you know from steps 1–3. Plot additional points as needed and complete the sketch.

EXAMPLE 5 Using the Graphing Strategy Follow the graphing strategy and analyze the function

$$f(x) = x^4 - 2x^3$$

State all the pertinent information and sketch the graph of f.

SOLUTION

Step 1 *Analyze $f(x)$.* Since f is a polynomial, its domain is $(-\infty, \infty)$.

x intercept: $f(x) = 0$
$$x^4 - 2x^3 = 0$$
$$x^3(x - 2) = 0$$
$$x = 0, 2$$

y intercept: $f(0) = 0$

---

*We will modify this summary in Section 4.4 to include additional information about the graph of f.

Step 2   *Analyze $f'(x)$.* $f'(x) = 4x^3 - 6x^2 = 4x^2(x - \frac{3}{2})$

Partition numbers for $f'(x)$: 0 and $\frac{3}{2}$

Critical numbers of $f(x)$: 0 and $\frac{3}{2}$

Sign chart for $f'(x)$:

So $f(x)$ is decreasing on $(-\infty, \frac{3}{2})$, is increasing on $(\frac{3}{2}, \infty)$, and has a local minimum at $x = \frac{3}{2}$. The local minimum is $f(\frac{3}{2}) = -\frac{27}{16}$.

Step 3   *Analyze $f''(x)$.* $f''(x) = 12x^2 - 12x = 12x(x - 1)$

Partition numbers for $f''(x)$: 0 and 1

Sign chart for $f''(x)$:

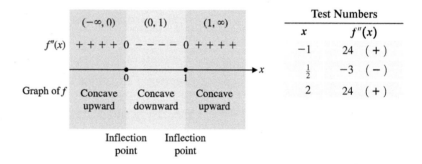

So the graph of f is concave upward on $(-\infty, 0)$ and $(1, \infty)$, is concave downward on $(0, 1)$, and has inflection points at $x = 0$ and $x = 1$. Since $f(0) = 0$ and $f(1) = -1$, the inflection points are $(0, 0)$ and $(1, -1)$.

Step 4   *Sketch the graph of f.*

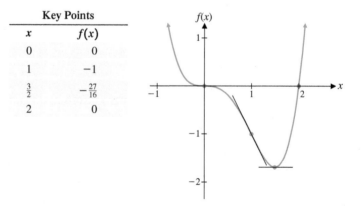

Key Points	
x	$f(x)$
0	0
1	-1
$\frac{3}{2}$	$-\frac{27}{16}$
2	0

Matched Problem 5   Follow the graphing strategy and analyze the function $f(x) = x^4 + 4x^3$. State all the pertinent information and sketch the graph of f.

CONCEPTUAL INSIGHT

Refer to the solution of Example 5. Combining the sign charts for $f'(x)$ and $f''(x)$ (Fig. 10) partitions the real-number line into intervals on which neither $f'(x)$ nor $f''(x)$ changes sign. On each of these intervals, the graph of $f(x)$ must have one of four basic shapes (see also Fig. 3, parts A, C, D, and F on page 256). This reduces sketching the graph of a function to plotting the points identified in the graphing strategy and connecting them with one of the basic shapes.

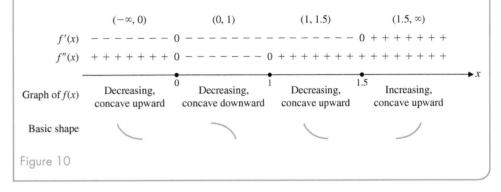

Figure 10

EXAMPLE 6   Using the Graphing Strategy Follow the graphing strategy and analyze the function

$$f(x) = 3x^{5/3} - 20x$$

State all the pertinent information and sketch the graph of f. Round any decimal values to two decimal places.

SOLUTION

Step 1 *Analyze $f(x)$.* $f(x) = 3x^{5/3} - 20x$

Since x^p is defined for any x and any positive p, the domain of f is $(-\infty, \infty)$.

x intercepts: Solve $f(x) = 0$
$$3x^{5/3} - 20x = 0$$
$$3x\left(x^{2/3} - \frac{20}{3}\right) = 0 \quad (a^2 - b^2) = (a - b)(a + b)$$
$$3x\left(x^{1/3} - \sqrt{\frac{20}{3}}\right)\left(x^{1/3} + \sqrt{\frac{20}{3}}\right) = 0$$

The x intercepts of f are

$$x = 0, \quad x = \left(\sqrt{\frac{20}{3}}\right)^3 \approx 17.21, \quad x = \left(-\sqrt{\frac{20}{3}}\right)^3 \approx -17.21$$

y intercept: $f(0) = 0$.

Step 2 Analyze $f'(x)$.
$$f'(x) = 5x^{2/3} - 20$$
$$= 5(x^{2/3} - 4) \qquad \text{Again, } a^2 - b^2 = (a - b)(a + b)$$
$$= 5(x^{1/3} - 2)(x^{1/3} + 2)$$

Partition numbers for f': $x = 2^3 = 8$ and $x = (-2)^3 = -8$.

Critical numbers of f: $-8, 8$

Sign chart for $f'(x)$:

	$(-\infty, -8)$	$(-8, 8)$	$(8, \infty)$
$f'(x)$	$+\,+\,+\,+$ 0	$-\,-\,-\,-$ 0	$+\,+\,+\,+$
	-8	8	
	Increasing	Decreasing	Increasing
	Local maximum	Local minimum	

Test Numbers

x	$f'(x)$
-12	$6.21\ (+)$
0	$-20\ (-)$
12	$6.21\ (+)$

So f is increasing on $(-\infty, -8)$ and $(8, \infty)$ and decreasing on $(-8, 8)$. Therefore, $f(-8) = 64$ is a local maximum, and $f(8) = -64$ is a local minimum.

Step 3 *Analyze $f''(x)$.*

$$f'(x) = 5x^{2/3} - 20$$

$$f''(x) = \frac{10}{3}x^{-1/3} = \frac{10}{3x^{1/3}}$$

Partition number for f'': 0

Sign chart for $f''(x)$:

	$(-\infty, 0)$	$(0, \infty)$
$f''(x)$	$-\,-\,-\,-$ ND	$+\,+\,+\,+$
	0	
	Concave downward	Concave upward
	Inflection point	

Test Numbers

x	$f''(x)$
-8	$-1.67\ (-)$
8	$1.67\ (+)$

So f is concave downward on $(-\infty, 0)$, is concave upward on $(0, \infty)$, and has an inflection point at $x = 0$. Since $f(0) = 0$, the inflection point is $(0, 0)$.

Step 4 *Sketch the graph of f.*

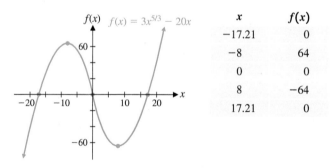

x	$f(x)$
-17.21	0
-8	64
0	0
8	-64
17.21	0

Matched Problem 6 Follow the graphing strategy and analyze the function $f(x) = 3x^{2/3} - x$. State all the pertinent information and sketch the graph of f. Round any decimal values to two decimal places.

Point of Diminishing Returns

If a company decides to increase spending on advertising, it would expect sales to increase. At first, sales will increase at an increasing rate and then increase at a decreasing rate. The dollar amount x at which the rate of change of sales goes from increasing to decreasing is called the **point of diminishing returns**. This is also the amount at which the rate of change has a maximum value. Money spent beyond this amount may increase sales but at a lower rate.

EXAMPLE 7 Maximum Rate of Change Currently, a discount appliance store is selling 200 large-screen TVs monthly. If the store invests x thousand in an advertising campaign, the ad company estimates that monthly sales will be given by

$$N(x) = 3x^3 - 0.25x^4 + 200 \qquad 0 \le x \le 9$$

When is the rate of change of sales increasing and when is it decreasing? What is the point of diminishing returns and the maximum rate of change of sales? Graph N and N' on the same coordinate system.

SOLUTION The rate of change of sales with respect to advertising expenditures is

$$N'(x) = 9x^2 - x^3 = x^2(9 - x)$$

To determine when $N'(x)$ is increasing and decreasing, we find $N''(x)$, the derivative of $N'(x)$:

$$N''(x) = 18x - 3x^2 = 3x(6 - x)$$

The information obtained by analyzing the signs of $N'(x)$ and $N''(x)$ is summarized in Table 2 (sign charts are omitted).

Table 2

x	$N''(x)$	$N'(x)$	$N'(x)$	$N(x)$
$0 < x < 6$	+	+	Increasing	Increasing, concave upward
$x = 6$	0	+	Local maximum	Inflection point
$6 < x < 9$	−	+	Decreasing	Increasing, concave downward

Examining Table 2, we see that $N'(x)$ is increasing on $(0, 6)$ and decreasing on $(6, 9)$. The point of diminishing returns is $x = 6$ and the maximum rate of change is $N'(6) = 108$. Note that $N'(x)$ has a local maximum and $N(x)$ has an inflection point at $x = 6$ [the inflection point of $N(x)$ is $(6, 524)$].

So if the store spends $6,000 on advertising, monthly sales are expected to be 524 TVs, and sales are expected to increase at a rate of 108 TVs per thousand dollars spent on advertising. Money spent beyond the $6,000 would increase sales, but at a lower rate.

Point of diminishing returns

Matched Problem 7 Repeat Example 7 for

$$N(x) = 4x^3 - 0.25x^4 + 500 \qquad 0 \le x \le 12$$

Exercises 4.2

Skills Warm-up Exercises

In Problems 1–8, inspect the graph of the function to determine whether it is concave up, concave down, or neither, on the given interval. (If necessary, review Section 1.2).

1. The square function, $h(x) = x^2$, on $(-\infty, \infty)$

2. The identity function, $f(x) = x$, on $(-\infty, \infty)$

3. The cube function, $m(x) = x^3$, on $(-\infty, 0)$

4. The cube function, $m(x) = x^3$, on $(0, \infty)$

5. The square root function, $n(x) = \sqrt{x}$, on $(0, \infty)$

6. The cube root function, $p(x) = \sqrt[3]{x}$, on $(-\infty, 0)$

7. The absolute value function, $g(x) = |x|$, on $(-\infty, 0)$

8. The cube root function, $p(x) = \sqrt[3]{x}$, on $(0, \infty)$

9. Use the graph of $y = f(x)$, assuming $f''(x) > 0$ if $x = b$ or f, to identify

  (A) Intervals on which the graph of f is concave upward

  (B) Intervals on which the graph of f is concave downward

  (C) Intervals on which $f''(x) < 0$

  (D) Intervals on which $f''(x) > 0$

  (E) Intervals on which $f'(x)$ is increasing

  (F) Intervals on which $f'(x)$ is decreasing

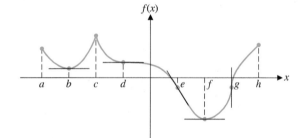

10. Use the graph of $y = g(x)$, assuming $g''(x) > 0$ if $x = c$ or g, to identify

  (A) Intervals on which the graph of g is concave upward

  (B) Intervals on which the graph of g is concave downward

  (C) Intervals on which $g''(x) < 0$

  (D) Intervals on which $g''(x) > 0$

  (E) Intervals on which $g'(x)$ is increasing

  (F) Intervals on which $g'(x)$ is decreasing

11. Use the graph of $y = f(x)$ to identify

  (A) The local extrema of $f(x)$.

  (B) The inflection points of $f(x)$.

  (C) The numbers u for which $f'(u)$ is a local extremum of $f'(x)$.

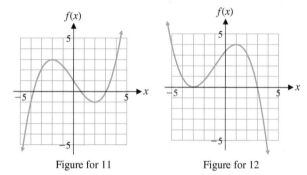

Figure for 11   Figure for 12

12. Use the graph of $y = f(x)$ to identify

  (A) The local extrema of $f(x)$.

  (B) The inflection points of $f(x)$.

  (C) The numbers u for which $f'(u)$ is a local extremum of $f'(x)$.

In Problems 13–16, match the indicated conditions with one of the graphs (A)–(D) shown in the figure.

13. $f'(x) > 0$ and $f''(x) > 0$ on (a, b)

14. $f'(x) > 0$ and $f''(x) < 0$ on (a, b)

15. $f'(x) < 0$ and $f''(x) > 0$ on (a, b)

16. $f'(x) < 0$ and $f''(x) < 0$ on (a, b)

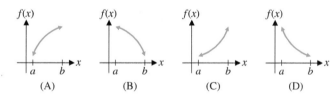

In Problems 17–24, find the indicated derivative for each function.

17. $f''(x)$ for $f(x) = 2x^3 - 4x^2 + 5x - 6$

18. $g''(x)$ for $g(x) = -x^3 + 2x^2 - 3x + 9$

19. $h''(x)$ for $h(x) = 2x^{-1} - 3x^{-2}$

20. $k''(x)$ for $k(x) = -6x^{-2} + 12x^{-3}$

21. d^2y/dx^2 for $y = x^2 - 18x^{1/2}$

22. d^2y/dx^2 for $y = x^3 - 24x^{1/3}$

23. y'' for $y = (x^2 + 9)^4$

24. y'' for $y = (x^2 - 16)^5$

In Problems 25–30, find the x and y coordinates of all inflection points.

25. $f(x) = x^3 + 30x^2$ **26.** $f(x) = x^3 - 24x^2$

27. $f(x) = x^{5/3} + 2$

28. $f(x) = 5 - x^{4/3}$

29. $f(x) = 1 + x + x^{2/5}$

30. $f(x) = x^{3/5} - 6x + 7$

In Problems 31–40, find the intervals on which the graph of f is concave upward, the intervals on which the graph of f is concave downward, and the x coordinates of the inflection points.

31. $f(x) = x^4 + 6x^2$

32. $f(x) = x^4 + 6x$

33. $f(x) = x^3 - 4x^2 + 5x - 2$

34. $f(x) = -x^3 - 5x^2 + 4x - 3$

35. $f(x) = -x^4 + 12x^3 - 12x + 24$

36. $f(x) = x^4 - 2x^3 - 36x + 12$

37. $f(x) = \ln(x^2 - 2x + 10)$

38. $f(x) = \ln(x^2 + 6x + 13)$

39. $f(x) = 8e^x - e^{2x}$

40. $f(x) = e^{3x} - 9e^x$

In Problems 41–48, f(x) is continuous on $(-\infty, \infty)$. Use the given information to sketch the graph of f.

41.

x	−4	−2	−1	0	2	4
$f(x)$	0	3	1.5	0	−1	−3

42.

x	−4	−2	−1	0	2	4
$f(x)$	0	−2	−1	0	1	3

43.

x	−3	0	1	2	4	5
$f(x)$	−4	0	2	1	−1	0

44.

x	−4	−2	0	2	4	6
$f(x)$	0	3	0	−2	0	3

45. $f(0) = 2, f(1) = 0, f(2) = -2;$

$f'(0) = 0, f'(2) = 0;$

$f'(x) > 0$ on $(-\infty, 0)$ and $(2, \infty)$;

$f'(x) < 0$ on $(0, 2)$;

$f''(1) = 0;$

$f''(x) > 0$ on $(1, \infty)$;

$f''(x) < 0$ on $(-\infty, 1)$

46. $f(-2) = -2, f(0) = 1, f(2) = 4;$

$f'(-2) = 0, f'(2) = 0;$

$f'(x) > 0$ on $(-2, 2)$;

$f'(x) < 0$ on $(-\infty, -2)$ and $(2, \infty)$;

$f''(0) = 0;$

$f''(x) > 0$ on $(-\infty, 0)$;

$f''(x) < 0$ on $(0, \infty)$

47. $f(-1) = 0, f(0) = -2, f(1) = 0;$

$f'(0) = 0, f'(-1)$ and $f'(1)$ are not defined;

$f'(x) > 0$ on $(0, 1)$ and $(1, \infty)$;

$f'(x) < 0$ on $(-\infty, -1)$ and $(-1, 0)$;

$f''(-1)$ and $f''(1)$ are not defined;

$f''(x) > 0$ on $(-1, 1)$;

$f''(x) < 0$ on $(-\infty, -1)$ and $(1, \infty)$

48. $f(0) = -2, f(1) = 0, f(2) = 4;$

$f'(0) = 0, f'(2) = 0, f'(1)$ is not defined;

$f'(x) > 0$ on $(0, 1)$ and $(1, 2)$;

$f'(x) < 0$ on $(-\infty, 0)$ and $(2, \infty)$;

$f''(1)$ is not defined;

$f''(x) > 0$ on $(-\infty, 1)$;

$f''(x) < 0$ on $(1, \infty)$

In Problems 49–70, summarize the pertinent information obtained by applying the graphing strategy and sketch the graph of $y = f(x)$.

49. $f(x) = (x - 2)(x^2 - 4x - 8)$

50. $f(x) = (x - 3)(x^2 - 6x - 3)$

51. $f(x) = (x + 1)(x^2 - x + 2)$

52. $f(x) = (1 - x)(x^2 + x + 4)$

53. $f(x) = -0.25x^4 + x^3$

54. $f(x) = 0.25x^4 - 2x^3$

55. $f(x) = 16x(x - 1)^3$

56. $f(x) = -4x(x + 2)^3$

57. $f(x) = (x^2 + 3)(9 - x^2)$

58. $f(x) = (x^2 + 3)(x^2 - 1)$

59. $f(x) = (x^2 - 4)^2$

60. $f(x) = (x^2 - 1)(x^2 - 5)$

61. $f(x) = 2x^6 - 3x^5$

62. $f(x) = 3x^5 - 5x^4$

63. $f(x) = 1 - e^{-x}$

64. $f(x) = 2 - 3e^{-2x}$

65. $f(x) = e^{0.5x} + 4e^{-0.5x}$

66. $f(x) = 2e^{0.5x} + e^{-0.5x}$

67. $f(x) = -4 + 2 \ln x$

68. $f(x) = 5 - 3 \ln x$

69. $f(x) = \ln(x + 4) - 2$

70. $f(x) = 1 - \ln(x - 3)$

In Problems 71–74, use the graph of $y = f'(x)$ to discuss the graph of $y = f(x)$. Organize your conclusions in a table (see Example 4), and sketch a possible graph of $y = f(x)$.

71.

72.

73.

74.

In Problems 75–82, apply steps 1–3 of the graphing strategy to *$f(x)$. Use a graphing calculator to approximate (to two decimal places) x intercepts, critical numbers, and inflection points. Summarize all the pertinent information.*

75. $f(x) = x^4 - 5x^3 + 3x^2 + 8x - 5$

76. $f(x) = x^4 + 2x^3 - 5x^2 - 4x + 4$

77. $f(x) = x^4 - 21x^3 + 100x^2 + 20x + 100$

78. $f(x) = x^4 - 12x^3 + 28x^2 + 76x - 50$

79. $f(x) = -x^4 - x^3 + 2x^2 - 2x + 3$

80. $f(x) = -x^4 + x^3 + x^2 + 6$

81. $f(x) = 0.1x^5 + 0.3x^4 - 4x^3 - 5x^2 + 40x + 30$

82. $f(x) = x^5 + 4x^4 - 7x^3 - 20x^2 + 20x - 20$

Applications

83. Inflation. One commonly used measure of inflation is the annual rate of change of the Consumer Price Index (CPI). A TV news story says that the annual rate of change of the CPI is increasing. What does this say about the shape of the graph of the CPI?

84. Inflation. Another commonly used measure of inflation is the annual rate of change of the Producer Price Index (PPI). A government report states that the annual rate of change of the PPI is decreasing. What does this say about the shape of the graph of the PPI?

85. Cost analysis. A company manufactures a variety of camp stoves at different locations. The total cost $C(x)$ (in dollars) of producing x camp stoves per week at plant A is shown in the figure. Discuss the graph of the marginal cost function $C'(x)$ and interpret the graph of $C'(x)$ in terms of the efficiency of the production process at this plant.

Production costs at plant A

86. Cost analysis. The company in Problem 85 produces the same camp stove at another plant. The total cost $C(x)$ (in dollars) of producing x camp stoves per week at plant B is shown in the figure. Discuss the graph of the marginal cost function $C'(x)$ and interpret the graph of $C'(x)$ in terms of the efficiency of the production process at plant B. Compare the production processes at the two plants.

Production costs at plant B

87. Revenue. The marketing research department of a computer company used a large city to test market the firm's new laptop. The department found that the relationship between price p (dollars per unit) and the demand x (units per week) was given approximately by

$$p = 1,296 - 0.12x^2 \qquad 0 < x < 80$$

So, weekly revenue can be approximated by

$$R(x) = xp = 1,296x - 0.12x^3 \qquad 0 < x < 80$$

(A) Find the local extrema for the revenue function.

(B) On which intervals is the graph of the revenue function concave upward? Concave downward?

88. Profit. Suppose that the cost equation for the company in Problem 87 is

$$C(x) = 830 + 396x$$

(A) Find the local extrema for the profit function.

(B) On which intervals is the graph of the profit function concave upward? Concave downward?

89. Revenue. A dairy is planning to introduce and promote a new line of organic ice cream. After test marketing the new line in a large city, the marketing research department found that the demand in that city is given approximately by

$$p = 10e^{-x} \qquad 0 \le x \le 5$$

where x thousand quarts were sold per week at a price of $\$p$ each.

(A) Find the local extrema for the revenue function.

(B) On which intervals is the graph of the revenue function concave upward? Concave downward?

90. Revenue. A national food service runs food concessions for sporting events throughout the country. The company's marketing research department chose a particular football stadium to test market a new jumbo hot dog. It was found that the demand for the new hot dog is given approximately by

$$p = 8 - 2 \ln x \qquad 5 \le x \le 50$$

where x is the number of hot dogs (in thousands) that can be sold during one game at a price of $\$p$.

(A) Find the local extrema for the revenue function.

(B) On which intervals is the graph of the revenue function concave upward? Concave downward?

91. Production: point of diminishing returns. A T-shirt manufacturer is planning to expand its workforce. It estimates that the number of T-shirts produced by hiring x new workers is given by

$$T(x) = -0.25x^4 + 5x^3 \qquad 0 \le x \le 15$$

When is the rate of change of T-shirt production increasing and when is it decreasing? What is the point of diminishing returns and the maximum rate of change of T-shirt production? Graph T and T' on the same coordinate system.

92. Production: point of diminishing returns. A baseball cap manufacturer is planning to expand its workforce. It estimates that the number of baseball caps produced by hiring x new workers is given by

$$T(x) = -0.25x^4 + 6x^3 \qquad 0 \le x \le 18$$

When is the rate of change of baseball cap production increasing and when is it decreasing? What is the point of diminishing returns and the maximum rate of change of baseball cap production? Graph T and T' on the same coordinate system.

93. Advertising: point of diminishing returns. A company estimates that it will sell $N(x)$ units of a product after spending $\$x$ thousand on advertising, as given by

$$N(x) = -0.25x^4 + 23x^3 - 540x^2 + 80,000 \qquad 24 \le x \le 45$$

When is the rate of change of sales increasing and when is it decreasing? What is the point of diminishing returns and the maximum rate of change of sales? Graph N and N' on the same coordinate system.

94. Advertising: point of diminishing returns. A company estimates that it will sell $N(x)$ units of a product after spending $\$x$ thousand on advertising, as given by

$$N(x) = -0.25x^4 + 13x^3 - 180x^2 + 10,000 \qquad 15 \le x \le 24$$

When is the rate of change of sales increasing and when is it decreasing? What is the point of diminishing returns and the maximum rate of change of sales? Graph N and N' on the same coordinate system.

95. Advertising. An automobile dealer uses TV advertising to promote car sales. On the basis of past records, the dealer arrived at the following data, where x is the number of ads placed monthly and y is the number of cars sold that month:

Number of Ads	Number of Cars
x	y
10	325
12	339
20	417
30	546
35	615
40	682
50	795

(A) Enter the data in a graphing calculator and find a cubic regression equation for the number of cars sold monthly as a function of the number of ads.

(B) How many ads should the dealer place each month to maximize the rate of change of sales with respect to the number of ads, and how many cars can the dealer expect to sell with this number of ads? Round answers to the nearest integer.

96. Advertising. A sporting goods chain places TV ads to promote golf club sales. The marketing director used past records to determine the following data, where x is the number of ads placed monthly and y is the number of golf clubs sold that month.

Number of Ads	Number of Golf Clubs
x	y
10	345
14	488
20	746
30	1,228
40	1,671
50	1,955

(A) Enter the data in a graphing calculator and find a cubic regression equation for the number of golf clubs sold monthly as a function of the number of ads.

(B) How many ads should the store manager place each month to maximize the rate of change of sales with respect to the number of ads, and how many golf clubs can the manager expect to sell with this number of ads? Round answers to the nearest integer.

97. Population growth: bacteria. A drug that stimulates reproduction is introduced into a colony of bacteria. After t minutes, the number of bacteria is given approximately by

$$N(t) = 1,000 + 30t^2 - t^3 \qquad 0 \le t \le 20$$

(A) When is the rate of growth, $N'(t)$, increasing? Decreasing?

(B) Find the inflection points for the graph of N.

(C) Sketch the graphs of N and N' on the same coordinate system.

(D) What is the maximum rate of growth?

98. Drug sensitivity. One hour after x milligrams of a particular drug are given to a person, the change in body temperature $T(x)$, in degrees Fahrenheit, is given by

$$T(x) = x^2\left(1 - \frac{x}{9}\right) \qquad 0 \le x \le 6$$

The rate $T'(x)$ at which $T(x)$ changes with respect to the size of the dosage x is called the *sensitivity* of the body to the dosage.

(A) When is $T'(x)$ increasing? Decreasing?

(B) Where does the graph of T have inflection points?

(C) Sketch the graphs of T and T' on the same coordinate system.

(D) What is the maximum value of $T'(x)$?

99. Learning. The time T (in minutes) it takes a person to learn a list of length n is

$$T(n) = 0.08n^3 - 1.2n^2 + 6n \qquad n \ge 0$$

(A) When is the rate of change of T with respect to the length of the list increasing? Decreasing?

(B) Where does the graph of T have inflection points?

(C) Graph T and T' on the same coordinate system.

(D) What is the minimum value of $T'(n)$?

Answers to Matched Problems

1. (A) Concave downward on $(-\infty, \infty)$

(B) Concave upward on $(0, \infty)$

(C) Concave upward on $(-\infty, 0)$ and concave downward on $(0, \infty)$

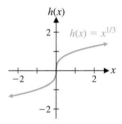

2. The only inflection point is $(3, f(3)) = (3, 8)$.

3. The inflection points are $(-1, f(-1)) = (-1, \ln 8)$ and $(3, f(3)) = (3, \ln 8)$.

4.

x	$f'(x)$	$f(x)$
$-\infty < x < -1$	Positive and decreasing	Increasing and concave downward
$x = -1$	Local minimum	Inflection point
$-1 < x < 1$	Positive and increasing	Increasing and concave upward
$x = 1$	Local maximum	Inflection point
$1 < x < 2$	Positive and decreasing	Increasing and concave downward
$x = 2$	x intercept	Local maximum
$2 < x < \infty$	Negative and decreasing	Decreasing and concave downward

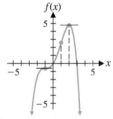

5. Domain: All real numbers
x intercepts: $-4, 0$; y intercept: $f(0) = 0$

Decreasing on $(-\infty, -3)$; increasing on $(-3, \infty)$; local minimum: $f(-3) = -27$

Concave upward on $(-\infty, -2)$ and $(0, \infty)$; concave downward on $(-2, 0)$

Inflection points: $(-2, -16)$, $(0, 0)$

x	$f(x)$
-4	0
-3	-27
-2	-16
0	0

6. Domain: All real numbers

x intercepts: 0, 27; y intercept: $f(0) = 0$

Decreasing on $(-\infty, 0)$ and $(8, \infty)$; increasing on $(0, 8)$; local minimum: $f(0) = 0$; local maximum: $f(8) = 4$

Concave downward on $(-\infty, 0)$ and $(0, \infty)$; no inflection points

x	$f(x)$
0	0
8	4
27	0

7. $N'(x)$ is increasing on $(0, 8)$ and decreasing on $(8, 12)$.

The point of diminishing returns is $x = 8$ and the maximum rate of change is $N'(8) = 256$.

4.3 L'Hôpital's Rule

- Introduction
- L'Hôpital's Rule and the Indeterminate Form 0/0
- One-Sided Limits and Limits at ∞
- L'Hôpital's Rule and the Indeterminate Form ∞/∞

Introduction

The ability to evaluate a wide variety of different types of limits is one of the skills that are necessary to apply the techniques of calculus successfully. Limits play a fundamental role in the development of the derivative and are an important graphing tool. In order to deal effectively with graphs, we need to develop some more methods for evaluating limits.

In this section, we discuss a powerful technique for evaluating limits of quotients called *L'Hôpital's rule*. The rule is named after the French mathematician Marquis de L'Hôpital (1661–1704). To use L'Hôpital's rule, it is necessary to be familiar with the limit properties of some basic functions. Figure 1 reviews some limits involving powers of x that were discussed earlier.

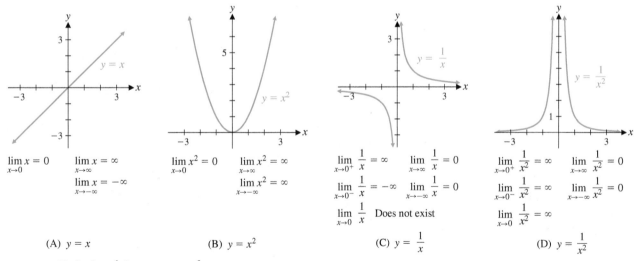

Figure 1 **Limits involving powers of x**

The limits in Figure 1 are easily extended to functions of the form $f(x) = (x - c)^n$ and $g(x) = 1/(x - c)^n$. In general, if n is an odd integer, then limits involving $(x - c)^n$ or $1/(x - c)^n$ as x approaches c (or $\pm\infty$) behave, respectively, like the limits of x and $1/x$ as x approaches 0 (or $\pm\infty$). If n is an even integer, then limits involving these expressions behave, respectively, like the limits of x^2 and $1/x^2$ as x approaches 0 (or $\pm\infty$).

EXAMPLE 1   Limits Involving Powers of $x - c$

(A) $\lim\limits_{x \to 2} \dfrac{5}{(x-2)^4} = \infty$ Compare with $\lim\limits_{x \to 0} \dfrac{1}{x^2}$ in Figure 1.

(B) $\lim\limits_{x \to -1^-} \dfrac{4}{(x+1)^3} = -\infty$ Compare with $\lim\limits_{x \to 0^-} \dfrac{1}{x}$ in Figure 1.

(C) $\lim\limits_{x \to \infty} \dfrac{4}{(x-9)^6} = 0$ Compare with $\lim\limits_{x \to \infty} \dfrac{1}{x^2}$ in Figure 1.

(D) $\lim\limits_{x \to -\infty} 3x^3 = -\infty$ Compare with $\lim\limits_{x \to -\infty} x$ in Figure 1.

Matched Problem 1   Evaluate each limit.

(A) $\lim\limits_{x \to 3^+} \dfrac{7}{(x-3)^5}$

(B) $\lim\limits_{x \to -4} \dfrac{6}{(x+4)^6}$

(C) $\lim\limits_{x \to -\infty} \dfrac{3}{(x+2)^3}$

(D) $\lim\limits_{x \to \infty} 5x^4$

Figure 2 reviews limits of exponential and logarithmic functions.

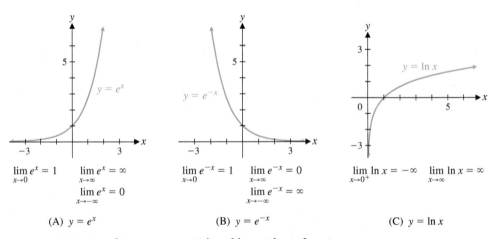

$\lim\limits_{x \to 0} e^x = 1$ $\lim\limits_{x \to \infty} e^x = \infty$

$\lim\limits_{x \to -\infty} e^x = 0$

(A) $y = e^x$

$\lim\limits_{x \to 0} e^{-x} = 1$ $\lim\limits_{x \to \infty} e^{-x} = 0$

$\lim\limits_{x \to -\infty} e^{-x} = \infty$

(B) $y = e^{-x}$

$\lim\limits_{x \to 0^+} \ln x = -\infty$ $\lim\limits_{x \to \infty} \ln x = \infty$

(C) $y = \ln x$

Figure 2 **Limits involving exponential and logarithmic functions**

The limits in Figure 2 also generalize to other simple exponential and logarithmic forms.

EXAMPLE 2   Limits Involving Exponential and Logarithmic Forms

(A) $\lim\limits_{x \to \infty} 2e^{3x} = \infty$ Compare with $\lim\limits_{x \to \infty} e^x$ in Figure 2.

(B) $\lim\limits_{x \to \infty} 4e^{-5x} = 0$ Compare with $\lim\limits_{x \to \infty} e^{-x}$ in Figure 2.

(C) $\lim\limits_{x \to \infty} \ln(x+4) = \infty$ Compare with $\lim\limits_{x \to \infty} \ln x$ in Figure 2.

(D) $\lim\limits_{x \to 2^+} \ln(x-2) = -\infty$ Compare with $\lim\limits_{x \to 0^+} \ln x$ in Figure 2.

Matched Problem 2   Evaluate each limit.

(A) $\lim\limits_{x \to -\infty} 2e^{-6x}$

(B) $\lim\limits_{x \to -\infty} 3e^{2x}$

(C) $\lim\limits_{x \to -4^+} \ln(x+4)$

(D) $\lim\limits_{x \to \infty} \ln(x-10)$

Now that we have reviewed the limit properties of some basic functions, we are ready to consider the main topic of this section: L'Hôpital's rule.

L'Hôpital's Rule and the Indeterminate Form 0/0

Recall that the limit

$$\lim_{x \to c} \frac{f(x)}{g(x)}$$

is a 0/0 indeterminate form if

$$\lim_{x \to c} f(x) = 0 \quad \text{and} \quad \lim_{x \to c} g(x) = 0$$

The quotient property for limits in Section 2.1 does not apply since $\lim_{x \to c} g(x) = 0$.

If we are dealing with a 0/0 indeterminate form, the limit may or may not exist, and we cannot tell which is true without further investigation.

Each of the following is a 0/0 indeterminate form:

$$\lim_{x \to 2} \frac{x^2 - 4}{x - 2} \quad \text{and} \quad \lim_{x \to 1} \frac{e^x - e}{x - 1} \tag{1}$$

The first limit can be evaluated by performing an algebraic simplification:

$$\lim_{x \to 2} \frac{x^2 - 4}{x - 2} = \lim_{x \to 2} \frac{(x - 2)(x + 2)}{x - 2} = \lim_{x \to 2} (x + 2) = 4$$

The second cannot. Instead, we turn to the powerful **L'Hôpital's rule**, which we state without proof. This rule can be used whenever a limit is a 0/0 indeterminate form, so can be used to evaluate both of the limits in (1).

THEOREM 1 L'Hôpital's Rule for 0/0 Indeterminate Forms: Version 1

For c a real number,
if $\lim_{x \to c} f(x) = 0$ and $\lim_{x \to c} g(x) = 0$, then

$$\lim_{x \to c} \frac{f(x)}{g(x)} = \lim_{x \to c} \frac{f'(x)}{g'(x)}$$

provided that the second limit exists or is ∞ or $-\infty$.

By L'Hôpital's rule,

$$\lim_{x \to 2} \frac{x^2 - 4}{x - 2} = \lim_{x \to 2} \frac{2x}{1} = 4$$

which agrees with the result obtained by algebraic simplification.

EXAMPLE 3 L'Hôpital's Rule   Evaluate $\lim_{x \to 1} \dfrac{e^x - e}{x - 1}$.

SOLUTION

Step 1   *Check to see if L'Hôpital's rule applies:*

$$\lim_{x \to 1} (e^x - e) = e^1 - e = 0 \quad \text{and} \quad \lim_{x \to 1} (x - 1) = 1 - 1 = 0$$

L'Hôpital's rule does apply.

Step 2   *Apply L'Hôpital's rule:*

0/0 form

$$\lim_{x \to 1} \frac{e^x - e}{x - 1} = \lim_{x \to 1} \frac{\dfrac{d}{dx}(e^x - e)}{\dfrac{d}{dx}(x - 1)}$$ Apply L'Hôpital's rule.

$$= \lim_{x \to 1} \frac{e^x}{1}$$ e^x is continuous at $x = 1$.

$$= \frac{e^1}{1} = e$$

Matched Problem 3⟩ Evaluate $\lim\limits_{x \to 4} \dfrac{e^x - e^4}{x - 4}$.

⚠ **CAUTION** In L'Hôpital's rule, the symbol $f'(x)/g'(x)$ represents the derivative of $f(x)$ divided by the derivative of $g(x)$, not the derivative of the quotient $f(x)/g(x)$.

> When applying L'Hôpital's rule to a 0/0 indeterminate form, do not use the quotient rule. Instead, evaluate the limit of the derivative of the numerator divided by the derivative of the denominator.   ▲

The functions

$$y_1 = \frac{e^x - e}{x - 1} \quad \text{and} \quad y_2 = \frac{e^x}{1}$$

of Example 3 are different functions (see Fig. 3), but both functions have the same limit e as x approaches 1. Although y_1 is undefined at $x = 1$, the graph of y_1 provides a check of the answer to Example 3.

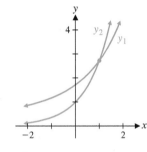

Figure 3

EXAMPLE 4   L'Hôpital's Rule   Evaluate $\lim\limits_{x \to 0} \dfrac{\ln(1 + x^2)}{x^4}$.

SOLUTION

Step 1   *Check to see if L'Hôpital's rule applies:*

$$\lim_{x \to 0} \ln(1 + x^2) = \ln 1 = 0 \quad \text{and} \quad \lim_{x \to 0} x^4 = 0$$

L'Hôpital's rule does apply.

Step 2   *Apply L'Hôpital's rule:*

0/0 form

$$\lim_{x \to 0} \frac{\ln(1 + x^2)}{x^4} = \lim_{x \to 0} \frac{\dfrac{d}{dx}\ln(1 + x^2)}{\dfrac{d}{dx}x^4}$$ Apply L'Hôpital's rule.

$$\lim_{x \to 0} \frac{\ln(1 + x^2)}{x^4} = \lim_{x \to 0} \frac{\dfrac{2x}{1 + x^2}}{4x^3}$$ Multiply numerator and denominator by $1/4x^3$.

$$= \lim_{x \to 0} \frac{\dfrac{2x}{1 + x^2}\dfrac{1}{4x^3}}{4x^3 \dfrac{1}{4x^3}}$$ Simplify.

$$= \lim_{x \to 0} \frac{1}{2x^2(1 + x^2)}$$

Apply Theorem 1 in Section 2.2 and compare with Fig. 1(D).

$$= \infty$$

Matched Problem 4 Evaluate $\lim_{x \to 1} \dfrac{\ln x}{(x - 1)^3}$.

EXAMPLE 5 L'Hôpital's Rule May Not Be Applicable Evaluate $\lim_{x \to 1} \dfrac{\ln x}{x}$.

SOLUTION

Step 1 *Check to see if L'Hôpital's rule applies:*

$$\lim_{x \to 1} \ln x = \ln 1 = 0, \qquad \text{but} \qquad \lim_{x \to 1} x = 1 \neq 0$$

L'Hôpital's rule does not apply.

Step 2 *Evaluate by another method.* The quotient property for limits from Section 2.1 does apply, and we have

$$\lim_{x \to 1} \frac{\ln x}{x} = \frac{\lim_{x \to 1} \ln x}{\lim_{x \to 1} x} = \frac{\ln 1}{1} = \frac{0}{1} = 0$$

Note that applying L'Hôpital's rule would give us an incorrect result:

$$\lim_{x \to 1} \frac{\ln x}{x} \neq \lim_{x \to 1} \frac{\frac{d}{dx} \ln x}{\frac{d}{dx} x} = \lim_{x \to 1} \frac{1/x}{1} = 1$$

Matched Problem 5 Evaluate $\lim_{x \to 0} \dfrac{x}{e^x}$.

⚠ **CAUTION** As Example 5 illustrates, some limits involving quotients are not $0/0$ indeterminate forms.

You must always check to see if L'Hôpital's rule applies before you use it. ▲

EXAMPLE 6 Repeated Application of L'Hôpital's Rule Evaluate

$$\lim_{x \to 0} \frac{x^2}{e^x - 1 - x}$$

SOLUTION

Step 1 *Check to see if L'Hôpital's rule applies:*

$$\lim_{x \to 0} x^2 = 0 \qquad \text{and} \qquad \lim_{x \to 0} (e^x - 1 - x) = 0$$

L'Hôpital's rule does apply.

Step 2 Apply L'Hôpital's rule:

$0/0$ form

$$\lim_{x \to 0} \frac{x^2}{e^x - 1 - x} = \lim_{x \to 0} \frac{\frac{d}{dx} x^2}{\frac{d}{dx} (e^x - 1 - x)} = \lim_{x \to 0} \frac{2x}{e^x - 1}$$

Since $\lim_{x \to 0} 2x = 0$ and $\lim_{x \to 0} (e^x - 1) = 0$, the new limit obtained is also a $0/0$ indeterminate form, and L'Hôpital's rule can be applied again.

Step 3 *Apply L'Hôpital's rule again:*

0/0 form

$$\lim_{x \to 0} \frac{2x}{e^x - 1} = \lim_{x \to 0} \frac{\frac{d}{dx} 2x}{\frac{d}{dx}(e^x - 1)} = \lim_{x \to 0} \frac{2}{e^x} = \frac{2}{e^0} = 2$$

Therefore,

$$\lim_{x \to 0} \frac{x^2}{e^x - 1 - x} = \lim_{x \to 0} \frac{2x}{e^x - 1} = \lim_{x \to 0} \frac{2}{e^x} = 2$$

Matched Problem 6 Evaluate $\lim_{x \to 0} \dfrac{e^{2x} - 1 - 2x}{x^2}$

One-Sided Limits and Limits at ∞

In addition to examining the limit as x approaches c, we have discussed one-sided limits and limits at ∞ in Chapter 3. L'Hôpital's rule is valid in these cases also.

THEOREM 2 L'Hôpital's Rule for 0/0 Indeterminate Forms: Version 2 (for one-sided limits and limits at infinity)

The first version of L'Hôpital's rule (Theorem 1) remains valid if the symbol $x \to c$ is replaced everywhere it occurs with one of the following symbols:

$$x \to c^+ \qquad x \to c^- \qquad x \to \infty \qquad x \to -\infty$$

For example, if $\lim_{x \to \infty} f(x) = 0$ and $\lim_{x \to \infty} g(x) = 0$, then

$$\lim_{x \to \infty} \frac{f(x)}{g(x)} = \lim_{x \to \infty} \frac{f'(x)}{g'(x)}$$

provided that the second limit exists or is $+\infty$ or $-\infty$. Similar rules can be written for $x \to c^+$, $x \to c^-$, and $x \to -\infty$.

EXAMPLE 7   L'Hôpital's Rule for One-Sided Limits   Evaluate $\lim_{x \to 1^+} \dfrac{\ln x}{(x - 1)^2}$.

SOLUTION

Step 1 *Check to see if L'Hôpital's rule applies:*

$$\lim_{x \to 1^+} \ln x = 0 \qquad \text{and} \qquad \lim_{x \to 1^+} (x - 1)^2 = 0$$

L'Hôpital's rule does apply.

Step 2 *Apply L'Hôpital's rule:*

0/0 form

$$\lim_{x \to 1^+} \frac{\ln x}{(x - 1)^2} = \lim_{x \to 1^+} \frac{\frac{d}{dx}(\ln x)}{\frac{d}{dx}(x - 1)^2} \qquad \text{Apply L'Hôpital's rule.}$$

$$= \lim_{x \to 1^+} \frac{1/x}{2(x - 1)} \qquad \text{Simplify.}$$

$$= \lim_{x \to 1^+} \frac{1}{2x(x - 1)}$$

$$= \infty$$

The limit as $x \to 1^+$ is ∞ because $1/2x(x - 1)$ has a vertical asymptote at $x = 1$ (Theorem 1, Section 2.2) and $x(x - 1) > 0$ for $x > 1$.

Matched Problem 7 ⌋ Evaluate $\displaystyle\lim_{x \to 1^-} \frac{\ln x}{(x - 1)^2}$.

EXAMPLE 8 L'Hôpital's Rule for Limits at Infinity Evaluate $\displaystyle\lim_{x \to \infty} \frac{\ln\left(1 + e^{-x}\right)}{e^{-x}}$.

SOLUTION

Step 1 *Check to see if L'Hôpital's rule applies:*

$$\lim_{x \to \infty} \ln(1 + e^{-x}) = \ln(1 + 0) = \ln 1 = 0 \quad \text{and} \quad \lim_{x \to \infty} e^{-x} = 0$$

L'Hôpital's rule does apply.

Step 2 *Apply L'Hôpital's rule:*

$$\lim_{x \to \infty} \frac{\ln\left(1 + e^{-x}\right)}{e^{-x}} \overset{\text{0/0 form}}{=} \lim_{x \to \infty} \frac{\dfrac{d}{dx}\left[\ln\left(1 + e^{-x}\right)\right]}{\dfrac{d}{dx} e^{-x}} \qquad \text{Apply L'Hôpital's rule.}$$

$$= \lim_{x \to \infty} \frac{-e^{-x}/(1 + e^{-x})}{-e^{-x}} \qquad \text{Multiply numerator and denominator by } -e^{x}.$$

$$= \lim_{x \to \infty} \frac{1}{1 + e^{-x}} \qquad \lim_{x \to \infty} e^{-x} = 0$$

$$= \frac{1}{1 + 0} = 1$$

Matched Problem 8 ⌋ Evaluate $\displaystyle\lim_{x \to -\infty} \frac{\ln(1 + 2e^x)}{e^x}$.

L'Hôpital's Rule and the Indeterminate Form ∞/∞

In Section 2.2, we discussed techniques for evaluating limits of rational functions such as

$$\lim_{x \to \infty} \frac{2x^2}{x^3 + 3} \qquad \lim_{x \to \infty} \frac{4x^3}{2x^2 + 5} \qquad \lim_{x \to \infty} \frac{3x^3}{5x^3 + 6} \tag{2}$$

Each of these limits is an ∞/∞ *indeterminate form*. In general, if $\lim_{x \to c} f(x) = \pm\infty$ and $\lim_{x \to c} g(x) = \pm\infty$, then

$$\lim_{x \to c} \frac{f(x)}{g(x)}$$

is called an **∞/∞ indeterminate form**. Furthermore, $x \to c$ can be replaced in all three limits above with $x \to c^+, x \to c^-, x \to \infty$, or $x \to -\infty$. It can be shown that L'Hôpital's rule also applies to these ∞/∞ indeterminate forms.

THEOREM 3   L'Hôpital's Rule for the Indeterminate Form ∞/∞: Version 3

Versions 1 and 2 of L'Hôpital's rule for the indeterminate form 0/0 are also valid if the limit of f and the limit of g are both infinite; that is, both $+\infty$ and $-\infty$ are permissible for either limit.

For example, if $\lim_{x \to c^+} f(x) = \infty$ and $\lim_{x \to c^+} g(x) = -\infty$, then L'Hôpital's rule can be applied to $\lim_{x \to c^+} [f(x)/g(x)]$.

Explore and Discuss 1　Evaluate each of the limits in (2) on page 277 in two ways:
1. Use Theorem 4 in Section 2.2.
2. Use L'Hôpital's rule.

Given a choice, which method would you choose? Why?

EXAMPLE 9　L'Hôpital's Rule for the Indeterminate Form ∞/∞　Evaluate $\lim_{x \to \infty} \dfrac{\ln x}{x^2}$.

SOLUTION

Step 1　*Check to see if L'Hôpital's rule applies:*
$$\lim_{x \to \infty} \ln x = \infty \qquad \text{and} \qquad \lim_{x \to \infty} x^2 = \infty$$
L'Hôpital's rule does apply.

Step 2　*Apply L'Hôpital's rule:*

∞/∞ form
$$\lim_{x \to \infty} \frac{\ln x}{x^2} = \lim_{x \to \infty} \frac{\dfrac{d}{dx}(\ln x)}{\dfrac{d}{dx} x^2} \qquad \text{Apply L'Hôpital's rule.}$$

$$= \lim_{x \to \infty} \frac{1/x}{2x} \qquad \text{Simplify.}$$

$$\lim_{x \to \infty} \frac{\ln x}{x^2} = \lim_{x \to \infty} \frac{1}{2x^2} \qquad \text{See Figure 1(D).}$$

$$= 0$$

Matched Problem 9　Evaluate $\lim_{x \to \infty} \dfrac{\ln x}{x}$.

EXAMPLE 10　L'Hôpital's Rule for the Indeterminate Form ∞/∞
Evaluate $\lim_{x \to \infty} \dfrac{e^x}{x^2}$.

SOLUTION

Step 1　*Check to see if L'Hôpital's rule applies:*
$$\lim_{x \to \infty} e^x = \infty \qquad \text{and} \qquad \lim_{x \to \infty} x^2 = \infty$$
L'Hôpital's rule does apply.

Step 2　*Apply L'Hôpital's rule:*

∞/∞ form
$$\lim_{x \to \infty} \frac{e^x}{x^2} = \lim_{x \to \infty} \frac{\dfrac{d}{dx} e^x}{\dfrac{d}{dx} x^2} = \lim_{x \to \infty} \frac{e^x}{2x}$$

Since $\lim_{x \to \infty} e^x = \infty$ and $\lim_{x \to \infty} 2x = \infty$, this limit is an ∞/∞ indeterminate form and L'Hôpital's rule can be applied again.

Step 3 *Apply L'Hôpital's rule again:*

∞ / ∞ form

$$\lim_{x\to\infty}\frac{e^x}{2x}=\lim_{x\to\infty}\frac{\frac{d}{dx}e^x}{\frac{d}{dx}2x}=\lim_{x\to\infty}\frac{e^x}{2}=\infty$$

Therefore,

$$\lim_{x\to\infty}\frac{e^x}{x^2}=\lim_{x\to\infty}\frac{e^x}{2x}=\lim_{x\to\infty}\frac{e^x}{2}=\infty$$

Matched Problem 10 Evaluate $\lim_{x\to\infty}\dfrac{e^{2x}}{x^2}$.

CONCEPTUAL INSIGHT

The three versions of L'Hôpital's rule cover a multitude of limits—far too many to remember case by case. Instead, we suggest you use the following pattern, common to all versions, as a memory aid:

1. All versions involve three limits: $\lim[f(x)/g(x)]$, $\lim f(x)$, and $\lim g(x)$.
2. The independent variable x must behave the same way in all three limits. The acceptable behaviors are $x\to c$, $x\to c^+$, $x\to c^-$, $x\to\infty$, or $x\to-\infty$.
3. The form of $\lim[f(x)/g(x)]$ must be $\frac{0}{0}$ or $\frac{\pm\infty}{\pm\infty}$ and both $\lim f(x)$ and $\lim g(x)$ must approach 0 or both must approach $\pm\infty$.

Exercises 4.3

Skills Warm-up Exercises

W *In Problems 1–8, round each expression to the nearest integer without using a calculator. (If necessary, review Section A.1).*

1. $\dfrac{5}{0.01}$ 2. $\dfrac{8}{0.002}$ 3. $\dfrac{3}{1,000}$

4. $\dfrac{2^8}{8}$ 5. $\dfrac{1}{2(1.01-1)}$ 6. $\dfrac{47}{106}$

7. $\dfrac{\ln 100}{100}$ 8. $\dfrac{e^5+5^2}{e^5}$

In Problems 9–16, even though the limit can be found using algebraic simplification as in Section 2.1, use L'Hôpital's rule to find the limit.

9. $\lim_{x\to3}\dfrac{x^2-9}{x-3}$ 10. $\lim_{x\to-3}\dfrac{x^2-9}{x+3}$

11. $\lim_{x\to-5}\dfrac{x+5}{x^2-25}$ 12. $\lim_{x\to4}\dfrac{x-4}{x^2-16}$

13. $\lim_{x\to1}\dfrac{x^2+5x-6}{x-1}$ 14. $\lim_{x\to10}\dfrac{x^2-5x-50}{x-10}$

15. $\lim_{x\to-9}\dfrac{x+9}{x^2+13x+36}$ 16. $\lim_{x\to-1}\dfrac{x+1}{x^2-7x-8}$

In Problems 17–24, even though the limit can be found using Theorem 4 of Section 2.2, use L'Hôpital's rule to find the limit.

17. $\lim_{x\to\infty}\dfrac{2x+3}{5x-1}$ 18. $\lim_{x\to\infty}\dfrac{6x-7}{7x-6}$

19. $\lim_{x\to\infty}\dfrac{3x^2-1}{x^3+4}$ 20. $\lim_{x\to\infty}\dfrac{5x^2+10x+1}{x^4+x^2+1}$

21. $\lim_{x\to-\infty}\dfrac{x^2-9}{x-3}$ 22. $\lim_{x\to-\infty}\dfrac{x^4-16}{x^2+4}$

23. $\lim_{x\to\infty}\dfrac{2x^2+3x+1}{3x^2-2x+1}$ 24. $\lim_{x\to\infty}\dfrac{5-4x^3}{1+7x^3}$

In Problems 25–32, use L'Hôpital's rule to find the limit. Note that in these problems, neither algebraic simplification nor Theorem 4 of Section 2.2 provides an alternative to L'Hôpital's rule.

25. $\lim_{x\to0}\dfrac{e^x-1}{2x}$ 26. $\lim_{x\to0}\dfrac{5x}{e^x-1}$

27. $\lim_{x\to1}\dfrac{x-1}{\ln x}$ 28. $\lim_{x\to1}\dfrac{x-1}{\ln x^4}$

29. $\lim_{x\to\infty}\dfrac{x^2}{e^x}$ 30. $\lim_{x\to\infty}\dfrac{x^3}{\ln x}$

31. $\lim_{x\to0}\dfrac{e^{4x}-1}{x}$ 32. $\lim_{x\to0}\dfrac{\ln(1-3x)}{x}$

✎ *In Problems 33–36, explain why L'Hôpital's rule does not apply. If the limit exists, find it by other means.*

33. $\lim_{x\to1}\dfrac{x^2+5x+4}{x^3+1}$ 34. $\lim_{x\to\infty}\dfrac{e^{-x}}{\ln x}$

35. $\lim_{x\to2}\dfrac{x+2}{(x-2)^4}$ 36. $\lim_{x\to-3}\dfrac{x^2}{(x+3)^5}$

Find each limit in Problems 37–60. Note that L'Hôpital's rule does not apply to every problem, and some problems will require more than one application of L'Hôpital's rule.

37. $\lim\limits_{x \to 0} \dfrac{e^{4x} - 1 - 4x}{x^2}$

38. $\lim\limits_{x \to 0} \dfrac{3x + 1 - e^{3x}}{x^2}$

39. $\lim\limits_{x \to 2} \dfrac{\ln(x - 1)}{x - 1}$

40. $\lim\limits_{x \to -1} \dfrac{\ln(x + 2)}{x + 2}$

41. $\lim\limits_{x \to 0^+} \dfrac{\ln(1 + x^2)}{x^3}$

42. $\lim\limits_{x \to 0^-} \dfrac{\ln(1 + 2x)}{x^2}$

43. $\lim\limits_{x \to 0^+} \dfrac{\ln(1 + \sqrt{x})}{x}$

44. $\lim\limits_{x \to 0^+} \dfrac{\ln(1 + x)}{\sqrt{x}}$

45. $\lim\limits_{x \to -2} \dfrac{x^2 + 2x + 1}{x^2 + x + 1}$

46. $\lim\limits_{x \to 1} \dfrac{2x^3 - 3x^2 + 1}{x^3 - 3x + 2}$

47. $\lim\limits_{x \to -1} \dfrac{x^3 + x^2 - x - 1}{x^3 + 4x^2 + 5x + 2}$

48. $\lim\limits_{x \to 3} \dfrac{x^3 + 3x^2 - x - 3}{x^2 + 6x + 9}$

49. $\lim\limits_{x \to 2} \dfrac{x^3 - 12x + 16}{x^3 - 6x^2 + 12x - 8}$

50. $\lim\limits_{x \to 1^+} \dfrac{x^3 + x^2 - x + 1}{x^3 + 3x^2 + 3x - 1}$

51. $\lim\limits_{x \to \infty} \dfrac{3x^2 + 5x}{4x^3 + 7}$

52. $\lim\limits_{x \to \infty} \dfrac{4x^2 + 9x}{5x^2 + 8}$

53. $\lim\limits_{x \to \infty} \dfrac{x^2}{e^{2x}}$

54. $\lim\limits_{x \to \infty} \dfrac{e^{3x}}{x^3}$

55. $\lim\limits_{x \to \infty} \dfrac{1 + e^{-x}}{1 + x^2}$

56. $\lim\limits_{x \to -\infty} \dfrac{1 + e^{-x}}{1 + x^2}$

57. $\lim\limits_{x \to \infty} \dfrac{e^{-x}}{\ln(1 + 4e^{-x})}$

58. $\lim\limits_{x \to \infty} \dfrac{\ln(1 + 2e^{-x})}{\ln(1 + e^{-x})}$

59. $\lim\limits_{x \to 0} \dfrac{e^x - e^{-x} - 2x}{x^3}$

60. $\lim\limits_{x \to 0} \dfrac{e^{2x} - 1 - 2x - 2x^2}{x^3}$

61. Find $\lim\limits_{x \to 0^+} (x \ln x)$.

[*Hint*: Write $x \ln x = (\ln x)/x^{-1}$.]

62. Find $\lim\limits_{x \to 0^+} (\sqrt{x} \ln x)$.

[*Hint*: Write $\sqrt{x} \ln x = (\ln x)/x^{-1/2}$.]

In Problems 63–66, n is a positive integer. Find each limit.

63. $\lim\limits_{x \to \infty} \dfrac{\ln x}{x^n}$

64. $\lim\limits_{x \to \infty} \dfrac{x^n}{\ln x}$

65. $\lim\limits_{x \to \infty} \dfrac{e^x}{x^n}$

66. $\lim\limits_{x \to \infty} \dfrac{x^n}{e^x}$

In Problems 67–70, show that the repeated application of L'Hôpital's rule does not lead to a solution. Then use algebraic manipulation to evaluate each limit. [Hint: If $x > 0$ and $n > 0$, then $\sqrt[n]{x^n} = x$.]

67. $\lim\limits_{x \to \infty} \dfrac{\sqrt{1 + x^2}}{x}$

68. $\lim\limits_{x \to -\infty} \dfrac{x}{\sqrt{4 + x^2}}$

69. $\lim\limits_{x \to -\infty} \dfrac{\sqrt[3]{x^3 + 1}}{x}$

70. $\lim\limits_{x \to \infty} \dfrac{x^2}{\sqrt[3]{(x^3 + 1)^2}}$

Answers to Matched Problems

1. (A) ∞ (B) ∞ (C) 0 (D) ∞
2. (A) ∞ (B) 0 (C) $-\infty$ (D) ∞
3. e^4 **4.** ∞ **5.** 0 **6.** 2
7. $-\infty$ **8.** 2 **9.** 0 **10.** ∞

4.4 Curve-Sketching Techniques

- Modifying the Graphing Strategy
- Using the Graphing Strategy
- Modeling Average Cost

When we summarized the graphing strategy in Section 4.2, we omitted one important topic: asymptotes. Polynomial functions do not have any asymptotes. Asymptotes of rational functions were discussed in Section 2.3, but what about all the other functions, such as logarithmic and exponential functions? Since investigating asymptotes always involves limits, we can now use L'Hôpital's rule (Section 4.3) as a tool for finding asymptotes of many different types of functions.

Modifying the Graphing Strategy

The first version of the graphing strategy in Section 4.2 made no mention of asymptotes. Including information about asymptotes produces the following (and final) version of the graphing strategy.

PROCEDURE Graphing Strategy (Final Version)

Step 1 *Analyze f(x).*

(A) Find the domain of *f*.

(B) Find the intercepts.

(C) Find asymptotes.

Step 2 *Analyze $f'(x)$.* Find the partition numbers for f' and the critical numbers of f. Construct a sign chart for $f'(x)$, determine the intervals on which f is increasing and decreasing, and find local maxima and minima of f.

Step 3 *Analyze $f''(x)$.* Find the partition numbers for $f''(x)$. Construct a sign chart for $f''(x)$, determine the intervals on which the graph of f is concave upward and concave downward, and find the inflection points of f.

Step 4 *Sketch the graph of f.* Draw asymptotes and locate intercepts, local maxima and minima, and inflection points. Sketch in what you know from steps 1–3. Plot additional points as needed and complete the sketch.

Using the Graphing Strategy

We will illustrate the graphing strategy with several examples. From now on, you should always use the final version of the graphing strategy. If a function does not have any asymptotes, simply state this fact.

EXAMPLE 1   Using the Graphing Strategy   Use the graphing strategy to analyze the function $f(x) = (x - 1)/(x - 2)$. State all the pertinent information and sketch the graph of f.

SOLUTION

Step 1 *Analyze $f(x)$.* $f(x) = \dfrac{x - 1}{x - 2}$

(A) Domain: All real x, except $x = 2$

(B) y intercept: $f(0) = \dfrac{0 - 1}{0 - 2} = \dfrac{1}{2}$

x intercepts: Since a fraction is 0 when its numerator is 0 and its denominator is not 0, the x intercept is $x = 1$.

(C) Horizontal asymptote: $\dfrac{a_m x^m}{b_n x^n} = \dfrac{x}{x} = 1$

So the line $y = 1$ is a horizontal asymptote.
Vertical asymptote: The denominator is 0 for $x = 2$, and the numerator is not 0 for this value. Therefore, the line $x = 2$ is a vertical asymptote.

Step 2 *Analyze $f'(x)$.* $f'(x) = \dfrac{(x - 2)(1) - (x - 1)(1)}{(x - 2)^2} = \dfrac{-1}{(x - 2)^2}$

Partition number for $f'(x)$: $x = 2$
Critical numbers of $f(x)$:   None
Sign chart for $f'(x)$:

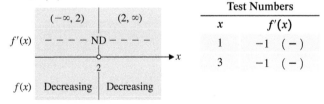

So $f(x)$ is decreasing on $(-\infty, 2)$ and $(2, \infty)$. There are no local extrema.

Step 3 *Analyze $f''(x)$.* $f''(x) = \dfrac{2}{(x - 2)^3}$

Partition number for $f''(x)$: $x = 2$
Sign chart for $f''(x)$:

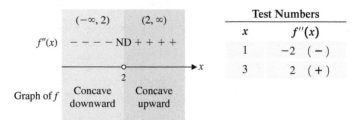

The graph of f is concave downward on $(-\infty, 2)$ and concave upward on $(2, \infty)$. Since $f(2)$ is not defined, there is no inflection point at $x = 2$, even though $f''(x)$ changes sign at $x = 2$.

Step 4   *Sketch the graph of f.* Insert intercepts and asymptotes, and plot a few additional points (for functions with asymptotes, plotting additional points is often helpful). Then sketch the graph.

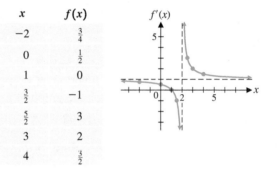

Matched Problem 1   Follow the graphing strategy and analyze the function $f(x) = 2x/(1 - x)$. State all the pertinent information and sketch the graph of f.

EXAMPLE 2   Using the Graphing Strategy   Use the graphing strategy to analyze the function

$$g(x) = \frac{2x - 1}{x^2}$$

State all pertinent information and sketch the graph of g.

SOLUTION

Step 1   *Analyze $g(x)$.*

(A) Domain: All real x, except $x = 0$

(B) x intercept: $x = \dfrac{1}{2} = 0.5$

y intercept: Since 0 is not in the domain of g, there is no y intercept.

(C) Horizontal asymptote: $y = 0$ (the x axis)

Vertical asymptote: The denominator of $g(x)$ is 0 at $x = 0$ and the numerator is not. So the line $x = 0$ (the y axis) is a vertical asymptote.

Step 2   *Analyze $g'(x)$.*

$$g(x) = \frac{2x - 1}{x^2} = \frac{2}{x} - \frac{1}{x^2} = 2x^{-1} - x^{-2}$$

$$g'(x) = -2x^{-2} + 2x^{-3} = -\frac{2}{x^2} + \frac{2}{x^3} = \frac{-2x + 2}{x^3}$$

$$= \frac{2(1 - x)}{x^3}$$

Partition numbers for $g'(x)$: $\quad x = 0, x = 1$

Critical number of $g(x)$: $\quad x = 1$

Sign chart for $g'(x)$:

Function $f(x)$ is decreasing on $(-\infty, 0)$ and $(1, \infty)$, is increasing on $(0, 1)$, and has a local maximum at $x = 1$. The local maximum is $g(1) = 1$.

Step 3 *Analyze $g''(x)$.*

$$g'(x) = -2x^{-2} + 2x^{-3}$$

$$g''(x) = 4x^{-3} - 6x^{-4} = \frac{4}{x^3} - \frac{6}{x^4} = \frac{4x - 6}{x^4} = \frac{2(2x - 3)}{x^4}$$

Partition numbers for $g''(x)$: $\quad x = 0, x = \dfrac{3}{2} = 1.5$

Sign chart for $g''(x)$:

Function $g(x)$ is concave downward on $(-\infty, 0)$ and $(0, 1.5)$, is concave upward on $(1.5, \infty)$, and has an inflection point at $x = 1.5$. Since $g(1.5) = 0.89$, the inflection point is $(1.5, 0.89)$.

Step 4 *Sketch the graph of g.* Plot key points, note that the coordinate axes are asymptotes, and sketch the graph.

x	$g(x)$
-10	-0.21
-1	-3
0.5	0
1	1
1.5	0.89
10	0.19

Matched Problem 2 Use the graphing strategy to analyze the function

$$h(x) = \frac{4x + 3}{x^2}$$

State all pertinent information and sketch the graph of h.

EXAMPLE 3 Graphing Strategy Follow the steps of the graphing strategy and analyze the function $f(x) = xe^x$. State all the pertinent information and sketch the graph of f.

SOLUTION

Step 1 *Analyze* $f(x)$: $f(x) = xe^x$.

(A) Domain: All real numbers

(B) *y* intercept: $f(0) = 0$

    x intercept: $xe^x = 0$ for $x = 0$ only, since $e^x > 0$ for all x.

(C) Vertical asymptotes: None

    Horizontal asymptotes: We use tables to determine the nature of the graph of *f* as $x \to \infty$ and $x \to -\infty$:

x	1	5	10	$\to \infty$
$f(x)$	2.72	742.07	220,264.66	$\to \infty$

x	-1	-5	-10	$\to -\infty$
$f(x)$	-0.37	-0.03	$-0.000\,45$	$\to 0$

Step 2 *Analyze* $f'(x)$:

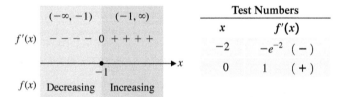

$$f'(x) = x\frac{d}{dx}e^x + e^x\frac{d}{dx}x$$

$$= xe^x + e^x = e^x(x + 1)$$

Partition number for $f'(x)$: -1
Critical number of $f(x)$: -1
Sign chart for $f'(x)$:

	$(-\infty, -1)$	$(-1, \infty)$		**Test Numbers**	
				x	$f'(x)$
$f'(x)$	$----$ 0	$++++$		-2	$-e^{-2}$ $(-)$
		-1		0	1 $(+)$
$f(x)$	Decreasing	Increasing			

So $f(x)$ decreases on $(-\infty, -1)$, has a local minimum at $x = -1$, and increases on $(-1, \infty)$. The local minimum is $f(-1) = -0.37$.

Step 3 *Analyze* $f''(x)$:

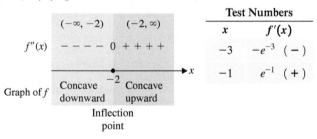

$$f''(x) = e^x\frac{d}{dx}(x + 1) + (x + 1)\frac{d}{dx}e^x$$

$$= e^x + (x + 1)e^x = e^x(x + 2)$$

Sign chart for $f''(x)$ (partition number is -2):

	$(-\infty, -2)$	$(-2, \infty)$		**Test Numbers**	
				x	$f'(x)$
$f''(x)$	$----$ 0	$++++$		-3	$-e^{-3}$ $(-)$
		-2		-1	e^{-1} $(+)$
Graph of f	Concave downward	Concave upward			
		Inflection point			

The graph of *f* is concave downward on $(-\infty, -2)$, has an inflection point at $x = -2$, and is concave upward on $(-2, \infty)$. Since $f(-2) = -0.27$, the inflection point is $(-2, -0.27)$.

Step 4   *Sketch the graph of f, using the information from steps 1 to 3:*

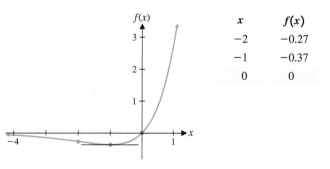

x	f(x)
−2	−0.27
−1	−0.37
0	0

Matched Problem 3   Analyze the function $f(x) = xe^{-0.5x}$. State all the pertinent information and sketch the graph of f.

Explore and Discuss 1   Refer to the discussion of asymptotes in the solution of Example 3. We used tables of values to estimate limits at infinity and determine horizontal asymptotes. In some cases, the functions involved in these limits can be written in a form that allows us to use L'Hôpital's rule.

$$\underset{x \to -\infty}{\lim} f(x) = \overset{-\infty \,\cdot\, 0 \text{ form}}{\underset{x \to -\infty}{\lim} xe^{x}} \qquad \text{Rewrite as a fraction.}$$

$$= \overset{-\infty\,/\,\infty \text{ form}}{\underset{x \to -\infty}{\lim} \frac{x}{e^{-x}}} \qquad \text{Apply L'Hôpital's rule.}$$

$$= \underset{x \to -\infty}{\lim} \frac{1}{-e^{-x}} \qquad \text{Simplify.}$$

$$= \underset{x \to -\infty}{\lim} (-e^{x}) \qquad \text{Property of } e^{x}$$

$$= 0$$

Use algebraic manipulation and L'Hôpital's rule to verify the value of each of the following limits:

(A) $\underset{x \to \infty}{\lim} xe^{-0.5x} = 0$

(B) $\underset{x \to 0^{+}}{\lim} x^{2}(\ln x - 0.5) = 0$

(C) $\underset{x \to 0^{+}}{\lim} x \ln x = 0$

EXAMPLE 4   Graphing Strategy   Let $f(x) = x^{2} \ln x - 0.5x^{2}$. Follow the steps in the graphing strategy and analyze this function. State all the pertinent information and sketch the graph of f.

SOLUTION

Step 1   *Analyze f(x):* $f(x) = x^{2} \ln x - 0.5x^{2} = x^{2}(\ln x - 0.5)$.

(A) Domain: $(0, \infty)$

(B) *y* intercept: None [$f(0)$ is not defined.]

  x intercept: Solve $x^{2}(\ln x - 0.5) = 0$

  $\ln x - 0.5 = 0$ or $x^{2} = 0$ Discard, since 0 is not in the domain of *f*.

  $\ln x = 0.5$ $\ln x = a$ if and only if $x = e^{a}$.

  $x = e^{0.5}$ *x* intercept

(C) Asymptotes: None. The following tables suggest the nature of the graph as $x \to 0^+$ and as $x \to \infty$:

x	0.1	0.01	0.001	$\to 0^+$
$f(x)$	−0.0280	−0.00051	−0.000007	$\to 0$

See Explore & Discuss 1(B).

x	10	100	1,000	$\to \infty$
$f(x)$	180	41,000	6,400,000	$\to \infty$

Step 2 *Analyze $f'(x)$:*

$$f'(x) = x^2 \frac{d}{dx} \ln x + (\ln x) \frac{d}{dx} x^2 - 0.5 \frac{d}{dx} x^2$$

$$= x^2 \frac{1}{x} + (\ln x)\, 2x - 0.5(2x)$$

$$= x + 2x \ln x - x$$

$$= 2x \ln x$$

Partition number for $f'(x)$: 1
Critical number of $f(x)$: 1
Sign chart for $f'(x)$:

Test Numbers	
x	$f'(x)$
0.5	−0.6931 (−)
2	2.7726 (+)

The function $f(x)$ decreases on $(0, 1)$, has a local minimum at $x = 1$, and increases on $(1, \infty)$. The local minimum is $f(1) = -0.5$.

Step 3 *Analyze $f''(x)$:*

$$f''(x) = 2x \frac{d}{dx}(\ln x) + (\ln x) \frac{d}{dx}(2x)$$

$$= 2x \frac{1}{x} + (\ln x)\, 2$$

$$= 2 + 2 \ln x = 0$$

$$2 \ln x = -2$$

$$\ln x = -1$$

$$x = e^{-1} \approx 0.3679$$

Sign chart for $f''(x)$ (partition number is e^{-1}):

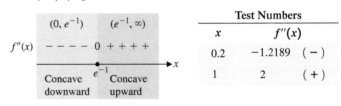

Test Numbers	
x	$f''(x)$
0.2	−1.2189 (−)
1 2	(+)

The graph of $f(x)$ is concave downward on $(0, e^{-1})$, has an inflection point at $x = e^{-1}$, and is concave upward on (e^{-1}, ∞). Since $f(e^{-1}) = -1.5e^{-2} \approx -0.20$, the inflection point is $(0.37, -0.20)$.

Step 4 *Sketch the graph of f, using the information from steps 1 to 3:*

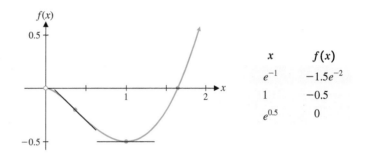

x	$f(x)$
e^{-1}	$-1.5e^{-2}$
1	-0.5
$e^{0.5}$	0

Matched Problem 4 Analyze the function $f(x) = x \ln x$. State all pertinent information and sketch the graph of f.

Modeling Average Cost

EXAMPLE 5 Average Cost Given the cost function $C(x) = 5,000 + 0.5x^2$, where x is the number of items produced, use the graphing strategy to analyze the graph of the average cost function. State all the pertinent information and sketch the graph of the average cost function. Find the marginal cost function and graph it on the same set of coordinate axes.

SOLUTION The average cost function is

$$\overline{C}(x) = \frac{5,000 + 0.5x^2}{x} = \frac{5,000}{x} + 0.5x$$

Step 1 *Analyze $\overline{C}(x)$.*

(A) Domain: Since negative values of x do not make sense and $\overline{C}(0)$ is not defined, the domain is the set of positive real numbers.

(B) Intercepts: None

(C) Horizontal asymptote: $\dfrac{a_m x^m}{b_n x^n} = \dfrac{0.5x^2}{x} = 0.5x$

So there is no horizontal asymptote.

Vertical asymptote: The line $x = 0$ is a vertical asymptote since the denominator is 0 and the numerator is not 0 for $x = 0$.

Oblique asymptotes: If a graph approaches a line that is neither horizontal nor vertical as x approaches ∞ or $-\infty$, then that line is called an **oblique asymptote**. If x is a large positive number, then $5,000/x$ is very small and

$$\overline{C}(x) = \frac{5,000}{x} + 0.5x \approx 0.5x$$

That is,

$$\lim_{x \to \infty} [\overline{C}(x) - 0.5x] = \lim_{x \to \infty} \frac{5,000}{x} = 0$$

This implies that the graph of $y = \overline{C}(x)$ approaches the line $y = 0.5x$ as x approaches ∞. That line is an oblique asymptote for the graph of $y = \overline{C}(x)$.*

---

*If $f(x) = n(x)/d(x)$ is a rational function for which the degree of $n(x)$ is 1 more than the degree of $d(x)$, then we can use polynomial long division to write $f(x) = mx + b + r(x)/d(x)$, where the degree of $r(x)$ is less than the degree of $d(x)$. The line $y = mx + b$ is then an oblique asymptote for the graph of $y = f(x)$.

Step 2   *Analyze* $\overline{C}'(x)$.

$$\overline{C}'(x) = -\frac{5,000}{x^2} + 0.5$$

$$= \frac{0.5x^2 - 5,000}{x^2}$$

$$= \frac{0.5(x - 100)(x + 100)}{x^2}$$

Partition numbers for $\overline{C}'(x)$:   0 and 100
Critical number of $\overline{C}(x)$:   100
Sign chart for $\overline{C}'(x)$:

| Test Numbers | |
x	$\overline{C}'(x)$
50	−1.5 (−)
125	0.18 (+)

So $\overline{C}(x)$ is decreasing on $(0, 100)$, is increasing on $(100, \infty)$, and has a local minimum at $x = 100$. The local minimum is $\overline{C}(100) = 100$.

Step 3   *Analyze* $\overline{C}''(x)$: $\overline{C}''(x) = \frac{10,000}{x^3}$.

$\overline{C}''(x)$ is positive for all positive x, so the graph of $y = \overline{C}(x)$ is concave upward on $(0, \infty)$.

Step 4   *Sketch the graph of* $\overline{C}$. The graph of $\overline{C}$ is shown in Figure 1.

Figure 1

The marginal cost function is $C'(x) = x$. The graph of this linear function is also shown in Figure 1.

Figure 1 illustrates an important principle in economics:

The minimum average cost occurs when the average cost is equal to the marginal cost.

Matched Problem 5   Given the cost function $C(x) = 1,600 + 0.25x^2$, where x is the number of items produced,

(A) Use the graphing strategy to analyze the graph of the average cost function. State all the pertinent information and sketch the graph of the average cost function. Find the marginal cost function and graph it on the same set of coordinate axes. Include any oblique asymptotes.

(B) Find the minimum average cost.

Exercises 4.4

W

Skills Warm-up Exercises

In Problems 1–8, find the domain of the function and all x or y intercepts. (If necessary, review Section 1.1).

1. $f(x) = 3x + 36$

2. $f(x) = -4x - 28$

3. $f(x) = \sqrt{25 - x}$

4. $f(x) = \sqrt{9 - x^2}$

5. $f(x) = \dfrac{x + 1}{x - 2}$

6. $f(x) = \dfrac{x^2 - 4}{x + 3}$

7. $f(x) = \dfrac{3}{x^2 - 1}$

8. $f(x) = \dfrac{x}{x^2 + 5x + 4}$

9. Use the graph of f in the figure to identify the following (assume that $f''(0) < 0, f''(b) > 0$, and $f''(g) > 0$):

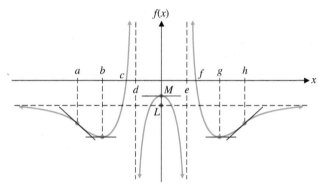

(A) the intervals on which $f'(x) < 0$

(B) the intervals on which $f'(x) > 0$

(C) the intervals on which $f(x)$ is increasing

(D) the intervals on which $f(x)$ is decreasing

(E) the x coordinate(s) of the point(s) where $f(x)$ has a local maximum

(F) the x coordinate(s) of the point(s) where $f(x)$ has a local minimum

(G) the intervals on which $f''(x) < 0$

(H) the intervals on which $f''(x) > 0$

(I) the intervals on which the graph of f is concave upward

(J) the intervals on which the graph of f is concave downward

(K) the x coordinate(s) of the inflection point(s)

(L) the horizontal asymptote(s)

(M) the vertical asymptote(s)

10. Repeat Problem 9 for the following graph of f (assume that $f''(d) < 0$):

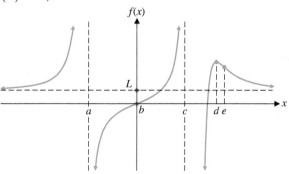

In Problems 11–18, use the given information to sketch the graph of f. Assume that f is continuous on its domain and that all intercepts are included in the table of values.

11. Domain: All real x; $\lim\limits_{x \to \pm\infty} f(x) = 2$

x	-4	-2	0	2	4
$f(x)$	0	-2	0	-2	0

$f'(x)$ $-\,-\,-\,-\,-\,-\,-\,0\,+\,+\,+ND-\,-\,-\,0\,+\,+\,+\,+\,+\,+\,+$
at -2, 0, 2

$f''(x)$ $-\,-\,-\,0\,+\,+\,+\,+\,+\,+$ ND $+\,+\,+\,+\,+\,0\,-\,-\,-$
at -4, 0, 4

12. Domain: All real x; $\lim\limits_{x \to -\infty} f(x) = -3$; $\lim\limits_{x \to \infty} f(x) = 3$

x	-2	-1	0	1	2
$f(x)$	0	2	0	-2	0

$f'(x)$ $+\,+\,+\,+\,+\,+\,+\,0\,-\,-\,-ND-\,-\,-\,0\,+\,+\,+\,+\,+\,+$
at -1, 0, 1

$f''(x)$ $+\,+\,+\,0\,-\,-\,-\,-\,-\,-$ ND $+\,+\,+\,+\,+\,+\,0\,-\,-\,-$
at -2, 0, 2

13. Domain: All real x, except $x = -2$;
$\lim\limits_{x \to -2^-} f(x) = \infty$; $\lim\limits_{x \to -2^+} f(x) = -\infty$; $\lim\limits_{x \to \infty} f(x) = 1$

x	-4	0	4	6
$f(x)$	0	0	3	2

$f'(x)$ $+\,+\,+$ ND $+\,+\,+\,0\,-\,-\,-\,-\,-\,-\,-\,-$
at -2, 4

$f''(x)$ $+\,+\,+$ ND $-\,-\,-\,-\,-\,-\,-\,-\,0\,+\,+\,+$
at -2, 6

14. Domain: All real x, except $x = 1$;
$\lim\limits_{x \to 1^-} f(x) = \infty$; $\lim\limits_{x \to 1^+} f(x) = \infty$; $\lim\limits_{x \to \infty} f(x) = -2$

x	-4	-2	0	2
$f(x)$	0	-2	0	0

$f'(x)$ $-\,-\,-\,0\,+\,+\,+$ ND $-\,-\,-$
at -2, 1

$f''(x)$ $+\,+\,+\,+\,+\,+\,+\,+$ND$+\,+\,+$
at 1

15. Domain: All real x, except $x = -1$;

$f(-3) = 2$, $f(-2) = 3$, $f(0) = -1$, $f(1) = 0$;

$f'(x) > 0$ on $(-\infty, -1)$ and $(-1, \infty)$;

$f''(x) > 0$ on $(-\infty, -1)$; $f''(x) < 0$ on $(-1, \infty)$;

vertical asymptote: $x = -1$;

horizontal asymptote: $y = 1$

16. Domain: All real x, except $x = 1$;

$f(0) = -2$, $f(2) = 0$;

$f'(x) < 0$ on $(-\infty, 1)$ and $(1, \infty)$;

$f''(x) < 0$ on $(-\infty, 1)$;

$f''(x) > 0$ on $(1, \infty)$;

vertical asymptote: $x = 1$;

horizontal asymptote: $y = -1$

17. Domain: All real x, except $x = -2$ and $x = 2$;

$f(-3) = -1$, $f(0) = 0$, $f(3) = 1$;

$f'(x) < 0$ on $(-\infty, -2)$ and $(2, \infty)$;

$f'(x) > 0$ on $(-2, 2)$;

$f''(x) < 0$ on $(-\infty, -2)$ and $(-2, 0)$;

$f''(x) > 0$ on $(0, 2)$ and $(2, \infty)$;

vertical asymptotes: $x = -2$ and $x = 2$;

horizontal asymptote: $y = 0$

18. Domain: All real x, except $x = -1$ and $x = 1$;

$f(-2) = 1$, $f(0) = 0$, $f(2) = 1$;

$f'(x) > 0$ on $(-\infty, -1)$ and $(0, 1)$;

$f'(x) < 0$ on $(-1, 0)$ and $(1, \infty)$;

$f''(x) > 0$ on $(-\infty, -1)$, $(-1, 1)$, and $(1, \infty)$;

vertical asymptotes: $x = -1$ and $x = 1$;

horizontal asymptote: $y = 0$

In Problems 19–58, summarize the pertinent information obtained by applying the graphing strategy and sketch the graph of $y = f(x)$.

19. $f(x) = \dfrac{x + 3}{x - 3}$

20. $f(x) = \dfrac{2x - 4}{x + 2}$

21. $f(x) = \dfrac{x}{x - 2}$

22. $f(x) = \dfrac{2 + x}{3 - x}$

23. $f(x) = 5 + 5e^{-0.1x}$

24. $f(x) = 3 + 7e^{-0.2x}$

25. $f(x) = 5xe^{-0.2x}$

26. $f(x) = 10xe^{-0.1x}$

27. $f(x) = \ln(1 - x)$

28. $f(x) = \ln(2x + 4)$

29. $f(x) = x - \ln x$

30. $f(x) = \ln(x^2 + 4)$

31. $f(x) = \dfrac{x}{x^2 - 4}$

32. $f(x) = \dfrac{1}{x^2 - 4}$

33. $f(x) = \dfrac{1}{1 + x^2}$

34. $f(x) = \dfrac{x^2}{1 + x^2}$

35. $f(x) = \dfrac{2x}{1 - x^2}$

36. $f(x) = \dfrac{2x}{x^2 - 9}$

37. $f(x) = \dfrac{-5x}{(x - 1)^2}$

38. $f(x) = \dfrac{x}{(x - 2)^2}$

39. $f(x) = \dfrac{x^2 + x - 2}{x^2}$

40. $f(x) = \dfrac{x^2 - 5x - 6}{x^2}$

41. $f(x) = \dfrac{x^2}{x - 1}$

42. $f(x) = \dfrac{x^2}{2 + x}$

43. $f(x) = \dfrac{3x^2 + 2}{x^2 - 9}$

44. $f(x) = \dfrac{2x^2 + 5}{4 - x^2}$

45. $f(x) = \dfrac{x^3}{x - 2}$

46. $f(x) = \dfrac{x^3}{4 - x}$

47. $f(x) = (3 - x)e^x$

48. $f(x) = (x - 2)e^x$

49. $f(x) = e^{-0.5x^2}$

50. $f(x) = e^{-2x^2}$

51. $f(x) = x^2 \ln x$

52. $f(x) = \dfrac{\ln x}{x}$

53. $f(x) = (\ln x)^2$

54. $f(x) = \dfrac{x}{\ln x}$

55. $f(x) = \dfrac{1}{x^2 + 2x - 8}$

56. $f(x) = \dfrac{1}{3 - 2x - x^2}$

57. $f(x) = \dfrac{x^3}{3 - x^2}$

58. $f(x) = \dfrac{x^3}{x^2 - 12}$

In Problems 59–66, show that the line $y = x$ is an oblique asymptote for the graph of $y = f(x)$, summarize all pertinent information obtained by applying the graphing strategy, and sketch the graph of $y = f(x)$.

59. $f(x) = x + \dfrac{4}{x}$

60. $f(x) = x - \dfrac{9}{x}$

61. $f(x) = x - \dfrac{4}{x^2}$

62. $f(x) = x + \dfrac{32}{x^2}$

63. $f(x) = x - \dfrac{9}{x^3}$

64. $f(x) = x + \dfrac{27}{x^3}$

65. $f(x) = x + \dfrac{1}{x} + \dfrac{4}{x^3}$

66. $f(x) = x - \dfrac{16}{x^3}$

In Problems 67–70, for the given cost function $C(x)$, find the oblique asymptote of the average cost function $\overline{C}(x)$.

67. $C(x) = 10,000 + 90x + 0.02x^2$

68. $C(x) = 7,500 + 65x + 0.01x^2$

69. $C(x) = 95,000 + 210x + 0.1x^2$

70. $C(x) = 120,000 + 340x + 0.4x^2$

In Problems 71–78, summarize all pertinent information obtained by applying the graphing strategy, and sketch the graph of $y = f(x)$. [Note: These rational functions are not reduced to lowest terms.]

71. $f(x) = \dfrac{x^2 + x - 6}{x^2 - 6x + 8}$

72. $f(x) = \dfrac{x^2 + x - 6}{x^2 - x - 12}$

73. $f(x) = \dfrac{2x^2 + x - 15}{x^2 - 9}$

74. $f(x) = \dfrac{2x^2 + 11x + 14}{x^2 - 4}$

75. $f(x) = \dfrac{x^3 - 5x^2 + 6x}{x^2 - x - 2}$

76. $f(x) = \dfrac{x^3 - 5x^2 - 6x}{x^2 + 3x + 2}$

77. $f(x) = \dfrac{x^2 + x - 2}{x^2 - 2x + 1}$

78. $f(x) = \dfrac{x^2 + x - 2}{x^2 + 4x + 4}$

Applications

79. Revenue. The marketing research department for a computer company used a large city to test market the firm's new laptop. The department found that the relationship between price p (dollars per unit) and demand x (units sold per week) was given approximately by

$$p = 1,296 - 0.12x^2 \qquad 0 \le x \le 80$$

So, weekly revenue can be approximated by

$$R(x) = xp = 1,296x - 0.12x^3 \qquad 0 \le x \le 80$$

Graph the revenue function R.

80. Profit. Suppose that the cost function $C(x)$ (in dollars) for the company in Problem 79 is

$$C(x) = 830 + 396x$$

(A) Write an equation for the profit $P(x)$.

(B) Graph the profit function P.

81. Pollution. In Silicon Valley, a number of computer firms were found to be contaminating underground water supplies with toxic chemicals stored in leaking underground containers. A water quality control agency ordered the companies to take immediate corrective action and contribute to a monetary pool for the testing and cleanup of the underground contamination. Suppose that the required monetary pool (in millions of dollars) is given by

$$P(x) = \frac{2x}{1 - x} \qquad 0 \le x < 1$$

where x is the percentage (expressed as a decimal fraction) of the total contaminant removed.

(A) Where is $P(x)$ increasing? Decreasing?

(B) Where is the graph of P concave upward? Downward?

(C) Find any horizontal and vertical asymptotes.

(D) Find the x and y intercepts.

(E) Sketch a graph of P.

82. Employee training. A company producing dive watches has established that, on average, a new employee can assemble $N(t)$ dive watches per day after t days of on-the-job training, as given by

$$N(t) = \frac{100t}{t + 9} \qquad t \ge 0$$

(A) Where is $N(t)$ increasing? Decreasing?

(B) Where is the graph of N concave upward? Downward?

(C) Find any horizontal and vertical asymptotes.

(D) Find the intercepts.

(E) Sketch a graph of N.

83. Replacement time. An outboard motor has an initial price of $3,200. A service contract costs $300 for the first year and increases $100 per year thereafter. The total cost of the outboard motor (in dollars) after n years is given by

$$C(n) = 3,200 + 250n + 50n^2 \qquad n \ge 1$$

(A) Write an expression for the average cost per year, $\overline{C}(n)$, for n years.

(B) Graph the average cost function found in part (A).

(C) When is the average cost per year at its minimum? (This time is frequently referred to as the **replacement time** for this piece of equipment.)

84. Construction costs. The management of a manufacturing plant wishes to add a fenced-in rectangular storage yard of 20,000 square feet, using a building as one side of the yard (see the figure). If x is the distance (in feet) from the building to the fence, show that the length of the fence required for the yard is given by

$$L(x) = 2x + \frac{20,000}{x} \qquad x > 0$$

Storage yard

x

(A) Graph L.

(B) What are the dimensions of the rectangle requiring the least amount of fencing?

85. Average and marginal costs. The total daily cost (in dollars) of producing x mountain bikes is given by

$$C(x) = 1,000 + 5x + 0.1x^2$$

(A) Sketch the graphs of the average cost function and the marginal cost function on the same set of coordinate axes. Include any oblique asymptotes.

(B) Find the minimum average cost.

86. Average and marginal costs. The total daily cost (in dollars) of producing x city bikes is given by

$$C(x) = 500 + 2x + 0.2x^2$$

(A) Sketch the graphs of the average cost function and the marginal cost function on the same set of coordinate axes. Include any oblique asymptotes.

(B) Find the minimum average cost.

87. Minimizing average costs. The table gives the total daily costs y (in dollars) of producing x pepperoni pizzas at various production levels.

Number of Pizzas	Total Costs
x	y
50	395
100	475
150	640
200	910
250	1,140
300	1,450

(A) Enter the data into a graphing calculator and find a quadratic regression equation for the total costs.

(B) Use the regression equation from part (A) to find the minimum average cost (to the nearest cent) and the corresponding production level (to the nearest integer).

88. Minimizing average costs. The table gives the total daily costs y (in dollars) of producing x deluxe pizzas at various production levels.

Number of Pizzas	Total Costs
x	y
50	595
100	755
150	1,110
200	1,380
250	1,875
300	2,410

(A) Enter the data into a graphing calculator and find a quadratic regression equation for the total costs.

(B) Use the regression equation from part (A) to find the minimum average cost (to the nearest cent) and the corresponding production level (to the nearest integer).

89. Medicine. A drug is injected into the bloodstream of a patient through her right arm. The drug concentration in the bloodstream of the left arm t hours after the injection is given by

$$C(t) = \frac{0.14t}{t^2 + 1}$$

Graph C.

90. Physiology. In a study on the speed of muscle contraction in frogs under various loads, researchers found that the speed of contraction decreases with increasing loads. More precisely, they found that the relationship between speed of contraction, S (in centimeters per second), and load w (in grams) is given approximately by

$$S(w) = \frac{26 + 0.06w}{w} \qquad w \geq 5$$

Graph S.

91. Psychology: retention. Each student in a psychology class is given one day to memorize the same list of 30 special characters. The lists are turned in at the end of the day, and for each succeeding day for 30 days, each student is asked to turn in

a list of as many of the symbols as can be recalled. Averages are taken, and it is found that

$$N(t) = \frac{5t + 20}{t} \qquad t \geq 1$$

provides a good approximation of the average number $N(t)$ of symbols retained after t days. Graph N.

Answers to Matched Problems

1. Domain: All real x, except $x = 1$

y intercept: $f(0) = 0$; x intercept: 0

Horizontal asymptote: $y = -2$;

Vertical asymptote: $x = 1$

Increasing on $(-\infty, 1)$ and $(1, \infty)$

Concave upward on $(-\infty, 1)$;

Concave downward on $(1, \infty)$

x	$f(x)$
-1	-1
0	0
$\frac{1}{2}$	2
$\frac{3}{2}$	-6
2	-4
5	$-\frac{5}{2}$

2. Domain: All real x, except $x = 0$

x intercept: $= -\frac{3}{4} = -0.75$

$h(0)$ is not defined

Vertical asymptote: $x = 0$ (the y axis)

Horizontal asymptote: $y = 0$ (the x axis)

Increasing on $(-1.5, 0)$

Decreasing on $(-\infty, -1.5)$ and $(0, \infty)$

Local minimum: $f(-1.5) = -1.33$

Concave upward on $(-2.25, 0)$ and $(0, \infty)$

Concave downward on $(-\infty, -2.25)$

Inflection point: $(-2.25, -1.19)$

x	$h(x)$
-10	-0.37
-2.25	-1.19
-1.5	-1.33
-0.75	0
2	2.75
10	0.43

3. Domain: $(-\infty, \infty)$

y intercept: $f(0) = 0$

x intercept: $x = 0$

Horizontal asymptote: $y = 0$ (the x axis)

Increasing on $(-\infty, 2)$

Decreasing on $(2, \infty)$

Local maximum: $f(2) = 2e^{-1} \approx 0.736$

Concave downward on $(-\infty, 4)$

Concave upward on $(4, \infty)$

Inflection point: $(4, 0.541)$

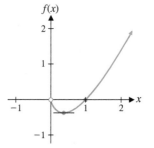

4. Domain: $(0, \infty)$

   y intercept: None $[f(0)$ is not defined$]$

   x intercept: $x = 1$

   Increasing on (e^{-1}, ∞)

   Decreasing on $(0, e^{-1})$

   Local minimum: $f(e^{-1}) = -e^{-1} \approx -0.368$

   Concave upward on $(0, \infty)$

x	5	10	100	$\to \infty$
$f(x)$	8.05	23.03	460.52	$\to \infty$

x	0.1	0.01	0.001	0.000 1	$\to 0$
$f(x)$	-0.23	-0.046	$-0.006\ 9$	$-0.000\ 92$	$\to 0$

5. (A) Domain: $(0, \infty)$

   Intercepts: None

   Vertical asymptote: $x = 0$; oblique asymptote: $y = 0.25x$

   Decreasing on $(0, 80)$; increasing on $(80, \infty)$;

   local minimum at $x = 80$

   Concave upward on $(0, \infty)$

(B) Minimum average cost is 40 at $x = 80$.

4.5 Absolute Maxima and Minima

- Absolute Maxima and Minima
- Second Derivative and Extrema

One of the most important applications of the derivative is to find the absolute maximum or minimum value of a function. An economist may be interested in the price or production level of a commodity that will bring a maximum profit; a doctor may be interested in the time it takes for a drug to reach its maximum concentration in the bloodstream after an injection; and a city planner might be interested in the location of heavy industry in a city in order to produce minimum pollution in residential and business areas. In this section, we develop the procedures needed to find the absolute maximum and absolute minimum values of a function.

Absolute Maxima and Minima

Recall that $f(c)$ is a local maximum if $f(x) \leq f(c)$ for x near c and a local minimum if $f(x) \geq f(c)$ for x near c. Now we are interested in finding the largest and the smallest values of $f(x)$ throughout the domain of f.

> **DEFINITION Absolute Maxima and Minima**
>
> If $f(c) \geq f(x)$ for all x in the domain of f, then $f(c)$ is called the **absolute maximum** of f. If $f(c) \leq f(x)$ for all x in the domain of f, then $f(c)$ is called the **absolute minimum** of f. An absolute maximum or absolute minimum is called an **absolute extremum.**

Figure 1 illustrates some typical examples.

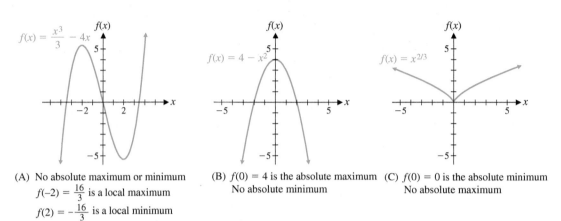

(A) No absolute maximum or minimum
$f(-2) = \frac{16}{3}$ is a local maximum
$f(2) = -\frac{16}{3}$ is a local minimum

(B) $f(0) = 4$ is the absolute maximum
No absolute minimum

(C) $f(0) = 0$ is the absolute minimum
No absolute maximum

Figure 1

In many applications, the domain of a function is restricted because of practical or physical considerations. If the domain is restricted to some closed interval, as is often the case, then Theorem 1 applies.

THEOREM 1 Extreme Value Theorem

A function f that is continuous on a closed interval $[a, b]$ has both an absolute maximum and an absolute minimum on that interval.

It is important to understand that the absolute maximum and absolute minimum depend on both the function f and the interval $[a, b]$. Figure 2 illustrates four cases.

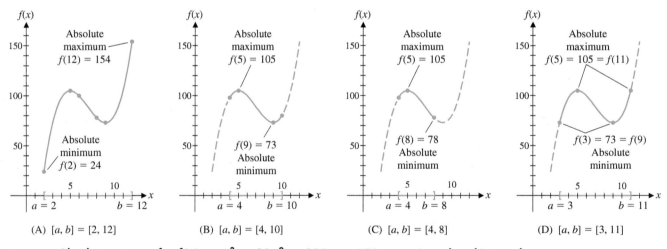

(A) $[a, b] = [2, 12]$

(B) $[a, b] = [4, 10]$

(C) $[a, b] = [4, 8]$

(D) $[a, b] = [3, 11]$

Figure 2 **Absolute extrema for $f(x) = x^3 - 21x^2 + 135x - 170$ on various closed intervals**

In all four cases illustrated in Figure 2, the absolute maximum and absolute minimum occur at a critical number or an endpoint. This property is generalized in Theorem 2. Note that both the absolute maximum and the absolute minimum are unique, but each can occur at more than one point in the interval (Fig. 2D).

THEOREM 2 Locating Absolute Extrema

Absolute extrema (if they exist) must occur at critical numbers or at endpoints.

To find the absolute maximum and minimum of a continuous function on a closed interval, we simply identify the endpoints and critical numbers in the interval, evaluate the function at each, and choose the largest and smallest values.

PROCEDURE Finding Absolute Extrema on a Closed Interval

Step 1 Check to make certain that f is continuous over $[a, b]$.

Step 2 Find the critical numbers in the interval (a, b).

Step 3 Evaluate f at the endpoints a and b and at the critical numbers found in step 2.

Step 4 The absolute maximum of f on $[a, b]$ is the largest value found in step 3.

Step 5 The absolute minimum of f on $[a, b]$ is the smallest value found in step 3.

EXAMPLE 1 *Finding Absolute Extrema* Find the absolute maximum and absolute minimum of

$$f(x) = x^3 + 3x^2 - 9x - 7$$

on each of the following intervals:

(A) $[-6, 4]$ (B) $[-4, 2]$ (C) $[-2, 2]$

SOLUTION

(A) The function is continuous for all values of x.

$$f'(x) = 3x^2 + 6x - 9 = 3(x - 1)(x + 3)$$

So, $x = -3$ and $x = 1$ are the critical numbers in the interval $(-6, 4)$. Evaluate f at the endpoints and critical numbers $(-6, -3, 1, \text{ and } 4)$, and choose the largest and smallest values.

$$f(-6) = -61 \quad \text{Absolute minimum}$$
$$f(-3) = 20$$
$$f(1) = -12$$
$$f(4) = 69 \quad \text{Absolute maximum}$$

The absolute maximum of f on $[-6, 4]$ is 69, and the absolute minimum is -61.

(B) Interval: $[-4, 2]$

x	$f(x)$	
-4	13	
-3	20	Absolute maximum
1	-12	Absolute minimum
2	-5	

The absolute maximum of f on $[-4, 2]$ is 20, and the absolute minimum is -12.

(C) Interval: $[-2, 2]$

x	$f(x)$	
-2	15	Absolute maximum
1	-12	Absolute minimum
2	-5	

Note that the critical number $x = -3$ is not included in the table, because it is not in the interval $[-2, 2]$. The absolute maximum of f on $[-2, 2]$ is 15, and the absolute minimum is -12.

Matched Problem 1 | Find the absolute maximum and absolute minimum of

$$f(x) = x^3 - 12x$$

on each of the following intervals:

(A) $[-5, 5]$ (B) $[-3, 3]$ (C) $[-3, 1]$

Now, suppose that we want to find the absolute maximum or minimum of a function that is continuous on an interval that is not closed. Since Theorem 1 no longer applies, we cannot be certain that the absolute maximum or minimum value exists. Figure 3 illustrates several ways that functions can fail to have absolute extrema.

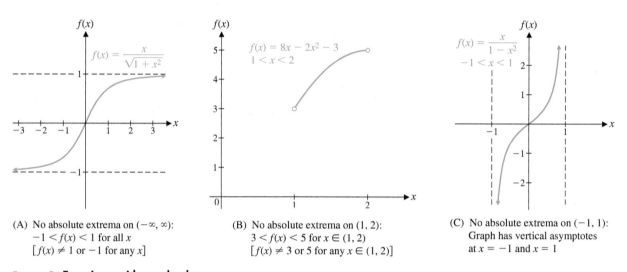

(A) No absolute extrema on $(-\infty, \infty)$:
$-1 < f(x) < 1$ for all x
$[f(x) \neq 1$ or -1 for any $x]$

(B) No absolute extrema on $(1, 2)$:
$3 < f(x) < 5$ for $x \in (1, 2)$
$[f(x) \neq 3$ or 5 for any $x \in (1, 2)]$

(C) No absolute extrema on $(-1, 1)$:
Graph has vertical asymptotes
at $x = -1$ and $x = 1$

Figure 3 **Functions with no absolute extrema**

In general, the best procedure to follow in searching for absolute extrema on an interval that is not of the form $[a, b]$ is to sketch a graph of the function. However, many applications can be solved with a new tool that does not require any graphing.

Second Derivative and Extrema

The second derivative can be used to classify the local extrema of a function. Suppose that f is a function satisfying $f'(c) = 0$ and $f''(c) > 0$. First, note that if $f''(c) > 0$, then it follows from the properties of limits* that $f''(x) > 0$ in some interval (m, n) containing c. Thus, the graph of f must be concave upward in this interval. But this implies that $f'(x)$ is increasing in the interval. Since $f'(c) = 0, f'(x)$ must change from negative to positive at $x = c$, and $f(c)$ is a local minimum (see Fig. 4). Reasoning in the same fashion, we conclude that if $f'(c) = 0$ and $f''(c) < 0$, then $f(c)$ is a local maximum. Of course, it is possible that both $f'(c) = 0$ and $f''(c) = 0$. In this case, the second derivative cannot be used to determine the shape of the graph around $x = c; f(c)$ may be a local minimum, a local maximum, or neither.

The sign of the second derivative provides a simple test for identifying local maxima and minima. This test is most useful when we do not want to draw the graph of the function. If we are interested in drawing the graph and have already constructed the sign chart for $f'(x)$, then the first-derivative test can be used to identify the local extrema.

---

*Actually, we are assuming that $f''(x)$ is continuous in an interval containing c. It is unlikely that we will encounter a function for which $f''(c)$ exists but $f''(x)$ is not continuous in an interval containing c.

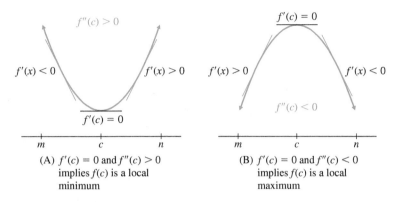

(A) $f'(c) = 0$ and $f''(c) > 0$
implies $f(c)$ is a local
minimum

(B) $f'(c) = 0$ and $f''(c) < 0$
implies $f(c)$ is a local
maximum

Figure 4 **Second derivative and local extrema**

RESULT   Second-Derivative Test for Local Extrema

Let c be a critical number of $f(x)$ such that $f'(c) = 0$. If the second derivative $f''(c) > 0$, then $f(c)$ is a local minimum. If $f''(c) < 0$, then $f(c)$ is a local maximum.

$f'(c)$	$f''(c)$	Graph of f is:	$f(c)$	Example
0	+	Concave upward	Local minimum	$\smile$
0	−	Concave downward	Local maximum	$\frown$
0	0	?	Test does not apply	

EXAMPLE 2   Testing Local Extrema Find the local maxima and minima for each function. Use the second-derivative test for local extrema when it applies.
(A) $f(x) = x^3 - 6x^2 + 9x + 1$
(B) $f(x) = xe^{-0.2x}$
(C) $f(x) = \frac{1}{6}x^6 - 4x^5 + 25x^4$

SOLUTION

(A) Find first and second derivatives and determine critical numbers:

$$f(x) = x^3 - 6x^2 + 9x + 1$$
$$f'(x) = 3x^2 - 12x + 9 = 3(x-1)(x-3)$$
$$f''(x) = 6x - 12 = 6(x-2)$$

Critical numbers are $x = 1$ and $x = 3$.

$$f''(1) = -6 < 0 \quad \text{\textit{f} has a local maximum at } x = 1.$$
$$f''(3) = 6 > 0 \quad \text{\textit{f} has a local minimum at } x = 3.$$

Substituting $x = 1$ in the expression for $f(x)$, we find that $f(1) = 5$ is a local maximum. Similarly, $f(3) = 1$ is a local minimum.

(B)
$$f(x) = xe^{-0.2x}$$
$$f'(x) = e^{-0.2x} + xe^{-0.2x}(-0.2)$$
$$= e^{-0.2x}(1 - 0.2x)$$
$$f''(x) = e^{-0.2x}(-0.2)(1 - 0.2x) + e^{-0.2x}(-0.2)$$
$$= e^{-0.2x}(0.04x - 0.4)$$

Critical number: $x = 1/0.2 = 5$

$$f''(5) = e^{-1}(-0.2) < 0 \quad \text{\textit{f} has a local maximum at } x = 5.$$

So $f(5) = 5e^{-0.2(5)} \approx 1.84$ is a local maximum.

(C)
$$f(x) = \tfrac{1}{6}x^6 - 4x^5 + 25x^4$$
$$f'(x) = x^5 - 20x^4 + 100x^3 = x^3(x-10)^2$$
$$f''(x) = 5x^4 - 80x^3 + 300x^2$$

Critical numbers are $x = 0$ and $x = 10$.

$f''(0) = 0$ The second-derivative test fails at both critical numbers, so
$f''(10) = 0$ the first-derivative test must be used.

Sign chart for $f'(x) = x^3(x-10)^2$ (partition numbers for f' are 0 and 10):

		Test Numbers	
		x	$f'(x)$
	$(-\infty, 0)$ $(0, 10)$ $(10, \infty)$		
$f'(x)$	$----0++++0++++$	-1	-121 $(-)$
		1	81 $(+)$
	0 10	11	$1{,}331$ $(+)$
$f(x)$	Decreasing Increasing Increasing		

From the chart, we see that $f(x)$ has a local minimum at $x = 0$ and does not have a local extremum at $x = 10$. So $f(0) = 0$ is a local minimum.

Matched Problem 2 Find the local maxima and minima for each function. Use the second-derivative test when it applies.

(A) $f(x) = x^3 - 9x^2 + 24x - 10$

(B) $f(x) = e^x - 5x$

(C) $f(x) = 10x^6 - 24x^5 + 15x^4$

CONCEPTUAL INSIGHT

The second-derivative test for local extrema does not apply if $f''(c) = 0$ or if $f''(c)$ is not defined. As Example 2C illustrates, if $f''(c) = 0$, then $f(c)$ may or may not be a local extremum. Some other method, such as the first-derivative test, must be used when $f''(c) = 0$ or $f''(c)$ does not exist.

The solution of many optimization problems involves searching for an absolute extremum. If the function in question has only one critical number, then the second-derivative test for local extrema not only classifies the local extremum but also guarantees that the local extremum is, in fact, the absolute extremum.

THEOREM 3   Second-Derivative Test for Absolute Extrema on an Open Interval

Let f be continuous on an open interval I with only one critical number c in I.

If $f'(c) = 0$ and $f''(c) > 0$, then $f(c)$ is the absolute minimum of f on I.

If $f'(c) = 0$ and $f''(c) < 0$, then $f(c)$ is the absolute maximum of f on I.

Since the second-derivative test for local extrema cannot be applied when $f''(c) = 0$ or $f''(c)$ does not exist, Theorem 3 makes no mention of these cases.

EXAMPLE 3 Finding Absolute Extrema on an Open Interval Find the absolute extrema of each function on $(0, \infty)$.

(A) $f(x) = x + \dfrac{4}{x}$ (B) $f(x) = (\ln x)^2 - 3\ln x$

SOLUTION

(A) $f(x) = x + \dfrac{4}{x}$

$f'(x) = 1 - \dfrac{4}{x^2} = \dfrac{x^2 - 4}{x^2} = \dfrac{(x-2)(x+2)}{x^2}$ Critical numbers are $x = -2$ and $x = 2$.

$f''(x) = \dfrac{8}{x^3}$

The only critical number in the interval $(0, \infty)$ is $x = 2$. Since $f''(2) = 1 > 0$, $f(2) = 4$ is the absolute minimum of f on $(0, \infty)$.

(B) $f(x) = (\ln x)^2 - 3 \ln x$

$f'(x) = (2 \ln x)\dfrac{1}{x} - \dfrac{3}{x} = \dfrac{2 \ln x - 3}{x}$ Critical number is $x = e^{3/2}$.

$f''(x) = \dfrac{x\dfrac{2}{x} - (2 \ln x - 3)}{x^2} = \dfrac{5 - 2 \ln x}{x^2}$

The only critical number in the interval $(0, \infty)$ is $x = e^{3/2}$. Since $f''(e^{3/2}) = 2/e^3 > 0$, $f(e^{3/2}) = -2.25$ is the absolute minimum of f on $(0, \infty)$.

Matched Problem 3 Find the absolute extrema of each function on $(0, \infty)$.

(A) $f(x) = 12 - x - \dfrac{5}{x}$ (B) $f(x) = 5 \ln x - x$

Exercises 4.5

Skills Warm-up Exercises

W In Problems 1–8, by inspecting the graph of the function, find the absolute maximum and absolute minimum on the given interval. (If necessary, review Section 1.2).

1. $f(x) = x$ on $[-2, 3]$ **2.** $g(x) = |x|$ on $[-1, 4]$

3. $h(x) = x^2$ on $[-5, 3]$ **4.** $m(x) = x^3$ on $[-3, 1]$

5. $n(x) = \sqrt{x}$ on $[3, 4]$ **6.** $p(x) = \sqrt[3]{x}$ on $[-125, 216]$

7. $q(x) = -\sqrt[3]{x}$ on $[27, 64]$ **8.** $r(x) = -x^2$ on $[-10, 11]$

Problems 9–18 refer to the graph of $y = f(x)$ shown here. Find the absolute minimum and the absolute maximum over the indicated interval.

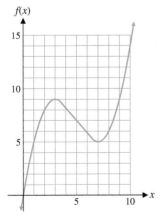

9. $[0, 10]$ **10.** $[2, 8]$ **11.** $[0, 8]$ **12.** $[2, 10]$

13. $[1, 10]$ **14.** $[0, 9]$ **15.** $[1, 9]$ **16.** $[0, 2]$

17. $[2, 5]$ **18.** $[5, 8]$

In Problems 19–22, find the absolute maximum and absolute minimum of each function on the indicated intervals.

19. $f(x) = 2x - 5$

   (A) $[0, 4]$ (B) $[0, 10]$ (C) $[-5, 10]$

20. $f(x) = 8 - x$

   (A) $[0, 1]$ (B) $[-1, 1]$ (C) $[-1, 6]$

21. $f(x) = x^2$

   (A) $[-1, 1]$ (B) $[1, 5]$ (C) $[-5, 5]$

22. $f(x) = 100 - x^2$

   (A) $[-10, 10]$ (B) $[0, 10]$ (C) $[10, 11]$

In Problems 23–26, find the absolute maximum and absolute minimum of each function on the given interval.

23. $f(x) = e^{-x}$ on $[-1, 1]$

24. $f(x) = \ln x$ on $[1, 2]$

25. $f(x) = 9 - x^2$ on $[-4, 4]$

26. $f(x) = x^2 - 6x + 7$ on $[0, 10]$

In Problems 27–42, find the absolute maximum and minimum, if either exists, for each function.

27. $f(x) = x^2 - 2x + 3$

28. $f(x) = x^2 + 4x - 3$

29. $f(x) = -x^2 - 6x + 9$

30. $f(x) = -x^2 + 2x + 4$

31. $f(x) = x^3 + x$

32. $f(x) = -x^3 - 2x$

33. $f(x) = 8x^3 - 2x^4$

34. $f(x) = x^4 - 4x^3$

35. $f(x) = x + \dfrac{16}{x}$

36. $f(x) = x + \dfrac{25}{x}$

37. $f(x) = \dfrac{x^2}{x^2 + 1}$

38. $f(x) = \dfrac{1}{x^2 + 1}$

39. $f(x) = \dfrac{2x}{x^2 + 1}$

40. $f(x) = \dfrac{-8x}{x^2 + 4}$

41. $f(x) = \dfrac{x^2 - 1}{x^2 + 1}$

42. $f(x) = \dfrac{9 - x^2}{x^2 + 4}$

In Problems 43–66, find the indicated extremum of each function on the given interval.

43. Absolute minimum value on $[0, \infty)$ for
$$f(x) = 2x^2 - 8x + 6$$

44. Absolute maximum value on $[0, \infty)$ for
$$f(x) = 6x - x^2 + 4$$

45. Absolute maximum value on $[0, \infty)$ for
$$f(x) = 3x^2 - x^3$$

46. Absolute minimum value on $[0, \infty)$ for
$$f(x) = x^3 - 6x^2$$

47. Absolute minimum value on $[0, \infty)$ for
$$f(x) = (x + 4)(x - 2)^2$$

48. Absolute minimum value on $[0, \infty)$ for
$$f(x) = (2 - x)(x + 1)^2$$

49. Absolute maximum value on $(0, \infty)$ for
$$f(x) = 2x^4 - 8x^3$$

50. Absolute maximum value on $(0, \infty)$ for
$$f(x) = 4x^3 - 8x^4$$

51. Absolute maximum value on $(0, \infty)$ for
$$f(x) = 20 - 3x - \dfrac{12}{x}$$

52. Absolute minimum value on $(0, \infty)$ for
$$f(x) = 4 + x + \dfrac{9}{x}$$

53. Absolute minimum value on $(0, \infty)$ for
$$f(x) = 10 + 2x + \dfrac{64}{x^2}$$

54. Absolute maximum value on $(0, \infty)$ for
$$f(x) = 20 - 4x - \dfrac{250}{x^2}$$

55. Absolute minimum value on $(0, \infty)$ for
$$f(x) = x + \dfrac{1}{x} + \dfrac{30}{x^3}$$

56. Absolute minimum value on $(0, \infty)$ for
$$f(x) = 2x + \dfrac{5}{x} + \dfrac{4}{x^3}$$

57. Absolute minimum value on $(0, \infty)$ for
$$f(x) = \dfrac{e^x}{x^2}$$

58. Absolute maximum value on $(0, \infty)$ for
$$f(x) = \dfrac{x^4}{e^x}$$

59. Absolute maximum value on $(0, \infty)$ for
$$f(x) = \dfrac{x^3}{e^x}$$

60. Absolute minimum value on $(0, \infty)$ for
$$f(x) = \dfrac{e^x}{x}$$

61. Absolute maximum value on $(0, \infty)$ for
$$f(x) = 5x - 2x \ln x$$

62. Absolute minimum value on $(0, \infty)$ for
$$f(x) = 4x \ln x - 7x$$

63. Absolute maximum value on $(0, \infty)$ for
$$f(x) = x^2(3 - \ln x)$$

64. Absolute minimum value on $(0, \infty)$ for
$$f(x) = x^3(\ln x - 2)$$

65. Absolute maximum value on $(0, \infty)$ for
$$f(x) = \ln(xe^{-x})$$

66. Absolute maximum value on $(0, \infty)$ for
$$f(x) = \ln(x^2 e^{-x})$$

In Problems 67–72, find the absolute maximum and minimum, if either exists, for each function on the indicated intervals.

67. $f(x) = x^3 - 6x^2 + 9x - 6$

    (A) $[-1, 5]$ (B) $[-1, 3]$ (C) $[2, 5]$

68. $f(x) = 2x^3 - 3x^2 - 12x + 24$

    (A) $[-3, 4]$ (B) $[-2, 3]$ (C) $[-2, 1]$

69. $f(x) = (x - 1)(x - 5)^3 + 1$

    (A) $[0, 3]$ (B) $[1, 7]$ (C) $[3, 6]$

70. $f(x) = x^4 - 8x^2 + 16$

    (A) $[-1, 3]$ (B) $[0, 2]$ (C) $[-3, 4]$

71. $f(x) = x^4 - 4x^3 + 5$

    (A) $[-1, 2]$ (B) $[0, 4]$ (C) $[-1, 1]$

72. $f(x) = x^4 - 18x^2 + 32$

(A) $[-4, 4]$ (B) $[-1, 1]$ (C) $[1, 3]$

In Problems 73–80, describe the graph of f at the given point relative to the existence of a local maximum or minimum with one of the following phrases: "Local maximum," "Local minimum," "Neither," or "Unable to determine from the given information." Assume that f(x) is continuous on $(-\infty, \infty)$.

73. $(2, f(2))$ if $f'(2) = 0$ and $f''(2) > 0$

74. $(4, f(4))$ if $f'(4) = 1$ and $f''(4) < 0$

75. $(-3, f(-3))$ if $f'(-3) = 0$ and $f''(-3) = 0$

76. $(-1, f(-1))$ if $f'(-1) = 0$ and $f''(-1) < 0$

77. $(6, f(6))$ if $f'(6) = 1$ and $f''(6)$ does not exist

78. $(5, f(5))$ if $f'(5) = 0$ and $f''(5)$ does not exist

79. $(-2, f(-2))$ if $f'(-2) = 0$ and $f''(-2) < 0$

80. $(1, f(1))$ if $f'(1) = 0$ and $f''(1) > 0$

Answers to Matched Problems

1. (A) Absolute maximum: $f(5) = 65$; absolute minimum: $f(-5) = -65$

(B) Absolute maximum: $f(-2) = 16$; absolute minimum: $f(2) = -16$

(C) Absolute maximum: $f(-2) = 16$; absolute minimum: $f(1) = -11$

2. (A) $f(2) = 10$ is a local maximum; $f(4) = 6$ is a local minimum.

(B) $f(\ln 5) = 5 - 5 \ln 5$ is a local minimum.

(C) $f(0) = 0$ is a local minimum; there is no local extremum at $x = 1$.

3. (A) $f(\sqrt{5}) = 12 - 2\sqrt{5}$ (B) $f(5) = 5 \ln 5 - 5$

4.6 Optimization

- Area and Perimeter
- Maximizing Revenue and Profit
- Inventory Control

Now we can use calculus to solve **optimization problems**—problems that involve finding the absolute maximum or the absolute minimum of a function. As you work through this section, note that the statement of the problem does not usually include the function to be optimized. Often, it is your responsibility to find the function and then to find the relevant absolute extremum.

Area and Perimeter

The techniques used to solve optimization problems are best illustrated through examples.

EXAMPLE 1 Maximizing Area A homeowner has $320 to spend on building a fence around a rectangular garden. Three sides of the fence will be constructed with wire fencing at a cost of $2 per linear foot. The fourth side will be constructed with wood fencing at a cost of $6 per linear foot. Find the dimensions and the area of the largest garden that can be enclosed with $320 worth of fencing.

SOLUTION To begin, we draw a figure (Fig. 1), introduce variables, and look for relationships among the variables.

Since we don't know the dimensions of the garden, the lengths of fencing are represented by the variables x and y. The costs of the fencing materials are fixed and are represented by constants.

Now we look for relationships among the variables. The area of the garden is

$$A = xy$$

while the cost of the fencing is

$$C = 2y + 2x + 2y + 6x$$
$$= 8x + 4y$$

The problem states that the homeowner has $320 to spend on fencing. We assume that enclosing the largest area will use all the money available for fencing. The problem has now been reduced to

Maximize $A = xy$ subject to $8x + 4y = 320$

Figure 1

Before we can use calculus to find the maximum area A, we must express A as a function of a single variable. We use the cost equation to eliminate one of the variables in the area expression (we choose to eliminate y—either will work).

$$8x + 4y = 320$$
$$4y = 320 - 8x$$
$$y = 80 - 2x$$
$$A = xy = x(80 - 2x) = 80x - 2x^2$$

Now we consider the permissible values of x. Because x is one of the dimensions of a rectangle, x must satisfy

$$x \geq 0 \quad \text{Length is always nonnegative.}$$

And because $y = 80 - 2x$ is also a dimension of a rectangle, y must satisfy

$$y = 80 - 2x \geq 0 \quad \text{Width is always nonnegative.}$$
$$80 \geq 2x$$
$$40 \geq x \quad \text{or} \quad x \leq 40$$

We summarize the preceding discussion by stating the following model for this optimization problem:

$$\text{Maximize} \quad A(x) = 80x - 2x^2 \quad \text{for } 0 \leq x \leq 40$$

Next, we find any critical numbers of A:

$$A'(x) = 80 - 4x = 0$$
$$80 = 4x$$
$$x = \frac{80}{4} = 20 \quad \text{Critical number}$$

Since $A(x)$ is continuous on $[0, 40]$, the absolute maximum of A, if it exists, must occur at a critical number or an endpoint. Evaluating A at these numbers (Table 1), we see that the maximum area is 800 when

$$x = 20 \quad \text{and} \quad y = 80 - 2(20) = 40$$

Finally, we must answer the questions posed in the problem. The dimensions of the garden with the maximum area of 800 square feet are 20 feet by 40 feet, with one 20-foot side of wood fencing.

Table 1

x	$A(x)$
0	0
20	800
40	0

Matched Problem 1 Repeat Example 1 if the wood fencing costs $8 per linear foot and all other information remains the same.

We summarize the steps in the solution of Example 1 in the following box:

PROCEDURE Strategy for Solving Optimization Problems

Step 1 Introduce variables, look for relationships among the variables, and construct a mathematical model of the form

$$\text{Maximize (or minimize) } f(x) \text{ on the interval } I$$

Step 2 Find the critical numbers of $f(x)$.

Step 3 Use the procedures developed in Section 4.5 to find the absolute maximum (or minimum) of $f(x)$ on the interval I and the numbers x where this occurs.

Step 4 Use the solution to the mathematical model to answer all the questions asked in the problem.

EXAMPLE 2 Minimizing Perimeter Refer to Example 1. The homeowner judges that an area of 800 square feet for the garden is too small and decides to increase the area to 1,250 square feet. What is the minimum cost of building a fence that will enclose a garden with an area of 1,250 square feet? What are the dimensions of this garden? Assume that the cost of fencing remains unchanged.

SOLUTION Refer to Figure 1 and the solution of Example 1. This time we want to minimize the cost of the fencing that will enclose 1,250 square feet. The problem can be expressed as

$$\text{Minimize} \quad C = 8x + 4y \quad \text{subject to} \quad xy = 1{,}250$$

Since x and y represent distances, we know that $x \geq 0$ and $y \geq 0$. But neither variable can equal 0 because their product must be 1,250.

$$xy = 1{,}250 \qquad\qquad \text{Solve the area equation for } y.$$

$$y = \frac{1{,}250}{x}$$

$$C(x) = 8x + 4\frac{1{,}250}{x} \qquad\qquad \text{Substitute for } y \text{ in the cost equation.}$$

$$= 8x + \frac{5{,}000}{x} \qquad x > 0$$

The model for this problem is

$$\text{Minimize} \quad C(x) = 8x + \frac{5{,}000}{x} \qquad \text{for } x > 0$$

$$= 8x + 5{,}000x^{-1}$$

$$C'(x) = 8 - 5{,}000x^{-2}$$

$$= 8 - \frac{5{,}000}{x^2} = 0$$

$$8 = \frac{5{,}000}{x^2}$$

$$x^2 = \frac{5{,}000}{8} = 625$$

$$x = \sqrt{625} = 25 \quad \begin{array}{l}\text{The negative square} \\ \text{root is discarded,} \\ \text{since } x > 0.\end{array}$$

We use the second derivative to determine the behavior at $x = 25$.

$$C'(x) = 8 - 5{,}000x^{-2}$$

$$C''(x) = 0 + 10{,}000x^{-3} = \frac{10{,}000}{x^3}$$

$$C''(25) = \frac{10{,}000}{25^3} = 0.64 > 0$$

The second-derivative test for local extrema shows that $C(x)$ has a local minimum at $x = 25$, and since $x = 25$ is the only critical number of $C(x)$ for $x > 0$, then $C(25)$ must be the absolute minimum for $x > 0$. When $x = 25$, the cost is

$$C(25) = 8(25) + \frac{5{,}000}{25} = 200 + 200 = \$400$$

and

$$y = \frac{1{,}250}{25} = 50$$

The minimum cost for enclosing a 1,250-square-foot garden is $400, and the dimensions are 25 feet by 50 feet, with one 25-foot side of wood fencing.

Matched Problem 2 Repeat Example 2 if the homeowner wants to enclose an 1,800-square-foot garden and all other data remain unchanged.

CONCEPTUAL INSIGHT

The restrictions on the variables in the solutions of Examples 1 and 2 are typical of problems involving areas or perimeters (or the cost of the perimeter):

$$8x + 4y = 320 \qquad \text{Cost of fencing (Example 1)}$$
$$xy = 1,250 \qquad \text{Area of garden (Example 2)}$$

The equation in Example 1 restricts the values of x to

$$0 \le x \le 40 \qquad \text{or} \qquad [0, 40]$$

The endpoints are included in the interval for our convenience (a closed interval is easier to work with than an open one). The area function is defined at each endpoint, so it does no harm to include them.

The equation in Example 2 restricts the values of x to

$$x > 0 \qquad \text{or} \qquad (0, \infty)$$

Neither endpoint can be included in this interval. We cannot include 0 because the area is not defined when $x = 0$, and we can never include ∞ as an endpoint. Remember, ∞ is not a number; it is a symbol that indicates the interval is unbounded.

Maximizing Revenue and Profit

EXAMPLE 3 Maximizing Revenue An office supply company sells x permanent markers per year at $\$p$ per marker. The price–demand equation for these markers is $p = 10 - 0.001x$. What price should the company charge for the markers to maximize revenue? What is the maximum revenue?

SOLUTION

$$\text{Revenue} = \text{price} \times \text{demand}$$
$$R(x) = (10 - 0.001x)x$$
$$= 10x - 0.001x^2$$

Both price and demand must be nonnegative, so

$$x \ge 0 \quad \text{and} \quad p = 10 - 0.001x \ge 0$$
$$10 \ge 0.001x$$
$$10,000 \ge x$$

The mathematical model for this problem is

$$\text{Maximize} \quad R(x) = 10x - 0.001x^2 \qquad 0 \le x \le 10,000$$
$$R'(x) = 10 - 0.002x$$
$$10 - 0.002x = 0$$
$$10 = 0.002x$$
$$x = \frac{10}{0.002} = 5,000 \qquad \text{Critical number}$$

Use the second-derivative test for absolute extrema:

$$R''(x) = -0.002 < 0 \quad \text{for all } x$$
$$\text{Max } R(x) = R(5,000) = \$25,000$$

When the demand is $x = 5,000$, the price is

$$10 - 0.001(5,000) = \$5 \quad p = 10 - 0.001x$$

The company will realize a maximum revenue of $25,000 when the price of a marker is $5.

Matched Problem 3) An office supply company sells x heavy-duty paper shredders per year at $\$p$ per shredder. The price–demand equation for these shredders is

$$p = 300 - \frac{x}{30}$$

What price should the company charge for the shredders to maximize revenue? What is the maximum revenue?

EXAMPLE 4 Maximizing Profit The total annual cost of manufacturing x permanent markers for the office supply company in Example 3 is

$$C(x) = 5,000 + 2x$$

What is the company's maximum profit? What should the company charge for each marker, and how many markers should be produced?

SOLUTION Using the revenue model in Example 3, we have

$$\text{Profit} = \text{Revenue} - \text{Cost}$$
$$P(x) = R(x) - C(x)$$
$$= 10x - 0.001x^2 - 5,000 - 2x$$
$$= 8x - 0.001x^2 - 5,000$$

The mathematical model for profit is

$$\text{Maximize} \quad P(x) = 8x - 0.001x^2 - 5,000 \qquad 0 \le x \le 10,000$$

The restrictions on x come from the revenue model in Example 3.

$$P'(x) = 8 - 0.002x = 0$$
$$8 = 0.002x$$
$$x = \frac{8}{0.002} = 4,000 \quad \text{Critical number}$$
$$P''(x) = -0.002 < 0 \quad \text{for all } x$$

Since $x = 4,000$ is the only critical number and $P''(x) < 0$,

$$\text{Max } P(x) = P(4,000) = \$11,000$$

Using the price–demand equation from Example 3 with $x = 4,000$, we find that

$$p = 10 - 0.001(4,000) = \$6 \quad p = 10 - 0.001x$$

A maximum profit of $11,000 is realized when 4,000 markers are manufactured annually and sold for $6 each.

The results in Examples 3 and 4 are illustrated in Figure 2.

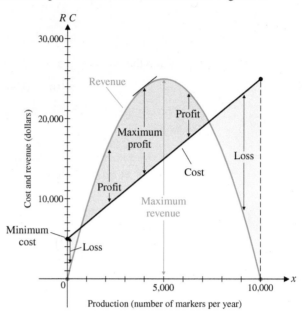

Figure 2

In Figure 2, notice that the maximum revenue and the maximum profit occur at different production levels. The maximum profit occurs when

$$P'(x) = R'(x) - C'(x) = 0$$

that is, when the marginal revenue is equal to the marginal cost. Notice that the slopes of the revenue function and the cost function are the same at this production level.

Matched Problem 4) The annual cost of manufacturing x paper shredders for the office supply company in Matched Problem 3 is $C(x) = 90{,}000 + 30x$. What is the company's maximum profit? What should it charge for each shredder, and how many shredders should it produce?

EXAMPLE 5   Maximizing Profit   The government decides to tax the company in Example 4 $2 for each marker produced. Taking into account this additional cost, how many markers should the company manufacture annually to maximize its profit? What is the maximum profit? How much should the company charge for the markers to realize the maximum profit?

SOLUTION   The tax of $2 per unit changes the company's cost equation:

$$C(x) = \text{original cost} + \text{tax}$$
$$= 5{,}000 + 2x + 2x$$
$$= 5{,}000 + 4x$$

The new profit function is

$$P(x) = R(x) - C(x)$$
$$= 10x - 0.001x^2 - 5{,}000 - 4x$$
$$= 6x - 0.001x^2 - 5{,}000$$

So, we must solve the following equation:

$$\text{Maximize} \quad P(x) = 6x - 0.001x^2 - 5{,}000 \qquad 0 \le x \le 10{,}000$$
$$P'(x) = 6 - 0.002x$$
$$6 - 0.002x = 0$$
$$x = 3{,}000 \quad \text{Critical number}$$
$$P''(x) = -0.002 < 0 \quad \text{for all } x$$
$$\text{Max } P(x) = P(3{,}000) = \$4{,}000$$

Using the price–demand equation (Example 3) with $x = 3{,}000$, we find that

$$p = 10 - 0.001(3{,}000) = \$7 \quad p = 10 - 0.001x$$

The company's maximum profit is $\$4{,}000$ when 3,000 markers are produced and sold annually at a price of $\$7$.

Even though the tax caused the company's cost to increase by $\$2$ per marker, the price that the company should charge to maximize its profit increases by only $\$1$. The company must absorb the other $\$1$, with a resulting decrease of $\$7{,}000$ in maximum profit.

Matched Problem 5) The government decides to tax the office supply company in Matched Problem 4 $\$20$ for each shredder produced. Taking into account this additional cost, how many shredders should the company manufacture annually to maximize its profit? What is the maximum profit? How much should the company charge for the shredders to realize the maximum profit?

EXAMPLE 6 Maximizing Revenue When a management training company prices its seminar on management techniques at $\$400$ per person, 1,000 people will attend the seminar. The company estimates that for each $\$5$ reduction in price, an additional 20 people will attend the seminar. How much should the company charge for the seminar in order to maximize its revenue? What is the maximum revenue?

SOLUTION Let x represent the number of $\$5$ price reductions.

$$400 - 5x = \text{price per customer}$$
$$1{,}000 + 20x = \text{number of customers}$$
$$\text{Revenue} = (\text{price per customer})(\text{number of customers})$$
$$R(x) = (400 - 5x) \times (1{,}000 + 20x)$$

Since price cannot be negative, we have

$$400 - 5x \ge 0$$
$$400 \ge 5x$$
$$80 \ge x \quad \text{or} \quad x \le 80$$

A negative value of x would result in a price increase. Since the problem is stated in terms of price reductions, we must restrict x so that $x \ge 0$. Putting all this together, we have the following model:

$$\text{Maximize} \quad R(x) = (400 - 5x)(1{,}000 + 20x) \quad \text{for } 0 \le x \le 80$$
$$R(x) = 400{,}000 + 3{,}000x - 100x^2$$
$$R'(x) = 3{,}000 - 200x = 0$$
$$3{,}000 = 200x$$
$$x = 15 \quad \text{Critical number}$$

Table 2

x	R(x)
0	400,000
15	422,500
80	0

Since $R(x)$ is continuous on the interval [0, 80], we can determine the behavior of the graph by constructing a table. Table 2 shows that $R(15) = \$422,500$ is the absolute maximum revenue. The price of attending the seminar at $x = 15$ is $400 - 5(15) = \$325$. The company should charge \$325 for the seminar in order to receive a maximum revenue of \$422,500.

Matched Problem 6) A walnut grower estimates from past records that if 20 trees are planted per acre, then each tree will average 60 pounds of nuts per year. If, for each additional tree planted per acre, the average yield per tree drops 2 pounds, then how many trees should be planted to maximize the yield per acre? What is the maximum yield?

EXAMPLE 7 Maximizing Revenue After additional analysis, the management training company in Example 6 decides that its estimate of attendance was too high. Its new estimate is that only 10 additional people will attend the seminar for each \$5 decrease in price. All other information remains the same. How much should the company charge for the seminar now in order to maximize revenue? What is the new maximum revenue?

SOLUTION Under the new assumption, the model becomes

$$\text{Maximize} \quad R(x) = (400 - 5x)(1,000 + 10x) \qquad 0 \le x \le 80$$
$$= 400,000 - 1,000x - 50x^2$$
$$R'(x) = -1,000 - 100x = 0$$
$$-1,000 = 100x$$
$$x = -10 \qquad \text{Critical number}$$

Table 3

x	R(x)
0	400,000
80	0

Note that $x = -10$ is not in the interval [0, 80]. Since $R(x)$ is continuous on [0, 80], we can use a table to find the absolute maximum revenue. Table 3 shows that the maximum revenue is $R(0) = \$400,000$. The company should leave the price at \$400. Any \$5 decreases in price will lower the revenue.

Matched Problem 7) After further analysis, the walnut grower in Matched Problem 6 determines that each additional tree planted will reduce the average yield by 4 pounds. All other information remains the same. How many additional trees per acre should the grower plant now in order to maximize the yield? What is the new maximum yield?

CONCEPTUAL INSIGHT

The solution in Example 7 is called an **endpoint solution** because the optimal value occurs at the endpoint of an interval rather than at a critical number in the interior of the interval.

Inventory Control

EXAMPLE 8 Inventory Control A multimedia company anticipates that there will be a demand for 20,000 copies of a certain DVD during the next year. It costs the company \$0.50 to store a DVD for one year. Each time it must make additional DVDs, it costs \$200 to set up the equipment. How many DVDs should the company make during each production run to minimize its total storage and setup costs?

SOLUTION This type of problem is called an **inventory control problem**. One of the basic assumptions made in such problems is that the demand is uniform. For example, if there are 250 working days in a year, then the daily demand would be 20,000 ÷ 250 = 80 DVDs. The company could decide to produce all 20,000 DVDs at the beginning of the year. This would certainly minimize the setup costs but would result in very large storage costs. At the other extreme, the company could produce 80 DVDs each day. This would minimize the storage costs but would result in very large setup costs. Somewhere between these two extremes is the optimal solution that will minimize the total storage and setup costs. Let

x = number of DVDs manufactured during each production run

y = number of production runs

It is easy to see that the total setup cost for the year is 200y, but what is the total storage cost? If the demand is uniform, then the number of DVDs in storage between production runs will decrease from x to 0, and the average number in storage each day is $x/2$. This result is illustrated in Figure 3.

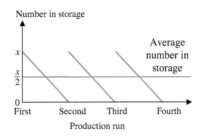

Figure 3

Since it costs $0.50 to store a DVD for one year, the total storage cost is $0.5(x/2) = 0.25x$ and the total cost is

$$\text{total cost} = \text{setup cost} + \text{storage cost}$$
$$C = 200y + 0.25x$$

In order to write the total cost C as a function of one variable, we must find a relationship between x and y. If the company produces x DVDs in each of y production runs, then the total number of DVDs produced is xy.

$$xy = 20{,}000$$
$$y = \frac{20{,}000}{x}$$

Certainly, x must be at least 1 and cannot exceed 20,000. We must solve the following equation:

Minimize $C(x) = 200\left(\dfrac{20{,}000}{x}\right) + 0.25x$ $1 \leq x \leq 20{,}000$

$$C(x) = \frac{4{,}000{,}000}{x} + 0.25x$$

$$C'(x) = -\frac{4{,}000{,}000}{x^2} + 0.25$$

$$-\frac{4{,}000{,}000}{x^2} + 0.25 = 0$$

$$x^2 = \frac{4{,}000{,}000}{0.25}$$

$$x^2 = 16{,}000{,}000 \quad \text{—4,000 is not a critical number, since}$$

$$x = 4{,}000 \qquad 1 \leq x \leq 20{,}000.$$

$$C''(x) = \frac{8{,}000{,}000}{x^3} > 0 \qquad \text{for } x \in (1, 20{,}000)$$

Therefore,

$$\text{Min } C(x) = C(4{,}000) = 2{,}000$$

$$y = \frac{20{,}000}{4{,}000} = 5$$

The company will minimize its total cost by making 4,000 DVDs five times during the year.

Matched Problem 8) Repeat Example 8 if it costs $250 to set up a production run and $0.40 to store a DVD for one year.

Exercises 4.6

W   *In Problems 1–8, express the given quantity as a function $f(x)$ of one variable x. (If necessary, review Section 1.1).*

1. The product of two numbers x and y whose sum is 28

2. The sum of two numbers x and y whose product is 36

3. The area of a circle of diameter x

4. The volume of a sphere of diameter x

5. The volume of a right circular cylinder of radius x and height equal to the radius

6. The volume of a right circular cylinder of diameter x and height equal to twice the diameter

7. The area of a rectangle of length x and width y that has a perimeter of 120 feet

8. The perimeter of a rectangle of length x and width y that has an area of 200 square meters

9. Find two numbers whose sum is 15 and whose product is a maximum.

10. Find two numbers whose sum is 21 and whose product is a maximum.

11. Find two numbers whose difference is 15 and whose product is a minimum.

12. Find two numbers whose difference is 21 and whose product is a minimum.

13. Find two positive numbers whose product is 15 and whose sum is a minimum.

14. Find two positive numbers whose product is 21 and whose sum is a minimum.

15. Find the dimensions of a rectangle with an area of 200 square feet that has the minimum perimeter.

16. Find the dimensions of a rectangle with an area of 108 square feet that has the minimum perimeter.

17. Find the dimensions of a rectangle with a perimeter of 148 feet that has the maximum area.

18. Find the dimensions of a rectangle with a perimeter of 76 feet that has the maximum area.

19. **Maximum revenue and profit.** A company manufactures and sells x smartphones per week. The weekly price–demand and cost equations are, respectively,

$$p = 500 - 0.5x \quad \text{and} \quad C(x) = 20{,}000 + 135x$$

(A) What price should the company charge for the phones, and how many phones should be produced to maximize the weekly revenue? What is the maximum weekly revenue?

(B) What is the maximum weekly profit? How much should the company charge for the phones, and how many phones should be produced to realize the maximum weekly profit?

20. **Maximum revenue and profit.** A company manufactures and sells x digital cameras per week. The weekly price–demand and cost equations are, respectively,

$$p = 400 - 0.4x \quad \text{and} \quad C(x) = 2{,}000 + 160x$$

(A) What price should the company charge for the cameras, and how many cameras should be produced to maximize the weekly revenue? What is the maximum revenue?

(B) What is the maximum weekly profit? How much should the company charge for the cameras, and how many cameras should be produced to realize the maximum weekly profit?

21. **Maximum revenue and profit.** A company manufactures and sells x television sets per month. The monthly cost and price–demand equations are

$$C(x) = 72{,}000 + 60x$$

$$p = 200 - \frac{x}{30} \quad 0 \le x \le 6{,}000$$

(A) Find the maximum revenue.

(B) Find the maximum profit, the production level that will realize the maximum profit, and the price the company should charge for each television set.

(C) If the government decides to tax the company $5 for each set it produces, how many sets should the company manufacture each month to maximize its profit? What is the maximum profit? What should the company charge for each set?

22. Maximum revenue and profit. Repeat Problem 21 for

$$C(x) = 60,000 + 60x$$

$$p = 200 - \frac{x}{50} \qquad 0 \leq x \leq 10,000$$

23. Maximum profit. The following table contains price–demand and total cost data for the production of extreme-cold sleeping bags, where p is the wholesale price (in dollars) of a sleeping bag for an annual demand of x sleeping bags and C is the total cost (in dollars) of producing x sleeping bags:

(A) Find a quadratic regression equation for the price–demand data, using x as the independent variable.

x	p	C
950	240	130,000
1,200	210	150,000
1,800	160	180,000
2,050	120	190,000

(B) Find a linear regression equation for the cost data, using x as the independent variable.

(C) What is the maximum profit? What is the wholesale price per extreme-cold sleeping bag that should be charged to realize the maximum profit? Round answers to the nearest dollar.

24. Maximum profit. The following table contains price–demand and total cost data for the production of regular sleeping bags, where p is the wholesale price (in dollars) of a sleeping bag for an annual demand of x sleeping bags and C is the total cost (in dollars) of producing x sleeping bags:

x	p	C
2,300	98	145,000
3,300	84	170,000
4,500	67	190,000
5,200	51	210,000

(A) Find a quadratic regression equation for the price–demand data, using x as the independent variable.

(B) Find a linear regression equation for the cost data, using x as the independent variable.

(C) What is the maximum profit? What is the wholesale price per regular sleeping bag that should be charged to realize the maximum profit? Round answers to the nearest dollar.

25. Maximum revenue. A deli sells 640 sandwiches per day at a price of $8 each.

(A) A market survey shows that for every $0.10 reduction in price, 40 more sandwiches will be sold. How much should the deli charge for a sandwich in order to maximize revenue?

(B) A different market survey shows that for every $0.20 reduction in the original $8 price, 15 more sandwiches

will be sold. Now how much should the deli charge for a sandwich in order to maximize revenue?

26. Maximum revenue. A university student center sells 1,600 cups of coffee per day at a price of $2.40.

(A) A market survey shows that for every $0.05 reduction in price, 50 more cups of coffee will be sold. How much should the student center charge for a cup of coffee in order to maximize revenue?

(B) A different market survey shows that for every $0.10 reduction in the original $2.40 price, 60 more cups of coffee will be sold. Now how much should the student center charge for a cup of coffee in order to maximize revenue?

27. Car rental. A car rental agency rents 200 cars per day at a rate of $30 per day. For each $1 increase in rate, 5 fewer cars are rented. At what rate should the cars be rented to produce the maximum income? What is the maximum income?

28. Rental income. A 300-room hotel in Las Vegas is filled to capacity every night at $80 a room. For each $1 increase in rent, 3 fewer rooms are rented. If each rented room costs $10 to service per day, how much should the management charge for each room to maximize gross profit? What is the maximum gross profit?

29. Agriculture. A commercial cherry grower estimates from past records that if 30 trees are planted per acre, then each tree will yield an average of 50 pounds of cherries per season. If, for each additional tree planted per acre (up to 20), the average yield per tree is reduced by 1 pound, how many trees should be planted per acre to obtain the maximum yield per acre? What is the maximum yield?

30. Agriculture. A commercial pear grower must decide on the optimum time to have fruit picked and sold. If the pears are picked now, they will bring 30¢ per pound, with each tree yielding an average of 60 pounds of salable pears. If the average yield per tree increases 6 pounds per tree per week for the next 4 weeks, but the price drops 2¢ per pound per week, when should the pears be picked to realize the maximum return per tree? What is the maximum return?

31. Manufacturing. A candy box is to be made out of a piece of cardboard that measures 8 by 12 inches. Squares of equal size will be cut out of each corner, and then the ends and sides will be folded up to form a rectangular box. What size square should be cut from each corner to obtain a maximum volume?

32. Packaging. A parcel delivery service will deliver a package only if the length plus girth (distance around) does not exceed 108 inches.

(A) Find the dimensions of a rectangular box with square ends that satisfies the delivery service's restriction and has maximum volume. What is the maximum volume?

(B) Find the dimensions (radius and height) of a cylindrical container that meets the delivery service's requirement and has maximum volume. What is the maximum volume?

Figure for 32

33. Construction costs. A fence is to be built to enclose a rectangular area of 800 square feet. The fence along three sides is to be made of material that costs $6 per foot. The material for the fourth side costs $18 per foot. Find the dimensions of the rectangle that will allow for the most economical fence to be built.

34. Construction costs. If a builder has only $840 to spend on a fence, but wants to use both $6 and $18 per foot fencing as in Problem 33, what is the maximum area that can be enclosed? What are its dimensions?

35. Construction costs. The owner of a retail lumber store wants to construct a fence to enclose an outdoor storage area adjacent to the store, using all of the store as part of one side of the area (see the figure). Find the dimensions that will enclose the largest area if

(A) 240 feet of fencing material are used.

(B) 400 feet of fencing material are used.

36. Construction costs. If the owner wants to enclose a rectangular area of 12,100 square feet as in Problem 35, what are the dimensions of the area that requires the least fencing? How many feet of fencing are required?

37. Inventory control. A paint manufacturer has a uniform annual demand for 16,000 cans of automobile primer. It costs $4 to store one can of paint for one year and $500 to set up the plant for production of the primer. How many times a year should the company produce this primer in order to minimize the total storage and setup costs?

38. Inventory control. A pharmacy has a uniform annual demand for 200 bottles of a certain antibiotic. It costs $10 to store one bottle for one year and $40 to place an order. How many times during the year should the pharmacy order the antibiotic in order to minimize the total storage and reorder costs?

39. Inventory control. A publishing company sells 50,000 copies of a certain book each year. It costs the company $1 to store a book for one year. Each time that it prints additional copies, it costs the company $1,000 to set up the presses. How many books should the company produce during each printing in order to minimize its total storage and setup costs?

40. Inventory control. A tool company has a uniform annual demand for 9,000 premium chainsaws. It costs $5 to store a chainsaw for a year and $2,500 to set up the plant for manufacture of the premium model. How many chainsaws should be manufactured in each production run in order to minimize the total storage and setup costs?

41. Operational costs. The cost per hour for fuel to run a train is $v^2/4$ dollars, where v is the speed of the train in miles per hour. (Note that the cost goes up as the square of the speed.) Other costs, including labor, are $300 per hour. How fast should the train travel on a 360-mile trip to minimize the total cost for the trip?

42. Operational costs. The cost per hour for fuel to drive a rental truck from Chicago to New York, a distance of 800 miles, is given by

$$f(v) = 0.03v^2 - 2.2v + 72$$

where v is the speed of the truck in miles per hour. Other costs are $40 per hour. How fast should you drive to minimize the total cost?

43. Construction costs. A freshwater pipeline is to be run from a source on the edge of a lake to a small resort community on an island 5 miles offshore, as indicated in the figure.

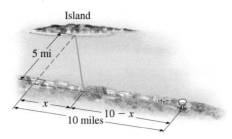

(A) If it costs 1.4 times as much to lay the pipe in the lake as it does on land, what should x be (in miles) to minimize the total cost of the project?

(B) If it costs only 1.1 times as much to lay the pipe in the lake as it does on land, what should x be to minimize the total cost of the project? [*Note:* Compare with Problem 46.]

44. Drug concentration. The concentration $C(t)$, in milligrams per cubic centimeter, of a particular drug in a patient's bloodstream is given by

$$C(t) = \frac{0.16t}{t^2 + 4t + 4}$$

where t is the number of hours after the drug is taken. How many hours after the drug is taken will the concentration be maximum? What is the maximum concentration?

45. Bacteria control. A lake used for recreational swimming is treated periodically to control harmful bacteria growth. Suppose that t days after a treatment, the concentration of bacteria per cubic centimeter is given by

$$C(t) = 30t^2 - 240t + 500 \qquad 0 \le t \le 8$$

How many days after a treatment will the concentration be minimal? What is the minimum concentration?

46. Bird flights. Some birds tend to avoid flights over large bodies of water during daylight hours. Suppose that an adult bird with this tendency is taken from its nesting area on the edge of a large lake to an island 5 miles offshore and is then released (see the figure).

(A) If it takes 1.4 times as much energy to fly over water as land, how far up the shore (x, in miles) should the bird head to minimize the total energy expended in returning to the nesting area?

(B) If it takes only 1.1 times as much energy to fly over water as land, how far up the shore should the bird head to minimize the total energy expended in returning to the nesting area? [*Note:* Compare with Problem 43.]

47. Botany. If it is known from past experiments that the height (in feet) of a certain plant after t months is given approximately by

$$H(t) = 4t^{1/2} - 2t \qquad 0 \le t \le 2$$

then how long, on average, will it take a plant to reach its maximum height? What is the maximum height?

48. Pollution. Two heavily industrial areas are located 10 miles apart, as shown in the figure. If the concentration of particulate matter (in parts per million) decreases as the reciprocal of the square of the distance from the source, and if area A_1 emits eight times the particulate matter as A_2, then the concentration of particulate matter at any point between the two areas is given by

$$C(x) = \frac{8k}{x^2} + \frac{k}{(10 - x)^2} \qquad 0.5 \le x \le 9.5, \quad k > 0$$

How far from A_1 will the concentration of particulate matter between the two areas be at a minimum?

49. Politics. In a newly incorporated city, the voting population (in thousands) is estimated to be

$$N(t) = 30 + 12t^2 - t^3 \qquad 0 \le t \le 8$$

where t is time in years. When will the rate of increase of $N(t)$ be most rapid?

50. Learning. A large grocery chain found that, on average, a checker can recall $P\%$ of a given price list x hours after starting work, as given approximately by

$$P(x) = 96x - 24x^2 \qquad 0 \le x \le 3$$

At what time x does the checker recall a maximum percentage? What is the maximum?

Answers to Matched Problems

1. The dimensions of the garden with the maximum area of 640 square feet are 16 feet by 40 feet, with one 16-foot side with wood fencing.

2. The minimum cost for enclosing a 1,800-square-foot garden is $480, and the dimensions are 30 feet by 60 feet, with one 30-foot side with wood fencing.

3. The company will realize a maximum revenue of $675,000 when the price of a shredder is $150.

4. A maximum profit of $456,750 is realized when 4,050 shredders are manufactured annually and sold for $165 each.

5. A maximum profit of $378,750 is realized when 3,750 shredders are manufactured annually and sold for $175 each.

6. The maximum yield is 1,250 pounds per acre when 5 additional trees are planted on each acre.

7. The maximum yield is 1,200 pounds when no additional trees are planted.

8. The company should produce 5,000 DVDs four times a year.

Important Terms, Symbols, and Concepts

4.1 First Derivative and Graphs

- A function f is **increasing** on an interval (a, b) if $f(x_2) > f(x_1)$ whenever $a < x_1 < x_2 < b$, and f is **decreasing** on (a, b) if $f(x_2) < f(x_1)$ whenever $a < x_1 < x_2 < b$.

- For the interval (a, b), if $f' > 0$, then f is increasing, and if $f' < 0$, then f is decreasing. So a sign chart for f' can be used to tell where f is increasing or decreasing.

- A real number x in the domain of f such that $f'(x) = 0$ or $f'(x)$ does not exist is called a **critical number** of f. So a critical number of f is a partition number for f' that also belongs to the domain of f.

- A value $f(c)$ is a **local maximum** if there is an interval (m, n) containing c such that $f(x) \leq f(c)$ for all x in (m, n). A value $f(c)$ is a **local minimum** if there is an interval (m, n) containing c such that $f(x) \geq f(c)$ for all x in (m, n). A local maximum or local minimum is called a **local extremum**.

- If $f(c)$ is a local extremum, then c is a critical number of f.

- The **first-derivative test for local extrema** identifies local maxima and minima of f by means of a sign chart for f'.

4.2 Second Derivative and Graphs

- The graph of f is **concave upward** on (a, b) if f' is increasing on (a, b), and is **concave downward** on (a, b) if f' is decreasing on (a, b).

- For the interval (a, b), if $f'' > 0$, then f is concave upward, and if $f'' < 0$, then f is concave downward. So a sign chart for f'' can be used to tell where f is concave upward or concave downward.

- An **inflection point** of f is a point $(c, f(c))$ on the graph of f where the concavity changes.

- The graphing strategy on page 261 is used to organize the information obtained from f' and f'' in order to sketch the graph of f.

- If sales $N(x)$ are expressed as a function of the amount x spent on advertising, then the dollar amount at which $N'(x)$, the rate of change of sales, goes from increasing to decreasing is called the **point of diminishing returns**. If d is the point of diminishing returns, then $(d, N(d))$ is an inflection point of $N(x)$.

4.3 L'Hôpital's Rule

- L'Hôpital's rule for 0/0 indeterminate forms: If $\lim_{x \to c} f(x) = 0$ and $\lim_{x \to c} g(x) = 0$, then

$$\lim_{x \to c} \frac{f(x)}{g(x)} = \lim_{x \to c} \frac{f'(x)}{g'(x)}$$

provided the second limit exists or is ∞ or $-\infty$.

- Always check to make sure that L'Hôpital's rule is applicable before using it.

- L'Hôpital's rule remains valid if the symbol $x \to c$ is replaced everywhere it occurs by one of

$$x \to c^+ \qquad x \to c^- \qquad x \to \infty \qquad x \to -\infty$$

- L'Hôpital's rule is also valid for indeterminate forms $\dfrac{\pm \infty}{\pm \infty}$.

4.4 Curve-Sketching Techniques

- The graphing strategy on pages 280 and 281 incorporates analyses of f, f', and f'' in order to sketch a graph of f, including intercepts and asymptotes.

- If $f(x) = n(x)/d(x)$ is a rational function and the degree of $n(x)$ is 1 more than the degree of $d(x)$, then the graph of $f(x)$ has an **oblique asymptote** of the form $y = mx + b$.

4.5 Absolute Maxima and Minima

- If $f(c) \geq f(x)$ for all x in the domain of f, then $f(c)$ is called the **absolute maximum** of f. If $f(c) \leq f(x)$ for all x in the domain of f, then $f(c)$ is called the **absolute minimum** of f. An absolute maximum or absolute minimum is called an **absolute extremum**.

- A function that is continuous on a closed interval $[a, b]$ has both an absolute maximum and an absolute minimum on that interval.

- Absolute extrema, if they exist, must occur at critical numbers or endpoints.
- To find the absolute maximum and absolute minimum of a continuous function f on a closed interval, identify the endpoints and critical numbers in the interval, evaluate the function f at each of them, and choose the largest and smallest values of f.
- **Second-derivative test for local extrema:** If $f'(c) = 0$ and $f''(c) > 0$, then $f(c)$ is a local minimum. If $f'(c) = 0$ and $f''(c) < 0$, then $f(c)$ is a local maximum. No conclusion can be drawn if $f''(c) = 0$. Ex. 2, p. 297
- The **second-derivative test for absolute extrema on an open interval** is applicable when there is only one critical number c in an open interval I and $f'(c) = 0$ and $f''(c) \neq 0$. Ex. 3, p. 298

4.6 Optimization

- The procedure on page 302 for solving optimization problems involves finding the absolute maximum or absolute minimum of a function $f(x)$ on an interval I. If the absolute maximum or absolute minimum occurs at an endpoint, not at a critical number in the interior of I, the extremum is called an **endpoint solution**. The procedure is effective in solving problems in business, including **inventory control problems**, manufacturing, construction, engineering, and many other fields.

Ex. 1, p. 301
Ex. 2, p. 303
Ex. 3, p. 304
Ex. 4, p. 305
Ex. 5, p. 306
Ex. 6, p. 307
Ex. 7, p. 308
Ex. 8, p. 308

Review Exercises

Work through all the problems in this chapter review, and check your answers in the back of the book. Answers to all review problems are there, along with section numbers in italics to indicate where each type of problem is discussed. Where weaknesses show up, review appropriate sections in the text.

Problems 1–8 refer to the following graph of $y = f(x)$. Identify the points or intervals on the x axis that produce the indicated behavior.

1. $f(x)$ is increasing.   **2.** $f'(x) < 0$

3. The graph of f is concave downward.

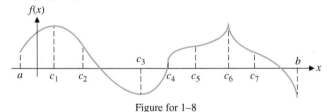

Figure for 1–8

4. Local minima   **5.** Absolute maxima

6. $f'(x)$ appears to be 0.

7. $f'(x)$ does not exist.

8. Inflection points

In Problems 9 and 10, use the given information to sketch the graph of f. Assume that f is continuous on its domain and that all intercepts are included in the information given.

9. Domain: All real x

x	-3	-2	-1	0	2	3
$f(x)$	0	3	2	0	-3	0

10. Domain: All real x

$$f(-2) = 1, f(0) = 0, f(2) = 1;$$
$$f'(0) = 0; f'(x) < 0 \text{ on } (-\infty, 0);$$
$$f'(x) > 0 \text{ on } (0, \infty);$$
$$f''(-2) = 0, f''(2) = 0;$$
$$f''(x) < 0 \text{ on } (-\infty, -2) \text{ and } (2, \infty);$$
$$f''(x) > 0 \text{ on } (-2, 2);$$
$$\lim_{x \to -\infty} f(x) = 2; \lim_{x \to \infty} f(x) = 2$$

11. Find $f''(x)$ for $f(x) = x^4 + 5x^3$.

12. Find y'' for $y = 3x + \dfrac{4}{x}$.

In Problems 13 and 14, find the domain and intercepts.

13. $f(x) = \dfrac{5 + x}{4 - x}$ **14.** $f(x) = \ln(x + 2)$

In Problems 15 and 16, find the horizontal and vertical asymptotes.

15. $f(x) = \dfrac{x + 3}{x^2 - 4}$ **16.** $f(x) = \dfrac{2x - 7}{3x + 10}$

In Problems 17 and 18, find the x and y coordinates of all inflection points.

17. $f(x) = x^4 - 12x^2$ **18.** $f(x) = (2x + 1)^{1/3} - 6$

In Problems 19 and 20, find (A) $f'(x)$, (B) the partition numbers for f', and (C) the critical numbers of f.

19. $f(x) = x^{1/5}$ **20.** $f(x) = x^{-1/5}$

In Problems 21–30, summarize all the pertinent information obtained by applying the final version of the graphing strategy (Section 4–4) to f, and sketch the graph of f.

21. $f(x) = x^3 - 18x^2 + 81x$

22. $f(x) = (x + 4)(x - 2)^2$

23. $f(x) = 8x^3 - 2x^4$ **24.** $f(x) = (x - 1)^3(x + 3)$

25. $f(x) = \dfrac{3x}{x + 2}$ **26.** $f(x) = \dfrac{x^2}{x^2 + 27}$

27. $f(x) = \dfrac{x}{(x + 2)^2}$ **28.** $f(x) = \dfrac{x^3}{x^2 + 3}$

29. $f(x) = 5 - 5e^{-x}$ **30.** $f(x) = x^3 \ln x$

Find each limit in Problems 31–40.

31. $\lim\limits_{x \to 0} \dfrac{e^{3x} - 1}{x}$ **32.** $\lim\limits_{x \to 2} \dfrac{x^2 - 5x + 6}{x^2 + x - 6}$

33. $\lim\limits_{x \to 0^-} \dfrac{\ln(1 + x)}{x^2}$ **34.** $\lim\limits_{x \to 0} \dfrac{\ln(1 + x)}{1 + x}$

35. $\lim\limits_{x \to \infty} \dfrac{e^{4x}}{x^2}$ **36.** $\lim\limits_{x \to 0} \dfrac{e^x + e^{-x} - 2}{x^2}$

37. $\lim\limits_{x \to 0^+} \dfrac{\sqrt{1 + x} - 1}{\sqrt{x}}$ **38.** $\lim\limits_{x \to \infty} \dfrac{\ln x}{x^5}$

39. $\lim\limits_{x \to \infty} \dfrac{\ln(1 + 6x)}{\ln(1 + 3x)}$ **40.** $\lim\limits_{x \to 0} \dfrac{\ln(1 + 6x)}{\ln(1 + 3x)}$

41. Use the graph of $y = f'(x)$ shown here to discuss the graph of $y = f(x)$. Organize your conclusions in a table (see Example 4, Section 4.2). Sketch a possible graph of $y = f(x)$.

Figure for 41 and 42

42. Refer to the above graph of $y = f'(x)$. Which of the following could be the graph of $y = f''(x)$?

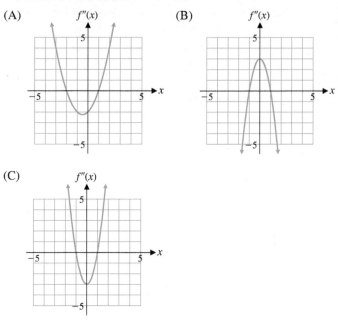

43. Use the second-derivative test to find any local extrema for
$$f(x) = x^3 - 6x^2 - 15x + 12$$

44. Find the absolute maximum and absolute minimum, if either exists, for
$$y = f(x) = x^3 - 12x + 12 \qquad -3 \le x \le 5$$

45. Find the absolute minimum, if it exists, for
$$y = f(x) = x^2 + \frac{16}{x^2} \qquad x > 0$$

46. Find the absolute maximum, if it exists, for
$$f(x) = 11x - 2x \ln x \qquad x > 0$$

47. Find the absolute maximum, if it exists, for
$$f(x) = 10xe^{-2x} \qquad x > 0$$

48. Let $y = f(x)$ be a polynomial function with local minima at $x = a$ and $x = b$, $a < b$. Must f have at least one local maximum between a and b? Justify your answer.

49. The derivative of $f(x) = x^{-1}$ is $f'(x) = -x^{-2}$. Since $f'(x) < 0$ for $x \ne 0$, is it correct to say that $f(x)$ is decreasing for all x except $x = 0$? Explain.

50. Discuss the difference between a partition number for $f'(x)$ and a critical number of $f(x)$, and illustrate with examples.

51. Find the absolute maximum for $f'(x)$ if
$$f(x) = 6x^2 - x^3 + 8$$
Graph f and f' on the same coordinate system for $0 \le x \le 4$.

52. Find two positive numbers whose product is 400 and whose sum is a minimum. What is the minimum sum?

In Problems 53 and 54, apply the graphing strategy and summarize the pertinent information. Round any approximate values to two decimal places.

53. $f(x) = x^4 + x^3 - 4x^2 - 3x + 4$

54. $f(x) = 0.25x^4 - 5x^3 + 31x^2 - 70x$

55. Find the absolute maximum, if it exists, for
$$f(x) = 3x - x^2 + e^{-x} \quad x > 0$$

56. Find the absolute maximum, if it exists, for
$$f(x) = \frac{\ln x}{e^x} \quad x > 0$$

Applications

57. Price analysis. The graph in the figure approximates the rate of change of the price of tomatoes over a 60-month period, where $p(t)$ is the price of a pound of tomatoes and t is time (in months).

   (A) Write a brief description of the graph of $y = p(t)$, including a discussion of local extrema and inflection points.

   (B) Sketch a possible graph of $y = p(t)$.

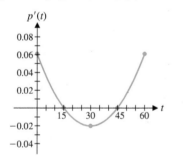

58. Maximum revenue and profit. A company manufactures and sells x e-book readers per month. The monthly cost and price–demand equations are, respectively,
$$C(x) = 350x + 50,000$$
$$p = 500 - 0.025x \qquad 0 \le x \le 20,000$$

   (A) Find the maximum revenue.

   (B) How many readers should the company manufacture each month to maximize its profit? What is the maximum monthly profit? How much should the company charge for each reader?

   (C) If the government decides to tax the company $20 for each reader it produces, how many readers should the company manufacture each month to maximize its profit? What is the maximum monthly profit? How much should the company charge for each reader?

59. Construction. A fence is to be built to enclose a rectangular area. The fence along three sides is to be made of material that costs $5 per foot. The material for the fourth side costs $15 per foot.

   (A) If the area is 5,000 square feet, find the dimensions of the rectangle that will allow for the most economical fence.

   (B) If $3,000 is available for the fencing, find the dimensions of the rectangle that will enclose the most area.

60. Rental income. A 200-room hotel in Reno is filled to capacity every night at a rate of $40 per room. For each $1 increase in the nightly rate, 4 fewer rooms are rented. If each rented room costs $8 a day to service, how much should the management charge per room in order to maximize gross profit? What is the maximum gross profit?

61. Inventory control. A computer store sells 7,200 boxes of storage disks annually. It costs the store $0.20 to store a box of disks for one year. Each time it reorders disks, the store must pay a $5.00 service charge for processing the order. How many times during the year should the store order disks to minimize the total storage and reorder costs?

62. Average cost. The total cost of producing x dorm refrigerators per day is given by
$$C(x) = 4,000 + 10x + 0.1x^2$$
Find the minimum average cost. Graph the average cost and the marginal cost functions on the same coordinate system. Include any oblique asymptotes.

63. Average cost. The cost of producing x wheeled picnic coolers is given by
$$C(x) = 200 + 50x - 50 \ln x \qquad x \ge 1$$
Find the minimum average cost.

64. Marginal analysis. The price–demand equation for a GPS device is
$$p(x) = 1,000e^{-0.02x}$$
where x is the monthly demand and p is the price in dollars. Find the production level and price per unit that produce the maximum revenue. What is the maximum revenue?

65. Maximum revenue. Graph the revenue function from Problem 64 for $0 \le x \le 100$.

66. Maximum profit. Refer to Problem 64. If the GPS devices cost the store $220 each, find the price (to the nearest cent) that maximizes the profit. What is the maximum profit (to the nearest dollar)?

67. Maximum profit. The data in the table show the daily demand x for cream puffs at a state fair at various price levels p. If it costs \$1 to make a cream puff, use logarithmic regression ($p = a + b \ln x$) to find the price (to the nearest cent) that maximizes profit.

Demand	Price per Cream Puff(\$)
x	p
3,125	1.99
3,879	1.89
5,263	1.79
5,792	1.69
6,748	1.59
8,120	1.49

68. Construction costs. The ceiling supports in a new discount department store are 12 feet apart. Lights are to be hung from these supports by chains in the shape of a "Y." If the lights are 10 feet below the ceiling, what is the shortest length of chain that can be used to support these lights?

69. Average cost. The table gives the total daily cost y (in dollars) of producing x dozen chocolate chip cookies at various production levels.

Dozens of Cookies	Total Cost
x	y
50	119
100	187
150	248
200	382
250	505
300	695

(A) Enter the data into a graphing calculator and find a quadratic regression equation for the total cost.

(B) Use the regression equation from part (A) to find the minimum average cost (to the nearest cent) and the corresponding production level (to the nearest integer).

70. Advertising—point of diminishing returns. A company estimates that it will sell $N(x)$ units of a product after spending \$$x$ thousand on advertising, as given by

$$N(x) = -0.25x^4 + 11x^3 - 108x^2 + 3,000$$
$$9 \le x \le 24$$

When is the rate of change of sales increasing and when is it decreasing? What is the point of diminishing returns and the maximum rate of change of sales? Graph N and N' on the same coordinate system.

71. Advertising. A chain of appliance stores uses TV ads to promote its HDTV sales. Analyzing past records produced the data in the following table, where x is the number of ads placed monthly and y is the number of HDTVs sold that month:

Number of Ads	Number of HDTVs
x	y
10	271
20	427
25	526
30	629
45	887
48	917

(A) Enter the data into a graphing calculator, set the calculator to display two decimal places, and find a cubic regression equation for the number of HDTVs sold monthly as a function of the number of ads.

(B) How many ads should be placed each month to maximize the rate of change of sales with respect to the number of ads, and how many HDTVs can be expected to be sold with that number of ads? Round answers to the nearest integer.

72. Bacteria control. If t days after a treatment the bacteria count per cubic centimeter in a body of water is given by

$$C(t) = 20t^2 - 120t + 800 \qquad 0 \le t \le 9$$

then in how many days will the count be a minimum?

73. Politics. In a new suburb, the number of registered voters is estimated to be

$$N(t) = 10 + 6t^2 - t^3 \qquad 0 \le t \le 5$$

where t is time in years and N is in thousands. When will the rate of increase of $N(t)$ be at its maximum?

5

Integration

Introduction

In the preceding three chapters, we studied the *derivative* and its applications. In Chapter 5, we introduce the *integral*, the second key concept of calculus. The integral can be used to calculate areas, volumes, the index of income concentration, and consumers' surplus. At first glance, the integral may appear to be unrelated to the derivative. There is, however, a close connection between these two concepts, which is made precise by the *fundamental theorem of calculus* (Section 5.5). We consider many applications of integrals and differential equations in Chapter 5. See, for example, Problem 91 in Section 5.3, which explores how the age of an archaeological site or artifact can be estimated.

5.1   Antiderivatives and Indefinite Integrals

- Antiderivatives
- Indefinite Integrals: Formulas and Properties
- Applications

Many operations in mathematics have reverses—addition and subtraction, multiplication and division, powers and roots. We now know how to find the derivatives of many functions. The reverse operation, *antidifferentiation* (the reconstruction of a function from its derivative), will receive our attention in this and the next two sections.

Antiderivatives

A function F is an **antiderivative** of a function f if $F'(x) = f(x)$.

The function $F(x) = \dfrac{x^3}{3}$ is an antiderivative of the function $f(x) = x^2$ because

$$\frac{d}{dx}\left(\frac{x^3}{3}\right) = x^2$$

However, $F(x)$ is not the only antiderivative of x^2. Note also that

$$\frac{d}{dx}\left(\frac{x^3}{3} + 2\right) = x^2 \qquad \frac{d}{dx}\left(\frac{x^3}{3} - \pi\right) = x^2 \qquad \frac{d}{dx}\left(\frac{x^3}{3} + \sqrt{5}\right) = x^2$$

Therefore,

$$\frac{x^3}{3} + 2 \qquad \frac{x^3}{3} - \pi \qquad \frac{x^3}{3} + \sqrt{5}$$

are also antiderivatives of x^2 because each has x^2 as a derivative. In fact, it appears that

$$\frac{x^3}{3} + C \qquad \text{for any real number } C$$

is an antiderivative of x^2 because

$$\frac{d}{dx}\left(\frac{x^3}{3} + C\right) = x^2$$

Antidifferentiation of a given function does not give a unique function, but an entire family of functions.

Does the expression

$$\frac{x^3}{3} + C \qquad \text{with } C \text{ any real number}$$

include all antiderivatives of x^2? Theorem 1 (stated without proof) indicates that the answer is yes.

THEOREM 1   Antiderivatives

If the derivatives of two functions are equal on an open interval (a, b), then the functions differ by at most a constant. Symbolically, if F and G are differentiable functions on the interval (a, b) and $F'(x) = G'(x)$ for all x in (a, b), then $F(x) = G(x) + k$ for some constant k.

CONCEPTUAL INSIGHT

Suppose that $F(x)$ is an antiderivative of $f(x)$. If $G(x)$ is any other antiderivative of $f(x)$, then by Theorem 1, the graph of $G(x)$ is a vertical translation of the graph of $F(x)$ (see Section 1.2).

EXAMPLE 1 A Family of Antiderivatives Note that

$$\frac{d}{dx}\left(\frac{x^2}{2}\right) = x$$

(A) Find all antiderivatives of $f(x) = x$.

(B) Graph the antiderivative of $f(x) = x$ that passes through the point $(0, 0)$; through the point $(0, 1)$; through the point $(0, 2)$.

(C) How are the graphs of the three antiderivatives in part (B) related?

SOLUTION

(A) By Theorem 1, any antiderivative of $f(x)$ has the form

$$F(x) = \frac{x^2}{2} + k$$

where k is a real number.

(B) Because $F(0) = (0^2/2) + k = k$, the functions

$$F_0(x) = \frac{x^2}{2}, \quad F_1(x) = \frac{x^2}{2} + 1, \quad \text{and} \quad F_2(x) = \frac{x^2}{2} + 2$$

pass through the points $(0, 0)$, $(0, 1)$, and $(0, 2)$, respectively (see Fig. 1).

(C) The graphs of the three antiderivatives are vertical translations of each other.

Figure 1

Matched Problem 1 Note that

$$\frac{d}{dx}(x^3) = 3x^2$$

(A) Find all antiderivatives of $f(x) = 3x^2$.

(B) Graph the antiderivative of $f(x) = 3x^2$ that passes through the point $(0, 0)$; through the point $(0, 1)$; through the point $(0, 2)$.

(C) How are the graphs of the three antiderivatives in part (B) related?

Indefinite Integrals: Formulas and Properties

Theorem 1 states that if the derivatives of two functions are equal, then the functions differ by at most a constant. We use the symbol

$$\int f(x)\, dx$$

called the **indefinite integral**, to represent the family of all antiderivatives of $f(x)$, and we write

$$\int f(x)\, dx = F(x) + C \qquad \text{if} \qquad F'(x) = f(x)$$

The symbol $\int$ is called an **integral sign**, and the function $f(x)$ is called the **integrand**. The symbol dx indicates that the antidifferentiation is performed with respect to the variable x. (We will have more to say about the symbols $\int$ and dx later in the chapter.) The arbitrary constant C is called the **constant of integration**. Referring to the preceding discussion, we can write

$$\int x^2\, dx = \frac{x^3}{3} + C \qquad \text{since} \qquad \frac{d}{dx}\left(\frac{x^3}{3} + C\right) = x^2$$

Of course, variables other than x can be used in indefinite integrals. For example,

$$\int t^2\, dt = \frac{t^3}{3} + C \qquad \text{since} \qquad \frac{d}{dt}\left(\frac{t^3}{3} + C\right) = t^2$$

or

$$\int u^2 \, du = \frac{u^3}{3} + C \qquad \text{since} \qquad \frac{d}{du}\left(\frac{u^3}{3} + C\right) = u^2$$

The fact that indefinite integration and differentiation are reverse operations, except for the addition of the constant of integration, can be expressed symbolically as

$$\frac{d}{dx}\left[\int f(x) \, dx\right] = f(x) \qquad \text{The derivative of the indefinite integral of } f(x) \text{ is } f(x).$$

and

$$\int F'(x) \, dx = F(x) + C \qquad \text{The indefinite integral of the derivative of } F(x) \text{ is } F(x) + C.$$

We can develop formulas for the indefinite integrals of certain basic functions from the formulas for derivatives in Chapters 2 and 3.

FORMULAS Indefinite Integrals of Basic Functions
For C a constant,

1. $\displaystyle\int x^n \, dx = \frac{x^{n+1}}{n+1} + C, \qquad n \neq -1$

2. $\displaystyle\int e^x \, dx = e^x + C$

3. $\displaystyle\int \frac{1}{x} \, dx = \ln|x| + C, \qquad x \neq 0$

Formula 3 involves the natural logarithm of the absolute value of x. Although the natural logarithm function is only defined for $x > 0$, $f(x) = \ln|x|$ is defined for all $x \neq 0$. Its graph is shown in Figure 2A. Note that $f(x)$ is decreasing for $x < 0$ but is increasing for $x > 0$. Therefore the derivative of f, which by formula 3 is $f'(x) = \dfrac{1}{x}$, is negative for $x < 0$ and positive for $x > 0$ (see Fig. 2B).

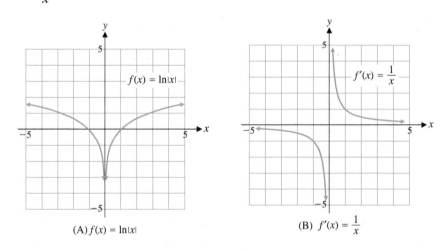

(A) $f(x) = \ln|x|$ \qquad (B) $f'(x) = \dfrac{1}{x}$

Figure 2

To justify the three formulas, show that the derivative of the right-hand side is the integrand of the left-hand side (see Problems 75–78 in Exercise 5.1). Note that formula 1 does not give the antiderivative of x^{-1} (because $x^{n+1}/(n+1)$ is undefined when $n = -1$), but formula 3 does.

Explore and Discuss 1   Formulas 1, 2, and 3 do *not* provide a formula for the indefinite integral of the function $\ln x$. Show that if $x > 0$, then

$$\int \ln x \, dx = x \ln x - x + C$$

by differentiating the right-hand side.

We can obtain properties of the indefinite integral from derivative properties that were established in Chapter 2.

PROPERTIES Indefinite Integrals
For k a constant,

4. $\displaystyle\int k f(x) \, dx = k \int f(x) \, dx$

5. $\displaystyle\int [f(x) \pm g(x)] \, dx = \int f(x) \, dx \pm \int g(x) \, dx$

Property 4 states that

> The indefinite integral of a constant times a function is the constant times the indefinite integral of the function.

Property 5 states that

> The indefinite integral of the sum of two functions is the sum of the indefinite integrals, and the indefinite integral of the difference of two functions is the difference of the indefinite integrals.

To establish property 4, let F be a function such that $F'(x) = f(x)$. Then

$$k \int f(x) \, dx = k \int F'(x) \, dx = k[F(x) + C_1] = kF(x) + kC_1$$

and since $[kF(x)]' = kF'(x) = kf(x)$, we have

$$\int kf(x) \, dx = \int kF'(x) \, dx = kF(x) + C_2$$

But $kF(x) + kC_1$ and $kF(x) + C_2$ describe the same set of functions, because C_1 and C_2 are arbitrary real numbers. Property 4 is established. Property 5 can be established in a similar manner (see Problems 79 and 80 in Exercise 5.1).

⚠ CAUTION Property 4 states that **a constant factor can be moved across an integral sign. A variable factor cannot be moved across an integral sign:**

CONSTANT FACTOR   VARIABLE FACTOR

$$\int 5x^{1/2} \, dx = 5 \int x^{1/2} \, dx \qquad\qquad \int xx^{1/2} \, dx \neq x \int x^{1/2} \, dx \qquad \blacktriangle$$

Indefinite integral formulas and properties can be used together to find indefinite integrals for many frequently encountered functions. If $n = 0$, then formula 1 gives

$$\int dx = x + C$$

Therefore, by property 4,

$$\int k\,dx = k(x + C) = kx + kC$$

Because kC is a constant, we replace it with a single symbol that denotes an arbitrary constant (usually C), and write

$$\int k\,dx = kx + C$$

In words,

The indefinite integral of a constant function with value k is $kx + C$.

Similarly, using property 5 and then formulas 2 and 3, we obtain

$$\int \left(e^x + \frac{1}{x}\right) dx = \int e^x\,dx + \int \frac{1}{x}\,dx$$

$$= e^x + C_1 + \ln|x| + C_2$$

Because $C_1 + C_2$ is a constant, we replace it with the symbol C and write

$$\int \left(e^x + \frac{1}{x}\right) dx = e^x + \ln|x| + C$$

EXAMPLE 2   Using Indefinite Integral Properties and Formulas

(A) $\displaystyle\int 5\,dx = 5x + C$

(B) $\displaystyle\int 9e^x\,dx = 9\int e^x\,dx = 9e^x + C$

(C) $\displaystyle\int 5t^7\,dt = 5\int t^7\,dt = 5\frac{t^8}{8} + C = \frac{5}{8}t^8 + C$

(D) $\displaystyle\int (4x^3 + 2x - 1)\,dx = \int 4x^3\,dx + \int 2x\,dx - \int dx$

Property 4 can be extended to the sum and difference of an arbitrary number of functions.

$$= 4\int x^3\,dx + 2\int x\,dx - \int dx$$

$$= \frac{4x^4}{4} + \frac{2x^2}{2} - x + C$$

$$= x^4 + x^2 - x + C$$

(E) $\displaystyle\int \left(2e^x + \frac{3}{x}\right) dx = 2\int e^x\,dx + 3\int \frac{1}{x}\,dx$

$$= 2e^x + 3\ln|x| + C$$

To check any of the results in Example 2, we differentiate the final result to obtain the integrand in the original indefinite integral. When you evaluate an indefinite integral, do not forget to include the arbitrary constant C.

Matched Problem 2   Find each indefinite integral:

(A) $\displaystyle\int 2\,dx$ (B) $\displaystyle\int 16e^t\,dt$ (C) $\displaystyle\int 3x^4\,dx$

(D) $\displaystyle\int (2x^5 - 3x^2 + 1)\,dx$ (E) $\displaystyle\int \left(\frac{5}{x} - 4e^x\right) dx$

EXAMPLE 3 Using Indefinite Integral Properties and Formulas

(A) $\displaystyle\int \frac{4}{x^3}\,dx = \int 4x^{-3}\,dx = \frac{4x^{-3+1}}{-3+1} + C = -2x^{-2} + C$

(B) $\displaystyle\int 5\sqrt[3]{u^2}\,du = 5\int u^{2/3}\,du = 5\frac{u^{(2/3)+1}}{\frac{2}{3}+1} + C$

$$= 5\frac{u^{5/3}}{\frac{5}{3}} + C = 3u^{5/3} + C$$

(C) $\displaystyle\int \frac{x^3 - 3}{x^2}\,dx = \int \left(\frac{x^3}{x^2} - \frac{3}{x^2}\right) dx$

$$= \int (x - 3x^{-2})\,dx$$

$$= \int x\,dx - 3\int x^{-2}\,dx$$

$$= \frac{x^{1+1}}{1+1} - 3\frac{x^{-2+1}}{-2+1} + C$$

$$= \tfrac{1}{2}x^2 + 3x^{-1} + C$$

(D) $\displaystyle\int \left(\frac{2}{\sqrt[3]{x}} - 6\sqrt{x}\right) dx = \int (2x^{-1/3} - 6x^{1/2})\,dx$

$$= 2\int x^{-1/3}\,dx - 6\int x^{1/2}\,dx$$

$$= 2\frac{x^{(-1/3)+1}}{-\frac{1}{3}+1} - 6\frac{x^{(1/2)+1}}{\frac{1}{2}+1} + C$$

$$= 2\frac{x^{2/3}}{\frac{2}{3}} - 6\frac{x^{3/2}}{\frac{3}{2}} + C$$

$$= 3x^{2/3} - 4x^{3/2} + C$$

(E) $\displaystyle\int x(x^2 + 2)\,dx = \int (x^3 + 2x)\,dx = \frac{x^4}{4} + x^2 + C$

Matched Problem 3 Find each indefinite integral:

(A) $\displaystyle\int \left(2x^{2/3} - \frac{3}{x^4}\right) dx$ 　　(B) $\displaystyle\int 4\sqrt[5]{w^3}\,dw$

(C) $\displaystyle\int \frac{x^4 - 8x^3}{x^2}\,dx$ 　　(D) $\displaystyle\int \left(8\sqrt[3]{x} - \frac{6}{\sqrt{x}}\right) dx$

(E) $\displaystyle\int (x^2 - 2)(x + 3)\,dx$

⚠ CAUTION

1. Note from Example 3E that

$$\int x(x^2 + 2)\,dx \neq \frac{x^2}{2}\left(\frac{x^3}{3} + 2x\right) + C$$

In general, the **indefinite integral of a product is not the product of the indefinite integrals.** (This is expected because the derivative of a product is not the product of the derivatives.)

2.
$$\int e^x \, dx \neq \frac{e^{x+1}}{x+1} + C$$

The power rule applies only to power functions of the form x^n, where the exponent n is a real constant not equal to -1 and the base x is the variable. The function e^x is an exponential function with variable exponent x and constant base e. The correct form is

$$\int e^x \, dx = e^x + C$$

3. Not all elementary functions have elementary antiderivatives. It is impossible, for example, to give a formula for the antiderivative of $f(x) = e^{x^2}$ in terms of elementary functions. Nevertheless, finding such a formula, when it exists, can markedly simplify the solution of certain problems.   ▲

Applications

Let's consider some applications of the indefinite integral.

EXAMPLE 4   Curves   Find the equation of the curve that passes through $(2, 5)$ if the slope of the curve is given by $dy/dx = 2x$ at any point x.

SOLUTION   We want to find a function $y = f(x)$ such that

$$\frac{dy}{dx} = 2x \tag{1}$$

and

$$y = 5 \quad \text{when} \quad x = 2 \tag{2}$$

If $dy/dx = 2x$, then

$$y = \int 2x \, dx \tag{3}$$

$$= x^2 + C$$

Since $y = 5$ when $x = 2$, we determine the *particular value of C* so that

$$5 = 2^2 + C$$

So $C = 1$, and

$$y = x^2 + 1$$

is the *particular antiderivative* out of all those possible from equation (3) that satisfies both equations (1) and (2) (see Fig. 3).

Matched Problem 4   Find the equation of the curve that passes through $(2, 6)$ if the slope of the curve is given by $dy/dx = 3x^2$ at any point x.

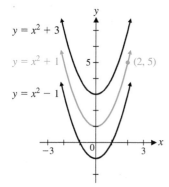

Figure 3 $y = x^2 + C$

In certain situations, it is easier to determine the rate at which something happens than to determine how much of it has happened in a given length of time (for example, population growth rates, business growth rates, the rate of healing of a wound, rates of learning or forgetting). If a rate function (derivative) is given and we know the value of the dependent variable for a given value of the independent variable, then we can often find the original function by integration.

EXAMPLE 5 Cost Function If the marginal cost of producing x units of a commodity is given by

$$C'(x) = 0.3x^2 + 2x$$

and the fixed cost is \$2,000, find the cost function $C(x)$ and the cost of producing 20 units.

SOLUTION Recall that marginal cost is the derivative of the cost function and that fixed cost is cost at a zero production level. So we want to find $C(x)$, given

$$C'(x) = 0.3x^2 + 2x \qquad C(0) = 2,000$$

We find the indefinite integral of $0.3x^2 + 2x$ and determine the arbitrary integration constant using $C(0) = 2,000$:

$$C'(x) = 0.3x^2 + 2x$$

$$C(x) = \int (0.3x^2 + 2x)\, dx$$

$$= 0.1x^3 + x^2 + K \qquad \text{Since } C \text{ represents the cost, we use } K \text{ for the constant of integration.}$$

But

$$C(0) = (0.1)0^3 + 0^2 + K = 2,000$$

So $K = 2,000$, and the cost function is

$$C(x) = 0.1x^3 + x^2 + 2,000$$

We now find $C(20)$, the cost of producing 20 units:

$$C(20) = (0.1)20^3 + 20^2 + 2,000$$

$$= \$3,200$$

See Figure 4 for a geometric representation.

Figure 4

Matched Problem 5 Find the revenue function $R(x)$ when the marginal revenue is

$$R'(x) = 400 - 0.4x$$

and no revenue results at a zero production level. What is the revenue at a production level of 1,000 units?

EXAMPLE 6 Advertising A satellite radio station is launching an aggressive advertising campaign in order to increase the number of daily listeners. The station currently has 27,000 daily listeners, and management expects the number of daily listeners, $S(t)$, to grow at the rate of

$$S'(t) = 60t^{1/2}$$

listeners per day, where t is the number of days since the campaign began. How long should the campaign last if the station wants the number of daily listeners to grow to 41,000?

SOLUTION We must solve the equation $S(t) = 41,000$ for t, given that

$$S'(t) = 60t^{1/2} \qquad \text{and} \qquad S(0) = 27,000$$

First, we use integration to find $S(t)$:

$$S(t) = \int 60t^{1/2}\, dt$$

$$= 60\frac{t^{3/2}}{\frac{3}{2}} + C$$

$$= 40t^{3/2} + C$$

Since

$$S(0) = 40(0)^{3/2} + C = 27{,}000$$

we have $C = 27{,}000$ and

$$S(t) = 40t^{3/2} + 27{,}000$$

Now we solve the equation $S(t) = 41{,}000$ for t:

$$40t^{3/2} + 27{,}000 = 41{,}000$$
$$40t^{3/2} = 14{,}000$$
$$t^{3/2} = 350$$
$$t = 350^{2/3} \qquad \text{Use a calculator.}$$
$$= 49.664\ 419\ldots$$

The advertising campaign should last approximately 50 days.

Matched Problem 6 There are 64,000 subscribers to an online fashion magazine. Due to competition from a new magazine, the number $C(t)$ of subscribers is expected to decrease at the rate of

$$C'(t) = -600t^{1/3}$$

subscribers per month, where t is the time in months since the new magazine began publication. How long will it take until the number of subscribers to the online fashion magazine drops to 46,000?

Exercises 5.1

W

Skills Warm-up Exercises

In Problems 1–8, write each function as a sum of terms of the form ax^n, where a is a constant. (If necessary, review Section A.6).

1. $f(x) = \dfrac{5}{x^4}$

2. $f(x) = -\dfrac{6}{x^9}$

3. $f(x) = \dfrac{3x - 2}{x^5}$

4. $f(x) = \dfrac{x^2 + 5x - 1}{x^3}$

5. $f(x) = \sqrt{x} + \dfrac{5}{\sqrt{x}}$

6. $f(x) = \sqrt[3]{x} - \dfrac{4}{\sqrt[3]{x}}$

7. $f(x) = \sqrt[3]{x}(4 + x - 3x^2)$

8. $f(x) = \sqrt{x}(1 - 5x + x^3)$

In Problems 9–24, find each indefinite integral. Check by differentiating.

9. $\displaystyle\int 7\, dx$

10. $\displaystyle\int 10\, dx$

11. $\displaystyle\int 8x\, dx$

12. $\displaystyle\int 14x\, dx$

13. $\displaystyle\int 9x^2\, dx$

14. $\displaystyle\int 15x^2\, dx$

15. $\displaystyle\int x^5\, dx$

16. $\displaystyle\int x^8\, dx$

17. $\displaystyle\int x^{-3}\, dx$

18. $\displaystyle\int x^{-4}\, dx$

19. $\displaystyle\int 10x^{3/2}\, dx$

20. $\displaystyle\int 8x^{1/3}\, dx$

21. $\displaystyle\int \dfrac{3}{z}\, dz$

22. $\displaystyle\int \dfrac{7}{z}\, dz$

23. $\displaystyle\int 16e^u\, du$

24. $\displaystyle\int 5e^u\, du$

25. Is $F(x) = (x + 1)(x + 2)$ an antiderivative of $f(x) = 2x + 3$? Explain.

26. Is $F(x) = (2x + 5)(x - 6)$ an antiderivative of $f(x) = 4x - 7$? Explain.

27. Is $F(x) = 1 + x \ln x$ an antiderivative of $f(x) = 1 + \ln x$? Explain.

28. Is $F(x) = x \ln x - x + e$ an antiderivative of $f(x) = \ln x$? Explain.

29. Is $F(x) = \dfrac{(2x + 1)^3}{3}$ an antiderivative of $f(x) = (2x + 1)^2$? Explain.

30. Is $F(x) = \dfrac{(3x - 2)^4}{4}$ an antiderivative of $f(x) = (3x - 2)^3$? Explain.

31. Is $F(x) = e^{x^3/3}$ an antiderivative of $f(x) = e^{x^2}$? Explain.

32. Is $F(x) = (e^x - 10)(e^x + 10)$ an antiderivative of $f(x) = 2e^{2x}$? Explain.

In Problems 33–38, discuss the validity of each statement. If the statement is always true, explain why. If not, give a counterexample.

33. The constant function $f(x) = \pi$ is an antiderivative of the constant function $k(x) = 0$.

34. The constant function $k(x) = 0$ is an antiderivative of the constant function $f(x) = \pi$.

35. If n is an integer, then $x^{n+1}/(n + 1)$ is an antiderivative of x^n.

36. The constant function $k(x) = 0$ is an antiderivative of itself.

37. The function $h(x) = 5e^x$ is an antiderivative of itself.

38. The constant function $g(x) = 5e^{\pi}$ is an antiderivative of itself.

In Problems 39–42, could the three graphs in each figure be antiderivatives of the same function? Explain.

39.

40.

41.

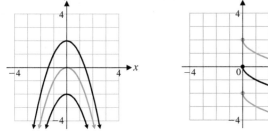

42.

In Problems 43–54, find each indefinite integral. (Check by differentiation.)

43. $\displaystyle \int 5x(1 - x)\, dx$

44. $\displaystyle \int x^2(1 + x^3)\, dx$

45. $\displaystyle \int \frac{du}{\sqrt{u}}$

46. $\displaystyle \int \frac{dt}{\sqrt[3]{t}}$

47. $\displaystyle \int \frac{dx}{4x^3}$

48. $\displaystyle \int \frac{6\, dm}{m^2}$

49. $\displaystyle \int \frac{4 + u}{u}\, du$

50. $\displaystyle \int \frac{1 - y^2}{3y}\, dy$

51. $\displaystyle \int (5e^z + 4)\, dz$

52. $\displaystyle \int \frac{e^t - t}{2}\, dt$

53. $\displaystyle \int \left(3x^2 - \frac{2}{x^2}\right) dx$

54. $\displaystyle \int \left(4x^3 + \frac{2}{x^3}\right) dx$

In Problems 55–62, find the particular antiderivative of each derivative that satisfies the given condition.

55. $C'(x) = 6x^2 - 4x;\ C(0) = 3,000$

56. $R'(x) = 600 - 0.6x;\ R(0) = 0$

57. $\dfrac{dx}{dt} = \dfrac{20}{\sqrt{t}};\ x(1) = 40$

58. $\dfrac{dR}{dt} = \dfrac{100}{t^2};\ R(1) = 400$

59. $\dfrac{dy}{dx} = 2x^{-2} + 3x^{-1} - 1;\ y(1) = 0$

60. $\dfrac{dy}{dx} = 3x^{-1} + x^{-2};\ y(1) = 1$

61. $\dfrac{dx}{dt} = 4e^t - 2;\ x(0) = 1$

62. $\dfrac{dy}{dt} = 5e^t - 4;\ y(0) = -1$

63. Find the equation of the curve that passes through $(2, 3)$ if its slope is given by

$$\frac{dy}{dx} = 4x - 3$$

for each x.

64. Find the equation of the curve that passes through $(1, 3)$ if its slope is given by

$$\frac{dy}{dx} = 12x^2 - 12x$$

for each x.

In Problems 65–70, find each indefinite integral.

65. $\displaystyle \int \frac{2x^4 - x}{x^3}\, dx$

66. $\displaystyle \int \frac{x^{-1} - x^4}{x^2}\, dx$

67. $\displaystyle \int \frac{x^5 - 2x}{x^4}\, dx$

68. $\displaystyle \int \frac{1 - 3x^4}{x^2}\, dx$

69. $\displaystyle \int \frac{x^2 e^x - 2x}{x^2}\, dx$

70. $\displaystyle \int \frac{1 - xe^x}{x}\, dx$

In Problems 71–74, find the derivative or indefinite integral as indicated.

71. $\dfrac{d}{dx}\left(\displaystyle\int x^3\, dx\right)$

72. $\dfrac{d}{dt}\left(\displaystyle\int \frac{\ln t}{t}\, dt\right)$

73. $\displaystyle \int \frac{d}{dx}(x^4 + 3x^2 + 1)\, dx$

74. $\displaystyle \int \frac{d}{du}(e^{u^2})\, du$

75. Use differentiation to justify the formula

$$\int x^n\, dx = \frac{x^{n+1}}{n + 1} + C$$

provided that $n \neq -1$.

76. Use differentiation to justify the formula

$$\int e^x\, dx = e^x + C$$

77. Assuming that $x > 0$, use differentiation to justify the formula

$$\int \frac{1}{x} \, dx = \ln|x| + C$$

78. Assuming that $x < 0$, use differentiation to justify the formula

$$\int \frac{1}{x} \, dx = \ln|x| + C$$

[*Hint:* Use the chain rule after noting that $\ln|x| = \ln(-x)$ for $x < 0$.]

79. Show that the indefinite integral of the sum of two functions is the sum of the indefinite integrals.

[*Hint:* Assume that $\int f(x)\,dx = F(x) + C_1$ and $\int g(x)\,dx = G(x) + C_2$. Using differentiation, show that $F(x) + C_1 + G(x) + C_2$ is the indefinite integral of the function $s(x) = f(x) + g(x)$.]

80. Show that the indefinite integral of the difference of two functions is the difference of the indefinite integrals.

Applications

81. Cost function. The marginal average cost of producing x sports watches is given by

$$\overline{C}'(x) = -\frac{1,000}{x^2} \qquad \overline{C}(100) = 25$$

where $\overline{C}(x)$ is the average cost in dollars. Find the average cost function and the cost function. What are the fixed costs?

82. Renewable energy. In 2012, U.S. consumption of renewable energy was 8.45 quadrillion Btu (or 8.45×10^{15} Btu). Since the 1960s, consumption has been growing at a rate (in quadrillion Btu per year) given by

$$f'(t) = 0.004t + 0.062$$

where t is years after 1960. Find $f(t)$ and estimate U.S. consumption of renewable energy in 2024.

83. Production costs. The graph of the marginal cost function from the production of x thousand bottles of sunscreen per month [where cost $C(x)$ is in thousands of dollars per month] is given in the figure.

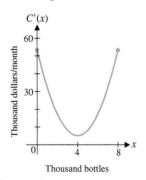

(A) Using the graph shown, describe the shape of the graph of the cost function $C(x)$ as x increases from 0 to 8,000 bottles per month.

(B) Given the equation of the marginal cost function,

$$C'(x) = 3x^2 - 24x + 53$$

find the cost function if monthly fixed costs at 0 output are \$30,000. What is the cost of manufacturing 4,000 bottles per month? 8,000 bottles per month?

(C) Graph the cost function for $0 \le x \le 8$. [Check the shape of the graph relative to the analysis in part (A).]

(D) Why do you think that the graph of the cost function is steeper at both ends than in the middle?

84. Revenue. The graph of the marginal revenue function from the sale of x sports watches is given in the figure.

(A) Using the graph shown, describe the shape of the graph of the revenue function $R(x)$ as x increases from 0 to 1,000.

(B) Find the equation of the marginal revenue function (the linear function shown in the figure).

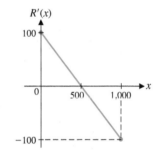

(C) Find the equation of the revenue function that satisfies $R(0) = 0$. Graph the revenue function over the interval $[0, 1,000]$. [Check the shape of the graph relative to the analysis in part (A).]

(D) Find the price–demand equation and determine the price when the demand is 700 units.

85. Sales analysis. Monthly sales of an SUV model are expected to increase at the rate of

$$S'(t) = -24t^{1/3}$$

SUVs per month, where t is time in months and $S(t)$ is the number of SUVs sold each month. The company plans to stop manufacturing this model when monthly sales reach 300 SUVs. If monthly sales now ($t = 0$) are 1,200 SUVs, find $S(t)$. How long will the company continue to manufacture this model?

86. Sales analysis. The rate of change of the monthly sales of a newly released football game is given by

$$S'(t) = 500t^{1/4} \qquad S(0) = 0$$

where t is the number of months since the game was released and $S(t)$ is the number of games sold each month. Find $S(t)$. When will monthly sales reach 20,000 games?

87. Sales analysis. Repeat Problem 85 if $S'(t) = -24t^{1/3} - 70$ and all other information remains the same. Use a graphing calculator to approximate the solution of the equation $S(t) = 300$ to two decimal places.

88. Sales analysis. Repeat Problem 86 if $S'(t) = 500t^{1/4} + 300$ and all other information remains the same. Use a graphing calculator to approximate the solution of the equation $S(t) = 20,000$ to two decimal places.

89. Labor costs. A defense contractor is starting production on a new missile control system. On the basis of data collected during the assembly of the first 16 control systems, the production manager obtained the following function describing the rate of labor use:

$$L'(x) = 2,400x^{-1/2}$$

For example, after assembly of 16 units, the rate of assembly is 600 labor-hours per unit, and after assembly of 25 units, the rate of assembly is 480 labor-hours per unit. The more units assembled, the more efficient the process. If 19,200 labor-hours are required to assemble of the first 16 units, how many labor-hours $L(x)$ will be required to assemble the first x units? The first 25 units?

90. Labor costs. If the rate of labor use in Problem 89 is

$$L'(x) = 2,000x^{-1/3}$$

and if the first 8 control units require 12,000 labor-hours, how many labor-hours, $L(x)$, will be required for the first x control units? The first 27 control units?

91. Weight–height. For an average person, the rate of change of weight W (in pounds) with respect to height h (in inches) is given approximately by

$$\frac{dW}{dh} = 0.0015h^2$$

Find $W(h)$ if $W(60) = 108$ pounds. Find the weight of an average person who is 5 feet, 10 inches, tall.

92. Wound healing. The area A of a healing wound changes at a rate given approximately by

$$\frac{dA}{dt} = -4t^{-3} \qquad 1 \le t \le 10$$

where t is time in days and $A(1) = 2$ square centimeters. What will the area of the wound be in 10 days?

93. Urban growth. The rate of growth of the population $N(t)$ of a new city t years after its incorporation is estimated to be

$$\frac{dN}{dt} = 400 + 600\sqrt{t} \qquad 0 \le t \le 9$$

If the population was 5,000 at the time of incorporation, find the population 9 years later.

94. Learning. A college language class was chosen for an experiment in learning. Using a list of 50 words, the experiment involved measuring the rate of vocabulary memorization at different times during a continuous 5-hour study session. It was found that the average rate of learning for the entire class was inversely proportional to the time spent studying and was given approximately by

$$V'(t) = \frac{15}{t} \qquad 1 \le t \le 5$$

If the average number of words memorized after 1 hour of study was 15 words, what was the average number of words memorized after t hours of study for $1 \le t \le 5$? After 4 hours of study? Round answer to the nearest whole number.

Answers to Matched Problems

1. (A) $x^3 + C$

(B)

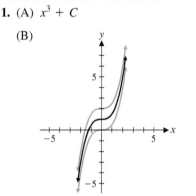

(C) The graphs are vertical translations of each other.

2. (A) $2x + C$ (B) $16e^t + C$ (C) $\frac{3}{5}x^5 + C$
   (D) $\frac{1}{3}x^6 - x^3 + x + C$ (E) $5\ln|x| - 4e^x + C$

3. (A) $\frac{6}{5}x^{5/3} + x^{-3} + C$ (B) $\frac{5}{2}w^{8/5} + C$
   (C) $\frac{1}{3}x^3 - 4x^2 + C$ (D) $6x^{4/3} - 12x^{1/2} + C$
   (E) $\frac{1}{4}x^4 + x^3 - x^2 - 6x + C$

4. $y = x^3 - 2$

5. $R(x) = 400x - 0.2x^2;\ R(1,000) = \$200,000$

6. $t = (40)^{3/4} \approx 16$ mo

5.2 Integration by Substitution

- Reversing the Chain Rule
- Integration by Substitution
- Additional Substitution Techniques
- Application

Many of the indefinite integral formulas introduced in the preceding section are based on corresponding derivative formulas studied earlier. We now consider indefinite integral formulas and procedures based on the chain rule for differentiation.

Reversing the Chain Rule

Recall the chain rule:

$$\frac{d}{dx}f[g(x)] = f'[g(x)]g'(x)$$

The expression on the right is formed from the expression on the left by taking the derivative of the outside function f and multiplying it by the derivative of the inside function g. If we recognize an integrand as a chain-rule form $E'[I(x)]I'(x)$, we can easily find an antiderivative and its indefinite integral:

$$\int E'[I(x)]I'(x)\,dx = E[I(x)] + C \tag{1}$$

We are interested in finding the indefinite integral

$$\int 3x^2 e^{x^3-1}\,dx \tag{2}$$

The integrand appears to be the chain-rule form $e^{g(x)}g'(x)$, which is the derivative of $e^{g(x)}$. Since

$$\frac{d}{dx}e^{x^3-1} = 3x^2 e^{x^3-1}$$

it follows that

$$\int 3x^2 e^{x^3-1}\,dx = e^{x^3-1} + C \tag{3}$$

How does the following indefinite integral differ from integral (2)?

$$\int x^2 e^{x^3-1}\,dx \tag{4}$$

It is missing the constant factor 3. That is, $x^2 e^{x^3-1}$ is within a constant factor of being the derivative of e^{x^3-1}. But because a constant factor can be moved across the integral sign, this causes us little trouble in finding the indefinite integral of $x^2 e^{x^3-1}$. We introduce the constant factor 3 and at the same time multiply by $\frac{1}{3}$ and move the $\frac{1}{3}$ factor outside the integral sign. This is equivalent to multiplying the integrand in integral (4) by 1:

$$\int x^2 e^{x^3-1}\,dx = \int \frac{3}{3}x^2 e^{x^3-1}\,dx \tag{5}$$

$$= \frac{1}{3}\int 3x^2 e^{x^3-1}\,dx = \frac{1}{3}e^{x^3-1} + C$$

The derivative of the rightmost side of equation (5) is the integrand of the indefinite integral (4). Check this.

How does the following indefinite integral differ from integral (2)?

$$\int 3x e^{x^3-1}\,dx \tag{6}$$

It is missing a variable factor x. This is more serious. As tempting as it might be, we *cannot* adjust integral (6) by introducing the variable factor x and moving $1/x$ outside the integral sign, as we did with the constant 3 in equation (5).

⚠ CAUTION A constant factor can be moved across an integral sign, but a variable factor cannot.   ▲

There is nothing wrong with educated guessing when you are looking for an antiderivative of a given function. You have only to check the result by differentiation. If you are right, you go on your way; if you are wrong, you simply try another approach.

In Section 3.4, we saw that the chain rule extends the derivative formulas for x^n, e^x, and $\ln x$ to derivative formulas for $[f(x)]^n$, $e^{f(x)}$, and $\ln[f(x)]$. The chain rule can also be used to extend the indefinite integral formulas discussed in Section 5.1. Some general formulas are summarized in the following box:

FORMULAS   General Indefinite Integral Formulas

1. $\displaystyle\int [f(x)]^n f'(x)\, dx = \frac{[f(x)]^{n+1}}{n+1} + C, n \neq -1$

2. $\displaystyle\int e^{f(x)} f'(x)\, dx = e^{f(x)} + C$

3. $\displaystyle\int \frac{1}{f(x)} f'(x)\, dx = \ln|f(x)| + C$

We can verify each formula by using the chain rule to show that the derivative of the function on the right is the integrand on the left. For example,

$$\frac{d}{dx}\left[e^{f(x)} + C\right] = e^{f(x)} f'(x)$$

verifies formula 2.

EXAMPLE 1   Reversing the Chain Rule

(A) $\displaystyle\int (3x + 4)^{10}(3)\, dx = \frac{(3x + 4)^{11}}{11} + C$ Formula 1 with $f(x) = 3x + 4$ and $f'(x) = 3$

Check:

$$\frac{d}{dx}\frac{(3x + 4)^{11}}{11} = 11\frac{(3x + 4)^{10}}{11}\frac{d}{dx}(3x + 4) = (3x + 4)^{10}(3)$$

(B) $\displaystyle\int e^{x^2}(2x)\, dx = e^{x^2} + C$ Formula 2 with $f(x) = x^2$ and $f'(x) = 2x$

Check:

$$\frac{d}{dx}e^{x^2} = e^{x^2}\frac{d}{dx}x^2 = e^{x^2}(2x)$$

(C) $\displaystyle\int \frac{1}{1 + x^3}3x^2\, dx = \ln|1 + x^3| + C$ Formula 3 with $f(x) = 1 + x^3$ and $f'(x) = 3x^2$

Check:

$$\frac{d}{dx}\ln|1 + x^3| = \frac{1}{1 + x^3}\frac{d}{dx}(1 + x^3) = \frac{1}{1 + x^3}3x^2$$

Matched Problem 1   Find each indefinite integral.

(A) $\displaystyle\int (2x^3 - 3)^{20}(6x^2)\, dx$ (B) $\displaystyle\int e^{5x}(5)\, dx$ (C) $\displaystyle\int \frac{1}{4 + x^2}2x\, dx$

Integration by Substitution

The key step in using formulas 1, 2, and 3 is recognizing the form of the integrand. Some people find it difficult to identify $f(x)$ and $f'(x)$ in these formulas and prefer to use a *substitution* to simplify the integrand. The *method of substitution,* which we now discuss, becomes increasingly useful as one progresses in studies of integration.

We start by recalling the definition of the *differential* (see Section 2.6, p. 158). We represent the derivative by the symbol *dy/dx* taken as a whole and now define *dy* and *dx* as two separate quantities with the property that their ratio is still equal to $f'(x)$:

DEFINITION Differentials

If $y = f(x)$ defines a differentiable function, then

1. The **differential dx** of the independent variable x is an arbitrary real number.
2. The **differential dy** of the dependent variable y is defined as the product of $f'(x)$ and *dx*:
$$dy = f'(x)\, dx$$

Differentials involve mathematical subtleties that are treated carefully in advanced mathematics courses. Here, we are interested in them mainly as a bookkeeping device to aid in the process of finding indefinite integrals. We can always check an indefinite integral by differentiating.

EXAMPLE 2 Differentials

(A) If $y = f(x) = x^2$, then
$$dy = f'(x)\, dx = 2x\, dx$$

(B) If $u = g(x) = e^{3x}$, then
$$du = g'(x)\, dx = 3e^{3x}\, dx$$

(C) If $w = h(t) = \ln(4 + 5t)$, then
$$dw = h'(t)\, dt = \frac{5}{4 + 5t}\, dt$$

Matched Problem 2

(A) Find *dy* for $y = f(x) = x^3$.
(B) Find *du* for $u = h(x) = \ln(2 + x^2)$.
(C) Find *dv* for $v = g(t) = e^{-5t}$.

The **method of substitution** is developed through Examples 3–6.

EXAMPLE 3 Using Substitution Find $\int (x^2 + 2x + 5)^5 (2x + 2)\, dx$.

SOLUTION If
$$u = x^2 + 2x + 5$$

then the differential of *u* is
$$du = (2x + 2)\, dx$$

Notice that *du* is one of the factors in the integrand. Substitute *u* for $x^2 + 2x + 5$ and *du* for $(2x + 2)\, dx$ to obtain

$$\int (x^2 + 2x + 5)^5 (2x + 2)\, dx = \int u^5\, du$$

$$= \frac{u^6}{6} + C$$

$$= \frac{1}{6}(x^2 + 2x + 5)^6 + C \quad \text{Since } u = x^2 + 2x + 5$$

Check:

$$\frac{d}{dx}\frac{1}{6}(x^2 + 2x + 5)^6 = \frac{1}{6}(6)(x^2 + 2x + 5)^5\frac{d}{dx}(x^2 + 2x + 5)$$

$$= (x^2 + 2x + 5)^5(2x + 2)$$

Matched Problem 3 Find $\int (x^2 - 3x + 7)^4(2x - 3)\ dx$ by substitution.

The substitution method is also called the **change-of-variable method** since u replaces the variable x in the process. Substituting $u = f(x)$ and $du = f'(x)\ dx$ in formulas 1, 2, and 3 produces the general indefinite integral formulas 4, 5, and 6:

FORMULAS General Indefinite Integral Formulas

4. $\int u^n\ du = \dfrac{u^{n+1}}{n+1} + C, \qquad n \neq -1$

5. $\int e^u\ du = e^u + C$

6. $\int \dfrac{1}{u}\ du = \ln|u| + C$

These formulas are valid if u is an independent variable, or if u is a function of another variable and du is the differential of u with respect to that variable.

The substitution method for evaluating certain indefinite integrals is outlined as follows:

PROCEDURE Integration by Substitution

Step 1 Select a substitution that appears to simplify the integrand. In particular, try to select u so that du is a factor in the integrand.

Step 2 Express the integrand entirely in terms of u and du, completely eliminating the original variable and its differential.

Step 3 Evaluate the new integral if possible.

Step 4 Express the antiderivative found in step 3 in terms of the original variable.

EXAMPLE 4 Using Substitution Use a substitution to find each indefinite integral.

(A) $\int (3x + 4)^6(3)\ dx$ \qquad\qquad (B) $\int e^{t^2}(2t)\ dt$

SOLUTION

(A) If we let $u = 3x + 4$, then $du = 3\ dx$, and

$$\int (3x + 4)^6(3)\ dx = \int u^6\ du \qquad \text{Use formula 4.}$$

$$= \frac{u^7}{7} + C$$

$$= \frac{(3x + 4)^7}{7} + C \qquad \text{Since } u = 3x + 4$$

Check:

$$\frac{d}{dx} \frac{(3x+4)^7}{7} = \frac{7(3x+4)^6}{7} \frac{d}{dx}(3x+4) = (3x+4)^6(3)$$

(B) If we let $u = t^2$, then $du = 2t \, dt$, and

$$\int e^{t^2}(2t) \, dt = \int e^u \, du \qquad \text{Use formula 5.}$$
$$= e^u + C$$
$$= e^{t^2} + C \qquad \text{Since } u = t^2$$

Check:

$$\frac{d}{dt} e^{t^2} = e^{t^2} \frac{d}{dt} t^2 = e^{t^2}(2t)$$

Matched Problem 4 Use a substitution to find each indefinite integral.

(A) $\displaystyle\int (2x^3 - 3)^4 (6x^2) \, dx$ (B) $\displaystyle\int e^{5w}(5) \, dw$

Additional Substitution Techniques

In order to use the substitution method, **the integrand must be expressed entirely in terms of u and du.** In some cases, the integrand must be modified before making a substitution and using one of the integration formulas. Example 5 illustrates this process.

EXAMPLE 5   Substitution Techniques   **Integrate.**

(A) $\displaystyle\int \frac{1}{4x+7} \, dx$ (B) $\displaystyle\int t e^{-t^2} \, dt$

(C) $\displaystyle\int 4x^2 \sqrt{x^3 + 5} \, dx$

SOLUTION

(A) If $u = 4x + 7$, then $du = 4 \, dx$ and, dividing both sides of the equation $du = 4 \, dx$ by 4, we have $dx = \frac{1}{4} \, du$. In the integrand, replace $4x + 7$ by u and replace dx by $\frac{1}{4} \, du$:

$$\int \frac{1}{4x+7} \, dx = \int \frac{1}{u}\left(\frac{1}{4} \, du\right) \qquad \begin{array}{l}\text{Move constant factor across}\\\text{the integral sign.}\end{array}$$

$$= \frac{1}{4} \int \frac{1}{u} \, du \qquad \text{Use formula 6.}$$

$$= \frac{1}{4} \ln|u| + C$$

$$= \frac{1}{4} \ln|4x+7| + C \qquad \text{Since } u = 4x + 7$$

Check:

$$\frac{d}{dx} \frac{1}{4} \ln|4x+7| = \frac{1}{4} \frac{1}{4x+7} \frac{d}{dx}(4x+7) = \frac{1}{4} \frac{1}{4x+7} 4 = \frac{1}{4x+7}$$

(B) If $u = -t^2$, then $du = -2t\,dt$ and, dividing both sides by -2, $-\frac{1}{2}\,du = t\,dt$. In the integrand, replace $-t^2$ by u and replace $t\,dt$ by $-\frac{1}{2}\,du$:

$$\int te^{-t^2}dt = \int e^u\left(-\frac{1}{2}\,du\right) \qquad \text{Move constant factor} \\ \text{across the integral sign.}$$

$$= -\frac{1}{2}\int e^u\,du \qquad \text{Use formula 5.}$$

$$= -\tfrac{1}{2}e^u + C$$

$$= -\tfrac{1}{2}e^{-t^2} + C \qquad \text{Since } u = -t^2$$

Check:

$$\frac{d}{dt}\left(-\tfrac{1}{2}e^{-t^2}\right) = -\tfrac{1}{2}e^{-t^2}\frac{d}{dt}(-t^2) = -\tfrac{1}{2}e^{-t^2}(-2t) = te^{-t^2}$$

(C) If $u = x^3 + 5$, then $du = 3x^2\,dx$ and, dividing both sides by 3, $\frac{1}{3}\,du = x^2\,dx$. In the integrand, replace $x^3 + 5$ by u and replace $x^2\,dx$ by $\frac{1}{3}\,du$:

$$\int 4x^2\sqrt{x^3 + 5}\,dx = \int 4\sqrt{u}\left(\frac{1}{3}\,du\right) \qquad \text{Move constant factors} \\ \text{across the integral sign.}$$

$$= \frac{4}{3}\int\sqrt{u}\,du$$

$$= \frac{4}{3}\int u^{1/2}\,du \qquad \text{Use formula 4.}$$

$$= \frac{4}{3}\cdot\frac{u^{3/2}}{\frac{3}{2}} + C$$

$$= \tfrac{8}{9}u^{3/2} + C$$

$$= \tfrac{8}{9}(x^3 + 5)^{3/2} + C \qquad \text{Since } u = x^3 + 5$$

Check:

$$\frac{d}{dx}\left[\tfrac{8}{9}(x^3 + 5)^{3/2}\right] = \tfrac{4}{3}(x^3 + 5)^{1/2}\frac{d}{dx}(x^3 + 5)$$

$$= \tfrac{4}{3}(x^3 + 5)^{1/2}(3x^2) = 4x^2\sqrt{x^3 + 5}$$

Matched Problem 5 Integrate.

(A) $\displaystyle\int e^{-3x}\,dx$

(B) $\displaystyle\int \frac{x}{x^2 - 9}\,dx$

(C) $\displaystyle\int 5t^2(t^3 + 4)^{-2}\,dt$

Even if it is not possible to find a substitution that makes an integrand match one of the integration formulas exactly, a substitution may simplify the integrand sufficiently so that other techniques can be used.

EXAMPLE 6   Substitution Techniques   Find $\int \dfrac{x}{\sqrt{x+2}}\,dx.$

SOLUTION   Proceeding as before, if we let $u = x + 2$, then $du = dx$ and

$$\int \frac{x}{\sqrt{x+2}}\,dx = \int \frac{x}{\sqrt{u}}\,du$$

Notice that this substitution is not complete because we have not expressed the integrand entirely in terms of u and du. As we noted earlier, only a constant factor can be moved across an integral sign, so we cannot move x outside the integral sign. Instead, we must return to the original substitution, solve for x in terms of u, and use the resulting equation to complete the substitution:

$$u = x + 2 \quad \text{Solve for } x \text{ in terms of } u.$$
$$u - 2 = x \quad \text{Substitute this expression for } x.$$

Thus,

$$\int \frac{x}{\sqrt{x+2}}\,dx = \int \frac{u-2}{\sqrt{u}}\,du \qquad\qquad \text{Simplify the integrand.}$$

$$= \int \frac{u-2}{u^{1/2}}\,du$$

$$= \int (u^{1/2} - 2u^{-1/2})\,du$$

$$= \int u^{1/2}\,du - 2\int u^{-1/2}\,du$$

$$= \frac{u^{3/2}}{\frac{3}{2}} - 2\frac{u^{1/2}}{\frac{1}{2}} + C$$

$$= \tfrac{2}{3}(x+2)^{3/2} - 4(x+2)^{1/2} + C \quad \text{Since } u = x + 2$$

Check:

$$\frac{d}{dx}\left[\tfrac{2}{3}(x+2)^{3/2} - 4(x+2)^{1/2}\right] = (x+2)^{1/2} - 2(x+2)^{-1/2}$$

$$= \frac{x+2}{(x+2)^{1/2}} - \frac{2}{(x+2)^{1/2}}$$

$$= \frac{x}{(x+2)^{1/2}}$$

Matched Problem 6)   Find $\int x\sqrt{x+1}\,dx.$

We can find the indefinite integral of some functions in more than one way. For example, we can use substitution to find

$$\int x(1+x^2)^2\,dx$$

by letting $u = 1 + x^2$. As a second approach, we can expand the integrand, obtaining

$$\int (x + 2x^3 + x^5)\,dx$$

for which we can easily calculate an antiderivative. In such a case, choose the approach that you prefer.

There are also some functions for which substitution is not an effective approach to finding the indefinite integral. For example, substitution is not helpful in finding

$$\int e^{x^2}\, dx \quad \text{or} \quad \int \ln x\, dx$$

Application

EXAMPLE 7   Price–Demand   The market research department of a supermarket chain has determined that, for one store, the marginal price $p'(x)$ at x tubes per week for a certain brand of toothpaste is given by

$$p'(x) = -0.015e^{-0.01x}$$

Find the price–demand equation if the weekly demand is 50 tubes when the price of a tube is \$4.35. Find the weekly demand when the price of a tube is \$3.89.

SOLUTION

$$p(x) = \int -0.015e^{-0.01x}\, dx$$

$$= -0.015 \int e^{-0.01x}\, dx$$

$$= -0.015 \int e^{-0.01x} \frac{-0.01}{-0.01}\, dx$$

$$= \frac{-0.015}{-0.01} \int e^{-0.01x}(-0.01)\, dx \qquad \text{Substitute } u = -0.01x \\ \text{and } du = -0.01\, dx.$$

$$= 1.5 \int e^{u}\, du$$

$$= 1.5e^{u} + C$$

$$= 1.5e^{-0.01x} + C \qquad \text{Since } u = -0.01x$$

We find C by noting that

$$p(50) = 1.5e^{-0.01(50)} + C = \$4.35$$

$$C = \$4.35 - 1.5e^{-0.5} \qquad \text{Use a calculator.}$$

$$= \$4.35 - 0.91$$

$$= \$3.44$$

So,

$$p(x) = 1.5e^{-0.01x} + 3.44$$

To find the demand when the price is \$3.89, we solve $p(x) = \$3.89$ for x:

$$1.5e^{-0.01x} + 3.44 = 3.89$$

$$1.5e^{-0.01x} = 0.45$$

$$e^{-0.01x} = 0.3$$

$$-0.01x = \ln 0.3$$

$$x = -100 \ln 0.3 \approx 120 \text{ tubes}$$

Matched Problem 7 The marginal price $p'(x)$ at a supply level of x tubes per week for a certain brand of toothpaste is given by

$$p'(x) = 0.001e^{0.01x}$$

Find the price–supply equation if the supplier is willing to supply 100 tubes per week at a price of $3.65 each. How many tubes would the supplier be willing to supply at a price of $3.98 each?

We conclude with two final cautions. The first was stated earlier, but it is worth repeating.

⚠ **CAUTION**

1. A variable cannot be moved across an integral sign.
2. An integral must be expressed entirely in terms of u and du before applying integration formulas 4, 5, and 6. ▲

Exercises 5.2

Skills Warm-up Exercises

W *In Problems 1–8, use the chain rule to find the derivative of each function. (If necessary, review Section 3.4).*

1. $f(x) = (5x + 1)^{10}$ **2.** $f(x) = (4x - 3)^6$

3. $f(x) = (x^2 + 1)^7$ **4.** $f(x) = (x^3 - 4)^5$

5. $f(x) = e^{x^2}$ **6.** $f(x) = 6e^{x^3}$

7. $f(x) = \ln(x^4 - 10)$ **8.** $f(x) = \ln(x^2 + 5x + 4)$

In Problems 9–44, find each indefinite integral and check the result by differentiating.

9. $\int (3x + 5)^2 (3) \, dx$ **10.** $\int (6x - 1)^3 (6) \, dx$

11. $\int (x^2 - 1)^5 (2x) \, dx$ **12.** $\int (x^6 + 1)^4 (6x^5) \, dx$

13. $\int (5x^3 + 1)^{-3} (15x^2) \, dx$ **14.** $\int (4x^2 - 3)^{-6} (8x) \, dx$

15. $\int e^{5x} (5) \, dx$ **16.** $\int e^{x^3} (3x^2) \, dx$

17. $\int \frac{1}{1 + x^2} (2x) \, dx$ **18.** $\int \frac{1}{5x - 7} (5) \, dx$

19. $\int \sqrt{1 + x^4} \, (4x^3) \, dx$ **20.** $\int (x^2 + 9)^{-1/2} (2x) \, dx$

21. $\int (x + 3)^{10} \, dx$ **22.** $\int (x - 3)^{-4} \, dx$

23. $\int (6t - 7)^{-2} \, dt$ **24.** $\int (5t + 1)^3 \, dt$

25. $\int (t^2 + 1)^5 \, t \, dt$ **26.** $\int (t^3 + 4)^{-2} \, t^2 \, dt$

27. $\int x e^{x^2} \, dx$ **28.** $\int e^{-0.01x} \, dx$

29. $\int \frac{1}{5x + 4} \, dx$ **30.** $\int \frac{x}{1 + x^2} \, dx$

31. $\int e^{1-t} \, dt$ **32.** $\int \frac{3}{2 - t} \, dt$

33. $\int \frac{t}{(3t^2 + 1)^4} \, dt$ **34.** $\int \frac{t^2}{(t^3 - 2)^5} \, dt$

35. $\int x \sqrt{x + 4} \, dx$ **36.** $\int x \sqrt{x - 9} \, dx$

37. $\int \frac{x}{\sqrt{x - 3}} \, dx$ **38.** $\int \frac{x}{\sqrt{x + 5}} \, dx$

39. $\int x(x - 4)^9 \, dx$ **40.** $\int x(x + 6)^8 \, dx$

41. $\int e^{2x} (1 + e^{2x})^3 \, dx$ **42.** $\int e^{-x} (1 - e^{-x})^4 \, dx$

43. $\int \frac{1 + x}{4 + 2x + x^2} \, dx$ **44.** $\int \frac{x^2 - 1}{x^3 - 3x + 7} \, dx$

In Problems 45–50, the indefinite integral can be found in more than one way. First use the substitution method to find the indefinite integral. Then find it without using substitution. Check that your answers are equivalent.

45. $\int 5(5x + 3) \, dx$ **46.** $\int -7(4 - 7x) \, dx$

47. $\int 2x(x^2 - 1) \, dx$ **48.** $\int 3x^2 (x^3 + 1) \, dx$

49. $\int 5x^4 (x^5)^4 \, dx$ **50.** $\int 8x^7 (x^8)^3 \, dx$

51. Is $F(x) = x^2 e^x$ an antiderivative of $f(x) = 2xe^x$? Explain.

52. Is $F(x) = \dfrac{1}{x}$ an antiderivative of $f(x) = \ln x$? Explain.

53. Is $F(x) = (x^2 + 4)^6$ an antiderivative of $f(x) = 12x(x^2 + 4)^5$? Explain.

54. Is $F(x) = (x^2 - 1)^{100}$ an antiderivative of $f(x) = 200x(x^2 - 1)^{99}$? Explain.

55. Is $F(x) = e^{2x} + 4$ an antiderivative of $f(x) = e^{2x}$? Explain.

56. Is $F(x) = 1 - 0.2e^{-5x}$ an antiderivative of $f(x) = e^{-5x}$? Explain.

57. Is $F(x) = 0.5(\ln x)^2 + 10$ an antiderivative of $f(x) = \dfrac{\ln x}{x}$? Explain.

58. Is $F(x) = \ln(\ln x)$ an antiderivative of $f(x) = \dfrac{l}{x \ln x}$? Explain.

In Problems 59–70, find each indefinite integral and check the result by differentiating.

59. $\displaystyle\int x\sqrt{3x^2 + 7}\, dx$

60. $\displaystyle\int x^2\sqrt{2x^3 + 1}\, dx$

61. $\displaystyle\int x(x^3 + 2)^2\, dx$

62. $\displaystyle\int x(x^2 + 2)^2\, dx$

63. $\displaystyle\int x^2(x^3 + 2)^2\, dx$

64. $\displaystyle\int (x^2 + 2)^2\, dx$

65. $\displaystyle\int \dfrac{x^3}{\sqrt{2x^4 + 3}}\, dx$

66. $\displaystyle\int \dfrac{x^2}{\sqrt{4x^3 - 1}}\, dx$

67. $\displaystyle\int \dfrac{(\ln x)^3}{x}\, dx$

68. $\displaystyle\int \dfrac{e^x}{1 + e^x}\, dx$

69. $\displaystyle\int \dfrac{1}{x^2}e^{-1/x}\, dx$

70. $\displaystyle\int \dfrac{1}{x \ln x}\, dx$

In Problems 71–76, find the family of all antiderivatives of each derivative.

71. $\dfrac{dx}{dt} = 7t^2(t^3 + 5)^6$

72. $\dfrac{dm}{dn} = 10n(n^2 - 8)^7$

73. $\dfrac{dy}{dt} = \dfrac{3t}{\sqrt{t^2 - 4}}$

74. $\dfrac{dy}{dx} = \dfrac{5x^2}{(x^3 - 7)^4}$

75. $\dfrac{dp}{dx} = \dfrac{e^x + e^{-x}}{(e^x - e^{-x})^2}$

76. $\dfrac{dm}{dt} = \dfrac{\ln(t - 5)}{t - 5}$

Applications

77. Price–demand equation. The marginal price for a weekly demand of x bottles of shampoo in a drugstore is given by

$$p'(x) = \dfrac{-6,000}{(3x + 50)^2}$$

Find the price–demand equation if the weekly demand is 150 when the price of a bottle of shampoo is \$8. What is the weekly demand when the price is \$6.50?

78. Price–supply equation. The marginal price at a supply level of x bottles of laundry detergent per week is given by

$$p'(x) = \dfrac{300}{(3x + 25)^2}$$

Find the price–supply equation if the distributor of the detergent is willing to supply 75 bottles a week at a price of \$5.00 per bottle. How many bottles would the supplier be willing to supply at a price of \$5.15 per bottle?

79. Cost function. The weekly marginal cost of producing x pairs of tennis shoes is given by

$$C'(x) = 12 + \dfrac{500}{x + 1}$$

where $C(x)$ is cost in dollars. If the fixed costs are \$2,000 per week, find the cost function. What is the average cost per pair of shoes if 1,000 pairs of shoes are produced each week?

80. Revenue function. The weekly marginal revenue from the sale of x pairs of tennis shoes is given by

$$R'(x) = 40 - 0.02x + \dfrac{200}{x + 1} \qquad R(0) = 0$$

where $R(x)$ is revenue in dollars. Find the revenue function. Find the revenue from the sale of 1,000 pairs of shoes.

81. Marketing. An automobile company is ready to introduce a new line of hybrid cars through a national sales campaign. After test marketing the line in a carefully selected city, the marketing research department estimates that sales (in millions of dollars) will increase at the monthly rate of

$$S'(t) = 10 - 10e^{-0.1t} \qquad 0 \le t \le 24$$

t months after the campaign has started.

(A) What will be the total sales $S(t)$ t months after the beginning of the national campaign if we assume no sales at the beginning of the campaign?

(B) What are the estimated total sales for the first 12 months of the campaign?

(C) When will the estimated total sales reach \$100 million? Use a graphing calculator to approximate the answer to two decimal places.

82. Marketing. Repeat Problem 81 if the monthly rate of increase in sales is found to be approximated by

$$S'(t) = 20 - 20e^{-0.05t} \qquad 0 \le t \le 24$$

83. Oil production. Using production and geological data, the management of an oil company estimates that oil will be pumped from a field producing at a rate given by

$$R(t) = \dfrac{100}{t + 1} + 5 \qquad 0 \le t \le 20$$

where $R(t)$ is the rate of production (in thousands of barrels per year) t years after pumping begins. How many barrels of oil $Q(t)$ will the field produce in the first t years if $Q(0) = 0$? How many barrels will be produced in the first 9 years?

84. Oil production. Assume that the rate in Problem 83 is found to be

$$R(t) = \frac{120t}{t^2 + 1} + 3 \qquad 0 \le t \le 20$$

(A) When is the rate of production greatest?

(B) How many barrels of oil $Q(t)$ will the field produce in the first t years if $Q(0) = 0$? How many barrels will be produced in the first 5 years?

(C) How long (to the nearest tenth of a year) will it take to produce a total of a quarter of a million barrels of oil?

85. Biology. A yeast culture is growing at the rate of $w'(t) = 0.2e^{0.1t}$ grams per hour. If the starting culture weighs 2 grams, what will be the weight of the culture $W(t)$ after t hours? After 8 hours?

86. Medicine. The rate of healing for a skin wound (in square centimeters per day) is approximated by $A'(t) = -0.9e^{-0.1t}$. If the initial wound has an area of 9 square centimeters, what will its area $A(t)$ be after t days? After 5 days?

87. Pollution. A contaminated lake is treated with a bactericide. The rate of increase in harmful bacteria t days after the treatment is given by

$$\frac{dN}{dt} = -\frac{2{,}000t}{1 + t^2} \qquad 0 \le t \le 10$$

where $N(t)$ is the number of bacteria per milliliter of water. Since dN/dt is negative, the count of harmful bacteria is decreasing.

(A) Find the minimum value of dN/dt.

(B) If the initial count was 5,000 bacteria per milliliter, find $N(t)$ and then find the bacteria count after 10 days.

(C) When (to two decimal places) is the bacteria count 1,000 bacteria per milliliter?

88. Pollution. An oil tanker aground on a reef is losing oil and producing an oil slick that is radiating outward at a rate given approximately by

$$\frac{dR}{dt} = \frac{60}{\sqrt{t + 9}} \qquad t \ge 0$$

where R is the radius (in feet) of the circular slick after t minutes. Find the radius of the slick after 16 minutes if the radius is 0 when $t = 0$.

89. Learning. An average student enrolled in an advanced typing class progressed at a rate of $N'(t) = 6e^{-0.1t}$ words per minute per week t weeks after enrolling in a 15-week course. If, at the beginning of the course, a student could type 40 words per minute, how many words per minute $N(t)$ would the student be expected to type t weeks into the course? After completing the course?

90. Learning. An average student enrolled in a stenotyping class progressed at a rate of $N'(t) = 12e^{-0.06t}$ words per minute per week t weeks after enrolling in a 15-week course. If, at the beginning of the course, a student could stenotype at zero words per minute, how many words per minute $N(t)$ would the student be expected to handle t weeks into the course? After completing the course?

91. College enrollment. The projected rate of increase in enrollment at a new college is estimated by

$$\frac{dE}{dt} = 5{,}000(t + 1)^{-3/2} \qquad t \ge 0$$

where $E(t)$ is the projected enrollment in t years. If enrollment is 2,000 now ($t = 0$), find the projected enrollment 15 years from now.

Answers to Matched Problems

1. (A) $\frac{1}{21}(2x^3 - 3)^{21} + C$ (B) $e^{5x} + C$
   (C) $\ln|4 + x^2| + C$ or $\ln(4 + x^2) + C$, since $4 + x^2 > 0$
2. (A) $dy = 3x^2\, dx$
   (B) $du = \frac{2x}{2 + x^2}dx$
   (C) $dv = -5e^{-5t}\, dt$
3. $\frac{1}{5}(x^2 - 3x + 7)^5 + C$
4. (A) $\frac{1}{6}(2x^3 - 3)^5 + C$ (B) $e^{5w} + C$
5. (A) $-\frac{1}{3}e^{-3x} + C$ (B) $\frac{1}{2}\ln|x^2 - 9| + C$
   (C) $-\frac{5}{3}(t^3 + 4)^{-1} + C$
6. $\frac{2}{5}(x + 1)^{5/2} - \frac{2}{3}(x + 1)^{3/2} + C$
7. $p(x) = 0.1e^{0.01x} + 3.38$; 179 tubes

5.3 Differential Equations; Growth and Decay

- Differential Equations and Slope Fields
- Continuous Compound Interest Revisited
- Exponential Growth Law
- Population Growth, Radioactive Decay, and Learning
- Comparison of Exponential Growth Phenomena

In the preceding section, we considered equations of the form

$$\frac{dy}{dx} = 6x^2 - 4x \qquad y' = -400e^{-0.04x}$$

These are examples of *differential equations*. In general, an equation is a **differential equation** if it involves an unknown function and one or more of its derivatives. Other examples of differential equations are

$$\frac{dy}{dx} = ky \qquad y'' - xy' + x^2 = 5 \qquad \frac{dy}{dx} = 2xy$$

The first and third equations are called **first-order** equations because each involves a first derivative but no higher derivative. The second equation is called a **second-order** equation because it involves a second derivative but no higher derivative.

A **solution** of a differential equation is a function $f(x)$ which, when substituted for y, satisfies the equation; that is, the left side and right side of the equation are the same function. Finding a solution of a given differential equation may be very difficult. However, it is easy to determine whether or not a given function is a solution of a given differential equation. Just substitute and check whether both sides of the differential equation are equal as functions. For example, even if you have trouble finding a function y that satisfies the differential equation

$$(x - 3)\frac{dy}{dx} = y + 4 \tag{1}$$

it is easy to determine whether or not the function $y = 5x - 19$ is a solution: Since $dy/dx = 5$, the left side of (1) is $(x - 3)5$ and the right side is $(5x - 19) + 4$, so the left and right sides are equal and $y = 5x - 19$ is a solution.

In this section, we emphasize a few special first-order differential equations that have immediate and significant applications. We start by looking at some first-order equations geometrically, in terms of *slope fields*. We then consider continuous compound interest as modeled by a first-order differential equation. From this treatment, we can generalize our approach to a wide variety of other types of growth phenomena.

Differential Equations and Slope Fields

We introduce the concept of *slope field* through an example. Consider the first-order differential equation

$$\frac{dy}{dx} = 0.2y \tag{2}$$

A function f is a solution of equation (2) if $y = f(x)$ satisfies equation (2) for all values of x in the domain of f. Geometrically interpreted, equation (2) gives us the slope of a solution curve that passes through the point (x, y). For example, if $y = f(x)$ is a solution of equation (2) that passes through the point $(0, 2)$, then the slope of f at $(0, 2)$ is given by

$$\frac{dy}{dx} = 0.2(2) = 0.4$$

We indicate this relationship by drawing a short segment of the tangent line at the point $(0, 2)$, as shown in Figure 1A. The procedure is repeated for points $(-3, 1)$ and $(2, 3)$. Assuming that the graph of f passes through all three points, we sketch an approximate graph of f in Figure 1B.

(A)   (B)

Figure 1

If we continue the process of drawing tangent line segments at each point grid in Figure 1—a task easily handled by computers, but not by hand—we obtain a *slope field*. A slope field for differential equation (2), drawn by a computer, is shown in Figure 2. In general, a **slope field** for a first-order differential equation is obtained by drawing tangent line segments determined by the equation at each point in a grid.

Explore and Discuss 1

(A) In Figure 1A (or a copy), draw tangent line segments for a solution curve of differential equation (2) that passes through $(-3, -1), (0, -2),$ and $(2, -3)$.

(B) In Figure 1B (or a copy), sketch an approximate graph of the solution curve that passes through the three points given in part (A). Repeat the tangent line segments first.

(C) What type of function, of all the elementary functions discussed in the first two chapters, appears to be a solution of differential equation (2)?

Figure 2

In Explore & Discuss 1, if you guessed that all solutions of equation (2) are exponential functions, you are to be congratulated. We now show that

$$y = Ce^{0.2x} \tag{3}$$

is a solution of equation (2) for any real number C. We substitute $y = Ce^{0.2x}$ into equation (2) to see if the left side is equal to the right side for all real x:

$$\frac{dy}{dx} = 0.2y$$

$$\textit{Left side:} \quad \frac{dy}{dx} = \frac{d}{dx}(Ce^{0.2x}) = 0.2Ce^{0.2x}$$

$$\textit{Right side:} \quad 0.2y = 0.2Ce^{0.2x}$$

So equation (3) is a solution of equation (2) for C any real number. Which values of C will produce solution curves that pass through $(0, 2)$ and $(0, -2)$, respectively? Substituting the coordinates of each point into equation (3) and solving for C, we obtain

$$y = 2e^{0.2x} \quad \text{and} \quad y = -2e^{0.2x} \tag{4}$$

The graphs of equations (4) are shown in Figure 3, and they confirm the results shown in Figure 1B. We say that (3) is the **general solution** of the differential equation (2), and the functions in (4) are the **particular solutions** that satisfy $y(0) = 2$ and $y(0) = -2$, respectively.

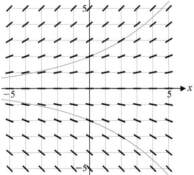

Figure 3

CONCEPTUAL INSIGHT

For a complicated first-order differential equation, say,

$$\frac{dy}{dx} = \frac{3 + \sqrt{xy}}{x^2 - 5y^4}$$

it may be impossible to find a formula analogous to (3) for its solutions. Nevertheless, it is routine to evaluate the right-hand side at each point in a grid. The resulting slope field provides a graphical representation of the solutions of the differential equation.

Drawing slope fields by hand is not a task for human beings: A 20-by-20 grid would require drawing 400 tangent line segments! Repetitive tasks of this type are what computers are for. A few problems in Exercises 5.3 involve interpreting slope fields, not drawing them.

Continuous Compound Interest Revisited

Let P be the initial amount of money deposited in an account, and let A be the amount in the account at any time t. Instead of assuming that the money in the account earns a particular rate of interest, suppose we say that the rate of growth of the amount of money in the account at any time t is proportional to the amount present at that time. Since dA/dt is the rate of growth of A with respect to t, we have

$$\frac{dA}{dt} = rA \qquad A(0) = P \qquad A, P > 0 \tag{5}$$

where r is an appropriate constant. We would like to find a function $A = A(t)$ that satisfies these conditions. Multiplying both sides of equation (5) by $1/A$, we obtain

$$\frac{1}{A}\frac{dA}{dt} = r$$

Now we integrate each side with respect to t:

$$\int \frac{1}{A}\frac{dA}{dt}dt = \int r\,dt \qquad \frac{dA}{dt}dt = A'(t)\,dt = dA$$

$$\int \frac{1}{A}dA = \int r\,dt$$

$$\ln|A| = rt + C \qquad |A| = A, \text{ since } A > 0$$

$$\ln A = rt + C$$

We convert this last equation into the equivalent exponential form

$$A = e^{rt+C} \qquad \text{Definition of logarithmic function:}$$
$$y = \ln x \text{ if and only if } x = e^y$$

$$= e^C e^{rt} \qquad \text{Property of exponents: } b^m b^n = b^{m+n}$$

Since $A(0) = P$, we evaluate $A(t) = e^C e^{rt}$ at $t = 0$ and set the result equal to P:

$$A(0) = e^C e^0 = e^C = P$$

Hence, $e^C = P$, and we can rewrite $A = e^C e^{rt}$ in the form

$$A = Pe^{rt}$$

This is the same continuous compound interest formula obtained in Section 4.1, where the principal P is invested at an annual nominal rate r compounded continuously for t years.

Exponential Growth Law

In general, if the rate of change of a quantity Q with respect to time is proportional to the amount of Q present and $Q(0) = Q_0$, then, proceeding in exactly the same way as we just did, we obtain the following theorem:

THEOREM 1 Exponential Growth Law

If $\dfrac{dQ}{dt} = rQ$ and $Q(0) = Q_0$, then $Q = Q_0 e^{rt}$,

where

$Q_0 = $ amount of Q at $t = 0$
$r = $ relative growth rate (expressed as a decimal)
$t = $ time
$Q = $ quantity at time t

The constant r in the exponential growth law is called the **relative growth rate**. If the relative growth rate is $r = 0.02$, then the quantity Q is growing at a rate $dQ/dt = 0.02Q$ (that is, 2% of the quantity Q per unit of time t). Note the distinction between the relative growth rate r and the rate of growth dQ/dt of the quantity Q. If $r < 0$, then $dQ/dt < 0$ and Q is decreasing. This type of growth is called **exponential decay**.

Once we know that the rate of growth is proportional to the amount present, we recognize exponential growth and can use Theorem 1 without solving the differential equation each time. The exponential growth law applies not only to money invested at interest compounded continuously, but also to many other types of problems—population growth, radioactive decay, the depletion of a natural resource, and so on.

Population Growth, Radioactive Decay, and Learning

The world population passed 1 billion in 1804, 2 billion in 1927, 3 billion in 1960, 4 billion in 1974, 5 billion in 1987, and 6 billion in 1999, as illustrated in Figure 4. **Population growth** over certain periods often can be approximated by the exponential growth law of Theorem 1.

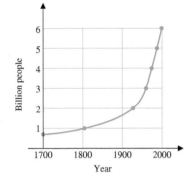

Figure 4 **World population growth**

EXAMPLE 1   Population Growth   India had a population of about 1.2 billion in 2010 $(t = 0)$. Let P represent the population (in billions) t years after 2010, and assume a growth rate of 1.5% compounded continuously.

(A) Find an equation that represents India's population growth after 2010, assuming that the 1.5% growth rate continues.

(B) What is the estimated population (to the nearest tenth of a billion) of India in the year 2030?

(C) Graph the equation found in part (A) from 2010 to 2030.

SOLUTION

(A) The exponential growth law applies, and we have

$$\frac{dP}{dt} = 0.015P \qquad P(0) = 1.2$$

Therefore,

$$P = 1.2e^{0.015t} \tag{6}$$

(B) Using equation (6), we can estimate the population in India in 2030 $(t = 20)$:

$$P = 1.2e^{0.015(20)} = 1.6 \text{ billion people}$$

(C) The graph is shown in Figure 5.

Figure 5 **Population of India**

Matched Problem 1   Assuming the same continuous compound growth rate as in Example 1, what will India's population be (to the nearest tenth of a billion) in the year 2020?

EXAMPLE 2   Population Growth   If the exponential growth law applies to Canada's population growth, at what continuous compound growth rate will the population double over the next 100 years?

SOLUTION   We must find r, given that $P = 2P_0$ and $t = 100$:

$$P = P_0e^{rt}$$
$$2P_0 = P_0e^{100r}$$
$$2 = e^{100r} \qquad \text{Take the natural logarithm}$$
$$100r = \ln 2 \qquad \text{of both sides and reverse}$$
$$r = \frac{\ln 2}{100} \qquad \text{the equation.}$$
$$\approx 0.0069 \quad \text{or} \quad 0.69\%$$

Matched Problem 2⌋ If the exponential growth law applies to population growth in Nigeria, find the doubling time (to the nearest year) of the population if it grows at 2.1% per year compounded continuously.

We now turn to another type of exponential growth: **radioactive decay**. In 1946, Willard Libby (who later received a Nobel Prize in chemistry) found that as long as a plant or animal is alive, radioactive carbon-14 is maintained at a constant level in its tissues. Once the plant or animal is dead, however, the radioactive carbon-14 diminishes by radioactive decay at a rate proportional to the amount present.

$$\frac{dQ}{dt} = rQ \qquad Q(0) = Q_0$$

This is another example of the exponential growth law. The continuous compound rate of decay for radioactive carbon-14 is 0.000 123 8, so $r = -0.000\ 123\ 8$, since decay implies a negative continuous compound growth rate.

EXAMPLE 3 Archaeology A human bone fragment was found at an archaeological site in Africa. If 10% of the original amount of radioactive carbon-14 was present, estimate the age of the bone (to the nearest 100 years).

SOLUTION By the exponential growth law for

$$\frac{dQ}{dt} = -0.000\ 123\ 8Q \qquad Q(0) = Q_0$$

we have

$$Q = Q_0 e^{-0.0001238t}$$

We must find t so that $Q = 0.1Q_0$ (since the amount of carbon-14 present now is 10% of the amount Q_0 present at the death of the person).

$$0.1Q_0 = Q_0 e^{-0.0001238t}$$
$$0.1 = e^{-0.0001238t}$$
$$\ln 0.1 = \ln e^{-0.0001238t}$$
$$t = \frac{\ln 0.1}{-0.000\ 123\ 8} \approx 18{,}600 \text{ years}$$

Figure 6 $y_1 = e^{-0.0001238x}$;
$y_2 = 0.1$

See Figure 6 for a graphical solution to Example 3.

Matched Problem 3⌋ Estimate the age of the bone in Example 3 (to the nearest 100 years) if 50% of the original amount of carbon-14 is present.

In learning certain skills, such as typing and swimming, one often assumes that there is a maximum skill attainable—say, M—and the rate of improvement is proportional to the difference between what has been achieved y and the maximum attainable M. Mathematically,

$$\frac{dy}{dt} = k(M - y) \qquad y(0) = 0$$

We solve this type of problem with the same technique used to obtain the exponential growth law. First, multiply both sides of the first equation by $1/(M - y)$ to get

$$\frac{1}{M - y}\frac{dy}{dt} = k$$

and then integrate each side with respect to t:

$$\int \frac{1}{M-y} \frac{dy}{dt} dt = \int k \, dt$$

$$-\int \frac{1}{M-y} \left(-\frac{dy}{dt}\right) dt = \int k \, dt \qquad \text{Substitute } u = M - y \text{ and}$$

$$-\int \frac{1}{u} du = \int k \, dt \qquad du = -dy = -\frac{dy}{dt} dt.$$

$$-\ln|u| = kt + C \qquad \text{Substitute } M - y, \text{ which is } > 0, \text{ for } u.$$
$$-\ln(M-y) = kt + C \qquad \text{Multiply both sides by } -1.$$
$$\ln(M-y) = -kt - C$$

Change this last equation to an equivalent exponential form:

$$M - y = e^{-kt-C}$$
$$M - y = e^{-C} e^{-kt}$$
$$y = M - e^{-C} e^{-kt}$$

Now, $y(0) = 0$; hence,

$$y(0) = M - e^{-C} e^0 = 0$$

Solving for e^{-C}, we obtain

$$e^{-C} = M$$

and our final solution is

$$y = M - Me^{-kt} = M(1 - e^{-kt})$$

EXAMPLE 4   Learning   For a particular person learning to swim, the distance y (in feet) that the person is able to swim in 1 minute after t hours of practice is given approximately by

$$y = 50(1 - e^{-0.04t})$$

What is the rate of improvement (to two decimal places) after 10 hours of practice?

SOLUTION

$$y = 50 - 50e^{-0.04t}$$
$$y'(t) = 2e^{-0.04t}$$
$$y'(10) = 2e^{-0.04(10)} \approx 1.34 \text{ feet per hour of practice}$$

Matched Problem 4   In Example 4, what is the rate of improvement (to two decimal places) after 50 hours of practice?

Comparison of Exponential Growth Phenomena

Table 1 compares four widely used growth models. Each model (column 2) consists of a first-order differential equation and an **initial condition** that specifies $y(0)$, the value of a solution y when $x = 0$. The differential equation has a family of solutions, but there is only one solution (the particular solution in column 3) that also satisfies the initial condition [just as there is a family, $y = x^2 + k$, of antiderivatives of $g(x) = 2x$, but only one antiderivative (the particular antiderivative $y = x^2 + 5$) that also satisfies the condition $y(0) = 5$]. A graph of the model's solution is shown in column 4 of Table 1, followed by a short (and necessarily incomplete) list of areas in which the model is used.

Table 1 **Exponential Growth**

Description	Model	Solution	Graph	Uses
Unlimited growth: Rate of growth is proportional to the amount present	$\dfrac{dy}{dt} = ky$ $k, t > 0$ $y(0) = c$	$y = ce^{kt}$		• Short-term population growth (people, bacteria, etc.) • Growth of money at continuous compound interest • Price–supply curves
Exponential decay: Rate of growth is proportional to the amount present	$\dfrac{dy}{dt} = -ky$ $k, t > 0$ $y(0) = c$	$y = ce^{-kt}$		• Depletion of natural resources • Radioactive decay • Absorption of light in water • Price–demand curves • Atmospheric pressure (t is altitude)
Limited growth: Rate of growth is proportional to the difference between the amount present and a fixed limit	$\dfrac{dy}{dt} = k(M - y)$ $k, t > 0$ $y(0) = 0$	$y = M(1 - e^{-kt})$		• Sales fads (for example, skateboards) • Depreciation of equipment • Company growth • Learning
Logistic growth: Rate of growth is proportional to the amount present and to the difference between the amount present and a fixed limit	$\dfrac{dy}{dt} = ky(M - y)$ $k, t > 0$ $y(0) = \dfrac{M}{1 + c}$	$y = \dfrac{M}{1 + ce^{-kMt}}$		• Long-term population growth • Epidemics • Sales of new products • Spread of a rumor • Company growth

Exercises 5.3

Skills Warm-up Exercises

W   *In Problems 1–8, express the relationship between $f'(x)$ and $f(x)$ in words, and write a differential equation that $f(x)$ satisfies. For example, the derivative of $f(x) = e^{3x}$ is 3 times $f(x)$; $y' = 3y$. (If necessary, review Section 3.4).*

1. $f(x) = e^{5x}$

2. $f(x) = e^{-2x}$

3. $f(x) = 10e^{-x}$

4. $f(x) = 25e^{0.04x}$

5. $f(x) = 3.2e^{x^2}$

6. $f(x) = e^{-x^2}$

7. $f(x) = 1 - e^{-x}$

8. $f(x) = 1 - e^{-3x}$

In Problems 9–20, find the general or particular solution, as indicated, for each first-order differential equation.

9. $\dfrac{dy}{dx} = 6x$

10. $\dfrac{dy}{dx} = 3x^{-2}$

11. $\dfrac{dy}{dx} = \dfrac{7}{x}$

12. $\dfrac{dy}{dx} = e^{0.1x}$

13. $\dfrac{dy}{dx} = e^{0.02x}$

14. $\dfrac{dy}{dx} = 8x^{-1}$

15. $\dfrac{dy}{dx} = x^2 - x; y(0) = 0$

16. $\dfrac{dy}{dx} = \sqrt{x}; y(0) = 0$

17. $\dfrac{dy}{dx} = -2xe^{-x^2}; y(0) = 3$

18. $\dfrac{dy}{dx} = e^{x-3}; y(3) = -5$

19. $\dfrac{dy}{dx} = \dfrac{2}{1 + x}; y(0) = 5$

20. $\dfrac{dy}{dx} = \dfrac{1}{4(3 - x)}; y(0) = 1$

In Problems 21–24, give the order (first, second, third, etc.) of each differential equation, where y represents a function of the variable x.

21. $y - 2y' + x^3y'' = 0$

22. $xy' + y^4 = e^x$

23. $y''' - 3y'' + 3y' - y = 0$

24. $y^3 + x^4y'' = \dfrac{5y}{1 + x^2}$

25. Is $y = 5x$ a solution of the differential equation $\dfrac{dy}{dx} = \dfrac{y}{x}$? Explain.

26. Is $y = 8x + 8$ a solution of the differential equation $\dfrac{dy}{dx} = \dfrac{y}{x + 1}$? Explain.

27. Is $y = \sqrt{9 + x^2}$ a solution of the differential equation $y' = \dfrac{x}{y}$? Explain.

28. Is $y = 5e^{x^2/2}$ a solution of the differential equation $y' = xy$? Explain.

29. Is $y = e^{3x}$ a solution of the differential equation $y'' - 4y' + 3y = 0$? Explain.

30. Is $y = -2e^x$ a solution of the differential equation $y'' - 4y' + 3y = 0$? Explain.

31. Is $y = 100e^{3x}$ a solution of the differential equation $y'' - 4y' + 3y = 0$? Explain.

32. Is $y = e^{-3x}$ a solution of the differential equation $y'' - 4y' + 3y = 0$? Explain.

Problems 33–38 refer to the following slope fields:

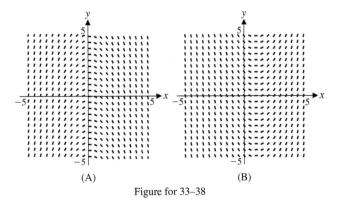

(A)   (B)

Figure for 33–38

33. Which slope field is associated with the differential equation $dy/dx = x - 1$? Briefly justify your answer.

34. Which slope field is associated with the differential equation $dy/dx = -x$? Briefly justify your answer.

35. Solve the differential equation $dy/dx = x - 1$ and find the particular solution that passes through $(0, -2)$.

36. Solve the differential equation $dy/dx = -x$ and find the particular solution that passes through $(0, 3)$.

37. Graph the particular solution found in Problem 35 in the appropriate Figure A or B (or a copy).

38. Graph the particular solution found in Problem 36 in the appropriate Figure A or B (or a copy).

In Problems 39–46, find the general or particular solution, as indicated, for each differential equation.

39. $\dfrac{dy}{dt} = 2y$

40. $\dfrac{dy}{dt} = -3y$

41. $\dfrac{dy}{dx} = -0.5y; \ y(0) = 100$

42. $\dfrac{dy}{dx} = 0.1y; \ y(0) = -2.5$

43. $\dfrac{dx}{dt} = -5x$

44. $\dfrac{dx}{dt} = 4t$

45. $\dfrac{dx}{dt} = -5t$

46. $\dfrac{dx}{dt} = 4x$

In Problems 47–50, does the given differential equation model unlimited growth, exponential decay, limited growth, or logistic growth?

47. $y' = 2.5y(300 - y)$

48. $y' = -0.0152y$

49. $y' = 0.43y$

50. $y' = 10,000 - y$

Problems 51–58 refer to the following slope fields:

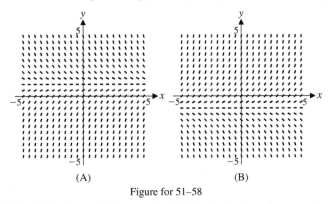

(A)   (B)

Figure for 51–58

51. Which slope field is associated with the differential equation $dy/dx = 1 - y$? Briefly justify your answer.

52. Which slope field is associated with the differential equation $dy/dx = y + 1$? Briefly justify your answer.

53. Show that $y = 1 - Ce^{-x}$ is a solution of the differential equation $dy/dx = 1 - y$ for any real number C. Find the particular solution that passes through $(0, 0)$.

54. Show that $y = Ce^x - 1$ is a solution of the differential equation $dy/dx = y + 1$ for any real number C. Find the particular solution that passes through $(0, 0)$.

55. Graph the particular solution found in Problem 53 in the appropriate Figure A or B (or a copy).

56. Graph the particular solution found in Problem 54 in the appropriate Figure A or B (or a copy).

57. Use a graphing calculator to graph $y = 1 - Ce^{-x}$ for $C = -2, -1, 1,$ and 2, for $-5 \le x \le 5, -5 \le y \le 5$, all in the same viewing window. Observe how the solution curves go with the flow of the tangent line segments in the corresponding slope field shown in Figure A or Figure B.

58. Use a graphing calculator to graph $y = Ce^x - 1$ for $C = -2, -1, 1,$ and 2, for $-5 \le x \le 5, -5 \le y \le 5$, all in the same viewing window. Observe how the solution curves go with the flow of the tangent line segments in the corresponding slope field shown in Figure A or Figure B.

59. Show that $y = \sqrt{C - x^2}$ is a solution of the differential equation $dy/dx = -x/y$ for any positive real number C. Find the particular solution that passes through $(3, 4)$.

60. Show that $y = \sqrt{x^2 + C}$ is a solution of the differential equation $dy/dx = x/y$ for any real number C. Find the particular solution that passes through $(-6, 7)$.

61. Show that $y = Cx$ is a solution of the differential equation $dy/dx = y/x$ for any real number C. Find the particular solution that passes through $(-8, 24)$.

62. Show that $y = C/x$ is a solution of the differential equation $dy/dx = -y/x$ for any real number C. Find the particular solution that passes through $(2, 5)$.

63. Show that $y = 1/(1 + ce^{-t})$ is a solution of the differential equation $dy/dt = y(1 - y)$ for any real number c. Find the particular solution that passes through $(0, -1)$.

64. Show that $y = 2/(1 + ce^{-6t})$ is a solution of the differential equation $dy/dt = 3y(2 - y)$ for any real number c. Find the particular solution that passes through $(0, 1)$.

In Problems 65–72, use a graphing calculator to graph the given examples of the various cases in Table 1 on page 349.

65. Unlimited growth:

$y = 1,000e^{0.08t}$
$0 \le t \le 15$
$0 \le y \le 3,500$

66. Unlimited growth:

$y = 5,250e^{0.12t}$
$0 \le t \le 10$
$0 \le y \le 20,000$

67. Exponential decay:

$p = 100e^{-0.05x}$
$0 \le x \le 30$
$0 \le p \le 100$

68. Exponential decay:

$p = 1,000e^{-0.08x}$
$0 \le x \le 40$
$0 \le p \le 1,000$

69. Limited growth:

$N = 100(1 - e^{-0.05t})$
$0 \le t \le 100$
$0 \le N \le 100$

70. Limited growth:

$N = 1,000(1 - e^{-0.07t})$
$0 \le t \le 70$
$0 \le N \le 1,000$

71. Logistic growth:

$N = \dfrac{1,000}{1 + 999e^{-0.4t}}$
$0 \le t \le 40$
$0 \le N \le 1,000$

72. Logistic growth:

$N = \dfrac{400}{1 + 99e^{-0.4t}}$
$0 \le t \le 30$
$0 \le N \le 400$

73. Show that the rate of logistic growth, $dy/dt = ky(M - y)$, has its maximum value when $y = M/2$.

74. Find the value of t for which the logistic function

$$y = \frac{M}{1 + ce^{-kMt}}$$

is equal to $M/2$.

75. Let $Q(t)$ denote the population of the world at time t. In 1999, the world population was 6.0 billion and increasing at 1.3% per year; in 2009, it was 6.8 billion and increasing at 1.2% per year. In which year, 1999 or 2009, was dQ/dt (the rate of growth of Q with respect to t) greater? Explain.

76. Refer to Problem 75. Explain why the world population function $Q(t)$ does not satisfy an exponential growth law.

Applications

77. Continuous compound interest. Find the amount A in an account after t years if

$$\frac{dA}{dt} = 0.03A \quad \text{and} \quad A(0) = 1,000$$

78. Continuous compound interest. Find the amount A in an account after t years if

$$\frac{dA}{dt} = 0.02A \quad \text{and} \quad A(0) = 5,250$$

79. Continuous compound interest. Find the amount A in an account after t years if

$$\frac{dA}{dt} = rA \quad A(0) = 8,000 \quad A(2) = 8,260.14$$

80. Continuous compound interest. Find the amount A in an account after t years if

$$\frac{dA}{dt} = rA \quad A(0) = 5,000 \quad A(5) = 5,581.39$$

81. Price–demand. The marginal price dp/dx at x units of demand per week is proportional to the price p. There is no weekly demand at a price of $100 per unit $[p(0) = 100]$, and there is a weekly demand of 5 units at a price of $77.88 per unit $[p(5) = 77.88]$.

(A) Find the price–demand equation.

(B) At a demand of 10 units per week, what is the price?

(C) Graph the price–demand equation for $0 \le x \le 25$.

82. Price–supply. The marginal price dp/dx at x units of supply per day is proportional to the price p. There is no supply at a price of $10 per unit $[p(0) = 10]$, and there is a daily supply of 50 units at a price of $12.84 per unit $[p(50) = 12.84]$.

(A) Find the price–supply equation.

(B) At a supply of 100 units per day, what is the price?

(C) Graph the price–supply equation for $0 \le x \le 250$.

83. Advertising. A company is trying to expose a new product to as many people as possible through TV ads. Suppose that the rate of exposure to new people is proportional to the number of those who have not seen the product out of L possible viewers (limited growth). No one is aware of the product at the start of the campaign, and after 10 days, 40% of L are aware of the product. Mathematically,

$$\frac{dN}{dt} = k(L - N) \quad N(0) = 0 \quad N(10) = 0.4L$$

(A) Solve the differential equation.

(B) What percent of L will have been exposed after 5 days of the campaign?

(C) How many days will it take to expose 80% of L?

(D) Graph the solution found in part (A) for $0 \le t \le 90$.

84. Advertising. Suppose that the differential equation for Problem 83 is

$$\frac{dN}{dt} = k(L - N) \quad N(0) = 0 \quad N(10) = 0.1L$$

(A) Explain what the equation $N(10) = 0.1L$ means.

(B) Solve the differential equation.

(C) How many days will it take to expose 50% of L?

(D) Graph the solution found in part (B) for $0 \le t \le 300$.

85. Biology. For relatively clear bodies of water, the intensity of light is reduced according to

$$\frac{dI}{dx} = -kI \quad I(0) = I_0$$

where I is the intensity of light at x feet below the surface. For the Sargasso Sea off the West Indies, $k = 0.00942$. Find I in terms of x, and find the depth at which the light is reduced to half of that at the surface.

86. Blood pressure. Under certain assumptions, the blood pressure P in the largest artery in the human body (the aorta) changes between beats with respect to time t according to

$$\frac{dP}{dt} = -aP \quad P(0) = P_0$$

where a is a constant. Find $P = P(t)$ that satisfies both conditions.

87. Drug concentration. A single injection of a drug is administered to a patient. The amount Q in the body then decreases at a rate proportional to the amount present. For a particular drug, the rate is 4% per hour. Thus,

$$\frac{dQ}{dt} = -0.04Q \qquad Q(0) = Q_0$$

where t is time in hours.

(A) If the initial injection is 3 milliliters $[Q(0) = 3]$, find $Q = Q(t)$ satisfying both conditions.

(B) How many milliliters (to two decimal places) are in the body after 10 hours?

(C) How many hours (to two decimal places) will it take for only 1 milliliter of the drug to be left in the body?

(D) Graph the solution found in part (A).

88. Simple epidemic. A community of 1,000 people is homogeneously mixed. One person who has just returned from another community has influenza. Assume that the home community has not had influenza shots and all are susceptible. One mathematical model assumes that influenza tends to spread at a rate in direct proportion to the number N who have the disease and to the number $1,000 - N$ who have not yet contracted the disease (logistic growth). Mathematically,

$$\frac{dN}{dt} = kN(1,000 - N) \qquad N(0) = 1$$

where N is the number of people who have contracted influenza after t days. For $k = 0.0004$, $N(t)$ is the logistic growth function

$$N(t) = \frac{1,000}{1 + 999e^{-0.4t}}$$

(A) How many people have contracted influenza after 10 days? After 20 days?

(B) How many days will it take until half the community has contracted influenza?

(C) Find $\lim_{t \to \infty} N(t)$.

(D) Graph $N = N(t)$ for $0 \le t \le 30$.

89. Nuclear accident. One of the dangerous radioactive isotopes detected after the Chernobyl nuclear disaster in 1986 was cesium-137. If 93.3% of the cesium-137 emitted during the disaster was still present 3 years later, find the continuous compound rate of decay of this isotope.

90. Insecticides. Many countries have banned the use of the insecticide DDT because of its long-term adverse effects. Five years after a particular country stopped using DDT, the amount of DDT in the ecosystem had declined to 75% of the amount present at the time of the ban. Find the continuous compound rate of decay of DDT.

91. Archaeology. A skull found in an ancient tomb has 5% of the original amount of radioactive carbon-14 present. Estimate the age of the skull. (See Example 3.)

92. Learning. For a person learning to type, the number N of words per minute that the person could type after t hours of practice was given by the limited growth function

$$N = 100(1 - e^{-0.02t})$$

What is the rate of improvement after 10 hours of practice? After 40 hours of practice?

93. Small-group analysis. In a study on small-group dynamics, sociologists found that when 10 members of a discussion group were ranked according to the number of times each participated, the number $N(k)$ of times that the kth-ranked person participated was given by

$$N(k) = N_1 e^{-0.11(k-1)} \qquad 1 \le k \le 10$$

where N_1 is the number of times that the first-ranked person participated in the discussion. If $N_1 = 180$, in a discussion group of 10 people, estimate how many times the sixth-ranked person participated. How about the 10th-ranked person?

94. Perception. The Weber–Fechner law concerns a person's sensed perception of various strengths of stimulation involving weights, sound, light, shock, taste, and so on. One form of the law states that the rate of change of sensed sensation S with respect to stimulus R is inversely proportional to the strength of the stimulus R. So

$$\frac{dS}{dR} = \frac{k}{R}$$

where k is a constant. If we let R_0 be the threshold level at which the stimulus R can be detected (the least amount of sound, light, weight, and so on, that can be detected), then

$$S(R_0) = 0$$

Find a function S in terms of R that satisfies these conditions.

95. Rumor propagation. Sociologists have found that a rumor tends to spread at a rate in direct proportion to the number x who have heard it and to the number $P - x$ who have not, where P is the total population (logistic growth). If a resident of a 400-student dormitory hears a rumor that there is a case of TB on campus, then $P = 400$ and

$$\frac{dx}{dt} = 0.001x(400 - x) \qquad x(0) = 1$$

where t is time (in minutes). From these conditions, it can be shown that $x(t)$ is the logistic growth function

$$x(t) = \frac{400}{1 + 399e^{-0.4t}}$$

(A) How many people have heard the rumor after 5 minutes? after 20 minutes?

(B) Find $\lim_{t \to \infty} x(t)$.

(C) Graph $x = x(t)$ for $0 \le t \le 30$.

96. Rumor propagation. In Problem 95, how long (to the nearest minute) will it take for half of the group of 400 to have heard the rumor?

Answers to Matched Problems

1. 1.4 billion people
2. 33 yr
3. 5,600 yr
4. 0.27 ft/hr

5.4 The Definite Integral

- Approximating Areas by Left and Right Sums

- The Definite Integral as a Limit of Sums

- Properties of the Definite Integral

The first three sections of this chapter focused on the *indefinite integral*. In this section, we introduce the *definite integral*. The definite integral is used to compute areas, probabilities, average values of functions, future values of continuous income streams, and many other quantities. Initially, the concept of the definite integral may seem unrelated to the notion of the indefinite integral. There is, however, a close connection between the two integrals. The fundamental theorem of calculus, discussed in Section 5.5, makes that connection precise.

Approximating Areas by Left and Right Sums

How do we find the shaded area in Figure 1? That is, how do we find the area bounded by the graph of $f(x) = 0.25x^2 + 1$, the x axis, and the vertical lines $x = 1$ and $x = 5$? [This cumbersome description is usually shortened to "the area under the graph of $f(x) = 0.25x^2 + 1$ from $x = 1$ to $x = 5$."] Our standard geometric area formulas do not apply directly, but the formula for the area of a rectangle can be used indirectly. To see how, we look at a method of approximating the area under the graph by using rectangles. This method will give us any accuracy desired, which is quite different from finding the area exactly. Our first area approximation is made by dividing the interval $[1, 5]$ on the x axis into four equal parts, each of length

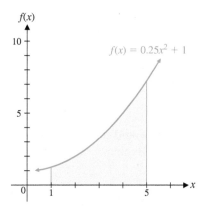

Figure 1 **What is the shaded area?**

$$\Delta x = \frac{5 - 1}{4} = 1*$$

We then place a **left rectangle** on each subinterval, that is, a rectangle whose base is the subinterval and whose height is the value of the function at the *left* endpoint of the subinterval (see Fig. 2).

Summing the areas of the left rectangles in Figure 2 results in a **left sum** of four rectangles, denoted by L_4, as follows:

$$L_4 = f(1) \cdot 1 + f(2) \cdot 1 + f(3) \cdot 1 + f(4) \cdot 1$$
$$= 1.25 + 2.00 + 3.25 + 5 = 11.5$$

From Figure 3, since $f(x)$ is increasing, we see that the left sum L_4 underestimates the area, and we can write

$$11.5 = L_4 < \text{Area}$$

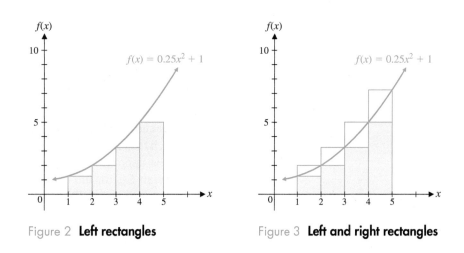

Figure 2 **Left rectangles**   Figure 3 **Left and right rectangles**

*It is customary to denote the length of the subintervals by Δx, which is read "delta x," since Δ is the Greek capital letter delta.

Explore and Discuss 1 If $f(x)$ were decreasing over the interval $[1, 5]$, would the left sum L_4 over- or underestimate the actual area under the curve? Explain.

Similarly, we use the *right* endpoint of each subinterval to find the height of the **right rectangle** placed on the subinterval. Superimposing right rectangles on Figure 2, we get Figure 3 on page 353.

Summing the areas of the right rectangles in Figure 3 results in a **right sum** of four rectangles, denoted by R_4, as follows (compare R_4 with L_4 and note that R_4 can be obtained from L_4 by deleting one rectangular area and adding one more):

$$R_4 = f(2) \cdot 1 + f(3) \cdot 1 + f(4) \cdot 1 + f(5) \cdot 1$$
$$= 2.00 + 3.25 + 5.00 + 7.25 = 17.5$$

From Figure 3, since $f(x)$ is increasing, we see that the right sum R_4 overestimates the area, and we conclude that the actual area is between 11.5 and 17.5. That is,

$$11.5 = L_4 < \text{Area} < R_4 = 17.5$$

Explore and Discuss 2 If $f(x)$ in Figure 3 were decreasing over the interval $[1, 5]$, would the right sum R_4 overestimate or underestimate the actual area under the curve? Explain.

The first approximation of the area under the curve in Figure 1 is fairly coarse, but the method outlined can be continued with increasingly accurate results by dividing the interval $[1, 5]$ into more and more subintervals of equal horizontal length. Of course, this is not a job for hand calculation, but a job that computers are designed to do.* Figure 4 shows left- and right-rectangle approximations for 16 equal subdivisions.

For this case,

$$\Delta x = \frac{5 - 1}{16} = 0.25$$

$$L_{16} = f(1) \cdot \Delta x + f(1.25) \cdot \Delta x + \cdots + f(4.75) \cdot \Delta x$$
$$= 13.59$$

$$R_{16} = f(1.25) \cdot \Delta x + f(1.50) \cdot \Delta x + \cdots + f(5) \cdot \Delta x$$
$$= 15.09$$

Figure 4

Now we know that the area under the curve is between 13.59 and 15.09. That is,

$$13.59 = L_{16} < \text{Area} < R_{16} = 15.09$$

For 100 equal subdivisions, computer calculations give us

$$14.214 = L_{100} < \text{Area} < R_{100} = 14.454$$

The **error in an approximation** is the absolute value of the difference between the approximation and the actual value. In general, neither the actual value nor the error in an approximation is known. However, it is often possible to calculate an **error bound**—a positive number such that the error is guaranteed to be less than or equal to that number.

The error in the approximation of the area under the graph of f from $x = 1$ to $x = 5$ by the left sum L_{16} (or the right sum R_{16}) is less than the sum of the areas of the small rectangles in Figure 4. By stacking those rectangles (see Fig. 5), we see that

$$\text{Error} = |\text{Area} - L_{16}| < |f(5) - f(1)| \cdot \Delta x = 1.5$$

Therefore, 1.5 is an error bound for the approximation of the area under f by L_{16}. We can apply the same stacking argument to any positive function that is increasing on $[a, b]$ or decreasing on $[a, b]$, to obtain the error bound in Theorem 1.

*The computer software that accompanies this book will perform these calculations (see the preface).

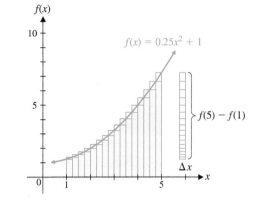

Figure 5

THEOREM 1 Error Bounds for Approximations of Area by Left or Right Sums

If $f(x) > 0$ and is either increasing on $[a, b]$ or decreasing on $[a, b]$, then

$$|f(b) - f(a)| \cdot \frac{b - a}{n}$$

is an error bound for the approximation of the area between the graph of f and the x axis, from $x = a$ to $x = b$, by L_n or R_n.

Because the error bound of Theorem 1 approaches 0 as $n \to \infty$, it can be shown that left and right sums, for certain functions, approach the same limit as $n \to \infty$.

THEOREM 2 Limits of Left and Right Sums

If $f(x) > 0$ and is either increasing on $[a, b]$ or decreasing on $[a, b]$, then its left and right sums approach the same real number as $n \to \infty$.

The number approached as $n \to \infty$ by the left and right sums in Theorem 2 is the area between the graph of f and the x axis from $x = a$ to $x = b$.

EXAMPLE 1 Approximating Areas Given the function $f(x) = 9 - 0.25x^2$, we want to approximate the area under $y = f(x)$ from $x = 2$ to $x = 5$.

(A) Graph the function over the interval $[0, 6]$. Then draw left and right rectangles for the interval $[2, 5]$ with $n = 6$.

(B) Calculate L_6, R_6, and error bounds for each.

(C) How large should n be in order for the approximation of the area by L_n or R_n to be within 0.05 of the true value?

SOLUTION

(A) $\Delta x = 0.5$:

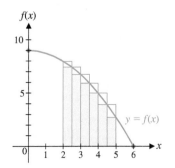

(B) $L_6 = f(2) \cdot \Delta x + f(2.5) \cdot \Delta x + f(3) \cdot \Delta x + f(3.5) \cdot \Delta x + f(4) \cdot \Delta x$
$\qquad + f(4.5) \cdot \Delta x = 18.53$

$R_6 = f(2.5) \cdot \Delta x + f(3) \cdot \Delta x + f(3.5) \cdot \Delta x + f(4) \cdot \Delta x$
$\qquad + f(4.5) \cdot \Delta x + f(5) \cdot \Delta x = 15.91$

The error bound for L_6 and R_6 is

$$\text{error} \leq |f(5) - f(2)| \frac{5 - 2}{6} = |2.75 - 8|(0.5) = 2.625$$

(C) For L_n and R_n, find n such that error ≤ 0.05:

$$|f(b) - f(a)| \frac{b - a}{n} \leq 0.05$$

$$|2.75 - 8| \frac{3}{n} \leq 0.05$$

$$|-5.25| \frac{3}{n} \leq 0.05$$

$$15.75 \leq 0.05n$$

$$n \geq \frac{15.75}{0.05} = 315$$

Matched Problem 1 Given the function $f(x) = 8 - 0.5x^2$, we want to approximate the area under $y = f(x)$ from $x = 1$ to $x = 3$.

(A) Graph the function over the interval $[0, 4]$. Then draw left and right rectangles for the interval $[1, 3]$ with $n = 4$.

(B) Calculate L_4, R_4, and error bounds for each.

(C) How large should n be in order for the approximation of the area by L_n or R_n to be within 0.5 of the true value?

> **CONCEPTUAL INSIGHT**
>
> Note from Example 1C that a relatively large value of n ($n = 315$) is required to approximate the area by L_n or R_n to within 0.05. In other words, 315 rectangles must be used, and 315 terms must be summed, to guarantee that the error does not exceed 0.05. We can obtain a more efficient approximation of the area (fewer terms are summed to achieve a given accuracy) by replacing rectangles with trapezoids. The resulting **trapezoidal rule** and other methods for approximating areas are discussed in Section 6.4.

The Definite Integral as a Limit of Sums

Left and right sums are special cases of more general sums, called *Riemann sums* [named after the German mathematician Georg Riemann (1826–1866)], that are used to approximate areas by means of rectangles.

Let f be a function defined on the interval $[a, b]$. We partition $[a, b]$ into n subintervals of equal length $\Delta x = (b - a)/n$ with endpoints

$$a = x_0 < x_1 < x_2 < \cdots < x_n = b$$

Then, using **summation notation** (see Appendix B.1), we have

$$\textbf{Left sum:} \quad L_n = f(x_0)\Delta x + f(x_1)\Delta x + \cdots + f(x_{n-1})\Delta x = \sum_{k=1}^{n} f(x_{k-1})\Delta x$$

$$\textbf{Right sum:} \quad R_n = f(x_1)\Delta x + f(x_2)\Delta x + \cdots + f(x_n)\Delta x = \sum_{k=1}^{n} f(x_k)\Delta x$$

Riemann sum: $S_n = f(c_1)\Delta x + f(c_2)\Delta x + \cdots + f(c_n)\Delta x = \displaystyle\sum_{k=1}^{n} f(c_k)\Delta x$

In a **Riemann sum,*** each c_k is required to belong to the subinterval $[x_{k-1}, x_k]$. Left and right sums are the special cases of Riemann sums in which c_k is the left endpoint or right endpoint, respectively, of the subinterval. If $f(x) > 0$, then each term of a Riemann sum S_n represents the area of a rectangle having height $f(c_k)$ and width Δx (see Fig. 6). If $f(x)$ has both positive and negative values, then some terms of S_n represent areas of rectangles, and others represent the negatives of areas of rectangles, depending on the sign of $f(c_k)$ (see Fig. 7).

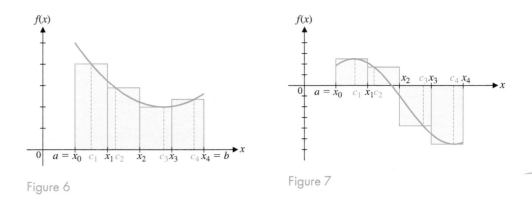

Figure 6

Figure 7

EXAMPLE 2 Riemann Sums Consider the function $f(x) = 15 - x^2$ on $[1, 5]$. Partition the interval $[1, 5]$ into four subintervals of equal length. For each subinterval $[x_{k-1}, x_k]$, let c_k be the midpoint. Calculate the corresponding Riemann sum S_4. (Riemann sums for which the c_k are the midpoints of the subintervals are called **midpoint sums.**)

SOLUTION $\Delta x = \dfrac{5 - 1}{4} = 1$

$$S_4 = f(c_1) \cdot \Delta x + f(c_2) \cdot \Delta x + f(c_3) \cdot \Delta x + f(c_4) \cdot \Delta x$$
$$= f(1.5) \cdot 1 + f(2.5) \cdot 1 + f(3.5) \cdot 1 + f(4.5) \cdot 1$$
$$= 12.75 + 8.75 + 2.75 - 5.25 = 19$$

Matched Problem 2 Consider the function $f(x) = x^2 - 2x - 10$ on $[2, 8]$. Partition the interval $[2, 8]$ into three subintervals of equal length. For each subinterval $[x_{k-1}, x_k]$, let c_k be the midpoint. Calculate the corresponding Riemann sum S_3.

By analyzing properties of a continuous function on a closed interval, it can be shown that the conclusion of Theorem 2 is valid if f is continuous. In that case, not just left and right sums, but Riemann sums, have the same limit as $n \rightarrow \infty$.

THEOREM 3 Limit of Riemann Sums

If f is a continuous function on $[a, b]$, then the Riemann sums for f on $[a, b]$ approach a real number limit I as $n \rightarrow \infty$.[†]

---

*The term *Riemann sum* is often applied to more general sums in which the subintervals $[x_{k-1}, x_k]$ are not required to have the same length. Such sums are not considered in this book.
[†]The precise meaning of this limit statement is as follows: For each $e > 0$, there exists some $d > 0$ such that $|S_n - I| < e$ whenever S_n is a Riemann sum for f on $[a, b]$ for which $\Delta x < d$.

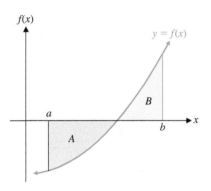

f(x)

y = f(x)

B

a

b   *x*

A

$\int_a^b f(x)dx = -A + B$

DEFINITION   Definite Integral

Let f be a continuous function on $[a, b]$. The limit I of Riemann sums for f on $[a, b]$, guaranteed to exist by Theorem 3, is called the **definite integral** of f from a to b and is denoted as

$$\int_a^b f(x)\, dx$$

The **integrand** is $f(x)$, the **lower limit of integration** is a, and the **upper limit of integration** is b.

Because area is a positive quantity, the definite integral has the following geometric interpretation:

$$\int_a^b f(x)\, dx$$

represents the cumulative sum of the signed areas between the graph of f and the x axis from $x = a$ to $x = b$, where the areas above the x axis are counted positively and the areas below the x axis are counted negatively (see Fig. 8, where A and B are the actual areas of the indicated regions).

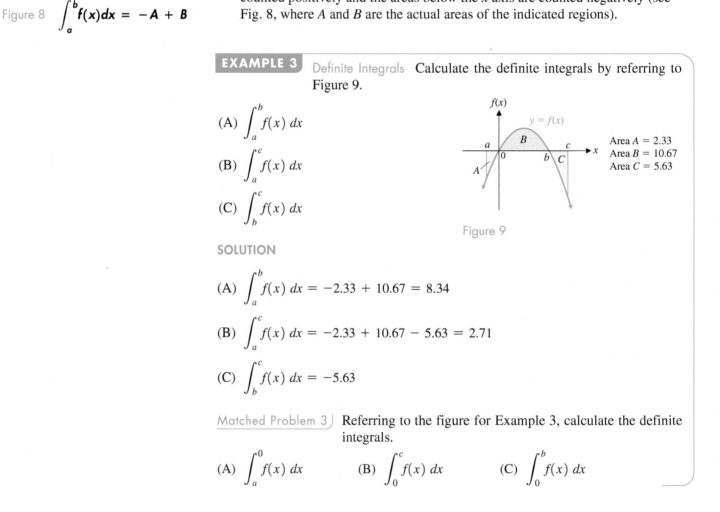

EXAMPLE 3   Definite Integrals   Calculate the definite integrals by referring to Figure 9.

(A) $\int_a^b f(x)\, dx$

(B) $\int_a^c f(x)\, dx$

(C) $\int_b^c f(x)\, dx$

f(x)

y = f(x)

a   *B*   *c*

0   *b*   *x*

A   *C*

Area A = 2.33
Area B = 10.67
Area C = 5.63

Figure 9

SOLUTION

(A) $\int_a^b f(x)\, dx = -2.33 + 10.67 = 8.34$

(B) $\int_a^c f(x)\, dx = -2.33 + 10.67 - 5.63 = 2.71$

(C) $\int_b^c f(x)\, dx = -5.63$

Matched Problem 3   Referring to the figure for Example 3, calculate the definite integrals.

(A) $\int_a^0 f(x)\, dx$ (B) $\int_0^c f(x)\, dx$ (C) $\int_0^b f(x)\, dx$

Properties of the Definite Integral

Because the definite integral is defined as the limit of Riemann sums, many properties of sums are also properties of the definite integral. Note that Properties 3 and 4 are similar to the indefinite integral properties given in Section 5.1.

Property 5 is illustrated by Figure 9 in Example 3: $2.71 = 8.34 + (-5.63)$. Property 1 follows from the special case of Property 5 in which b and c are both replaced by a. Property 2 follows from the special case of Property 5 in which c is replaced by a.

PROPERTIES Properties of Definite Integrals

1. $\displaystyle\int_a^a f(x)\, dx = 0$

2. $\displaystyle\int_a^b f(x)\, dx = -\int_b^a f(x)\, dx$

3. $\displaystyle\int_a^b kf(x)\, dx = k\int_a^b f(x)\, dx,\ k$ a constant

4. $\displaystyle\int_a^b [f(x) \pm g(x)]\, dx = \int_a^b f(x)\, dx \pm \int_a^b g(x)\, dx$

5. $\displaystyle\int_a^c f(x)\, dx = \int_a^b f(x)\, dx + \int_b^c f(x)\, dx$

EXAMPLE 4 Using Properties of the Definite Integral If

$$\int_0^2 x\, dx = 2 \qquad \int_0^2 x^2\, dx = \frac{8}{3} \qquad \int_2^3 x^2\, dx = \frac{19}{3}$$

then

(A) $\displaystyle\int_0^2 12x^2\, dx = 12\int_0^2 x^2\, dx = 12\left(\frac{8}{3}\right) = 32$

(B) $\displaystyle\int_0^2 (2x - 6x^2)\, dx = 2\int_0^2 x\, dx - 6\int_0^2 x^2\, dx = 2(2) - 6\left(\frac{8}{3}\right) = -12$

(C) $\displaystyle\int_3^2 x^2\, dx = -\int_2^3 x^2\, dx = -\frac{19}{3}$

(D) $\displaystyle\int_5^5 3x^2\, dx = 0$

(E) $\displaystyle\int_0^3 3x^2\, dx = 3\int_0^2 x^2\, dx + 3\int_2^3 x^2\, dx = 3\left(\frac{8}{3}\right) + 3\left(\frac{19}{3}\right) = 27$

Matched Problem 4 Using the same integral values given in Example 4, find

(A) $\displaystyle\int_2^3 6x^2\, dx$

(B) $\displaystyle\int_0^2 (9x^2 - 4x)\, dx$

(C) $\displaystyle\int_2^0 3x\, dx$

(D) $\displaystyle\int_{-2}^{-2} 3x\, dx$

(E) $\displaystyle\int_0^3 12x^2\, dx$

Skills Warm-up Exercises

In Problems 1–6, perform a mental calculation to find the answer and include the correct units. (If necessary, review Appendix C).

1. Find the total area enclosed by 5 non-overlapping rectangles, if each rectangle is 8 inches high and 2 inches wide.

2. Find the total area enclosed by 6 non-overlapping rectangles, if each rectangle is 10 centimeters high and 3 centimeters wide.

3. Find the total area enclosed by 4 non-overlapping rectangles, if each rectangle has width 2 meters and the heights of the rectangles are 3, 4, 5, and 6 meters, respectively.

4. Find the total area enclosed by 5 non-overlapping rectangles, if each rectangle has width 3 feet and the heights of the rectangles are 2, 4, 6, 8, and 10 feet, respectively.

5. A square is inscribed in a circle of radius 1 meter. Is the area inside the circle but outside the square less than 1 square meter?

6. A square is circumscribed around a circle of radius 1 foot. Is the area inside the square but outside the circle less than 1 square foot?

Problems 7–10 refer to the rectangles A, B, C, D, and E in the following figure.

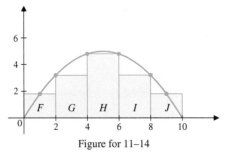

7. Which rectangles are left rectangles?

8. Which rectangles are right rectangles?

9. Which rectangles are neither left nor right rectangles?

10. Which rectangles are both left and right rectangles?

Problems 11–14 refer to the rectangles F, G, H, I, and J in the following figure.

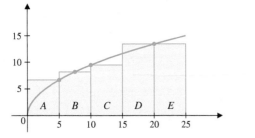

Figure for 11–14

11. Which rectangles are right rectangles?

12. Which rectangles are left rectangles?

13. Which rectangles are both left and right rectangles?

14. Which rectangles are neither left nor right rectangles?

Problems 15–22 involve estimating the area under the curves in Figures A–D from $x = 1$ to $x = 4$. For each figure, divide the interval $[1, 4]$ into three equal subintervals.

15. Draw in left and right rectangles for Figures A and B.

16. Draw in left and right rectangles for Figures C and D.

17. Using the results of Problem 15, compute L_3 and R_3 for Figure A and for Figure B.

18. Using the results of Problem 16, compute L_3 and R_3 for Figure C and for Figure D.

19. Replace the question marks with L_3 and R_3 as appropriate. Explain your choice.

$$? \leq \int_1^4 f(x)\, dx \leq ? \qquad ? \leq \int_1^4 g(x)\, dx \leq ?$$

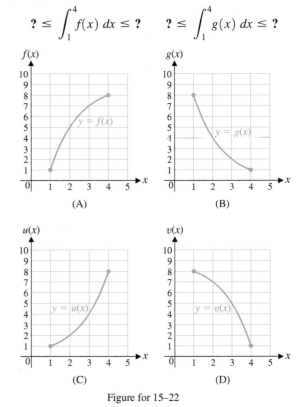

Figure for 15–22

20. Replace the question marks with L_3 and R_3 as appropriate. Explain your choice.

$$? \leq \int_1^4 u(x)\, dx \leq ? \qquad ? \leq \int_1^4 v(x)\, dx \leq ?$$

21. Compute error bounds for L_3 and R_3 found in Problem 17 for both figures.

22. Compute error bounds for L_3 and R_3 found in Problem 18 for both figures.

In Problems 23–26, calculate the indicated Riemann sum S_n for the function $f(x) = 25 - 3x^2$.

23. Partition $[-2, 8]$ into five subintervals of equal length, and for each subinterval $[x_{k-1}, x_k]$, let $c_k = (x_{k-1} + x_k)/2$.

24. Partition $[0, 12]$ into four subintervals of equal length, and for each subinterval $[x_{k-1}, x_k]$, let $c_k = (x_{k-1} + 2x_k)/3$.

25. Partition $[0, 12]$ into four subintervals of equal length, and for each subinterval $[x_{k-1}, x_k]$, let $c_k = (2x_{k-1} + x_k)/3$.

26. Partition $[-5, 5]$ into five subintervals of equal length, and for each subinterval $[x_{k-1}, x_k]$, let $c_k = (x_{k-1} + x_k)/2$.

In Problems 27–30, calculate the indicated Riemann sum S_n for the function $f(x) = x^2 - 5x - 6$.

27. Partition $[0, 3]$ into three subintervals of equal length, and let $c_1 = 0.7$, $c_2 = 1.8$, and $c_3 = 2.4$.

28. Partition $[0, 3]$ into three subintervals of equal length, and let $c_1 = 0.2$, $c_2 = 1.5$, and $c_3 = 2.8$.

29. Partition $[1, 7]$ into six subintervals of equal length, and let $c_1 = 1$, $c_2 = 3$, $c_3 = 3$, $c_4 = 5$, $c_5 = 5$, and $c_6 = 7$.

30. Partition $[1, 7]$ into six subintervals of equal length, and let $c_1 = 2$, $c_2 = 2$, $c_3 = 4$, $c_4 = 4$, $c_5 = 6$, and $c_6 = 6$.

In Problems 31–42, calculate the definite integral by referring to the figure with the indicated areas.

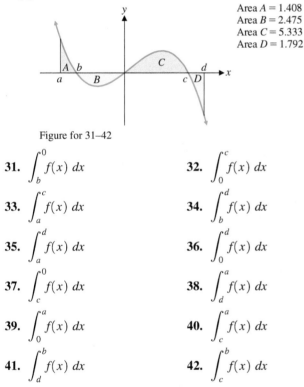

Area $A = 1.408$
Area $B = 2.475$
Area $C = 5.333$
Area $D = 1.792$

Figure for 31–42

31. $\int_b^0 f(x)\, dx$

32. $\int_0^c f(x)\, dx$

33. $\int_a^c f(x)\, dx$

34. $\int_b^d f(x)\, dx$

35. $\int_a^d f(x)\, dx$

36. $\int_0^d f(x)\, dx$

37. $\int_c^0 f(x)\, dx$

38. $\int_d^a f(x)\, dx$

39. $\int_0^a f(x)\, dx$

40. $\int_c^a f(x)\, dx$

41. $\int_d^b f(x)\, dx$

42. $\int_c^b f(x)\, dx$

In Problems 43–54, calculate the definite integral, given that

$$\int_1^4 x\, dx = 7.5 \qquad \int_1^4 x^2\, dx = 21 \qquad \int_4^5 x^2\, dx = \frac{61}{3}$$

43. $\int_1^4 2x\, dx$

44. $\int_1^4 3x^2\, dx$

45. $\int_1^4 (5x + x^2)\, dx$

46. $\int_1^4 (7x - 2x^2)\, dx$

47. $\int_1^4 (x^2 - 10x)\, dx$

48. $\int_1^4 (4x^2 - 9x)\, dx$

49. $\int_1^5 6x^2\, dx$

50. $\int_1^5 -4x^2\, dx$

51. $\int_4^4 (7x - 2)^2\, dx$

52. $\int_5^5 (10 - 7x + x^2)\, dx$

53. $\int_5^4 9x^2\, dx$

54. $\int_4^1 x(1 - x)\, dx$

In Problems 55–60, discuss the validity of each statement. If the statement is always true, explain why. If it is not always true, give a counterexample.

55. If $\int_a^b f(x)\, dx = 0$, then $f(x) = 0$ for all x in $[a, b]$.

56. If $f(x) = 0$ for all x in $[a, b]$, then $\int_a^b f(x)\, dx = 0$.

57. If $f(x) = 2x$ on $[0, 10]$, then there is a positive integer n for which the left sum L_n equals the exact area under the graph of f from $x = 0$ to $x = 10$.

58. If $f(x) = 2x$ on $[0, 10]$ and n is a positive integer, then there is some Riemann sum S_n that equals the exact area under the graph of f from $x = 0$ to $x = 10$.

59. If the area under the graph of f on $[a, b]$ is equal to both the left sum L_n and the right sum R_n for some positive integer n, then f is constant on $[a, b]$.

60. If f is a decreasing function on $[a, b]$, then the area under the graph of f is greater than the left sum L_n and less than the right sum R_n, for any positive integer n.

Problems 61 and 62 refer to the following figure showing two parcels of land along a river:

Figure for 61 and 62

61. You want to purchase both parcels of land shown in the figure and make a quick check on their combined area. There is no equation for the river frontage, so you use the average of the left and right sums of rectangles covering the area. The 1,000-foot baseline is divided into 10 equal parts. At the end of each subinterval, a measurement is made from the baseline to the river, and the results are tabulated. Let x be the distance from the left end of the baseline and let $h(x)$ be the distance from the baseline to the river at x. Use L_{10} to estimate the combined area of both parcels, and calculate an error bound for this estimate. How many subdivisions of the baseline would be required so that the error incurred in using L_n would not exceed 2,500 square feet?

x	0	100	200	300	400	500
$h(x)$	0	183	235	245	260	286

x	600	700	800	900	1,000
$h(x)$	322	388	453	489	500

62. Refer to Problem 61. Use R_{10} to estimate the combined area of both parcels, and calculate an error bound for this estimate. How many subdivisions of the baseline would be required so that the error incurred in using R_n would not exceed 1,000 square feet?

Problems 63 and 64 refer to the following figure:

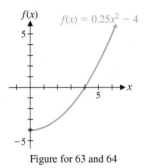

Figure for 63 and 64

63. Use L_6 and R_6 to approximate $\int_2^5 (0.25x^2 - 4)\,dx$. Compute error bounds for each. (Round answers to two decimal places.) Describe in geometric terms what the definite integral over the interval $[2, 5]$ represents.

64. Use L_5 and R_5 to approximate $\int_1^6 (0.25x^2 - 4)\,dx$. Compute error bounds for each. (Round answers to two decimal places.) Describe in geometric terms what the definite integral over the interval $[1, 6]$ represents.

For Problems 65–68, use a graphing calculator to determine the intervals on which each function is increasing or decreasing.

65. $f(x) = e^{-x^2}$

66. $f(x) = \dfrac{3}{1 + 2e^{-x}}$

67. $f(x) = x^4 - 2x^2 + 3$

68. $f(x) = e^{x^2}$

In Problems 69–72, the left sum L_n or the right sum R_n is used to approximate the definite integral to the indicated accuracy. How large must n be chosen in each case? (Each function is increasing over the indicated interval.)

69. $\displaystyle\int_1^3 \ln x\,dx = R_n \pm 0.1$

70. $\displaystyle\int_0^{10} \ln(x^2 + 1)\,dx = L_n \pm 0.5$

71. $\displaystyle\int_1^3 x^x\,dx = L_n \pm 0.5$

72. $\displaystyle\int_1^4 x^x\,dx = R_n \pm 0.5$

Applications

73. Employee training. A company producing electric motors has established that, on the average, a new employee can assemble $N(t)$ components per day after t days of on-the-job training, as shown in the following table (a new employee's productivity increases continuously with time on the job):

t	0	20	40	60	80	100	120
$N(t)$	10	51	68	76	81	84	86

Use left and right sums to estimate the area under the graph of $N(t)$ from $t = 0$ to $t = 60$. Use three subintervals of equal length for each. Calculate an error bound for each estimate.

74. Employee training. For a new employee in Problem 73, use left and right sums to estimate the area under the graph of $N(t)$ from $t = 20$ to $t = 100$. Use four equal subintervals for each. Replace the question marks with the values of L_4 or R_4 as appropriate:

$$? \leq \int_{20}^{100} N(t)\,dt \leq ?$$

75. Medicine. The rate of healing, $A'(t)$ (in square centimeters per day), for a certain type of skin wound is given approximately by the following table:

t	0	1	2	3	4	5
$A'(t)$	0.90	0.81	0.74	0.67	0.60	0.55
t	6	7	8	9	10	
$A'(t)$	0.49	0.45	0.40	0.36	0.33	

(A) Use left and right sums over five equal subintervals to approximate the area under the graph of $A'(t)$ from $t = 0$ to $t = 5$.

(B) Replace the question marks with values of L_5 and R_5 as appropriate:

$$? \leq \int_0^5 A'(t)\,dt \leq ?$$

76. Medicine. Refer to Problem 75. Use left and right sums over five equal subintervals to approximate the area under the graph of $A'(t)$ from $t = 5$ to $t = 10$. Calculate an error bound for this estimate.

77. Learning. A psychologist found that, on average, the rate of learning a list of special symbols in a code $N'(x)$ after x days of practice was given approximately by the following table values:

x	0	2	4	6	8	10	12
$N'(x)$	29	26	23	21	19	17	15

Use left and right sums over three equal subintervals to approximate the area under the graph of $N'(x)$ from $x = 6$ to $x = 12$. Calculate an error bound for this estimate.

78. Learning. For the data in Problem 77, use left and right sums over three equal subintervals to approximate the area under the graph of $N'(x)$ from $x = 0$ to $x = 6$. Replace the question marks with values of L_3 and R_3 as appropriate:

$$? \leq \int_0^6 N'(x)\,dx \leq ?$$

Answers to Matched Problems

1. (A) $\Delta x = 0.5$:

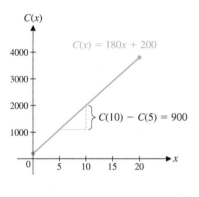

(B) $L_4 = 12.625$, $R_4 = 10.625$; error for L_4 and $R_4 = 2$

(C) $n > 16$ for L_n and R_n

2. $S_3 = 46$

3. (A) -2.33 (B) 5.04 (C) 10.67

4. (A) 38 (B) 16 (C) -6

(D) 0 (E) 108

5.5 The Fundamental Theorem of Calculus

- Introduction to the Fundamental Theorem

- Evaluating Definite Integrals

- Recognizing a Definite Integral: Average Value

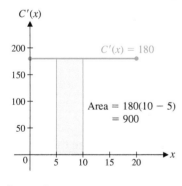

Figure 1

The definite integral of a function f on an interval $[a, b]$ is a number, the area (if $f(x) > 0$) between the graph of f and the x axis from $x = a$ to $x = b$. The indefinite integral of a function is a family of antiderivatives. In this section, we explain the connection between these two integrals, a connection made precise by the fundamental theorem of calculus.

Introduction to the Fundamental Theorem

Suppose that the daily cost function for a small manufacturing firm is given (in dollars) by

$$C(x) = 180x + 200 \qquad 0 \le x \le 20$$

Then the marginal cost function is given (in dollars per unit) by

$$C'(x) = 180$$

What is the change in cost as production is increased from $x = 5$ units to $x = 10$ units? That change is equal to

$$C(10) - C(5) = (180 \cdot 10 + 200) - (180 \cdot 5 + 200)$$
$$= 180(10 - 5)$$
$$= \$900$$

Notice that $180(10 - 5)$ is equal to the area between the graph of $C'(x)$ and the x axis from $x = 5$ to $x = 10$. Therefore,

$$C(10) - C(5) = \int_5^{10} 180 \, dx$$

In other words, the change in cost from $x = 5$ to $x = 10$ is equal to the area between the marginal cost function and the x axis from $x = 5$ to $x = 10$ (see Fig. 1).

CONCEPTUAL INSIGHT

Consider the formula for the slope of a line:

$$m = \frac{y_2 - y_1}{x_2 - x_1}$$

Multiplying both sides of this equation by $x_2 - x_1$ gives

$$y_2 - y_1 = m(x_2 - x_1)$$

The right-hand side, $m(x_2 - x_1)$, is equal to the area of a rectangle of height m and width $x_2 - x_1$. So the change in y coordinates is equal to the area under the constant function with value m from $x = x_1$ to $x = x_2$.

EXAMPLE 1 Change in Cost vs Area under Marginal Cost The daily cost function for a company (in dollars) is given by

$$C(x) = -5x^2 + 210x + 400 \qquad 0 \le x \le 20$$

(A) Graph $C(x)$ for $0 \le x \le 20$, calculate the change in cost from $x = 5$ to $x = 10$, and indicate that change in cost on the graph.

(B) Graph the marginal cost function $C'(x)$ for $0 \le x \le 20$, and use geometric formulas (see Appendix C) to calculate the area between $C'(x)$ and the x axis from $x = 5$ to $x = 10$.

(C) Compare the results of the calculations in parts (A) and (B).

SOLUTION

(A) $C(10) - C(5) = 2,000 - 1,325 = 675$, and this change in cost is indicated in Figure 2A.

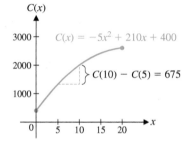

Figure 2A

(B) $C'(x) = -10x + 210$, so the area between $C'(x)$ and the x axis from $x = 5$ to $x = 10$ (see Fig. 2B) is the area of a trapezoid (geometric formulas are given in Appendix C):

$$\text{Area} = \frac{C'(5) + C'(10)}{2}(10 - 5) = \frac{160 + 110}{2}(5) = 675$$

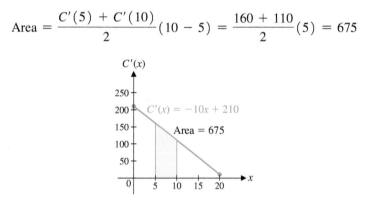

Figure 2B

(C) The change in cost from $x = 5$ to $x = 10$ is equal to the area between the marginal cost function and the x axis from $x = 5$ to $x = 10$.

Matched Problem 1   Repeat Example 1 for the daily cost function

$$C(x) = -7.5x^2 + 305x + 625$$

The connection illustrated in Example 1, between the change in a function from $x = a$ to $x = b$ and the area under the derivative of the function, provides the link between antiderivatives (or indefinite integrals) and the definite integral. This link is known as the fundamental theorem of calculus. (See Problems 67 and 68 in Exercise 5.5 for an outline of its proof.)

THEOREM 1   Fundamental Theorem of Calculus

If f is a continuous function on $[a, b]$, and F is any antiderivative of f, then

$$\int_a^b f(x)\, dx = F(b) - F(a)$$

CONCEPTUAL INSIGHT

Because a definite integral is the limit of Riemann sums, we expect that it would be difficult to calculate definite integrals exactly. The fundamental theorem, however, gives us an easy method for evaluating definite integrals, *provided that we can find an antiderivative $F(x)$ of $f(x)$*: Simply calculate the difference $F(b) - F(a)$. But what if we are unable to find an antiderivative of $f(x)$? In that case, we must resort to left sums, right sums, or other approximation methods to approximate the definite integral. However, it is often useful to remember that such an approximation is also an estimate of the change $F(b) - F(a)$.

Evaluating Definite Integrals

By the fundamental theorem, we can evaluate $\int_a^b f(x)\, dx$ easily and exactly whenever we can find an antiderivative $F(x)$ of $f(x)$. We simply calculate the difference $F(b) - F(a)$. If $G(x)$ is another antiderivative of $f(x)$, then $G(x) = F(x) + C$ for some constant C. So

$$G(b) - G(a) = F(b) + C - [F(a) + C]$$
$$= F(b) - F(a)$$

In other words:

> Any antiderivative of $f(x)$ can be used in the fundamental theorem. One generally chooses the simplest antiderivative by letting $C = 0$, since any other value of C will drop out in computing the difference $F(b) - F(a)$.

Now you know why we studied techniques of indefinite integration before this section—so that we would have methods of finding antiderivatives of large classes of elementary functions for use with the fundamental theorem.

In evaluating definite integrals by the fundamental theorem, it is convenient to use the notation $F(x)\big|_a^b$, which represents the change in $F(x)$ from $x = a$ to $x = b$, as an intermediate step in the calculation. This technique is illustrated in the following examples.

EXAMPLE 2   Evaluating Definite Integrals   Evaluate $\displaystyle\int_1^2 \left(2x + 3e^x - \frac{4}{x}\right) dx.$

SOLUTION $\displaystyle\int_1^2 \left(2x + 3e^x - \frac{4}{x}\right) dx = 2\int_1^2 x\, dx + 3\int_1^2 e^x\, dx - 4\int_1^2 \frac{1}{x}\, dx$

$$= 2\frac{x^2}{2}\bigg|_1^2 + 3e^x\bigg|_1^2 - 4\ln|x|\,\bigg|_1^2$$

$$= (2^2 - 1^2) + (3e^2 - 3e^1) - (4\ln 2 - 4\ln 1)$$

$$= 3 + 3e^2 - 3e - 4\ln 2 \approx 14.24$$

Matched Problem 2   Evaluate $\displaystyle\int_1^3 \left(4x - 2e^x + \frac{5}{x}\right) dx.$

The evaluation of a definite integral is a two-step process: First, find an antiderivative. Then find the change in that antiderivative. If *substitution techniques* are required to find the antiderivative, there are two different ways to proceed. The next example illustrates both methods.

EXAMPLE 3   Definite Integrals and Substitution Techniques   Evaluate

$$\int_0^5 \frac{x}{x^2 + 10}\,dx$$

SOLUTION   We solve this problem using substitution in two different ways.

Method 1. Use substitution in an indefinite integral to find an antiderivative as a function of x. Then evaluate the definite integral.

$$\int \frac{x}{x^2 + 10}\,dx = \frac{1}{2}\int \frac{1}{x^2 + 10}2x\,dx \qquad \text{Substitute } u = x^2 + 10$$
$$\text{and } du = 2x\,dx.$$

$$= \frac{1}{2}\int \frac{1}{u}\,du$$

$$= \tfrac{1}{2}\ln|u| + C$$

$$= \tfrac{1}{2}\ln(x^2 + 10) + C \quad \text{Since } u = x^2 + 10 > 0$$

We choose $C = 0$ and use the antiderivative $\frac{1}{2}\ln(x^2 + 10)$ to evaluate the definite integral.

$$\int_0^5 \frac{x}{x^2 + 10}\,dx = \frac{1}{2}\ln(x^2 + 10)\Big|_0^5$$

$$= \tfrac{1}{2}\ln 35 - \tfrac{1}{2}\ln 10 \approx 0.626$$

Method 2. Substitute directly into the definite integral, changing both the variable of integration and the limits of integration. In the definite integral

$$\int_0^5 \frac{x}{x^2 + 10}\,dx$$

the upper limit is $x = 5$ and the lower limit is $x = 0$. When we make the substitution $u = x^2 + 10$ in this definite integral, we must change the limits of integration to the corresponding values of u:

$$x = 5 \qquad \text{implies} \qquad u = 5^2 + 10 = 35 \quad \text{New upper limit}$$
$$x = 0 \qquad \text{implies} \qquad u = 0^2 + 10 = 10 \quad \text{New lower limit}$$

We have

$$\int_0^5 \frac{x}{x^2 + 10}\,dx = \frac{1}{2}\int_0^5 \frac{1}{x^2 + 10}2x\,dx$$

$$= \frac{1}{2}\int_{10}^{35} \frac{1}{u}\,du$$

$$= \frac{1}{2}\left(\ln|u|\,\Big|_{10}^{35}\right)$$

$$= \tfrac{1}{2}(\ln 35 - \ln 10) \approx 0.626$$

Matched Problem 3   Use both methods described in Example 3 to evaluate

$$\int_0^1 \frac{1}{2x + 4}\,dx.$$

EXAMPLE 4 Definite Integrals and Substitution   Use method 2 described in Example 3 to evaluate

$$\int_{-4}^{1} \sqrt{5-t}\, dt$$

SOLUTION If $u = 5 - t$, then $du = -dt$, and

$$t = 1 \qquad \text{implies} \qquad u = 5 - 1 = 4 \qquad \text{New upper limit}$$
$$t = -4 \qquad \text{implies} \qquad u = 5 - (-4) = 9 \qquad \text{New lower limit}$$

Notice that the lower limit for u is larger than the upper limit. Be careful not to reverse these two values when substituting into the definite integral:

$$\int_{-4}^{1} \sqrt{5-t}\, dt = -\int_{-4}^{1} \sqrt{5-t}\,(-dt)$$

$$= -\int_{9}^{4} \sqrt{u}\, du$$

$$= -\int_{9}^{4} u^{1/2}\, du$$

$$= -\left(\frac{u^{3/2}}{\frac{3}{2}}\Big|_{9}^{4}\right)$$

$$= -\left[\tfrac{2}{3}(4)^{3/2} - \tfrac{2}{3}(9)^{3/2}\right]$$

$$= -\left[\tfrac{16}{3} - \tfrac{54}{3}\right] = \tfrac{38}{3} \approx 12.667$$

Matched Problem 4 Use method 2 described in Example 3 to evaluate

$$\int_{2}^{5} \frac{1}{\sqrt{6-t}}\, dt.$$

EXAMPLE 5 Change in Profit   A company manufactures x HDTVs per month. The monthly marginal profit (in dollars) is given by

$$P'(x) = 165 - 0.1x \qquad 0 \le x \le 4{,}000$$

The company is currently manufacturing 1,500 HDTVs per month, but is planning to increase production. Find the change in the monthly profit if monthly production is increased to 1,600 HDTVs.

SOLUTION

$$P(1{,}600) - P(1{,}500) = \int_{1{,}500}^{1{,}600} (165 - 0.1x)\, dx$$

$$= \left(165x - 0.05x^2\right)\Big|_{1{,}500}^{1{,}600}$$

$$= \left[165(1{,}600) - 0.05(1{,}600)^2\right]$$
$$\quad - \left[165(1{,}500) - 0.05(1{,}500)^2\right]$$

$$= 136{,}000 - 135{,}000$$

$$= 1{,}000$$

Increasing monthly production from 1,500 units to 1,600 units will increase the monthly profit by $1,000.

Matched Problem 5 Repeat Example 5 if

$$P'(x) = 300 - 0.2x \qquad 0 \le x \le 3,000$$

and monthly production is increased from 1,400 to 1,500 HDTVs.

EXAMPLE 6 Useful Life An amusement company maintains records for each video game installed in an arcade. Suppose that $C(t)$ and $R(t)$ represent the total accumulated costs and revenues (in thousands of dollars), respectively, t years after a particular game has been installed. Suppose also that

$$C'(t) = 2 \qquad R'(t) = 9e^{-0.5t}$$

The value of t for which $C'(t) = R'(t)$ is called the **useful life** of the game.

(A) Find the useful life of the game, to the nearest year.

(B) Find the total profit accumulated during the useful life of the game.

SOLUTION

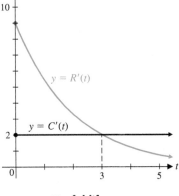

(A) $R'(t) = C'(t)$

$9e^{-0.5t} = 2$

$e^{-0.5t} = \frac{2}{9}$ Convert to equivalent logarithmic form.

$-0.5t = \ln\frac{2}{9}$

$t = -2\ln\frac{2}{9} \approx 3$ years

Thus, the game has a useful life of 3 years. This is illustrated graphically in Figure 3.

Figure 3 Useful life

(B) The total profit accumulated during the useful life of the game is

$$P(3) - P(0) = \int_0^3 P'(t)\, dt$$

$$= \int_0^3 [R'(t) - C'(t)]\, dt$$

$$= \int_0^3 (9e^{-0.5t} - 2)\, dt$$

$$= \left(\frac{9}{-0.5}e^{-0.5t} - 2t\right)\Big|_0^3 \quad\quad \text{Recall: } \int e^{ax}\, dx = \frac{1}{a}e^{ax} + C$$

$$= (-18e^{-0.5t} - 2t)\big|_0^3$$

$$= (-18e^{-1.5} - 6) - (-18e^0 - 0)$$

$$= 12 - 18e^{-1.5} \approx 7.984 \quad \text{or} \quad \$7,984$$

Matched Problem 6 Repeat Example 6 if $C'(t) = 1$ and $R'(t) = 7.5e^{-0.5t}$.

  EXAMPLE 7 Numerical Integration on a Graphing Calculator Evaluate

$$\int_{-1}^2 e^{-x^2}\, dx \text{ to three decimal places.}$$

SOLUTION The integrand e^{-x^2} does not have an elementary antiderivative, so we are unable to use the fundamental theorem to evaluate the definite integral.

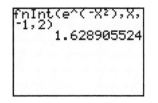

Figure 4

Instead, we use a numerical integration routine that has been preprogrammed into a graphing calculator. (Consult your user's manual for specific details.) Such a routine is an approximation algorithm, more powerful than the left-sum and right-sum methods discussed in Section 5.4. From Figure 4,

$$\int_{-1}^{2} e^{-x^2}\, dx = 1.629$$

Matched Problem 7 Evaluate $\displaystyle\int_{1.5}^{4.3} \frac{x}{\ln x}\, dx$ to three decimal places.

Recognizing a Definite Integral: Average Value

Recall that the derivative of a function f was defined in Section 2.4 by

$$f'(x) = \lim_{h \to 0} \frac{f(x + h) - f(x)}{h}$$

This form is generally not easy to compute directly but is easy to recognize in certain practical problems (slope, instantaneous velocity, rates of change, and so on). Once we know that we are dealing with a derivative, we proceed to try to compute the derivative with the use of derivative formulas and rules.

Similarly, evaluating a definite integral with the use of the definition

$$\int_{a}^{b} f(x)\, dx = \lim_{n \to \infty} [f(c_1)\Delta x_1 + f(c_2)\Delta x_2 + \cdots + f(c_n)\Delta x_n] \qquad (1)$$

is generally not easy, but the form on the right occurs naturally in many practical problems. We can use the fundamental theorem to evaluate the definite integral (once it is recognized) if an antiderivative can be found; otherwise, we will approximate it with a rectangle sum. We will now illustrate these points by finding the *average value* of a continuous function.

Suppose that the temperature F (in degrees Fahrenheit) in the middle of a small shallow lake from 8 AM ($t = 0$) to 6 PM ($t = 10$) during the month of May is given approximately by $F(t) = -t^2 + 10t + 50$ as shown in Figure 5.

How can we compute the average temperature from 8 AM to 6 PM? We know that the average of a finite number of values $a_1, a_2, \ldots, a_n$ is given by

$$\text{average} = \frac{a_1 + a_2 + \cdots + a_n}{n}$$

But how can we handle a continuous function with infinitely many values? It would seem reasonable to divide the time interval [0, 10] into n equal subintervals, compute the temperature at a point in each subinterval, and then use the average of the temperatures as an approximation of the average value of the continuous function $F = F(t)$ over [0, 10]. We would expect the approximations to improve as n increases. In fact, we would define the limit of the average of n values as $n \to \infty$ as the *average value of F over* [0, 10] if the limit exists. This is exactly what we will do:

$$\begin{pmatrix} \text{average temperature} \\ \text{for } n \text{ values} \end{pmatrix} = \frac{1}{n}[F(t_1) + F(t_2) + \cdots + F(t_n)] \qquad (2)$$

Here t_k is a point in the kth subinterval. We will call the limit of equation (2) as $n \to \infty$ the *average temperature over the time interval* [0, 10].

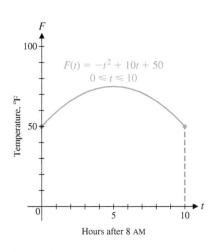

Figure 5

$F(t) = -t^2 + 10t + 50$
$0 \leqslant t \leqslant 10$

Temperature, °F

Hours after 8 AM

Form (2) resembles form (1), but we are missing the Δt_k. We take care of this by multiplying equation (2) by $(b - a)/(b - a)$, which will change the form of equation (2) without changing its value:

$$\frac{b - a}{b - a} \cdot \frac{1}{n} \left[F(t_1) + F(t_2) + \cdots + F(t_n) \right] = \frac{1}{b - a} \cdot \frac{b - a}{n} \left[F(t_1) + F(t_2) + \cdots + F(t_n) \right]$$

$$= \frac{1}{b - a} \left[F(t_1) \frac{b - a}{n} + F(t_2) \frac{b - a}{n} + \cdots + F(t_n) \frac{b - a}{n} \right]$$

$$= \frac{1}{b - a} \left[F(t_1) \Delta t + F(t_2) \Delta t + \cdots + F(t_n) \Delta t \right]$$

Therefore,

$$\left(\begin{array}{c} \text{average temperature} \\ \text{over } [a, b] = [0, 10] \end{array} \right) = \lim_{n \to \infty} \left\{ \frac{1}{b - a} \left[F(t_1) \Delta t + F(t_2) \Delta t + \cdots + F(t_n) \Delta t \right] \right\}$$

$$= \frac{1}{b - a} \left\{ \lim_{n \to \infty} \left[F(t_1) \Delta t + F(t_2) \Delta t + \cdots + F(t_n) \Delta t \right] \right\}$$

The limit inside the braces is of form (1)—that is, a definite integral. So

$$\left(\begin{array}{c} \text{average temperature} \\ \text{over } [a, b] = [0, 10] \end{array} \right) = \frac{1}{b - a} \int_a^b F(t) \, dt$$

$$= \frac{1}{10 - 0} \int_0^{10} (-t^2 + 10t + 50) \, dt$$

$$= \frac{1}{10} \left(-\frac{t^3}{3} + 5t^2 + 50t \right) \Big|_0^{10}$$

$$= \frac{200}{3} \approx 67°\text{F}$$

We now use the fundamental theorem to evaluate the definite integral.

Proceeding as before for an arbitrary continuous function f over an interval $[a, b]$, we obtain the following general formula:

DEFINITION Average Value of a Continuous Function f over $[a, b]$

$$\frac{1}{b - a} \int_a^b f(x) \, dx$$

Explore and Discuss 1   In Figure 6, the rectangle shown has the same area as the area under the graph of $y = f(x)$ from $x = a$ to $x = b$. Explain how the average value of $f(x)$ over the interval $[a, b]$ is related to the height of the rectangle.

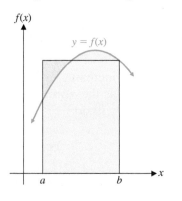

Figure 6

EXAMPLE 8 Average Value of a Function Find the average value of $f(x) = x - 3x^2$ over the interval $[-1, 2]$.

SOLUTION

$$\frac{1}{b-a} \int_a^b f(x)\, dx = \frac{1}{2-(-1)} \int_{-1}^{2} (x - 3x^2)\, dx$$

$$= \frac{1}{3} \left(\frac{x^2}{2} - x^3 \right) \Big|_{-1}^{2} = -\frac{5}{2}$$

Matched Problem 8 Find the average value of $g(t) = 6t^2 - 2t$ over the interval $[-2, 3]$.

EXAMPLE 9 Average Price Given the demand function

$$p = D(x) = 100e^{-0.05x}$$

find the average price (in dollars) over the demand interval [40, 60].

SOLUTION

$$\text{Average price} = \frac{1}{b-a} \int_a^b D(x)\, dx$$

$$= \frac{1}{60-40} \int_{40}^{60} 100e^{-0.05x}\, dx$$

$$= \frac{100}{20} \int_{40}^{60} e^{-0.05x}\, dx \qquad \text{Use } \int e^{ax}\, dx = \frac{1}{a} e^{ax}, a \neq 0.$$

$$= -\frac{5}{0.05} e^{-0.05x} \Big|_{40}^{60}$$

$$= 100(e^{-2} - e^{-3}) \approx \$8.55$$

Matched Problem 9 Given the supply equation

$$p = S(x) = 10e^{0.05x}$$

find the average price (in dollars) over the supply interval [20, 30].

Exercises 5.5

Skills Warm-up Exercises

W *In Problems 1–8, use geometric formulas to find the unsigned area between the graph of $y = f(x)$ and the x axis over the indicated interval. (If necessary, review Appendix C.)*

1. $f(x) = 100; [1, 6]$

2. $f(x) = -50; [8, 12]$

3. $f(x) = x + 5; [0, 4]$

4. $f(x) = x - 2; [-3, -1]$

5. $f(x) = 3x; [-4, 4]$

6. $f(x) = -10x; [-100, 50]$

7. $f(x) = \sqrt{9 - x^2}; [-3, 3]$

8. $f(x) = -\sqrt{25 - x^2}; [-5, 5]$

In Problems 9–12,

(A) *Calculate the change in $F(x)$ from $x = 10$ to $x = 15$.*

(B) *Graph $F'(x)$ and use geometric formulas (see Appendix C) to calculate the area between the graph of $F'(x)$ and the x axis from $x = 10$ to $x = 15$.*

(C) *Verify that your answers to (A) and (B) are equal, as is guaranteed by the fundamental theorem of calculus.*

9. $F(x) = 3x^2 + 160$

10. $F(x) = 9x + 120$

11. $F(x) = -x^2 + 42x + 240$

12. $F(x) = x^2 + 30x + 210$

Evaluate the integrals in Problems 13–32.

13. $\displaystyle\int_0^{10} 4\,dx$

14. $\displaystyle\int_0^8 9x\,dx$

15. $\displaystyle\int_0^6 x^2\,dx$

16. $\displaystyle\int_0^4 x^3\,dx$

17. $\displaystyle\int_1^4 (5x + 3)\,dx$

18. $\displaystyle\int_2^5 (2x - 1)\,dx$

19. $\displaystyle\int_0^1 e^x\,dx$

20. $\displaystyle\int_0^2 4e^x\,dx$

21. $\displaystyle\int_1^2 \frac{1}{x}\,dx$

22. $\displaystyle\int_1^5 \frac{2}{x}\,dx$

23. $\displaystyle\int_{-2}^2 (x^3 + 7x)\,dx$

24. $\displaystyle\int_0^8 (0.25x - 1)\,dx$

25. $\displaystyle\int_2^5 (2x + 9)\,dx$

26. $\displaystyle\int_1^4 (6x - 5)\,dx$

27. $\displaystyle\int_5^2 (2x + 9)\,dx$

28. $\displaystyle\int_4^1 (6x - 5)\,dx$

29. $\displaystyle\int_2^3 (6 - x^3)\,dx$

30. $\displaystyle\int_6^9 (5 - x^2)\,dx$

31. $\displaystyle\int_6^6 (x^2 - 5x + 1)^{10}\,dx$

32. $\displaystyle\int_{-3}^{-3} (x^2 + 4x + 2)^8\,dx$

Evaluate the integrals in Problems 33–48.

33. $\displaystyle\int_1^2 (2x^{-2} - 3)\,dx$

34. $\displaystyle\int_1^2 (5 - 16x^{-3})\,dx$

35. $\displaystyle\int_1^4 3\sqrt{x}\,dx$

36. $\displaystyle\int_4^{25} \frac{2}{\sqrt{x}}\,dx$

37. $\displaystyle\int_2^3 12(x^2 - 4)^5 x\,dx$

38. $\displaystyle\int_0^1 32(x^2 + 1)^7 x\,dx$

39. $\displaystyle\int_3^9 \frac{1}{x - 1}\,dx$

40. $\displaystyle\int_2^8 \frac{1}{x + 1}\,dx$

41. $\displaystyle\int_{-5}^{10} e^{-0.05x}\,dx$

42. $\displaystyle\int_{-10}^{25} e^{-0.01x}\,dx$

43. $\displaystyle\int_1^e \frac{\ln t}{t}\,dt$

44. $\displaystyle\int_e^{e^2} \frac{(\ln t)^2}{t}\,dt$

45. $\displaystyle\int_0^1 xe^{-x^2}\,dx$

46. $\displaystyle\int_0^1 xe^{x^2}\,dx$

47. $\displaystyle\int_1^1 e^{x^2}\,dx$

48. $\displaystyle\int_{-1}^{-1} e^{-x^2}\,dx$

In Problems 49–56,

(A) Find the average value of each function over the indicated interval.

(B) Use a graphing calculator to graph the function and its average value over the indicated interval in the same viewing window.

49. $f(x) = 500 - 50x; [0, 10]$

50. $g(x) = 2x + 7; [0, 5]$

51. $f(t) = 3t^2 - 2t; [-1, 2]$

52. $g(t) = 4t - 3t^2; [-2, 2]$

53. $f(x) = \sqrt[3]{x}; [1, 8]$

54. $g(x) = \sqrt{x + 1}; [3, 8]$

55. $f(x) = 4e^{-0.2x}; [0, 10]$

56. $f(x) = 64e^{0.08x}; [0, 10]$

Evaluate the integrals in Problems 57–62.

57. $\displaystyle\int_2^3 x\sqrt{2x^2 - 3}\,dx$

58. $\displaystyle\int_0^1 x\sqrt{3x^2 + 2}\,dx$

59. $\displaystyle\int_0^1 \frac{x - 1}{x^2 - 2x + 3}\,dx$

60. $\displaystyle\int_1^2 \frac{x + 1}{2x^2 + 4x + 4}\,dx$

61. $\displaystyle\int_{-1}^1 \frac{e^{-x} - e^x}{(e^{-x} + e^x)^2}\,dx$

62. $\displaystyle\int_6^7 \frac{\ln(t - 5)}{t - 5}\,dt$

Use a numerical integration routine to evaluate each definite integral in Problems 63–66 (to three decimal places).

63. $\displaystyle\int_{1.7}^{3.5} x\ln x\,dx$

64. $\displaystyle\int_{-1}^1 e^{x^2}\,dx$

65. $\displaystyle\int_{-2}^2 \frac{1}{1 + x^2}\,dx$

66. $\displaystyle\int_0^3 \sqrt{9 - x^2}\,dx$

67. The **mean value theorem** states that if $F(x)$ is a differentiable function on the interval $[a, b]$, then there exists some number c between a and b such that

$$F'(c) = \frac{F(b) - F(a)}{b - a}$$

Explain why the mean value theorem implies that if a car averages 60 miles per hour in some 10-minute interval, then the car's instantaneous velocity is 60 miles per hour at least once in that interval.

68. The fundamental theorem of calculus can be proved by showing that, for every positive integer n, there is a Riemann sum for f on $[a, b]$ that is equal to $F(b) - F(a)$. By the mean value theorem (see Problem 67), within each subinterval $[x_{k-1}, x_k]$ that belongs to a partition of $[a, b]$, there is some c_k such that

$$f(c_k) = F'(c_k) = \frac{F(x_k) - F(x_{k-1})}{x_k - x_{k-1}}$$

Multiplying by the denominator $x_k - x_{k-1}$, we get

$$f(c_k)(x_k - x_{k-1}) = F(x_k) - F(x_{k-1})$$

Show that the Riemann sum

$$S_n = \sum_{k=1}^n f(c_k)(x_k - x_{k-1})$$

is equal to $F(b) - F(a)$.

Applications

69. Cost. A company manufactures mountain bikes. The research department produced the marginal cost function

$$C'(x) = 500 - \frac{x}{3} \qquad 0 \le x \le 900$$

where $C'(x)$ is in dollars and x is the number of bikes produced per month. Compute the increase in cost going from a production level of 300 bikes per month to 900 bikes per month. Set up a definite integral and evaluate it.

70. Cost. Referring to Problem 69, compute the increase in cost going from a production level of 0 bikes per month to 600 bikes per month. Set up a definite integral and evaluate it.

71. Salvage value. A new piece of industrial equipment will depreciate in value, rapidly at first and then less rapidly as time goes on. Suppose that the rate (in dollars per year) at which the book value of a new milling machine changes is given approximately by

$$V'(t) = f(t) = 500(t - 12) \qquad 0 \le t \le 10$$

where $V(t)$ is the value of the machine after t years. What is the total loss in value of the machine in the first 5 years? In the second 5 years? Set up appropriate integrals and solve.

72. Maintenance costs. Maintenance costs for an apartment house generally increase as the building gets older. From past records, the rate of increase in maintenance costs (in dollars per year) for a particular apartment complex is given approximately by

$$M'(x) = f(x) = 90x^2 + 5,000$$

where x is the age of the apartment complex in years and $M(x)$ is the total (accumulated) cost of maintenance for x years. Write a definite integral that will give the total maintenance costs from the end of the second year to the end of the seventh year, and evaluate the integral.

73. Employee training. A company producing computer components has established that, on the average, a new employee can assemble $N(t)$ components per day after t days of on-the-job training, as indicated in the following table (a new employee's productivity usually increases with time on the job, up to a leveling-off point):

t	0	20	40	60	80	100	120
$N(t)$	10	51	68	76	81	84	85

(A) Find a quadratic regression equation for the data, and graph it and the data set in the same viewing window.

(B) Use the regression equation and a numerical integration routine on a graphing calculator to approximate the number of units assembled by a new employee during the first 100 days on the job.

74. Employee training. Refer to Problem 73.

(A) Find a cubic regression equation for the data, and graph it and the data set in the same viewing window.

(B) Use the regression equation and a numerical integration routine on a graphing calculator to approximate the number of units assembled by a new employee during the second 60 days on the job.

75. Useful life. The total accumulated costs $C(t)$ and revenues $R(t)$ (in thousands of dollars), respectively, for a photocopying machine satisfy

$$C'(t) = \tfrac{1}{11}t \qquad \text{and} \qquad R'(t) = 5te^{-t^2}$$

where t is time in years. Find the useful life of the machine, to the nearest year. What is the total profit accumulated during the useful life of the machine?

76. Useful life. The total accumulated costs $C(t)$ and revenues $R(t)$ (in thousands of dollars), respectively, for a coal mine satisfy

$$C'(t) = 3 \qquad \text{and} \qquad R'(t) = 15e^{-0.1t}$$

where t is the number of years that the mine has been in operation. Find the useful life of the mine, to the nearest year. What is the total profit accumulated during the useful life of the mine?

77. Average cost. The total cost (in dollars) of manufacturing x auto body frames is $C(x) = 60,000 + 300x$.

(A) Find the average cost per unit if 500 frames are produced. [*Hint*: Recall that $\overline{C}(x)$ is the average cost per unit.]

(B) Find the average value of the cost function over the interval [0, 500].

(C) Discuss the difference between parts (A) and (B).

78. Average cost. The total cost (in dollars) of printing x dictionaries is $C(x) = 20,000 + 10x$.

(A) Find the average cost per unit if 1,000 dictionaries are produced.

(B) Find the average value of the cost function over the interval [0, 1,000].

(C) Discuss the difference between parts (A) and (B).

79. Cost. The marginal cost at various levels of output per month for a company that manufactures sunglasses is shown in the following table, with the output x given in thousands of units per month and the total cost $C(x)$ given in thousands of dollars per month:

x	0	1	2	3	4	5	6	7	8
$C'(x)$	58	30	18	9	5	7	17	33	51

(A) Find a quadratic regression equation for the data, and graph it and the data set in the same viewing window.

(B) Use the regression equation and a numerical integration routine on a graphing calculator to approximate (to the nearest dollar) the increased cost in going from a production level of 2 thousand sunglasses per month to 8 thousand sunglasses per month.

80. Cost. Refer to Problem 79.

(A) Find a cubic regression equation for the data, and graph it and the data set in the same viewing window.

(B) Use the regression equation and a numerical integration routine on a graphing calculator to approximate (to the nearest dollar) the increased cost in going from a production level of 1 thousand sunglasses per month to 7 thousand sunglasses per month.

81. Supply function. Given the supply function

$$p = S(x) = 10(e^{0.02x} - 1)$$

find the average price (in dollars) over the supply interval [20, 30].

82. Demand function. Given the demand function

$$p = D(x) = \frac{1,000}{x}$$

find the average price (in dollars) over the demand interval [400, 600].

83. Labor costs and learning. A defense contractor is starting production on a new missile control system. On the basis of data collected during assembly of the first 16 control systems, the production manager obtained the following function for the rate of labor use:

$$L'(x) = 2,400x^{-1/2}$$

Approximately how many labor-hours will be required to assemble the 17th through the 25th control units? [*Hint*: Let $a = 16$ and $b = 25$.]

84. Labor costs and learning. If the rate of labor use in Problem 83 is

$$L'(x) = 2,000x^{-1/3}$$

then approximately how many labor-hours will be required to assemble the 9th through the 27th control units? [*Hint*: Let $a = 8$ and $b = 27$.]

85. Inventory. A store orders 600 units of a product every 3 months. If the product is steadily depleted to 0 by the end of each 3 months, the inventory on hand I at any time t during the year is shown in the following figure:

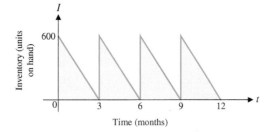

Time (months)

(A) Write an inventory function (assume that it is continuous) for the first 3 months. [The graph is a straight line joining (0, 600) and (3, 0).]

(B) What is the average number of units on hand for a 3-month period?

86. Repeat Problem 85 with an order of 1,200 units every 4 months.

87. Oil production. Using production and geological data, the management of an oil company estimates that oil will be pumped from a producing field at a rate given by

$$R(t) = \frac{100}{t + 1} + 5 \qquad 0 \le t \le 20$$

where $R(t)$ is the rate of production (in thousands of barrels per year) t years after pumping begins. Approximately how many barrels of oil will the field produce during the first

10 years of production? From the end of the 10th year to the end of the 20th year of production?

88. Oil production. In Problem 87, if the rate is found to be

$$R(t) = \frac{120t}{t^2 + 1} + 3 \qquad 0 \le t \le 20$$

then approximately how many barrels of oil will the field produce during the first 5 years of production? The second 5 years of production?

89. Biology. A yeast culture weighing 2 grams is expected to grow at the rate of $W'(t) = 0.2e^{0.1t}$ grams per hour at a higher controlled temperature. How much will the weight of the culture increase during the first 8 hours of growth? How much will the weight of the culture increase from the end of the 8th hour to the end of the 16th hour of growth?

90. Medicine. The rate at which the area of a skin wound is increasing is given (in square centimeters per day) by $A'(t) = -0.9e^{-0.1t}$. The initial wound has an area of 9 square centimeters. How much will the area change during the first 5 days? The second 5 days?

91. Temperature. If the temperature in an aquarium (in degrees Celsius) is given by

$$C(t) = t^3 - 2t + 10 \qquad 0 \le t \le 2$$

over a 2-hour period, what is the average temperature over this period?

92. Medicine. A drug is injected into the bloodstream of a patient through her right arm. The drug concentration in the bloodstream of the left arm t hours after the injection is given by

$$C(t) = \frac{0.14t}{t^2 + 1}$$

What is the average drug concentration in the bloodstream of the left arm during the first hour after the injection? During the first 2 hours after the injection?

93. Politics. Public awareness of a congressional candidate before and after a successful campaign was approximated by

$$P(t) = \frac{8.4t}{t^2 + 49} + 0.1 \qquad 0 \le t \le 24$$

where t is time in months after the campaign started and $P(t)$ is the fraction of the number of people in the congressional district who could recall the candidate's name. What is the average fraction of the number of people who could recall the candidate's name during the first 7 months of the campaign? During the first 2 years of the campaign?

94. Population composition. The number of children in a large city was found to increase and then decrease rather drastically. If the number of children (in millions) over a 6-year period was given by

$$N(t) = -\tfrac{1}{4}t^2 + t + 4 \qquad 0 \le t \le 6$$

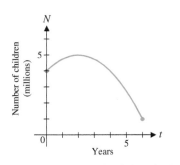

what was the average number of children in the city over the 6-year period? [Assume that $N = N(t)$ is continuous.]

1. (A) $C(x)$

(B) $C'(x)$

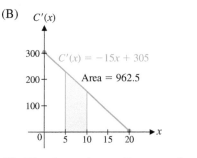

(C) The change in cost from $x = 5$ to $x = 10$ is equal to the area between the marginal cost function and the x axis from $x = 5$ to $x = 10$.

2. $16 + 2e - 2e^3 + 5 \ln 3 \approx -13.241$

3. $\frac{1}{2}(\ln 6 - \ln 4) \approx 0.203$

4. 2

5. $1,000

6. (A) $-2 \ln\frac{2}{15} \approx 4$ yr   (B) $11 - 15e^{-2} \approx 8.970$ or $8,970

7. 8.017

8. 13

9. $35.27

Chapter 5   Summary and Review

Important Terms, Symbols, and Concepts

5.1 Antiderivatives and Indefinite Integrals

EXAMPLES

- A function F is an **antiderivative** of a function f if $F'(x) = f(x)$.

Ex. 1, p. 321

- If F and G are both antiderivatives of f, then F and G differ by a constant; that is, $F(x) = G(x) + k$ for some constant k.

- We use the symbol $\int f(x)\, dx$, called an **indefinite integral,** to represent the family of all antiderivatives of f, and we write

$$\int f(x)\, dx = F(x) + C$$

The symbol $\int$ is called an **integral sign,** $f(x)$ is the **integrand,** and C is the **constant of integration.**

Ex. 2, p. 324
Ex. 3, p. 325
Ex. 4, p. 326

- Indefinite integrals of basic functions are given by the formulas on page 322.

- Properties of indefinite integrals are given on page 323; in particular, a constant factor can be moved across an integral sign. However, a variable factor *cannot* be moved across an integral sign.

Ex. 5, p. 327
Ex. 6, p. 327

5.2 Integration by Substitution

- The **method of substitution** (also called the **change-of-variable method**) is a technique for finding indefinite integrals. It is based on the following formula, which is obtained by reversing the chain rule:

Ex. 1, p. 333

$$\int E'[I(x)]I'(x)\, dx = E[I(x)] + C$$

- This formula implies the general indefinite integral formulas on page 333.

- When using the method of substitution, it is helpful to use differentials as a bookkeeping device:

Ex. 2, p. 334
Ex. 3, p. 334

1. The **differential dx** of the independent variable x is an arbitrary real number.

Ex. 4, p. 335
Ex. 5, p. 336

2. The **differential dy** of the dependent variable y is defined by $dy = f'(x)\, dx$.

Ex. 6, p. 338

- Guidelines for using the substitution method are given by the procedure on page 335.

Ex. 7, p. 339

5.3 Differential Equations; Growth and Decay

- An equation is a **differential equation** if it involves an unknown function and one or more of the function's derivatives.

- The equation

$$\frac{dy}{dx} = 3x(1 + xy^2)$$

is a **first-order** differential equation because it involves the first derivative of the unknown function y but no second or higher-order derivative.

- A **slope field** can be constructed for the preceding differential equation by drawing a tangent line segment with slope $3x(1 + xy^2)$ at each point (x, y) of a grid. The slope field gives a graphical representation of the functions that are solutions of the differential equation.

- The differential equation

$$\frac{dQ}{dt} = rQ$$

Ex. 1, p. 346
Ex. 2, p. 346
Ex. 3, p. 347

(in words, the rate at which the unknown function Q increases is proportional to Q) is called the **exponential growth law**. The constant r is called the **relative growth rate**. The solutions of the exponential growth law are the functions

$$Q(t) = Q_0 e^{rt}$$

where Q_0 denotes $Q(0)$, the amount present at time $t = 0$. These functions can be used to solve problems in population growth, continuous compound interest, radioactive decay, blood pressure, and light absorption.

- Table 1 on page 349 gives the solutions of other first-order differential equations that can be used to model the limited or logistic growth of epidemics, sales, and corporations.

Ex. 4, p. 348

5.4 The Definite Integral

- If the function f is positive on $[a, b]$, then the area between the graph of f and the x axis from $x = a$ to $x = b$ can be approximated by partitioning $[a, b]$ into n subintervals $[x_{k-1}, x_k]$ of equal length $\Delta x = (b - a)/n$ and summing the areas of n rectangles. This can be done using **left sums, right sums,** or, more generally, **Riemann sums:**

Ex. 1, p. 355
Ex. 2, p. 357

Left sum: $L_n = \displaystyle\sum_{k=1}^{n} f(x_{k-1}) \Delta x$

Right sum: $R_n = \displaystyle\sum_{k=1}^{n} f(x_k) \Delta x$

Riemann sum: $S_n = \displaystyle\sum_{k=1}^{n} f(c_k) \Delta x$

In a Riemann sum, each c_k is required to belong to the subinterval $[x_{k-1}, x_k]$. Left sums and right sums are the special cases of Riemann sums in which c_k is the left endpoint and right endpoint, respectively, of the subinterval.

- The **error in an approximation** is the absolute value of the difference between the approximation and the actual value. An **error bound** is a positive number such that the error is guaranteed to be less than or equal to that number.

- Theorem 1 on page 355 gives error bounds for the approximation of the area between the graph of a positive function f and the x axis from $x = a$ to $x = b$, by left sums or right sums, if f is either increasing or decreasing.

- If $f(x) > 0$ and is either increasing on $[a, b]$ or decreasing on $[a, b]$, then the left and right sums of $f(x)$ approach the same real number as $n \to \infty$ (Theorem 2, page 355).

- If f is a continuous function on $[a, b]$, then the Riemann sums for f on $[a, b]$ approach a real-number limit I as $n \to \infty$ (Theorem 3, page 357).

- Let f be a continuous function on $[a, b]$. Then the limit I of Riemann sums for f on $[a, b]$, guaranteed to exist by Theorem 3, is called the **definite integral** of f from a to b and is denoted

$$\int_a^b f(x)\, dx$$

The **integrand** is $f(x)$, the **lower limit of integration** is a, and the **upper limit of integration** is b.   Ex. 3, p. 358

- Geometrically, the definite integral

$$\int_a^b f(x)\, dx$$

represents the cumulative sum of the signed areas between the graph of f and the x axis from $x = a$ Ex. 4, p. 359
to $x = b$.

- Properties of the definite integral are given on page 359.

5.5 The Fundamental Theorem of Calculus

- If f is a continuous function on $[a, b]$ and F is any antiderivative of f, then   Ex. 1, p. 364
                                                                                            Ex. 2, p. 365

$$\int_a^b f(x)\, dx = F(b) - F(a)$$

This is the fundamental theorem of calculus (see page 365).   Ex. 3, p. 366

- The fundamental theorem gives an easy and exact method for evaluating definite integrals, provided   Ex. 4, p. 367
that we can find an antiderivative $F(x)$ of $f(x)$. In practice, we first find an antiderivative $F(x)$ Ex. 5, p. 367
(when possible), using techniques for computing indefinite integrals. Then we calculate the difference   Ex. 6, p. 368
$F(b) - F(a)$. If it is impossible to find an antiderivative, we must resort to left or right sums, or other   Ex. 7, p. 368
approximation methods, to evaluate the definite integral. Graphing calculators have a built-in numerical
approximation routine, more powerful than left- or right-sum methods, for this purpose.

- If f is a continuous function on $[a, b]$, then the **average value** of f over $[a, b]$ is defined to be   Ex. 8, p. 371
                                                                                                                  Ex. 9, p. 371

$$\frac{1}{b - a} \int_a^b f(x)\, dx$$

Review Exercises

Work through all the problems in this chapter review and check your answers in the back of the book. Answers to all review problems are there, along with section numbers in italics to indicate where each type of problem is discussed. Where weaknesses show up, review appropriate sections of the text.

Find each integral in Problems 1–6.

1. $\displaystyle\int (6x + 3)\, dx$

2. $\displaystyle\int_{10}^{20} 5\, dx$

3. $\displaystyle\int_0^9 (4 - t^2)\, dt$

4. $\displaystyle\int (1 - t^2)^3 t\, dt$

5. $\displaystyle\int \frac{1 + u^4}{u}\, du$

6. $\displaystyle\int_0^1 xe^{-2x^2}\, dx$

7. Is $F(x) = \ln x^2$ an antiderivative of $f(x) = \ln (2x)$? Explain.

8. Is $F(x) = \ln x^2$ an antiderivative of $f(x) = \dfrac{2}{x}$? Explain.

9. Is $F(x) = (\ln x)^2$ an antiderivative of $f(x) = 2 \ln x$? Explain.

10. Is $F(x) = (\ln x)^2$ an antiderivative of $f(x) = \dfrac{2 \ln x}{x}$? Explain.

11. Is $y = 3x + 17$ a solution of the differential equation $(x + 5)y' = y - 2$? Explain.

12. Is $y = 4x^3 + 7x^2 - 5x + 2$ a solution of the differential equation $(x + 2)y''' - 24x = 48$? Explain.

In Problems 13 and 14, find the derivative or indefinite integral as indicated.

13. $\dfrac{d}{dx}\left(\displaystyle\int e^{-x^2}\, dx\right)$

14. $\displaystyle\int \dfrac{d}{dx}\left(\sqrt{4 + 5x}\right) dx$

15. Find a function $y = f(x)$ that satisfies both conditions:

$$\frac{dy}{dx} = 3x^2 - 2 \qquad f(0) = 4$$

16. Find all antiderivatives of

(A) $\dfrac{dy}{dx} = 8x^3 - 4x - 1$

(B) $\dfrac{dx}{dt} = e^t - 4t^{-1}$

17. Approximate $\int_1^5 (x^2 + 1)\, dx$, using a right sum with $n = 2$. Calculate an error bound for this approximation.

18. Evaluate the integral in Problem 17, using the fundamental theorem of calculus, and calculate the actual error $|I - R_2|$ produced by using R_2.

19. Use the following table of values and a left sum with $n = 4$ to approximate $\int_1^{17} f(x)\, dx$:

x	1	5	9	13	17
$f(x)$	1.2	3.4	2.6	0.5	0.1

20. Find the average value of $f(x) = 6x^2 + 2x$ over the interval $[-1, 2]$.

21. Describe a rectangle that has the same area as the area under the graph of $f(x) = 6x^2 + 2x$ from $x = -1$ to $x = 2$ (see Problem 20).

In Problems 22 and 23, calculate the indicated Riemann sum S_n for the function $f(x) = 100 - x^2$.

22. Partition $[3, 11]$ into four subintervals of equal length, and for each subinterval $[x_{i-1}, x_i]$, let $c_i = (x_{i-1} + x_i)/2$.

23. Partition $[-5, 5]$ into five subintervals of equal length and let $c_1 = -4$, $c_2 = -1$, $c_3 = 1$, $c_4 = 2$, and $c_5 = 5$.

Use the graph and actual areas of the indicated regions in the figure to evaluate the integrals in Problems 24–31:

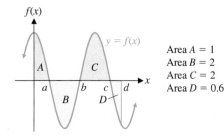

Area $A = 1$
Area $B = 2$
Area $C = 2$
Area $D = 0.6$

Figure for 24–31

24. $\int_a^b 5f(x)\, dx$

25. $\int_b^c \dfrac{f(x)}{5}\, dx$

26. $\int_b^d f(x)\, dx$

27. $\int_a^c f(x)\, dx$

28. $\int_0^d f(x)\, dx$

29. $\int_b^a f(x)\, dx$

30. $\int_c^b f(x)\, dx$

31. $\int_d^0 f(x)\, dx$

Problems 32–37 refer to the slope field shown in the figure:

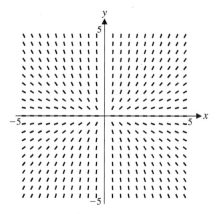

Figure for 32–37

32. (A) For $dy/dx = (2y)/x$, what is the slope of a solution curve at $(2, 1)$? At $(-2, -1)$?

   (B) For $dy/dx = (2x)/y$, what is the slope of a solution curve at $(2, 1)$? At $(-2, -1)$?

33. Is the slope field shown in the figure for $dy/dx = (2x)/y$ or for $dy/dx = (2y)/x$? Explain.

34. Show that $y = Cx^2$ is a solution of $dy/dx = (2y)/x$ for any real number C.

35. Referring to Problem 34, find the particular solution of $dy/dx = (2y)/x$ that passes through $(2, 1)$. Through $(-2, -1)$.

36. Graph the two particular solutions found in Problem 35 in the slope field shown (or a copy).

37. Use a graphing calculator to graph, in the same viewing window, graphs of $y = Cx^2$ for $C = -2, -1, 1$, and 2 for $-5 \le x \le 5$ and $-5 \le y \le 5$.

Find each integral in Problems 38–48.

38. $\int_{-1}^{1} \sqrt{1 + x}\, dx$

39. $\int_{-1}^{0} x^2 (x^3 + 2)^{-2}\, dx$

40. $\int 5e^{-t}\, dt$

41. $\int_1^e \dfrac{1 + t^2}{t}\, dt$

42. $\int x e^{3x^2}\, dx$

43. $\int_{-3}^{1} \dfrac{1}{\sqrt{2 - x}}\, dx$

44. $\int_0^3 \dfrac{x}{1 + x^2}\, dx$

45. $\int_0^3 \dfrac{x}{(1 + x^2)^2}\, dx$

46. $\int x^3 (2x^4 + 5)^5\, dx$

47. $\int \dfrac{e^{-x}}{e^{-x} + 3}\, dx$

48. $\int \dfrac{e^x}{(e^x + 2)^2}\, dx$

49. Find a function $y = f(x)$ that satisfies both conditions:

$$\frac{dy}{dx} = 3x^{-1} - x^{-2} \qquad f(1) = 5$$

50. Find the equation of the curve that passes through (2, 10) if its slope is given by

$$\frac{dy}{dx} = 6x + 1$$

for each x.

51. (A) Find the average value of $f(x) = 3\sqrt{x}$ over the interval [1, 9].

(B) Graph $f(x) = 3\sqrt{x}$ and its average over the interval [1, 9] in the same coordinate system.

Find each integral in Problems 52–56.

52. $\displaystyle\int \frac{(\ln x)^2}{x}\, dx$

53. $\displaystyle\int x(x^3 - 1)^2\, dx$

54. $\displaystyle\int \frac{x}{\sqrt{6 - x}}\, dx$

55. $\displaystyle\int_0^7 x\sqrt{16 - x}\, dx$

56. $\displaystyle\int_1^1 (x + 1)^9 dx$

57. Find a function $y = f(x)$ that satisfies both conditions:

$$\frac{dy}{dx} = 9x^2 e^{x^3} \qquad f(0) = 2$$

58. Solve the differential equation

$$\frac{dN}{dt} = 0.06N \qquad N(0) = 800 \qquad N > 0$$

Graph Problems 59–62 on a graphing calculator, and identify each curve as unlimited growth, exponential decay, limited growth, or logistic growth:

59. $N = 50(1 - e^{-0.07t}); 0 \le t \le 80, 0 \le N \le 60$

60. $p = 500e^{-0.03x}; 0 \le x \le 100, 0 \le p \le 500$

61. $A = 200e^{0.08t}; 0 \le t \le 20, 0 \le A \le 1,000$

62. $N = \dfrac{100}{1 + 9e^{-0.3t}}; 0 \le t \le 25, 0 \le N \le 100$

Use a numerical integration routine to evaluate each definite integral in Problems 63–65 (to three decimal places).

63. $\displaystyle\int_{-0.5}^{0.6} \frac{1}{\sqrt{1 - x^2}}\, dx$

64. $\displaystyle\int_{-2}^3 x^2 e^x\, dx$

65. $\displaystyle\int_{0.5}^{2.5} \frac{\ln x}{x^2}\, dx$

Applications

66. Cost. A company manufactures downhill skis. The research department produced the marginal cost graph shown in the accompanying figure, where $C'(x)$ is in dollars and x is the number of pairs of skis produced per week. Estimate the increase in cost going from a production level of 200 to 600 pairs of skis per week. Use left and right sums over two equal subintervals. Replace the question marks with the values of L_2 and R_2 as appropriate:

$$? \le \int_{200}^{600} C'(x)\, dx \le ?$$

Figure for 66

67. Cost. Assuming that the marginal cost function in Problem 66 is linear, find its equation and write a definite integral that represents the increase in costs going from a production level of 200 to 600 pairs of skis per week. Evaluate the definite integral.

68. Profit and production. The weekly marginal profit for an output of x units is given approximately by

$$P'(x) = 150 - \frac{x}{10} \qquad 0 \le x \le 40$$

What is the total change in profit for a change in production from 10 units per week to 40 units? Set up a definite integral and evaluate it.

69. Profit function. If the marginal profit for producing x units per day is given by

$$P'(x) = 100 - 0.02x \qquad P(0) = 0$$

where $P(x)$ is the profit in dollars, find the profit function P and the profit on 10 units of production per day.

70. Resource depletion. An oil well starts out producing oil at the rate of 60,000 barrels of oil per year, but the production rate is expected to decrease by 4,000 barrels per year. Thus, if $P(t)$ is the total production (in thousands of barrels) in t years, then

$$P'(t) = f(t) = 60 - 4t \qquad 0 \le t \le 15$$

Write a definite integral that will give the total production after 15 years of operation, and evaluate the integral.

71. Inventory. Suppose that the inventory of a certain item t months after the first of the year is given approximately by

$$I(t) = 10 + 36t - 3t^2 \qquad 0 \le t \le 12$$

What is the average inventory for the second quarter of the year?

72. Price–supply. Given the price–supply function

$$p = S(x) = 8(e^{0.05x} - 1)$$

find the average price (in dollars) over the supply interval [40, 50].

73. Useful life. The total accumulated costs $C(t)$ and revenues $R(t)$ (in thousands of dollars), respectively, for a coal mine satisfy

$$C'(t) = 3 \qquad \text{and} \qquad R'(t) = 20e^{-0.1t}$$

where t is the number of years that the mine has been in operation. Find the useful life of the mine, to the nearest year. What is the total profit accumulated during the useful life of the mine?

74. Marketing. The market research department for an automobile company estimates that sales (in millions of dollars) of a new electric car will increase at the monthly rate of

$$S'(t) = 4e^{-0.08t} \qquad 0 \le t \le 24$$

t months after the introduction of the car. What will be the total sales $S(t)$ t months after the car is introduced if we assume that there were 0 sales at the time the car entered the marketplace? What are the estimated total sales during the first 12 months after the introduction of the car? How long will it take for the total sales to reach $40 million?

75. Wound healing. The area of a healing skin wound changes at a rate given approximately by

$$\frac{dA}{dt} = -5t^{-2} \qquad 1 \le t \le 5$$

where t is time in days and $A(1) = 5$ square centimeters. What will be the area of the wound in 5 days?

76. Pollution. An environmental protection agency estimates that the rate of seepage of toxic chemicals from a waste dump (in gallons per year) is given by

$$R(t) = \frac{1,000}{(1 + t)^2}$$

where t is the time in years since the discovery of the seepage. Find the total amount of toxic chemicals that seep from the dump during the first 4 years of its discovery.

77. Population. The population of Mexico was 116 million in 2013 and was growing at a rate of 1.07% per year, compounded continuously.

(A) Assuming that the population continues to grow at this rate, estimate the population of Mexico in the year 2025.

(B) At the growth rate indicated, how long will it take the population of Mexico to double?

78. Archaeology. The continuous compound rate of decay for carbon-14 is $r = -0.000\,123\,8$. A piece of animal bone found at an archaeological site contains 4% of the original amount of carbon-14. Estimate the age of the bone.

79. Learning. An average student enrolled in a typing class progressed at a rate of $N'(t) = 7e^{-0.1t}$ words per minute t weeks after enrolling in a 15-week course. If a student could type 25 words per minute at the beginning of the course, how many words per minute $N(t)$ would the student be expected to type t weeks into the course? After completing the course?

6

Additional Integration Topics

Introduction

In Chapter 6 we explore additional applications and techniques of integration. We use the integral to find probabilities and to calculate several quantities that are important in business and economics: the total income and future value produced by a continuous income stream, consumers' and producers' surplus, and the Gini index of income concentration. The Gini index is a single number that measures the equality of a country's income distribution (see Problems 93 and 94, for example, in Section 6.1).

6.1   Area Between Curves

- Area Between Two Curves
- Application: Income Distribution

In Chapter 5, we found that the definite integral $\int_a^b f(x)\,dx$ represents the sum of the signed areas between the graph of $y = f(x)$ and the x axis from $x = a$ to $x = b$, where the areas above the x axis are counted positively and the areas below the x axis are counted negatively (see Fig. 1). In this section, we are interested in using the definite integral to find the actual area between a curve and the x axis or the actual area between two curves. These areas are always nonnegative quantities—**area measure is never negative**.

Area Between Two Curves

Consider the area bounded by $y = f(x)$ and $y = g(x)$, where $f(x) \geq g(x) \geq 0$, for $a \leq x \leq b$, as shown in Figure 2.

$$\begin{pmatrix} \text{Area } A \text{ between} \\ f(x) \text{ and } g(x) \end{pmatrix} = \begin{pmatrix} \text{area} \\ \text{under } f(x) \end{pmatrix} - \begin{pmatrix} \text{area} \\ \text{under } g(x) \end{pmatrix}$$ Areas are from $x = a$ to $x = b$ above the x axis.

$$= \int_a^b f(x)\,dx - \int_a^b g(x)\,dx$$ Use definite integral property 4 (Section 5.4).

$$= \int_a^b [f(x) - g(x)]\,dx$$

It can be shown that the preceding result does not require $f(x)$ or $g(x)$ to remain positive over the interval $[a, b]$. A more general result is stated in the following box:

THEOREM 1   Area Between Two Curves

If f and g are continuous and $f(x) \geq g(x)$ over the interval $[a, b]$, then the area bounded by $y = f(x)$ and $y = g(x)$ for $a \leq x \leq b$ is given exactly by

$$A = \int_a^b [f(x) - g(x)]\,dx$$

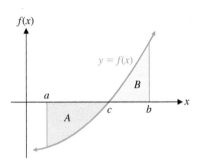

Figure 1 $\int_a^b f(x)\,dx = -A + B$

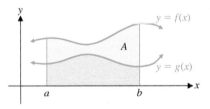

Figure 2

CONCEPTUAL   INSIGHT

Theorem 1 requires the graph of f to be *above* (or equal to) the graph of g throughout $[a, b]$, but f and g can be either positive, negative, or 0. In Section 5.4, we considered the special cases of Theorem 1 in which (1) f is positive and g is the zero function on $[a, b]$; and (2) f is the zero function and g is negative on $[a, b]$:

Special case 1. If f is continuous and positive over $[a, b]$, then the area bounded by the graph of f and the x axis for $a \leq x \leq b$ is given exactly by

$$\int_a^b f(x)\,dx$$

Special case 2. If g is continuous and negative over $[a, b]$, then the area bounded by the graph of g and the x axis for $a \leq x \leq b$ is given exactly by

$$\int_a^b [-g(x)]\,dx$$

EXAMPLE 1 Area Between a Curve and the x Axis Find the area bounded by $f(x) = 6x - x^2$ and $y = 0$ for $1 \leq x \leq 4$.

SOLUTION We sketch a graph of the region first (Fig. 3). The solution of every area problem should begin with a sketch. Since $f(x) \geq 0$ on $[1, 4]$,

$$A = \int_1^4 (6x - x^2)\, dx = \left(3x^2 - \frac{x^3}{3}\right)\Big|_1^4$$

$$= \left[3(4)^2 - \frac{(4)^3}{3}\right] - \left[3(1)^2 - \frac{(1)^3}{3}\right]$$

$$= 48 - \tfrac{64}{3} - 3 + \tfrac{1}{3}$$

$$= 48 - 21 - 3$$

$$= 24$$

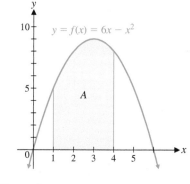

$y = f(x) = 6x - x^2$

A

Figure 3

Matched Problem 1 Find the area bounded by $f(x) = x^2 + 1$ and $y = 0$ for $-1 \leq x \leq 3$.

EXAMPLE 2 Area Between a Curve and the x Axis Find the area between the graph of $f(x) = x^2 - 2x$ and the x axis over the indicated intervals:

(A) $[1, 2]$ (B) $[-1, 1]$

SOLUTION We begin by sketching the graph of f, as shown in Figure 4.

(A) From the graph, we see that $f(x) \leq 0$ for $1 \leq x \leq 2$, so we integrate $-f(x)$:

$$A_1 = \int_1^2 [-f(x)]\, dx$$

$$= \int_1^2 (2x - x^2)\, dx$$

$$= \left(x^2 - \frac{x^3}{3}\right)\Big|_1^2$$

$$= \left[(2)^2 - \frac{(2)^3}{3}\right] - \left[(1)^2 - \frac{(1)^3}{3}\right]$$

$$= 4 - \tfrac{8}{3} - 1 + \tfrac{1}{3} = \tfrac{2}{3} \approx 0.667$$

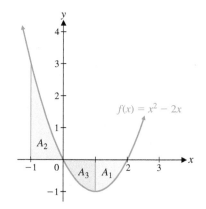

$f(x) = x^2 - 2x$

A_2

A_3 A_1

Figure 4

(B) Since the graph shows that $f(x) \geq 0$ on $[-1, 0]$ and $f(x) \leq 0$ on $[0, 1]$, the computation of this area will require two integrals:

$$A = A_2 + A_3$$

$$= \int_{-1}^0 f(x)\, dx + \int_0^1 [-f(x)]\, dx$$

$$= \int_{-1}^0 (x^2 - 2x)\, dx + \int_0^1 (2x - x^2)\, dx$$

$$= \left(\frac{x^3}{3} - x^2\right)\Big|_{-1}^0 + \left(x^2 - \frac{x^3}{3}\right)\Big|_0^1$$

$$= \tfrac{4}{3} + \tfrac{2}{3} = 2$$

Matched Problem 2 Find the area between the graph of $f(x) = x^2 - 9$ and the x axis over the indicated intervals:

(A) $[0, 2]$ (B) $[2, 4]$

Figure 5

EXAMPLE 3   Area Between Two Curves   Find the area bounded by the graphs of $f(x) = \frac{1}{2}x + 3$, $g(x) = -x^2 + 1$, $x = -2$, and $x = 1$.

SOLUTION   We first sketch the area (Fig. 5) and then set up and evaluate an appropriate definite integral. We observe from the graph that $f(x) \geq g(x)$ for $-2 \leq x \leq 1$, so

$$A = \int_{-2}^{1} [f(x) - g(x)] \, dx = \int_{-2}^{1} \left[\left(\frac{x}{2} + 3 \right) - (-x^2 + 1) \right] dx$$

$$= \int_{-2}^{1} \left(x^2 + \frac{x}{2} + 2 \right) dx$$

$$= \left(\frac{x^3}{3} + \frac{x^2}{4} + 2x \right) \Big|_{-2}^{1}$$

$$= \left(\frac{1}{3} + \frac{1}{4} + 2 \right) - \left(\frac{-8}{3} + \frac{4}{4} - 4 \right) = \frac{33}{4} = 8.25$$

Matched Problem 3   Find the area bounded by $f(x) = x^2 - 1$, $g(x) = -\frac{1}{2}x - 3$, $x = -1$, and $x = 2$.

EXAMPLE 4   Area Between Two Curves   Find the area bounded by $f(x) = 5 - x^2$ and $g(x) = 2 - 2x$.

SOLUTION   First, graph f and g on the same coordinate system, as shown in Figure 6. Since the statement of the problem does not include any limits on the values of x, we must determine the appropriate values from the graph. The graph of f is a parabola and the graph of g is a line. The area bounded by these two graphs extends from the intersection point on the left to the intersection point on the right. To find these intersection points, we solve the equation $f(x) = g(x)$ for x:

$$f(x) = g(x)$$
$$5 - x^2 = 2 - 2x$$
$$x^2 - 2x - 3 = 0$$
$$x = -1, 3$$

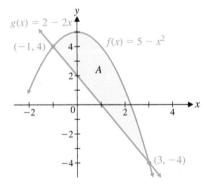

Figure 6

You should check these values in the original equations. (Note that the area between the graphs for $x < -1$ is unbounded on the left, and the area between the graphs for $x > 3$ is unbounded on the right.) Figure 6 shows that $f(x) \geq g(x)$ over the interval $[-1, 3]$, so we have

$$A = \int_{-1}^{3} [f(x) - g(x)] \, dx = \int_{-1}^{3} [5 - x^2 - (2 - 2x)] \, dx$$

$$= \int_{-1}^{3} (3 + 2x - x^2) \, dx$$

$$= \left(3x + x^2 - \frac{x^3}{3} \right) \Big|_{-1}^{3}$$

$$= \left[3(3) + (3)^2 - \frac{(3)^3}{3} \right] - \left[3(-1) + (-1)^2 - \frac{(-1)^3}{3} \right] = \frac{32}{3} \approx 10.667$$

Matched Problem 4   Find the area bounded by $f(x) = 6 - x^2$ and $g(x) = x$.

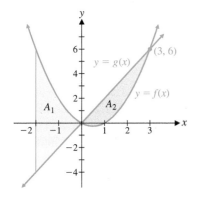

Figure 7

EXAMPLE 5 Area Between Two Curves Find the area bounded by $f(x) = x^2 - x$ and $g(x) = 2x$ for $-2 \le x \le 3$.

SOLUTION The graphs of f and g are shown in Figure 7. Examining the graph, we see that $f(x) \ge g(x)$ on the interval $[-2, 0]$, but $g(x) \ge f(x)$ on the interval $[0, 3]$. Thus, two integrals are required to compute this area:

$$A_1 = \int_{-2}^{0} [f(x) - g(x)] \, dx \qquad f(x) \ge g(x) \text{ on } [-2, 0]$$

$$= \int_{-2}^{0} [x^2 - x - 2x] \, dx$$

$$= \int_{-2}^{0} (x^2 - 3x) \, dx$$

$$= \left(\frac{x^3}{3} - \frac{3}{2} x^2 \right) \Big|_{-2}^{0}$$

$$= (0) - \left[\frac{(-2)^3}{3} - \frac{3}{2} (-2)^2 \right] = \frac{26}{3} \approx 8.667$$

$$A_2 = \int_{0}^{3} [g(x) - f(x)] \, dx \qquad g(x) \ge f(x) \text{ on } [0, 3]$$

$$= \int_{0}^{3} [2x - (x^2 - x)] \, dx$$

$$= \int_{0}^{3} (3x - x^2) \, dx$$

$$= \left(\frac{3}{2} x^2 - \frac{x^3}{3} \right) \Big|_{0}^{3}$$

$$= \left[\frac{3}{2} (3)^2 - \frac{(3)^3}{3} \right] - (0) = \frac{9}{2} = 4.5$$

The total area between the two graphs is

$$A = A_1 + A_2 = \frac{26}{3} + \frac{9}{2} = \frac{79}{6} \approx 13.167$$

Matched Problem 5) Find the area bounded by $f(x) = 2x^2$ and $g(x) = 4 - 2x$ for $-2 \le x \le 2$.

EXAMPLE 6 Computing Areas with a Numerical Integration Routine Find the area (to three decimal places) bounded by $f(x) = e^{-x^2}$ and $g(x) = x^2 - 1$.

SOLUTION First, we use a graphing calculator to graph the functions f and g and find their intersection points (see Fig. 8A). We see that the graph of f is bell shaped and the graph of g is a parabola. We note that $f(x) \ge g(x)$ on the interval $[-1.131, 1.131]$ and compute the area A by a numerical integration routine (see Fig. 8B):

$$A = \int_{-1.131}^{1.131} \left[e^{-x^2} - (x^2 - 1) \right] dx = 2.876$$

Figure 8   (A)   (B)

Matched Problem 6) Find the area (to three decimal places) bounded by the graphs of $f(x) = x^2 \ln x$ and $g(x) = 3x - 3$.

Application: Income Distribution

The U.S. Census Bureau compiles and analyzes a great deal of data having to do with the distribution of income among families in the United States. For 2011, the Bureau reported that the lowest 20% of families received 3% of all family income and the top 20% received 51%. Table 1 and Figure 9 give a detailed picture of the distribution of family income in 2011.

The graph of $y = f(x)$ in Figure 9 is called a **Lorenz curve** and is generally found by using *regression analysis,* a technique for fitting a function to a data set over a given interval. The variable **x represents the cumulative percentage of families at or below a given income level,** and **y represents the cumulative percentage of total family income received.** For example, data point (0.40, 0.11) in Table 1 indicates that the bottom 40% of families (those with incomes under $39,000) received 11% of the total income for all families in 2011, data point (0.60, 0.26) indicates that the bottom 60% of families received 26% of the total income for all families that year, and so on.

Table 1 **Family Income Distribution in the United States, 2011**

Income Level	x	y
Under $20,000	0.20	0.03
Under $39,000	0.40	0.11
Under $62,000	0.60	0.26
Under $102,000	0.80	0.49

Source: U.S. Census Bureau

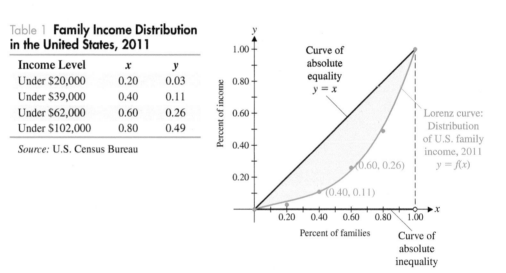

Figure 9 **Lorenz curve**

Absolute equality of income would occur if the area between the Lorenz curve and $y = x$ were 0. In this case, the Lorenz curve would be $y = x$ and all families would receive equal shares of the total income. That is, 5% of the families would receive 5% of the income, 20% of the families would receive 20% of the income, 65% of the families would receive 65% of the income, and so on. The maximum possible area between a Lorenz curve and $y = x$ is $\frac{1}{2}$, the area of the triangle below $y = x$. In this case, we would have **absolute inequality**: All the income would be in the hands of one family and the rest would have none. In actuality, Lorenz curves lie between these two extremes. But as the shaded area increases, the greater is the inequality of income distribution.

We use a single number, the **Gini index** [named after the Italian sociologist Corrado Gini (1884–1965)], to measure income concentration. The Gini index is the ratio of two areas: the area between $y = x$ and the Lorenz curve, and the area between $y = x$ and the x axis, from $x = 0$ to $x = 1$. The first area equals $\int_0^1 [x - f(x)] \, dx$ and the second (triangular) area equals $\frac{1}{2}$, giving the following definition:

DEFINITION   Gini Index of Income Concentration
If $y = f(x)$ is the equation of a Lorenz curve, then

$$\textbf{Gini index} = 2 \int_0^1 [x - f(x)]\, dx$$

The Gini index is always a number between 0 and 1:

A Gini index of 0 indicates absolute equality—all people share equally in the income. A Gini index of 1 indicates absolute inequality—one person has all the income and the rest have none.

The closer the index is to 0, the closer the income is to being equally distributed. The closer the index is to 1, the closer the income is to being concentrated in a few hands. The Gini index of income concentration is used to compare income distributions at various points in time, between different groups of people, before and after taxes are paid, between different countries, and so on.

EXAMPLE 7   Distribution of Income   The Lorenz curve for the distribution of income in a certain country in 2013 is given by $f(x) = x^{2.6}$. Economists predict that the Lorenz curve for the country in the year 2025 will be given by $g(x) = x^{1.8}$. Find the Gini index of income concentration for each curve, and interpret the results.

SOLUTION   The Lorenz curves are shown in Figure 10.

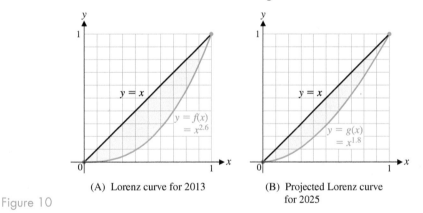

(A) Lorenz curve for 2013   (B) Projected Lorenz curve for 2025

Figure 10

The Gini index in 2013 is (see Fig. 10A)

$$2 \int_0^1 [x - f(x)]\, dx = 2 \int_0^1 [x - x^{2.6}]\, dx = 2 \left(\frac{1}{2}x^2 - \frac{1}{3.6}x^{3.6} \right)\Big|_0^1$$

$$= 2 \left(\frac{1}{2} - \frac{1}{3.6} \right) \approx 0.444$$

The projected Gini index in 2025 is (see Fig. 10B)

$$2 \int_0^1 [x - g(x)]\, dx = 2 \int_0^1 [x - x^{1.8}]\, dx = 2 \left(\frac{1}{2}x^2 - \frac{1}{2.8}x^{2.8} \right)\Big|_0^1$$

$$= 2 \left(\frac{1}{2} - \frac{1}{2.8} \right) \approx 0.286$$

If this projection is correct, the Gini index will decrease, and income will be more equally distributed in the year 2025 than in 2013.

Matched Problem 7)   Repeat Example 7 if the projected Lorenz curve in the year 2025 is given by $g(x) = x^{3.8}$.

Explore and Discuss 1   Do you agree or disagree with each of the following statements (explain your answers by referring to the data in Table 2):

(A) In countries with a low Gini index, there is little incentive for individuals to strive for success, and therefore productivity is low.

(B) In countries with a high Gini index, it is almost impossible to rise out of poverty, and therefore productivity is low.

Table 2

Country	Gini Index	Per Capita Gross Domestic Product
Brazil	0.52	$12,100
Canada	0.32	43,400
China	0.47	9,300
France	0.33	36,100
Germany	0.27	39,700
India	0.37	3,900
Japan	0.38	36,900
Jordan	0.40	6,100
Mexico	0.48	15,600
Russia	0.42	18,000
Sweden	0.23	41,900
United States	0.45	50,700

Source: The World Factbook, CIA

Exercises 6.1

Skills Warm-up Exercises

W   *In Problems 1–8, use geometric formulas to find the area between the graphs of $y = f(x)$ and $y = g(x)$ over the indicated interval. (If necessary, review Appendix C).*

1. $f(x) = 60, g(x) = 45; [2, 12]$

2. $f(x) = -30, g(x) = 20; [-3, 6]$

3. $f(x) = 6 + 2x, g(x) = 6 - x; [0, 5]$

4. $f(x) = 0.5x, g(x) = 0.5x - 4; [0, 8]$

5. $f(x) = -3 - x, g(x) = 4 + 2x; [-1, 2]$

6. $f(x) = 100 - 2x, g(x) = 10 + 3x; [5, 10]$

7. $f(x) = x, g(x) = \sqrt{4 - x^2}; [0, \sqrt{2}]$

8. $f(x) = \sqrt{16 - x^2}, g(x) = |x|; [-2\sqrt{2}, 2\sqrt{2}]$

Problems 9–14 refer to Figures A–D. Set up definite integrals in Problems 9–12 that represent the indicated shaded area.

9. Shaded area in Figure B

10. Shaded area in Figure A

11. Shaded area in Figure C

12. Shaded area in Figure D

13. Explain why $\int_a^b h(x)\, dx$ does not represent the area between the graph of $y = h(x)$ and the x axis from $x = a$ to $x = b$ in Figure C.

14. Explain why $\int_a^b [-h(x)]\, dx$ represents the area between the graph of $y = h(x)$ and the x axis from $x = a$ to $x = b$ in Figure C.

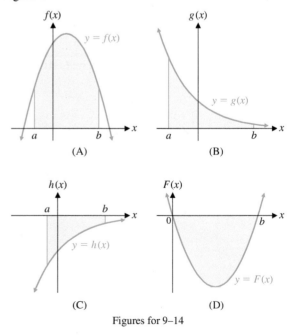

Figures for 9–14

In Problems 15–28, find the area bounded by the graphs of the indicated equations over the given interval. Compute answers to three decimal places.

15. $y = x + 4$; $y = 0$; $0 \le x \le 4$

16. $y = -x + 10$; $y = 0$; $-2 \le x \le 2$

17. $y = x^2 - 20$; $y = 0$; $-3 \le x \le 0$

18. $y = x^2 + 2$; $y = 0$; $0 \le x \le 3$

19. $y = -x^2 + 10$; $y = 0$; $-3 \le x \le 3$

20. $y = -2x^2$; $y = 0$; $-6 \le x \le 0$

21. $y = x^3 + 1$; $y = 0$; $0 \le x \le 2$

22. $y = -x^3 + 3$; $y = 0$; $-2 \le x \le 1$

23. $y = x(1 - x)$; $y = 0$; $-1 \le x \le 0$

24. $y = -x(3 - x)$; $y = 0$; $1 \le x \le 2$

25. $y = -e^x$; $y = 0$; $-1 \le x \le 1$

26. $y = e^x$; $y = 0$; $0 \le x \le 1$

27. $y = \dfrac{1}{x}$; $y = 0$; $1 \le x \le e$

28. $y = -\dfrac{1}{x}$; $y = 0$; $-1 \le x \le -\dfrac{1}{e}$

In Problems 29–32, base your answers on the Gini index of income concentration (see Table 2, page 388).

29. In which of Canada, Mexico, or the United States is income most equally distributed? Most unequally distributed?

30. In which of France, Germany, or Sweden is income most equally distributed? Most unequally distributed?

31. In which of Brazil, India, or Jordan is income most equally distributed? Most unequally distributed?

32. In which of China, Japan, or Russia is income most equally distributed? Most unequally distributed?

Problems 33–42 refer to Figures A and B. Set up definite integrals in Problems 33–40 that represent the indicated shaded areas over the given intervals.

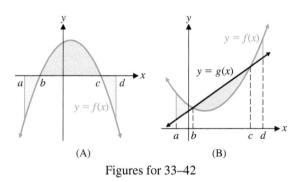

(A)   (B)

Figures for 33–42

33. Over interval $[a, b]$ in Figure A

34. Over interval $[c, d]$ in Figure A

35. Over interval $[b, d]$ in Figure A

36. Over interval $[a, c]$ in Figure A

37. Over interval $[c, d]$ in Figure B

38. Over interval $[a, b]$ in Figure B

39. Over interval $[a, c]$ in Figure B

40. Over interval $[b, d]$ in Figure B

41. Referring to Figure B, explain how you would use definite integrals and the functions f and g to find the area bounded by the two functions from $x = a$ to $x = d$.

42. Referring to Figure A, explain how you would use definite integrals to find the area between the graph of $y = f(x)$ and the x axis from $x = a$ to $x = d$.

In Problems 43–58, find the area bounded by the graphs of the indicated equations over the given intervals (when stated). Compute answers to three decimal places.

43. $y = -x$; $y = 0$; $-2 \le x \le 1$

44. $y = -x + 1$; $y = 0$; $-1 \le x \le 2$

45. $y = x^2 - 4$; $y = 0$; $0 \le x \le 3$

46. $y = 4 - x^2$; $y = 0$; $0 \le x \le 4$

47. $y = x^2 - 3x$; $y = 0$; $-2 \le x \le 2$

48. $y = -x^2 - 2x$; $y = 0$; $-2 \le x \le 1$

49. $y = -2x + 8$; $y = 12$; $-1 \le x \le 2$

50. $y = 2x + 6$; $y = 3$; $-1 \le x \le 2$

51. $y = 3x^2$; $y = 12$

52. $y = x^2$; $y = 9$

53. $y = 4 - x^2$; $y = -5$

54. $y = x^2 - 1$; $y = 3$

55. $y = x^2 + 1$; $y = 2x - 2$; $-1 \le x \le 2$

56. $y = x^2 - 1$; $y = x - 2$; $-2 \le x \le 1$

57. $y = e^{0.5x}$; $y = -\dfrac{1}{x}$; $1 \le x \le 2$

58. $y = \dfrac{1}{x}$; $y = -e^x$; $0.5 \le x \le 1$

In Problems 59–64, set up a definite integral that represents the area bounded by the graphs of the indicated equations over the given interval. Find the areas to three decimal places. [Hint: A circle of radius r, with center at the origin, has equation $x^2 + y^2 = r^2$ and area πr^2].

59. $y = \sqrt{9 - x^2}$; $y = 0$; $-3 \le x \le 3$

60. $y = \sqrt{25 - x^2}$; $y = 0$; $-5 \le x \le 5$

61. $y = -\sqrt{16 - x^2}$; $y = 0$; $0 \le x \le 4$

62. $y = -\sqrt{36 - x^2}$; $y = 0$; $-6 \le x \le 0$

63. $y = -\sqrt{4 - x^2}$; $y = \sqrt{4 - x^2}$; $-2 \le x \le 2$

64. $y = -\sqrt{100 - x^2}$; $y = \sqrt{100 - x^2}$; $-10 \le x \le 10$

In Problems 65–70, find the area bounded by the graphs of the indicated equations over the given interval (when stated). Compute answers to three decimal places.

65. $y = e^x$; $y = e^{-x}$; $0 \le x \le 4$

66. $y = e^x$; $y = -e^{-x}$; $1 \le x \le 2$

67. $y = x^3; y = 4x$

68. $y = x^3 + 1; y = x + 1$

69. $y = x^3 - 3x^2 - 9x + 12; y = x + 12$

70. $y = x^3 - 6x^2 + 9x; y = x$

In Problems 71–76, use a graphing calculator to graph the equations and find relevant intersection points. Then find the area bounded by the curves. Compute answers to three decimal places.

71. $y = x^3 - x^2 + 2; y = -x^3 + 8x - 2$

72. $y = 2x^3 + 2x^2 - x; y = -2x^3 - 2x^2 + 2x$

73. $y = e^{-x}; y = 3 - 2x$

74. $y = 2 - (x + 1)^2; y = e^{x+1}$

75. $y = e^x; y = 5x - x^3$

76. $y = 2 - e^x; y = x^3 + 3x^2$

In Problems 77–80, use a numerical integration routine on a graphing calculator to find the area bounded by the graphs of the indicated equations over the given interval (when stated). Compute answers to three decimal places.

77. $y = e^{-x}; y = \sqrt{\ln x}; 2 \le x \le 5$

78. $y = x^2 + 3x + 1; y = e^{e^x}; -3 \le x \le 0$

79. $y = e^{x^2}; y = x + 2$

80. $y = \ln(\ln x); y = 0.01x$

In Problems 81–84, find the constant c (to 2 decimal places) such that the Lorenz curve $f(x) = x^c$ has the given Gini index of income concentration.

81. 0.52

82. 0.23

83. 0.29

84. 0.65

Applications

In the applications that follow, it is helpful to sketch graphs to get a clearer understanding of each problem and to interpret results. A graphing calculator will prove useful if you have one, but it is not necessary.

85. *Oil production.* Using production and geological data, the management of an oil company estimates that oil will be pumped from a producing field at a rate given by

$$R(t) = \frac{100}{t + 10} + 10 \qquad 0 \le t \le 15$$

where $R(t)$ is the rate of production (in thousands of barrels per year) t years after pumping begins. Find the area between the graph of R and the t axis over the interval [5, 10] and interpret the results.

86. *Oil production.* In Problem 85, if the rate is found to be

$$R(t) = \frac{100t}{t^2 + 25} + 4 \qquad 0 \le t \le 25$$

then find the area between the graph of R and the t axis over the interval [5, 15] and interpret the results.

87. *Useful life.* An amusement company maintains records for each video game it installs in an arcade. Suppose that $C(t)$ and $R(t)$ represent the total accumulated costs and revenues (in thousands of dollars), respectively, t years after a particular game has been installed. If

$$C'(t) = 2 \qquad \text{and} \qquad R'(t) = 9e^{-0.3t}$$

then find the area between the graphs of C' and R' over the interval on the t axis from 0 to the useful life of the game and interpret the results.

88. *Useful life.* Repeat Problem 87 if

$$C'(t) = 2t \qquad \text{and} \qquad R'(t) = 5te^{-0.1t^2}$$

89. *Income distribution.* In a study on the effects of World War II on the U.S. economy, an economist used data from the U.S. Census Bureau to produce the following Lorenz curves for the distribution of U.S. income in 1935 and in 1947:

$$f(x) = x^{2.4} \qquad \text{Lorenz curve for 1935}$$

$$g(x) = x^{1.6} \qquad \text{Lorenz curve for 1947}$$

Find the Gini index of income concentration for each Lorenz curve and interpret the results.

90. *Income distribution.* Using data from the U.S. Census Bureau, an economist produced the following Lorenz curves for the distribution of U.S. income in 1962 and in 1972:

$$f(x) = \tfrac{3}{10}x + \tfrac{7}{10}x^2 \qquad \text{Lorenz curve for 1962}$$

$$g(x) = \tfrac{1}{2}x + \tfrac{1}{2}x^2 \qquad \text{Lorenz curve for 1972}$$

Find the Gini index of income concentration for each Lorenz curve and interpret the results.

91. *Distribution of wealth.* Lorenz curves also can provide a relative measure of the distribution of a country's total assets. Using data in a report by the U.S. Congressional Joint Economic Committee, an economist produced the following Lorenz curves for the distribution of total U.S. assets in 1963 and in 1983:

$$f(x) = x^{10} \qquad \text{Lorenz curve for 1963}$$

$$g(x) = x^{12} \qquad \text{Lorenz curve for 1983}$$

Find the Gini index of income concentration for each Lorenz curve and interpret the results.

92. *Income distribution.* The government of a small country is planning sweeping changes in the tax structure in order to provide a more equitable distribution of income. The Lorenz curves for the current income distribution and for the projected income distribution after enactment of the tax changes are as follows:

$$f(x) = x^{2.3} \qquad \text{Current Lorenz curve}$$

$$g(x) = 0.4x + 0.6x^2 \qquad \text{Projected Lorenz curve after changes in tax laws}$$

Find the Gini index of income concentration for each Lorenz curve. Will the proposed changes provide a more equitable income distribution? Explain.

93. *Distribution of wealth.* The data in the following table describe the distribution of wealth in a country:

x	0	0.20	0.40	0.60	0.80	1
y	0	0.12	0.31	0.54	0.78	1

(A) Use quadratic regression to find the equation of a Lorenz curve for the data.

(B) Use the regression equation and a numerical integration routine to approximate the Gini index of income concentration.

94. Distribution of wealth. Refer to Problem 93.

(A) Use cubic regression to find the equation of a Lorenz curve for the data.

(B) Use the cubic regression equation you found in Part (A) and a numerical integration routine to approximate the Gini index of income concentration.

95. Biology. A yeast culture is growing at a rate of $W'(t) = 0.3e^{0.1t}$ grams per hour. Find the area between the graph of W' and the t axis over the interval $[0, 10]$ and interpret the results.

96. Natural resource depletion. The instantaneous rate of change in demand for U.S. lumber since 1970 ($t = 0$), in billions of cubic feet per year, is given by

$$Q'(t) = 12 + 0.006t^2 \qquad 0 \leq t \leq 50$$

Find the area between the graph of Q' and the t axis over the interval $[35, 40]$, and interpret the results.

97. Learning. A college language class was chosen for a learning experiment. Using a list of 50 words, the experiment

measured the rate of vocabulary memorization at different times during a continuous 5-hour study session. The average rate of learning for the entire class was inversely proportional to the time spent studying and was given approximately by

$$V'(t) = \frac{15}{t} \qquad 1 \leq t \leq 5$$

Find the area between the graph of V' and the t axis over the interval $[2, 4]$, and interpret the results.

98. Learning. Repeat Problem 97 if $V'(t) = 13/t^{1/2}$ and the interval is changed to $[1, 4]$.

Answers to Matched Problems

1. $A = \int_{-1}^{3} (x^2 + 1)\, dx = \frac{40}{3} \approx 13.333$

2. (A) $A = \int_{0}^{2} (9 - x^2)\, dx = \frac{46}{3} \approx 15.333$

   (B) $A = \int_{2}^{3} (9 - x^2)\, dx + \int_{3}^{4} (x^2 - 9)\, dx = 6$

3. $A = \int_{-1}^{2} \left[(x^2 - 1) - \left(-\frac{x}{2} - 3 \right) \right] dx = \frac{39}{4} = 9.75$

4. $A = \int_{-3}^{2} [(6 - x^2) - x]\, dx = \frac{125}{6} \approx 20.833$

5. $A = \int_{-2}^{1} [(4 - 2x) - 2x^2]\, dx$
   $\quad + \int_{1}^{2} [2x^2 - (4 - 2x)]\, dx = \frac{38}{3} \approx 12.667$

6. 0.443

7. Gini index of income concentration ≈ 0.583; income will be less equally distributed in 2025.

6.2 Applications in Business and Economics

- Probability Density Functions
- Continuous Income Stream
- Future Value of a Continuous Income Stream
- Consumers' and Producers' Surplus

This section contains important applications of the definite integral to business and economics. Included are three independent topics: probability density functions, continuous income streams, and consumers' and producers' surplus. Any of the three may be covered in any order as time and interests dictate.

Probability Density Functions

We now take a brief, informal look at the use of the definite integral to determine probabilities. A more formal treatment of the subject requires the use of the special "improper" integral form $\int_{-\infty}^{\infty} f(x)\, dx$, which we will not discuss.

Suppose that an experiment is designed in such a way that any real number x on the interval $[c, d]$ is a possible outcome. For example, x may represent an IQ score, the height of a person in inches, or the life of a lightbulb in hours. Technically, we refer to x as a *continuous random variable*.

In certain situations, we can find a function f with x as an independent variable such that the function f can be used to determine Probability $(c \leq x \leq d)$, that is, the probability that the outcome x of an experiment will be in the interval $[c, d]$. Such a function, called a **probability density function**, must satisfy the following three conditions (see Fig. 1):

1. $f(x) \geq 0$ for all real x.
2. The area under the graph of $f(x)$ over the interval $(-\infty, \infty)$ is exactly 1.
3. If $[c, d]$ is a subinterval of $(-\infty, \infty)$, then

$$\text{Probability } (c \leq x \leq d) = \int_{c}^{d} f(x)\, dx$$

Figure 1 **Probability density function**

EXAMPLE 1 Duration of Telephone Calls Suppose that the length of telephone calls (in minutes) is a continuous random variable with the probability density function shown in Figure 2:

$$f(t) = \begin{cases} \frac{1}{4}e^{-t/4} & \text{if } t \geq 0 \\ 0 & \text{otherwise} \end{cases}$$

(A) Determine the probability that a call selected at random will last between 2 and 3 minutes.

(B) Find b (to two decimal places) so that the probability of a call selected at random lasting between 2 and b minutes is .5.

SOLUTION

(A) Probability $(2 \leq t \leq 3) = \displaystyle\int_2^3 \frac{1}{4}e^{-t/4}\,dt$

$$= \left(-e^{-t/4}\right)\Big|_2^3$$

$$= -e^{-3/4} + e^{-1/2} \approx .13$$

(B) We want to find b such that Probability $(2 \leq t \leq b) = .5$.

$$\int_2^b \frac{1}{4}e^{-t/4}\,dt = .5$$

$$-e^{-b/4} + e^{-1/2} = .5 \qquad \text{Solve for } b.$$

$$e^{-b/4} = e^{-.5} - .5$$

$$-\frac{b}{4} = \ln\left(e^{-.5} - .5\right)$$

$$b = 8.96 \text{ minutes}$$

So the probability of a call selected at random lasting from 2 to 8.96 minutes is .5.

Matched Problem 1

(A) In Example 1, find the probability that a call selected at random will last 4 minutes or less.

(B) Find b (to two decimal places) so that the probability of a call selected at random lasting b minutes or less is .9

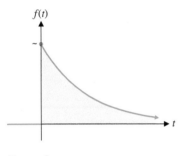

$f(t)$

t

Figure 2

CONCEPTUAL INSIGHT

The probability that a phone call in Example 1 lasts exactly 2 minutes (not 1.999 minutes, not 1.999 999 minutes) is given by

$$\text{Probability } (2 \leq t \leq 2) = \int_2^2 \frac{1}{4}e^{-t/4}\,dt \qquad \text{Use Property 1, Section 5.4}$$

$$= 0$$

In fact, for any *continuous* random variable x with probability density function $f(x)$, the probability that x is exactly equal to a constant c is equal to 0:

$$\text{Probability } (c \le x \le c) = \int_c^c f(x)\, dx \quad \text{Use Property 1, Section 5.4}$$

$$= 0$$

In this respect, a *continuous* random variable differs from a *discrete* random variable. If x, for example, is the discrete random variable that represents the number of dots that appear on the top face when a fair die is rolled, then

$$\text{Probability } (2 \le x \le 2) = \tfrac{1}{6}$$

One of the most important probability density functions, the **normal probability density function**, is defined as follows and graphed in Figure 3:

$$f(x) = \frac{1}{\sigma\sqrt{2\pi}} e^{-(x-\mu)^2/2\sigma^2} \quad \begin{array}{l} \mu \text{ is the mean.} \\ \sigma \text{ is the standard deviation.} \end{array}$$

It can be shown (but not easily) that the area under the normal curve in Figure 3 over the interval $(-\infty, \infty)$ is exactly 1. Since $\int e^{-x^2}\, dx$ is nonintegrable in terms of elementary functions (that is, the antiderivative cannot be expressed as a finite combination of simple functions), probabilities such as

$$\text{Probability } (c \le x \le d) = \frac{1}{\sigma\sqrt{2\pi}} \int_c^d e^{-(x-\mu)^2/2\sigma^2}\, dx$$

can be determined by making an appropriate substitution in the integrand and then using a table of areas under the standard normal curve (that is, the normal curve with $\mu = 0$ and $\sigma = 1$). As an alternative to a table, calculators and computers can be used to compute areas under normal curves.

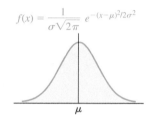

$$f(x) = \frac{1}{\sigma\sqrt{2\pi}} e^{-(x-\mu)^2/2\sigma^2}$$

Figure 3 **Normal curve**

Continuous Income Stream

We start with a simple example having an obvious solution and generalize the concept to examples having less obvious solutions.

Suppose that an aunt has established a trust that pays you $2,000 a year for 10 years. What is the total amount you will receive from the trust by the end of the 10th year? Since there are 10 payments of $2,000 each, you will receive

$$10 \times \$2,000 = \$20,000$$

We now look at the same problem from a different point of view. Let's assume that the income stream is continuous at a rate of $2,000 per year. In Figure 4, the area under the graph of $f(t) = 2,000$ from 0 to t represents the income accumulated t years after the start. For example, for $t = \tfrac{1}{4}$ year, the income would be $\tfrac{1}{4}(2,000) = \$500$; for $t = \tfrac{1}{2}$ year, the income would be $\tfrac{1}{2}(2,000) = \$1,000$; for $t = 1$ year, the income would be $1(2,000) = \$2,000$; for $t = 5.3$ years, the income would be $5.3(2,000) = \$10,600$; and for $t = 10$ years, the income would be $10(2,000) = \$20,000$. The total income over a 10-year period—that is, the area under the graph of $f(t) = 2,000$ from 0 to 10—is also given by the definite integral

$$\int_0^{10} 2,000\, dt = 2,000t \Big|_0^{10} = 2,000(10) - 2,000(0) = \$20,000$$

Figure 4 **Continuous income stream**

EXAMPLE 2   Continuous Income Stream   The rate of change of the income produced by a vending machine is given by

$$f(t) = 5{,}000e^{0.04t}$$

where t is time in years since the installation of the machine. Find the total income produced by the machine during the first 5 years of operation.

SOLUTION   The area under the graph of the rate-of-change function from 0 to 5 represents the total change in income over the first 5 years (Fig. 5), and is given by a definite integral:

$$
\begin{aligned}
\text{Total income} &= \int_0^5 5{,}000e^{0.04t}\, dt \\
&= 125{,}000e^{0.04t}\Big|_0^5 \\
&= 125{,}000e^{0.04(5)} - 125{,}000e^{0.04(0)} \\
&= 152{,}675 - 125{,}000 \\
&= \$27{,}675 \qquad \text{Rounded to the nearest dollar}
\end{aligned}
$$

Figure 5 **Continuous income stream**

The vending machine produces a total income of $27,675 during the first 5 years of operation.

Matched Problem 2   Referring to Example 2, find the total income produced (to the nearest dollar) during the second 5 years of operation.

In Example 2, we assumed that the rate of change of income was given by the continuous function f. The assumption is reasonable because income from a vending machine is often collected daily. In such situations, we assume that income is received in a **continuous stream**; that is, we assume that the rate at which income is received is a continuous function of time. The rate of change is called the **rate of flow** of the continuous income stream.

DEFINITION   Total Income for a Continuous Income Stream
If $f(t)$ is the rate of flow of a continuous income stream, then the **total income** produced during the period from $t = a$ to $t = b$ is

$$\text{Total income} = \int_a^b f(t)\, dt$$

Future Value of a Continuous Income Stream

In Section 3.1, we discussed the continuous compound interest formula

$$A = Pe^{rt}$$

where P is the principal (or present value), A is the amount (or future value), r is the annual rate of continuous compounding (expressed as a decimal), and t is time in years. For example, if money is worth 12% compounded continuously, then the future value of a \$10,000 investment in 5 years is (to the nearest dollar)

$$A = 10{,}000e^{0.12(5)} = \$18{,}221$$

We want to apply the future value concept to the income produced by a continuous income stream. Suppose that $f(t)$ is the rate of flow of a continuous income stream, and the income produced by this continuous income stream is invested as soon as it is received at a rate r, compounded continuously. We already know how to find the total income produced after T years, but how can we find the total of the income produced and the interest earned by this income? Since the income is received in a continuous flow, we cannot just use the formula $A = Pe^{rt}$. This formula is valid only for a single deposit P, not for a continuous flow of income. Instead, we use a Riemann sum approach that will allow us to apply the formula $A = Pe^{rt}$ repeatedly. To begin, we divide the time interval $[0, T]$ into n equal subintervals of length Δt and choose an arbitrary point c_k in each subinterval, as shown in Figure 6.

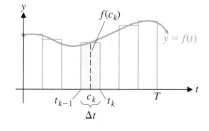

Figure 6

The total income produced during the period from $t = t_{k-1}$ to $t = t_k$ is equal to the area under the graph of $f(t)$ over this subinterval and is approximately equal to $f(c_k)\, \Delta t$, the area of the shaded rectangle in Figure 6. The income received during this period will earn interest for approximately $T - c_k$ years. So, from the future-value formula $A = Pe^{rt}$ with $P = f(c_k)\, \Delta t$ and $t = T - c_k$, the future value of the income produced during the period from $t = t_{k-1}$ to $t = t_k$ is approximately equal to

$$f(c_k)\, \Delta t e^{(T-c_k)r}$$

The total of these approximate future values over n subintervals is then

$$f(c_1)\, \Delta t e^{(T-c_1)r} + f(c_2)\, \Delta t e^{(T-c_2)r} + \cdots + f(c_n)\, \Delta t e^{(T-c_n)r} = \sum_{k=1}^{n} f(c_k) e^{r(T-c_k)}\, \Delta t$$

This equation has the form of a Riemann sum, the limit of which is a definite integral. (See the definition of the definite integral in Section 5.4.) Therefore, the *future value FV* of the income produced by the continuous income stream is given by

$$FV = \int_0^T f(t) e^{r(T-t)}\, dt$$

Since r and T are constants, we also can write

$$FV = \int_0^T f(t) e^{rT} e^{-rt}\, dt = e^{rT} \int_0^T f(t) e^{-rt}\, dt \tag{1}$$

This last form is preferable, since the integral is usually easier to evaluate than the first form.

DEFINITION Future Value of a Continuous Income Stream
If $f(t)$ is the rate of flow of a continuous income stream, $0 \leq t \leq T$, and if the income is continuously invested at a rate r, compounded continuously, then the **future value FV** at the end of T years is given by

$$FV = \int_0^T f(t) e^{r(T-t)}\, dt = e^{rT} \int_0^T f(t) e^{-rt}\, dt$$

The future value of a continuous income stream is the total value of all money produced by the continuous income stream (income and interest) at the end of T years.

We return to the trust that your aunt set up for you. Suppose that the $2,000 per year you receive from the trust is invested as soon as it is received at 8%, compounded continuously. We consider the trust income to be a continuous income stream with a flow rate of $2,000 per year. What is its future value (to the nearest dollar) by the end of the 10th year? Using the definite integral for future value from the preceding box, we have

$$FV = e^{rT} \int_0^T f(t)e^{-rt} \, dt$$

$$FV = e^{0.08(10)} \int_0^{10} 2{,}000 e^{-0.08t} \, dt \qquad r = 0.08, \; T = 10, \; f(t) = 2{,}000$$

$$= 2{,}000 e^{0.8} \int_0^{10} e^{-0.08t} \, dt$$

$$= 2{,}000 e^{0.8} \left[\frac{e^{-0.08t}}{-0.08} \right] \Big|_0^{10}$$

$$= 2{,}000 e^{0.8} \left[-12.5 e^{-0.8} + 12.5 \right] = \$30{,}639$$

At the end of 10 years, you will have received $30,639, including interest. How much is interest? Since you received $20,000 in income from the trust, the interest is the difference between the future value and income. So,

$$\$30{,}639 - \$20{,}000 = \$10{,}639$$

is the interest earned by the income received from the trust over the 10-year period.

EXAMPLE 3 Future Value of a Continuous Income Stream   Using the continuous income rate of flow for the vending machine in Example 2, namely,

$$f(t) = 5{,}000 e^{0.04t}$$

find the future value of this income stream at 12%, compounded continuously for 5 years, and find the total interest earned. Compute answers to the nearest dollar.

SOLUTION   Using the formula

$$FV = e^{rT} \int_0^T f(t)e^{-rt} \, dt$$

with $r = 0.12$, $T = 5$, and $f(t) = 5{,}000 e^{0.04t}$, we have

$$FV = e^{0.12(5)} \int_0^5 5{,}000 e^{0.04t} e^{-0.12t} \, dt$$

$$= 5{,}000 e^{0.6} \int_0^5 e^{-0.08t} \, dt$$

$$= 5{,}000 e^{0.6} \left(\frac{e^{-0.08t}}{-0.08} \right) \Big|_0^5$$

$$= 5{,}000 e^{0.6} \left(-12.5 e^{-0.4} + 12.5 \right)$$

$$= \$37{,}545 \qquad \text{Rounded to the nearest dollar}$$

The future value of the income stream at 12% compounded continuously at the end of 5 years is $37,545.

In Example 2, we saw that the total income produced by this vending machine over a 5-year period was $27,675. The difference between future value and income is interest. So,

$$\$37{,}545 - \$27{,}675 = \$9{,}870$$

is the interest earned by the income produced by the vending machine during the 5-year period.

Matched Problem 3 Repeat Example 3 if the interest rate is 9%, compounded continuously.

Consumers' and Producers' Surplus

Let $p = D(x)$ be the price–demand equation for a product, where x is the number of units of the product that consumers will purchase at a price of p per unit. Suppose that $\bar{p}$ is the current price and $\bar{x}$ is the number of units that can be sold at that price. Then the price–demand curve in Figure 7 shows that if the price is higher than $\bar{p}$, the demand x is less than $\bar{x}$, but some consumers are still willing to pay the higher price. Consumers who are willing to pay more than $\bar{p}$, but who are still able to buy the product at $\bar{p}$, have saved money. We want to determine the total amount saved by all the consumers who are willing to pay a price higher than $\bar{p}$ for the product.

To do this, consider the interval $[c_k, c_k + \Delta x]$, where $c_k + \Delta x < \bar{x}$. If the price remained constant over that interval, the savings on each unit would be the difference between $D(c_k)$, the price consumers are willing to pay, and $\bar{p}$, the price they actually pay. Since Δx represents the number of units purchased by consumers over the interval, the total savings to consumers over this interval is approximately equal to

$$[D(c_k) - \bar{p}]\,\Delta x \quad \text{(savings per unit)} \times \text{(number of units)}$$

which is the area of the shaded rectangle shown in Figure 7. If we divide the interval $[0, \bar{x}]$ into n equal subintervals, then the total savings to consumers is approximately equal to

$$[D(c_1) - \bar{p}]\,\Delta x + [D(c_2) - \bar{p}]\,\Delta x + \cdots + [D(c_n) - \bar{p}]\,\Delta x = \sum_{k=1}^{n}[D(c_k) - \bar{p}]\,\Delta x$$

which we recognize as a Riemann sum for the integral

$$\int_0^{\bar{x}}[D(x) - \bar{p}]\,dx$$

We define the *consumers' surplus* to be this integral.

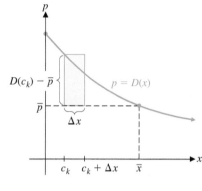

$D(c_k) - \bar{p}$ $p = D(x)$

Δx

$c_k \quad c_k + \Delta x \quad \bar{x}$

Figure 7

DEFINITION   Consumers' Surplus

If $(\bar{x}, \bar{p})$ is a point on the graph of the price–demand equation $p = D(x)$ for a particular product, then the **consumers' surplus CS** at a price level of $\bar{p}$ is

$$CS = \int_0^{\bar{x}}[D(x) - \bar{p}]\,dx$$

which is the area between $p = \bar{p}$ and $p = D(x)$ from $x = 0$ to $x = \bar{x}$, as shown in Figure 8.

The consumers' surplus represents the total savings to consumers who are willing to pay more than $\bar{p}$ for the product but are still able to buy the product for $\bar{p}$.

$p = D(x)$

CS

$\bar{p}$

$\bar{x}$

Figure 8

EXAMPLE 4 Consumers' Surplus Find the consumers' surplus at a price level of $8 for the price–demand equation

$$p = D(x) = 20 - 0.05x$$

SOLUTION

Step 1   Find $\bar{x}$, the demand when the price is $\bar{p} = 8$:

$$\bar{p} = 20 - 0.05\bar{x}$$
$$8 = 20 - 0.05\bar{x}$$
$$0.05\bar{x} = 12$$
$$\bar{x} = 240$$

Step 2   Sketch a graph, as shown in Figure 9.

Step 3   Find the consumers' surplus (the shaded area in the graph):

$$CS = \int_0^{\bar{x}} [D(x) - \bar{p}] \, dx$$

$$= \int_0^{240} (20 - 0.05x - 8) \, dx$$

$$= \int_0^{240} (12 - 0.05x) \, dx$$

$$= (12x - 0.025x^2) \Big|_0^{240}$$

$$= 2{,}880 - 1{,}440 = \$1{,}440$$

The total savings to consumers who are willing to pay a higher price for the product is $1,440.

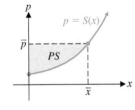

Figure 9

Matched Problem 4   Repeat Example 4 for a price level of $4.

If $p = S(x)$ is the price–supply equation for a product, $\bar{p}$ is the current price, and $\bar{x}$ is the current supply, then some suppliers are still willing to supply some units at a lower price than $\bar{p}$. The additional money that these suppliers gain from the higher price is called the *producers' surplus* and can be expressed in terms of a definite integral (proceeding as we did for the consumers' surplus).

DEFINITION   Producers' Surplus

If $(\bar{x}, \bar{p})$ is a point on the graph of the price–supply equation $p = S(x)$, then the **producers' surplus PS** at a price level of $\bar{p}$ is

$$PS = \int_0^{\bar{x}} [\bar{p} - S(x)] \, dx$$

which is the area between $p = \bar{p}$ and $p = S(x)$ from $x = 0$ to $x = \bar{x}$, as shown in Figure 10.

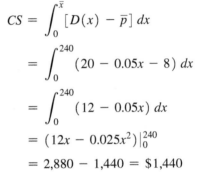

Figure 10

The producers' surplus represents the total gain to producers who are willing to supply units at a lower price than $\bar{p}$ but are still able to supply units at $\bar{p}$.

EXAMPLE 5   Producers' Surplus   Find the producers' surplus at a price level of $20 for the price–supply equation

$$p = S(x) = 2 + 0.0002x^2$$

SOLUTION

Step 1   Find $\bar{x}$, the supply when the price is $\bar{p} = 20$:

$$\bar{p} = 2 + 0.0002\bar{x}^2$$
$$20 = 2 + 0.0002\bar{x}^2$$
$$0.0002\bar{x}^2 = 18$$
$$\bar{x}^2 = 90{,}000$$
$$\bar{x} = 300 \qquad \text{There is only one solution, since } \bar{x} \geq 0.$$

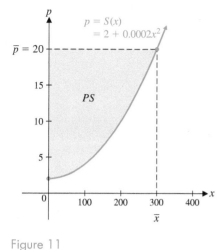

Figure 11

Step 2 Sketch a graph, as shown in Figure 11.

Step 3 Find the producers' surplus (the shaded area in the graph):

$$PS = \int_0^{\bar{x}} [\bar{p} - S(x)] \, dx = \int_0^{300} [20 - (2 + 0.0002x^2)] \, dx$$

$$= \int_0^{300} (18 - 0.0002x^2) \, dx = \left(18x - 0.0002\frac{x^3}{3}\right)\Big|_0^{300}$$

$$= 5{,}400 - 1{,}800 = \$3{,}600$$

The total gain to producers who are willing to supply units at a lower price is \$3,600.

Matched Problem 5   Repeat Example 5 for a price level of \$4.

In a free competitive market, the price of a product is determined by the relationship between supply and demand. If $p = D(x)$ and $p = S(x)$ are the price–demand and price–supply equations, respectively, for a product and if $(\bar{x}, \bar{p})$ is the point of intersection of these equations, then $\bar{p}$ is called the **equilibrium price** and $\bar{x}$ is called the **equilibrium quantity**. If the price stabilizes at the equilibrium price $\bar{p}$, then this is the price level that will determine both the consumers' surplus and the producers' surplus.

EXAMPLE 6   Equilibrium Price and Consumers' and Producers' Surplus   Find the equilibrium price and then find the consumers' surplus and producers' surplus at the equilibrium price level, if

$$p = D(x) = 20 - 0.05x \qquad \text{and} \qquad p = S(x) = 2 + 0.0002x^2$$

SOLUTION

Step 1 Find the equilibrium quantity. Set $D(x)$ equal to $S(x)$ and solve:

$$D(x) = S(x)$$
$$20 - 0.05x = 2 + 0.0002x^2$$
$$0.0002x^2 + 0.05x - 18 = 0$$
$$x^2 + 250x - 90{,}000 = 0$$
$$x = 200, -450$$

Since x cannot be negative, the only solution is $\bar{x} = 200$. The equilibrium price can be determined by using $D(x)$ or $S(x)$. We will use both to check our work:

$$\bar{p} = D(200) \qquad\qquad \bar{p} = S(200)$$
$$= 20 - 0.05(200) = 10 \qquad = 2 + 0.0002(200)^2 = 10$$

The equilibrium price is $\bar{p} = 10$, and the equilibrium quantity is $\bar{x} = 200$.

Step 2 Sketch a graph, as shown in Figure 12.

Step 3 Find the consumers' surplus:

$$CS = \int_0^{\bar{x}} [D(x) - \bar{p}] \, dx = \int_0^{200} (20 - 0.05x - 10) \, dx$$

$$= \int_0^{200} (10 - 0.05x) \, dx$$

$$= (10x - 0.025x^2)\Big|_0^{200}$$

$$= 2{,}000 - 1{,}000 = \$1{,}000$$

Figure 12

(A)

(B)

Figure 13

Step 4 Find the producers' surplus:

$$PS = \int_0^{\bar{x}} [\bar{p} - S(x)] \, dx$$

$$= \int_0^{200} [10 - (2 + 0.0002x^2)] \, dx$$

$$= \int_0^{200} (8 - 0.0002x^2) \, dx$$

$$= \left(8x - 0.0002\frac{x^3}{3} \right) \Big|_0^{200}$$

$$= 1{,}600 - \frac{1{,}600}{3} \approx \$1{,}067 \qquad \text{Rounded to the nearest dollar}$$

A graphing calculator offers an alternative approach to finding the equilibrium point for Example 6 (Fig. 13A). A numerical integration command can then be used to find the consumers' and producers' surplus (Fig. 13B).

Matched Problem 6 Repeat Example 6 for

$$p = D(x) = 25 - 0.001x^2 \qquad \text{and} \qquad p = S(x) = 5 + 0.1x$$

Exercises 6.2

Skills Warm-up Exercises

W In Problems 1–8, find real numbers b and c such that $f(t) = e^b e^{ct}$. (If necessary, review Section 1.5).

1. $f(t) = e^{5(4-t)}$

2. $f(t) = e^{3(15-t)}$

3. $f(t) = e^{0.04(8-t)}$

4. $f(t) = e^{0.02(12-t)}$

5. $f(t) = e^{0.05t}e^{0.08(20-t)}$

6. $f(t) = e^{0.03t}e^{0.09(30-t)}$

7. $f(t) = e^{0.09t}e^{0.07(25-t)}$

8. $f(t) = e^{0.14t}e^{0.11(15-t)}$

In Problems 9–14, evaluate each definite integral to two decimal places.

9. $\int_0^8 e^{0.06(8-t)} \, dt$

10. $\int_1^{10} e^{0.07(10-t)} \, dt$

11. $\int_0^{20} e^{0.08t}e^{0.12(20-t)} \, dt$

12. $\int_0^{15} e^{0.05t}e^{0.06(15-t)} \, dt$

13. $\int_0^{30} 500\, e^{0.02t}e^{0.09(30-t)} \, dt$

14. $\int_0^{25} 900\, e^{0.03t}e^{0.04(25-t)} \, dt$

In Problems 15 and 16, explain which of (A), (B), and (C) are equal before evaluating the expressions. Then evaluate each expression to two decimal places.

15. (A) $\int_0^8 e^{0.07(8-t)} \, dt$ (B) $\int_0^8 (e^{0.56} - e^{0.07t}) \, dt$

(C) $e^{0.56} \int_0^8 e^{-0.07t} \, dt$

16. (A) $\int_0^{10} 2{,}000 e^{0.05t}e^{0.12(10-t)} \, dt$

(B) $2{,}000 e^{1.2} \int_0^{10} e^{-0.07t} \, dt$

(C) $2{,}000 e^{0.05} \int_0^{10} e^{0.12(10-t)} \, dt$

In Problems 17–20, use a graphing calculator to graph the normal probability density function

$$f(x) = \frac{1}{\sigma\sqrt{2\pi}} e^{-(x-\mu)^2/2\sigma^2}$$

that has the given mean μ and standard deviation σ.

17. $\mu = 0, \sigma = 1$ **18.** $\mu = 20, \sigma = 5$

19. $\mu = 500, \sigma = 100$ **20.** $\mu = 300, \sigma = 25$

In Problems 21–24, use a numerical integration routine on a graphing calculator.

21. For the normal probability density function of Problem 17, find:

(A) Probability $(-1 \le x \le 1)$

(B) Probability $(-2 \le x \le 2)$

(C) Probability $(-3 \le x \le 3)$

22. For the normal probability density function of Problem 18, find:

(A) Probability $(15 \le x \le 25)$

(B) Probability $(10 \le x \le 30)$

(C) Probability $(5 \le x \le 35)$

23. For the normal probability density function of Problem 19, find:

(A) Probability $(400 \le x \le 600)$

(B) Probability $(300 \le x \le 700)$

(C) Probability $(200 \le x \le 800)$

24. For the normal probability density function of Problem 20, find:

(A) Probability $(275 \le x \le 325)$

(B) Probability $(250 \le x \le 350)$

(C) Probability $(225 \le x \le 375)$

Applications

Unless stated to the contrary, compute all monetary answers to the nearest dollar.

25. The life expectancy (in years) of a microwave oven is a continuous random variable with probability density function

$$f(x) = \begin{cases} 2/(x+2)^2 & \text{if } x \ge 0 \\ 0 & \text{otherwise} \end{cases}$$

(A) Find the probability that a randomly selected microwave oven lasts at most 6 years.

(B) Find the probability that a randomly selected microwave oven lasts from 6 to 12 years.

(C) Graph $y = f(x)$ for [0, 12] and show the shaded region for part (A).

26. The shelf life (in years) of a laser pointer battery is a continuous random variable with probability density function

$$f(x) = \begin{cases} 1/(x+1)^2 & \text{if } x \ge 0 \\ 0 & \text{otherwise} \end{cases}$$

(A) Find the probability that a randomly selected laser pointer battery has a shelf life of 3 years or less.

(B) Find the probability that a randomly selected laser pointer battery has a shelf life of from 3 to 9 years.

(C) Graph $y = f(x)$ for [0, 10] and show the shaded region for part (A).

27. In Problem 25, find d so that the probability of a randomly selected microwave oven lasting d years or less is .8.

28. In Problem 26, find d so that the probability of a randomly selected laser pointer battery lasting d years or less is .5.

29. A manufacturer guarantees a product for 1 year. The time to failure of the product after it is sold is given by the probability density function

$$f(t) = \begin{cases} .01e^{-.01t} & \text{if } t \ge 0 \\ 0 & \text{otherwise} \end{cases}$$

where t is time in months. What is the probability that a buyer chosen at random will have a product failure

(A) During the warranty period?

(B) During the second year after purchase?

30. In a certain city, the daily use of water (in hundreds of gallons) per household is a continuous random variable with probability density function

$$f(x) = \begin{cases} .15e^{-.15x} & \text{if } x \ge 0 \\ 0 & \text{otherwise} \end{cases}$$

Find the probability that a household chosen at random will use

(A) At most 400 gallons of water per day

(B) Between 300 and 600 gallons of water per day

31. In Problem 29, what is the probability that the product will last at least 1 year? [*Hint:* Recall that the total area under the probability density function curve is 1.]

32. In Problem 30, what is the probability that a household will use more than 400 gallons of water per day? [See the hint in Problem 31.]

33. Find the total income produced by a continuous income stream in the first 5 years if the rate of flow is $f(t) = 2,500$.

34. Find the total income produced by a continuous income stream in the first 10 years if the rate of flow is $f(t) = 3,000$.

35. Interpret the results of Problem 33 with both a graph and a description of the graph.

36. Interpret the results of Problem 34 with both a graph and a description of the graph.

37. Find the total income produced by a continuous income stream in the first 3 years if the rate of flow is $f(t) = 400e^{0.05t}$.

38. Find the total income produced by a continuous income stream in the first 2 years if the rate of flow is $f(t) = 600e^{0.06t}$.

39. Interpret the results of Problem 37 with both a graph and a description of the graph.

40. Interpret the results of Problem 38 with both a graph and a description of the graph.

41. Starting at age 25, you deposit $2,000 a year into an IRA account. Treat the yearly deposits into the account as a continuous income stream. If money in the account earns 5%, compounded continuously, how much will be in the account 40 years later, when you retire at age 65? How much of the final amount is interest?

42. Suppose in Problem 41 that you start the IRA deposits at age 30, but the account earns 6%, compounded continuously. Treat the yearly deposits into the account as a continuous income stream. How much will be in the account 35 years later when you retire at age 65? How much of the final amount is interest?

43. Find the future value at 3.25% interest, compounded continuously for 4 years, of the continuous income stream with rate of flow $f(t) = 1,650e^{-0.02t}$.

44. Find the future value, at 2.95% interest, compounded continuously for 6 years, of the continuous income stream with rate of flow $f(t) = 2,000e^{0.06t}$.

45. Compute the interest earned in Problem 43.

46. Compute the interest earned in Problem 44.

47. An investor is presented with a choice of two investments: an established clothing store and a new computer store. Each choice requires the same initial investment and each produces a continuous income stream of 4%, compounded continuously. The rate of flow of income from the clothing store is $f(t) = 12,000$, and the rate of flow of income from the computer store is expected to be $g(t) = 10,000e^{0.05t}$. Compare the future values of these investments to determine which is the better choice over the next 5 years.

48. Refer to Problem 47. Which investment is the better choice over the next 10 years?

49. An investor has $10,000 to invest in either a bond that matures in 5 years or a business that will produce a continuous stream of income over the next 5 years with rate of flow $f(t) = 2,150$. If both the bond and the continuous income stream earn 3.75%, compounded continuously, which is the better investment?

50. Refer to Problem 49. Which is the better investment if the rate of the income from the business is $f(t) = 2,250$?

51. A business is planning to purchase a piece of equipment that will produce a continuous stream of income for 8 years with rate of flow $f(t) = 9,000$. If the continuous income stream earns 6.95%, compounded continuously, what single deposit into an account earning the same interest rate will produce the same future value as the continuous income stream? (This deposit is called the **present value** of the continuous income stream.)

52. Refer to Problem 51. Find the present value of a continuous income stream at 7.65%, compounded continuously for 12 years, if the rate of flow is $f(t) = 1,000e^{0.03t}$.

53. Find the future value at a rate r, compounded continuously for T years, of a continuous income stream with rate of flow $f(t) = k$, where k is a constant.

54. Find the future value at a rate r, compounded continuously for T years, of a continuous income stream with rate of flow $f(t) = ke^{ct}$, where c and k are constants, $c \neq r$.

55. Find the consumers' surplus at a price level of $\bar{p} = \$150$ for the price–demand equation

$$p = D(x) = 400 - 0.05x$$

56. Find the consumers' surplus at a price level of $\bar{p} = \$120$ for the price–demand equation

$$p = D(x) = 200 - 0.02x$$

57. Interpret the results of Problem 55 with both a graph and a description of the graph.

58. Interpret the results of Problem 56 with both a graph and a description of the graph.

59. Find the producers' surplus at a price level of $\bar{p} = \$67$ for the price–supply equation

$$p = S(x) = 10 + 0.1x + 0.0003x^2$$

60. Find the producers' surplus at a price level of $\bar{p} = \$55$ for the price–supply equation

$$p = S(x) = 15 + 0.1x + 0.003x^2$$

61. Interpret the results of Problem 59 with both a graph and a description of the graph.

62. Interpret the results of Problem 60 with both a graph and a description of the graph.

In Problems 63–70, find the consumers' surplus and the producers' surplus at the equilibrium price level for the given price–demand and price–supply equations. Include a graph that identifies the consumers' surplus and the producers' surplus. Round all values to the nearest integer.

63. $p = D(x) = 50 - 0.1x; p = S(x) = 11 + 0.05x$

64. $p = D(x) = 25 - 0.004x^2; p = S(x) = 5 + 0.004x^2$

65. $p = D(x) = 80e^{-0.001x}; p = S(x) = 30e^{0.001x}$

66. $p = D(x) = 185e^{-0.005x}; p = S(x) = 25e^{0.005x}$

67. $p = D(x) = 80 - 0.04x; p = S(x) = 30e^{0.001x}$

68. $p = D(x) = 190 - 0.2x; p = S(x) = 25e^{0.005x}$

69. $p = D(x) = 80e^{-0.001x}; p = S(x) = 15 + 0.0001x^2$

70. $p = D(x) = 185e^{-0.005x}; p = S(x) = 20 + 0.002x^2$

71. The following tables give price–demand and price–supply data for the sale of soybeans at a grain market, where x is the number of bushels of soybeans (in thousands of bushels) and p is the price per bushel (in dollars):

Tables for 71–72

Price–Demand		Price–Supply	
x	$p = D(x)$	x	$p = S(x)$
0	6.70	0	6.43
10	6.59	10	6.45
20	6.52	20	6.48
30	6.47	30	6.53
40	6.45	40	6.62

Use quadratic regression to model the price–demand data and linear regression to model the price–supply data.

(A) Find the equilibrium quantity (to three decimal places) and equilibrium price (to the nearest cent).

(B) Use a numerical integration routine to find the consumers' surplus and producers' surplus at the equilibrium price level.

72. Repeat Problem 71, using quadratic regression to model both sets of data.

Answers to Matched Problems

1. (A) .63   (B) 9.21 min

2. $33,803   **3.** $FV = \$34,691$; interest $= \$7,016$

4. $2,560   **5.** $133

6. $\bar{p} = 15$; $CS = \$667$; $PS = \$500$

6.3   Integration by Parts

In Section 5.1, we promised to return later to the indefinite integral

$$\int \ln x \, dx$$

since none of the integration techniques considered up to that time could be used to find an antiderivative for ln x. We now develop a very useful technique, called *integration by parts,* that will enable us to find not only the preceding integral, but also many others, including integrals such as

$$\int x \ln x \, dx \qquad \text{and} \qquad \int xe^x \, dx$$

The method of integration by parts is based on the product formula for derivatives. If f and g are differentiable functions, then

$$\frac{d}{dx}[f(x)g(x)] = f(x)g'(x) + g(x)f'(x)$$

which can be written in the equivalent form

$$f(x)g'(x) = \frac{d}{dx}[f(x)g(x)] - g(x)f'(x)$$

Integrating both sides, we obtain

$$\int f(x)g'(x) \, dx = \int \frac{d}{dx}[f(x)g(x)] \, dx - \int g(x)f'(x) \, dx$$

The first integral to the right of the equal sign is $f(x)g(x) + C$. Why? We will leave out the constant of integration for now, since we can add it after integrating the second integral to the right of the equal sign. So,

$$\int f(x)g'(x) \, dx = f(x)g(x) - \int g(x)f'(x) \, dx$$

This equation can be transformed into a more convenient form by letting $u = f(x)$ and $v = g(x)$; then $du = f'(x) \, dx$ and $dv = g'(x) \, dx$. Making these substitutions, we obtain the **integration-by-parts formula**:

Integration-by-Parts Formula

$$\int u \, dv = uv - \int v \, du$$

This formula can be very useful when the integral on the left is difficult or impossible to integrate with standard formulas. If u and dv are chosen with care—this is the crucial part of the process—then the integral on the right side may be easier to integrate than the one on the left. The formula provides us with another tool that is helpful in many, but not all, cases. We are able to easily check the results by differentiating to get the original integrand, a good habit to develop.

EXAMPLE 1   Integration by Parts   Find $\int xe^x \, dx$, using integration by parts, and check the result.

SOLUTION First, write the integration-by-parts formula:

$$\int u \, dv = uv - \int v \, du \qquad (1)$$

Now try to identify u and dv in $\int xe^x \, dx$ so that $\int v \, du$ on the right side of (1) is easier to integrate than $\int u \, dv = \int xe^x \, dx$ on the left side. There are essentially two reasonable choices in selecting u and dv in $\int xe^x \, dx$:

We pursue choice 1 and leave choice 2 for you to explore (see Explore and Discuss 1 following this example).

From choice 1, $u = x$ and $dv = e^x \, dx$. Looking at formula (1), we need du and v to complete the right side. Let

$$u = x \qquad dv = e^x \, dx$$

Then,

$$du = dx \qquad \int dv = \int e^x \, dx$$

$$v = e^x$$

Any constant may be added to v, but we will always choose 0 for simplicity. The general arbitrary constant of integration will be added at the end of the process.

Substituting these results into formula (1), we obtain

$$\int u \, dv = uv - \int v \, du$$

$$\int xe^x \, dx = xe^x - \int e^x \, dx \qquad \text{The right integral is easy to integrate.}$$

$$= xe^x - e^x + C \qquad \text{Now add the arbitrary constant } C.$$

Check:

$$\frac{d}{dx}(xe^x - e^x + C) = xe^x + e^x - e^x = xe^x$$

Explore and Discuss 1   Pursue choice 2 in Example 1, using the integration-by-parts formula, and explain why this choice does not work out.

Matched Problem 1   Find $\int xe^{2x} \, dx$.

EXAMPLE 2   Integration by Parts   Find $\int x \ln x \, dx$.

SOLUTION As before, we have essentially two choices in choosing u and dv:

Choice 1   Choice 2

$$\int \overset{u}{\overbrace{x}} \; \overset{dv}{\overbrace{\ln x \, dx}} \qquad \int \overset{u}{\overbrace{\ln x}} \; \overset{dv}{\overbrace{x \, dx}}$$

Choice 1 is rejected since we do not yet know how to find an antiderivative of $\ln x$. So we move to choice 2 and choose $u = \ln x$ and $dv = x\, dx$. Then we proceed as in Example 1. Let

$$u = \ln x \qquad dv = x\, dx$$

Then,

$$du = \frac{1}{x}dx \qquad \int dv = \int x\, dx$$

$$v = \frac{x^2}{2}$$

Substitute these results into the integration-by-parts formula:

$$\int u\, dv = uv - \int v\, du$$

$$\int x \ln x\, dx = (\ln x)\left(\frac{x^2}{2}\right) - \int \left(\frac{x^2}{2}\right)\left(\frac{1}{x}\right) dx$$

$$= \frac{x^2}{2} \ln x - \int \frac{x}{2}dx \qquad \text{An easy integral to evaluate}$$

$$= \frac{x^2}{2} \ln x - \frac{x^2}{4} + C$$

Check:

$$\frac{d}{dx}\left(\frac{x^2}{2} \ln x - \frac{x^2}{4} + C\right) = x \ln x + \left(\frac{x^2}{2} \cdot \frac{1}{x}\right) - \frac{x}{2} = x \ln x$$

Matched Problem 2   Find $\int x \ln 2x\, dx$.

CONCEPTUAL INSIGHT

As you may have discovered in Explore and Discuss 1, some choices for u and dv will lead to integrals that are more complicated than the original integral. This does not mean that there is an error in either the calculations or the integration-by-parts formula. It simply means that the particular choice of u and dv does not change the problem into one we can solve. When this happens, we must look for a different choice of u and dv. In some problems, it is possible that no choice will work.

Guidelines for selecting u and dv for integration by parts are summarized in the following box:

SUMMARY   Integration by Parts: Selection of u and dv
For $\int u\, dv = uv - \int v\, du$,

1. The product $u\, dv$ must equal the original integrand.
2. It must be possible to integrate dv (preferably by using standard formulas or simple substitutions).
3. The new integral $\int v\, du$ should not be more complicated than the original integral $\int u\, dv$.
4. For integrals involving $x^p e^{ax}$, try

$$u = x^p \qquad \text{and} \qquad dv = e^{ax}\, dx$$

5. For integrals involving $x^p(\ln x)^q$, try

$$u = (\ln x)^q \qquad \text{and} \qquad dv = x^p\, dx$$

In some cases, repeated use of the integration-by-parts formula will lead to the evaluation of the original integral. The next example provides an illustration of such a case.

EXAMPLE 3   Repeated Use of Integration by Parts   Find $\int x^2 e^{-x}\,dx$.

SOLUTION   Following suggestion 4 in the box, we choose

$$u = x^2 \qquad dv = e^{-x}\,dx$$

Then,

$$du = 2x\,dx \qquad v = -e^{-x}$$

and

$$\int x^2 e^{-x}\,dx = x^2(-e^{-x}) - \int (-e^{-x})2x\,dx$$

$$= -x^2 e^{-x} + 2\int xe^{-x}\,dx \qquad (2)$$

The new integral is not one we can evaluate by standard formulas, but it is simpler than the original integral. Applying the integration-by-parts formula to it will produce an even simpler integral. For the integral $\int xe^{-x}\,dx$, we choose

$$u = x \qquad dv = e^{-x}\,dx$$

Then,

$$du = dx \qquad v = -e^{-x}$$

and

$$\int xe^{-x}\,dx = x(-e^{-x}) - \int (-e^{-x})\,dx$$

$$= -xe^{-x} + \int e^{-x}\,dx$$

$$= -xe^{-x} - e^{-x} \qquad \text{Choose 0 for the constant.} \qquad (3)$$

Substituting equation (3) into equation (2), we have

$$\int x^2 e^{-x}\,dx = -x^2 e^{-x} + 2(-xe^{-x} - e^{-x}) + C \qquad \text{Add an arbitrary constant here.}$$

$$= -x^2 e^{-x} - 2xe^{-x} - 2e^{-x} + C$$

Check:

$$\frac{d}{dx}(-x^2 e^{-x} - 2xe^{-x} - 2e^{-x} + C) = x^2 e^{-x} - 2xe^{-x} + 2xe^{-x} - 2e^{-x} + 2e^{-x}$$

$$= x^2 e^{-x}$$

Matched Problem 3   Find $\int x^2 e^{2x}\,dx$.

EXAMPLE 4   Using Integration by Parts   Find $\int_1^e \ln x\,dx$ and interpret the result geometrically.

SOLUTION   First, we find $\int \ln x\,dx$. Then we return to the definite integral. Following suggestion 5 in the box (with $p = 0$), we choose

$$u = \ln x \qquad dv = dx$$

Then,

$$du = \frac{1}{x}dx \qquad v = x$$

$$\int \ln x\, dx = (\ln x)(x) - \int (x)\frac{1}{x}dx$$

$$= x \ln x - x + C$$

This is the important result we mentioned at the beginning of this section. Now we have

$$\int_1^e \ln x\, dx = (x \ln x - x)\Big|_1^e$$

$$= (e \ln e - e) - (1 \ln 1 - 1)$$

$$= (e - e) - (0 - 1)$$

$$= 1$$

The integral represents the area under the curve $y = \ln x$ from $x = 1$ to $x = e$, as shown in Figure 1.

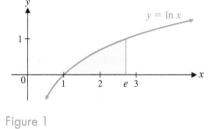

Figure 1

Matched Problem 4 Find $\int_1^2 \ln 3x\, dx$.

Explore and Discuss 2 Try using the integration-by-parts formula on $\int e^{x^2}\, dx$, and explain why it does not work.

Exercises 6.3

Skills Warm-up Exercises

In Problems 1–8, find the derivative of $f(x)$ and the indefinite integral of $g(x)$. (If necessary, review Sections 3.2 and 5.1).

1. $f(x) = 5x; g(x) = x^3$

2. $f(x) = x^2; g(x) = e^x$

3. $f(x) = x^3; g(x) = 5x$

4. $f(x) = e^x; g(x) = x^2$

5. $f(x) = e^{4x}; g(x) = \dfrac{1}{x}$

6. $f(x) = \sqrt{x}; g(x) = e^{-2x}$

7. $f(x) = \dfrac{1}{x}; g(x) = e^{4x}$

8. $f(x) = e^{-2x}; g(x) = \sqrt{x}$

In Problems 9–12, integrate by parts. Assume that $x > 0$ whenever the natural logarithm function is involved.

9. $\displaystyle\int xe^{3x}\, dx$

10. $\displaystyle\int xe^{4x}\, dx$

11. $\displaystyle\int x^2 \ln x\, dx$

12. $\displaystyle\int x^3 \ln x\, dx$

13. If you want to use integration by parts to find $\int (x + 1)^5 (x + 2)\, dx$, which is the better choice for u: $u = (x + 1)^5$ or $u = x + 2$? Explain your choice and then integrate.

14. If you want to use integration by parts to find $\int (5x - 7)(x - 1)^4\, dx$, which is the better choice for u: $u = 5x - 7$ or $u = (x - 1)^4$? Explain your choice and then integrate.

Problems 15–28 are mixed—some require integration by parts, and others can be solved with techniques considered earlier. Integrate as indicated, assuming $x > 0$ whenever the natural logarithm function is involved.

15. $\displaystyle\int xe^{-x}\, dx$

16. $\displaystyle\int (x - 1)e^{-x}\, dx$

17. $\displaystyle\int xe^{x^2}\, dx$

18. $\displaystyle\int xe^{-x^2}\, dx$

19. $\displaystyle\int_0^1 (x - 3)e^x\, dx$

20. $\displaystyle\int_0^1 (x + 1)e^x\, dx$

21. $\displaystyle\int_1^3 \ln 2x\, dx$

22. $\displaystyle\int_1^2 \ln\left(\frac{x}{2}\right)dx$

23. $\displaystyle\int \frac{2x}{x^2 + 1}\, dx$

24. $\displaystyle\int \frac{x^2}{x^3 + 5}\, dx$

25. $\displaystyle\int \frac{\ln x}{x}\, dx$

26. $\displaystyle\int \frac{e^x}{e^x + 1}\, dx$

27. $\displaystyle\int \sqrt{x} \ln x\, dx$

28. $\displaystyle\int \frac{\ln x}{\sqrt{x}}\, dx$

In Problems 29–32, the integral can be found in more than one way. First use integration by parts, then use a method that does not involve integration by parts. Which method do you prefer?

29. $\int (x - 3)(x + 1)^2 \, dx$ **30.** $\int (x + 2)(x - 1)^2 \, dx$

31. $\int (2x + 1)(x - 2)^2 \, dx$ **32.** $\int (5x - 1)(x + 2)^2 \, dx$

In Problems 33–36, illustrate each integral graphically and describe what the integral represents in terms of areas.

33. Problem 19   **34.** Problem 20

35. Problem 21   **36.** Problem 22

Problems 37–58 are mixed—some may require use of the integration-by-parts formula along with techniques we have considered earlier; others may require repeated use of the integration-by-parts formula. Assume that $g(x) > 0$ whenever $\ln g(x)$ is involved.

37. $\int x^2 e^x \, dx$ **38.** $\int x^3 e^x \, dx$

39. $\int x e^{ax} \, dx, a \neq 0$ **40.** $\int \ln(ax) \, dx, a > 0$

41. $\int_1^e \frac{\ln x}{x^2} \, dx$ **42.** $\int_1^2 x^3 e^{x^2} \, dx$

43. $\int_0^2 \ln(x + 4) \, dx$ **44.** $\int_0^2 \ln(4 - x) \, dx$

45. $\int x e^{x-2} \, dx$ **46.** $\int x e^{x+1} \, dx$

47. $\int x \ln(1 + x^2) \, dx$ **48.** $\int x \ln(1 + x) \, dx$

49. $\int e^x \ln(1 + e^x) \, dx$ **50.** $\int \frac{\ln(1 + \sqrt{x})}{\sqrt{x}} \, dx$

51. $\int (\ln x)^2 \, dx$ **52.** $\int x(\ln x)^2 \, dx$

53. $\int (\ln x)^3 \, dx$ **54.** $\int x(\ln x)^3 \, dx$

55. $\int_1^e \ln(x^2) \, dx$ **56.** $\int_1^e \ln(x^4) \, dx$

57. $\int_0^1 \ln(e^{x^2}) \, dx$ **58.** $\int_1^2 \ln(x e^x) \, dx$

In Problems 59–62, use a graphing calculator to graph each equation over the indicated interval and find the area between the curve and the x axis over that interval. Find answers to two decimal places.

59. $y = x - 2 - \ln x; 1 \leq x \leq 4$

60. $y = 6 - x^2 - \ln x; 1 \leq x \leq 4$

61. $y = 5 - x e^x; 0 \leq x \leq 3$

62. $y = x e^x + x - 6; 0 \leq x \leq 3$

Applications

63. Profit. If the marginal profit (in millions of dollars per year) is given by

$$P'(t) = 2t - t e^{-t}$$

use an appropriate definite integral to find the total profit (to the nearest million dollars) earned over the first 5 years of operation.

64. Production. An oil field is estimated to produce oil at a rate of $R(t)$ thousand barrels per month t months from now, as given by

$$R(t) = 10t e^{-0.1t}$$

Use an appropriate definite integral to find the total production (to the nearest thousand barrels) in the first year of operation.

65. Profit. Interpret the results of Problem 63 with both a graph and a description of the graph.

66. Production. Interpret the results of Problem 64 with both a graph and a description of the graph.

67. Continuous income stream. Find the future value at 3.95%, compounded continuously, for 5 years of a continuous income stream with a rate of flow of

$$f(t) = 1,000 - 200t$$

68. Continuous income stream. Find the interest earned at 4.15%, compounded continuously, for 4 years for a continuous income stream with a rate of flow of

$$f(t) = 1,000 - 250t$$

69. Income distribution. Find the Gini index of income concentration for the Lorenz curve with equation

$$y = x e^{x-1}$$

70. Income distribution. Find the Gini index of income concentration for the Lorenz curve with equation

$$y = x^2 e^{x-1}$$

71. Income distribution. Interpret the results of Problem 69 with both a graph and a description of the graph.

72. Income distribution. Interpret the results of Problem 70 with both a graph and a description of the graph.

73. Sales analysis. Monthly sales of a particular personal computer are expected to increase at the rate of

$$S'(t) = -4t e^{0.1t}$$

computers per month, where t is time in months and $S(t)$ is the number of computers sold each month. The company plans to stop manufacturing this computer when monthly sales reach 800 computers. If monthly sales now $(t = 0)$ are 2,000 computers, find $S(t)$. How long, to the nearest month, will the company continue to manufacture the computer?

74. Sales analysis. The rate of change of the monthly sales of a new basketball game is given by

$$S'(t) = 350 \ln(t + 1) \qquad S(0) = 0$$

where t is the number of months since the game was released and $S(t)$ is the number of games sold each month. Find $S(t)$.

When, to the nearest month, will monthly sales reach 15,000 games?

75. Consumers' surplus. Find the consumers' surplus (to the nearest dollar) at a price level of $\bar{p} = \$2.089$ for the price–demand equation

$$p = D(x) = 9 - \ln(x + 4)$$

Use $\bar{x}$ computed to the nearest higher unit.

76. Producers' surplus. Find the producers' surplus (to the nearest dollar) at a price level of $\bar{p} = \$26$ for the price–supply equation

$$p = S(x) = 5 \ln(x + 1)$$

Use $\bar{x}$ computed to the nearest higher unit.

77. Consumers' surplus. Interpret the results of Problem 75 with both a graph and a description of the graph.

78. Producers' surplus. Interpret the results of Problem 76 with both a graph and a description of the graph.

79. Pollution. The concentration of particulate matter (in parts per million) t hours after a factory ceases operation for the day is given by

$$C(t) = \frac{20 \ln(t + 1)}{(t + 1)^2}$$

Find the average concentration for the period from $t = 0$ to $t = 5$.

80. Medicine. After a person takes a pill, the drug contained in the pill is assimilated into the bloodstream. The rate of assimilation t minutes after taking the pill is

$$R(t) = te^{-0.2t}$$

Find the total amount of the drug that is assimilated into the bloodstream during the first 10 minutes after the pill is taken.

81. Learning. A student enrolled in an advanced typing class progressed at a rate of

$$N'(t) = (t + 6)e^{-0.25t}$$

words per minute per week t weeks after enrolling in a 15-week course. If a student could type 40 words per minute at the beginning of the course, then how many words per minute $N(t)$ would the student be expected to type t weeks into the course? How long, to the nearest week, should it take the student to achieve the 70-word-per-minute level? How many words per minute should the student be able to type by the end of the course?

82. Learning. A student enrolled in a stenotyping class progressed at a rate of

$$N'(t) = (t + 10)e^{-0.1t}$$

words per minute per week t weeks after enrolling in a 15-week course. If a student had no knowledge of stenotyping (that is, if the student could stenotype at 0 words per minute) at the beginning of the course, then how many words per minute $N(t)$ would the student be expected to handle t weeks into the course? How long, to the nearest week, should it take the student to achieve 90 words per minute? How many words per minute should the student be able to handle by the end of the course?

83. Politics. The number of voters (in thousands) in a certain city is given by

$$N(t) = 20 + 4t - 5te^{-0.1t}$$

where t is time in years. Find the average number of voters during the period from $t = 0$ to $t = 5$.

Answers to Matched Problems

1. $\dfrac{x}{2}e^{2x} - \dfrac{1}{4}e^{2x} + C$

2. $\dfrac{x^2}{2}\ln 2x - \dfrac{x^2}{4} + C$

3. $\dfrac{x^2}{2}e^{2x} - \dfrac{x}{2}e^{2x} + \dfrac{1}{4}e^{2x} + C$

4. $2 \ln 6 - \ln 3 - 1 \approx 1.4849$

6.4 Other Integration Methods

- The Trapezoidal Rule
- Simpson's Rule
- Using a Table of Integrals
- Substitution and Integral Tables
- Reduction Formulas
- Application

In Chapter 5 we used left and right sums to approximate the definite integral of a function, and, if an antiderivative could be found, calculated the exact value using the fundamental theorem of calculus. Now we discuss other methods for approximating definite integrals, and a procedure for finding exact values of definite integrals of many standard functions.

Approximation of definite integrals by left sums and right sums is instructive and important, but not efficient. A large number of rectangles must be used, and many terms must be summed, to get good approximations. The *trapezoidal rule* and *Simpson's rule* provide more efficient approximations of definite integrals in the sense that fewer terms must be summed to achieve a given accuracy.

A **table of integrals** can be used to find antiderivatives of many standard functions (see Table II of Appendix C on pages 574–576). Definite integrals of such functions can therefore be found exactly by means of the fundamental theorem of calculus.

The Trapezoidal Rule

The trapezoid in Figure 1 is a more accurate approximation of the area under the graph of f and above the x axis than the left rectangle or the right rectangle. Using Δx to denote $x_1 - x_0$,

$$\text{Area of left rectangle: } f(x_0)\,\Delta x$$

$$\text{Area of right rectangle: } f(x_1)\,\Delta x$$

$$\text{Area of trapezoid: } \frac{f(x_0) + f(x_1)}{2}\Delta x \tag{1}$$

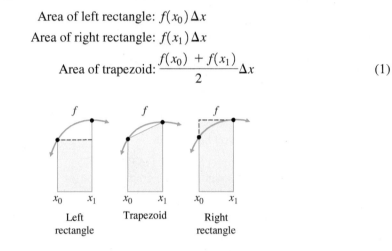

Left rectangle   Trapezoid   Right rectangle

Figure 1

Note that the area of the trapezoid in Figure 1 [also see formula (1)] is the average of the areas of the left and right rectangles. So the average T_4 of the left sum L_4 and the right sum R_4 for a function f on an interval $[a, b]$ is equal to the sum of the areas of four trapezoids (Fig. 2).

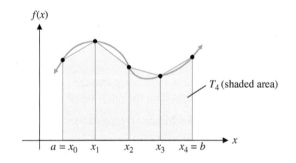

T_4 (shaded area)

Figure 2

Adding L_4 and R_4 and dividing by 2 gives a formula for T_4:

$$L_4 = [f(x_0) + f(x_1) + f(x_2) + f(x_3)]\Delta x$$
$$R_4 = [f(x_1) + f(x_2) + f(x_3) + f(x_4)]\Delta x$$
$$T_4 = [f(x_0) + 2f(x_1) + 2f(x_2) + 2f(x_3) + f(x_4)]\Delta x/2$$

The **trapezoidal sum** T_4 is the case $n = 4$ of the **trapezoidal rule**.

TRAPEZOIDAL RULE

Let f be a function defined on an interval $[a, b]$. Partition $[a, b]$ into n subintervals of equal length $\Delta x = (b - a)/n$ with endpoints

$$a = x_0 < x_1 < x_2 < \cdots < x_n = b.$$

Then

$$T_n = [f(x_0) + 2f(x_1) + 2f(x_2) + \cdots + 2f(x_{n-1}) + f(x_n)]\Delta x/2$$

is an approximation of $\int_a^b f(x)\,dx$.

EXAMPLE 1 Trapezoidal rule Use the trapezoidal rule with $n = 5$ to approximate $\int_2^4 \sqrt{100 + x^2}\, dx$. Round function values to 4 decimal places and the final answer to 2 decimal places.

SOLUTION Partition $[2, 4]$ into 5 equal subintervals of width $(4 - 2)/5 = 0.4$. The endpoints are $x_0 = 2$, $x_1 = 2.4$, $x_2 = 2.8$, $x_3 = 3.2$, $x_4 = 3.6$, and $x_5 = 4$. We calculate the value of the function $f(x) = \sqrt{100 + x^2}$ at each endpoint:

x	$f(x)$
2.0	10.1980
2.4	10.2840
2.8	10.3846
3.2	10.4995
3.6	10.6283
4.0	10.7703

By the trapezoidal rule,

$$
\begin{aligned}
T_5 &= [f(2) + 2f(2.4) + 2f(2.8) + 2f(3.2) + 2f(3.6) + f(4)](0.4/2) \\
&= [10.1980 + 2(10.2840) + 2(10.3846) + 2(10.4995) + 2(10.6283) + 10.7703](0.2) \\
&= 20.91
\end{aligned}
$$

Matched Problem 1 Use the trapezoidal rule with $n = 5$ to approximate $\int_2^4 \sqrt{81 + x^5}\, dx$ (round function values to 4 decimal places and the final answer to 2 decimal places).

Simpson's Rule

The trapezoidal sum provides a better approximation of the definite integral of a function that is increasing (or decreasing) than either the left or right sum. Similarly, the **midpoint sum**,

$$
M_n = \left[f\left(\frac{x_0 + x_1}{2}\right) + f\left(\frac{x_1 + x_2}{2}\right) + \cdots + f\left(\frac{x_{n-1} + x_n}{2}\right) \right] \Delta x
$$

(see Example 2, Section 5.4) is a better approximation of the definite integral of a function that is increasing (or decreasing) than either the left or right sum. How do T_n and M_n compare? A midpoint sum rectangle has the same area as the corresponding tangent line trapezoid (the larger trapezoid in Fig. 3). It appears from Figure 3, and can be proved in general, that the trapezoidal sum error is about double the midpoint sum error when the graph of the function is concave up or concave down.

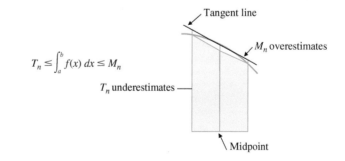

$$T_n \le \int_a^b f(x)\, dx \le M_n$$

T_n underestimates

Tangent line

M_n overestimates

Midpoint

Figure 3

This suggests that a weighted average of the two estimates, with the midpoint sum being counted double the trapezoidal sum, might be an even better estimate than either separately. This weighted average,

$$
S_{2n} = \frac{2M_n + T_n}{3} \tag{2}
$$

leads to a formula called *Simpson's rule*. To simplify notation, we agree to divide the interval $[a, b]$ into $2n$ equal subintervals when Simpson's rule is applied. So, if $n = 2$, for example, then $[a, b]$ is divided into $2n = 4$ equal subintervals, of length Δx, with endpoints

$$a = x_0 < x_1 < x_2 < x_3 < x_4 = b.$$

There are two equal subintervals for M_2 and T_2, each of length $2\Delta x$, with endpoints

$$a = x_0 < x_2 < x_4 = b.$$

Therefore,

$$M_2 = [f(x_1) + f(x_3)](2\Delta x)$$
$$T_2 = [f(x_0) + 2f(x_2) + f(x_4)](2\Delta x)/2$$

We use equation (2) to get a formula for S_4:

$$S_4 = [f(x_0) + 4f(x_1) + 2f(x_2) + 4f(x_3) + f(x_4)]\Delta x/3$$

The formula for S_4 is the case $n = 2$ of **Simpson's rule**.

Simpson's Rule

Let f be a function defined on an interval $[a, b]$. Partition $[a, b]$ into $2n$ subintervals of equal length $\Delta x = (b - a)/n$ with endpoints

$$a = x_0 < x_1 < x_2 < \cdots < x_{2n} = b.$$

Then

$$S_{2n} = [f(x_0) + 4f(x_1) + 2f(x_2) + 4f(x_3) + 2f(x_4) + \cdots + 4f(x_{2n-1}) + f(x_{2n})]\Delta x/3$$

is an approximation of $\int_a^b f(x)\,dx$.

⚠ CAUTION Simpson's rule always requires an *even* number of subintervals of $[a, b]$. ▲

EXAMPLE 2 Simpson's rule Use Simpson's rule with $n = 2$ to approximate $\int_2^{10} \frac{x^4}{\ln x}\,dx$. Round function values to 4 decimal places and the final answer to 2 decimal places.

SOLUTION Partition the interval $[2, 10]$ into $2n = 4$ equal subintervals of width $(10 - 2)/4 = 2$. The endpoints are $x_0 = 2, x_1 = 4, x_2 = 6, x_3 = 8$, and $x_4 = 10$. We calculate the value of the function $f(x) = \frac{x^4}{\ln x}$ at each endpoint:

x	$f(x)$
2	23.0831
4	184.6650
6	723.3114
8	1,969.7596
10	4,342.9448

By Simpson's rule,

$$S_4 = [f(2) + 4f(4) + 2f(6) + 4f(8) + f(10)](2/3)$$
$$= [23.0831 + 4(184.6650) + 2(723.3114) + 4(1,969.7596) + 4,342.9448](2/3)$$
$$= 9,620.23$$

Matched Problem 2 Use Simpson's rule with $n = 2$ to approximate $\int_2^{10} \frac{1}{\ln x}\,dx$ (round function values to 4 decimal places and the final answer to 2 decimal places).

CONCEPTUAL INSIGHT

The trapezoidal rule and Simpson's rule require the values of a function at the endpoints of the subintervals of a partition, but neither requires a formula for the function. So either rule can be used on data that give the values of a function at the required points. It is not necessary to use regression techniques to find a formula for the function.

Using a Table of Integrals

The formulas in Table II on pages 574–576 are organized by categories, such as "Integrals Involving $a + bu$," "Integrals Involving $\sqrt{u^2 - a^2}$," and so on. The variable u is the variable of integration. All other symbols represent constants. To use a table to evaluate an integral, you must first find the category that most closely agrees with the form of the integrand and then find a formula in that category that you can make to match the integrand exactly by assigning values to the constants in the formula.

EXAMPLE 3 Integration Using Tables Use Table II to find

$$\int \frac{x}{(5 + 2x)(4 - 3x)}\,dx$$

SOLUTION Since the integrand

$$f(x) = \frac{x}{(5 + 2x)(4 - 3x)}$$

is a rational function involving terms of the form $a + bu$ and $c + du$, we examine formulas 15 to 20 in Table II on page 575 to see if any of the integrands in these formulas can be made to match $f(x)$ exactly. Comparing the integrand in formula 16 with $f(x)$, we see that this integrand will match $f(x)$ if we let $a = 5$, $b = 2$, $c = 4$, and $d = -3$. Letting $u = x$ and substituting for $a, b, c,$ and d in formula 16, we have

$$\int \frac{u}{(a + bu)(c + du)}\,du = \frac{1}{ad - bc}\left(\frac{a}{b}\ln|a + bu| - \frac{c}{d}\ln|c + du|\right) \quad \text{Formula 16}$$

$$\int \frac{x}{\underset{a\ \ b\ \ c\ \ d}{(5 + 2x)(4 - 3x)}}\,dx = \frac{1}{\underset{a\cdot d - b\cdot c\, =\, 5\cdot(-3)\, -\, 2\cdot 4\, =\, -23}{5\cdot(-3) - 2\cdot 4}}\left(\frac{5}{2}\ln|5 + 2x| - \frac{4}{-3}\ln|4 - 3x|\right) + C$$

$$= -\tfrac{5}{46}\ln|5 + 2x| - \tfrac{4}{69}\ln|4 - 3x| + C$$

Notice that the constant of integration, C, is not included in any of the formulas in Table II. However, you must still include C in all antiderivatives.

Matched Problem 3 Use Table II to find $\displaystyle\int \frac{1}{(5 + 3x)^2(1 + x)}\,dx.$

EXAMPLE 4 Integration Using Tables Evaluate $\displaystyle\int_3^4 \frac{1}{x\sqrt{25 - x^2}}\,dx.$

SOLUTION First, we use Table II to find

$$\int \frac{1}{x\sqrt{25 - x^2}}\,dx$$

Since the integrand involves the expression $\sqrt{25 - x^2}$, we examine formulas 29 to 31 in Table II and select formula 29 with $a^2 = 25$ and $a = 5$:

$$\int \frac{1}{u\sqrt{a^2 - u^2}}\,du = -\frac{1}{a}\ln\left|\frac{a + \sqrt{a^2 - u^2}}{u}\right| \qquad \text{Formula 29}$$

$$\int \frac{1}{x\sqrt{25 - x^2}}\,dx = -\frac{1}{5}\ln\left|\frac{5 + \sqrt{25 - x^2}}{x}\right| + C$$

So

$$\int_3^4 \frac{1}{x\sqrt{25 - x^2}}\,dx = -\frac{1}{5}\ln\left|\frac{5 + \sqrt{25 - x^2}}{x}\right|\Bigg|_3^4$$

$$= -\frac{1}{5}\ln\left|\frac{5 + 3}{4}\right| + \frac{1}{5}\ln\left|\frac{5 + 4}{3}\right|$$

$$= -\tfrac{1}{5}\ln 2 + \tfrac{1}{5}\ln 3 = \tfrac{1}{5}\ln 1.5 \approx 0.0811$$

Matched Problem 4 Evaluate $\displaystyle\int_6^8 \frac{1}{x^2\sqrt{100 - x^2}}\,dx.$

Substitution and Integral Tables

As Examples 3 and 4 illustrate, if the integral we want to evaluate can be made to match one in the table exactly, then evaluating the indefinite integral consists simply of substituting the correct values of the constants into the formula. But what happens if we cannot match an integral with one of the formulas in the table? In many cases, a substitution will change the given integral into one that corresponds to a table entry.

EXAMPLE 5   Integration Using Substitution and Tables   Find $\displaystyle\int \frac{x^2}{\sqrt{16x^2 - 25}}\,dx.$

SOLUTION   In order to relate this integral to one of the formulas involving $\sqrt{u^2 - a^2}$ (formulas 40 to 45 in Table II), we observe that if $u = 4x$, then

$$u^2 = 16x^2 \qquad \text{and} \qquad \sqrt{16x^2 - 25} = \sqrt{u^2 - 25}$$

So, we will use the substitution $u = 4x$ to change this integral into one that appears in the table:

$$\int \frac{x^2}{\sqrt{16x^2 - 25}}\,dx = \frac{1}{4}\int \frac{\tfrac{1}{16}u^2}{\sqrt{u^2 - 25}}\,du \qquad \begin{array}{l}\text{Substitution:}\\ u = 4x,\ du = 4\,dx,\ x = \tfrac{1}{4}u\end{array}$$

$$= \frac{1}{64}\int \frac{u^2}{\sqrt{u^2 - 25}}\,du$$

This last integral can be evaluated with the aid of formula 44 in Table II with $a = 5$:

$$\int \frac{u^2}{\sqrt{u^2 - a^2}}\,du = \frac{1}{2}\left(u\sqrt{u^2 - a^2} + a^2\ln\left|u + \sqrt{u^2 - a^2}\right|\right) \qquad \text{Formula 44}$$

$$\int \frac{x^2}{\sqrt{16x^2 - 25}}\,dx = \frac{1}{64}\int \frac{u^2}{\sqrt{u^2 - 25}}\,du \qquad \text{Use formula 44 with } a = 5.$$

$$= \tfrac{1}{128}\left(u\sqrt{u^2 - 25} + 25\ln\left|u + \sqrt{u^2 - 25}\right|\right) + C \qquad \text{Substitute } u = 4x.$$

$$= \tfrac{1}{128}\left(4x\sqrt{16x^2 - 25} + 25\ln\left|4x + \sqrt{16x^2 - 25}\right|\right) + C$$

Matched Problem 5 Find $\displaystyle\int \sqrt{9x^2 - 16}\,dx.$

EXAMPLE 6 Integration Using Substitution and Tables Find $\int \dfrac{x}{\sqrt{x^4+1}}\,dx.$

SOLUTION None of the formulas in Table II involve fourth powers; however, if we let $u = x^2$, then

$$\sqrt{x^4+1} = \sqrt{u^2+1}$$

and this form does appear in formulas 32 to 39. Thus, we substitute $u = x^2$:

$$\int \frac{1}{\sqrt{x^4+1}}\,x\,dx = \frac{1}{2}\int \frac{1}{\sqrt{u^2+1}}\,du \qquad \begin{array}{l}\text{Substitution:}\\ u = x^2,\ du = 2x\,dx\end{array}$$

We recognize the last integral as formula 36 with $a = 1$:

$$\int \frac{1}{\sqrt{u^2+a^2}}\,du = \ln|u + \sqrt{u^2+a^2}| \qquad \text{Formula 36}$$

$$\int \frac{x}{\sqrt{x^4+1}}\,dx = \frac{1}{2}\int \frac{1}{\sqrt{u^2+1}}\,du \qquad \text{Use formula 36 with } a = 1.$$

$$= \tfrac{1}{2}\ln|u + \sqrt{u^2+1}| + C \qquad \text{Substitute } u = x^2.$$

$$= \tfrac{1}{2}\ln|x^2 + \sqrt{x^4+1}| + C$$

Matched Problem 6) Find $\int x\sqrt{x^4+1}\,dx.$

Reduction Formulas

EXAMPLE 7 Using Reduction Formulas Use Table II to find $\int x^2 e^{3x}\,dx.$

SOLUTION Since the integrand involves the function e^{3x}, we examine formulas 46–48 and conclude that formula 47 can be used for this problem. Letting $u = x$, $n = 2$, and $a = 3$ in formula 47, we have

$$\int u^n e^{au}\,du = \frac{u^n e^{au}}{a} - \frac{n}{a}\int u^{n-1} e^{au}\,du \qquad \text{Formula 47}$$

$$\int x^2 e^{3x}\,dx = \frac{x^2 e^{3x}}{3} - \frac{2}{3}\int x e^{3x}\,dx$$

Notice that the expression on the right still contains an integral, but the exponent of x has been reduced by 1. Formulas of this type are called **reduction formulas** and are designed to be applied repeatedly until an integral that can be evaluated is obtained. Applying formula 47 to $\int x e^{3x}\,dx$ with $n = 1$, we have

$$\int x^2 e^{3x}\,dx = \frac{x^2 e^{3x}}{3} - \frac{2}{3}\left(\frac{x e^{3x}}{3} - \frac{1}{3}\int e^{3x}\,dx\right)$$

$$= \frac{x^2 e^{3x}}{3} - \frac{2x e^{3x}}{9} + \frac{2}{9}\int e^{3x}\,dx$$

This last expression contains an integral that is easy to evaluate:

$$\int e^{3x}\,dx = \tfrac{1}{3}e^{3x}$$

After making a final substitution and adding a constant of integration, we have

$$\int x^2 e^{3x}\,dx = \frac{x^2 e^{3x}}{3} - \frac{2x e^{3x}}{9} + \frac{2}{27}e^{3x} + C$$

Matched Problem 7) Use Table II to find $\int (\ln x)^2\,dx.$

Application

EXAMPLE 8 Producers' Surplus Find the producers' surplus at a price level of $20 for the price–supply equation

$$p = S(x) = \frac{5x}{500 - x}$$

SOLUTION

Step 1 Find $\bar{x}$, the supply when the price is $\bar{p} = 20$:

$$\bar{p} = \frac{5\bar{x}}{500 - \bar{x}}$$

$$20 = \frac{5\bar{x}}{500 - \bar{x}}$$

$$10,000 - 20\bar{x} = 5\bar{x}$$

$$10,000 = 25\bar{x}$$

$$\bar{x} = 400$$

Step 2 Sketch a graph, as shown in Figure 4.

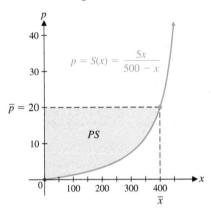

Figure 4

Step 3 Find the producers' surplus (the shaded area of the graph):

$$PS = \int_0^{\bar{x}} [\bar{p} - S(x)] \, dx$$

$$= \int_0^{400} \left(20 - \frac{5x}{500 - x} \right) dx$$

$$= \int_0^{400} \frac{10,000 - 25x}{500 - x} dx$$

Use formula 20 with $a = 10,000$, $b = -25$, $c = 500$, and $d = -1$:

$$\int \frac{a + bu}{c + du} du = \frac{bu}{d} + \frac{ad - bc}{d^2} \ln|c + du| \qquad \text{Formula 20}$$

$$PS = (25x + 2,500 \ln|500 - x|)\Big|_0^{400}$$

$$= 10,000 + 2,500 \ln|100| - 2,500 \ln|500|$$

$$\approx \$5,976$$

Matched Problem 8 Find the consumers' surplus at a price level of $10 for the price–demand equation

$$p = D(x) = \frac{20x - 8,000}{x - 500}$$

Exercises 6.4

In Problems 1–8, round function values to 4 decimal places and the final answer to 2 decimal places.

1. Use the trapezoidal rule with $n = 3$ to approximate $\int_0^6 \sqrt{1 + x^4}\,dx$.

2. Use the trapezoidal rule with $n = 2$ to approximate $\int_0^8 \sqrt{1 + x^2}\,dx$.

3. Use the trapezoidal rule with $n = 6$ to approximate $\int_0^6 \sqrt{1 + x^4}\,dx$.

4. Use the trapezoidal rule with $n = 4$ to approximate $\int_0^8 \sqrt{1 + x^2}\,dx$.

5. Use Simpson's rule with $n = 1$ (so there are $2n = 2$ subintervals) to approximate $\int_1^3 \dfrac{1}{1 + x^2}\,dx$.

6. Use Simpson's rule with $n = 1$ (so there are $2n = 2$ subintervals) to approximate $\int_2^{10} \dfrac{x^2}{\ln x}\,dx$.

7. Use Simpson's rule with $n = 2$ (so there are $2n = 4$ subintervals) to approximate $\int_1^3 \dfrac{1}{1 + x^2}\,dx$.

8. Use Simpson's rule with $n = 2$ (so there are $2n = 4$ subintervals) to approximate $\int_2^{10} \dfrac{x^2}{\ln x}\,dx$.

Use Table II on pages 574–576 to find each indefinite integral in Problems 9–22.

9. $\displaystyle\int \dfrac{1}{x(1 + x)}\,dx$

10. $\displaystyle\int \dfrac{1}{x^2(1 + x)}\,dx$

11. $\displaystyle\int \dfrac{1}{(3 + x)^2(5 + 2x)}\,dx$

12. $\displaystyle\int \dfrac{x}{(5 + 2x)^2(2 + x)}\,dx$

13. $\displaystyle\int \dfrac{x}{\sqrt{16 + x}}\,dx$

14. $\displaystyle\int \dfrac{1}{x\sqrt{16 + x}}\,dx$

15. $\displaystyle\int \dfrac{1}{x\sqrt{1 - x^2}}\,dx$

16. $\displaystyle\int \dfrac{\sqrt{9 - x^2}}{x}\,dx$

17. $\displaystyle\int \dfrac{1}{x\sqrt{x^2 + 4}}\,dx$

18. $\displaystyle\int \dfrac{1}{x^2\sqrt{x^2 - 16}}\,dx$

19. $\displaystyle\int x^2 \ln x\,dx$

20. $\displaystyle\int x^3 \ln x\,dx$

21. $\displaystyle\int \dfrac{1}{1 + e^x}\,dx$

22. $\displaystyle\int \dfrac{1}{5 + 2e^{3x}}\,dx$

Evaluate each definite integral in Problems 23–28. Use Table II on pages 574–576 to find the antiderivative.

23. $\displaystyle\int_1^3 \dfrac{x^2}{3 + x}\,dx$

24. $\displaystyle\int_2^6 \dfrac{x}{(6 + x)^2}\,dx$

25. $\displaystyle\int_0^7 \dfrac{1}{(3 + x)(1 + x)}\,dx$

26. $\displaystyle\int_0^7 \dfrac{x}{(3 + x)(1 + x)}\,dx$

27. $\displaystyle\int_0^4 \dfrac{1}{\sqrt{x^2 + 9}}\,dx$

28. $\displaystyle\int_4^5 \sqrt{x^2 - 16}\,dx$

29. Use the trapezoidal rule with $n = 5$ to approximate $\int_3^{13} x^2 dx$ and use the fundamental theorem of calculus to find the exact value of the definite integral.

30. Use the trapezoidal rule with $n = 5$ to approximate $\int_1^{11} x^3 dx$ and use the fundamental theorem of calculus to find the exact value of the definite integral.

31. Use Simpson's rule with $n = 4$ (so there are $2n = 8$ subintervals) to approximate $\int_1^5 \dfrac{1}{x}\,dx$ and use the fundamental theorem of calculus to find the exact value of the definite integral.

32. Use Simpson's rule with $n = 4$ (so there are $2n = 8$ subintervals) to approximate $\int_1^5 x^4 dx$ and use the fundamental theorem of calculus to find the exact value of the definite integral.

33. Use the trapezoidal rule with $n = 3$ to approximate $\int_5^8 (4x - 3)\,dx$ and use the fundamental theorem of calculus to find the exact value of the definite integral.

34. Use the trapezoidal rule with $n = 3$ to approximate $\int_7^{10} (2 - 9x)\,dx$ and use the fundamental theorem of calculus to find the exact value of the definite integral.

35. Use Simpson's rule with $n = 2$ (so there are $2n = 4$ subintervals) to approximate $\int_5^9 (3x^2 + 5x + 3)\,dx$ and use the fundamental theorem of calculus to find the exact value of the definite integral.

36. Use Simpson's rule with $n = 2$ (so there are $2n = 4$ subintervals) to approximate $\int_{-2}^2 (x^3 - 3x^2 + 2x + 8)\,dx$ and use the fundamental theorem of calculus to find the exact value of the definite integral.

In Problems 37–48, use substitution techniques and Table II to find each indefinite integral.

37. $\displaystyle\int \dfrac{\sqrt{4x^2 + 1}}{x^2}\,dx$

38. $\displaystyle\int x^2\sqrt{9x^2 - 1}\,dx$

39. $\displaystyle\int \dfrac{x}{\sqrt{x^4 - 16}}\,dx$

40. $\displaystyle\int x\sqrt{x^4 - 16}\,dx$

41. $\displaystyle\int x^2\sqrt{x^6 + 4}\,dx$

42. $\displaystyle\int \dfrac{x^2}{\sqrt{x^6 + 4}}\,dx$

43. $\displaystyle\int \dfrac{1}{x^3\sqrt{4 - x^4}}\,dx$

44. $\displaystyle\int \dfrac{\sqrt{x^4 + 4}}{x}\,dx$

45. $\displaystyle\int \dfrac{e^x}{(2 + e^x)(3 + 4e^x)}\,dx$

46. $\displaystyle\int \dfrac{e^x}{(4 + e^x)^2(2 + e^x)}\,dx$

47. $\displaystyle\int \dfrac{\ln x}{x\sqrt{4 + \ln x}}\,dx$

48. $\displaystyle\int \dfrac{1}{x\ln x\sqrt{4 + \ln x}}\,dx$

In Problems 49–54, use Table II to find each indefinite integral.

49. $\int x^2 e^{5x}\, dx$

50. $\int x^2 e^{-4x}\, dx$

51. $\int x^3 e^{-x}\, dx$

52. $\int x^3 e^{2x}\, dx$

53. $\int (\ln x)^3\, dx$

54. $\int (\ln x)^4\, dx$

Problems 55–62 are mixed—some require the use of Table II, and others can be solved with techniques considered earlier.

55. $\int_3^5 x\sqrt{x^2 - 9}\, dx$

56. $\int_3^5 x^2\sqrt{x^2 - 9}\, dx$

57. $\int_2^4 \dfrac{1}{x^2 - 1}\, dx$

58. $\int_2^4 \dfrac{x}{(x^2 - 1)^2}\, dx$

59. $\int \dfrac{\ln x}{x^2}\, dx$

60. $\int \dfrac{(\ln x)^2}{x}\, dx$

61. $\int \dfrac{x}{\sqrt{x^2 - 1}}\, dx$

62. $\int \dfrac{x^2}{\sqrt{x^2 - 1}}\, dx$

63. If $f(x) = ax^2 + bx + c$, where a, b, and c are any real numbers, use Simpson's rule with $n = 1$ (so there are $2n = 2$ subintervals) to show that

$$S_2 = \int_{-1}^{1} f(x)\, dx.$$

64. If $f(x) = ax^3 + bx^2 + cx + d$, where a, b, c, and d are any real numbers, use Simpson's rule with $n = 1$ (so there are $2n = 2$ subintervals) to show that

$$S_2 = \int_{-1}^{1} f(x)\, dx.$$

In Problems 65–68, find the area bounded by the graphs of $y = f(x)$ and $y = g(x)$ to two decimal places. Use a graphing calculator to approximate intersection points to two decimal places.

65. $f(x) = \dfrac{10}{\sqrt{x^2 + 1}}$; $g(x) = x^2 + 3x$

66. $f(x) = \sqrt{1 + x^2}$; $g(x) = 5x - x^2$

67. $f(x) = x\sqrt{4 + x}$; $g(x) = 1 + x$

68. $f(x) = \dfrac{x}{\sqrt{x + 4}}$; $g(x) = x - 2$

Applications

Use Table II to evaluate all integrals involved in any solutions of Problems 69–92.

69. Consumers' surplus. Find the consumers' surplus at a price level of $\bar{p} = \$15$ for the price–demand equation

$$p = D(x) = \dfrac{7,500 - 30x}{300 - x}$$

70. Producers' surplus. Find the producers' surplus at a price level of $\bar{p} = \$20$ for the price–supply equation

$$p = S(x) = \dfrac{10x}{300 - x}$$

71. Consumers' surplus. Graph the price–demand equation and the price-level equation $\bar{p} = 15$ of Problem 69 in the same coordinate system. What region represents the consumers' surplus?

72. Producers' surplus. Graph the price–supply equation and the price-level equation $\bar{p} = 20$ of Problem 70 in the same coordinate system. What region represents the producers' surplus?

73. Cost. A company manufactures downhill skis. It has fixed costs of $25,000 and a marginal cost given by

$$C'(x) = \dfrac{250 + 10x}{1 + 0.05x}$$

where $C(x)$ is the total cost at an output of x pairs of skis. Find the cost function $C(x)$ and determine the production level (to the nearest unit) that produces a cost of $150,000. What is the cost (to the nearest dollar) for a production level of 850 pairs of skis?

74. Cost. A company manufactures a portable DVD player. It has fixed costs of $11,000 per week and a marginal cost given by

$$C'(x) = \dfrac{65 + 20x}{1 + 0.4x}$$

where $C(x)$ is the total cost per week at an output of x players per week. Find the cost function $C(x)$ and determine the production level (to the nearest unit) that produces a cost of $52,000 per week. What is the cost (to the nearest dollar) for a production level of 700 players per week?

75. Continuous income stream. Find the future value at 4.4%, compounded continuously, for 10 years for the continuous income stream with rate of flow $f(t) = 50t^2$.

76. Continuous income stream. Find the interest earned at 3.7%, compounded continuously, for 5 years for the continuous income stream with rate of flow $f(t) = 200t$.

77. Income distribution. Find the Gini index of income concentration for the Lorenz curve with equation

$$y = \tfrac{1}{2}x\sqrt{1 + 3x}$$

78. Income distribution. Find the Gini index of income concentration for the Lorenz curve with equation

$$y = \tfrac{1}{2}x^2\sqrt{1 + 3x}$$

79. Income distribution. Graph $y = x$ and the Lorenz curve of Problem 77 over the interval $[0, 1]$. Discuss the effect of the area bounded by $y = x$ and the Lorenz curve getting smaller relative to the equitable distribution of income.

80. Income distribution. Graph $y = x$ and the Lorenz curve of Problem 78 over the interval $[0, 1]$. Discuss the effect of the area bounded by $y = x$ and the Lorenz curve getting larger relative to the equitable distribution of income.

81. Marketing. After test marketing a new high-fiber cereal, the market research department of a major food producer estimates that monthly sales (in millions of dollars) will grow at the monthly rate of

$$S'(t) = \frac{t^2}{(1 + t)^2}$$

t months after the cereal is introduced. If we assume 0 sales at the time the cereal is introduced, find $S(t)$, the total sales *t* months after the cereal is introduced. Find the total sales during the first 2 years that the cereal is on the market.

82. Average price. At a discount department store, the price–demand equation for premium motor oil is given by

$$p = D(x) = \frac{50}{\sqrt{100 + 6x}}$$

where *x* is the number of cans of oil that can be sold at a price of $p. Find the average price over the demand interval [50, 250].

83. Marketing. For the cereal of Problem 81, show the sales over the first 2 years geometrically, and describe the geometric representation.

84. Price–demand. For the motor oil of Problem 82, graph the price–demand equation and the line representing the average price in the same coordinate system over the interval [50, 250]. Describe how the areas under the two curves over the interval [50, 250] are related.

85. Profit. The marginal profit for a small car agency that sells *x* cars per week is given by

$$P'(x) = x\sqrt{2 + 3x}$$

where $P(x)$ is the profit in dollars. The agency's profit on the sale of only 1 car per week is −$2,000. Find the profit function and the number of cars that must be sold (to the nearest unit) to produce a profit of $13,000 per week. How much weekly profit (to the nearest dollar) will the agency have if 80 cars are sold per week?

86. Revenue. The marginal revenue for a company that manufactures and sells *x* graphing calculators per week is given by

$$R'(x) = \frac{x}{\sqrt{1 + 2x}} \qquad R(0) = 0$$

where $R(x)$ is the revenue in dollars. Find the revenue function and the number of calculators that must be sold (to the nearest unit) to produce $10,000 in revenue per week. How much weekly revenue (to the nearest dollar) will the company have if 1,000 calculators are sold per week?

87. Pollution. An oil tanker is producing an oil slick that is radiating outward at a rate given approximately by

$$\frac{dR}{dt} = \frac{100}{\sqrt{t^2 + 9}} \qquad t \ge 0$$

where *R* is the radius (in feet) of the circular slick after *t* minutes. Find the radius of the slick after 4 minutes if the radius is 0 when $t = 0$.

88. Pollution. The concentration of particulate matter (in parts per million) during a 24-hour period is given approximately by

$$C(t) = t\sqrt{24 - t} \qquad 0 \le t \le 24$$

where *t* is time in hours. Find the average concentration during the period from $t = 0$ to $t = 24$.

89. Learning. A person learns *N* items at a rate given approximately by

$$N'(t) = \frac{60}{\sqrt{t^2 + 25}} \qquad t \ge 0$$

where *t* is the number of hours of continuous study. Determine the total number of items learned in the first 12 hours of continuous study.

90. Politics. The number of voters (in thousands) in a metropolitan area is given approximately by

$$f(t) = \frac{500}{2 + 3e^{-t}} \qquad t \ge 0$$

where *t* is time in years. Find the average number of voters during the period from $t = 0$ to $t = 10$.

91. Learning. Interpret Problem 89 geometrically. Describe the geometric interpretation.

92. Politics. For the voters of Problem 90, graph $y = f(t)$ and the line representing the average number of voters over the interval [0, 10] in the same coordinate system. Describe how the areas under the two curves over the interval [0, 10] are related.

Answers to Matched Problems

1. 38.85   2. 5.20
3. $\frac{1}{2}\left(\frac{1}{5 + 3x}\right) + \frac{1}{4} \ln\left|\frac{1 + x}{5 + 3x}\right| + C$
4. $\frac{7}{1,200} \approx 0.0058$
5. $\frac{1}{6}\left(3x\sqrt{9x^2 - 16} - 16 \ln|3x + \sqrt{9x^2 - 16}|\right) + C$
6. $\frac{1}{4}\left(x^2\sqrt{x^4 + 1} + \ln|x^2 + \sqrt{x^4 + 1}|\right) + C$
7. $x(\ln x)^2 - 2x \ln x + 2x + C$
8. $3,000 + 2,000 \ln 200 - 2,000 \ln 500 \approx \$1,167$

Important Terms, Symbols, and Concepts

6.1 Area Between Curves

EXAMPLES

Ex. 1, p. 383
Ex. 2, p. 383
Ex. 3, p. 384
Ex. 4, p. 384
Ex. 5, p. 385
Ex. 6, p. 385

- If f and g are continuous and $f(x) \geq g(x)$ over the interval $[a, b]$, then the area bounded by $y = f(x)$ and $y = g(x)$ for $a \leq x \leq b$ is given exactly by

$$A = \int_a^b [f(x) - g(x)] \, dx$$

- A graphical representation of the distribution of income among a population can be found by plotting data points (x, y), where **x represents the cumulative percentage of families at or below a given income level** and **y represents the cumulative percentage of total family income received.** Regression analysis can be used to find a particular function $y = f(x)$, called a **Lorenz curve,** that best fits the data.

- A single number, the **Gini index,** measures income concentration:

Ex. 7, p. 387

$$\text{Gini index} = 2 \int_0^1 [x - f(x)] \, dx$$

A Gini index of 0 indicates **absolute equality:** All families share equally in the income. A Gini index of 1 indicates **absolute inequality:** One family has all of the income and the rest have none.

6.2 Applications in Business and Economics

- ***Probability Density Functions*** If any real number x in an interval is a possible outcome of an experiment, then x is said to be a **continuous random variable.** The probability distribution of a continuous random variable is described by a **probability density function** f that satisfies the following conditions:

Ex. 1, p. 392

1. $f(x) \geq 0$ for all real x.

2. The area under the graph of $f(x)$ over the interval $(-\infty, \infty)$ is exactly 1.

3. If $[c, d]$ is a subinterval of $(-\infty, \infty)$, then

$$\text{Probability} \quad (c \leq x \leq d) = \int_c^d f(x) \, dx$$

- ***Continuous Income Stream*** If the rate at which income is received—its **rate of flow**—is a continuous function $f(t)$ of time, then the income is said to be a **continuous income stream.** The **total income** produced by a continuous income stream from $t = a$ to $t = b$ is

Ex. 2, p. 394

$$\text{Total income} = \int_a^b f(t) \, dt$$

- The **future value** of a continuous income stream that is invested at rate r, compounded continuously, for $0 \leq t \leq T$, is

Ex. 3, p. 396

$$FV = \int_0^T f(t) e^{r(T-t)} \, dt$$

- ***Consumers' and Producers' Surplus*** If $(\bar{x}, \bar{p})$ is a point on the graph of a price–demand equation $p = D(x)$, then the **consumers' surplus** at a price level of $\bar{p}$ is

Ex. 4, p. 397

$$CS = \int_0^{\bar{x}} [D(x) - \bar{p}] \, dx$$

The consumers' surplus represents the total savings to consumers who are willing to pay more than $\bar{p}$ but are still able to buy the product for $\bar{p}$.

Similarly, for a point $(\bar{x}, \bar{p})$ on the graph of a price–supply equation $p = S(x)$, the **producers' surplus** at a price level of $\bar{p}$ is

Ex. 5, p. 398

$$PS = \int_0^{\bar{x}} [\bar{p} - S(x)]\, dx$$

The producers' surplus represents the total gain to producers who are willing to supply units at a lower price $\bar{p}$, but are still able to supply units at $\bar{p}$.

If $(\bar{x}, \bar{p})$ is the intersection point of a price–demand equation $p = D(x)$ and a price–supply equation $p = S(x)$, then $\bar{p}$ is called the **equilibrium price** and $\bar{x}$ is called the **equilibrium quantity**.

Ex. 6, p. 399

6.3 Integration by Parts

- Some indefinite integrals, but not all, can be found by means of the **integration-by-parts formula**

$$\int u\, dv = uv - \int v\, du$$

- Select u and dv with the help of the guidelines in the summary on page 405.

Ex. 1, p. 403
Ex. 2, p. 404
Ex. 3, p. 406
Ex. 4, p. 406

6.4 Other Integration Methods

- The **trapezoidal rule** and **Simpson's rule** provide approximations of the definite integral that are more efficient than approximations by left or right sums: Fewer terms must be summed to achieve a given accuracy.

- **Trapezoidal Rule** Let f be a function defined on an interval $[a, b]$. Partition $[a, b]$ into n subintervals of equal length $\Delta x = (b - a)/n$ with endpoints

Ex. 1, p. 411

$$a = x_0 < x_1 < x_2 < \cdots < x_n = b.$$

Then

$$T_n = [f(x_0) + 2f(x_1) + 2f(x_2) + \cdots + 2f(x_{n-1}) + f(x_n)]\Delta x/2$$

is an approximation of $\int_a^b f(x)\, dx$.

- **Simpson's Rule** Let f be a function defined on an interval $[a, b]$. Partition $[a, b]$ into $2n$ subintervals of equal length $\Delta x = (b - a)/n$ with endpoints

Ex. 2, p. 412

$$a = x_0 < x_1 < x_2 < \cdots < x_{2n} = b.$$

Then

$$S_{2n} = [f(x_0) + 4f(x_1) + 2f(x_2) + 4f(x_3) + 2f(x_4) + \cdots + 4f(x_{2n-1}) + f(x_{2n})]\Delta x/3$$

is an approximation of $\int_a^b f(x)\, dx$.

- A **table of integrals** is a list of integration formulas that can be used to find indefinite or definite integrals of frequently encountered functions. Such a list appears in Table II of Appendix C on pages 574–576.

Ex. 3, p. 413
Ex. 4, p. 413
Ex. 5, p. 414
Ex. 6, p. 415
Ex. 7, p. 415
Ex. 8, p. 416

Review Exercises

Work through all the problems in this chapter review and check your answers in the back of the book. Answers to all review problems are there, along with section numbers in italics to indicate where each type of problem is discussed. Where weaknesses show up, review appropriate sections of the text.

Compute all numerical answers to three decimal places unless directed otherwise.

In Problems 1–3, set up definite integrals that represent the shaded areas in the figure over the indicated intervals.

1. Interval $[a, b]$ **2.** Interval $[b, c]$

3. Interval $[a, c]$

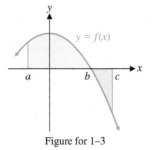

Figure for 1–3

4. Sketch a graph of the area between the graphs of $y = \ln x$ and $y = 0$ over the interval $[0.5, e]$ and find the area.

In Problems 5–10, evaluate each integral.

5. $\int xe^{4x}\, dx$

6. $\int x \ln x\, dx$

7. $\int \frac{\ln x}{x}\, dx$

8. $\int \frac{x}{1 + x^2}\, dx$

9. $\int \frac{1}{x(1 + x)^2}\, dx$

10. $\int \frac{1}{x^2\sqrt{1 + x}}\, dx$

In Problems 11–16, find the area bounded by the graphs of the indicated equations over the given interval.

11. $y = 5 - 2x - 6x^2; y = 0, 1 \le x \le 2$

12. $y = 5x + 7; y = 12, -3 \le x \le 1$

13. $y = -x + 2; y = x^2 + 3, -1 \le x \le 4$

14. $y = \frac{1}{x}; y = -e^{-x}, 1 \le x \le 2$

15. $y = x; y = -x^3, -2 \le x \le 2$

16. $y = x^2; y = -x^4; -2 \le x \le 2$

17. The Gini indices of Indonesia and Malaysia are 0.37 and 0.46, respectively. In which country is income more equally distributed?

18. The Gini indices of Thailand and Vietnam are 0.54 and 0.38, respectively. In which country is income more equally distributed?

In Problems 19–22, set up definite integrals that represent the shaded areas in the figure over the indicated intervals.

19. Interval $[a, b]$

20. Interval $[b, c]$

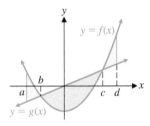

Figure for 19–22

21. Interval $[b, d]$

22. Interval $[a, d]$

23. Sketch a graph of the area bounded by the graphs of $y = x^2 - 6x + 9$ and $y = 9 - x$ and find the area.

In Problems 24–29, evaluate each integral.

24. $\int_0^1 xe^x\, dx$

25. $\int_0^3 \frac{x^2}{\sqrt{x^2 + 16}}\, dx$

26. $\int \sqrt{9x^2 - 49}\, dx$

27. $\int te^{-0.5t}\, dt$

28. $\int x^2 \ln x\, dx$

29. $\int \frac{1}{1 + 2e^x}\, dx$

30. Sketch a graph of the area bounded by the indicated graphs, and find the area. In part (B), approximate intersection points and area to two decimal places.

(A) $y = x^3 - 6x^2 + 9x; y = x$

(B) $y = x^3 - 6x^2 + 9x; y = x + 1$

In Problems 31–34, round function values to 4 decimal places and the final answer to 2 decimal places.

31. Use the trapezoidal rule with $n = 3$ to approximate $\int_0^3 e^{x^2}dx$.

32. Use the trapezoidal rule with $n = 5$ to approximate $\int_0^3 e^{x^2}dx$.

33. Use Simpson's rule with $n = 2$ (so there are $2n = 4$ subintervals) to approximate $\int_1^5 (\ln x)^2 dx$.

34. Use Simpson's rule with $n = 4$ (so there are $2n = 8$ subintervals) to approximate $\int_1^5 (\ln x)^2 dx$.

In Problems 35–42, evaluate each integral.

35. $\int \frac{(\ln x)^2}{x}\, dx$

36. $\int x(\ln x)^2\, dx$

37. $\int \frac{x}{\sqrt{x^2 - 36}}\, dx$

38. $\int \frac{x}{\sqrt{x^4 - 36}}\, dx$

39. $\int_0^4 x \ln(10 - x)\, dx$

40. $\int (\ln x)^2\, dx$

41. $\int xe^{-2x^2}\, dx$

42. $\int x^2 e^{-2x}\, dx$

43. Use a numerical integration routine on a graphing calculator to find the area in the first quadrant that is below the graph of

$$y = \frac{6}{2 + 5e^{-x}}$$

and above the graph of $y = 0.2x + 1.6$.

Applications

44. *Product warranty.* A manufacturer warrants a product for parts and labor for 1 year and for parts only for a second year. The time to a failure of the product after it is sold is given by the probability density function

$$f(t) = \begin{cases} 0.21e^{-0.21t} & \text{if } t \ge 0 \\ 0 & \text{otherwise} \end{cases}$$

What is the probability that a buyer chosen at random will have a product failure

(A) During the first year of warranty?

(B) During the second year of warranty?

45. *Product warranty.* Graph the probability density function for Problem 44 over the interval $[0, 3]$, interpret part (B) of Problem 44 geometrically and describe the geometric representation.

46. Revenue function. The weekly marginal revenue from the sale of x hair dryers is given by

$$R'(x) = 65 - 6 \ln(x + 1) \qquad R(0) = 0$$

where $R(x)$ is the revenue in dollars. Find the revenue function and the production level (to the nearest unit) for a revenue of $20,000 per week. What is the weekly revenue (to the nearest dollar) at a production level of 1,000 hair dryers per week?

47. Continuous income stream. The rate of flow (in dollars per year) of a continuous income stream for a 5-year period is given by

$$f(t) = 2,500e^{0.05t} \qquad 0 \leq t \leq 5$$

(A) Graph $y = f(t)$ over [0, 5] and shade the area that represents the total income received from the end of the first year to the end of the fourth year.

(B) Find the total income received, to the nearest dollar, from the end of the first year to the end of the fourth year.

48. Future value of a continuous income stream. The continuous income stream in Problem 47 is invested at 4%, compounded continuously.

(A) Find the future value (to the nearest dollar) at the end of the 5-year period.

(B) Find the interest earned (to the nearest dollar) during the 5-year period.

49. Income distribution. An economist produced the following Lorenz curves for the current income distribution and the projected income distribution 10 years from now in a certain country:

$$f(x) = 0.1x + 0.9x^2 \qquad \text{Current Lorenz curve}$$

$$g(x) = x^{1.5} \qquad \text{Projected Lorenz curve}$$

(A) Graph $y = x$ and the current Lorenz curve on one set of coordinate axes for [0, 1] and graph $y = x$ and the projected Lorenz curve on another set of coordinate axes over the same interval.

(B) Looking at the areas bounded by the Lorenz curves and $y = x$, can you say that the income will be more or less equitably distributed 10 years from now?

(C) Compute the Gini index of income concentration (to one decimal place) for the current and projected curves. What can you say about the distribution of income 10 years from now? Is it more equitable or less?

50. Consumers' and producers' surplus. Find the consumers' surplus and the producers' surplus at the equilibrium price level for each pair of price–demand and price–supply equations. Include a graph that identifies the consumers' surplus and the producers' surplus. Round all values to the nearest integer.

(A) $p = D(x) = 70 - 0.2x$;
$\quad p = S(x) = 13 + 0.0012x^2$

(B) $p = D(x) = 70 - 0.2x$;
$\quad p = S(x) = 13e^{0.006x}$

51. Producers' surplus. The accompanying table gives price–supply data for the sale of hogs at a livestock market, where x is the number of pounds (in thousands) and p is the price per pound (in cents):

Price–Supply	
x	$p = S(x)$
0	43.50
10	46.74
20	50.05
30	54.72
40	59.18

(A) Using quadratic regression to model the data, find the demand at a price of 52.50 cents per pound.

(B) Use a numerical integration routine to find the producers' surplus (to the nearest dollar) at a price level of 52.50 cents per pound.

52. Drug assimilation. The rate at which the body eliminates a certain drug (in milliliters per hour) is given by

$$R(t) = \frac{60t}{(t + 1)^2(t + 2)}$$

where t is the number of hours since the drug was administered. How much of the drug is eliminated during the first hour after it was administered? During the fourth hour?

53. With the aid of a graphing calculator, illustrate Problem 52 geometrically.

54. Medicine. For a particular doctor, the length of time (in hours) spent with a patient per office visit has the probability density function

$$f(t) = \begin{cases} \dfrac{\frac{4}{3}}{(t + 1)^2} & \text{if } 0 \leq t \leq 3 \\ 0 & \text{otherwise} \end{cases}$$

(A) What is the probability that this doctor will spend less than 1 hour with a randomly selected patient?

(B) What is the probability that this doctor will spend more than 1 hour with a randomly selected patient?

55. Medicine. Illustrate part (B) in Problem 54 geometrically. Describe the geometric interpretation.

56. Politics. The rate of change of the voting population of a city with respect to time t (in years) is estimated to be

$$N'(t) = \frac{100t}{(1 + t^2)^2}$$

where $N(t)$ is in thousands. If $N(0)$ is the current voting population, how much will this population increase during the next 3 years?

57. Psychology. Rats were trained to go through a maze by rewarding them with a food pellet upon successful completion of the run. After the seventh successful run, the probability density function for length of time (in minutes) until success on the eighth trial was given by

$$f(t) = \begin{cases} .5e^{-.5t} & \text{if } t \geq 0 \\ 0 & \text{otherwise} \end{cases}$$

What is the probability that a rat selected at random after seven successful runs will take 2 or more minutes to complete the eighth run successfully? [Recall that the area under a probability density function curve from $-\infty$ to ∞ is 1.]

7

Multivariable Calculus

Introduction

In previous chapters, we have applied the key concepts of calculus, the derivative and the integral, to functions with one independent variable. The graph of such a function is a curve in the plane. In Chapter 7, we extend the key concepts of calculus to functions with two independent variables. Graphs of such functions are surfaces in a three-dimensional coordinate system. We use functions with two independent variables to study how production depends on both labor and capital; how braking distance depends on both the weight and speed of a car; how resistance in a blood vessel depends on both its length and radius. In Section 7.5, we justify the method of least squares and use the method to construct linear models (see, for example, Problem 37 in Section 7.5 on global warming).

7.1 Functions of Several Variables

Functions of Two or More Independent Variables

In Section 1.1, we introduced the concept of a function with one independent variable. Now we broaden the concept to include functions with more than one independent variable.

A small manufacturing company produces a standard type of surfboard. If fixed costs are \$500 per week and variable costs are \$70 per board produced, the weekly cost function is given by

$$C(x) = 500 + 70x \qquad (1)$$

where x is the number of boards produced per week. The cost function is a function of a single independent variable x. For each value of x from the domain of C, there exists exactly one value of $C(x)$ in the range of C.

Now, suppose that the company decides to add a high-performance competition board to its line. If the fixed costs for the competition board are \$200 per week and the variable costs are \$100 per board, then the cost function (1) must be modified to

$$C(x, y) = 700 + 70x + 100y \qquad (2)$$

where $C(x, y)$ is the cost for a weekly output of x standard boards and y competition boards. Equation (2) is an example of a function with two independent variables x and y. Of course, as the company expands its product line even further, its weekly cost function must be modified to include more and more independent variables, one for each new product produced.

In general, an equation of the form

$$z = f(x, y)$$

describes a **function of two independent variables** if, for each permissible ordered pair (x, y), there is one and only one value of z determined by $f(x, y)$. The variables x and y are **independent variables**, and the variable z is a **dependent variable**. The set of all ordered pairs of permissible values of x and y is the **domain** of the function, and the set of all corresponding values $f(x, y)$ is the **range** of the function. Unless otherwise stated, we will assume that the domain of a function specified by an equation of the form $z = f(x, y)$ is the set of all ordered pairs of real numbers (x, y) such that $f(x, y)$ is also a real number. It should be noted, however, that certain conditions in practical problems often lead to further restrictions on the domain of a function.

We can similarly define functions of three independent variables, $w = f(x, y, z)$; of four independent variables, $u = f(w, x, y, z)$; and so on. In this chapter, we concern ourselves primarily with functions of two independent variables.

EXAMPLE 1 Evaluating a Function of Two Independent Variables For the cost function $C(x, y) = 700 + 70x + 100y$ described earlier, find $C(10, 5)$.

SOLUTION

$$C(10, 5) = 700 + 70(10) + 100(5)$$
$$= \$1,900$$

Matched Problem 1 Find $C(20, 10)$ for the cost function in Example 1.

EXAMPLE 2 Evaluating a Function of Three Independent Variables For the function $f(x, y, z) = 2x^2 - 3xy + 3z + 1$, find $f(3, 0, -1)$.

SOLUTION

$$f(3, 0, -1) = 2(3)^2 - 3(3)(0) + 3(-1) + 1$$
$$= 18 - 0 - 3 + 1 = 16$$

Matched Problem 2 Find $f(-2, 2, 3)$ for f in Example 2.

EXAMPLE 3 Revenue, Cost, and Profit Functions Suppose the surfboard company discussed earlier has determined that the demand equations for its two types of boards are given by

$$p = 210 - 4x + y$$
$$q = 300 + x - 12y$$

where p is the price of the standard board, q is the price of the competition board, x is the weekly demand for standard boards, and y is the weekly demand for competition boards.

(A) Find the weekly revenue function $R(x, y)$, and evaluate $R(20, 10)$.

(B) If the weekly cost function is

$$C(x, y) = 700 + 70x + 100y$$

find the weekly profit function $P(x, y)$ and evaluate $P(20, 10)$.

SOLUTION

(A)

$$\text{Revenue} = \begin{pmatrix} \text{demand for} \\ \text{standard} \\ \text{boards} \end{pmatrix} \times \begin{pmatrix} \text{price of a} \\ \text{standard} \\ \text{board} \end{pmatrix} + \begin{pmatrix} \text{demand for} \\ \text{competition} \\ \text{boards} \end{pmatrix} \times \begin{pmatrix} \text{price of a} \\ \text{competition} \\ \text{board} \end{pmatrix}$$

$$R(x, y) = xp + yq$$
$$= x(210 - 4x + y) + y(300 + x - 12y)$$
$$= 210x + 300y - 4x^2 + 2xy - 12y^2$$
$$R(20, 10) = 210(20) + 300(10) - 4(20)^2 + 2(20)(10) - 12(10)^2$$
$$= \$4,800$$

(B)   Profit = revenue − cost

$$P(x, y) = R(x, y) - C(x, y)$$
$$= 210x + 300y - 4x^2 + 2xy - 12y^2 - 700 - 70x - 100y$$
$$= 140x + 200y - 4x^2 + 2xy - 12y^2 - 700$$
$$P(20, 10) = 140(20) + 200(10) - 4(20)^2 + 2(20)(10) - 12(10)^2 - 700$$
$$= \$1,700$$

Matched Problem 3 Repeat Example 3 if the demand and cost equations are given by

$$p = 220 - 6x + y$$
$$q = 300 + 3x - 10y$$
$$C(x, y) = 40x + 80y + 1,000$$

Examples of Functions of Several Variables

A number of concepts can be considered as functions of two or more variables.

Area of a rectangle $A(x, y) = xy$

A = area y

     x

Volume of a box $V(x, y, z) = xyz$

V = volume

     z

     x y

Volume of a right circular cylinder $V(r, h) = \pi r^2 h$

     r h

Simple interest $A(P, r, t) = P(1 + rt)$

A = amount
P = principal
r = annual rate
t = time in years

Compound interest $A(P, r, t, n) = P\left(1 + \dfrac{r}{n}\right)^{nt}$

A = amount
P = principal
r = annual rate
t = time in years
n = number of compound periods per year

IQ $Q(M, C) = \dfrac{M}{C}(100)$

Q = IQ = intelligence quotient
M = MA = mental age
C = CA
    = chronological age

Resistance for blood flow in a vessel (Poiseuille's law) $R(L, r) = k\dfrac{L}{r^4}$

R = resistance
L = length of vessel
r = radius of vessel
k = constant

EXAMPLE 4   Package Design   A company uses a box with a square base and an open top for a bath assortment (see figure). If x is the length (in inches) of each side of the base and y is the height (in inches), find the total amount of material $M(x, y)$ required to construct one of these boxes, and evaluate $M(5, 10)$.

SOLUTION

$$\text{Area of base} = x^2$$
$$\text{Area of one side} = xy$$
$$\text{Total material} = (\text{area of base}) + 4(\text{area of one side})$$
$$M(x, y) = x^2 + 4xy$$
$$M(5, 10) = (5)^2 + 4(5)(10)$$
$$= 225 \text{ square inches}$$

Matched Problem 4   For the box in Example 4, find the volume $V(x, y)$ and evaluate $V(5, 10)$.

The next example concerns the **Cobb–Douglas production function**

$$f(x, y) = kx^m y^n$$

where k, m, and n are positive constants with $m + n = 1$. Economists use this function to describe the number of units $f(x, y)$ produced from the utilization of x units of labor and y units of capital (for equipment such as tools, machinery, buildings, and so on). Cobb–Douglas production functions are also used to describe the productivity of a single industry, of a group of industries producing the same product, or even of an entire country.

EXAMPLE 5 Productivity The productivity of a steel-manufacturing company is given approximately by the function

$$f(x, y) = 10x^{0.2}y^{0.8}$$

with the utilization of x units of labor and y units of capital. If the company uses 3,000 units of labor and 1,000 units of capital, how many units of steel will be produced?

SOLUTION The number of units of steel produced is given by

$$f(3,000, 1,000) = 10(3,000)^{0.2}(1,000)^{0.8} \quad \text{Use a calculator.}$$
$$\approx 12,457 \text{ units}$$

Matched Problem 5 Refer to Example 5. Find the steel production if the company uses 1,000 units of labor and 2,000 units of capital.

Three-Dimensional Coordinate Systems

We now take a brief look at graphs of functions of two independent variables. Since functions of the form $z = f(x, y)$ involve two independent variables x and y, and one dependent variable z, we need a *three-dimensional coordinate system* for their graphs. A **three-dimensional coordinate system** is formed by three mutually perpendicular number lines intersecting at their origins (see Fig. 1). In such a system, every ordered **triplet of numbers** (x, y, z) can be associated with a unique point, and conversely.

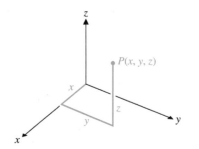

Figure 1 **Rectangular coordinate system**

EXAMPLE 6 Three-Dimensional Coordinates Locate $(-3, 5, 2)$ in a rectangular coordinate system.

SOLUTION

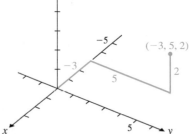

Matched Problem 6 Find the coordinates of the corners A, C, G, and D of the rectangular box shown in the following figure.

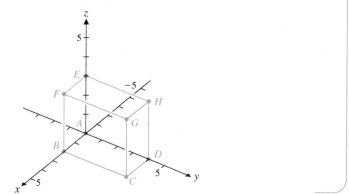

Explore and Discuss 1 Imagine that you are facing the front of a classroom whose rectangular walls meet at right angles. Suppose that the point of intersection of the floor, front wall, and left-side wall is the origin of a three-dimensional coordinate system in which every point in the room has nonnegative coordinates. Then the plane $z = 0$ (or, equivalently, the xy plane) can be described as "the floor," and the plane $z = 2$ can be described as "the plane parallel to, but 2 units above, the floor." Give similar descriptions of the following planes:

(A) $x = 0$ (B) $x = 3$ (C) $y = 0$ (D) $y = 4$ (E) $x = -1$

What does the graph of $z = x^2 + y^2$ look like? If we let $x = 0$ and graph $z = 0^2 + y^2 = y^2$ in the yz plane, we obtain a parabola; if we let $y = 0$ and graph $z = x^2 + 0^2 = x^2$ in the xz plane, we obtain another parabola. The graph of $z = x^2 + y^2$ is either one of these parabolas rotated around the z axis (see Fig. 2). This cup-shaped figure is a *surface* and is called a **paraboloid**.

In general, the graph of any function of the form $z = f(x, y)$ is called a **surface**. The graph of such a function is the graph of all ordered triplets of numbers (x, y, z) that satisfy the equation. Graphing functions of two independent variables is a difficult task, and the general process will not be dealt with in this book. We present only a few simple graphs to suggest extensions of earlier geometric interpretations of the derivative and local maxima and minima to functions of two variables. Note that $z = f(x, y) = x^2 + y^2$ appears (see Fig. 2) to have a local minimum at $(x, y) = (0, 0)$. Figure 3 shows a local maximum at $(x, y) = (0, 0)$.

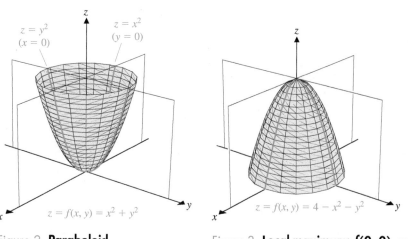

Figure 2 **Paraboloid**

Figure 3 **Local maximum: $f(0, 0) = 4$**

Figure 4 shows a point at $(x, y) = (0, 0)$, called a **saddle point**, that is neither a local minimum nor a local maximum. Note that in the cross section $x = 0$, the saddle point is a local minimum, and in the cross section $y = 0$, the saddle point is a local maximum. More will be said about local maxima and minima in Section 7.3.

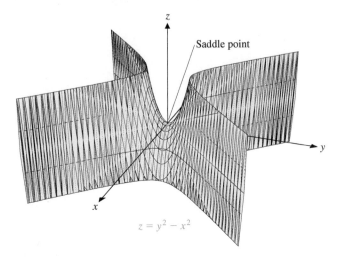

Figure 4 **Saddle point at (0, 0, 0)**

Some graphing calculators are designed to draw graphs (like those of Figs. 2, 3, and 4) of functions of two independent variables. Others, such as the graphing calculator used for the displays in this book, are designed to draw graphs of functions of one independent variable. When using the latter type of calculator, we can graph cross sections produced by cutting surfaces with planes parallel to the xz plane or yz plane to gain insight into the graph of a function of two independent variables.

EXAMPLE 7   Graphing Cross Sections

(A) Describe the cross sections of $f(x, y) = 2x^2 + y^2$ in the planes $y = 0$, $y = 1, y = 2, y = 3$, and $y = 4$.

(B) Describe the cross sections of $f(x, y) = 2x^2 + y^2$ in the planes $x = 0$, $x = 1, x = 2, x = 3$, and $x = 4$.

SOLUTION

(A) The cross section of $f(x, y) = 2x^2 + y^2$ produced by cutting it with the plane $y = 0$ is the graph of the function $f(x, 0) = 2x^2$ in this plane. We can examine the shape of this cross section by graphing $y_1 = 2x^2$ on a graphing calculator (Fig. 5). Similarly, the graphs of $y_2 = f(x, 1) = 2x^2 + 1$, $y_3 = f(x, 2) = 2x^2 + 4$, $y_4 = f(x, 3) = 2x^2 + 9$, and $y_5 = f(x, 4) = 2x^2 + 16$ show the shapes of the other four cross sections (see Fig. 5). Each of these is a parabola that opens upward. Note the correspondence between the graphs in Figure 5 and the actual cross sections of $f(x, y) = 2x^2 + y^2$ shown in Figure 6.

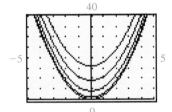

Figure 5

$y_1 = 2x^2$

$y_2 = 2x^2 + 1$

$y_3 = 2x^2 + 4$

$y_4 = 2x^2 + 9$

$y_5 = 2x^2 + 16$

Figure 6

Figure 7

$y_1 = x^2$ $y_4 = 18 + x^2$
$y_2 = 2 + x^2$ $y_5 = 32 + x^2$
$y_3 = 8 + x^2$

(B) The five cross sections are represented by the graphs of the functions $f(0, y) = y^2$, $f(1, y) = 2 + y^2$, $f(2, y) = 8 + y^2$, $f(3, y) = 18 + y^2$, and $f(4, y) = 32 + y^2$. These five functions are graphed in Figure 7. (Note that changing the name of the independent variable from y to x for graphing purposes does not affect the graph displayed.) Each of the five cross sections is a parabola that opens upward.

Matched Problem 7

(A) Describe the cross sections of $g(x, y) = y^2 - x^2$ in the planes $y = 0$, $y = 1$, $y = 2$, $y = 3$, and $y = 4$.

(B) Describe the cross sections of $g(x, y) = y^2 - x^2$ in the planes $x = 0$, $x = 1$, $x = 2$, $x = 3$, and $x = 4$.

CONCEPTUAL INSIGHT

The graph of the *equation*

$$x^2 + y^2 + z^2 = 4 \tag{3}$$

is the graph of all ordered triplets of numbers (x, y, z) that satisfy the equation. The Pythagorean theorem can be used to show that the distance from the point (x, y, z) to the origin $(0, 0, 0)$ is equal to

$$\sqrt{x^2 + y^2 + z^2}$$

Therefore, the graph of (3) consists of all points that are at a distance 2 from the origin—that is, all points on the sphere of radius 2 and with center at the origin. Recall that a circle in the plane is *not* the graph of a function $y = f(x)$, because it fails the vertical-line test (Section 1.1). Similarly, a sphere is *not* the graph of a *function* $z = f(x, y)$ of two variables.

Exercises 7.1

Skills Warm-up Exercises

W

In Problems 1–8, find the indicated value of the function of two or three variables. (If necessary, review Appendix C).

1. The height of a trapezoid is 3 feet and the lengths of its parallel sides are 5 feet and 8 feet. Find the area.

2. The height of a trapezoid is 4 meters and the lengths of its parallel sides are 25 meters and 32 meters. Find the area.

3. The length, width, and height of a rectangular box are 12 inches, 5 inches, and 4 inches, respectively. Find the volume.

4. The length, width, and height of a rectangular box are 30 centimeters, 15 centimeters, and 10 centimeters, respectively. Find the volume.

5. The height of a right circular cylinder is 8 meters and the radius is 2 meters. Find the volume.

6. The height of a right circular cylinder is 6 feet and the diameter is also 6 feet. Find the total surface area.

7. The height of a right circular cone is 48 centimeters and the radius is 20 centimeters. Find the total surface area.

8. The height of a right circular cone is 42 inches and the radius is 7 inches. Find the volume.

In Problems 9–16, find the indicated values of the functions

$$f(x, y) = 2x + 7y - 5 \quad \text{and} \quad g(x, y) = \frac{88}{x^2 + 3y}$$

9. $f(4, -1)$ **10.** $f(0, 10)$

11. $f(8, 0)$ **12.** $f(5, 6)$

13. $g(1, 7)$ **14.** $g(-2, 0)$

15. $g(3, -3)$ **16.** $g(0, 0)$

In Problems 17–20, find the indicated values of

$$f(x, y, z) = 2x - 3y^2 + 5z^3 - 1$$

17. $f(0, 0, 0)$ **18.** $f(0, 0, 2)$

19. $f(6, -5, 0)$ **20.** $f(-10, 4, -3)$

In Problems 21–30, find the indicated value of the given function.

21. $P(13, 5)$ for $P(n, r) = \dfrac{n!}{(n - r)!}$

22. $C(13, 5)$ for $C(n, r) = \dfrac{n!}{r!(n - r)!}$

23. $V(4, 12)$ for $V(R, h) = \pi R^2 h$

24. $T(4, 12)$ for $T(R, h) = 2\pi R(R + h)$

25. $S(3, 10)$ for $S(R, h) = \pi R \sqrt{R^2 + h^2}$

26. $W(3, 10)$ for $W(R, h) = \dfrac{1}{3} \pi R^2 h$

27. $A(100, 0.06, 3)$ for $A(P, r, t) = P + Prt$

28. $A(10, 0.04, 3, 2)$ for $A(P, r, t, n) = P\left(1 + \dfrac{r}{n}\right)^{tn}$

29. $P(0.05, 12)$ for $P(r, T) = \displaystyle\int_0^T 4{,}000 e^{-rt}\, dt$

30. $F(0.07, 10)$ for $F(r, T) = \displaystyle\int_0^T 4{,}000 e^{r(T-t)}\, dt$

In Problems 31–36, find the indicated function f of a single variable.

31. $f(x) = G(x, 0)$ for $G(x, y) = x^2 + 3xy + y^2 - 7$

32. $f(y) = H(0, y)$ for $H(x, y) = x^2 - 5xy - y^2 + 2$

33. $f(y) = K(4, y)$ for $K(x, y) = 10xy + 3x - 2y + 8$

34. $f(x) = L(x, -2)$ for $L(x, y) = 25 - x + 5y - 6xy$

35. $f(y) = M(y, y)$ for $M(x, y) = x^2 y - 3xy^2 + 5$

36. $f(x) = N(x, 2x)$ for $N(x, y) = 3xy + x^2 - y^2 + 1$

37. Let $F(x, y) = 2x + 3y - 6$. Find all values of y such that $F(0, y) = 0$.

38. Let $F(x, y) = 5x - 4y + 12$. Find all values of x such that $F(x, 0) = 0$.

39. Let $F(x, y) = 2xy + 3x - 4y - 1$. Find all values of x such that $F(x, x) = 0$.

40. Let $F(x, y) = xy + 2x^2 + y^2 - 25$. Find all values of y such that $F(y, y) = 0$.

41. Let $F(x, y) = x^2 + e^x y - y^2$. Find all values of x such that $F(x, 2) = 0$.

42. Let $G(a, b, c) = a^3 + b^3 + c^3 - (ab + ac + bc) - 6$. Find all values of b such that $G(2, b, 1) = 0$.

43. For the function $f(x, y) = x^2 + 2y^2$, find

$$\frac{f(x + h, y) - f(x, y)}{h}$$

44. For the function $f(x, y) = x^2 + 2y^2$, find

$$\frac{f(x, y + k) - f(x, y)}{k}$$

45. For the function $f(x, y) = 2xy^2$, find

$$\frac{f(x + h, y) - f(x, y)}{h}$$

46. For the function $f(x, y) = 2xy^2$, find

$$\frac{f(x, y + k) - f(x, y)}{k}$$

47. Find the coordinates of E and F in the figure for Matched Problem 6 on page 429.

48. Find the coordinates of B and H in the figure for Matched Problem 6 on page 429.

In Problems 49–54, use a graphing calculator as necessary to explore the graphs of the indicated cross sections.

49. Let $f(x, y) = x^2$.

(A) Explain why the cross sections of the surface $z = f(x, y)$ produced by cutting it with planes parallel to $y = 0$ are parabolas.

(B) Describe the cross sections of the surface in the planes $x = 0$, $x = 1$, and $x = 2$.

(C) Describe the surface $z = f(x, y)$.

50. Let $f(x, y) = \sqrt{4 - y^2}$.

(A) Explain why the cross sections of the surface $z = f(x, y)$ produced by cutting it with planes parallel to $x = 0$ are semicircles of radius 2.

(B) Describe the cross sections of the surface in the planes $y = 0$, $y = 2$, and $y = 3$.

(C) Describe the surface $z = f(x, y)$.

51. Let $f(x, y) = \sqrt{36 - x^2 - y^2}$.

(A) Describe the cross sections of the surface $z = f(x, y)$ produced by cutting it with the planes $y = 1$, $y = 2$, $y = 3$, $y = 4$, and $y = 5$.

(B) Describe the cross sections of the surface in the planes $x = 0$, $x = 1$, $x = 2$, $x = 3$, $x = 4$, and $x = 5$.

(C) Describe the surface $z = f(x, y)$.

52. Let $f(x, y) = 100 + 10x + 25y - x^2 - 5y^2$.

(A) Describe the cross sections of the surface $z = f(x, y)$ produced by cutting it with the planes $y = 0$, $y = 1$, $y = 2$, and $y = 3$.

(B) Describe the cross sections of the surface in the planes $x = 0$, $x = 1$, $x = 2$, and $x = 3$.

(C) Describe the surface $z = f(x, y)$.

53. Let $f(x, y) = e^{-(x^2 + y^2)}$.

(A) Explain why $f(a, b) = f(c, d)$ whenever (a, b) and (c, d) are points on the same circle centered at the origin in the xy plane.

(B) Describe the cross sections of the surface $z = f(x, y)$ produced by cutting it with the planes $x = 0$, $y = 0$, and $x = y$.

(C) Describe the surface $z = f(x, y)$.

54. Let $f(x, y) = 4 - \sqrt{x^2 + y^2}$.

(A) Explain why $f(a, b) = f(c, d)$ whenever (a, b) and (c, d) are points on the same circle with center at the origin in the xy plane.

(B) Describe the cross sections of the surface $z = f(x, y)$ produced by cutting it with the planes $x = 0$, $y = 0$, and $x = y$.

(C) Describe the surface $z = f(x, y)$.

Applications

55. *Cost function.* A small manufacturing company produces two models of a surfboard: a standard model and a competition model. If the standard model is produced at a variable cost of $210 each and the competition model at a variable cost of $300 each, and if the total fixed costs per month are $6,000, then the monthly cost function is given by

$$C(x, y) = 6,000 + 210x + 300y$$

where x and y are the numbers of standard and competition models produced per month, respectively. Find $C(20, 10)$, $C(50, 5)$, and $C(30, 30)$.

56. *Advertising and sales.* A company spends x thousand per week on online advertising and y thousand per week on TV advertising. Its weekly sales are found to be given by

$$S(x, y) = 5x^2y^3$$

Find $S(3, 2)$ and $S(2, 3)$.

57. *Revenue function.* A supermarket sells two brands of coffee: brand A at p per pound and brand B at q per pound. The daily demand equations for brands A and B are, respectively,

$$x = 200 - 5p + 4q$$
$$y = 300 + 2p - 4q$$

(both in pounds). Find the daily revenue function $R(p, q)$. Evaluate $R(2, 3)$ and $R(3, 2)$.

58. *Revenue, cost, and profit functions.* A company manufactures 10- and 3-speed bicycles. The weekly demand and cost equations are

$$p = 230 - 9x + y$$
$$q = 130 + x - 4y$$
$$C(x, y) = 200 + 80x + 30y$$

where p is the price of a 10-speed bicycle, q is the price of a 3-speed bicycle, x is the weekly demand for 10-speed bicycles, y is the weekly demand for 3-speed bicycles, and $C(x, y)$ is the cost function. Find the weekly revenue function $R(x, y)$ and the weekly profit function $P(x, y)$. Evaluate $R(10, 15)$ and $P(10, 15)$.

59. *Productivity.* The Cobb–Douglas production function for a petroleum company is given by

$$f(x, y) = 20x^{0.4}y^{0.6}$$

where x is the utilization of labor and y is the utilization of capital. If the company uses 1,250 units of labor and 1,700 units of capital, how many units of petroleum will be produced?

60. *Productivity.* The petroleum company in Problem 59 is taken over by another company that decides to double both the units of labor and the units of capital utilized in the production of petroleum. Use the Cobb–Douglas production function given in Problem 59 to find the amount of petroleum that will be produced by this increased utilization of labor and capital. What is the effect on productivity of doubling both the units of labor and the units of capital?

61. *Future value.* At the end of each year, $5,000 is invested into an IRA earning 3% compounded annually.

(A) How much will be in the account at the end of 30 years? Use the annuity formula

$$F(P, i, n) = P\frac{(1 + i)^n - 1}{i}$$

where

$P = $ periodic payment

$i = $ rate per period

$n = $ number of payments (periods)

$F = $ FV $= $ future value

(B) Use graphical approximation methods to determine the rate of interest that would produce $300,000 in the account at the end of 30 years.

62. *Package design.* The packaging department in a company has been asked to design a rectangular box with no top and a partition down the middle (see the figure). Let x, y, and z be the dimensions of the box (in inches). Ignore the thickness of the material from which the box will be made.

(A) Find the total area of material $M(x, y, z)$ used in constructing one of these boxes, and evaluate $M(10, 12, 6)$.

(B) Suppose that the box will have a square base and a volume of 720 cubic inches. Use graphical approximation methods to determine the dimensions that require the least material.

63. *Marine biology.* For a diver using scuba-diving gear, a marine biologist estimates the time (duration) of a dive according to the equation

$$T(V, x) = \frac{33V}{x + 33}$$

where

$T = $ time of dive in minutes

$V = $ volume of air, at sea level pressure, compressed into tanks

$x = $ depth of dive in feet

Find $T(70, 47)$ and $T(60, 27)$.

64. *Blood flow.* Poiseuille's law states that the resistance R for blood flowing in a blood vessel varies directly as the length L of the vessel and inversely as the fourth power of its radius r. Stated as an equation,

$$R(L, r) = k\frac{L}{r^4} \qquad k \text{ a constant}$$

Find $R(8, 1)$ and $R(4, 0.2)$.

65. Physical anthropology. Anthropologists use an index called the *cephalic index.* The cephalic index C varies directly as the width W of the head and inversely as the length L of the head (both viewed from the top). In terms of an equation,

$$C(W, L) = 100\frac{W}{L}$$

where

W = width in inches

L = length in inches

Find $C(6, 8)$ and $C(8.1, 9)$.

66. Safety research. Under ideal conditions, if a person driving a car slams on the brakes and skids to a stop, the length of the skid marks (in feet) is given by the formula

$$L(w, v) = kwv^2$$

where

k = constant

w = weight of car in pounds

v = speed of car in miles per hour

For $k = 0.000\ 013\ 3$, find $L(2,000, 40)$ and $L(3,000, 60)$.

67. Psychology. The intelligence quotient (IQ) is defined to be the ratio of mental age (MA), as determined by certain tests, to chronological age (CA), multiplied by 100. Stated as an equation,

$$Q(M, C) = \frac{M}{C} \cdot 100$$

where

$$Q = \text{IQ} \qquad M = \text{MA} \qquad C = \text{CA}$$

Find $Q(12, 10)$ and $Q(10, 12)$.

Answers to Matched Problems

1. $3,100   2. 30
3. (A) $R(x, y) = 220x + 300y - 6x^2 + 4xy - 10y^2$; $R(20, 10) = \$4,800$
   (B) $P(x, y) = 180x + 220y - 6x^2 + 4xy - 10y^2 - 1,000$; $P(20, 10) = \$2,200$
4. $V(x, y) = x^2y$; $V(5, 10) = 250$ in.^{3}
5. 17,411 units
6. $A(0, 0, 0)$; $C(2, 4, 0)$; $G(2, 4, 3)$; $D(0, 4, 0)$
7. (A) Each cross section is a parabola that opens downward.
   (B) Each cross section is a parabola that opens upward.

7.2 Partial Derivatives

- Partial Derivatives
- Second-Order Partial Derivatives

Partial Derivatives

We know how to differentiate many kinds of functions of one independent variable and how to interpret the derivatives that result. What about functions with two or more independent variables? Let's return to the surfboard example considered on page 426.

For the company producing only the standard board, the cost function was

$$C(x) = 500 + 70x$$

Differentiating with respect to x, we obtain the marginal cost function

$$C'(x) = 70$$

Since the marginal cost is constant, $70 is the change in cost for a 1-unit increase in production at any output level.

For the company producing two types of boards—a standard model and a competition model—the cost function was

$$C(x, y) = 700 + 70x + 100y$$

Now suppose that we differentiate with respect to x, holding y fixed, and denote the resulting function by $C_x(x, y)$; or suppose we differentiate with respect to y, holding x fixed, and denote the resulting function by $C_y(x, y)$. Differentiating in this way, we obtain

$$C_x(x, y) = 70 \qquad C_y(x, y) = 100$$

Each of these functions is called a **partial derivative**, and, in this example, each represents marginal cost. The first is the change in cost due to a 1-unit increase in production of the standard board with the production of the competition model held fixed. The second is the change in cost due to a 1-unit increase in production of the competition board with the production of the standard board held fixed.

In general, if $z = f(x, y)$, then the **partial derivative of f with respect to x**, denoted $\partial z / \partial x, f_x$, or $f_x(x, y)$, is defined by

$$\frac{\partial z}{\partial x} = \lim_{h \to 0} \frac{f(x + h, y) - f(x, y)}{h}$$

provided that the limit exists. We recognize this formula as the ordinary derivative of f with respect to x, holding y constant. We can continue to use all the derivative rules and properties discussed in Chapters 2 to 4 and apply them to partial derivatives.

Similarly, the **partial derivative of f with respect to y**, denoted $\partial z / \partial y, f_y$, or $f_y(x, y)$, is defined by

$$\frac{\partial z}{\partial y} = \lim_{k \to 0} \frac{f(x, y + k) - f(x, y)}{k}$$

which is the ordinary derivative with respect to y, holding x constant.

Parallel definitions and interpretations hold for functions with three or more independent variables.

EXAMPLE 1 Partial Derivatives For $z = f(x, y) = 2x^2 - 3x^2y + 5y + 1$, find

(A) $\partial z / \partial x$ (B) $f_x(2, 3)$

SOLUTION

(A) $z = 2x^2 - 3x^2y + 5y + 1$

Differentiating with respect to x, holding y constant (that is, treating y as a constant), we obtain

$$\frac{\partial z}{\partial x} = 4x - 6xy$$

(B) $f(x, y) = 2x^2 - 3x^2y + 5y + 1$

First, differentiate with respect to x. From part (A), we have

$$f_x(x, y) = 4x - 6xy$$

Then evaluate this equation at $(2, 3)$:

$$f_x(2, 3) = 4(2) - 6(2)(3) = -28$$

Figure 1 $y_1 = -7x^2 + 16$

In part 1B, an alternative approach would be to substitute $y = 3$ into $f(x, y)$ and graph the function $f(x, 3) = -7x^2 + 16$, which represents the cross section of the surface $z = f(x, y)$ produced by cutting it with the plane $y = 3$. Then determine the slope of the tangent line when $x = 2$. Again, we conclude that $f_x(2, 3) = -28$ (see Fig. 1).

Matched Problem 1 For f in Example 1, find

(A) $\partial z / \partial y$ (B) $f_y(2, 3)$

EXAMPLE 2 Partial Derivatives Using the Chain Rule For $z = f(x, y) = e^{x^2 + y^2}$, find

(A) $\partial z / \partial x$ (B) $f_y(2, 1)$

SOLUTION

(A) Using the chain rule [thinking of $z = e^u$, $u = u(x)$; y is held constant], we obtain

$$\frac{\partial z}{\partial x} = e^{x^2 + y^2} \frac{\partial(x^2 + y^2)}{\partial x}$$

$$= 2xe^{x^2 + y^2}$$

(B) $f_y(x, y) = e^{x^2+y^2} \dfrac{\partial(x^2 + y^2)}{\partial y} = 2ye^{x^2+y^2}$

$f_y(2, 1) = 2(1)e^{(2)^2+(1)^2}$

$\qquad\quad = 2e^5$

Matched Problem 2 For $z = f(x, y) = (x^2 + 2xy)^5$, find

(A) $\partial z/\partial y$ (B) $f_x(1, 0)$

EXAMPLE 3 Profit The profit function for the surfboard company in Example 3 of Section 7.1 was

$$P(x, y) = 140x + 200y - 4x^2 + 2xy - 12y^2 - 700$$

Find $P_x(15, 10)$ and $P_x(30, 10)$, and interpret the results.

SOLUTION

$$P_x(x, y) = 140 - 8x + 2y$$
$$P_x(15, 10) = 140 - 8(15) + 2(10) = 40$$
$$P_x(30, 10) = 140 - 8(30) + 2(10) = -80$$

At a production level of 15 standard and 10 competition boards per week, increasing the production of standard boards by 1 unit and holding the production of competition boards fixed at 10 will increase profit by approximately $40. At a production level of 30 standard and 10 competition boards per week, increasing the production of standard boards by 1 unit and holding the production of competition boards fixed at 10 will decrease profit by approximately $80.

Matched Problem 3 For the profit function in Example 3, find $P_y(25, 10)$ and $P_y(25, 15)$, and interpret the results.

EXAMPLE 4 Productivity The productivity of a major computer manufacturer is given approximately by the Cobb–Douglas production function

$$f(x, y) = 15x^{0.4}y^{0.6}$$

with the utilization of x units of labor and y units of capital. The partial derivative $f_x(x, y)$ represents the rate of change of productivity with respect to labor and is called the **marginal productivity of labor**. The partial derivative $f_y(x, y)$ represents the rate of change of productivity with respect to capital and is called the **marginal productivity of capital**. If the company is currently utilizing 4,000 units of labor and 2,500 units of capital, find the marginal productivity of labor and the marginal productivity of capital. For the greatest increase in productivity, should the management of the company encourage increased use of labor or increased use of capital?

SOLUTION

$$f_x(x, y) = 6x^{-0.6}y^{0.6}$$
$$f_x(4,000, 2,500) = 6(4,000)^{-0.6}(2,500)^{0.6}$$
$$\approx 4.53 \qquad \text{Marginal productivity of labor}$$
$$f_y(x, y) = 9x^{0.4}y^{-0.4}$$
$$f_y(4,000, 2,500) = 9(4,000)^{0.4}(2,500)^{-0.4}$$
$$\approx 10.86 \qquad \text{Marginal productivity of capital}$$

At the current level of utilization of 4,000 units of labor and 2,500 units of capital, each 1-unit increase in labor utilization (keeping capital utilization fixed at 2,500 units) will increase production by approximately 4.53 units, and each 1-unit increase in capital utilization (keeping labor utilization fixed at 4,000 units) will increase production by approximately 10.86 units. The management of the company should encourage increased use of capital.

Matched Problem 4 The productivity of an airplane-manufacturing company is given approximately by the Cobb–Douglas production function

$$f(x, y) = 40x^{0.3}y^{0.7}$$

(A) Find $f_x(x, y)$ and $f_y(x, y)$.

(B) If the company is currently using 1,500 units of labor and 4,500 units of capital, find the marginal productivity of labor and the marginal productivity of capital.

(C) For the greatest increase in productivity, should the management of the company encourage increased use of labor or increased use of capital?

Partial derivatives have simple geometric interpretations, as shown in Figure 2. If we hold x fixed at $x = a$, then $f_y(a, y)$ is the slope of the curve obtained by intersecting the surface $z = f(x, y)$ with the plane $x = a$. A similar interpretation is given to $f_x(x, b)$.

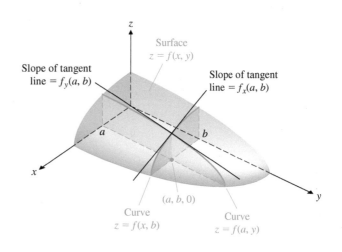

Figure 2

Second-Order Partial Derivatives

The function

$$z = f(x, y) = x^4 y^7$$

has two **first-order partial derivatives**:

$$\frac{\partial z}{\partial x} = f_x = f_x(x, y) = 4x^3 y^7 \qquad \text{and} \qquad \frac{\partial z}{\partial y} = f_y = f_y(x, y) = 7x^4 y^6$$

Each of these partial derivatives, in turn, has two partial derivatives called **second-order partial derivatives** of $z = f(x, y)$. Generalizing the various notations we have for first-order partial derivatives, we write the four second-order partial derivatives of $z = f(x, y) = x^4 y^7$ as

Equivalent notations

$$f_{xx} = f_{xx}(x, y) = \frac{\partial^2 z}{\partial x^2} = \frac{\partial}{\partial x}\left(\frac{\partial z}{\partial x}\right) = \frac{\partial}{\partial x}(4x^3y^7) = 12x^2y^7$$

$$f_{xy} = f_{xy}(x, y) = \frac{\partial^2 z}{\partial y\,\partial x} = \frac{\partial}{\partial y}\left(\frac{\partial z}{\partial x}\right) = \frac{\partial}{\partial y}(4x^3y^7) = 28x^3y^6$$

$$f_{yx} = f_{yx}(x, y) = \frac{\partial^2 z}{\partial x\,\partial y} = \frac{\partial}{\partial x}\left(\frac{\partial z}{\partial y}\right) = \frac{\partial}{\partial x}(7x^4y^6) = 28x^3y^6$$

$$f_{yy} = f_{yy}(x, y) = \frac{\partial^2 z}{\partial y^2} = \frac{\partial}{\partial y}\left(\frac{\partial z}{\partial y}\right) = \frac{\partial}{\partial y}(7x^4y^6) = 42x^4y^5$$

In the mixed partial derivative $\partial^2 z/\partial y\,\partial x = f_{xy}$, we started with $z = f(x, y)$ and first differentiated with respect to x (holding y constant). Then we differentiated with respect to y (holding x constant). In the other mixed partial derivative, $\partial^2 z/\partial x\,\partial y = f_{yx}$, the order of differentiation was reversed; however, the final result was the same—that is, $f_{xy} = f_{yx}$. Although it is possible to find functions for which $f_{xy} \neq f_{yx}$, such functions rarely occur in applications involving partial derivatives. For all the functions in this book, we will assume that $f_{xy} = f_{yx}$.

In general, we have the following definitions:

DEFINITION   Second-Order Partial Derivatives
If $z = f(x, y)$, then

$$f_{xx} = f_{xx}(x, y) = \frac{\partial^2 z}{\partial x^2} = \frac{\partial}{\partial x}\left(\frac{\partial z}{\partial x}\right)$$

$$f_{xy} = f_{xy}(x, y) = \frac{\partial^2 z}{\partial y\,\partial x} = \frac{\partial}{\partial y}\left(\frac{\partial z}{\partial x}\right)$$

$$f_{yx} = f_{yx}(x, y) = \frac{\partial^2 z}{\partial x\,\partial y} = \frac{\partial}{\partial x}\left(\frac{\partial z}{\partial y}\right)$$

$$f_{yy} = f_{yy}(x, y) = \frac{\partial^2 z}{\partial y^2} = \frac{\partial}{\partial y}\left(\frac{\partial z}{\partial y}\right)$$

EXAMPLE 5   Second-Order Partial Derivatives   For $z = f(x, y) = 3x^2 - 2xy^3 + 1$, find

(A) $\dfrac{\partial^2 z}{\partial x\,\partial y}, \dfrac{\partial^2 z}{\partial y\,\partial x}$ (B) $\dfrac{\partial^2 z}{\partial x^2}$ (C) $f_{yx}(2, 1)$

SOLUTION

(A) First differentiate with respect to y and then with respect to x:

$$\frac{\partial z}{\partial y} = -6xy^2 \qquad \frac{\partial^2 z}{\partial x\,\partial y} = \frac{\partial}{\partial x}\left(\frac{\partial z}{\partial y}\right) = \frac{\partial}{\partial x}(-6xy^2) = -6y^2$$

Now differentiate with respect to x and then with respect to y:

$$\frac{\partial z}{\partial x} = 6x - 2y^3 \qquad \frac{\partial^2 z}{\partial y\,\partial x} = \frac{\partial}{\partial y}\left(\frac{\partial z}{\partial x}\right) = \frac{\partial}{\partial y}(6x - 2y^3) = -6y^2$$

(B) Differentiate with respect to x twice:

$$\frac{\partial z}{\partial x} = 6x - 2y^3 \qquad \frac{\partial^2 z}{\partial x^2} = \frac{\partial}{\partial x}\left(\frac{\partial z}{\partial x}\right) = 6$$

(C) First find $f_{yx}(x, y)$; then evaluate the resulting equation at $(2, 1)$. Again, remember that f_{yx} signifies differentiation first with respect to y and then with respect to x.

$$f_y(x, y) = -6xy^2 \qquad f_{yx}(x, y) = -6y^2$$

and

$$f_{yx}(2, 1) = -6(1)^2 = -6$$

Matched Problem 5 For $z = f(x, y) = x^3y - 2y^4 + 3$, find

(A) $\dfrac{\partial^2 z}{\partial y \, \partial x}$

(B) $\dfrac{\partial^2 z}{\partial y^2}$

(C) $f_{xy}(2, 3)$

(D) $f_{yx}(2, 3)$

CONCEPTUAL INSIGHT

Although the mixed second-order partial derivatives f_{xy} and f_{yx} are equal for all functions considered in this book, it is a good idea to compute both of them, as in Example 5A, as a check on your work. By contrast, the other two second-order partial derivatives, f_{xx} and f_{yy}, are generally not equal to each other. For example, for the function

$$f(x, y) = 3x^2 - 2xy^3 + 1$$

of Example 5,

$$f_{xx} = 6 \qquad \text{and} \qquad f_{yy} = -12xy$$

Exercises 7.2

W Skills Warm-up Exercises

In Problems 1–8, find the indicated derivative. (If necessary, review Sections 3.3 and 3.4).

1. $f'(x)$ if $f(x) = \pi x^3 + x\pi^3$

2. $f'(x)$ if $f(x) = (\pi x + 3)^5 - x^4$

3. $f'(x)$ if $f(x) = x^e + e^x$

4. $f'(x)$ if $f(x) = x \ln \pi + \pi \ln x$

5. $\dfrac{dz}{dx}$ if $z = \dfrac{x}{e} + \dfrac{e}{x}$

6. $\dfrac{dz}{dx}$ if $z = x^3 \ln \pi + 4\pi^2 e^x$

7. $\dfrac{dz}{dx}$ if $z = \ln(x^2 + e^2)$

8. $\dfrac{dz}{dx}$ if $z = e^7 - 2ex^7$

In Problems 9–16, find the indicated first-order partial derivative for each function $z = f(x, y)$.

9. $f_x(x, y)$ if $f(x, y) = 4x - 3y + 6$

10. $f_x(x, y)$ if $f(x, y) = 7x + 8y - 2$

11. $f_y(x, y)$ if $f(x, y) = x^2 - 3xy + 2y^2$

12. $f_y(x, y)$ if $f(x, y) = 3x^2 + 2xy - 7y^2$

13. $\dfrac{\partial z}{\partial x}$ if $z = x^3 + 4x^2y + 2y^3$

14. $\dfrac{\partial z}{\partial y}$ if $z = 4x^2y - 5xy^2$

15. $\dfrac{\partial z}{\partial y}$ if $z = (5x + 2y)^{10}$

16. $\dfrac{\partial z}{\partial x}$ if $z = (2x - 3y)^8$

In Problems 17–24, find the indicated value.

17. $f_x(1, 3)$ if $f(x, y) = 5x^3y - 4xy^2$

18. $f_x(4, 1)$ if $f(x, y) = x^2y^2 - 5xy^3$

19. $f_y(1, 0)$ if $f(x, y) = 3xe^y$

20. $f_y(2, 4)$ if $f(x, y) = x^4 \ln y$

21. $f_y(2, 1)$ if $f(x, y) = e^{x^2} - 4y$

22. $f_y(3, 3)$ if $f(x, y) = e^{3x} - y^2$

23. $f_x(1, -1)$ if $f(x, y) = \dfrac{2xy}{1 + x^2y^2}$

24. $f_x(-1, 2)$ if $f(x, y) = \dfrac{x^2 - y^2}{1 + x^2}$

In Problems 25–30, $M(x, y) = 68 + 0.3x - 0.8y$ gives the mileage (in mpg) of a new car as a function of tire pressure x (in psi) and speed (in mph). Find the indicated quantity (include the appropriate units) and explain what it means.

25. $M(32, 40)$ **26.** $M(22, 40)$

27. $M(32, 50)$ **28.** $M(22, 50)$

29. $M_x(32, 50)$ **30.** $M_y(32, 50)$

In Problems 31–42, find the indicated second-order partial derivative for each function $f(x, y)$.

31. $f_{xx}(x, y)$ if $f(x, y) = 6x - 5y + 3$

32. $f_{yx}(x, y)$ if $f(x, y) = -2x + y + 8$

33. $f_{xy}(x, y)$ if $f(x, y) = 4x^2 + 6y^2 - 10$

34. $f_{yy}(x, y)$ if $f(x, y) = x^2 + 9y^2 - 4$

35. $f_{xy}(x, y)$ if $f(x, y) = e^{xy^2}$

36. $f_{yx}(x, y)$ if $f(x, y) = e^{3x+2y}$

37. $f_{yy}(x, y)$ if $f(x, y) = \dfrac{\ln x}{y}$

38. $f_{xx}(x, y)$ if $f(x, y) = \dfrac{3 \ln x}{y^2}$

39. $f_{xx}(x, y)$ if $f(x, y) = (2x + y)^5$

40. $f_{yx}(x, y)$ if $f(x, y) = (3x - 8y)^6$

41. $f_{xy}(x, y)$ if $f(x, y) = (x^2 + y^4)^{10}$

42. $f_{yy}(x, y)$ if $f(x, y) = (1 + 2xy^2)^8$

In Problems 43–52, find the indicated function or value if $C(x, y) = 3x^2 + 10xy - 8y^2 + 4x - 15y - 120$.

43. $C_x(x, y)$ **44.** $C_y(x, y)$

45. $C_x(3, -2)$ **46.** $C_y(3, -2)$

47. $C_{xx}(x, y)$ **48.** $C_{yy}(x, y)$

49. $C_{xy}(x, y)$ **50.** $C_{yx}(x, y)$

51. $C_{xx}(3, -2)$ **52.** $C_{yy}(3, -2)$

In Problems 53–58, $S(T, r) = 50(T - 40)(5 - r)$ gives an ice cream shop's daily sales as a function of temperature T (in °F) and rain r (in inches). Find the indicated quantity (include the appropriate units) and explain what it means.

53. $S(60, 2)$ **54.** $S(80, 0)$

55. $S_r(90, 1)$ **56.** $S_T(90, 1)$

57. $S_{Tr}(90, 1)$ **58.** $S_{rT}(90, 1)$

59. (A) Let $f(x, y) = y^3 + 4y^2 - 5y + 3$. Show that $\partial f/\partial x = 0$.

(B) Explain why there are an infinite number of functions $g(x, y)$ such that $\partial g/\partial x = 0$.

60. (A) Find an example of a function $f(x, y)$ such that $\partial f/\partial x = 3$ and $\partial f/\partial y = 2$.

(B) How many such functions are there? Explain.

In Problems 61–66, find $f_{xx}(x, y)$, $f_{xy}(x, y)$, $f_{yx}(x, y)$, and $f_{yy}(x, y)$ for each function f.

61. $f(x, y) = x^2y^2 + x^3 + y$

62. $f(x, y) = x^3y^3 + x + y^2$

63. $f(x, y) = \dfrac{x}{y} - \dfrac{y}{x}$ **64.** $f(x, y) = \dfrac{x^2}{y} - \dfrac{y^2}{x}$

65. $f(x, y) = xe^{xy}$ **66.** $f(x, y) = x \ln(xy)$

67. For
$$P(x, y) = -x^2 + 2xy - 2y^2 - 4x + 12y - 5$$
find all values of x and y such that
$$P_x(x, y) = 0 \quad \text{and} \quad P_y(x, y) = 0$$
simultaneously.

68. For
$$C(x, y) = 2x^2 + 2xy + 3y^2 - 16x - 18y + 54$$
find all values of x and y such that
$$C_x(x, y) = 0 \quad \text{and} \quad C_y(x, y) = 0$$
simultaneously.

69. For
$$F(x, y) = x^3 - 2x^2y^2 - 2x - 4y + 10$$
find all values of x and y such that
$$F_x(x, y) = 0 \quad \text{and} \quad F_y(x, y) = 0$$
simultaneously.

70. For
$$G(x, y) = x^2 \ln y - 3x - 2y + 1$$
find all values of x and y such that
$$G_x(x, y) = 0 \quad \text{and} \quad G_y(x, y) = 0$$
simultaneously.

71. Let $f(x, y) = 3x^2 + y^2 - 4x - 6y + 2$.

(A) Find the minimum value of $f(x, y)$ when $y = 1$.

(B) Explain why the answer to part (A) is not the minimum value of the function $f(x, y)$.

72. Let $f(x, y) = 5 - 2x + 4y - 3x^2 - y^2$.

(A) Find the maximum value of $f(x, y)$ when $x = 2$.

(B) Explain why the answer to part (A) is not the maximum value of the function $f(x, y)$.

73. Let $f(x, y) = 4 - x^4y + 3xy^2 + y^5$.

(A) Use graphical approximation methods to find c (to three decimal places) such that $f(c, 2)$ is the maximum value of $f(x, y)$ when $y = 2$.

(B) Find $f_x(c, 2)$ and $f_y(c, 2)$.

74. Let $f(x, y) = e^x + 2e^y + 3xy^2 + 1$.

   (A) Use graphical approximation methods to find d (to three decimal places) such that $f(1, d)$ is the minimum value of $f(x, y)$ when $x = 1$.

   (B) Find $f_x(1, d)$ and $f_y(1, d)$.

75. For $f(x, y) = x^2 + 2y^2$, find

   (A) $\displaystyle\lim_{h \to 0} \frac{f(x + h, y) - f(x, y)}{h}$

   (B) $\displaystyle\lim_{k \to 0} \frac{f(x, y + k) - f(x, y)}{k}$

76. For $f(x, y) = 2xy^2$, find

   (A) $\displaystyle\lim_{h \to 0} \frac{f(x + h, y) - f(x, y)}{h}$

   (B) $\displaystyle\lim_{k \to 0} \frac{f(x, y + k) - f(x, y)}{k}$

Applications

77. Profit function. A firm produces two types of calculators each week, x of type A and y of type B. The weekly revenue and cost functions (in dollars) are

$$R(x, y) = 80x + 90y + 0.04xy - 0.05x^2 - 0.05y^2$$
$$C(x, y) = 8x + 6y + 20{,}000$$

Find $P_x(1{,}200, 1{,}800)$ and $P_y(1{,}200, 1{,}800)$, and interpret the results.

78. Advertising and sales. A company spends \$$x$ per week on online advertising and \$$y$ per week on TV advertising. Its weekly sales were found to be given by

$$S(x, y) = 10x^{0.4}y^{0.8}$$

Find $S_x(3{,}000, 2{,}000)$ and $S_y(3{,}000, 2{,}000)$, and interpret the results.

79. Demand equations. A supermarket sells two brands of coffee: brand A at \$$p$ per pound and brand B at \$$q$ per pound. The daily demands x and y (in pounds) for brands A and B, respectively, are given by

$$x = 200 - 5p + 4q$$
$$y = 300 + 2p - 4q$$

Find $\partial x / \partial p$ and $\partial y / \partial p$, and interpret the results.

80. Revenue and profit functions. A company manufactures 10- and 3-speed bicycles. The weekly demand and cost functions are

$$p = 230 - 9x + y$$
$$q = 130 + x - 4y$$
$$C(x, y) = 200 + 80x + 30y$$

where \$$p$ is the price of a 10-speed bicycle, \$$q$ is the price of a 3-speed bicycle, x is the weekly demand for 10-speed

bicycles, y is the weekly demand for 3-speed bicycles, and $C(x, y)$ is the cost function. Find $R_x(10, 5)$ and $P_x(10, 5)$, and interpret the results.

81. Productivity. The productivity of a certain third-world country is given approximately by the function

$$f(x, y) = 10x^{0.75}y^{0.25}$$

with the utilization of x units of labor and y units of capital.

   (A) Find $f_x(x, y)$ and $f_y(x, y)$.

   (B) If the country is now using 600 units of labor and 100 units of capital, find the marginal productivity of labor and the marginal productivity of capital.

   (C) For the greatest increase in the country's productivity, should the government encourage increased use of labor or increased use of capital?

82. Productivity. The productivity of an automobile-manufacturing company is given approximately by the function

$$f(x, y) = 50\sqrt{xy} = 50x^{0.5}y^{0.5}$$

with the utilization of x units of labor and y units of capital.

   (A) Find $f_x(x, y)$ and $f_y(x, y)$.

   (B) If the company is now using 250 units of labor and 125 units of capital, find the marginal productivity of labor and the marginal productivity of capital.

   (C) For the greatest increase in the company's productivity, should the management encourage increased use of labor or increased use of capital?

Problems 83–86 refer to the following: If a decrease in demand for one product results in an increase in demand for another product, the two products are said to be **competitive**, *or* **substitute**, **products**. *(Real whipping cream and imitation whipping cream are examples of competitive, or substitute, products.) If a decrease in demand for one product results in a decrease in demand for another product, the two products are said to be* **complementary products**. *(Fishing boats and outboard motors are examples of complementary products.) Partial derivatives can be used to test whether two products are competitive, complementary, or neither. We start with demand functions for two products such that the demand for either depends on the prices for both:*

$$x = f(p, q) \quad \text{Demand function for product } A$$
$$y = g(p, q) \quad \text{Demand function for product } B$$

The variables x and y represent the number of units demanded of products A and B, respectively, at a price p for 1 unit of product A and a price q for 1 unit of product B. Normally, if the price of A increases while the price of B is held constant, then the demand for A will decrease; that is, $f_p(p, q) < 0$. Then, if A and B are competitive products, the demand for B will increase; that is, $g_p(p, q) > 0$. Similarly, if the price of B increases while the price of A is held constant, the demand for B will decrease; that is, $g_q(p, q) < 0$. Then, if A and B are competitive products, the demand for A will increase; that is,

$f_q(p, q) > 0$. *Reasoning similarly for complementary products, we arrive at the following test:*

Test for Competitive and Complementary Products

Partial Derivatives	Products A and B
$f_q(p, q) > 0$ and $g_p(p, q) > 0$	Competitive (substitute)
$f_q(p, q) < 0$ and $g_p(p, q) < 0$	Complementary
$f_q(p, q) \geq 0$ and $g_p(p, q) \leq 0$	Neither
$f_q(p, q) \leq 0$ and $g_p(p, q) \geq 0$	Neither

Use this test in Problems 83–86 to determine whether the indicated products are competitive, complementary, or neither.

83. Product demand. The weekly demand equations for the sale of butter and margarine in a supermarket are

$$x = f(p, q) = 8,000 - 0.09p^2 + 0.08q^2 \quad \text{Butter}$$
$$y = g(p, q) = 15,000 + 0.04p^2 - 0.3q^2 \quad \text{Margarine}$$

84. Product demand. The daily demand equations for the sale of brand A coffee and brand B coffee in a supermarket are

$$x = f(p, q) = 200 - 5p + 4q \quad \text{Brand } A \text{ coffee}$$
$$y = g(p, q) = 300 + 2p - 4q \quad \text{Brand } B \text{ coffee}$$

85. Product demand. The monthly demand equations for the sale of skis and ski boots in a sporting goods store are

$$x = f(p, q) = 800 - 0.004p^2 - 0.003q^2 \quad \text{Skis}$$
$$y = g(p, q) = 600 - 0.003p^2 - 0.002q^2 \quad \text{Ski boots}$$

86. Product demand. The monthly demand equations for the sale of tennis rackets and tennis balls in a sporting goods store are

$$x = f(p, q) = 500 - 0.5p - q^2 \quad \text{Tennis rackets}$$
$$y = g(p, q) = 10,000 - 8p - 100q^2 \quad \text{Tennis balls (cans)}$$

87. Medicine. The following empirical formula relates the surface area A (in square inches) of an average human body to its weight w (in pounds) and its height h (in inches):

$$A = f(w, h) = 15.64w^{0.425}h^{0.725}$$

(A) Find $f_w(w, h)$ and $f_h(w, h)$.

(B) For a 65-pound child who is 57 inches tall, find $f_w(65, 57)$ and $f_h(65, 57)$, and interpret the results.

88. Blood flow. Poiseuille's law states that the resistance R for blood flowing in a blood vessel varies directly as the length L of the vessel and inversely as the fourth power of its radius r. Stated as an equation,

$$R(L, r) = k\frac{L}{r^4} \quad k \text{ a constant}$$

Find $R_L(4, 0.2)$ and $R_r(4, 0.2)$, and interpret the results.

89. Physical anthropology. Anthropologists use the cephalic index C, which varies directly as the width W of the head and inversely as the length L of the head (both viewed from the top). In terms of an equation,

$$C(W, L) = 100\frac{W}{L}$$

where

$$W = \text{width in inches}$$
$$L = \text{length in inches}$$

Find $C_W(6, 8)$ and $C_L(6, 8)$, and interpret the results.

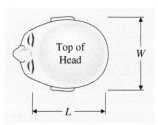

90. Safety research. Under ideal conditions, if a person driving a car slams on the brakes and skids to a stop, the length of the skid marks (in feet) is given by the formula

$$L(w, v) = kwv^2$$

where

$$k = \text{constant}$$
$$w = \text{weight of car in pounds}$$
$$v = \text{speed of car in miles per hour}$$

For $k = 0.000\ 013\ 3$, find $L_w(2,500, 60)$ and $L_v(2,500, 60)$, and interpret the results.

Answers to Matched Problems

1. (A) $\partial z/\partial y = -3x^2 + 5$ 　　(B) $f_y(2, 3) = -7$
2. (A) $10x(x^2 + 2xy)^4$ 　　(B) 10
3. $P_y(25, 10) = 10$: At a production level of $x = 25$ and $y = 10$, increasing y by 1 unit and holding x fixed at 25 will increase profit by approximately \$10; $P_y(25, 15) = -110$: At a production level of $x = 25$ and $y = 15$, increasing y by 1 unit and holding x fixed at 25 will decrease profit by approximately \$110
4. (A) $f_x(x, y) = 12x^{-0.7}y^{0.7}; f_y(x, y) = 28x^{0.3}y^{-0.3}$
   (B) Marginal productivity of labor ≈ 25.89; marginal productivity of capital ≈ 20.14
   (C) Labor
5. (A) $3x^2$ 　(B) $-24y^2$ 　(C) 12 　(D) 12

7.3 Maxima and Minima

We are now ready to undertake a brief, but useful, analysis of local maxima and minima for functions of the type $z = f(x, y)$. We will extend the second-derivative test developed for functions of a single independent variable. We assume that all second-order partial derivatives exist for the function f in some circular region in the xy plane. This guarantees that the surface $z = f(x, y)$ has no sharp points, breaks, or ruptures. In other words, we are dealing only with smooth surfaces with no edges (like the edge of a box), breaks (like an earthquake fault), or sharp points (like the bottom point of a golf tee). (See Figure 1.)

Figure 1

In addition, we will not concern ourselves with boundary points or absolute maxima–minima theory. Despite these restrictions, the procedure we will describe will help us solve a large number of useful problems.

What does it mean for $f(a, b)$ to be a local maximum or a local minimum? We say that $f(a, b)$ **is a local maximum** if there exists a circular region in the domain of f with (a, b) as the center, such that

$$f(a, b) \geq f(x, y)$$

for all (x, y) in the region. Similarly, we say that $f(a, b)$ **is a local minimum** if there exists a circular region in the domain of f with (a, b) as the center, such that

$$f(a, b) \leq f(x, y)$$

for all (x, y) in the region. Figure 2A illustrates a local maximum, Figure 2B a local minimum, and Figure 2C a **saddle point**, which is neither a local maximum nor a local minimum.

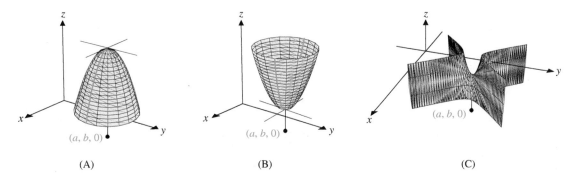

Figure 2

What happens to $f_x(a, b)$ and $f_y(a, b)$ if $f(a, b)$ is a local minimum or a local maximum and the partial derivatives of f exist in a circular region containing (a, b)? Figure 2 suggests that $f_x(a, b) = 0$ and $f_y(a, b) = 0$, since the tangent lines to the given curves are horizontal. Theorem 1 indicates that our intuitive reasoning is correct.

THEOREM 1   Local Extrema and Partial Derivatives

Let $f(a, b)$ be a local extremum (a local maximum or a local minimum) for the function f. If both f_x and f_y exist at (a, b), then

$$f_x(a, b) = 0 \quad \text{and} \quad f_y(a, b) = 0 \tag{1}$$

The converse of this theorem is false. If $f_x(a, b) = 0$ and $f_y(a, b) = 0$, then $f(a, b)$ may or may not be a local extremum; for example, the point $(a, b, f(a, b))$ may be a saddle point (see Fig. 2C).

Theorem 1 gives us *necessary* (but not *sufficient*) conditions for $f(a, b)$ to be a local extremum. We find all points (a, b) such that $f_x(a, b) = 0$ and $f_y(a, b) = 0$ and test these further to determine whether $f(a, b)$ is a local extremum or a saddle point. Points (a, b) such that conditions (1) hold are called **critical points**.

Explore and Discuss 1

(A) Let $f(x, y) = y^2 + 1$. Explain why $f(x, y)$ has a local minimum at every point on the x axis. Verify that every point on the x axis is a critical point. Explain why the graph of $z = f(x, y)$ could be described as a trough.

(B) Let $g(x, y) = x^3$. Show that every point on the y axis is a critical point. Explain why no point on the y axis is a local extremum. Explain why the graph of $z = g(x, y)$ could be described as a slide.

The next theorem, using second-derivative tests, gives us *sufficient* conditions for a critical point to produce a local extremum or a saddle point.

THEOREM 2   Second-Derivative Test for Local Extrema

If

1. $z = f(x, y)$
2. $f_x(a, b) = 0$ and $f_y(a, b) = 0$ $[(a, b)$ is a critical point]
3. All second-order partial derivatives of f exist in some circular region containing (a, b) as center.
4. $A = f_{xx}(a, b), \quad B = f_{xy}(a, b), \quad C = f_{yy}(a, b)$

Then

Case 1. If $AC - B^2 > 0$ and $A < 0$, then $f(a, b)$ is a local maximum.
Case 2. If $AC - B^2 > 0$ and $A > 0$, then $f(a, b)$ is a local minimum.
Case 3. If $AC - B^2 < 0$, then f has a saddle point at (a, b).
Case 4. If $AC - B^2 = 0$, the test fails.

CONCEPTUAL INSIGHT

The condition $A = f_{xx}(a, b) < 0$ in case 1 of Theorem 2 is analogous to the condition $f''(c) < 0$ in the second-derivative test for local extrema for a function of one variable (Section 4.5), which implies that the function is concave downward and therefore has a local maximum. Similarly, the condition $A = f_{xx}(a, b) > 0$ in case 2 is analogous to the condition $f''(c) > 0$ in the earlier second-derivative test, which implies that the function is concave upward and therefore has a local minimum.

Figure 3

To illustrate the use of Theorem 2, we find the local extremum for a very simple function whose solution is almost obvious: $z = f(x, y) = x^2 + y^2 + 2$. From the function f itself and its graph (Fig. 3), it is clear that a local minimum is found at $(0, 0)$. Let us see how Theorem 2 confirms this observation.

Step 1 Find critical points: Find (x, y) such that $f_x(x, y) = 0$ and $f_y(x, y) = 0$ simultaneously:

$$f_x(x, y) = 2x = 0 \qquad f_y(x, y) = 2y = 0$$
$$x = 0 \qquad\qquad\quad y = 0$$

The only critical point is $(a, b) = (0, 0)$.

Step 2 Compute $A = f_{xx}(0, 0)$, $B = f_{xy}(0, 0)$, and $C = f_{yy}(0, 0)$:

$$f_{xx}(x, y) = 2; \quad \text{so,} \quad A = f_{xx}(0, 0) = 2$$
$$f_{xy}(x, y) = 0; \quad \text{so,} \quad B = f_{xy}(0, 0) = 0$$
$$f_{yy}(x, y) = 2; \quad \text{so,} \quad C = f_{yy}(0, 0) = 2$$

Step 3 Evaluate $AC - B^2$ and try to classify the critical point $(0, 0)$ by using Theorem 2:

$$AC - B^2 = (2)(2) - (0)^2 = 4 > 0 \qquad \text{and} \qquad A = 2 > 0$$

Therefore, case 2 in Theorem 2 holds. That is, $f(0, 0) = 2$ is a local minimum. We will now use Theorem 2 to analyze extrema without the aid of graphs.

EXAMPLE 1 Finding Local Extrema Use Theorem 2 to find local extrema of

$$f(x, y) = -x^2 - y^2 + 6x + 8y - 21$$

SOLUTION

Step 1 Find critical points: Find (x, y) such that $f_x(x, y) = 0$ and $f_y(x, y) = 0$ simultaneously:

$$f_x(x, y) = -2x + 6 = 0 \qquad f_y(x, y) = -2y + 8 = 0$$
$$x = 3 \qquad\qquad\qquad\quad y = 4$$

The only critical point is $(a, b) = (3, 4)$.

Step 2 Compute $A = f_{xx}(3, 4)$, $B = f_{xy}(3, 4)$, and $C = f_{yy}(3, 4)$:

$$f_{xx}(x, y) = -2; \quad \text{so,} \quad A = f_{xx}(3, 4) = -2$$
$$f_{xy}(x, y) = 0; \quad \text{so,} \quad B = f_{xy}(3, 4) = 0$$
$$f_{yy}(x, y) = -2; \quad \text{so,} \quad C = f_{yy}(3, 4) = -2$$

Step 3 Evaluate $AC - B^2$ and try to classify the critical point $(3, 4)$ by using Theorem 2:

$$AC - B^2 = (-2)(-2) - (0)^2 = 4 > 0 \qquad \text{and} \qquad A = -2 < 0$$

Therefore, case 1 in Theorem 2 holds, and $f(3, 4) = 4$ is a local maximum.

Matched Problem 1 Use Theorem 2 to find local extrema of

$$f(x, y) = x^2 + y^2 - 10x - 2y + 36$$

EXAMPLE 2 Finding Local Extrema: Multiple Critical Points Use Theorem 2 to find local extrema of

$$f(x, y) = x^3 + y^3 - 6xy$$

SOLUTION

Step 1 Find critical points of $f(x, y) = x^3 + y^3 - 6xy$:

$$f_x(x, y) = 3x^2 - 6y = 0 \qquad \text{Solve for } y.$$
$$6y = 3x^2$$
$$y = \tfrac{1}{2}x^2 \qquad\qquad\qquad\qquad\qquad (2)$$
$$f_y(x, y) = 3y^2 - 6x = 0$$
$$3y^2 = 6x \qquad \text{Use equation (2) to eliminate } y.$$
$$3\left(\tfrac{1}{2}x^2\right)^2 = 6x$$
$$\tfrac{3}{4}x^4 = 6x \qquad \text{Solve for } x.$$
$$3x^4 - 24x = 0$$
$$3x(x^3 - 8) = 0$$
$$x = 0 \quad \text{or} \quad x = 2$$
$$y = 0 \qquad\qquad y = \tfrac{1}{2}(2)^2 = 2$$

The critical points are $(0, 0)$ and $(2, 2)$.

Since there are two critical points, steps 2 and 3 must be performed twice.

Test (0, 0)

Step 2 Compute $A = f_{xx}(0, 0)$, $B = f_{xy}(0, 0)$, and $C = f_{yy}(0, 0)$:

$$f_{xx}(x, y) = 6x; \qquad \text{so,} \qquad A = f_{xx}(0, 0) = 0$$
$$f_{xy}(x, y) = -6; \qquad \text{so,} \qquad B = f_{xy}(0, 0) = -6$$
$$f_{yy}(x, y) = 6y; \qquad \text{so,} \qquad C = f_{yy}(0, 0) = 0$$

Step 3 Evaluate $AC - B^2$ and try to classify the critical point $(0, 0)$ by using Theorem 2:

$$AC - B^2 = (0)(0) - (-6)^2 = -36 < 0$$

Therefore, case 3 in Theorem 2 applies. That is, f has a saddle point at $(0, 0)$.

Now we will consider the second critical point, $(2, 2)$:

Test (2, 2)

Step 2 Compute $A = f_{xx}(2, 2)$, $B = f_{xy}(2, 2)$, and $C = f_{yy}(2, 2)$:

$$f_{xx}(x, y) = 6x; \qquad \text{so,} \qquad A = f_{xx}(2, 2) = 12$$
$$f_{xy}(x, y) = -6; \qquad \text{so,} \qquad B = f_{xy}(2, 2) = -6$$
$$f_{yy}(x, y) = 6y; \qquad \text{so,} \qquad C = f_{yy}(2, 2) = 12$$

Step 3 Evaluate $AC - B^2$ and try to classify the critical point $(2, 2)$ by using Theorem 2:

$$AC - B^2 = (12)(12) - (-6)^2 = 108 > 0 \qquad \text{and} \qquad A = 12 > 0$$

So, case 2 in Theorem 2 applies, and $f(2, 2) = -8$ is a local minimum.

Our conclusions in Example 2 may be confirmed geometrically by graphing cross sections of the function f. The cross sections of f in the planes $y = 0$, $x = 0$, $y = x$, and $y = -x$ [each of these planes contains $(0, 0)$] are represented by the graphs of the functions $f(x, 0) = x^3, f(0, y) = y^3, f(x, x) = 2x^3 - 6x^2$, and $f(x, -x) = 6x^2$, respectively, as shown in Figure 4A (note that the first two functions have the same graph). The cross sections of f in the planes $y = 2, x = 2, y = x$, and $y = 4 - x$ [each of these planes contains $(2, 2)$] are represented by the graphs of $f(x, 2) = x^3 - 12x + 8, f(2, y) = y^3 - 12y + 8, f(x, x) = 2x^3 - 6x^2$, and $f(x, 4 - x) = x^3 + (4 - x)^3 + 6x^2 - 24x$, respectively, as shown in Figure 4B (the first two functions have the same graph). Figure 4B illustrates the fact that since f has a local minimum at $(2, 2)$, each of the cross sections of f through $(2, 2)$ has a local minimum of -8 at $(2, 2)$. Figure 4A, by contrast, indicates that some cross sections of f through $(0, 0)$ have a local minimum, some a local maximum, and some neither one, at $(0, 0)$.

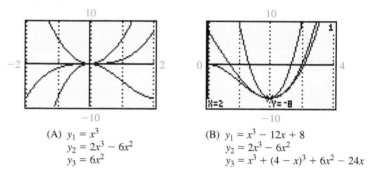

(A) $y_1 = x^3$
$y_2 = 2x^3 - 6x^2$
$y_3 = 6x^2$

(B) $y_1 = x^3 - 12x + 8$
$y_2 = 2x^3 - 6x^2$
$y_3 = x^3 + (4 - x)^3 + 6x^2 - 24x$

Figure 4

Matched Problem 2 Use Theorem 2 to find local extrema for $f(x, y) = x^3 + y^2 - 6xy$.

EXAMPLE 3 Profit Suppose that the surfboard company discussed earlier has developed the yearly profit equation

$$P(x, y) = -22x^2 + 22xy - 11y^2 + 110x - 44y - 23$$

where x is the number (in thousands) of standard surfboards produced per year, y is the number (in thousands) of competition surfboards produced per year, and P is profit (in thousands of dollars). How many of each type of board should be produced per year to realize a maximum profit? What is the maximum profit?

SOLUTION

Step 1 Find critical points:

$$P_x(x, y) = -44x + 22y + 110 = 0$$
$$P_y(x, y) = 22x - 22y - 44 = 0$$

Solving this system, we obtain $(3, 1)$ as the only critical point.

Step 2 Compute $A = P_{xx}(3, 1)$, $B = P_{xy}(3, 1)$, and $C = P_{yy}(3, 1)$:

$$P_{xx}(x, y) = -44; \quad \text{so,} \quad A = P_{xx}(3, 1) = -44$$
$$P_{xy}(x, y) = 22; \quad \text{so,} \quad B = P_{xy}(3, 1) = 22$$
$$P_{yy}(x, y) = -22; \quad \text{so,} \quad C = P_{yy}(3, 1) = -22$$

Step 3 Evaluate $AC - B^2$ and try to classify the critical point $(3, 1)$ by using Theorem 2:

$$AC - B^2 = (-44)(-22) - 22^2 = 484 > 0 \quad \text{and} \quad A = -44 < 0$$

Therefore, case 1 in Theorem 2 applies. That is, $P(3, 1) = 120$ is a local maximum. A maximum profit of $120,000 is obtained by producing and selling 3,000 standard boards and 1,000 competition boards per year.

Matched Problem 3 Repeat Example 3 with

$$P(x, y) = -66x^2 + 132xy - 99y^2 + 132x - 66y - 19$$

EXAMPLE 4 Package Design The packaging department in a company is to design a rectangular box with no top and a partition down the middle. The box must have a volume of 48 cubic inches. Find the dimensions that will minimize the area of material used to construct the box.

SOLUTION Refer to Figure 5. The area of material used in constructing this box is

$$M = \underset{\text{Base}}{xy} + \underset{\substack{\text{Front,} \\ \text{back}}}{2xz} + \underset{\substack{\text{Sides,} \\ \text{partition}}}{3yz} \tag{3}$$

The volume of the box is

$$V = xyz = 48 \tag{4}$$

Since Theorem 2 applies only to functions with two independent variables, we must use equation (4) to eliminate one of the variables in equation (3):

$$M = xy + 2xz + 3yz \qquad \text{Substitute } z = 48/xy.$$

$$= xy + 2x\left(\frac{48}{xy}\right) + 3y\left(\frac{48}{xy}\right)$$

$$= xy + \frac{96}{y} + \frac{144}{x}$$

So, we must find the minimum value of

$$M(x, y) = xy + \frac{96}{y} + \frac{144}{x} \qquad x > 0 \qquad \text{and} \qquad y > 0$$

Step 1 Find critical points:

$$M_x(x, y) = y - \frac{144}{x^2} = 0$$

$$y = \frac{144}{x^2} \tag{5}$$

$$M_y(x, y) = x - \frac{96}{y^2} = 0$$

$$x = \frac{96}{y^2} \qquad \text{Solve for } y^2.$$

$$y^2 = \frac{96}{x} \qquad \text{Use equation (5) to eliminate } y \text{ and solve for } x.$$

$$\left(\frac{144}{x^2}\right)^2 = \frac{96}{x}$$

$$\frac{20{,}736}{x^4} = \frac{96}{x} \qquad \text{Multiply both sides by } x^4/96 \text{ (recall that } x > 0).$$

$$x^3 = \frac{20{,}736}{96} = 216$$

$$x = 6 \qquad \text{Use equation (5) to find } y.$$

$$y = \frac{144}{36} = 4$$

Therefore, $(6, 4)$ is the only critical point.

Figure 5

Step 2 Compute $A = M_{xx}(6, 4), B = M_{xy}(6, 4),$ and $C = M_{yy}(6, 4)$:

$$M_{xx}(x, y) = \frac{288}{x^3}; \quad \text{so,} \quad A = M_{xx}(6, 4) = \frac{288}{216} = \frac{4}{3}$$

$$M_{xy}(x, y) = 1; \quad \text{so,} \quad B = M_{xy}(6, 4) = 1$$

$$M_{yy}(x, y) = \frac{192}{y^3}; \quad \text{so,} \quad C = M_{yy}(6, 4) = \frac{192}{64} = 3$$

Step 3 Evaluate $AC - B^2$ and try to classify the critical point $(6, 4)$ by using Theorem 2:

$$AC - B^2 = \left(\frac{4}{3}\right)(3) - (1)^2 = 3 > 0 \quad \text{and} \quad A = \frac{4}{3} > 0$$

Case 2 in Theorem 2 applies, and $M(x, y)$ has a local minimum at $(6, 4)$. If $x = 6$ and $y = 4$, then

$$z = \frac{48}{xy} = \frac{48}{(6)(4)} = 2$$

2 inches

4 inches

6 inches

Figure 6

The dimensions that will require the least material are 6 inches by 4 inches by 2 inches (see Fig. 6).

Matched Problem 4 If the box in Example 4 must have a volume of 384 cubic inches, find the dimensions that will require the least material.

Exercises 7.3

Skills Warm-up Exercises

W *In Problems 1–8, find $f'(0)$, $f''(0)$, and determine whether f has a local minimum, local maximum, or neither at $x = 0$. (If necessary, review the second derivative test for local extrema in Section 4.5).*

1. $f(x) = 2x^3 - 9x^2 + 4$

2. $f(x) = 4x^3 + 6x^2 + 100$

3. $f(x) = \dfrac{1}{1 - x^2}$

4. $f(x) = \dfrac{1}{1 + x^2}$

5. $f(x) = e^{-x^2}$

6. $f(x) = e^{x^2}$

7. $f(x) = x^3 - x^2 + x - 1$

8. $f(x) = (3x + 1)^2$

In Problems 9–12, find $f_x(x, y)$ and $f_y(x, y)$, and explain, using Theorem 1, why $f(x, y)$ has no local extrema.

9. $f(x, y) = 4x + 5y - 6$

10. $f(x, y) = 10 - 2x - 3y + x^2$

11. $f(x, y) = 3.7 - 1.2x + 6.8y + 0.2y^3 + x^4$

12. $f(x, y) = x^3 - y^2 + 7x + 3y + 1$

Use Theorem 2 to find local extrema in Problems 13–32.

13. $f(x, y) = 6 - x^2 - 4x - y^2$

14. $f(x, y) = 3 - x^2 - y^2 + 6y$

15. $f(x, y) = x^2 + y^2 + 2x - 6y + 14$

16. $f(x, y) = x^2 + y^2 - 4x + 6y + 23$

17. $f(x, y) = xy + 2x - 3y - 2$

18. $f(x, y) = x^2 - y^2 + 2x + 6y - 4$

19. $f(x, y) = -3x^2 + 2xy - 2y^2 + 14x + 2y + 10$

20. $f(x, y) = -x^2 + xy - 2y^2 + x + 10y - 5$

21. $f(x, y) = 2x^2 - 2xy + 3y^2 - 4x - 8y + 20$

22. $f(x, y) = 2x^2 - xy + y^2 - x - 5y + 8$

23. $f(x, y) = e^{xy}$

24. $f(x, y) = x^2y - xy^2$

25. $f(x, y) = x^3 + y^3 - 3xy$

26. $f(x, y) = 2y^3 - 6xy - x^2$

27. $f(x, y) = 2x^4 + y^2 - 12xy$

28. $f(x, y) = 16xy - x^4 - 2y^2$

29. $f(x, y) = x^3 - 3xy^2 + 6y^2$

30. $f(x, y) = 2x^2 - 2x^2y + 6y^3$

31. $f(x, y) = y^3 + 2x^2y^2 - 3x - 2y + 8$

32. $f(x, y) = x \ln y + x^2 - 4x - 5y + 3$

33. Explain why $f(x, y) = x^2$ has a local extremum at infinitely many points.

34. (A) Find the local extrema of the functions $f(x, y) = x + y$, $g(x, y) = x^2 + y^2$, and $h(x, y) = x^3 + y^3$.

    (B) Discuss the local extrema of the function $k(x, y) = x^n + y^n$, where n is a positive integer.

35. (A) Show that $(0, 0)$ is a critical point of the function $f(x, y) = x^4 e^y + x^2 y^4 + 1$, but that the second-derivative test for local extrema fails.

(B) Use cross sections, as in Example 2, to decide whether f has a local maximum, a local minimum, or a saddle point at $(0, 0)$.

36. (A) Show that $(0, 0)$ is a critical point of the function $g(x, y) = e^{xy^2} + x^2 y^3 + 2$, but that the second-derivative test for local extrema fails.

(B) Use cross sections, as in Example 2, to decide whether g has a local maximum, a local minimum, or a saddle point at $(0, 0)$.

Applications

37. Product mix for maximum profit. A firm produces two types of earphones per year: x thousand of type A and y thousand of type B. If the revenue and cost equations for the year are (in millions of dollars)

$$R(x, y) = 2x + 3y$$
$$C(x, y) = x^2 - 2xy + 2y^2 + 6x - 9y + 5$$

determine how many of each type of earphone should be produced per year to maximize profit. What is the maximum profit?

38. Automation–labor mix for minimum cost. The annual labor and automated equipment cost (in millions of dollars) for a company's production of HDTVs is given by

$$C(x, y) = 2x^2 + 2xy + 3y^2 - 16x - 18y + 54$$

where x is the amount spent per year on labor and y is the amount spent per year on automated equipment (both in millions of dollars). Determine how much should be spent on each per year to minimize this cost. What is the minimum cost?

39. Maximizing profit. A store sells two brands of camping chairs. The store pays $60 for each brand A chair and $80 for each brand B chair. The research department has estimated the weekly demand equations for these two competitive products to be

$$x = 260 - 3p + q \quad \text{Demand equation for brand } A$$
$$y = 180 + p - 2q \quad \text{Demand equation for brand } B$$

where p is the selling price for brand A and q is the selling price for brand B.

(A) Determine the demands x and y when $p = \$100$ and $q = \$120$; when $p = \$110$ and $q = \$110$.

(B) How should the store price each chair to maximize weekly profits? What is the maximum weekly profit? [*Hint:* $C = 60x + 80y$, $R = px + qy$, and $P = R - C$.]

40. Maximizing profit. A store sells two brands of laptop sleeves. The store pays $25 for each brand A sleeve and $30 for each brand B sleeve. A consulting firm has estimated the daily demand equations for these two competitive products to be

$$x = 130 - 4p + q \quad \text{Demand equation for brand } A$$
$$y = 115 + 2p - 3q \quad \text{Demand equation for brand } B$$

where p is the selling price for brand A and q is the selling price for brand B.

(A) Determine the demands x and y when $p = \$40$ and $q = \$50$; when $p = \$45$ and $q = \$55$.

(B) How should the store price each brand of sleeve to maximize daily profits? What is the maximum daily profit? [*Hint:* $C = 25x + 30y$, $R = px + qy$, and $P = R - C$.]

41. Minimizing cost. A satellite TV station is to be located at $P(x, y)$ so that the sum of the squares of the distances from P to the three towns A, B, and C is a minimum (see the figure). Find the coordinates of P, the location that will minimize the cost of providing satellite TV for all three towns.

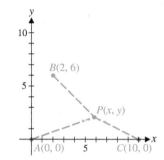

42. Minimizing cost. Repeat Problem 41, replacing the coordinates of B with $B(6, 9)$ and the coordinates of C with $C(9, 0)$.

43. Minimum material. A rectangular box with no top and two parallel partitions (see the figure) must hold a volume of 64 cubic inches. Find the dimensions that will require the least material.

44. Minimum material. A rectangular box with no top and two intersecting partitions (see the figure) must hold a volume of 72 cubic inches. Find the dimensions that will require the least material.

45. Maximum volume. A mailing service states that a rectangular package cannot have the sum of its length and girth exceed 120 inches (see the figure). What are the dimensions of the largest (in volume) mailing carton that can be constructed to meet these restrictions?

Length

Girth

46. Maximum shipping volume. A shipping box is to be reinforced with steel bands in all three directions, as shown in the figure. A total of 150 inches of steel tape is to be used, with 6 inches of waste because of a 2-inch overlap in each direction.

Find the dimensions of the box with maximum volume that can be taped as described.

Answers to Matched Problems

1. $f(5, 1) = 10$ is a local minimum
2. f has a saddle point at $(0, 0)$; $f(6, 18) = -108$ is a local minimum
3. Local maximum for $x = 2$ and $y = 1$; $P(2, 1) = 80$; a maximum profit of \$80,000 is obtained by producing and selling 2,000 standard boards and 1,000 competition boards
4. 12 in. by 8 in. by 4 in.

7.4 Maxima and Minima Using Lagrange Multipliers

- Functions of Two Independent Variables

- Functions of Three Independent Variables

Existing fence

x

y

x

Figure 1

Functions of Two Independent Variables

We now consider a powerful method of solving a certain class of maxima–minima problems. Joseph Louis Lagrange (1736–1813), an eighteenth-century French mathematician, discovered this method, called the **method of Lagrange multipliers**. We introduce the method through an example.

A rancher wants to construct two feeding pens of the same size along an existing fence (see Fig. 1). If the rancher has 720 feet of fencing materials available, how long should x and y be in order to obtain the maximum total area? What is the maximum area?

The total area is given by

$$f(x, y) = xy$$

which can be made as large as we like, provided that there are no restrictions on x and y. But there are restrictions on x and y, since we have only 720 feet of fencing. The variables x and y must be chosen so that

$$3x + y = 720$$

This restriction on x and y, called a **constraint**, leads to the following maxima–minima problem:

Maximize $f(x, y) = xy$ (1)

subject to $3x + y = 720$,   or $3x + y - 720 = 0$ (2)

This problem is one of a general class of problems of the form

Maximize (or minimize) $z = f(x, y)$ (3)

subject to $g(x, y) = 0$ (4)

Of course, we could try to solve equation (4) for y in terms of x, or for x in terms of y, then substitute the result into equation (3), and use methods developed in Section 4.5 for functions of a single variable. But what if equation (4) is more complicated than equation (2), and solving for one variable in terms of the other is either very difficult or impossible? In the method of Lagrange multipliers, we will work with $g(x, y)$ directly and avoid solving equation (4) for one variable in terms of the other. In addition, the method generalizes to functions of arbitrarily many variables subject to one or more constraints.

Now to the method: We form a new function F, using functions f and g in equations (3) and (4), as follows:

$$F(x, y, \lambda) = f(x, y) + \lambda g(x, y) \tag{5}$$

Here, λ (the Greek lowercase letter lambda) is called a **Lagrange multiplier**. Theorem 1 gives the basis for the method.

THEOREM 1 Method of Lagrange Multipliers for Functions of Two Variables

Any local maxima or minima of the function $z = f(x, y)$ subject to the constraint $g(x, y) = 0$ will be among those points (x_0, y_0) for which (x_0, y_0, λ_0) is a solution of the system

$$F_x(x, y, \lambda) = 0$$
$$F_y(x, y, \lambda) = 0$$
$$F_\lambda(x, y, \lambda) = 0$$

where $F(x, y, \lambda) = f(x, y) + \lambda g(x, y)$, provided that all the partial derivatives exist.

We now use the method of Lagrange multipliers to solve the fence problem.

Step 1 Formulate the problem in the form of equations (3) and (4):

$$\text{Maximize} \quad f(x, y) = xy$$
$$\text{subject to} \quad g(x, y) = 3x + y - 720 = 0$$

Step 2 Form the function F, introducing the Lagrange multiplier λ:

$$F(x, y, \lambda) = f(x, y) + \lambda g(x, y)$$
$$= xy + \lambda(3x + y - 720)$$

Step 3 Solve the system $F_x = 0$, $F_y = 0$, $F_\lambda = 0$ (the solutions are **critical points** of F):

$$F_x = y + 3\lambda = 0$$
$$F_y = x + \lambda = 0$$
$$F_\lambda = 3x + y - 720 = 0$$

From the first two equations, we see that

$$y = -3\lambda$$
$$x = -\lambda$$

Substitute these values for x and y into the third equation and solve for λ:

$$-3\lambda - 3\lambda = 720$$
$$-6\lambda = 720$$
$$\lambda = -120$$

So,

$$y = -3(-120) = 360 \text{ feet}$$
$$x = -(-120) = 120 \text{ feet}$$

and $(x_0, y_0, \lambda_0) = (120, 360, -120)$ is the only critical point of F.

Step 4 According to Theorem 1, if the function $f(x, y)$, subject to the constraint $g(x, y) = 0$, has a local maximum or minimum, that maximum or minimum must occur at $x = 120$, $y = 360$. Although it is possible to develop a test similar to Theorem 2 in Section 7.3 to determine the nature of this local extremum, we will not do so. [Note that Theorem 2 cannot be applied to $f(x, y)$ at (120, 360), since this point is not a critical point of the unconstrained function $f(x, y)$.] We simply assume that the maximum value of $f(x, y)$ must occur for $x = 120$, $y = 360$.

$$\text{Max } f(x, y) = f(120, 360)$$
$$= (120)(360) = 43{,}200 \text{ square feet}$$

The key steps in applying the method of Lagrange multipliers are as follows:

PROCEDURE **Method of Lagrange Multipliers: Key Steps**

Step 1 Write the problem in the form

$$\text{Maximize (or minimize)} \quad z = f(x, y)$$
$$\text{subject to} \quad g(x, y) = 0$$

Step 2 Form the function F:

$$F(x, y, \lambda) = f(x, y) + \lambda g(x, y)$$

Step 3 Find the critical points of F; that is, solve the system

$$F_x(x, y, \lambda) = 0$$
$$F_y(x, y, \lambda) = 0$$
$$F_\lambda(x, y, \lambda) = 0$$

Step 4 If (x_0, y_0, λ_0) is the only critical point of F, we assume that (x_0, y_0) will always produce the solution to the problems we consider. If F has more than one critical point, we evaluate $z = f(x, y)$ at (x_0, y_0) for each critical point (x_0, y_0, λ_0) of F. For the problems we consider, we assume that the largest of these values is the maximum value of $f(x, y)$, subject to the constraint $g(x, y) = 0$, and the smallest is the minimum value of $f(x, y)$, subject to the constraint $g(x, y) = 0$.

EXAMPLE 1 Minimization Subject to a Constraint **Minimize** $f(x, y) = x^2 + y^2$ subject to $x + y = 10$.

SOLUTION

Step 1
$$\text{Minimize} \quad f(x, y) = x^2 + y^2$$
$$\text{subject to} \quad g(x, y) = x + y - 10 = 0$$

Step 2
$$F(x, y, \lambda) = x^2 + y^2 + \lambda(x + y - 10)$$

Step 3
$$F_x = 2x + \lambda = 0$$
$$F_y = 2y + \lambda = 0$$
$$F_\lambda = x + y - 10 = 0$$

From the first two equations, $x = -\lambda/2$ and $y = -\lambda/2$. Substituting these values into the third equation, we obtain

$$-\frac{\lambda}{2} - \frac{\lambda}{2} = 10$$
$$-\lambda = 10$$
$$\lambda = -10$$

The only critical point is $(x_0, y_0, \lambda_0) = (5, 5, -10)$.

Step 4   Since $(5, 5, -10)$ is the only critical point of F, we conclude that (see step 4 in the box)

$$\text{Min } f(x, y) = f(5, 5) = (5)^2 + (5)^2 = 50$$

Figure 2 $h(x) = x^2 + (10 - x)^2$

Since $g(x, y)$ in Example 1 has a relatively simple form, an alternative to the method of Lagrange multipliers is to solve $g(x, y) = 0$ for y and then substitute into $f(x, y)$ to obtain the function $h(x) = f(x, 10 - x) = x^2 + (10 - x)^2$ in the single variable x. Then we minimize h (see Fig. 2). From Figure 2, we conclude that min $f(x, y) = f(5, 5) = 50$. This technique depends on being able to solve the constraint for one of the two variables and so is not always available as an alternative to the method of Lagrange multipliers.

Matched Problem 1   Maximize $f(x, y) = 25 - x^2 - y^2$ subject to $x + y = 4$.

Figures 3 and 4 illustrate the results obtained in Example 1 and Matched Problem 1, respectively.

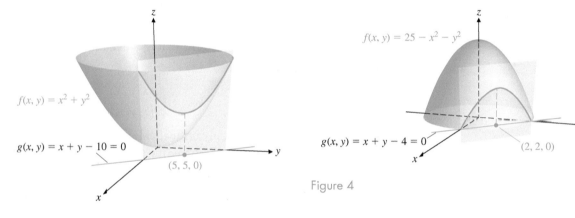

$f(x, y) = x^2 + y^2$

$g(x, y) = x + y - 10 = 0$

$(5, 5, 0)$

Figure 3

$f(x, y) = 25 - x^2 - y^2$

$g(x, y) = x + y - 4 = 0$

$(2, 2, 0)$

Figure 4

Explore and Discuss 1

Figure 5

Consider the problem of minimizing $f(x, y) = 3x^2 + 5y^2$ subject to the constraint $g(x, y) = 2x + 3y - 6 = 0$.

(A) Compute the value of $f(x, y)$ when x and y are integers, $0 \le x \le 3, 0 \le y \le 2$. Record your answers in the empty boxes next to the points (x, y) in Figure 5.

(B) Graph the constraint $g(x, y) = 0$.

(C) Estimate the minimum value of f on the basis of your graph and the computations from part (A).

(D) Use the method of Lagrange multipliers to solve the minimization problem.

EXAMPLE 2   Productivity   The Cobb–Douglas production function for a new product is given by

$$N(x, y) = 16x^{0.25}y^{0.75}$$

where x is the number of units of labor and y is the number of units of capital required to produce $N(x, y)$ units of the product. Each unit of labor costs \$50 and each unit of capital costs \$100. If \$500,000 has been budgeted for the production of this product, how should that amount be allocated between labor and capital in order to maximize production? What is the maximum number of units that can be produced?

SOLUTION The total cost of using x units of labor and y units of capital is $50x + 100y$. Thus, the constraint imposed by the \$500,000 budget is

$$50x + 100y = 500{,}000$$

Step 1
$$\text{Maximize} \quad N(x, y) = 16x^{0.25}y^{0.75}$$
$$\text{subject to} \quad g(x, y) = 50x + 100y - 500{,}000 = 0$$

Step 2
$$F(x, y, \lambda) = 16x^{0.25}y^{0.75} + \lambda(50x + 100y - 500{,}000)$$

Step 3
$$F_x = 4x^{-0.75}y^{0.75} + 50\lambda = 0$$
$$F_y = 12x^{0.25}y^{-0.25} + 100\lambda = 0$$
$$F_\lambda = 50x + 100y - 500{,}000 = 0$$

From the first two equations,

$$\lambda = -\tfrac{2}{25}x^{-0.75}y^{0.75} \quad \text{and} \quad \lambda = -\tfrac{3}{25}x^{0.25}y^{-0.25}$$

Therefore,

$$-\tfrac{2}{25}x^{-0.75}y^{0.75} = -\tfrac{3}{25}x^{0.25}y^{-0.25} \qquad \text{Multiply both sides by } x^{0.75}\, y^{0.25}.$$
$$-\tfrac{2}{25}y = -\tfrac{3}{25}x \qquad\qquad \text{(We can assume that } x \neq 0 \text{ and } y \neq 0.)$$
$$y = \tfrac{3}{2}x$$

Now substitute for y in the third equation and solve for x:

$$50x + 100\left(\tfrac{3}{2}x\right) - 500{,}000 = 0$$
$$200x = 500{,}000$$
$$x = 2{,}500$$

So,
$$y = \tfrac{3}{2}(2{,}500) = 3{,}750$$
and
$$\lambda = -\tfrac{2}{25}(2{,}500)^{-0.75}(3{,}750)^{0.75} \approx -0.1084$$

The only critical point of F is $(2{,}500, 3{,}750, -0.1084)$.

Step 4   Since F has only one critical point, we conclude that maximum productivity occurs when 2,500 units of labor and 3,750 units of capital are used (see step 4 in the method of Lagrange multipliers).

$$\text{Max } N(x, y) = N(2{,}500, 3{,}750)$$
$$= 16(2{,}500)^{0.25}(3{,}750)^{0.75}$$
$$\approx 54{,}216 \text{ units}$$

The negative of the value of the Lagrange multiplier found in step 3 is called the **marginal productivity of money** and gives the approximate increase in production for each additional dollar spent on production. In Example 2, increasing the production budget from \$500,000 to \$600,000 would result in an approximate increase in production of

$$0.1084(100{,}000) = 10{,}840 \text{ units}$$

Note that simplifying the constraint equation

$$50x + 100y - 500{,}000 = 0$$

to

$$x + 2y - 10{,}000 = 0$$

before forming the function $F(x, y, \lambda)$ would make it difficult to interpret $-\lambda$ correctly. **In marginal productivity problems, the constraint equation should not be simplified.**

Matched Problem 2 The Cobb–Douglas production function for a new product is given by

$$N(x, y) = 20x^{0.5}y^{0.5}$$

where x is the number of units of labor and y is the number of units of capital required to produce $N(x, y)$ units of the product. Each unit of labor costs $40 and each unit of capital costs $120.

(A) If $300,000 has been budgeted for the production of this product, how should that amount be allocated in order to maximize production? What is the maximum production?

(B) Find the marginal productivity of money in this case, and estimate the increase in production if an additional $40,000 is budgeted for production.

Explore and Discuss 2 Consider the problem of maximizing $f(x, y) = 4 - x^2 - y^2$ subject to the constraint $g(x, y) = y - x^2 + 1 = 0$.

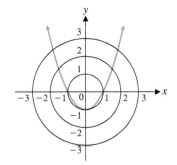

(A) Explain why $f(x, y) = 3$ whenever (x, y) is a point on the circle of radius 1 centered at the origin. What is the value of $f(x, y)$ when (x, y) is a point on the circle of radius 2 centered at the origin? On the circle of radius 3 centered at the origin? (See Fig. 6.)

(B) Explain why some points on the parabola $y - x^2 + 1 = 0$ lie inside the circle $x^2 + y^2 = 1$.

(C) In light of part (B), would you guess that the maximum value of $f(x, y)$ subject to the constraint is greater than 3? Explain.

(D) Use Lagrange multipliers to solve the maximization problem.

Figure 6

Functions of Three Independent Variables

The method of Lagrange multipliers can be extended to functions with arbitrarily many independent variables with one or more constraints. We now state a theorem for functions with three independent variables and one constraint, and we consider an example that demonstrates the advantage of the method of Lagrange multipliers over the method used in Section 7.3.

THEOREM 2 Method of Lagrange Multipliers for Functions of Three Variables

Any local maxima or minima of the function $w = f(x, y, z)$, subject to the constraint $g(x, y, z) = 0$, will be among the set of points (x_0, y_0, z_0) for which $(x_0, y_0, z_0, \lambda_0)$ is a solution of the system

$$F_x(x, y, z, \lambda) = 0$$
$$F_y(x, y, z, \lambda) = 0$$
$$F_z(x, y, z, \lambda) = 0$$
$$F_\lambda(x, y, z, \lambda) = 0$$

where $F(x, y, z, \lambda) = f(x, y, z) + \lambda g(x, y, z)$, provided that all the partial derivatives exist.

EXAMPLE 3 Package Design A rectangular box with an open top and one partition is to be constructed from 162 square inches of cardboard (Fig. 7). Find the dimensions that result in a box with the largest possible volume.

Figure 7

SOLUTION We must maximize

$$V(x, y, z) = xyz$$

subject to the constraint that the amount of material used is 162 square inches. So x, y, and z must satisfy

$$xy + 2xz + 3yz = 162$$

Step 1   Maximize $V(x, y, z) = xyz$

subject to $g(x, y, z) = xy + 2xz + 3yz - 162 = 0$

Step 2 $F(x, y, z, \lambda) = xyz + \lambda(xy + 2xz + 3yz - 162)$

Step 3
$$F_x = yz + \lambda(y + 2z) = 0$$
$$F_y = xz + \lambda(x + 3z) = 0$$
$$F_z = xy + \lambda(2x + 3y) = 0$$
$$F_\lambda = xy + 2xz + 3yz - 162 = 0$$

From the first two equations, we can write

$$\lambda = \frac{-yz}{y + 2z} \qquad \lambda = \frac{-xz}{x + 3z}$$

Eliminating λ, we have

$$\frac{-yz}{y + 2z} = \frac{-xz}{x + 3z}$$
$$-xyz - 3yz^2 = -xyz - 2xz^2$$
$$3yz^2 = 2xz^2 \qquad \text{We can assume that } z \neq 0.$$
$$3y = 2x$$
$$x = \tfrac{3}{2}y$$

From the second and third equations,

$$\lambda = \frac{-xz}{x + 3z} \qquad \lambda = \frac{-xy}{2x + 3y}$$

Eliminating λ, we have

$$\frac{-xz}{x + 3z} = \frac{-xy}{2x + 3y}$$
$$-2x^2z - 3xyz = -x^2y - 3xyz$$
$$2x^2z = x^2y \qquad \text{We can assume that } x \neq 0.$$
$$2z = y$$
$$z = \tfrac{1}{2}y$$

Substituting $x = \tfrac{3}{2}y$ and $z = \tfrac{1}{2}y$ into the fourth equation, we have

$$\left(\tfrac{3}{2}y\right)y + 2\left(\tfrac{3}{2}y\right)\left(\tfrac{1}{2}y\right) + 3y\left(\tfrac{1}{2}y\right) - 162 = 0$$
$$\tfrac{3}{2}y^2 + \tfrac{3}{2}y^2 + \tfrac{3}{2}y^2 = 162$$
$$y^2 = 36 \quad \text{We can assume that } y > 0.$$
$$y = 6$$
$$x = \tfrac{3}{2}(6) = 9 \quad \text{Using } x = \tfrac{3}{2}y$$
$$z = \tfrac{1}{2}(6) = 3 \quad \text{Using } z = \tfrac{1}{2}y$$

and finally,

$$\lambda = \frac{-(6)(3)}{6 + 2(3)} = -\frac{3}{2} \quad \text{Using } \lambda = \frac{-yz}{y + 2z}$$

The only critical point of F with x, y, and z all positive is $(9, 6, 3, -\tfrac{3}{2})$.

3 inches

6 inches

9 inches

Figure 8

Step 4 The box with the maximum volume has dimensions 9 inches by 6 inches by 3 inches (see Fig. 8).

Matched Problem 3 ⌐ A box of the same type as in Example 3 is to be constructed from 288 square inches of cardboard. Find the dimensions that result in a box with the largest possible volume.

CONCEPTUAL INSIGHT

An alternative to the method of Lagrange multipliers would be to solve Example 3 by means of Theorem 2 (the second-derivative test for local extrema) in Section 7.3. That approach involves solving the material constraint for one of the variables, say, z:

$$z = \frac{162 - xy}{2x + 3y}$$

Then we would eliminate z in the volume function to obtain a function of two variables:

$$V(x, y) = xy \frac{162 - xy}{2x + 3y}$$

The method of Lagrange multipliers allows us to avoid the formidable tasks of calculating the partial derivatives of V and finding the critical points of V in order to apply Theorem 2.

Exercises 7.4

Skills Warm-up Exercises

W *In Problems 1–6, maximize or minimize subject to the constraint without using the method of Lagrange multipliers; instead, solve the constraint for x or y and substitute into f(x, y). (If necessary, review Section 1.3).*

1. Minimize $f(x, y) = x^2 + xy + y^2$
   subject to $y = 4$

2. Maximize $f(x, y) = 64 + x^2 + 3xy - y^2$
   subject to $x = 6$

3. Minimize $f(x, y) = 4xy$
   subject to $x - y = 2$

4. Maximize $f(x, y) = 3xy$
   subject to $x + y = 1$

5. Maximize $f(x, y) = 2x + y$
   subject to $x^2 + y = 1$

6. Minimize $f(x, y) = 10x - y^2$
   subject to $x^2 + y^2 = 25$

Use the method of Lagrange multipliers in Problems 7–10.

7. Maximize $f(x, y) = 2xy$
   subject to $x + y = 6$

8. Minimize $f(x, y) = 6xy$
   subject to $y - x = 6$

9. Minimize $f(x, y) = x^2 + y^2$
   subject to $3x + 4y = 25$

10. Maximize $f(x, y) = 25 - x^2 - y^2$
   subject to $2x + y = 10$

In Problems 11 and 12, use Theorem 1 to explain why no maxima or minima exist.

11. Minimize $f(x, y) = 4y - 3x$
   subject to $2x + 5y = 3$

12. Maximize $f(x, y) = 6x + 5y + 24$
   subject to $3x + 2y = 4$

Use the method of Lagrange multipliers in Problems 13–22.

13. Find the maximum and minimum of $f(x, y) = 2xy$ subject to $x^2 + y^2 = 18$.

14. Find the maximum and minimum of $f(x, y) = x^2 - y^2$ subject to $x^2 + y^2 = 25$.

15. Maximize the product of two numbers if their sum must be 10.

16. Minimize the product of two numbers if their difference must be 10.

17. Minimize $f(x, y, z) = x^2 + y^2 + z^2$
   subject to $2x - y + 3z = -28$

18. Maximize $f(x, y, z) = xyz$
   subject to $2x + y + 2z = 120$

19. Maximize and Minimize $f(x, y, z) = x + y + z$
   subject to $x^2 + y^2 + z^2 = 12$

20. Maximize and Minimize $f(x, y, z) = 2x + 4y + 4z$
   subject to $x^2 + y^2 + z^2 = 9$

21. Maximize $f(x, y) = y + xy^2$
subject to $x + y^2 = 1$

22. Maximize and Minimize $f(x, y) = x + e^y$
subject to $x^2 + y^2 = 1$

In Problems 23 and 24, use Theorem 1 to explain why no maxima or minima exist.

23. Maximize $f(x, y) = e^x + 3e^y$
subject to $x - 2y = 6$

24. Minimize $f(x, y) = x^3 + 2y^3$
subject to $6x - 2y = 1$

25. Consider the problem of maximizing $f(x, y)$ subject to $g(x, y) = 0$, where $g(x, y) = y - 5$. Explain how the maximization problem can be solved without using the method of Lagrange multipliers.

26. Consider the problem of minimizing $f(x, y)$ subject to $g(x, y) = 0$, where $g(x, y) = 4x - y + 3$. Explain how the minimization problem can be solved without using the method of Lagrange multipliers.

27. Consider the problem of maximizing $f(x, y) = e^{-(x^2+y^2)}$ subject to the constraint $g(x, y) = x^2 + y - 1 = 0$.

(A) Solve the constraint equation for y, and then substitute into $f(x, y)$ to obtain a function $h(x)$ of the single variable x. Solve the original maximization problem by maximizing h (round answers to three decimal places).

(B) Confirm your answer by the method of Lagrange multipliers.

28. Consider the problem of minimizing

$$f(x, y) = x^2 + 2y^2$$

subject to the constraint $g(x, y) = ye^{x^2} - 1 = 0$.

(A) Solve the constraint equation for y, and then substitute into $f(x, y)$ to obtain a function $h(x)$ of the single variable x. Solve the original minimization problem by minimizing h (round answers to three decimal places).

(B) Confirm your answer by the method of Lagrange multipliers.

Applications

29. Budgeting for least cost. A manufacturing company produces two models of an HDTV per week, x units of model A and y units of model B at a cost (in dollars) of

$$C(x, y) = 6x^2 + 12y^2$$

If it is necessary (because of shipping considerations) that

$$x + y = 90$$

how many of each type of set should be manufactured per week to minimize cost? What is the minimum cost?

30. Budgeting for maximum production. A manufacturing firm has budgeted $60,000 per month for labor and materials.

If x thousand is spent on labor and y thousand is spent on materials, and if the monthly output (in units) is given by

$$N(x, y) = 4xy - 8x$$

then how should the $60,000 be allocated to labor and materials in order to maximize N? What is the maximum N?

31. Productivity. A consulting firm for a manufacturing company arrived at the following Cobb–Douglas production function for a particular product:

$$N(x, y) = 50x^{0.8}y^{0.2}$$

In this equation, x is the number of units of labor and y is the number of units of capital required to produce $N(x, y)$ units of the product. Each unit of labor costs $40 and each unit of capital costs $80.

(A) If $400,000 is budgeted for production of the product, determine how that amount should be allocated to maximize production, and find the maximum production.

(B) Find the marginal productivity of money in this case, and estimate the increase in production if an additional $50,000 is budgeted for the production of the product.

32. Productivity. The research department of a manufacturing company arrived at the following Cobb–Douglas production function for a particular product:

$$N(x, y) = 10x^{0.6}y^{0.4}$$

In this equation, x is the number of units of labor and y is the number of units of capital required to produce $N(x, y)$ units of the product. Each unit of labor costs $30 and each unit of capital costs $60.

(A) If $300,000 is budgeted for production of the product, determine how that amount should be allocated to maximize production, and find the maximum production.

(B) Find the marginal productivity of money in this case, and estimate the increase in production if an additional $80,000 is budgeted for the production of the product.

33. Maximum volume. A rectangular box with no top and two intersecting partitions is to be constructed from 192 square inches of cardboard (see the figure). Find the dimensions that will maximize the volume.

34. Maximum volume. A mailing service states that a rectangular package shall have the sum of its length and girth not to exceed 120 inches (see the figure). What are the dimensions of the largest (in volume) mailing carton that can be constructed to meet these restrictions?

Figure for 34

35. Agriculture. Three pens of the same size are to be built along an existing fence (see the figure). If 400 feet of fencing is available, what length should x and y be to produce the maximum total area? What is the maximum area?

36. Diet and minimum cost. A group of guinea pigs is to receive 25,600 calories per week. Two available foods produce $200xy$ calories for a mixture of x kilograms of type M food and y kilograms of type N food. If type M costs \$1 per kilogram and type N costs \$2 per kilogram, how much of each type of food should be used to minimize weekly food costs? What is the minimum cost?

Note: $x \geq 0$, $y \geq 0$

Answers to Matched Problems

1. Max $f(x, y) = f(2, 2) = 17$ (see Fig. 4)
2. (A) 3,750 units of labor and 1,250 units of capital;
   Max $N(x, y) = N(3,750, 1,250) \approx 43,301$ units
   (B) Marginal productivity of money ≈ 0.1443; increase in production $\approx 5,774$ units
3. 12 in. by 8 in. by 4 in.

7.5   Method of Least Squares

- Least Squares Approximation
- Applications

Least Squares Approximation

Regression analysis is the process of fitting an elementary function to a set of data points by the **method of least squares**. The mechanics of using regression techniques were introduced in Chapter 1. Now, using the optimization techniques of Section 7.3, we can develop and explain the mathematical foundation of the method of least squares. We begin with **linear regression**, the process of finding the equation of the line that is the "best" approximation to a set of data points.

Suppose that a manufacturer wants to approximate the cost function for a product. The value of the cost function has been determined for certain levels of production, as listed in Table 1. Although these points do not all lie on a line (see Fig. 1), they are very close to being linear. The manufacturer would like to approximate the cost function by a linear function—that is, determine values a and b so that the line

$$y = ax + b$$

is, in some sense, the "best" approximation to the cost function.

Table 1

Number of Units x (hundreds)	Cost y (thousand \$)
2	4
5	6
6	7
9	8

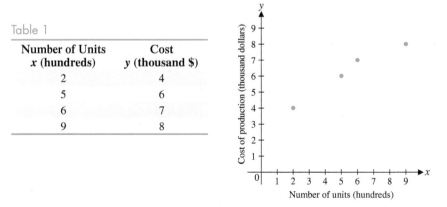

Figure 1

What do we mean by "best"? Since the line $y = ax + b$ will not go through all four points, it is reasonable to examine the differences between the y coordinates of the points listed in the table and the y coordinates of the corresponding points on the line. Each of these differences is called the **residual** at that point (see Fig. 2). For example, at $x = 2$, the point from Table 1 is $(2, 4)$ and the point on the line is $(2, 2a + b)$, so the residual is

$$4 - (2a + b) = 4 - 2a - b$$

All the residuals are listed in Table 2.

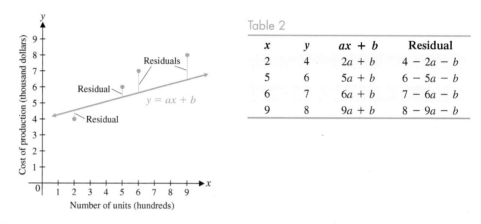

Table 2

x	y	$ax + b$	Residual
2	4	$2a + b$	$4 - 2a - b$
5	6	$5a + b$	$6 - 5a - b$
6	7	$6a + b$	$7 - 6a - b$
9	8	$9a + b$	$8 - 9a - b$

Figure 2

Our criterion for the "best" approximation is the following: Determine the values of a and b that *minimize the sum of the squares* of the residuals. The resulting line is called the **least squares line**, or the **regression line**. To this end, we minimize

$$F(a, b) = (4 - 2a - b)^2 + (6 - 5a - b)^2 + (7 - 6a - b)^2 + (8 - 9a - b)^2$$

Step 1 Find critical points:

$$\begin{aligned} F_a(a, b) &= 2(4 - 2a - b)(-2) + 2(6 - 5a - b)(-5) \\ &\quad + 2(7 - 6a - b)(-6) + 2(8 - 9a - b)(-9) \\ &= -304 + 292a + 44b = 0 \\ F_b(a, b) &= 2(4 - 2a - b)(-1) + 2(6 - 5a - b)(-1) \\ &\quad + 2(7 - 6a - b)(-1) + 2(8 - 9a - b)(-1) \\ &= -50 + 44a + 8b = 0 \end{aligned}$$

After dividing each equation by 2, we solve the system

$$\begin{aligned} 146a + 22b &= 152 \\ 22a + 4b &= 25 \end{aligned}$$

obtaining $(a, b) = (0.58, 3.06)$ as the only critical point.

Step 2 Compute $A = F_{aa}(a, b)$, $B = F_{ab}(a, b)$, and $C = F_{bb}(a, b)$:

$$\begin{aligned} F_{aa}(a, b) = 292; &\quad \text{so,} \quad A = F_{aa}(0.58, 3.06) = 292 \\ F_{ab}(a, b) = 44; &\quad \text{so,} \quad B = F_{ab}(0.58, 3.06) = 44 \\ F_{bb}(a, b) = 8; &\quad \text{so,} \quad C = F_{bb}(0.58, 3.06) = 8 \end{aligned}$$

Step 3 Evaluate $AC - B^2$ and try to classify the critical point (a, b) by using Theorem 2 in Section 7.3:

$$AC - B^2 = (292)(8) - (44)^2 = 400 > 0 \quad \text{and} \quad A = 292 > 0$$

Therefore, case 2 in Theorem 2 applies, and $F(a, b)$ has a local minimum at the critical point $(0.58, 3.06)$.

So, the least squares line for the given data is

$$y = 0.58x + 3.06 \qquad \text{Least squares line}$$

The sum of the squares of the residuals is minimized for this choice of a and b (see Fig. 3).

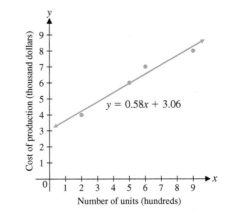

Figure 3

This linear function can now be used by the manufacturer to estimate any of the quantities normally associated with the cost function—such as costs, marginal costs, average costs, and so on. For example, the cost of producing 2,000 units is approximately

$$y = (0.58)(20) + 3.06 = 14.66, \qquad \text{or} \qquad \$14,660$$

The marginal cost function is

$$\frac{dy}{dx} = 0.58$$

The average cost function is

$$\bar{y} = \frac{0.58x + 3.06}{x}$$

In general, if we are given a set of n points (x_1, y_1), (x_2, y_2), . . . , (x_n, y_n), we want to determine the line $y = ax + b$ for which the sum of the squares of the residuals is minimized. Using summation notation, we find that the sum of the squares of the residuals is given by

$$F(a, b) = \sum_{k=1}^{n} (y_k - ax_k - b)^2$$

Note that in this expression the variables are a and b, and the x_k and y_k are all known values. To minimize $F(a, b)$, we thus compute the partial derivatives with respect to a and b and set them equal to 0:

$$F_a(a, b) = \sum_{k=1}^{n} 2(y_k - ax_k - b)(-x_k) = 0$$

$$F_b(a, b) = \sum_{k=1}^{n} 2(y_k - ax_k - b)(-1) = 0$$

Dividing each equation by 2 and simplifying, we see that the coefficients a and b of the least squares line $y = ax + b$ must satisfy the following system of *normal equations*:

$$\left(\sum_{k=1}^{n} x_k^2 \right) a + \left(\sum_{k=1}^{n} x_k \right) b = \sum_{k=1}^{n} x_k y_k$$

$$\left(\sum_{k=1}^{n} x_k \right) a + nb = \sum_{k=1}^{n} y_k$$

Solving this system for a and b produces the formulas given in Theorem 1.

THEOREM 1 Least Squares Approximation

For a set of n points $(x_1, y_1), (x_2, y_2), \ldots, (x_n, y_n)$, the coefficients of the least squares line $y = ax + b$ are the solutions of the system of **normal equations**

$$\left(\sum_{k=1}^{n} x_k^2\right)a + \left(\sum_{k=1}^{n} x_k\right)b = \sum_{k=1}^{n} x_k y_k \tag{1}$$

$$\left(\sum_{k=1}^{n} x_k\right)a + nb = \sum_{k=1}^{n} y_k$$

and are given by the formulas

$$a = \frac{n\left(\sum_{k=1}^{n} x_k y_k\right) - \left(\sum_{k=1}^{n} x_k\right)\left(\sum_{k=1}^{n} y_k\right)}{n\left(\sum_{k=1}^{n} x_k^2\right) - \left(\sum_{k=1}^{n} x_k\right)^2} \tag{2}$$

$$b = \frac{\sum_{k=1}^{n} y_k - a\left(\sum_{k=1}^{n} x_k\right)}{n} \tag{3}$$

Now we return to the data in Table 1 and tabulate the sums required for the normal equations and their solution in Table 3.

Table 3

	x_k	y_k	$x_k y_k$	x_k^2
	2	4	8	4
	5	6	30	25
	6	7	42	36
	9	8	72	81
Totals	22	25	152	146

The normal equations (1) are then

$$146a + 22b = 152$$
$$22a + 4b = 25$$

The solution of the normal equations given by equations (2) and (3) is

$$a = \frac{4(152) - (22)(25)}{4(146) - (22)^2} = 0.58$$

$$b = \frac{25 - 0.58(22)}{4} = 3.06$$

Compare these results with step 1 on page 461. Note that Table 3 provides a convenient format for the computation of step 1.

Many graphing calculators have a linear regression feature that solves the system of normal equations obtained by setting the partial derivatives of the sum of squares of the residuals equal to 0. Therefore, in practice, we simply enter the given data points and use the linear regression feature to determine the line $y = ax + b$ that best fits the data (see Fig. 4). There is no need to compute partial derivatives or even to tabulate sums (as in Table 3).

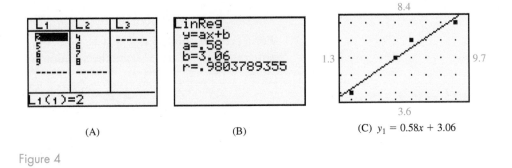

(A)   (B)   (C) $y_1 = 0.58x + 3.06$

Figure 4

Explore and Discuss 1   (A) Plot the four points $(0, 0)$, $(0, 1)$, $(10, 0)$, and $(10, 1)$. Which line would you guess "best" fits these four points? Use formulas (2) and (3) to test your conjecture.

(B) Plot the four points $(0, 0)$, $(0, 10)$, $(1, 0)$ and $(1, 10)$. Which line would you guess "best" fits these four points? Use formulas (2) and (3) to test your conjecture.

(C) If either of your conjectures was wrong, explain how your reasoning was mistaken.

CONCEPTUAL INSIGHT

Formula (2) for a is undefined if the denominator equals 0. When can this happen? Suppose $n = 3$. Then

$$n\left(\sum_{k=1}^{n} x_k^2\right) - \left(\sum_{k=1}^{n} x_k\right)^2$$

$$= 3(x_1^2 + x_2^2 + x_3^2) - (x_1 + x_2 + x_3)^2$$
$$= 3(x_1^2 + x_2^2 + x_3^2) - (x_1^2 + x_2^2 + x_3^2 + 2x_1x_2 + 2x_1x_3 + 2x_2x_3)$$
$$= 2(x_1^2 + x_2^2 + x_3^2) - (2x_1x_2 + 2x_1x_3 + 2x_2x_3)$$
$$= (x_1^2 + x_2^2) + (x_1^2 + x_3^2) + (x_2^2 + x_3^2) - (2x_1x_2 + 2x_1x_3 + 2x_2x_3)$$
$$= (x_1^2 - 2x_1x_2 + x_2^2) + (x_1^2 - 2x_1x_3 + x_3^2) + (x_2^2 - 2x_2x_3 + x_3^2)$$
$$= (x_1 - x_2)^2 + (x_1 - x_3)^2 + (x_2 - x_3)^2$$

and the last expression is equal to 0 if and only if $x_1 = x_2 = x_3$ (i.e., if and only if the three points all lie on the same vertical line). A similar algebraic manipulation works for any integer $n > 1$, showing that, in formula (2) for a, the denominator equals 0 if and only if all n points lie on the same vertical line.

The method of least squares can also be applied to find the quadratic equation $y = ax^2 + bx + c$ that best fits a set of data points. In this case, the sum of the squares of the residuals is a function of three variables:

$$F(a, b, c) = \sum_{k=1}^{n} (y_k - ax_k^2 - bx_k - c)^2$$

There are now three partial derivatives to compute and set equal to 0:

$$F_a(a, b, c) = \sum_{k=1}^{n} 2(y_k - ax_k^2 - bx_k - c)(-x_k^2) = 0$$

$$F_b(a, b, c) = \sum_{k=1}^{n} 2(y_k - ax_k^2 - bx_k - c)(-x_k) = 0$$

$$F_c(a, b, c) = \sum_{k=1}^{n} 2(y_k - ax_k^2 - bx_k - c)(-1) = 0$$

The resulting set of three linear equations in the three variables *a, b,* and *c* is called the *set of normal equations for quadratic regression.*

A quadratic regression feature on a calculator is designed to solve such normal equations after the given set of points has been entered. Figure 5 illustrates the computation for the data of Table 1.

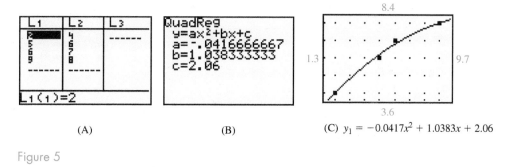

(A) (B) (C) $y_1 = -0.0417x^2 + 1.0383x + 2.06$

Figure 5

Explore and Discuss 2

(A) Use the graphs in Figures 4 and 5 to predict which technique, linear regression or quadratic regression, yields the smaller sum of squares of the residuals for the data of Table 1. Explain.

(B) Confirm your prediction by computing the sum of squares of the residuals in each case.

The method of least squares can also be applied to other regression equations—for example, cubic, quartic, logarithmic, exponential, and power regression models. Details are explored in some of the exercises at the end of this section.

Applications

EXAMPLE 1 Exam Scores Table 4 lists the midterm and final examination scores of 10 students in a calculus course.

Table 4

Midterm	Final	Midterm	Final
49	61	78	77
53	47	83	81
67	72	85	79
71	76	91	93
74	68	99	99

(A) Use formulas (1), (2), and (3) to find the normal equations and the least squares line for the data given in Table 4.

(B) Use the linear regression feature on a graphing calculator to find and graph the least squares line.

(C) Use the least squares line to predict the final examination score of a student who scored 95 on the midterm examination.

SOLUTION

(A) Table 5 shows a convenient way to compute all the sums in the formulas for *a* and *b.*

Table 5

x_k	y_k	$x_k y_k$	x_k^2
49	61	2,989	2,401
53	47	2,491	2,809
67	72	4,824	4,489
71	76	5,396	5,041
74	68	5,032	5,476
78	77	6,006	6,084
83	81	6,723	6,889
85	79	6,715	7,225
91	93	8,463	8,281
99	99	9,801	9,801
Totals 750	753	58,440	58,496

From the last line in Table 5, we have

$$\sum_{k=1}^{10} x_k = 750 \qquad \sum_{k=1}^{10} y_k = 753 \qquad \sum_{k=1}^{10} x_k y_k = 58,440 \qquad \sum_{k=1}^{10} x_k^2 = 58,496$$

and the normal equations are

$$58,496a + 750b = 58,440$$
$$750a + 10b = 753$$

Using formulas (2) and (3), we obtain

$$a = \frac{10(58,440) - (750)(753)}{10(58,496) - (750)^2} = \frac{19,650}{22,460} \approx 0.875$$

$$b = \frac{753 - 0.875(750)}{10} = 9.675$$

The least squares line is given (approximately) by

$$y = 0.875x + 9.675$$

(B) We enter the data and use the linear regression feature, as shown in Figure 6. [The discrepancy between values of a and b in the preceding calculations and those in Figure 6B is due to rounding in part (A).]

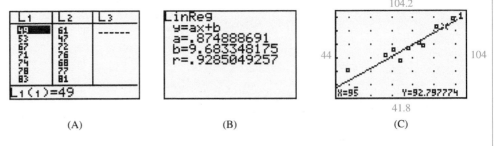

(A)   (B)   (C)

Figure 6

(C) If $x = 95$, then $y = 0.875(95) + 9.675 \approx 92.8$ is the predicted score on the final exam. This is also indicated in Figure 6C. If we assume that the exam score must be an integer, then we would predict a score of 93.

Matched Problem 1 Repeat Example 1 for the scores listed in Table 6.

Table 6

Midterm	Final	Midterm	Final
54	50	84	80
60	66	88	95
75	80	89	85
76	68	97	94
78	71	99	86

EXAMPLE 2 Energy Consumption The use of fuel oil for home heating in the United States has declined steadily for several decades. Table 7 lists the percentage of occupied housing units in the United States that were heated by fuel oil for various years between 1960 and 2009. Use the data in the table and linear regression to estimate the percentage of occupied housing units in the United States that were heated by fuel oil in the year 1995.

Table 7 **Occupied Housing Units Heated by Fuel Oil**

Year	Percent	Year	Percent
1960	32.4	1989	13.3
1970	26.0	1999	9.8
1979	19.5	2009	7.3

SOLUTION We enter the data, with $x = 0$ representing 1960, $x = 10$ representing 1970, and so on, and use linear regression as shown in Figure 7.

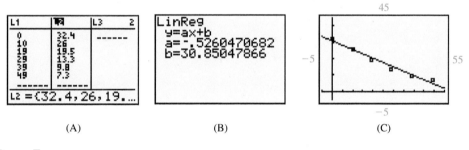

(A)   (B)   (C)

Figure 7

Figure 7 indicates that the least squares line is $y = -0.526x + 30.85$. To estimate the percentage of occupied housing units heated by fuel oil in the year 1995 (corresponding to $x = 35$), we substitute $x = 35$ in the equation of the least squares line: $-0.526(35) + 30.85 = 12.44$. The estimated percentage for 1995 is 12.44%.

Matched Problem 2 In 1950, coal was still a major source of fuel for home energy consumption, and the percentage of occupied housing units heated by fuel oil was only 22.1%. Add the data for 1950 to the data for Example 2, and compute the new least squares line and the new estimate for the percentage of occupied housing units heated by fuel oil in the year 1995. Discuss the discrepancy between the two estimates. (As in Example 2, let $x = 0$ represent 1960.)

Exercises 7.5

Skills Warm-up Exercises

W *Problems 1–6 refer to the n = 5 data points $(x_1, y_1) = (0, 4)$, $(x_2, y_2) = (1, 5)$, $(x_3, y_3) = (2, 7)$, $(x_4, y_4) = (3, 9)$, and $(x_5, y_5) = (4, 13)$. Calculate the indicated sum or product of sums. (If necessary, review Section B.1).*

1. $\sum_{k=1}^{5} x_k$

2. $\sum_{k=1}^{5} y_k$

3. $\sum_{k=1}^{5} x_k y_k$

4. $\sum_{k=1}^{5} x_k^2$

5. $\sum_{k=1}^{5} x_k \sum_{k=1}^{5} y_k$

6. $\left(\sum_{k=1}^{5} x_k \right)^2$

In Problems 7–12, find the least squares line. Graph the data and the least squares line.

7.

x	y
1	1
2	3
3	4
4	3

8.

x	y
1	-2
2	-1
3	3
4	5

9.

x	y
1	8
2	5
3	4
4	0

10.

x	y
1	20
2	14
3	11
4	3

11.

x	y
1	3
2	4
3	5
4	6

12.

x	y
1	2
2	3
3	3
4	2

In Problems 13–20, find the least squares line and use it to estimate y for the indicated value of x. Round answers to two decimal places.

13.

x	y
1	3
2	1
2	2
3	0

Estimate y when x = 2.5.

14.

x	y
1	0
3	1
3	6
3	4

Estimate y when x = 3.

15.

x	y
0	10
5	22
10	31
15	46
20	51

Estimate y when x = 25.

16.

x	y
-5	60
0	50
5	30
10	20
15	15

Estimate y when x = 20.

17.

x	y
-1	14
1	12
3	8
5	6
7	5

Estimate y when x = 2.

18.

x	y
2	-4
6	0
10	8
14	12
18	14

Estimate y when x = 15.

19.

x	y	x	y
0.5	25	9.5	12
2	22	11	11
3.5	21	12.5	8
5	21	14	5
6.5	18	15.5	1

Estimate y when x = 8.

20.

x	y	x	y
0	-15	12	11
2	-9	14	13
4	-7	16	19
6	-7	18	25
8	-1	20	33

Estimate y when x = 10.

21. To find the coefficients of the parabola

$$y = ax^2 + bx + c$$

that is the "best" fit to the points $(1, 2)$, $(2, 1)$, $(3, 1)$, and $(4, 3)$, minimize the sum of the squares of the residuals

$$F(a, b, c) = (a + b + c - 2)^2$$
$$+ (4a + 2b + c - 1)^2$$
$$+ (9a + 3b + c - 1)^2$$
$$+ (16a + 4b + c - 3)^2$$

by solving the system of normal equations

$$F_a(a, b, c) = 0 \qquad F_b(a, b, c) = 0 \qquad F_c(a, b, c) = 0$$

for a, b, and c. Graph the points and the parabola.

22. Repeat Problem 21 for the points $(-1, -2)$, $(0, 1)$, $(1, 2)$, and $(2, 0)$.

Problems 23 and 24 refer to the system of normal equations and the formulas for a and b given on page 463.

23. Verify formulas (2) and (3) by solving the system of normal equations (1) for a and b.

24. If

$$\bar{x} = \frac{1}{n} \sum_{k=1}^{n} x_k \qquad \text{and} \qquad \bar{y} = \frac{1}{n} \sum_{k=1}^{n} y_k$$

are the averages of the x and y coordinates, respectively, show that the point $(\bar{x}, \bar{y})$ satisfies the equation of the least squares line, $y = ax + b$.

25. (A) Suppose that $n = 5$ and the x coordinates of the data points (x_1, y_1), (x_2, y_2), ..., (x_n, y_n) are $-2, -1, 0, 1, 2$. Show that system (1) in the text implies that

$$a = \frac{\sum x_k y_k}{\sum x_k^2}$$

and that b is equal to the average of the values of y_k.

(B) Show that the conclusion of part (A) holds whenever the average of the x coordinates of the data points is 0.

26. (A) Give an example of a set of six data points such that half of the points lie above the least squares line and half lie below.

(B) Give an example of a set of six data points such that just one of the points lies above the least squares line and five lie below.

27. (A) Find the linear and quadratic functions that best fit the data points $(0, 1.3)$, $(1, 0.6)$, $(2, 1.5)$, $(3, 3.6)$, and $(4, 7.4)$. Round coefficients to two decimal places.

(B) Which of the two functions best fits the data? Explain.

28. (A) Find the linear, quadratic, and logarithmic functions that best fit the data points $(1, 3.2)$, $(2, 4.2)$, $(3, 4.7)$, $(4, 5.0)$, and $(5, 5.3)$. (Round coefficients to two decimal places.)

(B) Which of the three functions best fits the data? Explain.

29. Describe the normal equations for cubic regression. How many equations are there? What are the variables? What techniques could be used to solve the equations?

30. Describe the normal equations for quartic regression. How many equations are there? What are the variables? What techniques could be used to solve the equations?

Applications

31. *Crime rate.* Data on U.S. property crimes (in number of crimes per 100,000 population) are given in the table for the years 2001 through 2011.

U.S. Property Crime Rates

Year	Rate
2001	3,658
2003	3,591
2005	3,431
2007	3,276
2009	3,041
2011	2,908

(A) Find the least squares line for the data, using $x = 0$ for 2000.

(B) Use the least squares line to predict the property crime rate in 2024.

32. *Cable TV revenue.* Data for cable TV revenue are given in the table for the years 2002 through 2010.

Cable TV Revenue

Year	Millions of dollars
2002	47,989
2004	58,586
2006	71,887
2008	85,232
2010	93,368

(A) Find the least squares line for the data, using $x = 0$ for 2000.

(B) Use the least squares line to predict cable TV revenue in 2025.

33. *Maximizing profit.* The market research department for a drugstore chain chose two summer resort areas to test market a new sunscreen lotion packaged in 4-ounce plastic bottles. After a summer of varying the selling price and recording the monthly demand, the research department arrived at the following demand table, where y is the number of bottles purchased per month (in thousands) at x dollars per bottle:

x	y
5.0	2.0
5.5	1.8
6.0	1.4
6.5	1.2
7.0	1.1

(A) Use the method of least squares to find a demand equation.

(B) If each bottle of sunscreen costs the drugstore chain $4, how should the sunscreen be priced to achieve a maximum monthly profit? [*Hint:* Use the result of part (A), with $C = 4y$, $R = xy$, and $P = R - C$.]

34. *Maximizing profit.* A market research consultant for a supermarket chain chose a large city to test market a new brand of mixed nuts packaged in 8-ounce cans. After a year of varying the selling price and recording the monthly demand, the consultant arrived at the following demand table, where y is the number of cans purchased per month (in thousands) at x dollars per can:

x	y
4.0	4.2
4.5	3.5
5.0	2.7
5.5	1.5
6.0	0.7

(A) Use the method of least squares to find a demand equation.

(B) If each can of nuts costs the supermarket chain $3, how should the nuts be priced to achieve a maximum monthly profit?

35. *Olympic Games.* The table gives the winning heights in the pole vault in the Olympic Games from 1980 to 2012.

Olympic Pole Vault Winning Height

Year	Height (ft)
1980	18.96
1984	18.85
1988	19.35
1992	19.02
1996	19.42
2000	19.35
2004	19.52
2008	19.56
2012	19.59

(A) Use a graphing calculator to find the least squares line for the data, letting $x = 0$ for 1980.

(B) Estimate the winning height in the pole vault in the Olympic Games of 2024.

36. *Biology.* In biology, there is an approximate rule, called the *bioclimatic rule for temperate climates*. This rule states that in spring and early summer, periodic phenomena such as the blossoming of flowers, the appearance of insects, and the ripening of fruit usually come about 4 days later for each 500 feet of altitude. Stated as a formula, the rule becomes

$$d = 8h \qquad 0 \le h \le 4$$

where d is the change in days and h is the altitude (in thousands of feet). To test this rule, an experiment was set up to record the difference in blossoming times of the same type of apple tree at different altitudes. A summary of the results is given in the following table:

h	d
0	0
1	7
2	18
3	28
4	33

(A) Use the method of least squares to find a linear equation relating h and d. Does the bioclimatic rule $d = 8h$ appear to be approximately correct?

(B) How much longer will it take this type of apple tree to blossom at 3.5 thousand feet than at sea level? [Use the linear equation found in part (A).]

37. Global warming. Average global temperatures from 1885 to 2005 are given in the table.

Average Global Temperatures

Year	°F	Year	°F
1885	56.65	1955	57.06
1895	56.64	1965	57.05
1905	56.52	1975	57.04
1915	56.57	1985	57.36
1925	56.74	1995	57.64
1935	57.00	2005	58.59
1945	57.13		

(A) Find the least squares line for the data, using $x = 0$ for 1885.

(B) Use the least squares line to estimate the average global temperature in 2085.

38. Organic Farming. The table gives the number of acres of certified organic farmland in the United States from 2000 to 2008.

Certified Organic Farmland in the United States

Year	Acres
2000	1,776,000
2002	1,926,000
2004	3,045,000
2006	2,936,000
2008	4,816,000

(A) Find the least squares line for the data, using $x = 0$ for the year 2000.

(B) Use the least squares line to estimate the number of acres of certified organic farmland in the United States in 2023.

Answers to Matched Problems

1. (A) $y = 0.85x + 9.47$

(B)

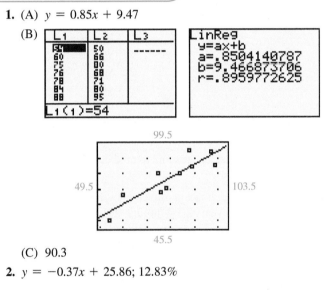

(C) 90.3

2. $y = -0.37x + 25.86$; 12.83%

7.6 Double Integrals over Rectangular Regions

- Introduction
- Definition of the Double Integral
- Average Value over Rectangular Regions
- Volume and Double Integrals

Introduction

We have generalized the concept of differentiation to functions with two or more independent variables. How can we do the same with integration, and how can we interpret the results? Let's look first at the operation of antidifferentiation. We can antidifferentiate a function of two or more variables with respect to one of the variables by treating all the other variables as though they were constants. Thus, this operation is the reverse operation of partial differentiation, just as ordinary antidifferentiation is the reverse operation of ordinary differentiation. We write $\int f(x, y)\, dx$ to indicate that we are to antidifferentiate $f(x, y)$ with respect to x, holding y fixed; we write $\int f(x, y)\, dy$ to indicate that we are to antidifferentiate $f(x, y)$ with respect to y, holding x fixed.

EXAMPLE 1 Partial Antidifferentiation Evaluate

(A) $\displaystyle\int (6xy^2 + 3x^2)\, dy$

(B) $\displaystyle\int (6xy^2 + 3x^2)\, dx$

SOLUTION

(A) Treating x as a constant and using the properties of antidifferentiation from Section 5.1, we have

$$\int (6xy^2 + 3x^2)\, dy = \int 6xy^2\, dy + \int 3x^2\, dy$$

> The dy tells us that we are looking for the antiderivative of $6xy^2 + 3x^2$ with respect to y only, holding x constant.

$$= 6x\int y^2\, dy + 3x^2 \int dy$$

$$= 6x\left(\frac{y^3}{3}\right) + 3x^2(y) + C(x)$$

$$= 2xy^3 + 3x^2y + C(x)$$

Note that the constant of integration can be *any function of x alone* since for any such function,

$$\frac{\partial}{\partial y} C(x) = 0$$

Check:

We can verify that our answer is correct by using partial differentiation:

$$\frac{\partial}{\partial y}[2xy^3 + 3x^2y + C(x)] = 6xy^2 + 3x^2 + 0$$

$$= 6xy^2 + 3x^2$$

(B) We treat y as a constant:

$$\int (6xy^2 + 3x^2)\, dx = \int 6xy^2\, dx + \int 3x^2\, dx$$

$$= 6y^2 \int x\, dx + 3\int x^2\, dx$$

$$= 6y^2\left(\frac{x^2}{2}\right) + 3\left(\frac{x^3}{3}\right) + E(y)$$

$$= 3x^2y^2 + x^3 + E(y)$$

The antiderivative contains an arbitrary function $E(y)$ of y alone.

Check:

$$\frac{\partial}{\partial x}[3x^2y^2 + x^3 + E(y)] = 6xy^2 + 3x^2 + 0$$

$$= 6xy^2 + 3x^2$$

Matched Problem 1 Evaluate

(A) $\displaystyle\int (4xy + 12x^2y^3)\, dy$

(B) $\displaystyle\int (4xy + 12x^2y^3)\, dx$

Now that we have extended the concept of antidifferentiation to functions with two variables, we also can evaluate definite integrals of the form

$$\int_a^b f(x, y)\, dx \quad \text{or} \quad \int_c^d f(x, y)\, dy$$

EXAMPLE 2 Evaluating a Partial Antiderivative Evaluate, substituting the limits of integration in y if dy is used and in x if dx is used:

(A) $\displaystyle\int_0^2 (6xy^2 + 3x^2)\,dy$

(B) $\displaystyle\int_0^1 (6xy^2 + 3x^2)\,dx$

SOLUTION

(A) From Example 1A, we know that

$$\int (6xy^2 + 3x^2)\,dy = 2xy^3 + 3x^2y + C(x)$$

According to properties of the definite integral for a function of one variable, we can use any antiderivative to evaluate the definite integral. Thus, choosing $C(x) = 0$, we have

$$\int_0^2 (6xy^2 + 3x^2)\,dy = (2xy^3 + 3x^2y)\big|_{y=0}^{y=2}$$

$$= [2x(2)^3 + 3x^2(2)] - [2x(0)^3 + 3x^2(0)]$$

$$= 16x + 6x^2$$

(B) From Example 1B, we know that

$$\int (6xy^2 + 3x^2)\,dx = 3x^2y^2 + x^3 + E(y)$$

Choosing $E(y) = 0$, we have

$$\int_0^1 (6xy^2 + 3x^2)\,dx = (3x^2y^2 + x^3)\big|_{x=0}^{x=1}$$

$$= [3y^2(1)^2 + (1)^3] - [3y^2(0)^2 + (0)^3]$$

$$= 3y^2 + 1$$

Matched Problem 2 Evaluate

(A) $\displaystyle\int_0^1 (4xy + 12x^2y^3)\,dy$

(B) $\displaystyle\int_0^3 (4xy + 12x^2y^3)\,dx$

Integrating and evaluating a definite integral with integrand $f(x, y)$ with respect to y produces a function of x alone (or a constant). Likewise, integrating and evaluating a definite integral with integrand $f(x, y)$ with respect to x produces a function of y alone (or a constant). Each of these results, involving at most one variable, can now be used as an integrand in a second definite integral.

EXAMPLE 3 Evaluating Integrals Evaluate

(A) $\displaystyle\int_0^1 \left[\int_0^2 (6xy^2 + 3x^2)\,dy \right] dx$

(B) $\displaystyle\int_0^2 \left[\int_0^1 (6xy^2 + 3x^2)\,dx \right] dy$

SOLUTION

(A) Example 2A showed that

$$\int_0^2 (6xy^2 + 3x^2)\,dy = 16x + 6x^2$$

Therefore,

$$\int_0^1 \left[\int_0^2 (6xy^2 + 3x^2)\, dy \right] dx = \int_0^1 (16x + 6x^2)\, dx$$

$$= (8x^2 + 2x^3)\big|_{x=0}^{x=1}$$

$$= [8(1)^2 + 2(1)^3] - [8(0)^2 + 2(0)^3] = 10$$

(B) Example 2B showed that

$$\int_0^1 (6xy^2 + 3x^2)\, dx = 3y^2 + 1$$

Therefore,

$$\int_0^2 \left[\int_0^1 (6xy^2 + 3x^2)\, dx \right] dy = \int_0^2 (3y^2 + 1)\, dy$$

$$= (y^3 + y)\big|_{y=0}^{y=2}$$

$$= [(2)^3 + 2] - [(0)^3 + 0] = 10$$

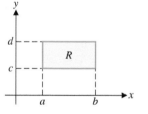

A numerical integration command can be used as an alternative to the fundamental theorem of calculus to evaluate the last integrals in Examples 3A and 3B, $\int_0^1 (16x + 6x^2)\, dx$ and $\int_0^2 (3y^2 + 1)\, dy$, since the integrand in each case is a function of a single variable (see Fig. 1).

Figure 1

Matched Problem 3 Evaluate

(A) $\displaystyle \int_0^3 \left[\int_0^1 (4xy + 12x^2y^3)\, dy \right] dx$ 　　　(B) $\displaystyle \int_0^1 \left[\int_0^3 (4xy + 12x^2y^3)\, dx \right] dy$

Definition of the Double Integral

Notice that the answers in Examples 3A and 3B are identical. This is not an accident. In fact, it is this property that enables us to define the *double integral,* as follows:

DEFINITION Double Integral

The **double integral** of a function $f(x, y)$ over a rectangle

$$R = \{(x, y)\,|\, a \le x \le b, c \le y \le d\}$$

is

$$\iint_R f(x, y)\, dA = \int_a^b \left[\int_c^d f(x, y)\, dy \right] dx$$

$$= \int_c^d \left[\int_a^b f(x, y)\, dx \right] dy$$

In the double integral $\iint_R f(x, y)\, dA, f(x, y)$ is called the **integrand**, and R is called the **region of integration**. The expression dA indicates that this is an integral over a two-dimensional region. The integrals

$$\int_a^b \left[\int_c^d f(x, y)\, dy \right] dx \qquad \text{and} \qquad \int_c^d \left[\int_a^b f(x, y)\, dx \right] dy$$

are referred to as **iterated integrals** (the brackets are often omitted), and the order in which dx and dy are written indicates the order of integration. This is not the most general definition of the double integral over a rectangular region; however, it is equivalent to the general definition for all the functions we will consider.

EXAMPLE 4   Evaluating a Double Integral   **Evaluate**

$$\iint\limits_R (x + y)\, dA \qquad \text{over} \qquad R = \{(x, y)\,|\,1 \leq x \leq 3,\ -1 \leq y \leq 2\}$$

SOLUTION   Region R is illustrated in Figure 2. We can choose either order of iteration. As a check, we will evaluate the integral both ways:

$$\iint\limits_R (x + y)\, dA = \int_1^3 \int_{-1}^2 (x + y)\, dy\, dx$$

$$= \int_1^3 \left[\left(xy + \frac{y^2}{2} \right) \Big|_{y=-1}^{y=2} \right] dx$$

$$= \int_1^3 \left[(2x + 2) - \left(-x + \tfrac{1}{2} \right) \right] dx$$

$$= \int_1^3 \left(3x + \tfrac{3}{2} \right) dx$$

$$= \left(\tfrac{3}{2}x^2 + \tfrac{3}{2}x \right) \Big|_{x=1}^{x=3}$$

$$= \left(\tfrac{27}{2} + \tfrac{9}{2} \right) - \left(\tfrac{3}{2} + \tfrac{3}{2} \right) = 18 - 3 = 15$$

$$\iint\limits_R (x + y)\, dA = \int_{-1}^2 \int_1^3 (x + y)\, dx\, dy$$

$$= \int_{-1}^2 \left[\left(\frac{x^2}{2} + xy \right) \Big|_{x=1}^{x=3} \right] dy$$

$$= \int_{-1}^2 \left[\left(\tfrac{9}{2} + 3y \right) - \left(\tfrac{1}{2} + y \right) \right] dy$$

$$= \int_{-1}^2 (4 + 2y)\, dy$$

$$= (4y + y^2) \Big|_{y=-1}^{y=2}$$

$$= (8 + 4) - (-4 + 1) = 12 - (-3) = 15$$

Matched Problem 4   **Evaluate**

$$\iint\limits_R (2x - y)\, dA \qquad \text{over} \qquad R = \{(x, y)\,|\,-1 \leq x \leq 5,\ 2 \leq y \leq 4\}$$

both ways.

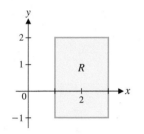

Figure 2

EXAMPLE 5   Double Integral of an Exponential Function   **Evaluate**

$$\iint\limits_R 2xe^{x^2+y}\, dA \qquad \text{over} \qquad R = \{(x, y)\,|\,0 \leq x \leq 1,\ -1 \leq y \leq 1\}$$

SOLUTION   Region R is illustrated in Figure 3.

$$\iint\limits_R 2xe^{x^2+y}\, dA = \int_{-1}^1 \int_0^1 2xe^{x^2+y}\, dx\, dy$$

$$= \int_{-1}^1 \left[(e^{x^2+y}) \Big|_{x=0}^{x=1} \right] dy$$

Figure 3

$$= \int_{-1}^{1} (e^{1+y} - e^{y}) \, dy$$

$$= (e^{1+y} - e^{y})|_{y=-1}^{y=1}$$

$$= (e^{2} - e) - (e^{0} - e^{-1})$$

$$= e^{2} - e - 1 + e^{-1}$$

Matched Problem 5 | Evaluate

$$\iint_{R} \frac{x}{y^2} e^{x/y} \, dA \qquad \text{over} \qquad R = \{(x, y)|0 \le x \le 1, \quad 1 \le y \le 2\}.$$

Average Value over Rectangular Regions

In Section 5.5, the average value of a function $f(x)$ over an interval $[a, b]$ was defined as

$$\frac{1}{b-a} \int_{a}^{b} f(x) \, dx$$

This definition is easily extended to functions of two variables over rectangular regions as follows (notice that the denominator $(b - a)(d - c)$ is simply the area of the rectangle R):

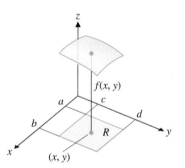

DEFINITION Average Value over Rectangular Regions

The **average value** of the function $f(x, y)$ over the rectangle

$$R = \{(x, y)|a \le x \le b, \quad c \le y \le d\}$$

is

$$\frac{1}{(b - a)(d - c)} \iint_{R} f(x, y) \, dA$$

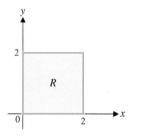

Figure 4

EXAMPLE 6 Average Value Find the average value of $f(x, y) = 4 - \frac{1}{2}x - \frac{1}{2}y$ over the rectangle $R = \{(x, y)|0 \le x \le 2, \quad 0 \le y \le 2\}$.

SOLUTION Region R is illustrated in Figure 4. We have

$$\frac{1}{(b - a)(d - c)} \iint_{R} f(x, y) \, dA = \frac{1}{(2 - 0)(2 - 0)} \iint_{R} \left(4 - \frac{1}{2}x - \frac{1}{2}y\right) dA$$

$$= \frac{1}{4} \int_{0}^{2} \int_{0}^{2} \left(4 - \frac{1}{2}x - \frac{1}{2}y\right) dy \, dx$$

$$= \frac{1}{4} \int_{0}^{2} \left[\left(4y - \frac{1}{2}xy - \frac{1}{4}y^2\right)\Big|_{y=0}^{y=2}\right] dx$$

$$= \frac{1}{4} \int_{0}^{2} (7 - x) \, dx$$

$$= \frac{1}{4}\left(7x - \frac{1}{2}x^2\right)|_{x=0}^{x=2}$$

$$= \frac{1}{4}(12) = 3$$

Figure 5 illustrates the surface $z = f(x, y)$, and our calculations show that 3 is the average of the z values over the region R.

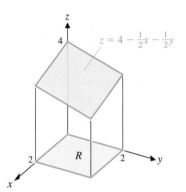

$$z = 4 - \tfrac{1}{2}x - \tfrac{1}{2}y$$

Figure 5

Matched Problem 6) Find the average value of $f(x, y) = x + 2y$ over the rectangle
$R = \{(x, y)\,|\,0 \le x \le 2, \quad 0 \le y \le 1\}$

Explore and Discuss 1   (A) Which of the functions $f(x, y) = 4 - x^2 - y^2$ and $g(x, y) = 4 - x - y$
would you guess has the greater average value over the rectangle
$R = \{(x, y)\,|\,0 \le x \le 1, \quad 0 \le y \le 1\}$? Explain.

(B) Use double integrals to check the correctness of your guess in part (A).

Volume and Double Integrals

One application of the definite integral of a function with one variable is the calculation of areas, so it is not surprising that the definite integral of a function of two variables can be used to calculate volumes of solids.

THEOREM 1   Volume under a Surface

If $f(x, y) \ge 0$ over a rectangle $R = \{(x, y)\,|\,a \le x \le b, \quad c \le y \le d\}$, then the volume of the solid formed by graphing f over the rectangle R is given by

$$V = \iint_R f(x, y)\ dA$$

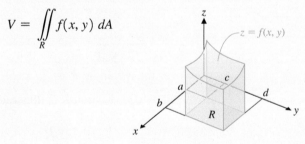

EXAMPLE 7   Volume   Find the volume of the solid under the graph of $f(x, y) = 1 + x^2 + y^2$ over the rectangle $R = \{(x, y)\,|\,0 \le x \le 1, \quad 0 \le y \le 1\}$.

SOLUTION   Figure 6 shows the region R, and Figure 7 illustrates the volume under consideration.

$$V = \iint_R (1 + x^2 + y^2)\ dA$$

$$= \int_0^1 \int_0^1 (1 + x^2 + y^2)\ dx\ dy$$

$$= \int_0^1 \left[(x + \tfrac{1}{3}x^3 + xy^2) \Big|_{x=0}^{x=1} \right] dy$$

Figure 6

$$= \int_0^1 \left(\tfrac{4}{3} + y^2 \right) dy$$

$$= \left(\tfrac{4}{3}y + \tfrac{1}{3}y^3 \right) \Big|_{y=0}^{y=1} = \tfrac{5}{3} \text{ cubic units}$$

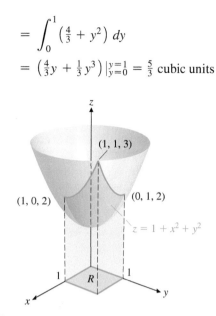

Figure 7

Matched Problem 7 Find the volume of the solid under the graph of $f(x, y) = 1 + x + y$ over the rectangle $R = \{(x, y) \,|\, 0 \le x \le 1, \ \ 0 \le y \le 2\}$.

CONCEPTUAL INSIGHT

Double integrals can be defined over regions that are more general than rectangles. For example, let $R > 0$. Then the function $f(x, y) = \sqrt{R^2 - (x^2 + y^2)}$ can be integrated over the circular region $C = \{(x, y) \,|\, x^2 + y^2 \le R^2\}$. In fact, it can be shown that

$$\iint\limits_C \sqrt{R^2 - (x^2 + y^2)} \, dx \, dy = \frac{2\pi R^3}{3}$$

Because $x^2 + y^2 + z^2 = R^2$ is the equation of a sphere of radius R centered at the origin, the double integral over C represents the volume of the upper hemisphere. Therefore, the volume of a sphere of radius R is given by

$$V = \frac{4\pi R^3}{3} \qquad \text{Volume of sphere of radius } R$$

Double integrals can also be used to obtain volume formulas for other geometric figures (see Table 1, Appendix C).

Exercises 7.6

Skills Warm-up Exercises

W *In Problems 1–6, find each antiderivative. (If necessary, review Sections 5.1 and 5.2).*

1. $\displaystyle \int (\pi + x) \, dx$

2. $\displaystyle \int (x\pi^2 + \pi x^2) \, dx$

3. $\displaystyle \int \left(1 + \frac{\pi}{x} \right) dx$

4. $\displaystyle \int \left(1 + \frac{x}{\pi} \right) dx$

5. $\displaystyle \int e^{\pi x} \, dx$

6. $\displaystyle \int \frac{\ln x}{\pi x} \, dx$

In Problems 7–14, find each antiderivative. Then use the antiderivative to evaluate the definite integral.

7. (A) $\displaystyle \int 12x^2 y^3 \, dy$ **(B)** $\displaystyle \int_0^1 12x^2 y^3 \, dy$

8. (A) $\displaystyle \int 12x^2 y^3 \, dx$ **(B)** $\displaystyle \int_{-1}^2 12x^2 y^3 \, dx$

9. (A) $\displaystyle \int (4x + 6y + 5) \, dx$ **(B)** $\displaystyle \int_{-2}^3 (4x + 6y + 5) \, dx$

10. (A) $\int (4x + 6y + 5)\, dy$ **(B)** $\int_1^4 (4x + 6y + 5)\, dy$

11. (A) $\int \dfrac{x}{\sqrt{y + x^2}}\, dx$ **(B)** $\int_0^2 \dfrac{x}{\sqrt{y + x^2}}\, dx$

12. (A) $\int \dfrac{x}{\sqrt{y + x^2}}\, dy$ **(B)** $\int_1^5 \dfrac{x}{\sqrt{y + x^2}}\, dy$

13. (A) $\int \dfrac{\ln x}{xy}\, dy$ **(B)** $\int_1^{e^2} \dfrac{\ln x}{xy}\, dy$

14. (A) $\int \dfrac{\ln x}{xy}\, dx$ **(B)** $\int_1^{e} \dfrac{\ln x}{xy}\, dx$

In Problems 15–22, evaluate each iterated integral. (See the indicated problem for the evaluation of the inner integral.)

15. $\int_{-1}^2 \int_0^1 12x^2y^3\, dy\, dx$

(See Problem 7.)

16. $\int_0^1 \int_{-1}^2 12x^2y^3\, dx\, dy$

(See Problem 8.)

17. $\int_1^4 \int_{-2}^3 (4x + 6y + 5)\, dx\, dy$

(See Problem 9.)

18. $\int_{-2}^3 \int_1^4 (4x + 6y + 5)\, dy\, dx$

(See Problem 10.)

19. $\int_1^5 \int_0^2 \dfrac{x}{\sqrt{y + x^2}}\, dx\, dy$

(See Problem 11.)

20. $\int_0^2 \int_1^5 \dfrac{x}{\sqrt{y + x^2}}\, dy\, dx$

(See Problem 12.)

21. $\int_1^{e} \int_1^{e^2} \dfrac{\ln x}{xy}\, dy\, dx$

(See Problem 13.)

22. $\int_1^{e^2} \int_1^{e} \dfrac{\ln x}{xy}\, dx\, dy$

(See Problem 14.)

Use both orders of iteration to evaluate each double integral in Problems 23–26.

23. $\iint\limits_R xy\, dA; R = \{(x, y)\,|\,0 \le x \le 2,\ 0 \le y \le 4\}$

24. $\iint\limits_R \sqrt{xy}\, dA; R = \{(x, y)\,|\,1 \le x \le 4,\ 1 \le y \le 9\}$

25. $\iint\limits_R (x + y)^5\, dA; R = \{(x, y)\,|-1 \le x \le 1,\ 1 \le y \le 2\}$

26. $\iint\limits_R xe^y\, dA; R = \{(x, y)\,|-2 \le x \le 3,\ 0 \le y \le 2\}$

In Problems 27–30, find the average value of each function over the given rectangle.

27. $f(x, y) = (x + y)^2$;

$R = \{(x, y)\,|\,1 \le x \le 5,\ -1 \le y \le 1\}$

28. $f(x, y) = x^2 + y^2$;

$R = \{(x, y)\,|-1 \le x \le 2,\ 1 \le y \le 4\}$

29. $f(x, y) = x/y; R = \{(x, y)\,|\,1 \le x \le 4,\ 2 \le y \le 7\}$

30. $f(x, y) = x^2y^3; R = \{(x, y)\,|-1 \le x \le 1,\ 0 \le y \le 2\}$

In Problems 31–34, find the volume of the solid under the graph of each function over the given rectangle.

31. $f(x, y) = 2 - x^2 - y^2$;

$R = \{(x, y)\,|\,0 \le x \le 1,\ 0 \le y \le 1\}$

32. $f(x, y) = 5 - x$;

$R = \{(x, y)\,|\,0 \le x \le 5,\ 0 \le y \le 5\}$

33. $f(x, y) = 4 - y^2; R = \{(x, y)\,|\,0 \le x \le 2,\ 0 \le y \le 2\}$

34. $f(x, y) = e^{-x-y}; R = \{(x, y)\,|\,0 \le x \le 1,\ 0 \le y \le 1\}$

Evaluate each double integral in Problems 35–38. Select the order of integration carefully; each problem is easy to do one way and difficult the other.

35. $\iint\limits_R xe^{xy}\, dA; R = \{(x, y)\,|\,0 \le x \le 1,\ 1 \le y \le 2\}$

36. $\iint\limits_R xye^{x^2y}\, dA; R = \{(x, y)\,|\,0 \le x \le 1,\ 1 \le y \le 2\}$

37. $\iint\limits_R \dfrac{2y + 3xy^2}{1 + x^2}\, dA$;

$R = \{(x, y)\,|\,0 \le x \le 1,\ -1 \le y \le 1\}$

38. $\iint\limits_R \dfrac{2x + 2y}{1 + 4y + y^2}\, dA$;

$R = \{(x, y)\,|\,1 \le x \le 3,\ 0 \le y \le 1\}$

39. Show that $\int_0^2 \int_0^2 (1 - y)\, dx\, dy = 0$. Does the double integral represent the volume of a solid? Explain.

40. (A) Find the average values of the functions $f(x, y) = x + y$, $g(x, y) = x^2 + y^2$, and $h(x, y) = x^3 + y^3$ over the rectangle

$R = \{(x, y)\,|\,0 \le x \le 1,\ 0 \le y \le 1\}$

(B) Does the average value of $k(x, y) = x^n + y^n$ over the rectangle

$R_1 = \{(x, y)\,|\,0 \le x \le 1,\ 0 \le y \le 1\}$

increase or decrease as n increases? Explain.

(C) Does the average value of $k(x, y) = x^n + y^n$ over the rectangle

$R_2 = \{(x, y)\,|\,0 \le x \le 2,\ 0 \le y \le 2\}$

increase or decrease as n increases? Explain.

41. Let $f(x, y) = x^3 + y^2 - e^{-x} - 1$.

(A) Find the average value of $f(x, y)$ over the rectangle

$$R = \{(x, y)|-2 \le x \le 2, \quad -2 \le y \le 2\}.$$

(B) Graph the set of all points (x, y) in R for which $f(x, y) = 0$.

(C) For which points (x, y) in R is $f(x, y)$ greater than 0? Less than 0? Explain.

42. Find the dimensions of the square S centered at the origin for which the average value of $f(x, y) = x^2 e^y$ over S is equal to 100.

Applications

43. Multiplier principle. Suppose that Congress enacts a one-time-only 10% tax rebate that is expected to infuse y billion, $5 \le y \le 7$, into the economy. If every person and every corporation is expected to spend a proportion x, $0.6 \le x \le 0.8$, of each dollar received, then, by the **multiplier principle** in economics, the total amount of spending S (in billions of dollars) generated by this tax rebate is given by

$$S(x, y) = \frac{y}{1 - x}$$

What is the average total amount of spending for the indicated ranges of the values of x and y? Set up a double integral and evaluate it.

44. Multiplier principle. Repeat Problem 43 if $6 \le y \le 10$ and $0.7 \le x \le 0.9$.

45. Cobb–Douglas production function. If an industry invests x thousand labor-hours, $10 \le x \le 20$, and y million, $1 \le y \le 2$, in the production of N thousand units of a certain item, then N is given by

$$N(x, y) = x^{0.75}y^{0.25}$$

What is the average number of units produced for the indicated ranges of x and y? Set up a double integral and evaluate it.

46. Cobb–Douglas production function. Repeat Problem 45 for

$$N(x, y) = x^{0.5}y^{0.5}$$

where $10 \le x \le 30$ and $1 \le y \le 3$.

47. Population distribution. In order to study the population distribution of a certain species of insect, a biologist has constructed an artificial habitat in the shape of a rectangle 16 feet long and 12 feet wide. The only food available to the insects in this habitat is located at its center. The biologist has determined that the concentration C of insects per square foot at a point d units from the food supply (see the figure) is given approximately by

$$C = 10 - \tfrac{1}{10}d^2$$

What is the average concentration of insects throughout the habitat? Express C as a function of x and y, set up a double integral, and evaluate it.

Figure for 47

48. Population distribution. Repeat Problem 47 for a square habitat that measures 12 feet on each side, where the insect concentration is given by

$$C = 8 - \tfrac{1}{10}d^2$$

49. Pollution. A heavy industrial plant located in the center of a small town emits particulate matter into the atmosphere. Suppose that the concentration of particulate matter (in parts per million) at a point d miles from the plant (see the figure) is given by

$$C = 100 - 15d^2$$

If the boundaries of the town form a rectangle 4 miles long and 2 miles wide, what is the average concentration of particulate matter throughout the town? Express C as a function of x and y, set up a double integral, and evaluate it.

50. Pollution. Repeat Problem 49 if the boundaries of the town form a rectangle 8 miles long and 4 miles wide and the concentration of particulate matter is given by

$$C = 100 - 3d^2$$

51. Safety research. Under ideal conditions, if a person driving a car slams on the brakes and skids to a stop, the length of the skid marks (in feet) is given by the formula

$$L = 0.000\ 013\ 3xy^2$$

where x is the weight of the car (in pounds) and y is the speed of the car (in miles per hour). What is the average length of the skid marks for cars weighing between 2,000 and 3,000 pounds and traveling at speeds between 50 and 60 miles per hour? Set up a double integral and evaluate it.

52. Safety research. Repeat Problem 51 for cars weighing between 2,000 and 2,500 pounds and traveling at speeds between 40 and 50 miles per hour.

53. Psychology. The intelligence quotient Q for a person with mental age x and chronological age y is given by

$$Q(x, y) = 100\frac{x}{y}$$

In a group of sixth-graders, the mental age varies between 8 and 16 years and the chronological age varies between

10 and 12 years. What is the average intelligence quotient for this group? Set up a double integral and evaluate it.

54. Psychology. Repeat Problem 53 for a group with mental ages between 6 and 14 years and chronological ages between 8 and 10 years.

7.7 Double Integrals over More General Regions

- Regular Regions
- Double Integrals over Regular Regions
- Reversing the Order of Integration
- Volume and Double Integrals

In this section, we extend the concept of double integration discussed in Section 7.6 to nonrectangular regions. We begin with an example and some new terminology.

Regular Regions

Let R be the region graphed in Figure 1. We can describe R with the following inequalities:

$$R = \{(x, y) \,|\, x \le y \le 6x - x^2, \quad 0 \le x \le 5\}$$

The region R can be viewed as a union of vertical line segments. For each x in the interval $[0, 5]$, the line segment from the point $(x, g(x))$ to the point $(x, f(x))$ lies in the region R. Any region that can be covered by vertical line segments in this manner is called a *regular x region*.

Now consider the region S in Figure 2. It can be described with the following inequalities:

$$S = \{(x, y) \,|\, y^2 \le x \le y + 2, \quad -1 \le y \le 2\}$$

The region S can be viewed as a union of horizontal line segments going from the graph of $h(y) = y^2$ to the graph of $k(y) = y + 2$ on the interval $[-1, 2]$. Regions that can be described in this manner are called *regular y regions*.

In general, *regular regions* are defined as follows:

Figure 1

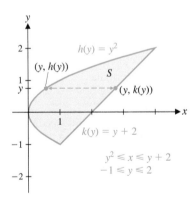

Figure 2

DEFINITION Regular Regions

A region R in the xy plane is a **regular x region** if there exist functions $f(x)$ and $g(x)$ and numbers a and b such that

$$R = \{(x, y) \,|\, g(x) \le y \le f(x), \quad a \le x \le b\}$$

A region R in the xy plane is a **regular y region** if there exist functions $h(y)$ and $k(y)$ and numbers c and d such that

$$R = \{(x, y) \,|\, h(y) \le x \le k(y), \quad c \le y \le d\}$$

See Figure 3 for a geometric interpretation.

CONCEPTUAL **INSIGHT**

If, for some region R, there is a horizontal line that has a nonempty intersection I with R, and if I is neither a closed interval nor a point, then R is *not* a regular y region. Similarly, if, for some region R, there is a vertical line that has a nonempty intersection I with R, and if I is neither a closed interval nor a point, then R is *not* a regular x region (see Fig. 3).

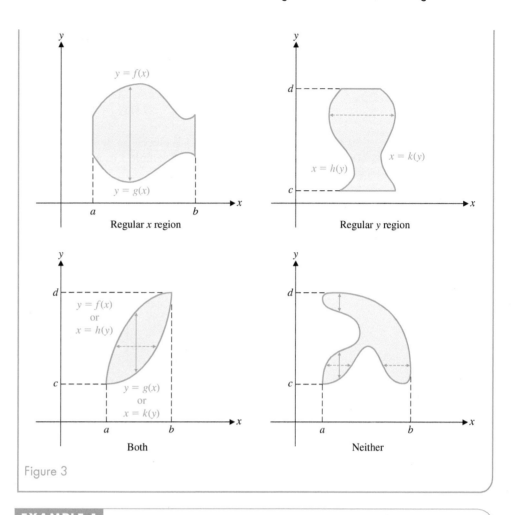

Figure 3

EXAMPLE 1 Describing a Regular x Region The region R is bounded by the graphs of $y = 4 - x^2$ and $y = x - 2$, $x \geq 0$, and the y axis. Graph R and use set notation with double inequalities to describe R as a regular x region.

SOLUTION As the solid line in the following figure indicates, R can be covered by vertical line segments that go from the graph of $y = x - 2$ to the graph of $y = 4 - x^2$. So, R is a regular x region. In terms of set notation with double inequalities, we can write

$$R = \{(x, y) \mid x - 2 \leq y \leq 4 - x^2, \ 0 \leq x \leq 2\}$$

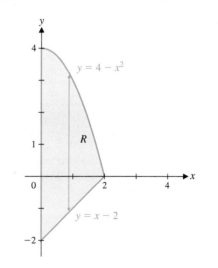

CONCEPTUAL INSIGHT

The region R of Example 1 is also a regular y region, since $R = \{(x, y) \mid 0 \le x \le k(y),\ -2 \le y \le 4\}$, where

$$k(y) = \begin{cases} 2 + y & \text{if } -2 \le y \le 0 \\ \sqrt{4 - y} & \text{if } \ \ 0 \le y \le 4 \end{cases}$$

But because $k(y)$ is piecewise defined, this description is more complicated than the description of R in Example 1 as a regular x region.

Matched Problem 1 | Describe the region R bounded by the graphs of $x = 6 - y$ and $x = y^2,\ y \ge 0$, and the x axis as a regular y region.

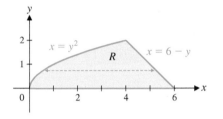

EXAMPLE 2 Describing Regular Regions The region R is bounded by the graphs of $x + y^2 = 9$ and $x + 3y = 9$. Graph R and describe R as a regular x region, a regular y region, both, or neither. Represent R in set notation with double inequalities.

SOLUTION

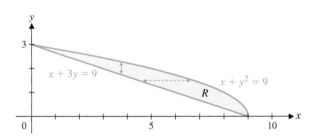

Region R can be covered by vertical line segments that go from the graph of $x + 3y = 9$ to the graph of $x + y^2 = 9$. Thus, R is a regular x region. In order to describe R with inequalities, we must solve each equation for y in terms of x:

$$x + 3y = 9 \qquad x + y^2 = 9$$
$$3y = 9 - x \qquad y^2 = 9 - x \qquad \text{We use the positive square}$$
$$y = 3 - \tfrac{1}{3}x \qquad y = \sqrt{9 - x} \qquad \begin{array}{l}\text{root, since the graph is in the}\\ \text{first quadrant.}\end{array}$$

So,

$$R = \{(x, y) \mid 3 - \tfrac{1}{3}x \le y \le \sqrt{9 - x},\ \ 0 \le x \le 9\}$$

Since region R also can be covered by horizontal line segments (see the dashed line in the preceding figure) that go from the graph of $x + 3y = 9$ to the graph of $x + y^2 = 9$, it is a regular y region. Now we must solve each equation for x in terms of y:

$$x + 3y = 9 \qquad x + y^2 = 9$$
$$x = 9 - 3y \qquad x = 9 - y^2$$

Therefore,

$$R = \{(x, y) \mid 9 - 3y \le x \le 9 - y^2,\ 0 \le y \le 3\}$$

Matched Problem 2 Repeat Example 2 for the region bounded by the graphs of $2y - x = 4$ and $y^2 - x = 4$, as shown in the following figure:

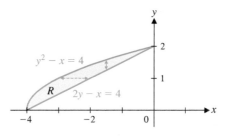

Explore and Discuss 1

A E I O U

Consider the vowels A, E, I, O, U, written in block letters as shown in the margin, to be regions of the plane. One of the vowels is a regular x region, but not a regular y region; one is a regular y region, but not a regular x region; one is both; two are neither. Explain.

Double Integrals over Regular Regions

Now we want to extend the definition of double integration to include regular x regions and regular y regions. The order of integration now depends on the nature of the region R. If R is a regular x region, we integrate with respect to y first, while if R is a regular y region, we integrate with respect to x first.

> Note that the variable limits of integration (when present) are always on the inner integral, and the constant limits of integration are always on the outer integral.

DEFINITION   Double Integration over Regular Regions
Regular x Region
If $R = \{(x, y) \,|\, g(x) \le y \le f(x), \quad a \le x \le b\}$, then

$$\iint\limits_{R} F(x, y)\, dA = \int_{a}^{b} \left[\int_{g(x)}^{f(x)} F(x, y)\, dy \right] dx$$

Regular y Region
If $R = \{(x, y) \,|\, h(y) \le x \le k(y), \quad c \le y \le d\}$, then

$$\iint\limits_{R} F(x, y)\, dA = \int_{c}^{d} \left[\int_{h(y)}^{k(y)} F(x, y)\, dx \right] dy$$

EXAMPLE 3   Evaluating a Double Integral   Evaluate $\iint\limits_{R} 2xy\, dA$, where R is the region bounded by the graphs of $y = -x$ and $y = x^2$, $x \geq 0$, and the graph of $x = 1$.

SOLUTION   From the graph, we can see that R is a regular x region described by

$$R = \{(x, y) \mid -x \leq y \leq x^2, \ 0 \leq x \leq 1\}$$

$$\iint\limits_{R} 2xy\, dA = \int_0^1 \left[\int_{-x}^{x^2} 2xy\, dy \right] dx$$

$$= \int_0^1 \left[xy^2 \Big|_{y=-x}^{y=x^2} \right] dx$$

$$= \int_0^1 \left[x(x^2)^2 - x(-x)^2 \right] dx$$

$$= \int_0^1 (x^5 - x^3)\, dx$$

$$= \left(\frac{x^6}{6} - \frac{x^4}{4} \right) \Big|_{x=0}^{x=1}$$

$$= \left(\tfrac{1}{6} - \tfrac{1}{4} \right) - (0 - 0) = -\tfrac{1}{12}$$

Matched Problem 3   Evaluate $\iint\limits_{R} 3xy^2\, dA$, where R is the region in Example 3.

EXAMPLE 4   Evaluating a Double Integral   Evaluate $\iint\limits_{R} (2x + y)\, dA$, where R is the region bounded by the graphs of $y = \sqrt{x}$, $x + y = 2$, and $y = 0$.

SOLUTION   From the graph, we can see that R is a regular y region. After solving each equation for x, we can write

$$R = \{(x, y) \mid y^2 \leq x \leq 2 - y, \ 0 \leq y \leq 1\}$$

$$\iint\limits_{R} (2x + y)\, dA = \int_0^1 \left[\int_{y^2}^{2-y} (2x + y)\, dx \right] dy$$

$$= \int_0^1 \left[(x^2 + yx) \Big|_{x=y^2}^{x=2-y} \right] dy$$

$$= \int_0^1 \{[(2 - y)^2 + y(2 - y)] - [(y^2)^2 + y(y^2)]\}\, dy$$

$$= \int_0^1 (4 - 2y - y^3 - y^4)\, dy$$

$$= \left(4y - y^2 - \tfrac{1}{4} y^4 - \tfrac{1}{5} y^5 \right) \Big|_{y=0}^{y=1}$$

$$= \left(4 - 1 - \tfrac{1}{4} - \tfrac{1}{5} \right) - 0 = \tfrac{51}{20}$$

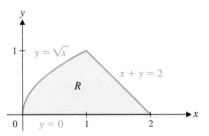

Matched Problem 4   Evaluate $\iint\limits_{R} (y - 4x)\, dA$, where R is the region in Example 4.

EXAMPLE 5 Evaluating a Double Integral The region R is bounded by the graphs of $y = \sqrt{x}$ and $y = \frac{1}{2}x$. Evaluate $\iint\limits_{R} 4xy^3\,dA$ two different ways.

SOLUTION Region R is both a regular x region and a regular y region:

$$R = \{(x, y)\mid \tfrac{1}{2}x \le y \le \sqrt{x},\ \ 0 \le x \le 4\} \quad \text{Regular } x \text{ region}$$

$$R = \{(x, y)\mid y^2 \le x \le 2y,\ \ 0 \le y \le 2\} \quad \text{Regular } y \text{ region}$$

Using the first representation (a regular x region), we obtain

$$\iint\limits_{R} 4xy^3\,dA = \int_0^4 \left[\int_{x/2}^{\sqrt{x}} 4xy^3\,dy\right] dx$$

$$= \int_0^4 \left[xy^4\,\Big|_{y=x/2}^{y=\sqrt{x}}\right] dx$$

$$= \int_0^4 \left[x(\sqrt{x})^4 - x(\tfrac{1}{2}x)^4\right] dx$$

$$= \int_0^4 \left(x^3 - \tfrac{1}{16}x^5\right) dx$$

$$= \left(\tfrac{1}{4}x^4 - \tfrac{1}{96}x^6\right)\Big|_{x=0}^{x=4}$$

$$= \left(64 - \tfrac{128}{3}\right) - 0 = \tfrac{64}{3}$$

Using the second representation (a regular y region), we obtain

$$\iint\limits_{R} 4xy^3\,dA = \int_0^2 \left[\int_{y^2}^{2y} 4xy^3\,dx\right] dy$$

$$= \int_0^2 \left[2x^2y^3\,\Big|_{x=y^2}^{x=2y}\right] dy$$

$$= \int_0^2 \left[2(2y)^2y^3 - 2(y^2)^2y^3\right] dy$$

$$= \int_0^2 \left(8y^5 - 2y^7\right) dy$$

$$= \left(\tfrac{4}{3}y^6 - \tfrac{1}{4}y^8\right)\Big|_{y=0}^{y=2}$$

$$= \left(\tfrac{256}{3} - 64\right) - 0 = \tfrac{64}{3}$$

Matched Problem 5 The region R is bounded by the graphs of $y = x$ and $y = \frac{1}{2}x^2$. Evaluate $\iint\limits_{R} 4xy^3\,dA$ two different ways.

Reversing the Order of Integration

Example 5 shows that

$$\iint\limits_{R} 4xy^3\,dA = \int_0^4 \left[\int_{x/2}^{\sqrt{x}} 4xy^3\,dy\right] dx = \int_0^2 \left[\int_{y^2}^{2y} 4xy^3\,dx\right] dy$$

In general, if R is both a regular x region and a regular y region, then the two iterated integrals are equal. In rectangular regions, reversing the order of integration in an

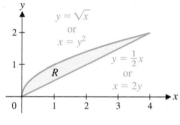

iterated integral was a simple matter. As Example 5 illustrates, the process is more complicated in nonrectangular regions. The next example illustrates how to start with an iterated integral and reverse the order of integration. Since we are interested in the reversal process and not in the value of either integral, the integrand will not be specified.

EXAMPLE 6 Reversing the Order of Integration Reverse the order of integration in

$$\int_1^3 \left[\int_0^{x-1} f(x, y) \, dy \right] dx$$

SOLUTION The order of integration indicates that the region of integration is a regular x region:

$$R = \{(x, y) \mid 0 \le y \le x - 1, \quad 1 \le x \le 3\}$$

Graph region R to determine whether it is also a regular y region. The graph shows that R is also a regular y region, and we can write

$$R = \{(x, y) \mid y + 1 \le x \le 3, \quad 0 \le y \le 2\}$$

$$\int_1^3 \left[\int_0^{x-1} f(x, y) \, dy \right] dx = \int_0^2 \left[\int_{y+1}^3 f(x, y) \, dx \right] dy$$

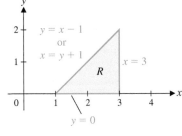

Matched Problem 6 Reverse the order of integration in $\int_2^4 \left[\int_0^{4-x} f(x, y) \, dy \right] dx$.

Explore and Discuss 2 Explain the difficulty in evaluating $\int_0^2 \int_{x^2}^4 xe^{y^2} dy \, dx$ and how it can be overcome by reversing the order of integration.

Volume and Double Integrals

In Section 7.6, we used the double integral to calculate the volume of a solid with a rectangular base. In general, if a solid can be described by the graph of a positive function $f(x, y)$ over a regular region R (not necessarily a rectangle), then the double integral of the function f over the region R still represents the volume of the corresponding solid.

EXAMPLE 7 Volume The region R is bounded by the graphs of $x + y = 1$, $y = 0$, and $x = 0$. Find the volume of the solid under the graph of $z = 1 - x - y$ over the region R.

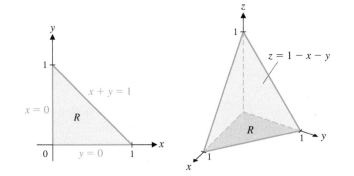

SOLUTION The graph of R shows that R is both a regular x region and a regular y region. We choose to use the regular x region:

$$R = \{(x, y) \mid 0 \le y \le 1 - x, \ 0 \le x \le 1\}$$

The volume of the solid is

$$
\begin{aligned}
V &= \iint_R (1 - x - y) \, dA = \int_0^1 \left[\int_0^{1-x} (1 - x - y) \, dy \right] dx \\
&= \int_0^1 \left[\left(y - xy - \tfrac{1}{2}y^2 \right) \Big|_{y=0}^{y=1-x} \right] dx \\
&= \int_0^1 \left[(1 - x) - x(1 - x) - \tfrac{1}{2}(1 - x)^2 \right] dx \\
&= \int_0^1 \left(\tfrac{1}{2} - x + \tfrac{1}{2}x^2 \right) dx \\
&= \left(\tfrac{1}{2}x - \tfrac{1}{2}x^2 + \tfrac{1}{6}x^3 \right) \Big|_{x=0}^{x=1} \\
&= \left(\tfrac{1}{2} - \tfrac{1}{2} + \tfrac{1}{6} \right) - 0 = \tfrac{1}{6}
\end{aligned}
$$

Matched Problem 7 The region R is bounded by the graphs of $y + 2x = 2$, $y = 0$, and $x = 0$. Find the volume of the solid under the graph of $z = 2 - 2x - y$ over the region R. [*Hint*: Sketch the region first; the solid does not have to be sketched.]

Exercises 7.7

In Problems 1–6, graph the region R bounded by the graphs of the equations. Use set notation and double inequalities to describe R as a regular x region and a regular y region in Problems 1 and 2, and as a regular x region or a regular y region, whichever is simpler, in Problems 3–6.

1. $y = 4 - x^2, y = 0, 0 \le x \le 2$

2. $y = x^2, y = 9, 0 \le x \le 3$

3. $y = x^3, y = 12 - 2x, x = 0$

4. $y = 5 - x, y = 1 + x, y = 0$

5. $y^2 = 2x, y = x - 4$

6. $y = 4 + 3x - x^2, x + y = 4$

Evaluate each integral in Problems 7–10.

7. $\int_0^1 \int_0^x (x + y) \, dy \, dx$

8. $\int_0^2 \int_0^y xy \, dx \, dy$

9. $\int_0^1 \int_{y^3}^{\sqrt{y}} (2x + y) \, dx \, dy$

10. $\int_1^4 \int_x^{x^2} (x^2 + 2y) \, dy \, dx$

In Problems 11–14, give a verbal description of the region R and determine whether R is a regular x region, a regular y region, both, or neither.

11. $R = \{(x, y) \mid |x| \le 2, \ |y| \le 3\}$

12. $R = \{(x, y) \mid 1 \le x^2 + y^2 \le 4\}$

13. $R = \{(x, y) \mid x^2 + y^2 \ge 1, \ |x| \le 2, \ 0 \le y \le 2\}$

14. $R = \{(x, y) \mid |x| + |y| \le 1\}$

In Problems 15–20, use the description of the region R to evaluate the indicated integral.

15. $\displaystyle \iint_R (x^2 + y^2) \, dA;$

$R = \{(x, y) \mid 0 \le y \le 2x, \ 0 \le x \le 2\}$

16. $\displaystyle \iint_R 2x^2 y \, dA;$

$R = \{(x, y) \mid 0 \le y \le 9 - x^2, \ -3 \le x \le 3\}$

17. $\displaystyle \iint_R (x + y - 2)^3 \, dA;$

$R = \{(x, y) \mid 0 \le x \le y + 2, \ 0 \le y \le 1\}$

18. $\displaystyle \iint_R (2x + 3y) \, dA;$

$R = \{(x, y) \mid y^2 - 4 \le x \le 4 - 2y, \ 0 \le y \le 2\}$

19. $\displaystyle \iint_R e^{x+y} \, dA;$

$R = \{(x, y) \mid -x \le y \le x, \ 0 \le x \le 2\}$

20. $\displaystyle \iint_R \frac{x}{\sqrt{x^2 + y^2}} \, dA;$

$R = \{(x, y) \mid 0 \le x \le \sqrt{4y - y^2}, \ 0 \le y \le 2\}$

In Problems 21–26, graph the region R bounded by the graphs of the indicated equations. Describe R in set notation with double inequalities, and evaluate the indicated integral.

21. $y = x + 1, y = 0, x = 0, x = 1;$ $\iint\limits_R \sqrt{1 + x + y}\, dA$

22. $y = x^2, \ y = \sqrt{x};$ $\iint\limits_R 12xy\, dA$

23. $y = 4x - x^2, \ y = 0;$ $\iint\limits_R \sqrt{y + x^2}\, dA$

24. $x = 1 + 3y, \ x = 1 - y, \ y = 1;$ $\iint\limits_R (x + y + 1)^3\, dA$

25. $y = 1 - \sqrt{x}, y = 1 + \sqrt{x}, x = 4;$ $\iint\limits_R x(y - 1)^2\, dA$

26. $y = \frac{1}{2}x, y = 6 - x, \ y = 1;$ $\iint\limits_R \frac{1}{x + y}\, dA$

In Problems 27–32, evaluate each integral. Graph the region of integration, reverse the order of integration, and then evaluate the integral with the order reversed.

27. $\int_0^3 \int_0^{3-x} (x + 2y)\, dy\, dx$

28. $\int_0^2 \int_0^y (y - x)^4\, dx\, dy$

29. $\int_0^1 \int_0^{1-x^2} x\sqrt{y}\, dy\, dx$

30. $\int_0^2 \int_{x^3}^{4x} (1 + 2y)\, dy\, dx$

31. $\int_0^4 \int_{x/4}^{\sqrt{x}/2} x\, dy\, dx$

32. $\int_0^4 \int_{y^2/4}^{2\sqrt{y}} (1 + 2xy)\, dx\, dy$

In Problems 33–36, find the volume of the solid under the graph of $f(x, y)$ over the region R bounded by the graphs of the indicated equations. Sketch the region R; the solid does not have to be sketched.

33. $f(x, y) = 4 - x - y;$ R is the region bounded by the graphs of $x + y = 4, y = 0, x = 0$

34. $f(x, y) = (x - y)^2;$ R is the region bounded by the graphs of $y = x, y = 2, x = 0$

35. $f(x, y) = 4;$ R is the region bounded by the graphs of $y = 1 - x^2$ and $y = 0$ for $0 \le x \le 1$

36. $f(x, y) = 4xy;$ R is the region bounded by the graphs of $y = \sqrt{1 - x^2}$ and $y = 0$ for $0 \le x \le 1$

In Problems 37–40, reverse the order of integration for each integral. Evaluate the integral with the order reversed. Do not attempt to evaluate the integral in the original form.

37. $\int_0^2 \int_{x^2}^4 \frac{4x}{1 + y^2}\, dy\, dx$

38. $\int_0^1 \int_y^1 \sqrt{1 - x^2}\, dx\, dy$

39. $\int_0^1 \int_{y^2}^1 4ye^{x^2}\, dx\, dy$

40. $\int_0^4 \int_{\sqrt{x}}^2 \sqrt{3x + y^2}\, dy\, dx$

In Problems 41–46, use a graphing calculator to graph the region R bounded by the graphs of the indicated equations. Use approximation techniques to find intersection points correct to two decimal places. Describe R in set notation with double inequalities, and evaluate the indicated integral correct to two decimal places.

41. $y = 1 + \sqrt{x}, \quad y = x^2, \quad x = 0;$ $\iint\limits_R x\, dA$

42. $y = 1 + \sqrt[3]{x}, y = x, x = 0;$ $\iint\limits_R x\, dA$

43. $y = \sqrt[3]{x}, y = 1 - x, y = 0;$ $\iint\limits_R 24xy\, dA$

44. $y = x^3, y = 1 - x, y = 0;$ $\iint\limits_R 48xy\, dA$

45. $y = e^{-x}, \ y = 3 - x;$ $\iint\limits_R 4y\, dA$

46. $y = e^x, \ y = 2 + x;$ $\iint\limits_R 8y\, dA$

Answers to Matched Problems

1. $R = \{(x, y)|y^2 \le x \le 6 - y, \ 0 \le y \le 2\}$

2. R is both a regular x region and a regular y region:
$R = \{(x, y)|\frac{1}{2}x + 2 \le y \le \sqrt{x + 4}, \ -4 \le x \le 0\}$
$R = \{(x, y)|y^2 - 4 \le x \le 2y - 4, \ 0 \le y \le 2\}$

3. $\frac{13}{40}$ **4.** $-\frac{77}{20}$ **5.** $\frac{64}{15}$

6. $\int_0^2 \int_2^{4-y} f(x, y)\, dx\, dy$

7. $\frac{2}{3}$

Chapter 7   Summary and Review

Important Terms, Symbols, and Concepts

7.1 Functions of Several Variables

- An equation of the form $z = f(x, y)$ describes a **function of two independent variables** if, for each permissible ordered pair (x, y), there is one and only one value of z determined by $f(x, y)$. The variables x and y are **independent variables**, and z is a **dependent variable**. The set of all ordered pairs of permissible values of x and y is the **domain** of the function, and the set of all corresponding values $f(x, y)$ is the **range**. Functions of more than two independent variables are defined similarly.

- The graph of $z = f(x, y)$ consists of all triples (x, y, z) in a **three-dimensional coordinate system** that satisfy the equation. The graphs of the functions $z = f(x, y) = x^2 + y^2$ and $z = g(x, y) = x^2 - y^2$, for example, are **surfaces**; the first has a local minimum, and the second has a **saddle point**, at $(0, 0)$.

7.2 Partial Derivatives

- If $z = f(x, y)$, then the **partial derivative of f with respect to x**, denoted as $\partial z/\partial x$, f_x, or $f_x(x, y)$, is

$$\frac{\partial z}{\partial x} = \lim_{h \to 0} \frac{f(x + h, y) - f(x, y)}{h}$$

Similarly, the **partial derivative of f with respect to y**, denoted as $\partial z/\partial y$, f_y, or $f_y(x, y)$, is

$$\frac{\partial z}{\partial y} = \lim_{k \to 0} \frac{f(x, y + k) - f(x, y)}{k}$$

The partial derivatives $\partial z/\partial x$ and $\partial z/\partial y$ are said to be **first-order partial derivatives**.

- There are four **second-order partial derivatives** of $z = f(x, y)$:

$$f_{xx} = f_{xx}(x, y) = \frac{\partial^2 z}{\partial x^2} = \frac{\partial}{\partial x}\left(\frac{\partial z}{\partial x}\right)$$

$$f_{xy} = f_{xy}(x, y) = \frac{\partial^2 z}{\partial y\, \partial x} = \frac{\partial}{\partial y}\left(\frac{\partial z}{\partial x}\right)$$

$$f_{yx} = f_{yx}(x, y) = \frac{\partial^2 z}{\partial x\, \partial y} = \frac{\partial}{\partial x}\left(\frac{\partial z}{\partial y}\right)$$

$$f_{yy} = f_{yy}(x, y) = \frac{\partial^2 z}{\partial y^2} = \frac{\partial}{\partial y}\left(\frac{\partial z}{\partial y}\right)$$

7.3 Maxima and Minima

- If $f(a, b) \geq f(x, y)$ for all (x, y) in a circular region in the domain of f with (a, b) as center, then $f(a, b)$ is a **local maximum**. If $f(a, b) \leq f(x, y)$ for all (x, y) in such a region, then $f(a, b)$ is a **local minimum**.

- If a function $f(x, y)$ has a local maximum or minimum at the point (a, b), and f_x and f_y exist at (a, b), then both first-order partial derivatives equal 0 at (a, b) [Theorem 1, p. 444].

- The second-derivative test for local extrema (Theorem 2, p. 444) gives conditions on the first- and second-order partial derivatives of $f(x, y)$, which guarantee that $f(a, b)$ is a local maximum, local minimum, or saddle point.

7.4 Maxima and Minima Using Lagrange Multipliers

- The **method of Lagrange multipliers** can be used to find local extrema of a function $z = f(x, y)$ subject to the constraint $g(x, y) = 0$. A procedure that lists the key steps in the method is given on page 453.

- The method of Lagrange multipliers can be extended to functions with arbitrarily many independent variables with one or more constraints (see Theorem 1, p. 452, and Theorem 2, p. 456, for the method when there are two and three independent variables, respectively).

7.5 Method of Least Squares

- **Linear regression** is the process of fitting a line $y = ax + b$ to a set of data points $(x_1, y_1), (x_2, y_2), \ldots, (x_n, y_n)$ by using the **method of least squares**.

- We minimize $F(a, b) = \displaystyle\sum_{k=1}^{n} (y_k - ax_k - b)^2$, the **sum of the squares of the residuals**, by computing the first-order partial derivatives of F and setting them equal to 0. Solving for a and b gives the formulas

$$a = \frac{n\left(\displaystyle\sum_{k=1}^{n} x_k y_k\right) - \left(\displaystyle\sum_{k=1}^{n} x_k\right)\left(\displaystyle\sum_{k=1}^{n} y_k\right)}{n\left(\displaystyle\sum_{k=1}^{n} x_k^2\right) - \left(\displaystyle\sum_{k=1}^{n} x_k\right)^2}$$

$$b = \frac{\displaystyle\sum_{k=1}^{n} y_k - a\left(\displaystyle\sum_{k=1}^{n} x_k\right)}{n}$$

- Graphing calculators have built-in routines to calculate linear—as well as quadratic, cubic, quartic, logarithmic, exponential, power, and trigonometric—regression equations.

7.6 Double Integrals over Rectangular Regions

- The **double integral** of a function $f(x, y)$ over a rectangle

$$R = \{(x, y) \,|\, a \le x \le b, \ c \le y \le d\}$$

is

$$\iint\limits_{R} f(x, y)\, dA = \int_{a}^{b} \left[\int_{c}^{d} f(x, y)\, dy \right] dx$$

$$= \int_{c}^{d} \left[\int_{a}^{b} f(x, y)\, dx \right] dy$$

- In the double integral $\iint_{R} f(x, y)\, dA$, $f(x, y)$ is called the **integrand** and R is called the **region of integration.** The expression dA indicates that this is an integral over a two-dimensional region. The integrals

$$\int_{a}^{b} \left[\int_{c}^{d} f(x, y)\, dy \right] dx \quad \text{and} \quad \int_{c}^{d} \left[\int_{a}^{b} f(x, y)\, dx \right] dy$$

are referred to as **iterated integrals** (the brackets are often omitted), and the order in which dx and dy are written indicates the order of integration.

- The **average value** of the function $f(x, y)$ over the rectangle

$$R = \{(x, y) \,|\, a \le x \le b, \ c \le y \le d\}$$

is

$$\frac{1}{(b - a)(d - c)} \iint\limits_{R} f(x, y)\, dA$$

- If $f(x, y) \ge 0$ over a rectangle $R = \{(x, y) \,|\, a \le x \le b, c \le y \le d\}$, then the volume of the solid formed by graphing f over the rectangle R is given by

$$V = \iint\limits_{R} f(x, y)\, dA$$

7.7 Double Integrals over More General Regions

- A region R in the xy plane is a **regular x region** if there exist functions $f(x)$ and $g(x)$ and numbers a and b such that

$$R = \{(x, y) \,|\, g(x) \le y \le f(x), \ a \le x \le b\}$$

- A region R in the xy plane is a **regular y region** if there exist functions $h(y)$ and $k(y)$ and numbers c and d such that

$$R = \{(x, y) \,|\, h(y) \le x \le k(y), \ c \le y \le d\}$$

- The double integral of a function $F(x, y)$ over a regular x region $R = \{(x, y) \,|\, g(x) \le y \le f(x),$ $a \le x \le b\}$ is

$$\iint\limits_{R} F(x, y)\, dA = \int_{a}^{b} \left[\int_{g(x)}^{f(x)} F(x, y)\, dy \right] dx$$

- The double integral of a function $F(x, y)$ over a regular y region $R = \{(x, y) \,|\, h(y) \le x \le k(y),$ $c \le y \le d\}$ is

$$\iint\limits_{R} F(x, y)\, dA = \int_{c}^{d} \left[\int_{h(y)}^{k(y)} F(x, y)\, dx \right] dy$$

Review Exercises

Work through all the problems in this chapter review and check your answers in the back of the book. Answers to all review problems are there, along with section numbers in italics to indicate where each type of problem is discussed. Where weaknesses show up, review appropriate sections of the text.

1. For $f(x, y) = 2,000 + 40x + 70y$, find $f(5, 10), f_x(x, y)$, and $f_y(x, y)$.

2. For $z = x^3y^2$, find $\partial^2 z/\partial x^2$ and $\partial^2 z/\partial x\, \partial y$.

3. Evaluate $\int (6xy^2 + 4y)\, dy$.

4. Evaluate $\int (6xy^2 + 4y)\, dx$.

5. Evaluate $\int_0^1 \int_0^1 4xy\, dy\, dx$.

6. For $f(x, y) = 6 + 5x - 2y + 3x^2 + x^3$, find $f_x(x, y)$, and $f_y(x, y)$, and explain why $f(x, y)$ has no local extrema.

7. For $f(x, y) = 3x^2 - 2xy + y^2 - 2x + 3y - 7$, find $f(2, 3)$ $f_y(x, y)$, and $f_y(2, 3)$.

8. For $f(x, y) = -4x^2 + 4xy - 3y^2 + 4x + 10y + 81$, find $[f_{xx}(2, 3)][f_{yy}(2, 3)] - [f_{xy}(2, 3)]^2$.

9. If $f(x, y) = x + 3y$ and $g(x, y) = x^2 + y^2 - 10$, find the critical points of $F(x, y, \lambda) = f(x, y) + \lambda g(x, y)$.

10. Use the least squares line for the data in the following table to estimate y when $x = 10$.

x	y
2	12
4	10
6	7
8	3

11. For $R = \{(x, y)\,|-1 \le x \le 1, \quad 1 \le y \le 2\}$, evaluate the following in two ways:

$$\iint_R (4x + 6y)\, dA$$

12. For $R = \{(x, y)\,|\sqrt{y} \le x \le 1, \quad 0 \le y \le 1\}$, evaluate

$$\iint_R (6x + y)\, dA$$

13. For $f(x, y) = e^{x^2 + 2y}$, find f_x, f_y, and f_{xy}.

14. For $f(x, y) = (x^2 + y^2)^5$, find f_x and f_{xy}.

15. Find all critical points and test for extrema for

$$f(x, y) = x^3 - 12x + y^2 - 6y$$

16. Use Lagrange multipliers to maximize $f(x, y) = xy$ subject to $2x + 3y = 24$.

17. Use Lagrange multipliers to minimize $f(x, y, z) = x^2 + y^2 + z^2$ subject to $2x + y + 2z = 9$.

18. Find the least squares line for the data in the following table.

x	y	x	y
10	50	60	80
20	45	70	85
30	50	80	90
40	55	90	90
50	65	100	110

19. Find the average value of $f(x, y) = x^{2/3}y^{1/3}$ over the rectangle

$$R = \{(x, y)\,|-8 \le x \le 8, \quad 0 \le y \le 27\}$$

20. Find the volume of the solid under the graph of $z = 3x^2 + 3y^2$ over the rectangle

$$R = \{(x, y)\,|\, 0 \le x \le 1, \quad -1 \le y \le 1\}$$

21. Without doing any computation, predict the average value of $f(x, y) = x + y$ over the rectangle $R = \{(x, y)\,|-10 \le x \le 10, \quad -10 \le y \le 10\}$. Then check the correctness of your prediction by evaluating a double integral.

22. (A) Find the dimensions of the square S centered at the origin such that the average value of

$$f(x, y) = \frac{e^x}{y + 10}$$

over S is equal to 5.

   (B) Is there a square centered at the origin over which

$$f(x, y) = \frac{e^x}{y + 10}$$

has average value 0.05? Explain.

23. Explain why the function $f(x, y) = 4x^3 - 5y^3$, subject to the constraint $3x + 2y = 7$, has no maxima or minima.

24. Find the volume of the solid under the graph of $F(x, y) = 60x^2y$ over the region R bounded by the graph of $x + y = 1$ and the coordinate axes.

Applications

25. **Maximizing profit.** A company produces x units of product A and y units of product B (both in hundreds per month). The monthly profit equation (in thousands of dollars) is given by

$$P(x, y) = -4x^2 + 4xy - 3y^2 + 4x + 10y + 81$$

   (A) Find $P_x(1, 3)$ and interpret the results.

   (B) How many of each product should be produced each month to maximize profit? What is the maximum profit?

26. Minimizing material. A rectangular box with no top and six compartments (see the figure) is to have a volume of 96 cubic inches. Find the dimensions that will require the least amount of material.

27. Profit. A company's annual profits (in millions of dollars) over a 5-year period are given in the following table. Use the least squares line to estimate the profit for the sixth year.

Year	Profit
1	2
2	2.5
3	3.1
4	4.2
5	4.3

28. Productivity. The Cobb–Douglas production function for a product is

$$N(x, y) = 10x^{0.8}y^{0.2}$$

where x is the number of units of labor and y is the number of units of capital required to produce N units of the product.

(A) Find the marginal productivity of labor and the marginal productivity of capital at $x = 40$ and $y = 50$. For the greatest increase in productivity, should management encourage increased use of labor or increased use of capital?

(B) If each unit of labor costs $100, each unit of capital costs $50, and $10,000 is budgeted for production of this product, use the method of Lagrange multipliers to determine the allocations of labor and capital that will maximize the number of units produced and find the maximum production. Find the marginal productivity of money and approximate the increase in production that would result from an increase of $2,000 in the amount budgeted for production.

(C) If $50 \le x \le 100$ and $20 \le y \le 40$, find the average number of units produced. Set up a double integral, and evaluate it.

29. Marine biology. When diving using scuba gear, the function used for timing the duration of the dive is

$$T(V, x) = \frac{33V}{x + 33}$$

where T is the time of the dive in minutes, V is the volume of air (in cubic feet, at sea-level pressure) compressed into tanks, and x is the depth of the dive in feet. Find $T_x(70, 17)$ and interpret the results.

30. Pollution. A heavy industrial plant located in the center of a small town emits particulate matter into the atmosphere. Suppose that the concentration of particulate matter (in parts per million) at a point d miles from the plant is given by

$$C = 100 - 24d^2$$

If the boundaries of the town form a square 4 miles long and 4 miles wide, what is the average concentration of particulate matter throughout the town? Express C as a function of x and y, and set up a double integral and evaluate it.

31. Sociology. A sociologist found that the number n of long-distance telephone calls between two cities during a given period varied (approximately) jointly as the populations P_1 and P_2 of the two cities and varied inversely as the distance d between the cities. An equation for a period of 1 week is

$$n(P_1, P_2, d) = 0.001\frac{P_1 P_2}{d}$$

Find $n(100{,}000, 50{,}000, 100)$.

32. Education. At the beginning of the semester, students in a foreign language course take a proficiency exam. The same exam is given at the end of the semester. The results for 5 students are shown in the following table. Use the least squares line to estimate the second exam score of a student who scored 40 on the first exam.

First Exam	Second Exam
30	60
50	75
60	80
70	85
90	90

33. Population density. The following table gives the U.S. population per square mile for the years 1960–2010:

U.S. Population Density

Year	Population (per square mile)
1960	50.6
1970	57.5
1980	64.1
1990	70.4
2000	79.7
2010	87.4

(A) Find the least squares line for the data, using $x = 0$ for 1960.

(B) Use the least squares line to estimate the population density in the United States in the year 2025.

(C) Now use quadratic regression and exponential regression to obtain the estimate of part (B).

34. Life expectancy. The following table gives life expectancies for males and females in a sample of Central and South American countries:

Life Expectancies for Central and South American Countries

Males	Females	Males	Females
62.30	67.50	70.15	74.10
68.05	75.05	62.93	66.58
72.40	77.04	68.43	74.88
63.39	67.59	66.68	72.80
55.11	59.43		

(A) Find the least squares line for the data.

(B) Use the least squares line to estimate the life expectancy of a female in a Central or South American country in which the life expectancy for males is 60 years.

(C) Now use quadratic regression and logarithmic regression to obtain the estimate of part (B).

8

Trigonometric Functions

Introduction

Business cycles, blood pressure in the aorta, seasonal growth, water waves, and amounts of pollution in the atmosphere are periodic (or cyclical) phenomena. To model such phenomena, we need functions that are periodic. The algebraic, exponential, and logarithmic functions studied in previous chapters do not have this property. But the trigonometric functions do. They are well suited to describe phenomena that repeat in cycles (see, for example, Problem 50 in Section 8.2 on air pollution). In Section 8.1, we provide a brief review of basic topics in trigonometry. In Sections 8.2 and 8.3, we study derivatives and integrals of the trigonometric functions.

8.1 Trigonometric Functions Review

Angles: Degree—Radian Measure

In a plane, an **angle** is formed by rotating a ray m, called the **initial side** of the angle, around its endpoint until the ray coincides with a ray n, called the **terminal side** of the angle. The common endpoint P of m and n is called the **vertex** (see Fig. 1).

There is no restriction on the amount or direction of rotation. A counterclockwise rotation produces a **positive** angle (Fig. 2A), and a clockwise rotation produces a **negative** angle (Fig. 2B). Two different angles may have the same initial and terminal sides, as shown in Figure 2C. Such angles are said to be **coterminal**.

Figure 1 **Angle θ**

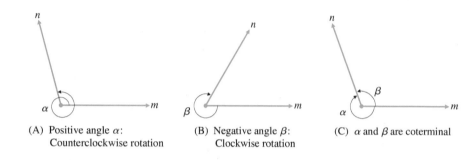

(A) Positive angle α: (B) Negative angle β: (C) α and β are coterminal
    Counterclockwise rotation   Clockwise rotation

Figure 2

There are two widely used measures of angles: the *degree* and the *radian*. When a central angle of a circle is subtended by an arc that is $\frac{1}{360}$ the circumference of the circle, the angle is said to have **degree measure 1**, written as **1°** (see Fig. 3A). It follows that a central angle subtended by an arc that is $\frac{1}{4}$ of the circumference has a degree measure of 90, $\frac{1}{2}$ of the circumference has a degree measure of 180, and the whole circumference of a circle has a degree measure of 360.

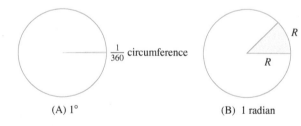

(A) 1°   (B) 1 radian

Figure 3 **Degree and radian measure**

The other measure of angles is radian measure. A central angle subtended by an arc of length equal to the radius (R) of the circle is said to have **radian measure 1**, written as **1 radian** or **1 rad** (see Fig. 3B). In general, a central angle subtended by an arc of length s has radian measure that is determined as follows:

Figure 4

$$\theta_{\text{rad}} = \text{radian measure of } \theta = \frac{\text{arc length}}{\text{radius}} = \frac{s}{R}$$

(See Figure 4.) [*Note*: If $R = 1$, then $\theta_{\text{rad}} = s$.]

What is the radian measure of a 180° angle? A central angle of 180° is subtended by an arc that is $\frac{1}{2}$ the circumference of a circle. Thus,

$$s = \frac{C}{2} = \frac{2\pi R}{2} = \pi R \qquad \text{and} \qquad \theta_{\text{rad}} = \frac{s}{R} = \frac{\pi R}{R} = \pi \text{ rad}$$

The following proportion can be used to convert degree measure to radian measure and vice versa:

Degree–Radian Conversion

$$\frac{\theta_{\text{deg}}}{180°} = \frac{\theta_{\text{rad}}}{\pi \text{ rad}}$$

EXAMPLE 1   From Degrees to Radians   Find the radian measure of 1°.

SOLUTION

$$\frac{1°}{180°} = \frac{\theta_{\text{rad}}}{\pi \text{ rad}}$$

$$\theta_{\text{rad}} = \frac{\pi}{180} \text{ rad} \approx 0.0175 \text{ rad}$$

Matched Problem 1   Find the degree measure of 1 rad.

A comparison of degree and radian measure for a few important angles is given in the following table:

Radian	0	$\pi/6$	$\pi/4$	$\pi/3$	$\pi/2$	π	2π
Degree	0	30°	45°	60°	90°	180°	360°

An angle in a rectangular coordinate system is said to be in **standard position** if its vertex is at the origin and its initial side is on the positive x axis. Figure 5 shows three angles in standard position.

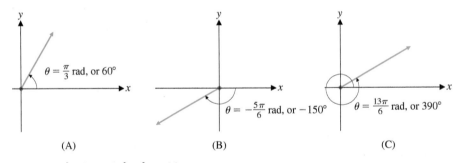

(A)   (B)   (C)

Figure 5 **Angles in standard position**

Trigonometric Functions

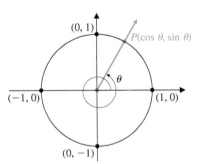

Figure 6

Consider a unit circle (radius 1) in a coordinate system with center at the origin (Fig. 6). The terminal side of any angle in standard position will pass through this circle at some point P. The abscissa of point P is called the **cosine of θ** (abbreviated **cos θ**), and the ordinate of the point is the **sine of θ** (abbreviated **sin θ**). The set of all ordered pairs of the form $(\theta, \cos \theta)$ and the set of all ordered pairs of the form $(\theta, \sin \theta)$ constitute, respectively, the **cosine and sine functions**. The **domain** of these two functions is the set of all angles, positive or negative, with measure either in degrees or radians. The **range** is a subset of the set of real numbers.

It is necessary for our work in calculus to define these two trigonometric functions in terms of real-number domains. This is done as follows:

DEFINITION   Sine and Cosine Functions with Real-Number Domains
For any real number x,

$$\sin x = \sin(x \text{ radians}) \quad \text{and} \quad \cos x = \cos(x \text{ radians})$$

EXAMPLE 2 Evaluating Sine and Cosine Functions   Referring to Figure 6, find

(A) $\cos 90°$ (B) $\sin(-\pi/2 \text{ rad})$ (C) $\cos \pi$

SOLUTION

(A) The terminal side of an angle of degree measure 90 passes through $(0, 1)$ on the unit circle. This point has abscissa 0. So

$$\cos 90° = 0$$

(B) The terminal side of an angle of radian measure $-\pi/2$ $(-90°)$ passes through $(0, -1)$ on the unit circle. This point has ordinate -1. So

$$\sin\left(-\frac{\pi}{2} \text{ rad}\right) = -1$$

(C) $\cos \pi = \cos(\pi \text{ rad}) = -1$, since the terminal side of an angle of radian measure $\pi(180°)$ passes through $(-1, 0)$ on the unit circle and this point has abscissa -1.

Matched Problem 2   Referring to Figure 6, find

(A) $\sin 180°$ (B) $\cos(2\pi \text{ rad})$ (C) $\sin(-\pi)$

Finding the value of either the sine or cosine function for any angle or any real number using the definition is not easy. Calculators with sin and cos keys are used. Calculators generally have degree and radian options, so we can use a calculator to evaluate these functions for most of the real numbers in which we might have an interest. The following table includes a few values produced by a calculator in radian mode:

x	1	-7	35.26	-105.9
$\sin x$	0.8415	-0.6570	-0.6461	0.7920
$\cos x$	0.5403	0.7539	-0.7632	0.6105

Explore and Discuss 1   Many errors in trigonometry can be traced to having the calculator in the wrong mode, radian instead of degree, or vice versa, when performing calculations. The calculator screen in Figure 7 gives two different values for cos 30. Experiment with your calculator and explain the discrepancy.

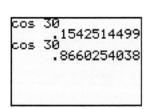

Figure 7

Exact values of the sine and cosine functions can be obtained for multiples of the special angles shown in Figure 8, because these triangles can be used to find the coordinate of the intersection of the terminal side of each angle with the unit circle.

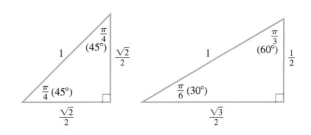

Figure 8

EXAMPLE 3   Finding Exact Values for Special "Angles"   Use Figure 8 to find the exact value of each of the following:

(A) $\cos\dfrac{\pi}{4}$ (B) $\sin\dfrac{\pi}{6}$ (C) $\sin\left(-\dfrac{\pi}{6}\right)$

SOLUTION

(A) $\cos\dfrac{\pi}{4} = \dfrac{\sqrt{2}}{2}$ (B) $\sin\dfrac{\pi}{6} = \dfrac{1}{2}$ (C) $\sin\left(-\dfrac{\pi}{6}\right) = -\dfrac{1}{2}$

Matched Problem 3   Use Figure 8 to find the exact value of each of the following:

(A) $\sin\dfrac{\pi}{4}$ (B) $\cos\dfrac{\pi}{3}$ (C) $\cos\left(-\dfrac{\pi}{3}\right)$

Graphs of the Sine and Cosine Functions

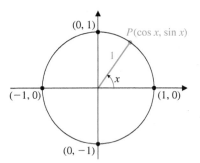

Figure 9

To graph $y = \sin x$ or $y = \cos x$ for x a real number, we could use a calculator to produce a table and then plot the ordered pairs from the table in a coordinate system. However, we can speed up the process by returning to basic definitions. Referring to Figure 9, since $\cos x$ and $\sin x$ are the coordinates of a point on the unit circle, we see that

$$-1 \le \sin x \le 1 \qquad \text{and} \qquad -1 \le \cos x \le 1$$

for all real numbers x. Furthermore, as x increases and P moves around the unit circle in a counterclockwise (positive) direction, both $\sin x$ and $\cos x$ behave in uniform ways, as indicated in the following table:

As x Increases from	$y = \sin x$	$y = \cos x$
0 to $\pi/2$	Increases from 0 to 1	Decreases from 1 to 0
$\pi/2$ to π	Decreases from 1 to 0	Decreases from 0 to −1
π to $3\pi/2$	Decreases from 0 to −1	Increases from −1 to 0
$3\pi/2$ to 2π	Increases from −1 to 0	Increases from 0 to 1

Note that P has completed one revolution and is back at its starting place. If we let x continue to increase, the second and third columns in the table will be repeated every 2π units. In general, it can be shown that

$$\sin(x + 2\pi) = \sin x \qquad \cos(x + 2\pi) = \cos x$$

for all real numbers x. Functions such that

$$f(x + p) = f(x)$$

for some positive constant p and all real numbers x for which the functions are defined are said to be **periodic**. The smallest such value of p is called the **period** of the function. Both the sine and cosine functions are periodic with period 2π.

Putting all this information together and adding a few values obtained from a calculator or Figure 8, we obtain the graphs of the sine and cosine functions illustrated in Figure 10. Notice that these curves are continuous. It can be shown that **the sine and cosine functions are continuous for all real numbers.**

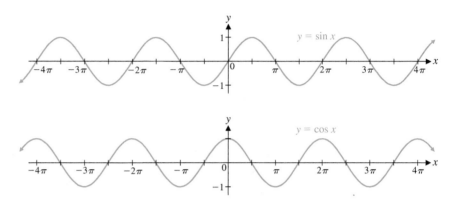

Figure 10

Four Other Trigonometric Functions

The sine and cosine functions are only two of six trigonometric functions. They are, however, the most important of the six for many applications. The other four trigonometric functions are the **tangent, cotangent, secant**, and **cosecant**.

DEFINITION Four Other Trigonometric Functions

$$\tan x = \frac{\sin x}{\cos x} \qquad \cos x \neq 0 \qquad\qquad \sec x = \frac{1}{\cos x} \qquad \cos x \neq 0$$

$$\cot x = \frac{\cos x}{\sin x} \qquad \sin x \neq 0 \qquad\qquad \csc x = \frac{1}{\sin x} \qquad \sin x \neq 0$$

CONCEPTUAL INSIGHT

The functions $\sin x$ and $\cos x$ are periodic with period 2π, so

$$\tan(x + 2\pi) = \frac{\sin(x + 2\pi)}{\cos(x + 2\pi)} = \frac{\sin x}{\cos x} = \tan x$$

One might guess that $\tan x$ is periodic with period 2π. However, 2π is not the *smallest* positive constant p such that $\tan(x + p) = \tan x$. Because the points $(\cos x, \sin x)$ and $(\cos(x + \pi), \sin(x + \pi))$ are diametrically opposed on the unit circle,

$$\sin(x + \pi) = -\sin x \qquad \text{and} \qquad \cos(x + \pi) = -\cos x$$

Therefore,

$$\tan(x + \pi) = \frac{\sin(x + \pi)}{\cos(x + \pi)} = \frac{-\sin x}{-\cos x} = \tan x$$

It follows that the functions $\tan x$ and $\cot x$ have period π. The other four trigonometric functions—$\sin x$, $\cos x$, $\sec x$, and $\csc x$—all have period 2π.

Skills Warm-up Exercises

W *In Problems 1–8, mentally convert each degree measure to radian measure, and each radian measure to degree measure.*

1. $60°$

2. $90°$

3. $135°$

4. $-30°$

5. $-\dfrac{\pi}{4}$ rad

6. $\dfrac{5\pi}{4}$ rad

7. $\dfrac{3\pi}{2}$ rad

8. $\dfrac{2\pi}{3}$ rad

In Problems 9–24, use Figure 6 or Figure 8 to find the exact value of each expression.

9. $\sin 60°$

10. $\sin 45°$

11. $\cos 135°$

12. $\cos 120°$

13. $\sin 90°$

14. $\cos 180°$

15. $\cos(-90°)$

16. $\sin(-180°)$

17. $\cos\left(\dfrac{5\pi}{4}\right)$

18. $\sin\left(\dfrac{3\pi}{4}\right)$

19. $\sin\left(-\dfrac{\pi}{6}\right)$

20. $\cos\left(-\dfrac{2\pi}{3}\right)$

21. $\sin\left(\dfrac{3\pi}{2}\right)$

22. $\cos(2\pi)$

23. $\cos\left(-\dfrac{11\pi}{6}\right)$

24. $\sin\left(-\dfrac{5\pi}{6}\right)$

25. Refer to Figure 6 and use the Pythagorean theorem to show that

$$(\sin x)^2 + (\cos x)^2 = 1$$

for all x.

26. Use the results of Problem 25 and basic definitions to show that

(A) $(\tan x)^2 + 1 = (\sec x)^2$

(B) $1 + (\cot x)^2 = (\csc x)^2$

In Problems 27–42, use Figure 6 or Figure 8 to find the exact value of each expression.

27. $\tan\left(\dfrac{3\pi}{4}\right)$

28. $\sec\left(\dfrac{\pi}{3}\right)$

29. $\csc\left(\dfrac{2\pi}{3}\right)$

30. $\cot\left(\dfrac{\pi}{4}\right)$

31. $\sec 90°$

32. $\csc(-30°)$

33. $\cot(-150°)$

34. $\tan(-90°)$

35. $\csc\left(\dfrac{7\pi}{6}\right)$

36. $\cot\left(\dfrac{5\pi}{6}\right)$

37. $\sec(-\pi)$

38. $\csc\left(-\dfrac{3\pi}{2}\right)$

39. $\tan 120°$

40. $\sec(135°)$

41. $\cot(-45°)$

42. $\tan(-720°)$

In Problems 43–54, use a calculator in radian or degree mode, as appropriate, to find the value of each expression to four decimal places.

43. $\sin 10°$

44. $\tan 141°$

45. $\cos(-52°)$

46. $\sec(-18°)$

47. $\tan 1$

48. $\cot(-2)$

49. $\sec(-1.56)$

50. $\cos 3.13$

51. $\csc 1°$

52. $\csc 182°$

53. $\cot\left(\dfrac{\pi}{10}\right)$

54. $\sin\left(\dfrac{4\pi}{5}\right)$

In Problems 55–58, use a graphing calculator set in radian mode to graph each function.

55. $y = 2 \sin \pi x;\ 0 \le x \le 2,\ -2 \le y \le 2$

56. $y = -0.5 \cos 2x;\ 0 \le x \le 2\pi,\ -0.5 \le y \le 0.5$

57. $y = 4 - 4\cos\dfrac{\pi x}{2};\ 0 \le x \le 8,\ 0 \le y \le 8$

58. $y = 6 + 6\sin\dfrac{\pi x}{26};\ 0 \le x \le 104,\ 0 \le y \le 12$

59. Find the domain of the tangent function.

60. Find the domain of the cotangent function.

61. Find the domain of the secant function.

62. Find the domain of the cosecant function.

63. Explain why the range of the cosecant function is $(-\infty, -1] \cup [1, \infty)$.

64. Explain why the range of the secant function is $(-\infty, -1] \cup [1, \infty)$.

65. Explain why the range of the cotangent function is $(-\infty, \infty)$.

66. Explain why the range of the tangent function is $(-\infty, \infty)$.

Applications

67. Seasonal business cycle. Suppose that profits on the sale of swimming suits over a 2-year period are given approximately by

$$P(t) = 5 - 5\cos\dfrac{\pi t}{26} \qquad 0 \le t \le 104$$

where P is profit (in hundreds of dollars) for a week of sales t weeks after January 1. The graph of the profit function is shown in the figure.

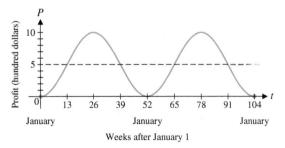

(A) Find the exact values of $P(13)$, $P(26)$, $P(39)$, and $P(52)$ without using a calculator.

(B) Use a calculator to find $P(30)$ and $P(100)$. Interpret the results.

(C) Use a graphing calculator to confirm the graph shown here for $y = P(t)$.

68. Seasonal business cycle. Revenues from sales of a soft drink over a 2-year period are given approximately by

$$R(t) = 4 - 3\cos\frac{\pi t}{6} \qquad 0 \le t \le 24$$

where $R(t)$ is revenue (in millions of dollars) for a month of sales t months after February 1. The graph of the revenue function is shown in the figure.

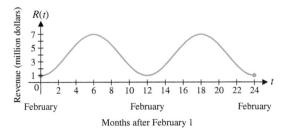

Months after February 1

(A) Find the exact values of $R(0)$, $R(2)$, $R(3)$, and $R(18)$ without using a calculator.

(B) Use a calculator to find $R(5)$ and $R(23)$. Interpret the results.

(C) Use a graphing calculator to confirm the graph shown here for $y = R(t)$.

69. Physiology. A normal seated adult inhales and exhales about 0.8 liter of air every 4 seconds. The volume $V(t)$ of air in the lungs t seconds after exhaling is given approximately by

$$V(t) = 0.45 - 0.35\cos\frac{\pi t}{2} \qquad 0 \le t \le 8$$

The graph for two complete respirations is shown in the figure.

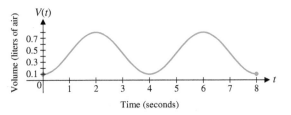

Time (seconds)

(A) Find the exact value of $V(0)$, $V(1)$, $V(2)$, $V(3)$, and $V(7)$ without using a calculator.

(B) Use a calculator to find $V(3.5)$ and $V(5.7)$. Interpret the results.

(C) Use a graphing calculator to confirm the graph shown here for $y = V(t)$.

70. Pollution. In a large city, the amount of sulfur dioxide pollutant released into the atmosphere due to the burning of coal and oil for heating purposes varies seasonally. Suppose that the number of tons of pollutant released into

the atmosphere during the nth week after January 1 is given approximately by

$$P(n) = 1 + \cos\frac{\pi n}{26} \qquad 0 \le n \le 104$$

The graph of the pollution function is shown in the figure.

Weeks after January 1

(A) Find the exact values of $P(0)$, $P(39)$, $P(52)$, and $P(65)$ without using a calculator.

(B) Use a calculator to find $P(10)$ and $P(95)$. Interpret the results.

(C) Use a graphing calculator to confirm the graph shown here for $y = P(n)$.

71. Psychology. Individuals perceive objects differently in different settings. Consider the well-known illusions shown in Figure A. Lines that appear parallel in one setting may appear to be curved in another (the two vertical lines are actually parallel). Lines of the same length may appear to be of different lengths in two different settings (the two horizontal lines are actually the same length). Psychologists Berliner and Berliner reported that when subjects were presented with a large tilted field of parallel lines and were asked to estimate the position of a horizontal line in the field, most of the subjects were consistently off (Figure B). They found that the difference d in degrees between the estimates and the actual horizontal could be approximated by the equation

$$d = a + b\sin 4\theta$$

where a and b are constants associated with a particular person and θ is the angle of tilt of the visual field (in degrees). Suppose that, for a given person, $a = -2.1$ and $b = -4$. Find d if

(A) $\theta = 30°$ \qquad\qquad (B) $\theta = 10°$

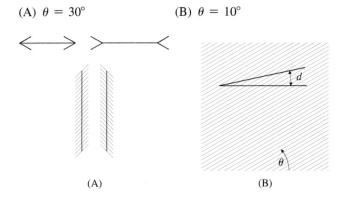

(A) \qquad\qquad\qquad (B)

Answers to Matched Problems

1. $180/\pi \approx 57.3°$

2. (A) 0 \qquad (B) 1 \qquad (C) 0

3. (A) $\sqrt{2}/2$ \qquad (B) $\frac{1}{2}$ \qquad (C) $\frac{1}{2}$

8.2 Derivatives of Trigonometric Functions

- Derivative Formulas
- Application

Derivative Formulas

In this section, we discuss derivative formulas for the sine and cosine functions. Once we have these formulas, we will automatically have integral formulas for the same functions, which we discuss in the next section.

From the definition of the derivative (Section 2.4),

$$\frac{d}{dx}\sin x = \lim_{h \to 0}\frac{\sin(x+h) - \sin x}{h}$$

On the basis of trigonometric identities and some special trigonometric limits, it can be shown that the limit on the right is cos x. Similarly, it can be shown that

$$\frac{d}{dx}\cos x = -\sin x$$

We now add the following important derivative formulas to our list of derivative formulas:

Derivative of Sine and Cosine
Basic Form

$$\frac{d}{dx}\sin x = \cos x \qquad \frac{d}{dx}\cos x = -\sin x$$

Generalized Form
For $u = u(x)$,

$$\frac{d}{dx}\sin u = \cos u\frac{du}{dx} \qquad \frac{d}{dx}\cos u = -\sin u\frac{du}{dx}$$

CONCEPTUAL INSIGHT

The derivative formula for the function $y = \sin x$ implies that each line tangent to the graph of the function has a slope between -1 and 1. Furthermore, the slope of the line tangent to $y = \sin x$ is equal to 1 if and only if cos $x = 1$—that is, at $x = 0, \pm 2\pi, \pm 4\pi, \ldots$. Similarly, the derivative formula for $y = \cos x$ implies that each line tangent to the graph of the function has a slope between -1 and 1. The slope of the tangent line is equal to 1 if and only if $-\sin x = 1$—that is, at $x = 3\pi/2, (3\pi/2) \pm 2\pi, (3\pi/2) \pm 4\pi, \ldots$. Note that these observations are consistent with the graphs of $y = \sin x$ and $y = \cos x$ shown in Figure 10, Section 8.1.

EXAMPLE 1   Derivatives Involving Sine and Cosine

(A) $\dfrac{d}{dx}\sin x^2 = (\cos x^2)\dfrac{d}{dx}x^2 = (\cos x^2)2x = 2x\cos x^2$

(B) $\dfrac{d}{dx}\cos(2x - 5) = -\sin(2x - 5)\dfrac{d}{dx}(2x - 5) = -2\sin(2x - 5)$

(C) $\dfrac{d}{dx}(3x^2 - x)\cos x = (3x^2 - x)\dfrac{d}{dx}\cos x + (\cos x)\dfrac{d}{dx}(3x^2 - x)$

$\qquad\qquad = -(3x^2 - x)\sin x + (6x - 1)\cos x$

$\qquad\qquad = (x - 3x^2)\sin x + (6x - 1)\cos x$

Matched Problem 1   Find each of the following derivatives:

(A) $\dfrac{d}{dx}\cos x^3$ 　　　(B) $\dfrac{d}{dx}\sin(5 - 3x)$ 　　　(C) $\dfrac{d}{dx}\dfrac{\sin x}{x}$

EXAMPLE 2 Slope Find the slope of the graph of $f(x) = \sin x$ at $(\pi/2, 1)$, and sketch in the line tangent to the graph at this point.

SOLUTION Slope at $(\pi/2, 1) = f'(\pi/2) = \cos(\pi/2) = 0$.

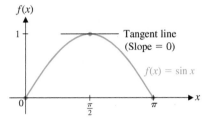

Matched Problem 2 Find the slope of the graph of $f(x) = \cos x$ at $(\pi/6, \sqrt{3}/2)$.

Explore and Discuss 1 From the graph of $y = f'(x)$ shown in Figure 1, describe the shape of the graph of $y = f(x)$ relative to where it is increasing, where it is decreasing, its concavity, and the locations of local maxima and minima. Make a sketch of a possible graph of $y = f(x), 0 \le x \le 2\pi$, given that it has x intercepts at $(0, 0)$, $(\pi, 0)$, and $(2\pi, 0)$. Can you identify $f(x)$ and $f'(x)$ in terms of sine or cosine functions?

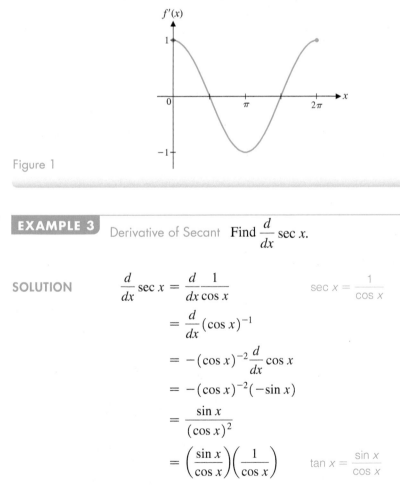

Figure 1

EXAMPLE 3 Derivative of Secant Find $\dfrac{d}{dx} \sec x$.

SOLUTION
$$\frac{d}{dx} \sec x = \frac{d}{dx} \frac{1}{\cos x} \qquad\qquad \sec x = \frac{1}{\cos x}$$

$$= \frac{d}{dx} (\cos x)^{-1}$$

$$= -(\cos x)^{-2} \frac{d}{dx} \cos x$$

$$= -(\cos x)^{-2} (-\sin x)$$

$$= \frac{\sin x}{(\cos x)^2}$$

$$= \left(\frac{\sin x}{\cos x}\right)\left(\frac{1}{\cos x}\right) \qquad \tan x = \frac{\sin x}{\cos x}$$

$$= \tan x \sec x$$

Matched Problem 3 Find $\dfrac{d}{dx} \csc x$.

Application

EXAMPLE 4   Revenue   Revenues from the sale of ski jackets are given approximately by

$$R(t) = 1.55 + 1.45 \cos \frac{\pi t}{26} \qquad 0 \le t \le 104$$

where $R(t)$ is revenue (in thousands of dollars) for a week of sales t weeks after January 1.

(A) What is the rate of change of revenue t weeks after the first of the year?

(B) What is the rate of change of revenue 10 weeks after the first of the year? 26 weeks after the first of the year? 40 weeks after the first of the year?

(C) Find all local maxima and minima for $0 < t < 104$.

(D) Find the absolute maximum and minimum for $0 \le t \le 104$.

(E) Illustrate the results from parts (A)–(D) by sketching a graph of $y = R(t)$ with the aid of a graphing calculator.

SOLUTION

(A) $R'(t) = -\dfrac{1.45\pi}{26} \sin \dfrac{\pi t}{26} \qquad 0 \le t \le 104$

(B) $R'(10) \approx -\$0.164$ thousand,   or $-\$164$ per week

$R'(26) = \$0$ per week

$R'(40) \approx \$0.174$ thousand,   or $\$174$ per week

(C) Find the critical points:

$$R'(t) = -\frac{1.45\pi}{26} \sin \frac{\pi t}{26} = 0 \qquad 0 < t < 104$$

$$\sin \frac{\pi t}{26} = 0$$

$$\frac{\pi t}{26} = \pi, 2\pi, 3\pi \quad \text{Note: } 0 < t < 104 \text{ implies that } 0 < \frac{\pi t}{26} < 4\pi.$$

$$t = 26, 52, 78$$

Differentiate $R'(t)$ to get $R''(t)$.

$$R''(t) = -\frac{1.45\pi^2}{26^2} \cos \frac{\pi t}{26}$$

Use the second-derivative test to get the results shown in Table 1.

Table 1

t	$R''(t)$	Graph of R
26	+	Local minimum
52	−	Local maximum
78	+	Local minimum

(D) Evaluate $R(t)$ at endpoints $t = 0$ and $t = 104$ and at the critical points found in part (C), as listed in Table 2. The absolute maximum is 3,000 and it occurs at $t = 0, 52$, and 104; the absolute minimum is 100 at it occurs at $t = 26$ and 78.

Table 2

t	$R(t)$	
0	$3,000	Absolute maximum
26	$100	Absolute minimum
52	$3,000	Absolute maximum
78	$100	Absolute minimum
104	$3,000	Absolute maximum

(E) The results from parts (A)–(D) can be visualized as shown in Figure 2.

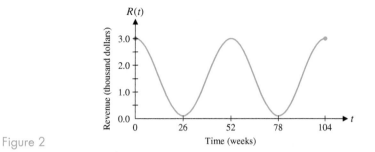

Figure 2

Matched Problem 4 Suppose that revenues from the sale of ski jackets are given approximately by

$$R(t) = 6.2 + 5.8 \cos \frac{\pi t}{6} \qquad 0 \le t \le 24$$

where $R(t)$ is revenue (in thousands of dollars) for a month of sales t months after January 1.

(A) What is the rate of change of revenue t months after the first of the year?

(B) What is the rate of change of revenue 2 months after the first of the year? 12 months after the first of the year? 23 months after the first of the year?

(C) Find all local maxima and minima for $0 < t < 24$.

(D) Find the absolute maximum and minimum for $0 \le t \le 24$.

(E) Illustrate the results from parts (A)–(D) by sketching a graph of $y = R(t)$ with the aid of a graphing calculator.

Exercises 8.2

Skills Warm-up Exercises

W *In Problems 1–4, by inspecting a graph of $y = \sin x$ or $y = \cos x$, determine whether the function is increasing or decreasing on the given interval.*

1. $y = \cos x$ on $(0, \pi)$

2. $y = \sin x$ on $(\pi/2, 3\pi/2)$

3. $y = \sin x$ on $(-\pi/2, \pi/2)$

4. $y = \cos x$ on $(\pi, 2\pi)$

In Problems 5–8, by inspecting a graph of $y = \sin x$ or $y = \cos x$, determine whether the graph is concave up or concave down on the given interval.

5. $y = \sin x$ on $(0, \pi)$

6. $y = \cos x$ on $(\pi/2, 3\pi/2)$

7. $y = \cos x$ on $(-\pi/2, \pi/2)$

8. $y = \sin x$ on $(-\pi, 0)$

Find the indicated derivatives in Problems 9–26.

9. $\dfrac{d}{dx}(5 \cos x)$

10. $\dfrac{d}{dx}(8 \sin x)$

11. $\dfrac{d}{dx} \cos (5x)$

12. $\dfrac{d}{dx} \sin (8x)$

13. $\dfrac{d}{dx} \sin (x^2 + 1)$

14. $\dfrac{d}{dx} \cos (x^3 - 1)$

15. $\dfrac{d}{dw} \sin (w + \pi)$

16. $\dfrac{d}{dt} \cos \left(\dfrac{\pi t}{2}\right)$

17. $\dfrac{d}{dt} t \sin t$

18. $\dfrac{d}{du} u \cos u$

19. $\dfrac{d}{dx} \sin x \cos x$

20. $\dfrac{d}{dx} \dfrac{\sin x}{\cos x}$

21. $\dfrac{d}{dx}(\sin x)^5$

22. $\dfrac{d}{dx}(\cos x)^8$

23. $\dfrac{d}{dx} \sqrt{\sin x}$

24. $\dfrac{d}{dx} \sqrt{\cos x}$

25. $\dfrac{d}{dx} \cos \sqrt{x}$

26. $\dfrac{d}{dx} \sin \sqrt{x}$

27. Find the slope of the graph of $f(x) = \sin x$ at $x = \pi/6$.

28. Find the slope of the graph of $f(x) = \cos x$ at $x = \pi/4$.

29. From the graph of $y = f'(x)$ shown here, describe the shape of the graph of $y = f(x)$ relative to where it is increasing, where it is decreasing, its concavity, and the locations of local maxima and minima. Make a sketch of a possible graph of $y = f(x)$, $-\pi \leq x \leq \pi$, given that it has x intercepts at $(-\pi/2, 0)$ and $(\pi/2, 0)$. Identify $f(x)$ and $f'(x)$ as particular trigonometric functions.

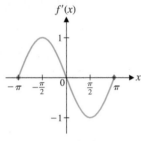

Figure for 29

30. From the graph of $y = f'(x)$ shown here, describe the shape of the graph of $y = f(x)$ relative to where it is increasing, where it is decreasing, its concavity, and the locations of local maxima and minima. Make a sketch of a possible graph of $y = f(x)$, $-\pi \leq x \leq \pi$, given that it has x intercepts at $(-\pi, 0)$ and $(\pi, 0)$. Identify $f(x)$ and $f'(x)$ as particular trigonometric functions.

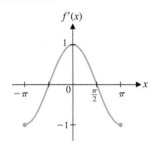

Find the indicated derivatives in Problems 31–38.

31. $\dfrac{d}{dx} \csc (\pi x)$

32. $\dfrac{d}{dx} \sec (x + \pi)$

33. $\dfrac{d}{dx} \cot \left(\dfrac{\pi x}{2} \right)$

34. $\dfrac{d}{dx} \tan (\pi x)$

35. $\dfrac{d}{dx} \cos (x e^x)$

36. $\dfrac{d}{dx} \sin (x e^x)$

37. $\dfrac{d}{dx} \tan (x^2)$

38. $\dfrac{d}{dx} \csc (x^3)$

In Problems 39 and 40, find $f''(x)$.

39. $f(x) = e^x \sin x$

40. $f(x) = e^x \cos x$

In Problems 41–46, graph each function on a graphing calculator.

41. $y = x \sin \pi x$; $0 \leq x \leq 9$, $-9 \leq y \leq 9$

42. $y = -x \cos \pi x$; $0 \leq x \leq 9$, $-9 \leq y \leq 9$

43. $y = \dfrac{\cos \pi x}{x}$; $0 \leq x \leq 8$, $-2 \leq y \leq 3$

44. $y = \dfrac{\sin \pi x}{0.5x}$; $0 \leq x \leq 8$, $-2 \leq y \leq 3$

45. $y = e^{-0.3x} \sin \pi x$; $0 \leq x \leq 10$, $-1 \leq y \leq 1$

46. $y = e^{-0.2x} \cos \pi x$; $0 \leq x \leq 10$, $-1 \leq y \leq 1$

Applications

47. Profit. Suppose that profits on the sale of swimming suits are given approximately by

$$P(t) = 5 - 5 \cos \frac{\pi t}{26} \qquad 0 \leq t \leq 104$$

where $P(t)$ is profit (in hundreds of dollars) for a week of sales t weeks after January 1.

(A) What is the rate of change of profit t weeks after the first of the year?

(B) What is the rate of change of profit 8 weeks after the first of the year? 26 weeks after the first of the year? 50 weeks after the first of the year?

(C) Find all local maxima and minima for $0 < t < 104$.

(D) Find the absolute maximum and minimum for $0 \leq t \leq 104$.

(E) Repeat part (C), using a graphing calculator.

48. Revenue. Revenues from sales of a soft drink over a 2-year period are given approximately by

$$R(t) = 4 - 3 \cos \frac{\pi t}{6} \qquad 0 \leq t \leq 24$$

where $R(t)$ is revenue (in millions of dollars) for a month of sales t months after February 1.

(A) What is the rate of change of revenue t months after February 1?

(B) What is the rate of change of revenue 1 month after February 1? 6 months after February 1? 11 months after February 1?

(C) Find all local maxima and minima for $0 < t < 24$.

(D) Find the absolute maximum and minimum for $0 \leq t \leq 24$.

(E) Repeat part (C), using a graphing calculator.

49. Physiology. A normal seated adult inhales and exhales about 0.8 liter of air every 4 seconds. The volume of air $V(t)$ in the lungs t seconds after exhaling is given approximately by

$$V(t) = 0.45 - 0.35 \cos \frac{\pi t}{2} \qquad 0 \leq t \leq 8$$

(A) What is the rate of flow of air t seconds after exhaling?

(B) What is the rate of flow of air 3 seconds after exhaling? 4 seconds after exhaling? 5 seconds after exhaling?

(C) Find all local maxima and minima for $0 < t < 8$.

(D) Find the absolute maximum and minimum for $0 \leq t \leq 8$.

(E) Repeat part (C), using a graphing calculator.

50. Pollution. In a large city, the amount of sulfur dioxide pollutant released into the atmosphere due to the burning of coal and oil for heating purposes varies seasonally. Suppose that the number of tons of pollutant released into the atmosphere during the nth week after January 1 is given approximately by

$$P(n) = 1 + \cos\frac{\pi n}{26} \qquad 0 \le n \le 104$$

(A) What is the rate of change of pollutant n weeks after the first of the year?

(B) What is the rate of change of pollutant 13 weeks after the first of the year? 26 weeks after the first of the year? 30 weeks after the first of the year?

(C) Find all local maxima and minima for $0 < t < 104$.

(D) Find the absolute maximum and minimum for $0 \le t \le 104$.

(E) Repeat part (C), using a graphing calculator.

1. (A) $-3x^2 \sin x^3$ (B) $-3\cos(5 - 3x)$

(C) $\dfrac{x\cos x - \sin x}{x^2}$

2. $-\frac{1}{2}$ 3. $-\cot x \csc x$

4. (A) $R'(t) = -\dfrac{5.8\pi}{6}\sin\dfrac{\pi t}{6}, 0 < t < 24$

(B) $R'(2) \approx -\$2.630$ thousand, or $-\$2,630$/month; $R'(12) = \$0$/month; $R'(23) \approx \$1.518$ thousand, or $\$1,518$ month

(C) Local minima at $t = 6$ and $t = 18$; local maximum at $t = 12$

(D)

	t	$R(t)$	
Endpoint	0	\$12,000	Absolute maximum
	6	\$400	Absolute minimum
	12	\$12,000	Absolute maximum
	18	\$400	Absolute minimum
Endpoint	24	\$12,000	Absolute maximum

(E)

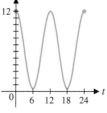

8.3   Integration of Trigonometric Functions

- Integral Formulas
- Application

Integral Formulas

Now that we know the derivative formulas

$$\frac{d}{dx}\sin x = \cos x \quad \text{and} \quad \frac{d}{dx}\cos x = -\sin x$$

we automatically have the two integral formulas from the definition of the indefinite integral of a function (Section 5.1):

$$\int \cos x \, dx = \sin x + C \quad \text{and} \quad \int \sin x \, dx = -\cos x + C$$

EXAMPLE 1 Area Under a Sine Curve Find the area under the sine curve $y = \sin x$ from 0 to π.

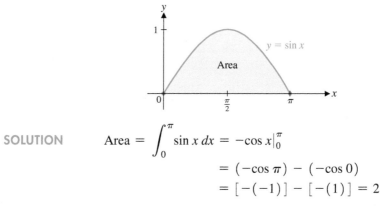

SOLUTION $\text{Area} = \displaystyle\int_0^\pi \sin x \, dx = -\cos x \big|_0^\pi$

$$= (-\cos \pi) - (-\cos 0)$$
$$= [-(-1)] - [-(1)] = 2$$

Matched Problem 1 Find the area under the cosine curve $y = \cos x$ from 0 to $\pi/2$.

From the general derivative formulas

$$\frac{d}{dx}\sin u = \cos u\,\frac{du}{dx} \quad \text{and} \quad \frac{d}{dx}\cos u = -\sin u\,\frac{du}{dx}$$

we obtain the following general integral formulas:

Indefinite Integrals of Sine and Cosine
For $u = u(x)$,

$$\int \sin u\, du = -\cos u + C \quad \text{and} \quad \int \cos u\, du = \sin u + C$$

EXAMPLE 2   Indefinite Integrals and Trigonometric Functions   Find $\int x \sin x^2\, dx$.

SOLUTION $\displaystyle \int x \sin x^2\, dx = \frac{1}{2}\int 2x \sin x^2\, dx$

$$= \frac{1}{2}\int (\sin x^2)\, 2x\, dx \qquad \text{Let } u = x^2;\ \text{then } du = 2x\, dx.$$

$$= \frac{1}{2}\int \sin u\, du$$

$$= -\frac{1}{2}\cos u + C$$

$$= -\frac{1}{2}\cos x^2 + C \qquad \text{Since } u = x^2$$

Check:
To check, we differentiate the result to obtain the original integrand:

$$\frac{d}{dx}\left(-\frac{1}{2}\cos x^2\right) = -\frac{1}{2}\frac{d}{dx}\cos x^2$$

$$= -\frac{1}{2}(-\sin x^2)\frac{d}{dx}x^2$$

$$= -\frac{1}{2}(-\sin x^2)(2x)$$

$$= x \sin x^2$$

Matched Problem 2   Find $\int \cos 20\pi t\, dt$.

EXAMPLE 3   Indefinite Integrals and Trigonometric Functions   Find $\int (\sin x)^5 \cos x\, dx$.

SOLUTION   This integrand is of the form $\int u^p\, du$, where $u = \sin x$ and $du = \cos x\, dx$. Thus,

$$\int (\sin x)^5 \cos x\, dx = \frac{(\sin x)^6}{6} + C$$

Matched Problem 3   Find $\int \sqrt{\sin x}\, \cos x\, dx$.

EXAMPLE 4 Definite Integrals and Trigonometric Functions Evaluate $\int_2^{3.5} \cos x \, dx$.

SOLUTION

$$\int_2^{3.5} \cos x \, dx = \sin x \Big|_2^{3.5}$$

$$= \sin 3.5 - \sin 2 \qquad \text{Use a calculator in radian mode.}$$

$$= -0.3508 - 0.9093$$

$$= -1.2601$$

Matched Problem 4 Use a calculator to evaluate $\int_1^{1.5} \sin x \, dx$.

CONCEPTUAL INSIGHT

Recall that $y = \sin x$ is a periodic function with period 2π, and let c be any real number. Then

$$\int_c^{c+2\pi} \cos x \, dx = \sin x \Big|_c^{c+2\pi} = \sin(c + 2\pi) - \sin c = 0$$

In other words, over any interval of the form $[c, c + 2\pi]$, the area that is above the x axis, but below the graph of $y = \cos x$, is equal to the area that is below the x axis, but above the graph of $y = \cos x$ (see Figure 10, Section 8.1). Similarly, for any real number c,

$$\int_c^{c+2\pi} \sin x \, dx = 0$$

Application

EXAMPLE 5 Total Revenue In Example 4 of Section 8.2, we were given the following revenue equation from the sale of ski jackets:

$$R(t) = 1.55 + 1.45 \cos \frac{\pi t}{26} \qquad 0 \le t \le 104$$

Here, $R(t)$ is revenue (in thousands of dollars) for a week of sales t weeks after January 1.

(A) Find the total revenue taken in over the 2-year period—that is, from $t = 0$ to $t = 104$.

(B) Find the total revenue taken in from $t = 39$ to $t = 65$.

SOLUTION

(A) The area under the graph of the revenue equation for the 2-year period approximates the total revenue taken in for that period:

Time (weeks)

This area (and therefore the total revenue) is given by the following definite integral:

$$\text{Total revenue} \approx \int_0^{104} \left(1.55 + 1.45 \cos \frac{\pi t}{26} \right) dt$$

$$= \left[1.55t + 1.45 \left(\frac{26}{\pi} \right) \sin \frac{\pi t}{26} \right] \Big|_0^{104}$$

$$= \$161.200 \text{ thousand}, \quad \text{or} \quad \$161{,}200$$

(B) The total revenue from $t = 39$ to $t = 65$ is approximated by the area under the curve from $t = 39$ to $t = 65$:

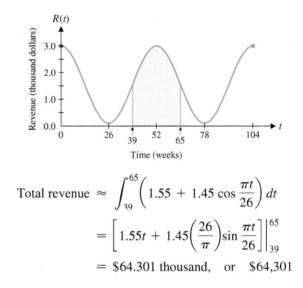

$$\text{Total revenue} \approx \int_{39}^{65} \left(1.55 + 1.45 \cos \frac{\pi t}{26} \right) dt$$

$$= \left[1.55t + 1.45 \left(\frac{26}{\pi} \right) \sin \frac{\pi t}{26} \right] \Big|_{39}^{65}$$

$$= \$64.301 \text{ thousand}, \quad \text{or} \quad \$64{,}301$$

Matched Problem 5 Suppose that revenues from the sale of ski jackets are given approximately by

$$R(t) = 6.2 + 5.8 \cos \frac{\pi t}{6} \quad 0 \le t \le 24$$

where $R(t)$ is revenue (in thousands of dollars) for a month of sales t months after January 1.

(A) Find the total revenue taken in over the 2 year-period—that is, from $t = 0$ to $t = 24$.

(B) Find the total revenue taken in from $t = 4$ to $t = 8$.

Exercises 8.3

Skills Warm-up Exercises

In Problems 1–8, by using only the unit circle definitions of the sine and cosine functions (see page 496), find the solution set of each equation or inequality on the given interval. (If necessary, review Section 1.3).

1. $\sin x \ge 0$ on $[0, 2\pi]$
2. $\cos x \ge 0$ on $[0, 2\pi]$
3. $\cos x > \frac{1}{2}$ on $[0, 2\pi]$
4. $\sin x > \frac{1}{2}$ on $[0, 2\pi]$
5. $|\sin x| = \frac{\sqrt{2}}{2}$ on $[0, 2\pi]$
6. $|\cos x| = \frac{\sqrt{2}}{2}$ on $[0, 2\pi]$
7. $\tan x \le 1$ on $(-\pi/2, \pi/2)$
8. $\cot x \ge 1$ on $(0, \pi)$

Find each of the indefinite integrals in Problems 9–18.

9. $\int \sin t \, dt$
10. $\int \cos w \, dw$
11. $\int \cos 3x \, dx$
12. $\int \sin 2x \, dx$
13. $\int (\sin x)^{12} \cos x \, dx$
14. $\int \sin x \cos x \, dx$
15. $\int \sqrt[3]{\cos x} \sin x \, dx$
16. $\int \frac{\cos x}{\sqrt{\sin x}} \, dx$

17. $\displaystyle\int x^2 \cos x^3 \, dx$ **18.** $\displaystyle\int (x + 1) \sin(x^2 + 2x) \, dx$

Evaluate each of the definite integrals in Problems 19–22.

19. $\displaystyle\int_0^{\pi/2} \cos x \, dx$ **20.** $\displaystyle\int_0^{\pi/4} \cos x \, dx$

21. $\displaystyle\int_{\pi/2}^{\pi} \sin x \, dx$ **22.** $\displaystyle\int_{\pi/6}^{\pi/3} \sin x \, dx$

23. Find the shaded area under the cosine curve in the figure:

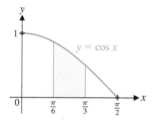

$y = \cos x$

24. Find the shaded area under the sine curve in the figure:

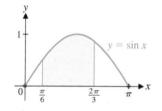

$y = \sin x$

Use a calculator to evaluate the definite integrals in Problems 25–28 after performing the indefinite integration. (Remember that the limits are real numbers, so radian mode must be used on the calculator.)

25. $\displaystyle\int_0^2 \sin x \, dx$ **26.** $\displaystyle\int_0^{0.5} \cos x \, dx$

27. $\displaystyle\int_1^2 \cos x \, dx$ **28.** $\displaystyle\int_1^3 \sin x \, dx$

Find each of the indefinite integrals in Problems 29–34.

29. $\displaystyle\int e^{\sin x} \cos x \, dx$ **30.** $\displaystyle\int e^{\cos x} \sin x \, dx$

31. $\displaystyle\int \frac{\cos x}{\sin x} \, dx$ **32.** $\displaystyle\int \frac{\sin x}{\cos x} \, dx$

33. $\displaystyle\int \tan x \, dx$ **34.** $\displaystyle\int \cot x \, dx$

35. Given the definite integral

$$I = \int_0^3 e^{-x} \sin x \, dx$$

(A) Graph the integrand $f(x) = e^{-x} \sin x$ over $[0, 3]$.

(B) Use the left sum L_6 (see Section 5.5) to approximate I.

36. Given the definite integral

$$I = \int_0^3 e^{-x} \cos x \, dx$$

(A) Graph the integrand $f(x) = e^{-x} \cos x$ over $[0, 3]$.

(B) Use the right sum R_6 (see Section 5.5) to approximate I.

Applications

37. *Seasonal business cycle.* Suppose that profits on the sale of swimming suits in a department store are given approximately by

$$P(t) = 5 - 5 \cos \frac{\pi t}{26} \qquad 0 \le t \le 104$$

where $P(t)$ is profit (in hundreds of dollars) for a week of sales t weeks after January 1. Use definite integrals to approximate

(A) The total profit earned during the 2-year period

(B) The total profit earned from $t = 13$ to $t = 26$

(C) Illustrate part (B) graphically with an appropriate shaded region representing the total profit earned.

38. *Seasonal business cycle.* Revenues from sales of a soft drink over a 2-year period are given approximately by

$$R(t) = 4 - 3 \cos \frac{\pi t}{6} \qquad 0 \le t \le 24$$

where $R(t)$ is revenue (in millions of dollars) for a month of sales t months after February 1. Use definite integrals to approximate

(A) Total revenues taken in over the 2-year period

(B) Total revenues taken in from $t = 8$ to $t = 14$

(C) Illustrate part (B) graphically with an appropriate shaded region representing the total revenues taken in.

39. *Pollution.* In a large city, the amount of sulfur dioxide pollutant released into the atmosphere due to the burning of coal and oil for heating purposes is given approximately by

$$P(n) = 1 + \cos \frac{\pi n}{26} \qquad 0 \le n \le 104$$

where $P(n)$ is the amount of sulfur dioxide (in tons) released during the nth week after January 1.

(A) How many tons of pollutants were emitted into the atmosphere over the 2-year period?

(B) How many tons of pollutants were emitted into the atmosphere from $n = 13$ to $n = 52$?

(C) Illustrate part (B) graphically with an appropriate shaded region representing the total tons of pollutants emitted into the atmosphere.

Answers to Matched Problems

1. 1   **2.** $\dfrac{1}{20\pi} \sin 20\pi t + C$ **3.** $\dfrac{2}{3} (\sin x)^{3/2} + C$

4. 0.4696

5. (A) $148.8 thousand, or $148,800

    (B) $5.614 thousand, or $5,614

Important Terms, Symbols, and Concepts

8.1 Trigonometric Functions Review

- In a plane, an **angle** is formed by rotating a ray m, called the **initial side** of the angle, around its endpoint until the ray coincides with a ray n, called the **terminal side** of the angle. The common endpoint of m and n is called the **vertex.**

- A counterclockwise rotation produces a **positive** angle, and a clockwise rotation produces a **negative** angle.

- Two angles with the same initial and terminal sides are said to be **coterminal**.

- An angle of **degree measure 1** is $\frac{1}{360}$ of a complete rotation. In a circle, an angle of **radian measure 1** is the central angle subtended by an arc having the same length as the radius of the circle.

- Degree measure can be converted to radian measure, and vice versa, by the proportion

Ex. 1, p. 496

$$\frac{\theta_{\deg}}{180°} = \frac{\theta_{\text{rad}}}{\pi \text{ rad}}$$

- An angle in a rectangular coordinate system is in **standard position** if its vertex is at the origin and its initial side is on the positive x axis.

- If θ is an angle in standard position, its terminal side intersects the unit circle at a point P. We denote the coordinates of P by $(\cos \theta, \sin \theta)$ [see Fig. 6, p. 496].

- The set of all ordered pairs of the form $(\theta, \sin \theta)$ is the **sine function**, and the set of all ordered pairs of the form $(\theta, \cos \theta)$ is the **cosine function**. For work in calculus, we define these functions for angles measured in radians. (See Fig. 10, p. 499, for the graphs of $y = \sin x$ and $y = \cos x$.)

Ex. 2, p. 497
Ex. 3, p. 498

- A function is **periodic** if $f(x + p) = f(x)$ for some positive constant p and all real numbers x for which $f(x)$ is defined. The smallest such constant p is called the **period**. Both $\sin x$ and $\cos x$ are periodic continuous functions with period 2π.

- Four additional trigonometric functions—the **tangent, cotangent, secant**, and **cosecant** functions—are defined in terms of $\sin x$ and $\cos x$:

$$\tan x = \frac{\sin x}{\cos x} \quad \cos x \neq 0 \qquad \sec x = \frac{1}{\cos x} \quad \cos x \neq 0$$

$$\cot x = \frac{\cos x}{\sin x} \quad \sin x \neq 0 \qquad \csc x = \frac{1}{\sin x} \quad \sin x \neq 0$$

8.2 Derivatives of Trigonometric Functions

- The derivatives of the functions $\sin x$ and $\cos x$ are

Ex. 1, p. 502
Ex. 2, p. 503
Ex. 3, p. 503
Ex. 4, p. 504

$$\frac{d}{dx} \sin x = \cos x \qquad \frac{d}{dx} \cos x = -\sin x$$

For $u = u(x)$,

$$\frac{d}{dx} \sin u = \cos u \frac{du}{dx} \qquad \frac{d}{du} \cos u = -\sin u \frac{du}{dx}$$

8.3 Integration of Trigonometric Functions

- Indefinite integrals of the functions $\sin x$ and $\cos x$ are

Ex. 1, p. 507
Ex. 2, p. 508
Ex. 3, p. 508
Ex. 4, p. 509
Ex. 5, p. 509

$$\int \sin u \, du = -\cos u + C \quad \text{and} \quad \int \cos u \, du = \sin u + C$$

Review Exercises

Work through all the problems in this chapter review and check your answers in the back of the book. Answers to all review problems are there, along with section numbers in italics to indicate where each type of problem is discussed. Where weaknesses show up, review appropriate sections of the text.

1. Convert to radian measure in terms of π:

(A) $30°$ (B) $45°$ (C) $60°$ (D) $90°$

2. Evaluate without using a calculator:

(A) $\cos \pi$ (B) $\sin 0$ (C) $\sin \dfrac{\pi}{2}$

In Problems 3–6, find each derivative or integral.

3. $\dfrac{d}{dm} \cos m$

4. $\dfrac{d}{du} \sin u$

5. $\dfrac{d}{dx} \sin(x^2 - 2x + 1)$

6. $\displaystyle\int \sin 3t \, dt$

7. Convert to degree measure:

(A) $\pi/6$ (B) $\pi/4$ (C) $\pi/3$ (D) $\pi/2$

8. Evaluate without using a calculator:

(A) $\sin \dfrac{\pi}{6}$ (B) $\cos \dfrac{\pi}{4}$ (C) $\sin \dfrac{\pi}{3}$

9. Evaluate with the use of a calculator:

(A) $\cos 33.7$ (B) $\sin(-118.4)$

In Problems 10–16, find each derivative or integral.

10. $\dfrac{d}{dx}(x^2 - 1) \sin x$

11. $\dfrac{d}{dx}(\sin x)^6$

12. $\dfrac{d}{dx} \sqrt[3]{\sin x}$

13. $\displaystyle\int t \cos(t^2 - 1) \, dt$

14. $\displaystyle\int_0^\pi \sin u \, du$

15. $\displaystyle\int_0^{\pi/3} \cos x \, dx$

16. $\displaystyle\int_1^{2.5} \cos x \, dx$

17. Find the slope of the cosine curve $y = \cos x$ at $x = \pi/4$.

18. Find the area under the sine curve $y = \sin x$ from $x = \pi/4$ to $x = 3\pi/4$.

19. Given the definite integral

$$I = \int_1^5 \frac{\sin x}{x} dx$$

(A) Graph the integrand

$$f(x) = \frac{\sin x}{x}$$

over $[1, 5]$.

(B) Use the right sum R_4 to approximate I.

20. Convert $15°$ to radian measure.

21. Evaluate without using a calculator:

(A) $\sin \dfrac{3\pi}{2}$ (B) $\cos \dfrac{5\pi}{6}$ (C) $\sin\left(\dfrac{-\pi}{6}\right)$

In Problems 22–26, find each derivative or integral.

22. $\dfrac{d}{du} \tan u$

23. $\dfrac{d}{dx} e^{\cos x^2}$

24. $\displaystyle\int e^{\sin x} \cos x \, dx$

25. $\displaystyle\int \tan x \, dx$

26. $\displaystyle\int_2^5 (5 + 2 \cos 2x) \, dx$

In Problems 27–29, graph each function on a graphing calculator set in radian mode.

27. $y = \dfrac{\sin \pi x}{0.2x}$; $1 \le x \le 8$, $-4 \le y \le 4$

28. $y = 0.5x \cos \pi x$; $0 \le x \le 8$, $-5 \le y \le 5$

29. $y = 3 - 2 \cos \pi x$; $0 \le x \le 6$, $0 \le y \le 5$

Applications

Problems 30–32 refer to the following: Revenues from sweater sales in a sportswear chain are given approximately by

$$R(t) = 3 + 2 \cos \frac{\pi t}{6} \qquad 0 \le t \le 24$$

where $R(t)$ is the revenue (in thousands of dollars) for a month of sales t months after January 1.

30. (A) Find the exact values of $R(0)$, $R(2)$, $R(3)$, and $R(6)$ without using a calculator.

(B) Use a calculator to find $R(1)$ and $R(22)$. Interpret the results.

31. (A) What is the rate of change of revenue t months after January 1?

(B) What is the rate of change of revenue 3 months after January 1? 10 months after January 1? 18 months after January 1?

(C) Find all local maxima and minima for $0 < t < 24$.

(D) Find the absolute maximum and minimum for $0 \le t \le 24$.

(E) Repeat part (C), using a graphing calculator.

32. (A) Find the total revenues taken in over the 2-year period.

(B) Find the total revenues taken in from $t = 5$ to $t = 9$.

(C) Illustrate part (B) graphically with an appropriate shaded region representing the total revenue taken in.

A Basic Algebra Review

Appendix A reviews some important basic algebra concepts usually studied in earlier courses. The material may be studied systematically before beginning the rest of the book or reviewed as needed.

A.1   Real Numbers

- Set of Real Numbers
- Real Number Line
- Basic Real Number Properties
- Further Properties
- Fraction Properties

The rules for manipulating and reasoning with symbols in algebra depend, in large measure, on properties of the real numbers. In this section we look at some of the important properties of this number system. To make our discussions here and elsewhere in the book clearer and more precise, we occasionally make use of simple *set* concepts and notation.

Set of Real Numbers

Informally, a **real number** is any number that has a decimal representation. Table 1 describes the set of real numbers and some of its important subsets. Figure 1 illustrates how these sets of numbers are related.

The set of integers contains all the natural numbers and something else—their negatives and 0. The set of rational numbers contains all the integers and something else—noninteger ratios of integers. And the set of real numbers contains all the rational numbers and something else—irrational numbers.

Table 1 **Set of Real Numbers**

Symbol	Name	Description	Examples
N	Natural numbers	Counting numbers (also called positive integers)	$1, 2, 3, \ldots$
Z	Integers	Natural numbers, their negatives, and 0	$\ldots, -2, -1, 0, 1, 2, \ldots$
Q	Rational numbers	Numbers that can be represented as a/b, where a and b are integers and $b \neq 0$; decimal representations are repeating or terminating	$-4, 0, 1, 25, \frac{-3}{5}, \frac{2}{3}, 3.67, -0.33\overline{3}, 5.272\,7\overline{27}$*
I	Irrational numbers	Numbers that can be represented as nonrepeating and nonterminating decimal numbers	$\sqrt{2}, \pi, \sqrt[3]{7}, 1.414\,213\ldots, 2.718\,281\,82\ldots$
R	Real numbers	Rational and irrational numbers	

*The overbar indicates that the number (or block of numbers) repeats indefinitely. The space after every third digit is used to help keep track of the number of decimal places.

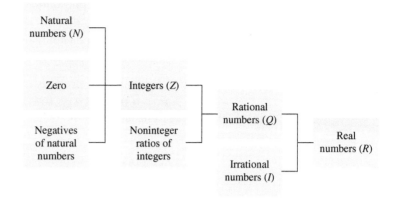

Figure 1 **Real numbers and important subsets**

Real Number Line

A one-to-one correspondence exists between the set of real numbers and the set of points on a line. That is, each real number corresponds to exactly one point, and each point corresponds to exactly one real number. A line with a real number associated with each point, and vice versa, as shown in Figure 2, is called a **real number line**, or simply a **real line**. Each number associated with a point is called the coordinate of the point.

The point with coordinate 0 is called the **origin**. The arrow on the right end of the line indicates a positive direction. The coordinates of all points to the right of the origin are called **positive real numbers**, and those to the left of the origin are called **negative real numbers**. The real number 0 is neither positive nor negative.

Figure 2 **Real number line**

Basic Real Number Properties

We now take a look at some of the basic properties of the real number system that enable us to convert algebraic expressions into *equivalent forms*.

SUMMARY Basic Properties of the Set of Real Numbers
Let a, b, and c be arbitrary elements in the set of real numbers R.

Addition Properties

Associative: $(a + b) + c = a + (b + c)$

Commutative: $a + b = b + a$

Identity: 0 is the additive identity; that is, $0 + a = a + 0 = a$ for all a in R, and 0 is the only element in R with this property.

Inverse: For each a in R, $-a$, is its unique additive inverse; that is, $a + (-a) = (-a) + a = 0$ and $-a$ is the only element in R relative to a with this property.

Multiplication Properties

Associative: $(ab)c = a(bc)$

Commutative: $ab = ba$

Identity: 1 is the multiplicative identity; that is, $(1)a = a(1) = a$ for all a in R, and 1 is the only element in R with this property.

Inverse: For each a in R, $a \neq 0$, $1/a$ is its unique multiplicative inverse; that is, $a(1/a) = (1/a)a = 1$, and $1/a$ is the only element in R relative to a with this property.

Distributive Properties

$$a(b + c) = ab + ac \qquad (a + b)c = ac + bc$$

You are already familiar with the **commutative properties** for addition and multiplication. They indicate that the order in which the addition or multiplication of two numbers is performed does not matter. For example,

$$7 + 2 = 2 + 7 \quad \text{and} \quad 3 \cdot 5 = 5 \cdot 3$$

Is there a commutative property relative to subtraction or division? That is, does $a - b = b - a$ or does $a \div b = b \div a$ for all real numbers a and b (division by 0 excluded)? The answer is no, since, for example,

$$8 - 6 \neq 6 - 8 \quad \text{and} \quad 10 \div 5 \neq 5 \div 10$$

When computing

$$3 + 2 + 6 \quad \text{or} \quad 3 \cdot 2 \cdot 6$$

why don't we need parentheses to indicate which two numbers are to be added or multiplied first? The answer is to be found in the **associative properties**. These properties allow us to write

$$(3 + 2) + 6 = 3 + (2 + 6) \quad \text{and} \quad (3 \cdot 2) \cdot 6 = 3 \cdot (2 \cdot 6)$$

so it does not matter how we group numbers relative to either operation. Is there an associative property for subtraction or division? The answer is no, since, for example,

$$(12 - 6) - 2 \neq 12 - (6 - 2) \quad \text{and} \quad (12 \div 6) \div 2 \neq 12 \div (6 \div 2)$$

Evaluate each side of each equation to see why.

What number added to a given number will give that number back again? What number times a given number will give that number back again? The answers are 0 and 1, respectively. Because of this, 0 and 1 are called the **identity elements** for the real numbers. Hence, for any real numbers a and b,

$$0 + 5 = 5 \quad \text{and} \quad (a + b) + 0 = a + b$$
$$1 \cdot 4 = 4 \quad \text{and} \quad (a + b) \cdot 1 = a + b$$

We now consider **inverses**. For each real number a, there is a unique real number $-a$ such that $a + (-a) = 0$. The number $-a$ is called the **additive inverse** of a, or the **negative** of a. For example, the additive inverse (or negative) of 7 is -7, since $7 + (-7) = 0$. The additive inverse (or negative) of -7 is $-(-7) = 7$, since $-7 + [-(-7)] = 0$.

CONCEPTUAL INSIGHT

Do not confuse negation with the sign of a number. If a is a real number, $-a$ is the negative of a and may be positive or negative. Specifically, if a is negative, then $-a$ is positive and if a is positive, then $-a$ is negative.

For each nonzero real number a, there is a unique real number $1/a$ such that $a(1/a) = 1$. The number $1/a$ is called the **multiplicative inverse** of a, or the **reciprocal** of a. For example, the multiplicative inverse (or reciprocal) of 4 is $\frac{1}{4}$, since $4\left(\frac{1}{4}\right) = 1$. (Also note that 4 is the multiplicative inverse of $\frac{1}{4}$.) The number 0 has no multiplicative inverse.

We now turn to the **distributive properties**, which involve both multiplication and addition. Consider the following two computations:

$$5(3 + 4) = 5 \cdot 7 = 35 \qquad 5 \cdot 3 + 5 \cdot 4 = 15 + 20 = 35$$

Thus,

$$5(3 + 4) = 5 \cdot 3 + 5 \cdot 4$$

and we say that multiplication by 5 *distributes* over the sum $(3 + 4)$. In general, **multiplication distributes over addition** in the real number system. Two more illustrations are

$$9(m + n) = 9m + 9n \qquad (7 + 2)u = 7u + 2u$$

EXAMPLE 1 Real Number Properties State the real number property that justifies the indicated statement.

Statement	Property Illustrated
(A) $x(y + z) = (y + z)x$	Commutative ($\cdot$)
(B) $5(2y) = (5 \cdot 2)y$	Associative ($\cdot$)
(C) $2 + (y + 7) = 2 + (7 + y)$	Commutative (+)
(D) $4z + 6z = (4 + 6)z$	Distributive
(E) If $m + n = 0$, then $n = -m$.	Inverse (+)

Matched Problem 1 State the real number property that justifies the indicated statement.

(A) $8 + (3 + y) = (8 + 3) + y$

(B) $(x + y) + z = z + (x + y)$

(C) $(a + b)(x + y) = a(x + y) + b(x + y)$

(D) $5xy + 0 = 5xy$

(E) If $xy = 1$, $x \neq 0$, then $y = 1/x$.

Further Properties

Subtraction and *division* can be defined in terms of addition and multiplication, respectively:

DEFINITION Subtraction and Division

For all real numbers a and b,

Subtraction: $\qquad a - b = a + (-b) \qquad 7 - (-5) = 7 + [-(-5)]$
$$= 7 + 5 = 12$$

Division: $\qquad a \div b = a\left(\dfrac{1}{b}\right), b \neq 0 \qquad 9 \div 4 = 9\left(\dfrac{1}{4}\right) = \dfrac{9}{4}$

To subtract b from a, add the negative (the additive inverse) of b to a. To divide a by b, multiply a by the reciprocal (the multiplicative inverse) of b. Note that division by 0 is not defined, since 0 does not have a reciprocal. **0 can never be used as a divisor!**

The following properties of negatives can be proved using the preceding assumed properties and definitions.

THEOREM 1 Negative Properties

For all real numbers a and b,

1. $-(-a) = a$

2. $(-a)b = -(ab)$
   $\qquad = a(-b) = -ab$

3. $(-a)(-b) = ab$

4. $(-1)a = -a$

5. $\dfrac{-a}{b} = -\dfrac{a}{b} = \dfrac{a}{-b}, b \neq 0$

6. $\dfrac{-a}{-b} = -\dfrac{-a}{b} = -\dfrac{a}{-b} = \dfrac{a}{b}, b \neq 0$

We now state two important properties involving 0.

THEOREM 2 Zero Properties

For all real numbers a and b,

1. $a \cdot 0 = 0 \qquad 0 \cdot 0 = 0 \quad (-35)(0) = 0$

2. $ab = 0 \qquad$ if and only if $\quad a = 0 \quad$ or $\quad b = 0$

   If $(3x + 2)(x - 7) = 0$, then either $3x + 2 = 0$ or $x - 7 = 0$.

Fraction Properties

Recall that the quotient $a \div b(b \neq 0)$ written in the form a/b is called a **fraction**. The quantity a is called the **numerator**, and the quantity b is called the **denominator**.

THEOREM 3   Fraction Properties

For all real numbers a, b, c, d, and k (division by 0 excluded):

1. $\dfrac{a}{b} = \dfrac{c}{d}$ if and only if $ad = bc$ $\dfrac{4}{6} = \dfrac{6}{9}$ since $4 \cdot 9 = 6 \cdot 6$

2. $\dfrac{ka}{kb} = \dfrac{a}{b}$
$\dfrac{7 \cdot 3}{7 \cdot 5} = \dfrac{3}{5}$

3. $\dfrac{a}{b} \cdot \dfrac{c}{d} = \dfrac{ac}{bd}$
$\dfrac{3}{5} \cdot \dfrac{7}{8} = \dfrac{3 \cdot 7}{5 \cdot 8}$

4. $\dfrac{a}{b} \div \dfrac{c}{d} = \dfrac{a}{b} \cdot \dfrac{d}{c}$
$\dfrac{2}{3} \div \dfrac{5}{7} = \dfrac{2}{3} \cdot \dfrac{7}{5}$

5. $\dfrac{a}{b} + \dfrac{c}{b} = \dfrac{a+c}{b}$
$\dfrac{3}{6} + \dfrac{5}{6} = \dfrac{3+5}{6}$

6. $\dfrac{a}{b} - \dfrac{c}{b} = \dfrac{a-c}{b}$
$\dfrac{7}{8} - \dfrac{3}{8} = \dfrac{7-3}{8}$

7. $\dfrac{a}{b} + \dfrac{c}{d} = \dfrac{ad + bc}{bd}$
$\dfrac{2}{3} + \dfrac{3}{5} = \dfrac{2 \cdot 5 + 3 \cdot 3}{3 \cdot 5}$

A fraction is a quotient, not just a pair of numbers. So if a and b are real numbers with $b \neq 0$, then $\frac{a}{b}$ corresponds to a point on the real number line. For example, $\frac{17}{2}$ corresponds to the point halfway between $\frac{16}{2} = 8$ and $\frac{18}{2} = 9$. Similarly, $-\frac{21}{5}$ corresponds to the point that is $\frac{1}{5}$ unit to the left of -4.

EXAMPLE 2   Estimation   Round $\frac{22}{7} + \frac{18}{19}$ to the nearest integer.

SOLUTION   Note that a calculator is not required: $\frac{22}{7}$ is a little greater than 3, and $\frac{18}{19}$ is a little less than 1. Therefore the sum, rounded to the nearest integer, is 4.

Matched Problem 2   Round $\frac{6}{93}$ to the nearest integer.

Fractions with denominator 100 are called **percentages**. They are used so often that they have their own notation:

$$\frac{3}{100} = 3\% \qquad \frac{7.5}{100} = 7.5\% \qquad \frac{110}{100} = 110\%$$

So 3% is equivalent to 0.03, 7.5% is equivalent to 0.075, and so on.

EXAMPLE 3   State Sales Tax   Find the sales tax that is owed on a purchase of $947.69 if the tax rate is 6.5%.

SOLUTION $6.5\%(\$947.69) = 0.065(947.69) = \$61.60$

Matched Problem 3   You intend to give a 20% tip, rounded to the nearest dollar, on a restaurant bill of $78.47. How much is the tip?

Exercises A.1

All variables represent real numbers.

In Problems 1–6, replace each question mark with an appropriate expression that will illustrate the use of the indicated real number property.

1. Commutative property ($\cdot$): $uv = ?$

2. Commutative property ($+$): $x + 7 = ?$

3. Associative property ($+$): $3 + (7 + y) = ?$

4. Associative property ($\cdot$): $x(yz) = ?$

5. Identity property ($\cdot$): $1(u + v) = ?$

6. Identity property ($+$): $0 + 9m = ?$

In Problems 7–26, indicate true (T) or false (F).

7. $5(8m) = (5 \cdot 8)m$

8. $a + cb = a + bc$

9. $5x + 7x = (5 + 7)x$

10. $uv(w + x) = uvw + uvx$

11. $-2(-a)(2x - y) = 2a(-4x + y)$

12. $8 \div (-5) = 8\left(\dfrac{1}{-5}\right)$

13. $(x + 3) + 2x = 2x + (x + 3)$

14. $\dfrac{x}{3y} \div \dfrac{5y}{x} = \dfrac{15y^2}{x^2}$

15. $\dfrac{2x}{-(x + 3)} = -\dfrac{2x}{x + 3}$

16. $-\dfrac{2x}{-(x - 3)} = \dfrac{2x}{x - 3}$

17. $(-3)\left(\dfrac{1}{-3}\right) = 1$

18. $(-0.5) + (0.5) = 0$

19. $-x^2y^2 = (-1)x^2y^2$

20. $[-(x + 2)](-x) = (x + 2)x$

21. $\dfrac{a}{b} + \dfrac{c}{d} = \dfrac{a + c}{b + d}$

22. $\dfrac{k}{k + b} = \dfrac{1}{1 + b}$

23. $(x + 8)(x + 6) = (x + 8)x + (x + 8)6$

24. $u(u - 2v) + v(u - 2v) = (u + v)(u - 2v)$

25. If $(x - 2)(2x + 3) = 0$, then either $x - 2 = 0$ or $2x + 3 = 0$.

26. If either $x - 2 = 0$ or $2x + 3 = 0$, then $(x - 2)(2x + 3) = 0$.

27. If $uv = 1$, does either u or v have to be 1? Explain.

28. If $uv = 0$, does either u or v have to be 0? Explain.

29. Indicate whether the following are true (T) or false (F):

   (A) All integers are natural numbers.

   (B) All rational numbers are real numbers.

   (C) All natural numbers are rational numbers.

30. Indicate whether the following are true (T) or false (F):

   (A) All natural numbers are integers.

   (B) All real numbers are irrational.

   (C) All rational numbers are real numbers.

31. Give an example of a real number that is not a rational number.

32. Give an example of a rational number that is not an integer.

33. Given the sets of numbers N (natural numbers), Z (integers), Q (rational numbers), and R (real numbers), indicate to which set(s) each of the following numbers belongs:

   (A) 8   (B) $\sqrt{2}$ (C) -1.414 (D) $\dfrac{-5}{2}$

34. Given the sets of numbers N, Z, Q, and R (see Problem 33), indicate to which set(s) each of the following numbers belongs:

   (A) -3 (B) 3.14   (C) π (D) $\dfrac{2}{3}$

35. Indicate true (T) or false (F), and for each false statement find real number replacements for a, b, and c that will provide a counterexample. For all real numbers a, b, and c,

   (A) $a(b - c) = ab - c$

   (B) $(a - b) - c = a - (b - c)$

   (C) $a(bc) = (ab)c$

   (D) $(a \div b) \div c = a \div (b \div c)$

36. Indicate true (T) or false (F), and for each false statement find real number replacements for a and b that will provide a counterexample. For all real numbers a and b,

   (A) $a + b = b + a$

   (B) $a - b = b - a$

   (C) $ab = ba$

   (D) $a \div b = b \div a$

37. If $c = 0.151515\ldots$, then $100c = 15.1515\ldots$ and

$$100c - c = 15.1515\ldots - 0.151515\ldots$$
$$99c = 15$$
$$c = \frac{15}{99} = \frac{5}{33}$$

Proceeding similarly, convert the repeating decimal $0.090909\ldots$ into a fraction. (All repeating decimals are rational numbers, and all rational numbers have repeating decimal representations.)

38. Repeat Problem 37 for $0.181818\ldots$.

Use a calculator to express each number in Problems 39 and 40 as a decimal to the capacity of your calculator. Observe the repeating decimal representation of the rational numbers and the nonrepeating decimal representation of the irrational numbers.

39. (A) $\dfrac{13}{6}$ (B) $\sqrt{21}$ (C) $\dfrac{7}{16}$ (D) $\dfrac{29}{111}$

40. (A) $\dfrac{8}{9}$ (B) $\dfrac{3}{11}$ (C) $\sqrt{5}$ (D) $\dfrac{11}{8}$

In Problems 41–44, without using a calculator, round to the nearest integer.

41. (A) $\dfrac{43}{13}$ (B) $\dfrac{37}{19}$

42. (A) $\dfrac{9}{17}$ (B) $-\dfrac{12}{25}$

43. (A) $\dfrac{7}{8} + \dfrac{11}{12}$ (B) $\dfrac{55}{9} - \dfrac{7}{55}$

44. (A) $\dfrac{5}{6} - \dfrac{18}{19}$ (B) $\dfrac{13}{5} + \dfrac{44}{21}$

Applications

45. *Sales tax.* Find the tax owed on a purchase of $182.39 if the state sales tax rate is 9%. (Round to the nearest cent).

46. *Sales tax.* If you paid $29.86 in tax on a purchase of $533.19, what was the sales tax rate? (Write as a percentage, rounded to one decimal place).

47. *Gasoline prices.* If the price per gallon of gas jumped from $4.25 to $4.37, what was the percentage increase? (Round to one decimal place).

48. *Gasoline prices.* The price of gas increased 4% in one week. If the price last week was $4.30 per gallon, what is the price now? (Round to the nearest cent).

Answers to Matched Problems

1. (A) Associative $(+)$ (B) Commutative $(+)$
(C) Distributive   (D) Identity $(+)$
(E) Inverse $(\cdot)$

2. 0   **3.** $16

A.2 Operations on Polynomials

- Natural Number Exponents
- Polynomials
- Combining Like Terms
- Addition and Subtraction
- Multiplication
- Combined Operations

This section covers basic operations on *polynomials*. Our discussion starts with a brief review of natural number exponents. Integer and rational exponents and their properties will be discussed in detail in subsequent sections. (Natural numbers, integers, and rational numbers are important parts of the real number system; see Table 1 and Figure 1 in Appendix A.1.)

Natural Number Exponents

We define a **natural number exponent** as follows:

DEFINITION Natural Number Exponent
For n a natural number and b any real number,

$$b^n = b \cdot b \cdot \cdots \cdot b \qquad n \text{ factors of } b$$
$$3^5 = 3 \cdot 3 \cdot 3 \cdot 3 \cdot 3 \qquad 5 \text{ factors of } 3$$

where n is called the exponent and b is called the **base**.

Along with this definition, we state the **first property of exponents**:

THEOREM 1 First Property of Exponents
For any natural numbers m and n, and any real number b:

$$b^m b^n = b^{m+n} \qquad (2t^4)(5t^3) = 2 \cdot 5t^{4+3} = 10t^7$$

Polynomials

Algebraic expressions are formed by using constants and variables and the algebraic operations of addition, subtraction, multiplication, division, raising to powers, and taking roots. Special types of algebraic expressions are called *polynomials*. A **polynomial in one variable** x is constructed by adding or subtracting constants and terms of the form ax^n, where a is a real number and n is a natural number. A **polynomial in two variables** x and y is constructed by adding and subtracting constants and terms of the form $ax^m y^n$, where a is a real number and m and n are natural numbers. Polynomials in three and more variables are defined in a similar manner.

Polynomials		Not Polynomials	
8	0	$\dfrac{1}{x}$	$\dfrac{x-y}{x^2+y^2}$
$3x^3 - 6x + 7$	$6x + 3$		
$2x^2 - 7xy - 8y^2$	$9y^3 + 4y^2 - y + 4$	$\sqrt{x^3 - 2x}$	$2x^{-2} - 3x^{-1}$
$2x - 3y + 2$	$u^5 - 3u^3v^2 + 2uv^4 - v^4$		

Polynomial forms are encountered frequently in mathematics. For the efficient study of polynomials, it is useful to classify them according to their *degree*. If a term in a polynomial has only one variable as a factor, then the **degree of the term** is the power of the variable. If two or more variables are present in a term as factors, then the **degree of the term** is the sum of the powers of the variables. The **degree of a polynomial** is the degree of the nonzero term with the highest degree in the polynomial. Any nonzero constant is defined to be a **polynomial of degree 0**. The number 0 is also a polynomial but is not assigned a degree.

EXAMPLE 1 Degree

(A) The degree of the first term in $5x^3 + \sqrt{3}x - \frac{1}{2}$ is 3, the degree of the second term is 1, the degree of the third term is 0, and the degree of the whole polynomial is 3 (the same as the degree of the term with the highest degree).

(B) The degree of the first term in $8u^3v^2 - \sqrt{7}uv^2$ is 5, the degree of the second term is 3, and the degree of the whole polynomial is 5.

Matched Problem 1

(A) Given the polynomial $6x^5 + 7x^3 - 2$, what is the degree of the first term? The second term? The third term? The whole polynomial?

(B) Given the polynomial $2u^4v^2 - 5uv^3$, what is the degree of the first term? The second term? The whole polynomial?

In addition to classifying polynomials by degree, we also call a single-term polynomial a **monomial**, a two-term polynomial a **binomial**, and a three-term polynomial a **trinomial**.

Combining Like Terms

The concept of *coefficient* plays a central role in the process of combining *like terms*. A constant in a term of a polynomial, including the sign that precedes it, is called the **numerical coefficient**, or simply, the **coefficient**, of the term. If a constant does not appear, or only a + sign appears, the coefficient is understood to be 1. If only a − sign appears, the coefficient is understood to be −1. Given the polynomial

$$5x^4 - x^3 - 3x^2 + x - 7 \quad \boxed{= 5x^4 + (-1)x^3 + (-3)x^2 + 1x + (-7)}$$

the coefficient of the first term is 5, the coefficient of the second term is −1, the coefficient of the third term is −3, the coefficient of the fourth term is 1, and the coefficient of the fifth term is −7.

The following distributive properties are fundamental to the process of combining *like terms*.

THEOREM 2 Distributive Properties of Real Numbers

1. $a(b + c) = (b + c)a = ab + ac$
2. $a(b - c) = (b - c)a = ab - ac$
3. $a(b + c + \cdots + f) = ab + ac + \cdots + af$

Two terms in a polynomial are called **like terms** if they have exactly the same variable factors to the same powers. The numerical coefficients may or may not be the same. Since constant terms involve no variables, all constant terms are like terms. If a polynomial contains two or more like terms, these terms can be combined into a single term by making use of distributive properties. The following example illustrates the reasoning behind the process:

$$
\begin{aligned}
3x^2y - 5xy^2 + x^2y - 2x^2y\ &= 3x^2y + x^2y - 2x^2y - 5xy^2 \\
&= (3x^2y + 1x^2y - 2x^2y) - 5xy^2 \\
&= (3 + 1 - 2)x^2y - 5xy^2 \\
&= 2x^2y - 5xy^2
\end{aligned}
$$

Note the use of distributive properties.

Free use is made of the real number properties discussed in Appendix A.1.

How can we simplify expressions such as $4(x - 2y) - 3(2x - 7y)$? We clear the expression of parentheses using distributive properties, and combine like terms:

$$
\begin{aligned}
4(x - 2y) - 3(2x - 7y) &= 4x - 8y - 6x + 21y \\
&= -2x + 13y
\end{aligned}
$$

EXAMPLE 2   Removing Parentheses   Remove parentheses and simplify:

(A) $2(3x^2 - 2x + 5) + (x^2 + 3x - 7)$

$$
\begin{aligned}
&= 2(3x^2 - 2x + 5) + 1(x^2 + 3x - 7) \\
&= 6x^2 - 4x + 10 + x^2 + 3x - 7 \\
&= 7x^2 - x + 3
\end{aligned}
$$

(B) $(x^3 - 2x - 6) - (2x^3 - x^2 + 2x - 3)$

$$
\begin{aligned}
&= 1(x^3 - 2x - 6) + (-1)(2x^3 - x^2 + 2x - 3) \\
&= x^3 - 2x - 6 - 2x^3 + x^2 - 2x + 3 \\
&= -x^3 + x^2 - 4x - 3
\end{aligned}
$$

Be careful with the sign here

(C) $[3x^2 - (2x + 1)] - (x^2 - 1) = [3x^2 - 2x - 1] - (x^2 - 1)$

$$
\begin{aligned}
&= 3x^2 - 2x - 1 - x^2 + 1 \\
&= 2x^2 - 2x
\end{aligned}
$$

Remove inner parentheses first.

Matched Problem 2   Remove parentheses and simplify:

(A) $3(u^2 - 2v^2) + (u^2 + 5v^2)$

(B) $(m^3 - 3m^2 + m - 1) - (2m^3 - m + 3)$

(C) $(x^3 - 2) - [2x^3 - (3x + 4)]$

Addition and Subtraction

Addition and subtraction of polynomials can be thought of in terms of removing parentheses and combining like terms, as illustrated in Example 2. Horizontal and vertical arrangements are illustrated in the next two examples. You should be able to work either way, letting the situation dictate your choice.

EXAMPLE 3   Adding Polynomials   Add horizontally and vertically:

$$
x^4 - 3x^3 + x^2, \quad -x^3 - 2x^2 + 3x, \quad \text{and} \quad 3x^2 - 4x - 5
$$

SOLUTION   Add horizontally:

$$
\begin{aligned}
(x^4 - 3x^3 + x^2) &+ (-x^3 - 2x^2 + 3x) + (3x^2 - 4x - 5) \\
&= x^4 - 3x^3 + x^2 - x^3 - 2x^2 + 3x + 3x^2 - 4x - 5 \\
&= x^4 - 4x^3 + 2x^2 - x - 5
\end{aligned}
$$

Or vertically, by lining up like terms and adding their coefficients:

$$
\begin{array}{r}
x^4 - 3x^3 + x^2 \\
- x^3 - 2x^2 + 3x \\
3x^2 - 4x - 5 \\
\hline
x^4 - 4x^3 + 2x^2 - x - 5
\end{array}
$$

Matched Problem 3⟩ Add horizontally and vertically:

$$3x^4 - 2x^3 - 4x^2, \quad x^3 - 2x^2 - 5x, \quad \text{and} \quad x^2 + 7x - 2$$

EXAMPLE 4 Subtracting Polynomials Subtract $4x^2 - 3x + 5$ from $x^2 - 8$, both horizontally and vertically.

SOLUTION $(x^2 - 8) - (4x^2 - 3x + 5)$ or

$$= x^2 - 8 - 4x^2 + 3x - 5$$
$$= -3x^2 + 3x - 13$$

$$\begin{array}{r} x^2 \qquad - 8 \\ \underline{-4x^2 + 3x - 5} \leftarrow \text{Change} \\ -3x^2 + 3x - 13 \quad \text{signs and} \\ \text{add.} \end{array}$$

Matched Problem 4⟩ Subtract $2x^2 - 5x + 4$ from $5x^2 - 6$, both horizontally and vertically.

Multiplication

Multiplication of algebraic expressions involves the extensive use of distributive properties for real numbers, as well as other real number properties.

EXAMPLE 5 Multiplying Polynomials Multiply: $(2x - 3)(3x^2 - 2x + 3)$

SOLUTION

$$(2x - 3)(3x^2 - 2x + 3) \boxed{= 2x(3x^2 - 2x + 3) - 3(3x^2 - 2x + 3)}$$
$$= 6x^3 - 4x^2 + 6x - 9x^2 + 6x - 9$$
$$= 6x^3 - 13x^2 + 12x - 9$$

Or, using a vertical arrangement,

$$\begin{array}{r} 3x^2 - 2x + 3 \\ \underline{2x - 3} \\ 6x^3 - 4x^2 + 6x \\ \underline{- 9x^2 + 6x - 9} \\ 6x^3 - 13x^2 + 12x - 9 \end{array}$$

Matched Problem 5⟩ Multiply: $(2x - 3)(2x^2 + 3x - 2)$

Thus, to multiply two polynomials, multiply each term of one by each term of the other, and combine like terms.

Products of binomial factors occur frequently, so it is useful to develop procedures that will enable us to write down their products by inspection. To find the product $(2x - 1)(3x + 2)$ we proceed as follows:

$$(2x - 1)(3x + 2) \boxed{= 6x^2 + 4x - 3x - 2}$$ The inner and outer products
$$= 6x^2 + x - 2$$ are like terms, so combine into a single term.

To speed the process, we do the step in the dashed box mentally.

Products of certain binomial factors occur so frequently that it is useful to learn formulas for their products. The following formulas are easily verified by multiplying the factors on the left.

THEOREM 3 Special Products

  1. $(a - b)(a + b) = a^2 - b^2$
  2. $(a + b)^2 = a^2 + 2ab + b^2$
  3. $(a - b)^2 = a^2 - 2ab + b^2$

EXAMPLE 6 Special Products   Multiply mentally, where possible.

(A) $(2x - 3y)(5x + 2y)$

(B) $(3a - 2b)(3a + 2b)$

(C) $(5x - 3)^2$

(D) $(m + 2n)^3$

SOLUTION

(A) $(2x - 3y)(5x + 2y)$ $= 10x^2 + 4xy - 15xy - 6y^2$
$$= 10x^2 - 11xy - 6y^2$$

(B) $(3a - 2b)(3a + 2b)$ $= (3a)^2 - (2b)^2$
$$= 9a^2 - 4b^2$$

(C) $(5x - 3)^2 = (5x)^2 - 2(5x)(3) + 3^2$
$$= 25x^2 - 30x + 9$$

(D) $(m + 2n)^3 = (m + 2n)^2(m + 2n)$
$$= (m^2 + 4mn + 4n^2)(m + 2n)$$
$$= m^2(m + 2n) + 4mn(m + 2n) + 4n^2(m + 2n)$$
$$= m^3 + 2m^2n + 4m^2n + 8mn^2 + 4mn^2 + 8n^3$$
$$= m^3 + 6m^2n + 12mn^2 + 8n^3$$

Matched Problem 6 Multiply mentally, where possible.

(A) $(4u - 3v)(2u + v)$

(B) $(2xy + 3)(2xy - 3)$

(C) $(m + 4n)(m - 4n)$

(D) $(2u - 3v)^2$

(E) $(2x - y)^3$

Combined Operations

We complete this section by considering several examples that use all the operations just discussed. Note that in simplifying, we usually remove grouping symbols starting from the inside. That is, we remove parentheses ( ) first, then brackets [ ], and finally braces { }, if present. Also,

DEFINITION Order of Operations

Multiplication and division precede addition and subtraction, and taking powers precedes multiplication and division.

$$2 \cdot 3 + 4 = 6 + 4 = 10, \quad \text{not} \quad 2 \cdot 7 = 14$$
$$\frac{10^2}{2} = \frac{100}{2} = 50, \quad \text{not} \quad 5^2 = 25$$

EXAMPLE 7 Combined Operations   Perform the indicated operations and simplify:

(A) $3x - \{5 - 3[x - x(3 - x)]\} = 3x - \{5 - 3[x - 3x + x^2]\}$
$$= 3x - \{5 - 3x + 9x - 3x^2\}$$
$$= 3x - 5 + 3x - 9x + 3x^2$$
$$= 3x^2 - 3x - 5$$

(B) $(x - 2y)(2x + 3y) - (2x + y)^2 = 2x^2 - xy - 6y^2 - (4x^2 + 4xy + y^2)$
$$= 2x^2 - xy - 6y^2 - 4x^2 - 4xy - y^2$$
$$= -2x^2 - 5xy - 7y^2$$

Matched Problem 7 Perform the indicated operations and simplify:

(A) $2t - \{7 - 2[t - t(4 + t)]\}$

(B) $(u - 3v)^2 - (2u - v)(2u + v)$

Problems 1–8 refer to the following polynomials:

(A) $2x - 3$ (B) $2x^2 - x + 2$ (C) $x^3 + 2x^2 - x + 3$

1. What is the degree of (C)?

2. What is the degree of (A)?

3. Add (B) and (C).

4. Add (A) and (B).

5. Subtract (B) from (C).

6. Subtract (A) from (B).

7. Multiply (B) and (C).

8. Multiply (A) and (C).

In Problems 9–30, perform the indicated operations and simplify.

9. $2(u - 1) - (3u + 2) - 2(2u - 3)$

10. $2(x - 1) + 3(2x - 3) - (4x - 5)$

11. $4a - 2a[5 - 3(a + 2)]$

12. $2y - 3y[4 - 2(y - 1)]$

13. $(a + b)(a - b)$

14. $(m - n)(m + n)$

15. $(3x - 5)(2x + 1)$

16. $(4t - 3)(t - 2)$

17. $(2x - 3y)(x + 2y)$

18. $(3x + 2y)(x - 3y)$

19. $(3y + 2)(3y - 2)$

20. $(2m - 7)(2m + 7)$

21. $-(2x - 3)^2$

22. $-(5 - 3x)^2$

23. $(4m + 3n)(4m - 3n)$

24. $(3x - 2y)(3x + 2y)$

25. $(3u + 4v)^2$

26. $(4x - y)^2$

27. $(a - b)(a^2 + ab + b^2)$

28. $(a + b)(a^2 - ab + b^2)$

29. $[(x - y) + 3z][(x - y) - 3z]$

30. $[a - (2b - c)][a + (2b - c)]$

In Problems 31–44, perform the indicated operations and simplify.

31. $m - \{m - [m - (m - 1)]\}$

32. $2x - 3\{x + 2[x - (x + 5)] + 1\}$

33. $(x^2 - 2xy + y^2)(x^2 + 2xy + y^2)$

34. $(3x - 2y)^2(2x + 5y)$

35. $(5a - 2b)^2 - (2b + 5a)^2$

36. $(2x - 1)^2 - (3x + 2)(3x - 2)$

37. $(m - 2)^2 - (m - 2)(m + 2)$

38. $(x - 3)(x + 3) - (x - 3)^2$

39. $(x - 2y)(2x + y) - (x + 2y)(2x - y)$

40. $(3m + n)(m - 3n) - (m + 3n)(3m - n)$

41. $(u + v)^3$

42. $(x - y)^3$

43. $(x - 2y)^3$

44. $(2m - n)^3$

45. Subtract the sum of the last two polynomials from the sum of the first two: $2x^2 - 4xy + y^2$, $3xy - y^2$, $x^2 - 2xy - y^2$, $-x^2 + 3xy - 2y^2$

46. Subtract the sum of the first two polynomials from the sum of the last two: $3m^2 - 2m + 5$, $4m^2 - m$, $3m^2 - 3m - 2$, $m^3 + m^2 + 2$

In Problems 47–50, perform the indicated operations and simplify.

47. $[(2x - 1)^2 - x(3x + 1)]^2$

48. $[5x(3x + 1) - 5(2x - 1)^2]^2$

49. $2\{(x - 3)(x^2 - 2x + 1) - x[3 - x(x - 2)]\}$

50. $-3x\{x[x - x(2 - x)] - (x + 2)(x^2 - 3)\}$

51. If you are given two polynomials, one of degree m and the other of degree n, where m is greater than n, what is the degree of their product?

52. What is the degree of the sum of the two polynomials in Problem 51?

53. How does the answer to Problem 51 change if the two polynomials can have the same degree?

54. How does the answer to Problem 52 change if the two polynomials can have the same degree?

55. Show by example that, in general, $(a + b)^2 \neq a^2 + b^2$. Discuss possible conditions on a and b that would make this a valid equation.

56. Show by example that, in general, $(a - b)^2 \neq a^2 - b^2$. Discuss possible conditions on a and b that would make this a valid equation.

Applications

57. Investment. You have $10,000 to invest, part at 9% and the rest at 12%. If x is the amount invested at 9%, write an algebraic expression that represents the total annual income from both investments. Simplify the expression.

58. Investment. A person has $100,000 to invest. If $x are invested in a money market account yielding 7% and twice that amount in certificates of deposit yielding 9%, and if the rest is invested in high-grade bonds yielding 11%, write an algebraic expression that represents the total annual income from all three investments. Simplify the expression.

59. Gross receipts. Four thousand tickets are to be sold for a musical show. If x tickets are to be sold for $20 each and three times that number for $30 each, and if the rest are sold for $50 each, write an algebraic expression that represents the gross receipts from ticket sales, assuming all tickets are sold. Simplify the expression.

60. Gross receipts. Six thousand tickets are to be sold for a concert, some for $20 each and the rest for $35 each. If x is the number of $20 tickets sold, write an algebraic expression that represents the gross receipts from ticket sales, assuming all tickets are sold. Simplify the expression.

61. Nutrition. Food mix A contains 2% fat, and food mix B contains 6% fat. A 10-kilogram diet mix of foods A and B is formed. If x kilograms of food A are used, write an algebraic expression that represents the total number of kilograms of fat in the final food mix. Simplify the expression.

62. Nutrition. Each ounce of food M contains 8 units of calcium, and each ounce of food N contains 5 units of calcium. A 160-ounce diet mix is formed using foods M and N. If x is the number of ounces of food M used, write an algebraic expression that represents the total number of units of calcium in the diet mix. Simplify the expression.

Answers to Matched Problems

1. (A) 5, 3, 0, 5   (B) 6, 4, 6
2. (A) $4u^2 - v^2$ (B) $-m^3 - 3m^2 + 2m - 4$
   (C) $-x^3 + 3x + 2$
3. $3x^4 - x^3 - 5x^2 + 2x - 2$
4. $3x^2 + 5x - 10$ 5. $4x^3 - 13x + 6$
6. (A) $8u^2 - 2uv - 3v^2$ (B) $4x^2y^2 - 9$ (C) $m^2 - 16n^2$
   (D) $4u^2 - 12uv + 9v^2$ (E) $8x^3 - 12x^2y + 6xy^2 - y^3$
7. (A) $-2t^2 - 4t - 7$ (B) $-3u^2 - 6uv + 10v^2$

A.3 Factoring Polynomials

- Common Factors
- Factoring by Grouping
- Factoring Second Degree Polynomials
- Special Factoring Formulas
- Combined Factoring Techniques

A positive integer is **written in factored form** if it is written as the product of two or more positive integers; for example, $120 = 10 \cdot 12$. A positive integer is **factored completely** if each factor is prime; for example, $120 = 2 \cdot 2 \cdot 2 \cdot 3 \cdot 5$. (Recall that an integer $p > 1$ is **prime** if p cannot be factored as the product of two smaller positive integers. So the first ten primes are 2, 3, 5, 7, 11, 13, 17, 19, 23, and 29). A **tree diagram** is a helpful way to visualize a factorization (Fig 1).

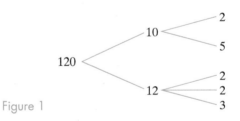

Figure 1

A polynomial is **written in factored form** if it is written as the product of two or more polynomials. The following polynomials are written in factored form:

$$4x^2y - 6xy^2 = 2xy(2x - 3y) \qquad 2x^3 - 8x = 2x(x - 2)(x + 2)$$
$$x^2 - x - 6 = (x - 3)(x + 2) \qquad 5m^2 + 20 = 5(m^2 + 4)$$

Unless stated to the contrary, we will limit our discussion of factoring polynomials to polynomials with integer coefficients.

A polynomial with integer coefficients is said to be **factored completely** if each factor cannot be expressed as the product of two or more polynomials with integer coefficients, other than itself or 1. All the polynomials above, as we will see by the conclusion of this section, are factored completely.

Writing polynomials in completely factored form is often a difficult task. But accomplishing it can lead to the simplification of certain algebraic expressions and to the solution of certain types of equations and inequalities. The distributive properties for real numbers are central to the factoring process.

Common Factors

Generally, a first step in any factoring procedure is to factor out all factors common to all terms.

EXAMPLE 1 Common Factors Factor out all factors common to all terms.

(A) $3x^3y - 6x^2y^2 - 3xy^3$

(B) $3y(2y + 5) + 2(2y + 5)$

SOLUTION

(A) $3x^3y - 6x^2y^2 - 3xy^3 = (3xy)x^2 - (3xy)2xy - (3xy)y^2$

$\qquad\qquad\qquad\qquad = 3xy(x^2 - 2xy - y^2)$

(B) $3y(2y + 5) + 2(2y + 5) = 3y(2y + 5) + 2(2y + 5)$

$\qquad\qquad\qquad\qquad\quad = (3y + 2)(2y + 5)$

Matched Problem 1 Factor out all factors common to all terms.

(A) $2x^3y - 8x^2y^2 - 6xy^3$ $\qquad$ (B) $2x(3x - 2) - 7(3x - 2)$

Factoring by Grouping

Occasionally, polynomials can be factored by grouping terms in such a way that we obtain results that look like Example 1B. We can then complete the factoring following the steps used in that example. This process will prove useful in the next subsection, where an efficient method is developed for factoring a second-degree polynomial as the product of two first-degree polynomials, if such factors exist.

EXAMPLE 2 Factoring by Grouping Factor by grouping.

(A) $3x^2 - 3x - x + 1$

(B) $4x^2 - 2xy - 6xy + 3y^2$

(C) $y^2 + xz + xy + yz$

SOLUTION

(A) $3x^2 - 3x - x + 1$

$\qquad = (3x^2 - 3x) - (x - 1)$ $\qquad$ Group the first two and the last two terms.

$\qquad = 3x(x - 1) - (x - 1)$ $\qquad$ Factor out any common factors from each group. The common factor $(x - 1)$ can be

$\qquad = (x - 1)(3x - 1)$ $\qquad$ taken out, and the factoring is complete.

(B) $4x^2 - 2xy - 6xy + 3y^2 = (4x^2 - 2xy) - (6xy - 3y^2)$

$\qquad\qquad\qquad\qquad\qquad = 2x(2x - y) - 3y(2x - y)$

$\qquad\qquad\qquad\qquad\qquad = (2x - y)(2x - 3y)$

(C) If, as in parts (A) and (B), we group the first two terms and the last two terms of $y^2 + xz + xy + yz$, no common factor can be taken out of each group to complete the factoring. However, if the two middle terms are reversed, we can proceed as before:

$$y^2 + xz + xy + yz = y^2 + xy + xz + yz$$
$$= (y^2 + xy) + (xz + yz)$$
$$= y(y + x) + z(x + y)$$
$$= y(x + y) + z(x + y)$$
$$= (x + y)(y + z)$$

Matched Problem 2 Factor by grouping.

(A) $6x^2 + 2x + 9x + 3$

(B) $2u^2 + 6uv - 3uv - 9v^2$

(C) $ac + bd + bc + ad$

Factoring Second-Degree Polynomials

We now turn our attention to factoring second-degree polynomials of the form

$$2x^2 - 5x - 3 \quad \text{and} \quad 2x^2 + 3xy - 2y^2$$

into the product of two first-degree polynomials with integer coefficients. Since many second-degree polynomials with integer coefficients cannot be factored in this way, it would be useful to know ahead of time that the factors we are seeking actually exist. The factoring approach we use, involving the *ac test*, determines at the beginning whether first-degree factors with integer coefficients do exist. Then, if they exist, the test provides a simple method for finding them.

THEOREM 1   ac Test for Factorability

If in polynomials of the form

$$ax^2 + bx + c \quad \text{or} \quad ax^2 + bxy + cy^2 \tag{1}$$

the product ac has two integer factors p and q whose sum is the coefficient b of the middle term; that is, if integers p and q exist so that

$$pq = ac \quad \text{and} \quad p + q = b \tag{2}$$

then the polynomials have first-degree factors with integer coefficients. If no integers p and q exist that satisfy equations (2), then the polynomials in equations (1) will not have first-degree factors with integer coefficients.

If integers p and q exist that satisfy equations (2) in the *ac* test, the factoring always can be completed as follows: Using $b = p + q$, split the middle terms in equations (1) to obtain

$$ax^2 + bx + c = ax^2 + px + qx + c$$
$$ax^2 + bxy + cy^2 = ax^2 + pxy + qxy + cy^2$$

Complete the factoring by grouping the first two terms and the last two terms as in Example 2. This process always works, and it does not matter if the two middle terms on the right are interchanged.

Several examples should make the process clear. After a little practice, you will perform many of the steps mentally and will find the process fast and efficient.

EXAMPLE 3   Factoring Second-Degree Polynomials   Factor, if possible, using integer coefficients.

(A) $4x^2 - 4x - 3$ (B) $2x^2 - 3x - 4$ (C) $6x^2 - 25xy + 4y^2$

SOLUTION

(A) $4x^2 - 4x - 3$

Step 1   Use the *ac* test to test for factorability. Comparing $4x^2 - 4x - 3$ with $ax^2 + bx + c$, we see that $a = 4$, $b = -4$, and $c = -3$. Multiply a and c to obtain

$$ac = (4)(-3) = -12$$

List all pairs of integers whose product is -12, as shown in the margin. These are called **factor pairs** of -12. Then try to find a factor pair that sums to $b = -4$, the coefficient of the middle term in $4x^2 - 4x - 3$. (In practice, this part of Step 1 is often done mentally and can be done rather quickly.) Notice that the factor pair 2 and -6 sums to -4. By the *ac* test, $4x^2 - 4x - 3$ has first-degree factors with integer coefficients.

pq

$(1)(-12)$ All factor pairs of
$(-1)(12)$ $-12 = ac$
$(2)(-6)$
$(-2)(6)$
$(3)(-4)$
$(-3)(4)$

Step 2 Split the middle term, using $b = p + q$, and complete the factoring by grouping. Using $-4 = 2 + (-6)$, we split the middle term in $4x^2 - 4x - 3$ and complete the factoring by grouping:

$$4x^2 - 4x - 3 = 4x^2 + 2x - 6x - 3$$
$$= (4x^2 + 2x) - (6x + 3)$$
$$= 2x(2x + 1) - 3(2x + 1)$$
$$= (2x + 1)(2x - 3)$$

The result can be checked by multiplying the two factors to obtain the original polynomial.

(B) $2x^2 - 3x - 4$

Step 1 Use the ac test to test for factorability:

$$ac = (2)(-4) = -8$$

pq

$(-1)(8)$ All factor pairs of

$(1)(-8)$ $-8 = ac$

$(-2)(4)$

$(2)(-4)$

Does -8 have a factor pair whose sum is -3? None of the factor pairs listed in the margin sums to $-3 = b$, the coefficient of the middle term in $2x^2 - 3x - 4$. According to the ac test, we can conclude that $2x^2 - 3x - 4$ does not have first-degree factors with integer coefficients, and we say that the polynomial is **not factorable**.

(C) $6x^2 - 25xy + 4y^2$

Step 1 Use the ac test to test for factorability:

$$ac = (6)(4) = 24$$

Mentally checking through the factor pairs of 24, keeping in mind that their sum must be $-25 = b$, we see that if $p = -1$ and $q = -24$, then

$$pq = (-1)(-24) = 24 = ac$$

and

$$p + q = (-1) + (-24) = -25 = b$$

So the polynomial is factorable.

Step 2 Split the middle term, using $b = p + q$, and complete the factoring by grouping. Using $-25 = (-1) + (-24)$, we split the middle term in $6x^2 - 25xy + 4y^2$ and complete the factoring by grouping:

$$6x^2 - 25xy + 4y^2 = 6x^2 - xy - 24xy + 4y^2$$
$$= (6x^2 - xy) - (24xy - 4y^2)$$
$$= x(6x - y) - 4y(6x - y)$$
$$= (6x - y)(x - 4y)$$

The check is left to the reader.

Matched Problem 3 Factor, if possible, using integer coefficients.

(A) $2x^2 + 11x - 6$

(B) $4x^2 + 11x - 6$

(C) $6x^2 + 5xy - 4y^2$

Special Factoring Formulas

The factoring formulas listed in the following box will enable us to factor certain polynomial forms that occur frequently. These formulas can be established by multiplying the factors on the right.

> **THEOREM 2**   Special Factoring Formulas
>
> | | |
> |---|---|
> | Perfect square: | 1. $u^2 + 2uv + v^2 = (u + v)^2$ |
> | Perfect square: | 2. $u^2 - 2uv + v^2 = (u - v)^2$ |
> | Difference of squares: | 3. $u^2 - v^2 = (u - v)(u + v)$ |
> | Difference of cubes: | 4. $u^3 - v^3 = (u - v)(u^2 + uv + v^2)$ |
> | Sum of cubes: | 5. $u^3 + v^3 = (u + v)(u^2 - uv + v^2)$ |

⚠ **CAUTION**   Notice that $u^2 + v^2$ is not included in the list of special factoring formulas. In fact,

$$u^2 + v^2 \neq (au + bv)(cu + dv)$$

for any choice of real number coefficients a, b, c, and d.   ▲

EXAMPLE 4   Factoring   Factor completely.

(A) $4m^2 - 12mn + 9n^2$ (B) $x^2 - 16y^2$ (C) $z^3 - 1$

(D) $m^3 + n^3$ (E) $a^2 - 4(b + 2)^2$

SOLUTION

(A) $4m^2 - 12mn + 9n^2 = (2m - 3n)^2$

(B) $x^2 - 16y^2 = x^2 - (4y)^2 = (x - 4y)(x + 4y)$

(C) $z^3 - 1 = (z - 1)(z^2 + z + 1)$ Use the *ac* test to verify that $z^2 + z + 1$ cannot be factored.

(D) $m^3 + n^3 = (m + n)(m^2 - mn + n^2)$ Use the *ac* test to verify that $m^2 - mn + n^2$ cannot be factored.

(E) $a^2 - 4(b + 2)^2 = [a - 2(b + 2)][a + 2(b + 2)]$

Matched Problem 4)   Factor completely:

(A) $x^2 + 6xy + 9y^2$ (B) $9x^2 - 4y^2$ (C) $8m^3 - 1$

(D) $x^3 + y^3z^3$ (E) $9(m - 3)^2 - 4n^2$

Combined Factoring Techniques

We complete this section by considering several factoring problems that involve combinations of the preceding techniques.

> **PROCEDURE**   Factoring Polynomials
>
> Step 1   Take out any factors common to all terms.
>
> Step 2   Use any of the special formulas listed in Theorem 2 that are applicable.
>
> Step 3   Apply the *ac* test to any remaining second-degree polynomial factors.
>
> **Note:** It may be necessary to perform some of these steps more than once. Furthermore, the order of applying these steps can vary.

EXAMPLE 5   Combined Factoring Techniques   Factor completely.

(A) $3x^3 - 48x$ (B) $3u^4 - 3u^3v - 9u^2v^2$

(C) $3m^2 - 24mn^3$ (D) $3x^4 - 5x^2 + 2$

SOLUTION

(A) $3x^3 - 48x = 3x(x^2 - 16) = 3x(x - 4)(x + 4)$

(B) $3u^4 - 3u^3v - 9u^2v^2 = 3u^2(u^2 - uv - 3v^2)$

(C) $3m^4 - 24mn^3 = 3m(m^3 - 8n^3) = 3m(m - 2n)(m^2 + 2mn + 4n^2)$

(D) $3x^4 - 5x^2 + 2 = (3x^2 - 2)(x^2 - 1) = (3x^2 - 2)(x - 1)(x + 1)$

Matched Problem 5 Factor completely.

(A) $18x^3 - 8x$

(B) $4m^3n - 2m^2n^2 + 2mn^3$

(C) $2t^4 - 16t$

(D) $2y^4 - 5y^2 - 12$

Exercises A.3

In Problems 1–8, factor out all factors common to all terms.

1. $6m^4 - 9m^3 - 3m^2$
2. $6x^4 - 8m^3 - 2x^2$

3. $8u^3v - 6u^2v^2 + 4uv^3$
4. $10x^3y + 20x^2y^2 - 15xy^3$

5. $7m(2m - 3) + 5(2m - 3)$

6. $5x(x + 1) - 3(x + 1)$

7. $4ab(2c + d) - (2c + d)$

8. $12a(b - 2c) - 15b(b - 2c)$

In Problems 9–18, factor by grouping.

9. $2x^2 - x + 4x - 2$
10. $x^2 - 3x + 2x - 6$

11. $3y^2 - 3y + 2y - 2$
12. $2x^2 - x + 6x - 3$

13. $2x^2 + 8x - x - 4$
14. $6x^2 + 9x - 2x - 3$

15. $wy - wz + xy - xz$
16. $ac + ad + bc + bd$

17. $am - 3bm + 2na - 6bn$
18. $ab + 6 + 2a + 3b$

In Problems 19–56, factor completely. If a polynomial cannot be factored, say so.

19. $3y^2 - y - 2$
20. $2x^2 + 5x - 3$

21. $u^2 - 2uv - 15v^2$
22. $x^2 - 4xy - 12y^2$

23. $m^2 - 6m - 3$
24. $x^2 + x - 4$

25. $w^2x^2 - y^2$
26. $25m^2 - 16n^2$

27. $9m^2 - 6mn + n^2$
28. $x^2 + 10xy + 25y^2$

29. $y^2 + 16$
30. $u^2 + 81$

31. $4z^2 - 28z + 48$
32. $6x^2 + 48x + 72$

33. $2x^4 - 24x^3 + 40x^2$
34. $2y^3 - 22y^2 + 48y$

35. $4xy^2 - 12xy + 9x$
36. $16x^2y - 8xy + y$

37. $6m^2 - mn - 12n^2$
38. $6s^2 + 7st - 3t^2$

39. $4u^3v - uv^3$
40. $x^3y - 9xy^3$

41. $2x^3 - 2x^2 + 8x$
42. $3m^3 - 6m^2 + 15m$

43. $8x^3 - 27y^3$
44. $5x^3 + 40y^3$

45. $x^4y + 8xy$
46. $8a^3 - 1$

47. $(x + 2)^2 - 9y^2$
48. $(a - b)^2 - 4(c - d)^2$

49. $5u^2 + 4uv - 2v^2$
50. $3x^2 - 2xy - 4y^2$

51. $6(x - y)^2 + 23(x - y) - 4$

52. $4(A + B)^2 - 5(A + B) - 6$

53. $y^4 - 3y^2 - 4$

54. $m^4 - n^4$

55. $15y(x - y)^3 + 12x(x - y)^2$

56. $15x^2(3x - 1)^4 + 60x^3(3x - 1)^3$

✎ In Problems 57–60, discuss the validity of each statement. If the statement is true, explain why. If not, give a counterexample.

57. If n is a positive integer greater than 1, then $u^n - v^n$ can be factored.

58. If m and n are positive integers and $m \neq n$, then $u^m - v^n$ is not factorable.

59. If n is a positive integer greater than 1, then $u^n + v^n$ can be factored.

60. If k is a positive integer, then $u^{2k+1} + v^{2k+1}$ can be factored.

Answers to Matched Problems

1. (A) $2xy(x^2 - 4xy - 3y^2)$ (B) $(2x - 7)(3x - 2)$
2. (A) $(3x + 1)(2x + 3)$ (B) $(u + 3v)(2u - 3v)$
    (C) $(a + b)(c + d)$
3. (A) $(2x - 1)(x + 6)$ (B) Not factorable
    (C) $(3x + 4y)(2x - y)$
4. (A) $(x + 3y)^2$ (B) $(3x - 2y)(3x + 2y)$
    (C) $(2m - 1)(4m^2 + 2m + 1)$
    (D) $(x + yz)(x^2 - xyz + y^2z^2)$
    (E) $[3(m - 3) - 2n][3(m - 3) + 2n]$
5. (A) $2x(3x - 2)(3x + 2)$ (B) $2mn(2m^2 - mn + n^2)$
    (C) $2t(t - 2)(t^2 + 2t + 4)$
    (D) $(2y^2 + 3)(y - 2)(y + 2)$

A.4 Operations on Rational Expressions

- Reducing to Lowest Terms
- Multiplication and Division
- Addition and Subtraction
- Compound Fractions

We now turn our attention to fractional forms. A quotient of two algebraic expressions (division by 0 excluded) is called a **fractional expression**. If both the numerator and the denominator are polynomials, the fractional expression is called a **rational expression**. Some examples of rational expressions are

$$\frac{1}{x^3 + 2x} \qquad \frac{5}{x} \qquad \frac{x + 7}{3x^2 - 5x + 1} \qquad \frac{x^2 - 2x + 4}{1}$$

In this section, we discuss basic operations on rational expressions. Since variables represent real numbers in the rational expressions we will consider, the properties of real number fractions summarized in Appendix A.1 will play a central role.

AGREEMENT   Variable Restriction

Even though not always explicitly stated, we always assume that variables are restricted so that division by 0 is excluded.

For example, given the rational expression

$$\frac{2x + 5}{x(x + 2)(x - 3)}$$

the variable x is understood to be restricted from being 0, -2, or 3, since these values would cause the denominator to be 0.

Reducing to Lowest Terms

Central to the process of reducing rational expressions to *lowest terms* is the *fundamental property of fractions*, which we restate here for convenient reference:

THEOREM 1   Fundamental Property of Fractions

If a, b, and k are real numbers with b, $k \neq 0$, then

$$\frac{ka}{kb} = \frac{a}{b} \qquad \frac{5 \cdot 2}{5 \cdot 7} = \frac{2}{7} \qquad \frac{x(x + 4)}{2(x + 4)} = \frac{x}{2} \quad x \neq -4$$

Using this property from left to right to eliminate all common factors from the numerator and the denominator of a given fraction is referred to as **reducing a fraction to lowest terms**. We are actually dividing the numerator and denominator by the same nonzero common factor.

Using the property from right to left—that is, multiplying the numerator and denominator by the same nonzero factor—is referred to as **raising a fraction to higher terms**. We will use the property in both directions in the material that follows.

EXAMPLE 1   Reducing to Lowest Terms   Reduce each fraction to lowest terms.

(A) $\dfrac{1 \cdot 2 \cdot 3 \cdot 4}{1 \cdot 2 \cdot 3 \cdot 4 \cdot 5 \cdot 6} = \dfrac{\cancel{1 \cdot 2 \cdot 3 \cdot 4}}{\cancel{1 \cdot 2 \cdot 3 \cdot 4} \cdot 5 \cdot 6} = \dfrac{1}{5 \cdot 6} = \dfrac{1}{30}$

(B) $\dfrac{2 \cdot 4 \cdot 6 \cdot 8}{1 \cdot 2 \cdot 3 \cdot 4} = \dfrac{\overset{2}{\cancel{2}} \cdot \overset{2}{\cancel{4}} \cdot \overset{2}{\cancel{6}} \cdot \overset{2}{\cancel{8}}}{\cancel{1 \cdot 2 \cdot 3 \cdot 4}} = 2 \cdot 2 \cdot 2 \cdot 2 = 16$

Matched Problem 1   Reduce each fraction to lowest terms.

(A) $\dfrac{1 \cdot 2 \cdot 3 \cdot 4 \cdot 5}{1 \cdot 2 \cdot 1 \cdot 2 \cdot 3}$ (B) $\dfrac{1 \cdot 4 \cdot 9 \cdot 16}{1 \cdot 2 \cdot 3 \cdot 4}$

CONCEPTUAL INSIGHT

Using Theorem 1 to divide the numerator and denominator of a fraction by a common factor is often referred to as **canceling**. This operation can be denoted by drawing a slanted line through each common factor and writing any remaining factors above or below the common factor. Canceling is often incorrectly applied to individual terms in the numerator or denominator, instead of to common factors. For example,

$$\frac{14 - 5}{2} = \frac{9}{2}$$ Theorem 1 does not apply. There are no common factors in the numerator.

$$\frac{14 - 5}{2} \neq \frac{\overset{7}{\cancel{14}} - 5}{\underset{1}{\cancel{2}}} = 2$$ Incorrect use of Theorem 1. To cancel 2 in the denominator, 2 must be a factor of each term in the numerator.

EXAMPLE 2 Reducing to Lowest Terms Reduce each rational expression to lowest terms.

(A) $\dfrac{6x^2 + x - 1}{2x^2 - x - 1} = \dfrac{(2x + 1)(3x - 1)}{(2x + 1)(x - 1)}$ Factor numerator and denominator completely.

$\qquad\qquad\quad = \dfrac{3x - 1}{x - 1}$ Divide numerator and denominator by the common factor $(2x + 1)$.

(B) $\dfrac{x^4 - 8x}{3x^3 - 2x^2 - 8x} = \dfrac{x(x - 2)(x^2 + 2x + 4)}{x(x - 2)(3x + 4)}$

$\qquad\qquad\qquad = \dfrac{x^2 + 2x + 4}{3x + 4}$

Matched Problem 2 Reduce each rational expression to lowest terms.

(A) $\dfrac{x^2 - 6x + 9}{x^2 - 9}$ (B) $\dfrac{x^3 - 1}{x^2 - 1}$

Multiplication and Division

Since we are restricting variable replacements to real numbers, multiplication and division of rational expressions follow the rules for multiplying and dividing real number fractions summarized in Appendix A.1.

THEOREM 2 Multiplication and Division

If a, b, c, and d are real numbers, then

1. $\dfrac{a}{b} \cdot \dfrac{c}{d} = \dfrac{ac}{bd}$, $b, d \neq 0$ $\qquad \dfrac{3}{5} \cdot \dfrac{x}{x + 5} = \dfrac{3x}{5(x + 5)}$

2. $\dfrac{a}{b} \div \dfrac{c}{d} = \dfrac{a}{b} \cdot \dfrac{d}{c}$, $b, c, d \neq 0$ $\qquad \dfrac{3}{5} \div \dfrac{x}{x + 5} = \dfrac{3}{5} \cdot \dfrac{x + 5}{x}$

EXAMPLE 3 Multiplication and Division Perform the indicated operations and reduce to lowest terms.

(A) $\dfrac{10x^3y}{3xy + 9y} \cdot \dfrac{x^2 - 9}{4x^2 - 12x}$ Factor numerators and denominators. Then divide any numerator and any denominator with a like common factor.

$\qquad = \dfrac{\overset{5x^2}{\cancel{10x^3y}}}{3\cancel{y}(x + 3)} \cdot \dfrac{\overset{1 \cdot 1}{(x - 3)(x + 3)}}{4x(x - 3)}$

$\qquad = \dfrac{5x^2}{6}$

(B) $\dfrac{4 - 2x}{4} \div (x - 2) = \dfrac{\overset{1}{2}(2 - x)}{\underset{2}{4}} \cdot \dfrac{1}{x - 2}$ $x - 2 = \dfrac{x - 2}{1}$

$\qquad\qquad\qquad = \dfrac{2 - x}{2(x - 2)} = \dfrac{\overset{-1}{-(x - 2)}}{2\underset{1}{(x - 2)}}$ $b - a = -(a - b)$, a useful change in some problems

$\qquad\qquad\qquad = -\dfrac{1}{2}$

Matched Problem 3 Perform the indicated operations and reduce to lowest terms.

(A) $\dfrac{12x^2y^3}{2xy^2 + 6xy} \cdot \dfrac{y^2 + 6y + 9}{3y^3 + 9y^2}$ (B) $(4 - x) \div \dfrac{x^2 - 16}{5}$

Addition and Subtraction

Again, because we are restricting variable replacements to real numbers, addition and subtraction of rational expressions follow the rules for adding and subtracting real number fractions.

THEOREM 3 Addition and Subtraction

For a, b, and c real numbers,

1. $\dfrac{a}{b} + \dfrac{c}{b} = \dfrac{a + c}{b}$, $b \neq 0$ $\dfrac{x}{x + 5} + \dfrac{8}{x + 5} = \dfrac{x + 8}{x + 5}$

2. $\dfrac{a}{b} - \dfrac{c}{b} = \dfrac{a - c}{b}$, $b \neq 0$ $\dfrac{x}{3x^2y^2} - \dfrac{x + 7}{3x^2y^2} = \dfrac{x - (x + 7)}{3x^2y^2}$

We add rational expressions with the same denominators by adding or subtracting their numerators and placing the result over the common denominator. If the denominators are not the same, we raise the fractions to higher terms, using the fundamental property of fractions to obtain common denominators, and then proceed as described.

Even though any common denominator will do, our work will be simplified if the *least common denominator (LCD)* is used. Often, the LCD is obvious, but if it is not, the steps in the next box describe how to find it.

PROCEDURE Least Common Denominator

The least common denominator (LCD) of two or more rational expressions is found as follows:

1. Factor each denominator completely, including integer factors.
2. Identify each different factor from all the denominators.
3. Form a product using each different factor to the highest power that occurs in any one denominator. This product is the LCD.

EXAMPLE 4 Addition and Subtraction Combine into a single fraction and reduce to lowest terms.

(A) $\dfrac{3}{10} + \dfrac{5}{6} - \dfrac{11}{45}$ (B) $\dfrac{4}{9x} - \dfrac{5x}{6y^2} + 1$ (C) $\dfrac{1}{x - 1} - \dfrac{1}{x} - \dfrac{2}{x^2 - 1}$

SOLUTION

(A) To find the LCD, factor each denominator completely:

$$\left.\begin{array}{l} 10 = 2 \cdot 5 \\ 6 = 2 \cdot 3 \\ 45 = 3^2 \cdot 5 \end{array}\right\} \quad LCD = 2 \cdot 3^2 \cdot 5 = 90$$

Now use the fundamental property of fractions to make each denominator 90:

$$\frac{3}{10} + \frac{5}{6} - \frac{11}{45} = \frac{9 \cdot 3}{9 \cdot 10} + \frac{15 \cdot 5}{15 \cdot 6} - \frac{2 \cdot 11}{2 \cdot 45}$$

$$= \frac{27}{90} + \frac{75}{90} - \frac{22}{90}$$

$$= \frac{27 + 75 - 22}{90} = \frac{80}{90} = \frac{8}{9}$$

(B) $\left.\begin{array}{l} 9x = 3^2 x \\ 6y^2 = 2 \cdot 3y^2 \end{array}\right\} \quad LCD = 2 \cdot 3^2 xy^2 = 18xy^2$

$$\frac{4}{9x} - \frac{5x}{6y^2} + 1 = \frac{2y^2 \cdot 4}{2y^2 \cdot 9x} - \frac{3x \cdot 5x}{3x \cdot 6y^2} + \frac{18xy^2}{18xy^2}$$

$$= \frac{8y^2 - 15x^2 + 18xy^2}{18xy^2}$$

(C) $\dfrac{1}{x-1} - \dfrac{1}{x} - \dfrac{2}{x^2 - 1}$

$$= \frac{1}{x-1} - \frac{1}{x} - \frac{2}{(x-1)(x+1)} \qquad LCD = x(x-1)(x+1)$$

$$= \frac{x(x+1) - (x-1)(x+1) - 2x}{x(x-1)(x+1)}$$

$$= \frac{x^2 + x - x^2 + 1 - 2x}{x(x-1)(x+1)}$$

$$= \frac{1 - x}{x(x-1)(x+1)}$$

$$= \frac{-(\overset{-1}{\cancel{x-1}})}{x\underset{1}{\cancel{(x-1)}}(x+1)} = \frac{-1}{x(x+1)}$$

Matched Problem 4 Combine into a single fraction and reduce to lowest terms.

(A) $\dfrac{5}{28} - \dfrac{1}{10} + \dfrac{6}{35}$

(B) $\dfrac{1}{4x^2} - \dfrac{2x+1}{3x^3} + \dfrac{3}{12x}$

(C) $\dfrac{2}{x^2 - 4x + 4} + \dfrac{1}{x} - \dfrac{1}{x-2}$

Compound Fractions

A fractional expression with fractions in its numerator, denominator, or both is called a **compound fraction**. It is often necessary to represent a compound fraction as a **simple fraction**—that is (in all cases we will consider), as the quotient of two polynomials. The process does not involve any new concepts. It is a matter of applying old concepts and processes in the correct sequence.

EXAMPLE 5   Simplifying Compound Fractions   Express as a simple fraction reduced to lowest terms:

(A) $\dfrac{\dfrac{1}{5+h} - \dfrac{1}{5}}{h}$

(B) $\dfrac{\dfrac{y}{x^2} - \dfrac{x}{y^2}}{\dfrac{y}{x} - \dfrac{x}{y}}$

SOLUTION   We will simplify the expressions in parts (A) and (B) using two different methods—each is suited to the particular type of problem.

(A) We simplify this expression by combining the numerator into a single fraction and using division of rational forms.

$$\frac{\dfrac{1}{5+h} - \dfrac{1}{5}}{h} = \left[\frac{1}{5+h} - \frac{1}{5}\right] \div \frac{h}{1}$$

$$= \frac{5 - 5 - h}{5(5+h)} \cdot \frac{1}{h}$$

$$= \frac{-h}{5(5+h)h} = \frac{-1}{5(5+h)}$$

(B) The method used here makes effective use of the fundamental property of fractions in the form

$$\frac{a}{b} = \frac{ka}{kb} \qquad b, k \neq 0$$

Multiply the numerator and denominator by the LCD of all fractions in the numerator and denominator—in this case, $x^2 y^2$:

$$\frac{x^2 y^2 \left(\dfrac{y}{x^2} - \dfrac{x}{y^2}\right)}{x^2 y^2 \left(\dfrac{y}{x} - \dfrac{x}{y}\right)} = \frac{x^2 y^2 \dfrac{y}{x^2} - x^2 y^2 \dfrac{x}{y^2}}{x^2 y^2 \dfrac{y}{x} - x^2 y^2 \dfrac{x}{y}} = \frac{y^3 - x^3}{xy^3 - x^3 y}$$

$$= \frac{(y - x)(y^2 + xy + x^2)}{xy(y - x)(y + x)}$$

$$= \frac{y^2 + xy + x^2}{xy(y + x)} \quad \text{or} \quad \frac{x^2 + xy + y^2}{xy(x + y)}$$

Matched Problem 5   Express as a simple fraction reduced to lowest terms:

(A) $\dfrac{\dfrac{1}{2+h} - \dfrac{1}{2}}{h}$

(B) $\dfrac{\dfrac{a}{b} - \dfrac{b}{a}}{\dfrac{a}{b} + 2 + \dfrac{b}{a}}$

Exercises A.4

In Problems 1–22, perform the indicated operations and reduce answers to lowest terms.

1. $\dfrac{5 \cdot 9 \cdot 13}{3 \cdot 5 \cdot 7}$

2. $\dfrac{10 \cdot 9 \cdot 8}{3 \cdot 2 \cdot 1}$

3. $\dfrac{12 \cdot 11 \cdot 10 \cdot 9}{4 \cdot 3 \cdot 2 \cdot 1}$

4. $\dfrac{15 \cdot 10 \cdot 5}{20 \cdot 15 \cdot 10}$

5. $\dfrac{d^5}{3a} \div \left(\dfrac{d^2}{6a^2} \cdot \dfrac{a}{4d^3}\right)$

6. $\left(\dfrac{d^5}{3a} \div \dfrac{d^2}{6a^2}\right) \cdot \dfrac{a}{4d^3}$

7. $\dfrac{x^2}{12} + \dfrac{x}{18} - \dfrac{1}{30}$

8. $\dfrac{2y}{18} - \dfrac{-1}{28} - \dfrac{y}{42}$

9. $\dfrac{4m-3}{18m^3} + \dfrac{3}{4m} - \dfrac{2m-1}{6m^2}$

10. $\dfrac{3x+8}{4x^2} - \dfrac{2x-1}{x^3} - \dfrac{5}{8x}$

11. $\dfrac{x^2-9}{x^2-3x} \div (x^2 - x - 12)$

12. $\dfrac{2x^2+7x+3}{4x^2-1} \div (x+3)$

13. $\dfrac{2}{x} - \dfrac{1}{x-3}$

14. $\dfrac{5}{m-2} - \dfrac{3}{2m+1}$

15. $\dfrac{2}{(x+1)^2} - \dfrac{5}{x^2-x-2}$

16. $\dfrac{3}{x^2-5x+6} - \dfrac{5}{(x-2)^2}$

17. $\dfrac{x+1}{x-1} - 1$

18. $m - 3 - \dfrac{m-1}{m-2}$

19. $\dfrac{3}{a-1} - \dfrac{2}{1-a}$

20. $\dfrac{5}{x-3} - \dfrac{2}{3-x}$

21. $\dfrac{2x}{x^2-16} - \dfrac{x-4}{x^2+4x}$

22. $\dfrac{m+2}{m^2-2m} - \dfrac{m}{m^2-4}$

In Problems 23–34, perform the indicated operations and reduce answers to lowest terms. Represent any compound fractions as simple fractions reduced to lowest terms.

23. $\dfrac{x^2}{x^2+2x+1} + \dfrac{x-1}{3x+3} - \dfrac{1}{6}$

24. $\dfrac{y}{y^2-y-2} - \dfrac{1}{y^2+5y-14} - \dfrac{2}{y^2+8y+7}$

25. $\dfrac{1-\dfrac{x}{y}}{2-\dfrac{y}{x}}$

26. $\dfrac{2}{5-\dfrac{3}{4x+1}}$

27. $\dfrac{c+2}{5c-5} - \dfrac{c-2}{3c-3} + \dfrac{c}{1-c}$

28. $\dfrac{x+7}{ax-bx} + \dfrac{y+9}{by-ay}$

29. $\dfrac{1+\dfrac{3}{x}}{x-\dfrac{9}{x}}$

30. $\dfrac{1-\dfrac{y^2}{x^2}}{1-\dfrac{y}{x}}$

31. $\dfrac{\dfrac{1}{2(x+h)} - \dfrac{1}{2x}}{h}$

32. $\dfrac{\dfrac{1}{x+h} - \dfrac{1}{x}}{h}$

33. $\dfrac{\dfrac{x}{y} - 2 + \dfrac{y}{x}}{\dfrac{x}{y} - \dfrac{y}{x}}$

34. $\dfrac{1+\dfrac{2}{x} - \dfrac{15}{x^2}}{1+\dfrac{4}{x} - \dfrac{5}{x^2}}$

In Problems 35–42, imagine that the indicated "solutions" were given to you by a student whom you were tutoring in this class.

(A) Is the solution correct? If the solution is incorrect, explain what is wrong and how it can be corrected.

(B) Show a correct solution for each incorrect solution.

35. $\dfrac{x^2+4x+3}{x+3} = \dfrac{x^2+4x}{x} = x + 4$

36. $\dfrac{x^2-3x-4}{x-4} = \dfrac{x^2-3x}{x} = x - 3$

37. $\dfrac{(x+h)^2 - x^2}{h} = (x+1)^2 - x^2 = 2x + 1$

38. $\dfrac{(x+h)^3 - x^3}{h} = (x+1)^3 - x^3 = 3x^2 + 3x + 1$

39. $\dfrac{x^2-3x}{x^2-2x-3} + x - 3 = \dfrac{x^2-3x+x-3}{x^2-2x-3} = 1$

40. $\dfrac{2}{x-1} - \dfrac{x+3}{x^2-1} = \dfrac{2x+2-x-3}{x^2-1} = \dfrac{1}{x+1}$

41. $\dfrac{2x^2}{x^2-4} - \dfrac{x}{x-2} = \dfrac{2x^2-x^2-2x}{x^2-4} = \dfrac{x}{x+2}$

42. $x + \dfrac{x-2}{x^2-3x+2} = \dfrac{x+x-2}{x^2-3x+2} = \dfrac{2}{x-2}$

Represent the compound fractions in Problems 43–46 as simple fractions reduced to lowest terms.

43. $\dfrac{\dfrac{1}{3(x+h)^2} - \dfrac{1}{3x^2}}{h}$

44. $\dfrac{\dfrac{1}{(x+h)^2} - \dfrac{1}{x^2}}{h}$

45. $x - \dfrac{2}{1-\dfrac{1}{x}}$

46. $2 - \dfrac{1}{1-\dfrac{2}{a+2}}$

Answers to Matched Problems

1. (A) 10   (B) 24

2. (A) $\dfrac{x-3}{x+3}$ (B) $\dfrac{x^2+x+1}{x+1}$

3. (A) $2x$ (B) $\dfrac{-5}{x+4}$

4. (A) $\dfrac{1}{4}$ (B) $\dfrac{3x^2-5x-4}{12x^3}$ (C) $\dfrac{4}{x(x-2)^2}$

5. (A) $\dfrac{-1}{2(2+h)}$ (B) $\dfrac{a-b}{a+b}$

A.5 Integer Exponents and Scientific Notation

- Integer Exponents
- Scientific Notation

We now review basic operations on integer exponents and scientific notation.

Integer Exponents

DEFINITION Integer Exponents

For n an integer and a a real number:

1. For n a positive integer,
$$a^n = a \cdot a \cdot \cdots \cdot a \quad n \text{ factors of } a \qquad 5^4 = 5 \cdot 5 \cdot 5 \cdot 5$$

2. For $n = 0$,
$$a^0 = 1 \quad a \neq 0 \qquad 12^0 = 1$$
$$0^0 \text{ is not defined.}$$

3. For n a negative integer,
$$a^n = \frac{1}{a^{-n}} \quad a \neq 0 \qquad a^{-3} = \frac{1}{a^{-(-3)}} = \frac{1}{a^3}$$

[If n is negative, then $(-n)$ is positive.]
Note: It can be shown that for *all* integers n,
$$a^{-n} = \frac{1}{a^n} \quad \text{and} \quad a^n = \frac{1}{a^{-n}} \quad a \neq 0 \qquad a^5 = \frac{1}{a^{-5}} \qquad a^{-5} = \frac{1}{a^5}$$

The following properties are very useful in working with integer exponents.

THEOREM 1 Exponent Properties

For n and m integers and a and b real numbers,

1. $a^m a^n = a^{m+n}$ $\qquad\qquad$ $a^8 a^{-3} = a^{8+(-3)} = a^5$
2. $(a^n)^m = a^{mn}$ $\qquad\qquad$ $(a^{-2})^3 = a^{3(-2)} = a^{-6}$
3. $(ab)^m = a^m b^m$ $\qquad\qquad$ $(ab)^{-2} = a^{-2} b^{-2}$
4. $\left(\dfrac{a}{b}\right)^m = \dfrac{a^m}{b^m} \quad b \neq 0$ $\qquad$ $\left(\dfrac{a}{b}\right)^5 = \dfrac{a^5}{b^5}$
5. $\dfrac{a^m}{a^n} = a^{m-n} = \dfrac{1}{a^{n-m}} \quad a \neq 0$ $\qquad$ $\dfrac{a^{-3}}{a^7} = \dfrac{1}{a^{7-(-3)}} = \dfrac{1}{a^{10}}$

Exponents are frequently encountered in algebraic applications. You should sharpen your skills in using exponents by reviewing the preceding basic definitions and properties and the examples that follow.

EXAMPLE 1 Simplifying Exponent Forms Simplify, and express the answers using positive exponents only.

(A) $(2x^3)(3x^5) = 2 \cdot 3 x^{3+5} = 6x^8$

(B) $x^5 x^{-9} = x^{-4} = \dfrac{1}{x^4}$

(C) $\dfrac{x^5}{x^7} = x^{5-7} = x^{-2} = \dfrac{1}{x^2}$ $\quad$ or $\quad$ $\dfrac{x^5}{x^7} = \dfrac{1}{x^{7-5}} = \dfrac{1}{x^2}$

(D) $\dfrac{x^{-3}}{y^{-4}} = \dfrac{y^4}{x^3}$

(E) $(u^{-3}v^2)^{-2} = (u^{-3})^{-2}(v^2)^{-2} = u^6v^{-4} = \dfrac{u^6}{v^4}$

(F) $\left(\dfrac{y^{-5}}{y^{-2}}\right)^{-2} = \dfrac{(y^{-5})^{-2}}{(y^{-2})^{-2}} = \dfrac{y^{10}}{y^4} = y^6$

(G) $\dfrac{4m^{-3}n^{-5}}{6m^{-4}n^3} = \dfrac{2m^{-3-(-4)}}{3n^{3-(-5)}} = \dfrac{2m}{3n^8}$

Matched Problem 1 Simplify, and express the answers using positive exponents only.

(A) $(3y^4)(2y^3)$ (B) m^2m^{-6} (C) $(u^3v^{-2})^{-2}$

(D) $\left(\dfrac{y^{-6}}{y^{-2}}\right)^{-1}$ (E) $\dfrac{8x^{-2}y^{-4}}{6x^{-5}y^2}$

EXAMPLE 2 Converting to a Simple Fraction Write $\dfrac{1-x}{x^{-1}-1}$ as a simple fraction with positive exponents.

SOLUTION First note that

$$\dfrac{1-x}{x^{-1}-1} \neq \dfrac{x(1-x)}{-1} \quad \text{A common error}$$

The original expression is a compound fraction, and we proceed to simplify it as follows:

$$\dfrac{1-x}{x^{-1}-1} = \dfrac{1-x}{\dfrac{1}{x}-1} \quad \begin{array}{l}\text{Multiply numerator and denominator}\\ \text{by } x \text{ to clear internal fractions.}\end{array}$$

$$= \dfrac{x(1-x)}{x\left(\dfrac{1}{x}-1\right)}$$

$$= \dfrac{x(1-x)}{1-x} = x$$

Matched Problem 2 Write $\dfrac{1+x^{-1}}{1-x^{-2}}$ as a simple fraction with positive exponents.

Scientific Notation

In the real world, one often encounters very large and very small numbers. For example,

- The public debt in the United States in 2013, to the nearest billion dollars, was

$$\$16,739,000,000,000$$

- The world population in the year 2025, to the nearest million, is projected to be

$$7,947,000,000$$

- The sound intensity of a normal conversation is

$$0.000\ 000\ 000\ 316 \text{ watt per square centimeter*}$$

---

*We write 0.000 000 000 316 in place of 0.000000000316, because it is then easier to keep track of the number of decimal places.

It is generally troublesome to write and work with numbers of this type in standard decimal form. The first and last example cannot even be entered into many calculators as they are written. But with exponents defined for all integers, we can now express any finite decimal form as the product of a number between 1 and 10 and an integer power of 10, that is, in the form

$$a \times 10^n \quad 1 \le a < 10, \quad a \text{ in decimal form}, \quad n \text{ an integer}$$

A number expressed in this form is said to be in **scientific notation**. The following are some examples of numbers in standard decimal notation and in scientific notation:

Decimal and Scientific Notation

$7 = 7 \times 10^0$	$0.5 = 5 \times 10^{-1}$
$67 = 6.7 \times 10$	$0.45 = 4.5 \times 10^{-1}$
$580 = 5.8 \times 10^2$	$0.0032 = 3.2 \times 10^{-3}$
$43,000 = 4.3 \times 10^4$	$0.000\,045 = 4.5 \times 10^{-5}$
$73,400,000 = 7.34 \times 10^7$	$0.000\,000\,391 = 3.91 \times 10^{-7}$

Note that the power of 10 used corresponds to the number of places we move the decimal to form a number between 1 and 10. The power is positive if the decimal is moved to the left and negative if it is moved to the right. Positive exponents are associated with numbers greater than or equal to 10; negative exponents are associated with positive numbers less than 1; and a zero exponent is associated with a number that is 1 or greater, but less than 10.

EXAMPLE 3   Scientific Notation

(A) Write each number in scientific notation:

$$7,320,000 \quad \text{and} \quad 0.000\,000\,54$$

(B) Write each number in standard decimal form:

$$4.32 \times 10^6 \quad \text{and} \quad 4.32 \times 10^{-5}$$

SOLUTION

(A) $7,320,000 = 7.320\,000. \times 10^6 = 7.32 \times 10^6$

    6 places left
    Positive exponent

$0.000\,000\,54 = 0.000\,000\,5.4 \times 10^{-7} = 5.4 \times 10^{-7}$

    7 places right
    Negative exponent

(B) $4.32 \times 10^6 = 4,320,000$ $4.32 \times 10^{-5} = \dfrac{4.32}{10^5} = 0.000\,043\,2$

    6 places right   5 places left
    Positive exponent 6   Negative exponent −5

Matched Problem 3

(A) Write each number in scientific notation: 47,100; 2,443,000,000; 1.45

(B) Write each number in standard decimal form: 3.07×10^8; 5.98×10^{-6}

In Problems 1–14, simplify and express answers using positive exponents only. Variables are restricted to avoid division by 0.

1. $2x^{-9}$

2. $3y^{-5}$

3. $\dfrac{3}{2w^{-7}}$

4. $\dfrac{5}{4x^{-9}}$

5. $2x^{-8}x^5$

6. $3c^{-9}c^4$

7. $\dfrac{w^{-8}}{w^{-3}}$

8. $\dfrac{m^{-11}}{m^{-5}}$

9. $(2a^{-3})^2$

10. $7d^{-4}d^4$

11. $(a^{-3})^2$

12. $(5b^{-2})^2$

13. $(2x^4)^{-3}$

14. $(a^{-3}b^4)^{-3}$

In Problems 15–20, write each number in scientific notation.

15. 82,300,000,000

16. 5,380,000

17. 0.783

18. 0.019

19. 0.000 034

20. 0.000 000 007 832

In Problems 21–28, write each number in standard decimal notation.

21. 4×10^4

22. 9×10^6

23. 7×10^{-3}

24. 2×10^{-5}

25. 6.171×10^7

26. 3.044×10^3

27. 8.08×10^{-4}

28. 1.13×10^{-2}

In Problems 29–38, simplify and express answers using positive exponents only. Assume that variables are nonzero.

29. $(22 + 31)^0$

30. $(2x^3y^4)^0$

31. $\dfrac{10^{-3} \cdot 10^4}{10^{-11} \cdot 10^{-2}}$

32. $\dfrac{10^{-17} \cdot 10^{-5}}{10^{-3} \cdot 10^{-14}}$

33. $(5x^2y^{-3})^{-2}$

34. $(2m^{-3}n^2)^{-3}$

35. $\left(\dfrac{-5}{2x^3}\right)^{-2}$

36. $\left(\dfrac{2a}{3b^2}\right)^{-3}$

37. $\dfrac{8x^{-3}y^{-1}}{6x^2y^{-4}}$

38. $\dfrac{9m^{-4}n^3}{12m^{-1}n^{-1}}$

In Problems 39–42, write each expression in the form $ax^p + bx^q$ or $ax^p + bx^q + cx^r$, where a, b, and c are real numbers and p, q, and r are integers. For example,

$$\dfrac{2x^4 - 3x^2 + 1}{2x^3} = \dfrac{2x^4}{2x^3} - \dfrac{3x^2}{2x^3} + \dfrac{1}{2x^3} = x - \dfrac{3}{2}x^{-1} + \dfrac{1}{2}x^{-3}$$

39. $\dfrac{7x^5 - x^2}{4x^5}$

40. $\dfrac{5x^3 - 2}{3x^2}$

41. $\dfrac{5x^4 - 3x^2 + 8}{2x^2}$

42. $\dfrac{2x^3 - 3x^2 + x}{2x^2}$

Write each expression in Problems 43–46 with positive exponents only, and as a single fraction reduced to lowest terms.

43. $\dfrac{3x^2(x-1)^2 - 2x^3(x-1)}{(x-1)^4}$

44. $\dfrac{5x^4(x+3)^2 - 2x^5(x+3)}{(x+3)^4}$

45. $2x^{-2}(x-1) - 2x^{-3}(x-1)^2$

46. $2x(x+3)^{-1} - x^2(x+3)^{-2}$

In Problems 47–50, convert each number to scientific notation and simplify. Express the answer in both scientific notation and in standard decimal form.

47. $\dfrac{9,600,000,000}{(1,600,000)(0.000\ 000\ 25)}$

48. $\dfrac{(60,000)(0.000\ 003)}{(0.0004)(1,500,000)}$

49. $\dfrac{(1,250,000)(0.000\ 38)}{0.0152}$

50. $\dfrac{(0.000\ 000\ 82)(230,000)}{(625,000)(0.0082)}$

51. What is the result of entering 2^{3^2} on a calculator?

52. Refer to Problem 51. What is the difference between $2^{(3^2)}$ and $(2^3)^2$? Which agrees with the value of 2^{3^2} obtained with a calculator?

53. If $n = 0$, then property 1 in Theorem 1 implies that $a^m a^0 = a^{m+0} = a^m$. Explain how this helps motivate the definition of a^0.

54. If $m = -n$, then property 1 in Theorem 1 implies that $a^{-n}a^n = a^0 = 1$. Explain how this helps motivate the definition of a^{-n}.

Write the fractions in Problems 55–58 as simple fractions reduced to lowest terms.

55. $\dfrac{u + v}{u^{-1} + v^{-1}}$

56. $\dfrac{x^{-2} - y^{-2}}{x^{-1} + y^{-1}}$

57. $\dfrac{b^{-2} - c^{-2}}{b^{-3} - c^{-3}}$

58. $\dfrac{xy^{-2} - yx^{-2}}{y^{-1} - x^{-1}}$

Applications

Problems 59 and 60 refer to Table 1.

Table 1 **U.S. Public Debt, Interest on Debt, and Population**

Year	Public Debt ($)	Interest on Debt ($)	Population
2000	5,674,000,000,000	362,000,000,000	281,000,000
2012	16,066,000,000,000	360,000,000,000	313,000,000

59. Public debt. Carry out the following computations using scientific notation, and write final answers in standard decimal form.

(A) What was the per capita debt in 2012 (to the nearest dollar)?

(B) What was the per capita interest paid on the debt in 2012 (to the nearest dollar)?

(C) What was the percentage interest paid on the debt in 2012 (to two decimal places)?

60. Public debt. Carry out the following computations using scientific notation, and write final answers in standard decimal form.

(A) What was the per capita debt in 2000 (to the nearest dollar)?

(B) What was the per capita interest paid on the debt in 2000 (to the nearest dollar)?

(C) What was the percentage interest paid on the debt in 2000 (to two decimal places)?

Air pollution. *Air quality standards establish maximum amounts of pollutants considered acceptable in the air. The amounts are frequently given in parts per million (ppm). A standard of 30 ppm also can be expressed as follows:*

$$30 \text{ ppm} = \frac{30}{1,000,000} = \frac{3 \times 10}{10^6}$$
$$= 3 \times 10^{-5} = 0.00003 = 0.003\%$$

In Problems 61 and 62, express the given standard:

(A) In scientific notation

(B) In standard decimal notation

(C) As a percent

61. 9 ppm, the standard for carbon monoxide, when averaged over a period of 8 hours

62. 0.03 ppm, the standard for sulfur oxides, when averaged over a year

63. Crime. In 2010, the United States had a violent crime rate of 404 per 100,000 people and a population of 309 million people. How many violent crimes occurred that year? Compute the answer using scientific notation and convert the answer to standard decimal form (to the nearest thousand).

64. Population density. The United States had a 2012 population of 313 million people and a land area of 3,539,000 square miles. What was the population density? Compute the answer using scientific notation and convert the answer to standard decimal form (to one decimal place).

Answers to Matched Problems

1. (A) $6y^7$ (B) $\dfrac{1}{m^4}$ (C) $\dfrac{v^4}{u^6}$ (D) y^4 (E) $\dfrac{4x^3}{3y^6}$

2. $\dfrac{x}{x-1}$

3. (A) 4.7×10^4; 2.443×10^9; 1.45×10^0

(B) 307,000,000; 0.000 005 98

A.6 Rational Exponents and Radicals

- *n*th Roots of Real Numbers
- Rational Exponents and Radicals
- Properties of Radicals

Square roots may now be generalized to *n*th roots, and the meaning of exponent may be generalized to include all rational numbers.

*n*th Roots of Real Numbers

Consider a square of side r with area 36 square inches. We can write

$$r^2 = 36$$

and conclude that side r is a number whose square is 36. We say that r is a **square root** of b if $r^2 = b$. Similarly, we say that r is a **cube root** of b if $r^3 = b$. And, in general,

> **DEFINITION** *n*th Root
> For any natural number n,
>
> $$r \text{ is an } \boldsymbol{n}\textbf{th root} \text{ of } b \text{ if } r^n = b$$

So 4 is a square root of 16, since $4^2 = 16$; -2 is a cube root of -8, since $(-2)^3 = -8$. Since $(-4)^2 = 16$, we see that -4 is also a square root of 16. It can be shown that any positive number has two real square roots, two real 4th roots, and, in general, two real *n*th roots if *n* is even. Negative numbers have no real square roots, no real 4th roots, and, in general, no real *n*th roots if *n* is even. The reason is that no real number raised to an even power can be negative. For odd roots, the situation is simpler. Every real number has exactly one real cube root, one real 5th root, and, in general, one real *n*th root if *n* is odd.

Additional roots can be considered in the *complex number system*. In this book, we restrict our interest to *real roots of real numbers*, and *root* will always be interpreted to mean "real root."

Rational Exponents and Radicals

We now turn to the question of what symbols to use to represent nth roots. For n a natural number greater than 1, we use

$$b^{1/n} \quad \text{or} \quad \sqrt[n]{b}$$

to represent a **real nth root of b**. The exponent form is motivated by the fact that $(b^{1/n})^n = b$ if exponent laws are to continue to hold for rational exponents. The other form is called an **nth root radical**. In the expression below, the symbol $\sqrt{}$ is called a **radical**, n is the **index** of the radical, and b is the **radicand**:

When the index is 2, it is usually omitted. That is, when dealing with square roots, we simply use $\sqrt{b}$ rather than $\sqrt[2]{b}$. If there are two real nth roots, both $b^{1/n}$ and $\sqrt[n]{b}$ denote the positive root, called the **principal nth root**.

EXAMPLE 1 Finding nth Roots Evaluate each of the following:

(A) $4^{1/2}$ and $\sqrt{4}$ (B) $-4^{1/2}$ and $-\sqrt{4}$ (C) $(-4)^{1/2}$ and $\sqrt{-4}$
(D) $8^{1/3}$ and $\sqrt[3]{8}$ (E) $(-8)^{1/3}$ and $\sqrt[3]{-8}$ (F) $-8^{1/3}$ and $-\sqrt[3]{8}$

SOLUTION

(A) $4^{1/2} = \sqrt{4} = 2 \quad (\sqrt{4} \neq \pm 2)$ (B) $-4^{1/2} = -\sqrt{4} = -2$
(C) $(-4)^{1/2}$ and $\sqrt{-4}$ are not real numbers
(D) $8^{1/3} = \sqrt[3]{8} = 2$ (E) $(-8)^{1/3} = \sqrt[3]{-8} = -2$
(F) $-8^{1/3} = -\sqrt[3]{8} = -2$

Matched Problem 1 Evaluate each of the following:
(A) $16^{1/2}$ (B) $-\sqrt{16}$ (C) $\sqrt[3]{-27}$ (D) $(-9)^{1/2}$ (E) $\left(\sqrt[4]{81}\right)^3$

⚠ **CAUTION** The symbol $\sqrt{4}$ represents the single number 2, not ± 2. Do not confuse $\sqrt{4}$ with the solutions of the equation $x^2 = 4$, which are usually written in the form $x = \pm\sqrt{4} = \pm 2$. ▲

We now define b^r for any rational number $r = m/n$.

DEFINITION Rational Exponents
If m and n are natural numbers without common prime factors, b is a real number, and b is nonnegative when n is even, then

$$b^{m/n} = \begin{cases} (b^{1/n})^m = (\sqrt[n]{b})^m & \quad 8^{2/3} = (8^{1/3})^2 = (\sqrt[3]{8})^2 = 2^2 = 4 \\ (b^m)^{1/n} = \sqrt[n]{b^m} & \quad 8^{2/3} = (8^2)^{1/3} = \sqrt[3]{8^2} = \sqrt[3]{64} = 4 \end{cases}$$

and

$$b^{-m/n} = \frac{1}{b^{m/n}} \quad b \neq 0 \qquad 8^{-2/3} = \frac{1}{8^{2/3}} = \frac{1}{4}$$

Note that the two definitions of $b^{m/n}$ are equivalent under the indicated restrictions on m, n, and b.

> ## CONCEPTUAL INSIGHT
>
> All the properties for integer exponents listed in Theorem 1 in Section A.5 also hold for rational exponents, provided that b is nonnegative when n is even. This restriction on b is necessary to avoid nonreal results. For example,
>
> $$(-4)^{3/2} = \sqrt{(-4)^3} = \sqrt{-64} \quad \text{Not a real number}$$
>
> To avoid nonreal results, all variables in the remainder of this discussion represent positive real numbers.

EXAMPLE 2   From Rational Exponent Form to Radical Form and Vice Versa   Change rational exponent form to radical form.

(A) $x^{1/7} = \sqrt[7]{x}$

(B) $(3u^2v^3)^{3/5} = \sqrt[5]{(3u^2v^3)^3}$ or $(\sqrt[5]{3u^2v^3})^3$ The first is usually preferred.

(C) $y^{-2/3} = \dfrac{1}{y^{2/3}} = \dfrac{1}{\sqrt[3]{y^2}}$ or $\sqrt[3]{y^{-2}}$ or $\sqrt[3]{\dfrac{1}{y^2}}$

Change radical form to rational exponent form.

(D) $\sqrt[5]{6} = 6^{1/5}$ 　　　　　　　　　　　 (E) $-\sqrt[3]{x^2} = -x^{2/3}$

(F) $\sqrt{x^2 + y^2} = (x^2 + y^2)^{1/2}$ Note that $(x^2 + y^2)^{1/2} \neq x + y$. Why?

Matched Problem 2   Convert to radical form.

(A) $u^{1/5}$ 　　　　　　(B) $(6x^2y^5)^{2/9}$ 　　　　　　(C) $(3xy)^{-3/5}$

Convert to rational exponent form.

(D) $\sqrt[4]{9u}$ 　　　　　　(E) $-\sqrt[7]{(2x)^4}$ 　　　　　　(F) $\sqrt[3]{x^3 + y^3}$

EXAMPLE 3   Working with Rational Exponents   Simplify each and express answers using positive exponents only. If rational exponents appear in final answers, convert to radical form.

(A) $(3x^{1/3})(2x^{1/2}) = 6x^{1/3+1/2} = 6x^{5/6} = 6\sqrt[6]{x^5}$

(B) $(-8)^{5/3} = [(-8)^{1/3}]^5 = (-2)^5 = -32$

(C) $(2x^{1/3}y^{-2/3})^3 = 8xy^{-2} = \dfrac{8x}{y^2}$

(D) $\left(\dfrac{4x^{1/3}}{x^{1/2}}\right)^{1/2} = \dfrac{4^{1/2}x^{1/6}}{x^{1/4}} = \dfrac{2}{x^{1/4-1/6}} = \dfrac{2}{x^{1/12}} = \dfrac{2}{\sqrt[12]{x}}$

Matched Problem 3   Simplify each and express answers using positive exponents only. If rational exponents appear in final answers, convert to radical form.

(A) $9^{3/2}$ 　　　(B) $(-27)^{4/3}$ 　　　(C) $(5y^{1/4})(2y^{1/3})$ 　　　(D) $(2x^{-3/4}y^{1/4})^4$

(E) $\left(\dfrac{8x^{1/2}}{x^{2/3}}\right)^{1/3}$

EXAMPLE 4   Working with Rational Exponents   Multiply, and express answers using positive exponents only.

(A) $3y^{2/3}(2y^{1/3} - y^2)$ 　　　　　　　　(B) $(2u^{1/2} + v^{1/2})(u^{1/2} - 3v^{1/2})$

SOLUTION

(A) $3y^{2/3}(2y^{1/3} - y^2) = 6y^{2/3+1/3} - 3y^{2/3+2}$

$\qquad\qquad\qquad\quad = 6y - 3y^{8/3}$

(B) $(2u^{1/2} + v^{1/2})(u^{1/2} - 3v^{1/2}) = 2u - 5u^{1/2}v^{1/2} - 3v$

Matched Problem 4) Multiply, and express answers using positive exponents only.

(A) $2c^{1/4}(5c^3 - c^{3/4})$ 　　　　　　(B) $(7x^{1/2} - y^{1/2})(2x^{1/2} + 3y^{1/2})$

EXAMPLE 5 Working with Rational Exponents Write the following expression in the form $ax^p + bx^q$, where a and b are real numbers and p and q are rational numbers:

$$\frac{2\sqrt{x} - 3\sqrt[3]{x^2}}{2\sqrt[3]{x}}$$

SOLUTION $\dfrac{2\sqrt{x} - 3\sqrt[3]{x^2}}{2\sqrt[3]{x}} = \dfrac{2x^{1/2} - 3x^{2/3}}{2x^{1/3}}$ 　　Change to rational exponent form.

$$= \frac{2x^{1/2}}{2x^{1/3}} - \frac{3x^{2/3}}{2x^{1/3}}$$ 　　Separate into two fractions.

$$= x^{1/6} - 1.5x^{1/3}$$

Matched Problem 5) Write the following expression in the form $ax^p + bx^q$, where a and b are real numbers and p and q are rational numbers:

$$\frac{5\sqrt[3]{x} - 4\sqrt{x}}{2\sqrt{x^3}}$$

Properties of Radicals

Changing or simplifying radical expressions is aided by several properties of radicals that follow directly from the properties of exponents considered earlier.

THEOREM 1 Properties of Radicals

If n is a natural number greater than or equal to 2, and if x and y are positive real numbers, then

1. $\sqrt[n]{x^n} = x$ 　　　　$\sqrt[3]{x^3} = x$

2. $\sqrt[n]{xy} = \sqrt[n]{x}\sqrt[n]{y}$ 　　$\sqrt[5]{xy} = \sqrt[5]{x}\,\sqrt[5]{y}$

3. $\sqrt[n]{\dfrac{x}{y}} = \dfrac{\sqrt[n]{x}}{\sqrt[n]{y}}$ 　　$\sqrt[4]{\dfrac{x}{y}} = \dfrac{\sqrt[4]{x}}{\sqrt[4]{y}}$

EXAMPLE 6 Applying Properties of Radicals Simplify using properties of radicals.

(A) $\sqrt[4]{(3x^4y^3)^4}$ 　　　　(B) $\sqrt[4]{8}\,\sqrt[4]{2}$ 　　　　(C) $\sqrt[3]{\dfrac{xy}{27}}$

SOLUTION

(A) $\sqrt[4]{(3x^4y^3)^4} = 3x^4y^3$ 　　　　　　　　Property 1

(B) $\sqrt[4]{8}\sqrt[4]{2} = \sqrt[4]{16} = \sqrt[4]{2^4} = 2$ 　　　　Properties 2 and 1

(C) $\sqrt[3]{\dfrac{xy}{27}} = \dfrac{\sqrt[3]{xy}}{\sqrt[3]{27}} = \dfrac{\sqrt[3]{xy}}{3}$ 　　or 　$\dfrac{1}{3}\sqrt[3]{xy}$ 　　Properties 3 and 1

Matched Problem 6) Simplify using properties of radicals.

(A) $\sqrt[7]{(x^3 + y^3)^7}$ 　　　(B) $\sqrt[3]{8y^3}$ 　　　(C) $\dfrac{\sqrt[3]{16x^4y}}{\sqrt[3]{2xy}}$

What is the best form for a radical expression? There are many answers, depending on what use we wish to make of the expression. In deriving certain formulas, it is sometimes useful to clear either a denominator or a numerator of radicals.

The process is referred to as **rationalizing** the denominator or numerator. Examples 7 and 8 illustrate the rationalizing process.

EXAMPLE 7 Rationalizing Denominators Rationalize each denominator.

(A) $\dfrac{6x}{\sqrt{2x}}$

(B) $\dfrac{6}{\sqrt{7} - \sqrt{5}}$

(C) $\dfrac{x-4}{\sqrt{x}+2}$

SOLUTION

(A) $\dfrac{6x}{\sqrt{2x}} = \dfrac{6x}{\sqrt{2x}} \cdot \dfrac{\sqrt{2x}}{\sqrt{2x}} = \dfrac{6x\sqrt{2x}}{2x} = 3\sqrt{2x}$

(B) $\dfrac{6}{\sqrt{7} - \sqrt{5}} = \dfrac{6}{\sqrt{7} - \sqrt{5}} \cdot \dfrac{\sqrt{7} + \sqrt{5}}{\sqrt{7} + \sqrt{5}}$

$\qquad = \dfrac{6(\sqrt{7} + \sqrt{5})}{2} = 3(\sqrt{7} + \sqrt{5})$

(C) $\dfrac{x-4}{\sqrt{x}+2} = \dfrac{x-4}{\sqrt{x}+2} \cdot \dfrac{\sqrt{x}-2}{\sqrt{x}-2}$

$\qquad = \dfrac{(x-4)(\sqrt{x}-2)}{x-4} = \sqrt{x} - 2$

Matched Problem 7 Rationalize each denominator.

(A) $\dfrac{12ab^2}{\sqrt{3ab}}$

(B) $\dfrac{9}{\sqrt{6} + \sqrt{3}}$

(C) $\dfrac{x^2 - y^2}{\sqrt{x} - \sqrt{y}}$

EXAMPLE 8 Rationalizing Numerators Rationalize each numerator.

(A) $\dfrac{\sqrt{2}}{2\sqrt{3}}$

(B) $\dfrac{3 + \sqrt{m}}{9 - m}$

(C) $\dfrac{\sqrt{2+h} - \sqrt{2}}{h}$

SOLUTION

(A) $\dfrac{\sqrt{2}}{2\sqrt{3}} = \dfrac{\sqrt{2}}{2\sqrt{3}} \cdot \dfrac{\sqrt{2}}{\sqrt{2}} = \dfrac{2}{2\sqrt{6}} = \dfrac{1}{\sqrt{6}}$

(B) $\dfrac{3 + \sqrt{m}}{9 - m} = \dfrac{3 + \sqrt{m}}{9 - m} \cdot \dfrac{3 - \sqrt{m}}{3 - \sqrt{m}} = \dfrac{9 - m}{(9 - m)(3 - \sqrt{m})} = \dfrac{1}{3 - \sqrt{m}}$

(C) $\dfrac{\sqrt{2+h} - \sqrt{2}}{h} = \dfrac{\sqrt{2+h} - \sqrt{2}}{h} \cdot \dfrac{\sqrt{2+h} + \sqrt{2}}{\sqrt{2+h} + \sqrt{2}}$

$\qquad = \dfrac{h}{h(\sqrt{2+h} + \sqrt{2})} = \dfrac{1}{\sqrt{2+h} + \sqrt{2}}$

Matched Problem 8 Rationalize each numerator.

(A) $\dfrac{\sqrt{3}}{3\sqrt{2}}$

(B) $\dfrac{2 - \sqrt{n}}{4 - n}$

(C) $\dfrac{\sqrt{3+h} - \sqrt{3}}{h}$

Exercises A.6

Change each expression in Problems 1–6 to radical form. Do not simplify.

1. $6x^{3/5}$

2. $7y^{2/5}$

3. $(32x^2y^3)^{3/5}$

4. $(7x^2y)^{5/7}$

5. $(x^2 + y^2)^{1/2}$

6. $x^{1/2} + y^{1/2}$

Change each expression in Problems 7–12 to rational exponent form. Do not simplify.

7. $5\sqrt[4]{x^3}$

8. $7m\sqrt[5]{n^2}$

9. $\sqrt[5]{(2x^2y)^3}$

10. $\sqrt[7]{(8x^4y)^3}$

11. $\sqrt[3]{x} + \sqrt[3]{y}$

12. $\sqrt[3]{x^2 + y^3}$

In Problems 13–24, find rational number representations for each, if they exist.

13. $25^{1/2}$ **14.** $64^{1/3}$ **15.** $16^{3/2}$

16. $16^{3/4}$ **17.** $-49^{1/2}$ **18.** $(-49)^{1/2}$

19. $-64^{2/3}$ **20.** $(-64)^{2/3}$ **21.** $\left(\dfrac{4}{25}\right)^{3/2}$

22. $\left(\dfrac{8}{27}\right)^{2/3}$ **23.** $9^{-3/2}$ **24.** $8^{-2/3}$

In Problems 25–34, simplify each expression and write answers using positive exponents only. All variables represent positive real numbers.

25. $x^{4/5}x^{-2/5}$ **26.** $y^{-3/7}y^{4/7}$ **27.** $\dfrac{m^{2/3}}{m^{-1/3}}$

28. $\dfrac{x^{1/4}}{x^{3/4}}$ **29.** $(8x^3y^{-6})^{1/3}$ **30.** $(4u^{-2}v^4)^{1/2}$

31. $\left(\dfrac{4x^{-2}}{y^4}\right)^{-1/2}$ **32.** $\left(\dfrac{w^4}{9x^{-2}}\right)^{-1/2}$

33. $\dfrac{(8x)^{-1/3}}{12x^{1/4}}$ **34.** $\dfrac{6a^{3/4}}{15a^{-1/3}}$

Simplify each expression in Problems 35–40 using properties of radicals. All variables represent positive real numbers.

35. $\sqrt[5]{(2x+3)^5}$ **36.** $\sqrt[3]{(7+2y)^3}$

37. $\sqrt{6x}\sqrt{15x^3}\sqrt{30x^7}$ **38.** $\sqrt[5]{16a^4}\sqrt[5]{4a^2}\sqrt[5]{8a^3}$

39. $\dfrac{\sqrt{6x}\sqrt{10}}{\sqrt{15x}}$ **40.** $\dfrac{\sqrt{8}\sqrt{12y}}{\sqrt{6y}}$

In Problems 41–48, multiply, and express answers using positive exponents only.

41. $3x^{3/4}(4x^{1/4}-2x^8)$

42. $2m^{1/3}(3m^{2/3}-m^6)$

43. $(3u^{1/2}-v^{1/2})(u^{1/2}-4v^{1/2})$

44. $(a^{1/2}+2b^{1/2})(a^{1/2}-3b^{1/2})$

45. $(6m^{1/2}+n^{-1/2})(6m-n^{-1/2})$

46. $(2x-3y^{1/3})(2x^{1/3}+1)$

47. $(3x^{1/2}-y^{1/2})^2$

48. $(x^{1/2}+2y^{1/2})^2$

Write each expression in Problems 49–54 in the form $ax^p + bx^q$, where a and b are real numbers and p and q are rational numbers.

49. $\dfrac{\sqrt[3]{x^2}+2}{2\sqrt[3]{x}}$ **50.** $\dfrac{12\sqrt{x}-3}{4\sqrt{x}}$ **51.** $\dfrac{2\sqrt[4]{x^3}+\sqrt[3]{x}}{3x}$

52. $\dfrac{3\sqrt[3]{x^2}+\sqrt{x}}{5x}$ **53.** $\dfrac{2\sqrt[3]{x}-\sqrt{x}}{4\sqrt{x}}$ **54.** $\dfrac{x^2-4\sqrt{x}}{2\sqrt[3]{x}}$

Rationalize the denominators in Problems 55–60.

55. $\dfrac{12mn^2}{\sqrt{3mn}}$ **56.** $\dfrac{14x^2}{\sqrt{7x}}$ **57.** $\dfrac{2(x+3)}{\sqrt{x}-2}$

58. $\dfrac{3(x+1)}{\sqrt{x+4}}$ **59.** $\dfrac{7(x-y)^2}{\sqrt{x}-\sqrt{y}}$ **60.** $\dfrac{3a-3b}{\sqrt{a}+\sqrt{b}}$

Rationalize the numerators in Problems 61–66.

61. $\dfrac{\sqrt{5xy}}{5x^2y^2}$ **62.** $\dfrac{\sqrt{3mn}}{3mn}$

63. $\dfrac{\sqrt{x+h}-\sqrt{x}}{h}$ **64.** $\dfrac{\sqrt{2(a+h)}-\sqrt{2a}}{h}$

65. $\dfrac{\sqrt{t}-\sqrt{x}}{t^2-x^2}$ **66.** $\dfrac{\sqrt{x}-\sqrt{y}}{\sqrt{x}+\sqrt{y}}$

Problems 67–70 illustrate common errors involving rational exponents. In each case, find numerical examples that show that the left side is not always equal to the right side.

67. $(x+y)^{1/2} \neq x^{1/2}+y^{1/2}$ **68.** $(x^3+y^3)^{1/3} \neq x+y$

69. $(x+y)^{1/3} \neq \dfrac{1}{(x+y)^3}$ **70.** $(x+y)^{-1/2} \neq \dfrac{1}{(x+y)^2}$

In Problems 71–82, discuss the validity of each statement. If the statement is true, explain why. If not, give a counterexample.

71. $\sqrt{x^2} = x$ for all real numbers x

72. $\sqrt{x^2} = |x|$ for all real numbers x

73. $\sqrt[3]{x^3} = |x|$ for all real numbers x

74. $\sqrt[3]{x^3} = x$ for all real numbers x

75. If $r < 0$, then r has no cube roots.

76. If $r < 0$, then r has no square roots.

77. If $r > 0$, then r has two square roots.

78. If $r > 0$, then r has three cube roots.

79. The fourth roots of 100 are $\sqrt{10}$ and $-\sqrt{10}$.

80. The square roots of $2\sqrt{6}-5$ are $\sqrt{3}-\sqrt{2}$ and $\sqrt{2}-\sqrt{3}$.

81. $\sqrt{355-60\sqrt{35}} = 5\sqrt{7}-6\sqrt{5}$

82. $\sqrt[3]{7-5\sqrt{2}} = 1-\sqrt{2}$

In Problems 83–88, simplify by writing each expression as a simple or single fraction reduced to lowest terms and without negative exponents.

83. $-\dfrac{1}{2}(x-2)(x+3)^{-3/2} + (x+3)^{-1/2}$

84. $2(x-2)^{-1/2} - \dfrac{1}{2}(2x+3)(x-2)^{-3/2}$

85. $\dfrac{(x-1)^{1/2} - x\left(\frac{1}{2}\right)(x-1)^{-1/2}}{x-1}$

86. $\dfrac{(2x-1)^{1/2} - (x+2)\left(\frac{1}{2}\right)(2x-1)^{-1/2}(2)}{2x-1}$

87. $\dfrac{(x+2)^{2/3} - x\left(\frac{2}{3}\right)(x+2)^{-1/3}}{(x+2)^{4/3}}$

88. $\dfrac{2(3x-1)^{1/3} - (2x+1)\left(\frac{1}{3}\right)(3x-1)^{-2/3}(3)}{(3x-1)^{2/3}}$

In Problems 89–94, evaluate using a calculator. (Refer to the instruction book for your calculator to see how exponential forms are evaluated.)

89. $22^{3/2}$

90. $15^{5/4}$

91. $827^{-3/8}$

92. $103^{-3/4}$

93. $37.09^{7/3}$

94. $2.876^{8/5}$

In Problems 95 and 96, evaluate each expression on a calculator and determine which pairs have the same value. Verify these results algebraically.

95. (A) $\sqrt{3} + \sqrt{5}$ (B) $\sqrt{2 + \sqrt{3}} + \sqrt{2 - \sqrt{3}}$

   (C) $1 + \sqrt{3}$ (D) $\sqrt[3]{10 + 6\sqrt{3}}$

   (E) $\sqrt{8 + \sqrt{60}}$ (F) $\sqrt{6}$

96. (A) $2\sqrt[3]{2} + \sqrt{5}$ (B) $\sqrt{8}$

   (C) $\sqrt{3} + \sqrt{7}$ (D) $\sqrt{3 + \sqrt{8}} + \sqrt{3 - \sqrt{8}}$

   (E) $\sqrt{10 + \sqrt{84}}$ (F) $1 + \sqrt{5}$

1. (A) 4   (B) -4

   (C) -3 (D) Not a real number   (E) 27

2. (A) $\sqrt[5]{u}$ (B) $\sqrt[9]{(6x^2y^5)^2}$ or $\left(\sqrt[9]{(6x^2y^5)}\right)^2$

   (C) $1/\sqrt[5]{(3xy)^3}$ (D) $(9u)^{1/4}$

   (E) $-(2x)^{4/7}$ (F) $(x^3 + y^3)^{1/3}$ (not $x + y$)

3. (A) 27   (B) 81

   (C) $10y^{7/12} = 10\sqrt[12]{y^7}$ (D) $16y/x^3$

   (E) $2/x^{1/18} = 2/\sqrt[18]{x}$

4. (A) $10c^{13/4} - 2c$ (B) $14x + 19x^{1/2}y^{1/2} - 3y$

5. $2.5x^{-7/6} - 2x^{-1}$

6. (A) $x^3 + y^3$ (B) $2y$ (C) $2x$

7. (A) $4b\sqrt{3ab}$ (B) $3(\sqrt{6} - \sqrt{3})$

   (C) $(x + y)(\sqrt{x} + \sqrt{y})$

8. (A) $\dfrac{1}{\sqrt{6}}$ (B) $\dfrac{1}{2 + \sqrt{n}}$ (C) $\dfrac{1}{\sqrt{3 + h} + \sqrt{3}}$

A.7 Quadratic Equations

- Solution by Square Root
- Solution by Factoring
- Quadratic Formula
- Quadratic Formula and Factoring
- Other Polynomial Equations
- Application: Supply and Demand

In this section we consider equations involving second-degree polynomials.

DEFINITION Quadratic Equation
A **quadratic equation** in one variable is any equation that can be written in the form

$$ax^2 + bx + c = 0 \qquad a \neq 0 \qquad \text{Standard form}$$

where x is a variable and a, b, and c are constants.

The equations

$$5x^2 - 3x + 7 = 0 \qquad \text{and} \qquad 18 = 32t^2 - 12t$$

are both quadratic equations, since they are either in the standard form or can be transformed into this form.

We restrict our review to finding real solutions to quadratic equations.

Solution by Square Root

The easiest type of quadratic equation to solve is the special form where the first-degree term is missing:

$$ax^2 + c = 0 \qquad a \neq 0$$

The method of solution of this special form makes direct use of the square-root property:

THEOREM 1 Square-Root Property
If $a^2 = b$, then $a = \pm\sqrt{b}$.

EXAMPLE 1 Square-Root Method Use the square-root property to solve each equation.

(A) $x^2 - 7 = 0$ (B) $2x^2 - 10 = 0$

(C) $3x^2 + 27 = 0$ (D) $(x - 8)^2 = 9$

SOLUTION

(A) $x^2 - 7 = 0$

$\qquad\quad x^2 = 7$ What real number squared is 7?

$\qquad\quad x = \pm\sqrt{7}$ Short for $\sqrt{7}$ and $-\sqrt{7}$

(B) $2x^2 - 10 = 0$

$\qquad\quad 2x^2 = 10$

$\qquad\quad x^2 = 5$ What real number squared is 5?

$\qquad\quad x = \pm\sqrt{5}$

(C) $3x^2 + 27 = 0$

$\qquad\quad 3x^2 = -27$

$\qquad\quad x^2 = -9$ What real number squared is -9?

No real solution, since no real number squared is negative.

(D) $(x - 8)^2 = 9$

$\qquad x - 8 = \pm\sqrt{9}$

$\qquad x - 8 = \pm 3$

$\qquad\quad x = 8 \pm 3 = 5$ or   11

Matched Problem 1 Use the square-root property to solve each equation.

(A) $x^2 - 6 = 0$ (B) $3x^2 - 12 = 0$

(C) $x^2 + 4 = 0$ (D) $(x + 5)^2 = 1$

Solution by Factoring

If the left side of a quadratic equation when written in standard form can be factored, the equation can be solved very quickly. The method of solution by factoring rests on a basic property of real numbers, first mentioned in Section A.1.

CONCEPTUAL INSIGHT

Theorem 2 in Section A.1 states that if a and b are real numbers, then $ab = 0$ if and only if $a = 0$ or $b = 0$. To see that this property is useful for solving quadratic equations, consider the following:

$$x^2 - 4x + 3 = 0 \qquad\qquad (1)$$

$$(x - 1)(x - 3) = 0$$

$$x - 1 = 0 \quad\text{ or }\quad x - 3 = 0$$

$$x = 1 \quad\text{ or }\quad x = 3$$

You should check these solutions in equation (1).

If one side of the equation is not 0, then this method cannot be used. For example, consider

$$x^2 - 4x + 3 = 8 \qquad\qquad (2)$$

$$(x - 1)(x - 3) = 8$$

$$x - 1 \neq 8 \quad\text{ or }\quad x - 3 \neq 8 \qquad \begin{array}{l} ab = 8 \text{ does not imply} \\ \text{that } a = 8 \text{ or } b = 8. \end{array}$$

$$x = 9 \quad\text{ or }\quad x = 11$$

Verify that neither $x = 9$ nor $x = 11$ is a solution for equation (2).

EXAMPLE 2 Factoring Method Solve by factoring using integer coefficients, if possible.

(A) $3x^2 - 6x - 24 = 0$ (B) $3y^2 = 2y$ (C) $x^2 - 2x - 1 = 0$

SOLUTION

(A) $3x^2 - 6x - 24 = 0$ Divide both sides by 3, since 3 is a factor of each coefficient.

$x^2 - 2x - 8 = 0$ Factor the left side, if possible.

$(x - 4)(x + 2) = 0$

$x - 4 = 0$ or $x + 2 = 0$

$x = 4$ or $x = -2$

(B) $3y^2 = 2y$

$3y^2 - 2y = 0$ We lose the solution $y = 0$ if both sides are divided by y

$y(3y - 2) = 0$ ($3y^2 = 2y$ and $3y = 2$ are not equivalent).

$y = 0$ or $3y - 2 = 0$

$3y = 2$

$y = \dfrac{2}{3}$

(C) $x^2 - 2x - 1 = 0$

This equation cannot be factored using integer coefficients. We will solve this type of equation by another method, considered below.

Matched Problem 2 Solve by factoring using integer coefficients, if possible.

(A) $2x^2 + 4x - 30 = 0$ (B) $2x^2 = 3x$ (C) $2x^2 - 8x + 3 = 0$

Note that an equation such as $x^2 = 25$ can be solved by either the square-root or the factoring method, and the results are the same (as they should be). Solve this equation both ways and compare.

Also, note that the factoring method can be extended to higher-degree polynomial equations. Consider the following:

$$x^3 - x = 0$$
$$x(x^2 - 1) = 0$$
$$x(x - 1)(x + 1) = 0$$
$$x = 0 \quad \text{or} \quad x - 1 = 0 \quad \text{or} \quad x + 1 = 0$$
$$\text{Solution: } x = 0, 1, -1$$

Check these solutions in the original equation.

The factoring and square-root methods are fast and easy to use when they apply. However, there are quadratic equations that look simple but cannot be solved by either method. For example, as was noted in Example 2C, the polynomial in

$$x^2 - 2x - 1 = 0$$

cannot be factored using integer coefficients. This brings us to the well-known and widely used *quadratic formula*.

Quadratic Formula

There is a method called *completing the square* that will work for all quadratic equations. After briefly reviewing this method, we will use it to develop the quadratic formula, which can be used to solve any quadratic equation.

The method of **completing the square** is based on the process of transforming a quadratic equation in standard form,

$$ax^2 + bx + c = 0$$

into the form

$$(x + A)^2 = B$$

where A and B are constants. Then, this last equation can be solved easily (if it has a real solution) by the square-root method discussed above.

Consider the equation from Example 2C:

$$x^2 - 2x - 1 = 0 \qquad (3)$$

Since the left side does not factor using integer coefficients, we add 1 to each side to remove the constant term from the left side:

$$x^2 - 2x = 1 \qquad (4)$$

Now we try to find a number that we can add to each side to make the left side a square of a first-degree polynomial. Note the following square of a binomial:

$$(x + m)^2 = x^2 + 2mx + m^2$$

We see that the third term on the right is the square of one-half the coefficient of x in the second term on the right. To complete the square in equation (4), we add the square of one-half the coefficient of x, $\left(-\frac{2}{2}\right)^2 = 1$, to each side. (This rule works only when the coefficient of x^2 is 1, that is, $a = 1$.) Thus,

$$x^2 - 2x + 1 = 1 + 1$$

The left side is the square of $x - 1$, and we write

$$(x - 1)^2 = 2$$

What number squared is 2?

$$x - 1 = \pm\sqrt{2}$$
$$x = 1 \pm \sqrt{2}$$

And equation (3) is solved!

Let us try the method on the general quadratic equation

$$ax^2 + bx + c = 0 \qquad a \neq 0 \qquad (5)$$

and solve it once and for all for x in terms of the coefficients a, b, and c. We start by multiplying both sides of equation (5) by $1/a$ to obtain

$$x^2 + \frac{b}{a}x + \frac{c}{a} = 0$$

Add $-c/a$ to both sides:

$$x^2 + \frac{b}{a}x = -\frac{c}{a}$$

Now we complete the square on the left side by adding the square of one-half the coefficient of x, that is, $(b/2a)^2 = b^2/4a^2$ to each side:

$$x^2 + \frac{b}{a}x + \frac{b^2}{4a^2} = \frac{b^2}{4a^2} - \frac{c}{a}$$

Writing the left side as a square and combining the right side into a single fraction, we obtain

$$\left(x + \frac{b}{2a}\right)^2 = \frac{b^2 - 4ac}{4a^2}$$

Now we solve by the square-root method:

$$x + \frac{b}{2a} = \pm\sqrt{\frac{b^2 - 4ac}{4a^2}}$$

$$x = -\frac{b}{2a} \pm \frac{\sqrt{b^3 - 4ac}}{2a} \qquad \text{Since } \pm\sqrt{4a^2} = \pm 2a \text{ for any real number } a$$

When this is written as a single fraction, it becomes the **quadratic formula**:

Quadratic Formula

If $ax^2 + bx + c = 0, a \neq 0$, then

$$x = \frac{-b \pm \sqrt{b^2 - 4ac}}{2a}$$

This formula is generally used to solve quadratic equations when the square-root or factoring methods do not work. The quantity $b^2 - 4ac$ under the radical is called the **discriminant**, and it gives us the useful information about solutions listed in Table 1.

Table 1

$b^2 - 4ac$	$ax^2 + bx + c = 0$
Positive	Two real solutions
Zero	One real solution
Negative	No real solutions

EXAMPLE 3 Quadratic Formula Method Solve $x^2 - 2x - 1 = 0$ using the quadratic formula.

SOLUTION

$$x^2 - 2x - 1 = 0$$

$$x = \frac{-b \pm \sqrt{b^2 - 4ac}}{2a} \qquad a = 1, b = -2, c = -1$$

$$= \frac{-(-2) \pm \sqrt{(-2)^2 - 4(1)(-1)}}{2(1)}$$

$$= \frac{2 \pm \sqrt{8}}{2} = \frac{2 \pm 2\sqrt{2}}{2} = 1 \pm \sqrt{2} \approx -0.414 \quad \text{or} \quad 2.414$$

CHECK

$$x^2 - 2x - 1 = 0$$
When $x = 1 + \sqrt{2}$,

$$(1 + \sqrt{2})^2 - 2(1 + \sqrt{2}) - 1 = 1 + 2\sqrt{2} + 2 - 2 - 2\sqrt{2} - 1 = 0$$

When $x = 1 - \sqrt{2}$,

$$(1 - \sqrt{2})^2 - 2(1 - \sqrt{2}) - 1 = 1 - 2\sqrt{2} + 2 - 2 + 2\sqrt{2} - 1 = 0$$

Matched Problem 3 Solve $2x^2 - 4x - 3 = 0$ using the quadratic formula.

If we try to solve $x^2 - 6x + 11 = 0$ using the quadratic formula, we obtain

$$x = \frac{6 \pm \sqrt{-8}}{2}$$

which is not a real number. (Why?)

Quadratic Formula and Factoring

As in Section A.3, we restrict our interest in factoring to polynomials with integer coefficients. If a polynomial cannot be factored as a product of lower-degree polynomials with integer coefficients, we say that the polynomial is **not factorable in the integers**.

How can you factor the quadratic polynomial $x^2 - 13x - 2{,}310$? We start by solving the corresponding quadratic equation using the quadratic formula:

$$x^2 - 13x - 2{,}310 = 0$$

$$x = \frac{-(-13) \pm \sqrt{(-13)^3 - 4(1)(-2{,}310)}}{2}$$

$$x = \frac{-(-13) \pm \sqrt{9{,}409}}{2}$$

$$= \frac{13 \pm 97}{2} = 55 \quad \text{or} \quad -42$$

Now we write

$$x^2 - 13x - 2{,}310 = [x - 55][x - (-42)] = (x - 55)(x + 42)$$

Multiplying the two factors on the right produces the second-degree polynomial on the left.

What is behind this procedure? The following two theorems justify and generalize the process:

THEOREM 2   Factorability Theorem

A second-degree polynomial, $ax^2 + bx + c$, with integer coefficients can be expressed as the product of two first-degree polynomials with integer coefficients if and only if $\sqrt{b^2 - 4ac}$ is an integer.

THEOREM 3   Factor Theorem

If r_1 and r_2 are solutions to the second-degree equation $ax^2 + bx + c = 0$, then

$$ax^2 + bx + c = a(x - r_1)(x - r_2)$$

EXAMPLE 4   Factoring with the Aid of the Discriminant   Factor, if possible, using integer coefficients.

(A) $4x^2 - 65x + 264$ (B) $2x^2 - 33x - 306$

SOLUTION   (A) $4x^2 - 65x + 264$

Step 1   Test for factorability:

$$\sqrt{b^2 - 4ac} = \sqrt{(-65)^2 - 4(4)(264)} = 1$$

Since the result is an integer, the polynomial has first-degree factors with integer coefficients.

Step 2   Factor, using the factor theorem. Find the solutions to the corresponding quadratic equation using the quadratic formula:

$$4x^2 - 65x + 264 = 0 \quad \text{From step 1}$$

$$x = \frac{-(-65) \pm 1}{2 \cdot 4} = \frac{33}{4} \quad \text{or} \quad 8$$

Thus,

$$4x^2 - 65x + 264 = 4\left(x - \frac{33}{4}\right)(x - 8)$$

$$= (4x - 33)(x - 8)$$

(B) $2x^2 - 33x - 306$

Step 1   Test for factorability:

$$\sqrt{b^2 - 4ac} = \sqrt{(-33)^2 - 4(2)(-306)} = \sqrt{3{,}537}$$

Since $\sqrt{3{,}537}$ is not an integer, the polynomial is not factorable in the integers.

Matched Problem 4   Factor, if possible, using integer coefficients.

(A) $3x^2 - 28x - 464$ (B) $9x^2 + 320x - 144$

Other Polynomial Equations

There are formulas that are analogous to the quadratic formula, but considerably more complicated, that can be used to solve any cubic (degree 3) or quartic (degree 4) polynomial equation. It can be shown that no such general formula exists for solving quintic (degree 5) or polynomial equations of degree greater than five. Certain polynomial equations, however, can be solved easily by taking roots.

EXAMPLE 5   Solving a Quartic Equation   Find all real solutions to $6x^4 - 486 = 0$.

SOLUTION

$$
\begin{aligned}
6x^4 - 486 &= 0 && \text{Add 486 to both sides} \\
6x^4 &= 486 && \text{Divide both sides by 6} \\
x^4 &= 81 && \text{Take the 4th root of both sides} \\
x &= \pm 3
\end{aligned}
$$

Matched Problem 5   Find all real solutions to $6x^5 + 192 = 0$.

Application: Supply and Demand

Supply-and-demand analysis is a very important part of business and economics. In general, producers are willing to supply more of an item as the price of an item increases and less of an item as the price decreases. Similarly, buyers are willing to buy less of an item as the price increases, and more of an item as the price decreases. We have a dynamic situation where the price, supply, and demand fluctuate until a price is reached at which the supply is equal to the demand. In economic theory, this point is called the **equilibrium point**. If the price increases from this point, the supply will increase and the demand will decrease; if the price decreases from this point, the supply will decrease and the demand will increase.

EXAMPLE 6   Supply and Demand   At a large summer beach resort, the weekly supply-and-demand equations for folding beach chairs are

$$p = \frac{x}{140} + \frac{3}{4} \qquad \text{Supply equation}$$

$$p = \frac{5{,}670}{x} \qquad \text{Demand equation}$$

The supply equation indicates that the supplier is willing to sell x units at a price of p dollars per unit. The demand equation indicates that consumers are willing to buy x units at a price of p dollars per unit. How many units are required for supply to equal demand? At what price will supply equal demand?

SOLUTION Set the right side of the supply equation equal to the right side of the demand equation and solve for x.

$$\frac{x}{140} + \frac{3}{4} = \frac{5{,}670}{x} \qquad \text{Multiply by } 140x \text{, the LCD.}$$

$$x^2 + 105x = 793{,}800 \qquad \text{Write in standard form.}$$

$$x^2 + 105x - 793{,}800 = 0 \qquad \text{Use the quadratic formula.}$$

$$x = \frac{-105 \pm \sqrt{105^2 - 4(1)(-793{,}800)}}{2}$$

$$x = 840 \text{ units}$$

The negative root is discarded since a negative number of units cannot be produced or sold. Substitute $x = 840$ back into either the supply equation or the demand equation to find the equilibrium price (we use the demand equation).

$$p = \frac{5{,}670}{x} = \frac{5{,}670}{840} = \$6.75$$

At a price of \$6.75 the supplier is willing to supply 840 chairs and consumers are willing to buy 840 chairs during a week.

Matched Problem 6   Repeat Example 6 if near the end of summer, the supply-and-demand equations are

$$p = \frac{x}{80} - \frac{1}{20} \qquad \text{Supply equation}$$

$$p = \frac{1{,}264}{x} \qquad \text{Demand equation}$$

Exercises A.7

Find only real solutions in the problems below. If there are no real solutions, say so.

Solve Problems 1–4 by the square-root method.

1. $2x^2 - 22 = 0$

2. $3m^2 - 21 = 0$

3. $(3x - 1)^2 = 25$

4. $(2x + 1)^2 = 16$

Solve Problems 5–8 by factoring.

5. $2u^2 - 8u - 24 = 0$

6. $3x^2 - 18x + 15 = 0$

7. $x^2 = 2x$

8. $n^2 = 3n$

Solve Problems 9–12 by using the quadratic formula.

9. $x^2 - 6x - 3 = 0$

10. $m^2 + 8m + 3 = 0$

11. $3u^2 + 12u + 6 = 0$

12. $2x^2 - 20x - 6 = 0$

Solve Problems 13–30 by using any method.

13. $\dfrac{2x^2}{3} = 5x$

14. $x^2 = -\dfrac{3}{4}x$

15. $4u^2 - 9 = 0$

16. $9y^2 - 25 = 0$

17. $8x^2 + 20x = 12$

18. $9x^2 - 6 = 15x$

19. $x^2 = 1 - x$

20. $m^2 = 1 - 3m$

21. $2x^2 = 6x - 3$

22. $2x^2 = 4x - 1$

23. $y^2 - 4y = -8$

24. $x^2 - 2x = -3$

25. $(2x + 3)^2 = 11$

26. $(5x - 2)^2 = 7$

27. $\dfrac{3}{p} = p$

28. $x - \dfrac{7}{x} = 0$

29. $2 - \dfrac{2}{m^2} = \dfrac{3}{m}$

30. $2 + \dfrac{5}{u} = \dfrac{3}{u^2}$

In Problems 31–38, factor, if possible, as the product of two first-degree polynomials with integer coefficients. Use the quadratic formula and the factor theorem.

31. $x^2 + 40x - 84$

32. $x^2 - 28x - 128$

33. $x^2 - 32x + 144$

34. $x^2 + 52x + 208$

35. $2x^2 + 15x - 108$

36. $3x^2 - 32x - 140$

37. $4x^2 + 241x - 434$

38. $6x^2 - 427x - 360$

39. Solve $A = P(1 + r)^2$ for r in terms of A and P; that is, isolate r on the left side of the equation (with coefficient 1) and end up with an algebraic expression on the right side involving A and P but not r. Write the answer using positive square roots only.

40. Solve $x^2 + 3mx - 3n = 0$ for x in terms of m and n.

✎ **41.** Consider the quadratic equation

$$x^2 + 4x + c = 0$$

where c is a real number. Discuss the relationship between the values of c and the three types of roots listed in Table 1 on page 552.

✎ **42.** Consider the quadratic equation

$$x^2 - 2x + c = 0$$

where c is a real number. Discuss the relationship between the values of c and the three types of roots listed in Table 1 on page 552.

In Problems 43–48, find all real solutions.

43. $x^3 + 8 = 0$

44. $x^3 - 8 = 0$

45. $5x^4 - 500 = 0$

46. $2x^3 + 250 = 0$

47. $x^4 - 8x^2 + 15 = 0$

48. $x^4 - 12x^2 + 32 = 0$

Applications

49. Supply and demand. A company wholesales shampoo in a particular city. Their marketing research department established the following weekly supply-and-demand equations:

$$p = \frac{x}{450} + \frac{1}{2} \quad \text{Supply equation}$$

$$p = \frac{6,300}{x} \quad \text{Demand equation}$$

How many units are required for supply to equal demand? At what price per bottle will supply equal demand?

50. Supply and demand. An importer sells an automatic camera to outlets in a large city. During the summer, the weekly supply-and-demand equations are

$$p = \frac{x}{6} + 9 \quad \text{Supply equation}$$

$$p = \frac{24,840}{x} \quad \text{Demand equation}$$

How many units are required for supply to equal demand? At what price will supply equal demand?

51. Interest rate. If P dollars are invested at $100r$ percent compounded annually, at the end of 2 years it will grow to $A = P(1 + r)^2$. At what interest rate will \$484 grow to \$625 in 2 years? (*Note:* If $A = 625$ and $P = 484$ find r.)

52. Interest rate. Using the formula in Problem 51, determine the interest rate that will make \$1,000 grow to \$1,210 in 2 years.

53. Ecology. To measure the velocity v (in feet per second) of a stream, we position a hollow L-shaped tube with one end under the water pointing upstream and the other end pointing straight up a couple of feet out of the water. The water will then be pushed up the tube a certain distance h (in feet) above the surface of the stream. Physicists have shown that $v^2 = 64h$. Approximately how fast is a stream flowing if $h = 1$ foot? If $h = 0.5$ foot?

54. Safety research. It is of considerable importance to know the least number of feet d in which a car can be stopped, including reaction time of the driver, at various speeds v (in miles per hour). Safety research has produced the formula $d = 0.044v^2 + 1.1v$. If it took a car 550 feet to stop, estimate the car's speed at the moment the stopping process was started.

Answers to Matched Problems

1. (A) $\pm\sqrt{6}$ (B) ± 2

   (C) No real solution   (D) $-6, -4$

2. (A) $-5, 3$ (B) $0, \frac{3}{2}$

   (C) Cannot be factored using integer coefficients

3. $(2 \pm \sqrt{10})/2$

4. (A) Cannot be factored using integer coefficients

   (B) $(9x - 4)(x + 36)$

5. -2

6. 320 chairs at \$3.95 each

Appendix

B

Special Topics

B.1 Sequences, Series, and Summation Notation

- Sequences
- Series and Summation Notation

If someone asked you to list all natural numbers that are perfect squares, you might begin by writing

$$1, 4, 9, 16, 25, 36$$

But you would soon realize that it is impossible to actually list all the perfect squares, since there are an infinite number of them. However, you could represent this collection of numbers in several different ways. One common method is to write

$$1, 4, 9, \ldots, n^2, \ldots \quad n \in N$$

where N is the set of natural numbers. A list of numbers such as this is generally called a *sequence*.

Sequences

Consider the function f given by

$$f(n) = 2n + 1 \tag{1}$$

where the domain of f is the set of natural numbers N. Note that

$$f(1) = 3, \quad f(2) = 5, \quad f(3) = 7, \quad \ldots$$

The function f is an example of a sequence. In general, a **sequence** is a function with domain a set of successive integers. Instead of the standard function notation used in equation (1), sequences are usually defined in terms of a special notation.

The range value $f(n)$ is usually symbolized more compactly with a symbol such as a_n. Thus, in place of equation (1), we write

$$a_n = 2n + 1$$

and the domain is understood to be the set of natural numbers unless something is said to the contrary or the context indicates otherwise. The elements in the range are called **terms of the sequence**; a_1 is the first term, a_2 is the second term, and a_n is the **nth term**, or **general term**.

$$a_1 = 2(1) + 1 = 3 \quad \text{First term}$$
$$a_2 = 2(2) + 1 = 5 \quad \text{Second term}$$
$$a_3 = 2(3) + 1 = 7 \quad \text{Third term}$$
$$\vdots$$
$$a_n = 2n + 1 \quad\quad\quad \text{General term}$$

The ordered list of elements

$$3, 5, 7, \ldots, 2n + 1, \ldots$$

obtained by writing the terms of the sequence in their natural order with respect to the domain values is often informally referred to as a sequence. A sequence also may be represented in the abbreviated form $\{a_n\}$, where a symbol for the nth term is written within braces. For example, we could refer to the sequence $3, 5, 7, \ldots, 2n + 1, \ldots$ as the sequence $\{2n + 1\}$.

If the domain of a sequence is a finite set of successive integers, then the sequence is called a **finite sequence**. If the domain is an infinite set of successive integers, then the sequence is called an **infinite sequence**. The sequence $\{2n + 1\}$ discussed above is an infinite sequence.

EXAMPLE 1 Writing the Terms of a Sequence Write the first four terms of each sequence:

(A) $a_n = 3n - 2$

(B) $\left\{\dfrac{(-1)^n}{n}\right\}$

SOLUTION

(A) $1, 4, 7, 10$

(B) $-1, \dfrac{1}{2}, \dfrac{-1}{3}, \dfrac{1}{4}$

Matched Problem 1 · Write the first four terms of each sequence:

(A) $a_n = -n + 3$

(B) $\left\{\dfrac{(-1)^n}{2^n}\right\}$

Now that we have seen how to use the general term to find the first few terms in a sequence, we consider the reverse problem. That is, can a sequence be defined just by listing the first three or four terms of the sequence? And can we then use these initial terms to find a formula for the nth term? In general, without other information, the answer to the first question is no. Many different sequences may start off with the same terms. Simply listing the first three terms (or any other finite number of terms) does not specify a particular sequence.

What about the second question? That is, given a few terms, can we find the general formula for at least one sequence whose first few terms agree with the given terms? The answer to this question is a qualified yes. If we can observe a simple pattern in the given terms, we usually can construct a general term that will produce that pattern. The next example illustrates this approach.

EXAMPLE 2 Finding the General Term of a Sequence Find the general term of a sequence whose first four terms are

(A) $3, 4, 5, 6, \ldots$ (B) $5, -25, 125, -625, \ldots$

SOLUTION

(A) Since these terms are consecutive integers, one solution is $a_n = n, n \geq 3$. If we want the domain of the sequence to be all natural numbers, another solution is $b_n = n + 2$.

(B) Each of these terms can be written as the product of a power of 5 and a power of -1:

$$5 = (-1)^0 5^1 = a_1$$
$$-25 = (-1)^1 5^2 = a_2$$
$$125 = (-1)^2 5^3 = a_3$$
$$-625 = (-1)^3 5^4 = a_4$$

If we choose the domain to be all natural numbers, a solution is

$$a_n = (-1)^{n-1} 5^n$$

Matched Problem 2 Find the general term of a sequence whose first four terms are

(A) $3, 6, 9, 12, \ldots$ (B) $1, -2, 4, -8, \ldots$

In general, there is usually more than one way of representing the nth term of a given sequence (see the solution of Example 2A). However, unless something is stated to the contrary, we assume that the domain of the sequence is the set of natural numbers N.

Series and Summation Notation

If $a_1, a_2, a_3, \ldots, a_n, \ldots$ is a sequence, the expression

$$a_1 + a_2 + a_3 + \cdots + a_n + \cdots$$

is called a **series**. If the sequence is finite, the corresponding series is a **finite series**. If the sequence is infinite, the corresponding series is an **infinite series**. We consider only finite series in this section. For example,

$$1, 3, 5, 7, 9 \qquad \text{Finite sequence}$$
$$1 + 3 + 5 + 7 + 9 \qquad \text{Finite series}$$

Notice that we can easily evaluate this series by adding the five terms:

$$1 + 3 + 5 + 7 + 9 = 25$$

Series are often represented in a compact form called **summation notation**. Consider the following examples:

$$\sum_{k=3}^{6} k^2 = 3^2 + 4^2 + 5^2 + 6^2$$

$$= 9 + 16 + 25 + 36 = 86$$

$$\sum_{k=0}^{2} (4k + 1) = (4 \cdot 0 + 1) + (4 \cdot 1 + 1) + (4 \cdot 2 + 1)$$

$$= 1 + 5 + 9 = 15$$

In each case, the terms of the series on the right are obtained from the expression on the left by successively replacing the **summing index k** with integers, starting with the number indicated below the **summation sign Σ** and ending with the number that appears above Σ. The summing index may be represented by letters other than k and may start at any integer and end at any integer greater than or equal to the starting integer. If we are given the finite sequence

$$\frac{1}{2}, \frac{1}{4}, \frac{1}{8}, \ldots, \frac{1}{2^n}$$

the corresponding series is

$$\frac{1}{2} + \frac{1}{4} + \frac{1}{8} + \cdots + \frac{1}{2^n} = \sum_{j=1}^{n} \frac{1}{2^j}$$

where we have used j for the summing index.

EXAMPLE 3 Summation Notation   Write

$$\sum_{k=1}^{5} \frac{k}{k^2 + 1}$$

without summation notation. Do not evaluate the sum.

SOLUTION

$$\sum_{k=1}^{5} \frac{k}{k^2 + 1} = \frac{1}{1^2 + 1} + \frac{2}{2^2 + 1} + \frac{3}{3^2 + 1} + \frac{4}{4^2 + 1} + \frac{5}{5^2 + 1}$$

$$= \frac{1}{2} + \frac{2}{5} + \frac{3}{10} + \frac{4}{17} + \frac{5}{26}$$

Matched Problem 3 Write

$$\sum_{k=1}^{5} \frac{k + 1}{k}$$

without summation notation. Do not evaluate the sum.

If the terms of a series are alternately positive and negative, we call the series an **alternating series**. The next example deals with the representation of such a series.

EXAMPLE 4 Summation Notation   Write the alternating series

$$\frac{1}{2} - \frac{1}{4} + \frac{1}{6} - \frac{1}{8} + \frac{1}{10} - \frac{1}{12}$$

using summation notation with

(A) The summing index k starting at 1

(B) The summing index j starting at 0

SOLUTION

(A) $(-1)^{k+1}$ provides the alternation of sign, and $1/(2k)$ provides the other part of each term. So, we can write

$$\frac{1}{2} - \frac{1}{4} + \frac{1}{6} - \frac{1}{8} + \frac{1}{10} - \frac{1}{12} = \sum_{k=1}^{6} \frac{(-1)^{k+1}}{2k}$$

(B) $(-1)^j$ provides the alternation of sign, and $1/[2(j + 1)]$ provides the other part of each term. So, we can write

$$\frac{1}{2} - \frac{1}{4} + \frac{1}{6} - \frac{1}{8} + \frac{1}{10} - \frac{1}{12} = \sum_{j=0}^{5} \frac{(-1)^j}{2(j + 1)}$$

Matched Problem 4 Write the alternating series

$$1 - \frac{1}{3} + \frac{1}{9} - \frac{1}{27} + \frac{1}{81}$$

using summation notation with

(A) The summing index k starting at 1

(B) The summing index j starting at 0

Summation notation provides a compact notation for the sum of any list of numbers, even if the numbers are not generated by a formula. For example, suppose that the results of an examination taken by a class of 10 students are given in the following list:

$$87, 77, 95, 83, 86, 73, 95, 68, 75, 86$$

If we let $a_1, a_2, a_3, \ldots, a_{10}$ represent these 10 scores, then the average test score is given by

$$\frac{1}{10}\sum_{k=1}^{10} a_k = \frac{1}{10}(87 + 77 + 95 + 83 + 86 + 73 + 95 + 68 + 75 + 86)$$

$$= \frac{1}{10}(825) = 82.5$$

More generally, in statistics, the **arithmetic mean** $\bar{a}$ of a list of n numbers $a_1, a_2, \ldots, a_n$ is defined as

$$\bar{a} = \frac{1}{n}\sum_{k=1}^{n} a_k$$

EXAMPLE 5 Arithmetic Mean Find the arithmetic mean of 3, 5, 4, 7, 4, 2, 3, and 6.

SOLUTION

$$\bar{a} = \frac{1}{8}\sum_{k=1}^{8} a_k = \frac{1}{8}(3 + 5 + 4 + 7 + 4 + 2 + 3 + 6) = \frac{1}{8}(34) = 4.25$$

Matched Problem 5 Find the arithmetic mean of 9, 3, 8, 4, 3, and 6.

Exercises B.1

Write the first four terms for each sequence in Problems 1–6.

1. $a_n = 2n + 3$

2. $a_n = 4n - 3$

3. $a_n = \dfrac{n + 2}{n + 1}$

4. $a_n = \dfrac{2n + 1}{2n}$

5. $a_n = (-3)^{n+1}$

6. $a_n = \left(-\frac{1}{4}\right)^{n-1}$

7. Write the 10th term of the sequence in Problem 1.

8. Write the 15th term of the sequence in Problem 2.

9. Write the 99th term of the sequence in Problem 3.

10. Write the 200th term of the sequence in Problem 4.

In Problems 11–16, write each series in expanded form without summation notation, and evaluate.

11. $\displaystyle\sum_{k=1}^{6} k$

12. $\displaystyle\sum_{k=1}^{5} k^2$

13. $\displaystyle\sum_{k=4}^{7} (2k - 3)$

14. $\displaystyle\sum_{k=0}^{4} (-2)^k$

15. $\displaystyle\sum_{k=0}^{3} \frac{1}{10^k}$

16. $\displaystyle\sum_{k=1}^{4} \frac{1}{2^k}$

Find the arithmetic mean of each list of numbers in Problems 17–20.

17. 5, 4, 2, 1, and 6

18. 7, 9, 9, 2, and 4

19. 96, 65, 82, 74, 91, 88, 87, 91, 77, and 74

20. 100, 62, 95, 91, 82, 87, 70, 75, 87, and 82

Write the first five terms of each sequence in Problems 21–26.

21. $a_n = \dfrac{(-1)^{n+1}}{2^n}$

22. $a_n = (-1)^n (n - 1)^2$

23. $a_n = n[1 + (-1)^n]$

24. $a_n = \dfrac{1 - (-1)^n}{n}$

25. $a_n = \left(-\dfrac{3}{2}\right)^{n-1}$

26. $a_n = \left(-\dfrac{1}{2}\right)^{n+1}$

In Problems 27–42, find the general term of a sequence whose first four terms agree with the given terms.

27. $-2, -1, 0, 1, \ldots$

28. $4, 5, 6, 7, \ldots$

29. $4, 8, 12, 16, \ldots$

30. $-3, -6, -9, -12, \ldots$

31. $\frac{1}{2}, \frac{3}{4}, \frac{5}{6}, \frac{7}{8}, \ldots$

32. $\frac{1}{2}, \frac{2}{3}, \frac{3}{4}, \frac{4}{5}, \ldots$

33. $1, -2, 3, -4, \ldots$

34. $-2, 4, -8, 16, \ldots$

35. $1, -3, 5, -7, \ldots$

36. $3, -6, 9, -12, \ldots$

37. $1, \frac{2}{5}, \frac{4}{25}, \frac{8}{125}, \ldots$

38. $\frac{4}{3}, \frac{16}{9}, \frac{64}{27}, \frac{256}{81}, \ldots$

39. $x, x^2, x^3, x^4, \ldots$

40. $1, 2x, 3x^2, 4x^3, \ldots$

41. $x, -x^3, x^5, -x^7, \ldots$

42. $x, \dfrac{x^2}{2}, \dfrac{x^3}{3}, \dfrac{x^4}{4}, \ldots$

Write each series in Problems 43–50 in expanded form without summation notation. Do not evaluate.

43. $\displaystyle\sum_{k=1}^{5} (-1)^{k+1}(2k-1)^2$

44. $\displaystyle\sum_{k=1}^{4} \dfrac{(-2)^{k+1}}{2k+1}$

45. $\displaystyle\sum_{k=2}^{5} \dfrac{2^k}{2k+3}$

46. $\displaystyle\sum_{k=3}^{7} \dfrac{(-1)^k}{k^2 - k}$

47. $\displaystyle\sum_{k=1}^{5} x^{k-1}$

48. $\displaystyle\sum_{k=1}^{3} \dfrac{1}{k} x^{k+1}$

49. $\displaystyle\sum_{k=0}^{4} \dfrac{(-1)^k x^{2k+1}}{2k+1}$

50. $\displaystyle\sum_{k=0}^{4} \dfrac{(-1)^k x^{2k}}{2k+2}$

Write each series in Problems 51–54 using summation notation with

(A) *The summing index k starting at* $k = 1$

(B) *The summing index j starting at* $j = 0$

51. $2 + 3 + 4 + 5 + 6$

52. $1^2 + 2^2 + 3^2 + 4^2$

53. $1 - \frac{1}{2} + \frac{1}{3} - \frac{1}{4}$

54. $1 - \frac{1}{3} + \frac{1}{5} - \frac{1}{7} + \frac{1}{9}$

Write each series in Problems 55–58 using summation notation with the summing index k starting at $k = 1$.

55. $2 + \dfrac{3}{2} + \dfrac{4}{3} + \cdots + \dfrac{n+1}{n}$

56. $1 + \dfrac{1}{2^2} + \dfrac{1}{3^2} + \cdots + \dfrac{1}{n^2}$

57. $\dfrac{1}{2} - \dfrac{1}{4} + \dfrac{1}{8} - \cdots + \dfrac{(-1)^{n+1}}{2^n}$

58. $1 - 4 + 9 - \cdots + (-1)^{n+1}n^2$

In Problems 59–62, discuss the validity of each statement. If the statement is true, explain why. If not, give a counterexample.

59. For each positive integer n, the sum of the series
$$1 + \frac{1}{2} + \frac{1}{3} + \cdots + \frac{1}{n} \text{ is less than 4.}$$

60. For each positive integer n, the sum of the series
$$\frac{1}{2} + \frac{1}{4} + \frac{1}{8} + \cdots + \frac{1}{2^n} \text{ is less than 1.}$$

61. For each positive integer n, the sum of the series
$$\frac{1}{2} - \frac{1}{4} + \frac{1}{8} - \cdots + \frac{(-1)^{n+1}}{2^n} \text{ is greater than or}$$
equal to $\dfrac{1}{4}$.

62. For each positive integer n, the sum of the series
$$1 - \frac{1}{2} + \frac{1}{3} - \frac{1}{4} + \cdots + \frac{(-1)^{n+1}}{n} \text{ is greater than or}$$
equal to $\dfrac{1}{2}$.

Some sequences are defined by a **recursion formula** *—that is, a formula that defines each term of the sequence in terms of one or more of the preceding terms. For example, if* $\{a_n\}$ *is defined by*

$$a_1 = 1 \quad and \quad a_n = 2a_{n-1} + 1 \quad for \quad n \geq 2$$

then

$$a_2 = 2a_1 + 1 = 2 \cdot 1 + 1 = 3$$
$$a_3 = 2a_2 + 1 = 2 \cdot 3 + 1 = 7$$
$$a_4 = 2a_3 + 1 = 2 \cdot 7 + 1 = 15$$

and so on. In Problems 63–66, write the first five terms of each sequence.

63. $a_1 = 2$ and $a_n = 3a_{n-1} + 2$ for $n \geq 2$

64. $a_1 = 3$ and $a_n = 2a_{n-1} - 2$ for $n \geq 2$

65. $a_1 = 1$ and $a_n = 2a_{n-1}$ for $n \geq 2$

66. $a_1 = 1$ and $a_n = -\frac{1}{3}a_{n-1}$ for $n \geq 2$

If A is a positive real number, the terms of the sequence defined by

$$a_1 = \frac{A}{2} \quad and \quad a_n = \frac{1}{2}\left(a_{n-1} + \frac{A}{a_{n-1}}\right) \quad for\ n \geq 2$$

can be used to approximate $\sqrt{A}$ *to any decimal place accuracy desired. In Problems 67 and 68, compute the first four terms of this sequence for the indicated value of A, and compare the fourth term with the value of* $\sqrt{A}$ *obtained from a calculator.*

67. $A = 2$

68. $A = 6$

69. The sequence defined recursively by $a_1 = 1, a_2 = 1$, $a_n = a_{n-1} + a_{n-2}$ for $n \geq 3$ is called the *Fibonacci sequence.* Find the first ten terms of the Fibonacci sequence.

70. The sequence defined by $b_n = \dfrac{\sqrt{5}}{5}\left(\dfrac{1 + \sqrt{5}}{2}\right)^n$ is related to the Fibonacci sequence. Find the first ten terms (to three decimal places) of the sequence $\{b_n\}$ and describe the relationship.

Answers to Matched Problems

1. (A) $2, 1, 0, -1$ 　　(B) $\frac{-1}{2}, \frac{1}{4}, \frac{-1}{8}, \frac{1}{16}$

2. (A) $a_n = 3n$ 　　(B) $a_n = (-2)^{n-1}$

3. $2 + \frac{3}{2} + \frac{4}{3} + \frac{5}{4} + \frac{6}{5}$

4. (A) $\displaystyle\sum_{k=1}^{5} \dfrac{(-1)^{k-1}}{3^{k-1}}$ 　　(B) $\displaystyle\sum_{j=0}^{4} \dfrac{(-1)^j}{3^j}$

5. 5.5

B.2 Arithmetic and Geometric Sequences

For most sequences, it is difficult to sum an arbitrary number of terms of the sequence without adding term by term. But particular types of sequences—*arithmetic sequences* and *geometric sequences*—have certain properties that lead to convenient and useful formulas for the sums of the corresponding *arithmetic series* and *geometric series*.

Arithmetic and Geometric Sequences

The sequence $5, 7, 9, 11, 13, \ldots, 5 + 2(n - 1), \ldots$, where each term after the first is obtained by adding 2 to the preceding term, is an example of an arithmetic sequence. The sequence $5, 10, 20, 40, 80, \ldots, 5(2)^{n-1}, \ldots$, where each term after the first is obtained by multiplying the preceding term by 2, is an example of a geometric sequence.

> **DEFINITION** Arithmetic Sequence
> A sequence of numbers
> $$a_1, a_2, a_3, \ldots, a_n, \ldots$$
> is called an **arithmetic sequence** if there is a constant d, called the **common difference**, such that
> $$a_n - a_{n-1} = d$$
> That is,
> $$a_n = a_{n-1} + d \quad \text{for every } n > 1$$

> **DEFINITION** Geometric Sequence
> A sequence of numbers
> $$a_1, a_2, a_3, \ldots, a_n, \ldots$$
> is called a **geometric sequence** if there exists a nonzero constant r, called a **common ratio**, such that
> $$\frac{a_n}{a_{n-1}} = r$$
> That is,
> $$a_n = r a_{n-1} \quad \text{for every } n > 1$$

EXAMPLE 1 Recognizing Arithmetic and Geometric Sequences Which of the following can be the first four terms of an arithmetic sequence? Of a geometric sequence?

(A) $1, 2, 3, 5, \ldots$ (B) $-1, 3, -9, 27, \ldots$

(C) $3, 3, 3, 3, \ldots$ (D) $10, 8.5, 7, 5.5, \ldots$

SOLUTION

(A) Since $2 - 1 \neq 5 - 3$, there is no common difference, so the sequence is not an arithmetic sequence. Since $2/1 \neq 3/2$, there is no common ratio, so the sequence is not geometric either.

(B) The sequence is geometric with common ratio -3. It is not arithmetic.

(C) The sequence is arithmetic with common difference 0, and is also geometric with common ratio 1.

(D) The sequence is arithmetic with common difference -1.5. It is not geometric.

Matched Problem 1 Which of the following can be the first four terms of an arithmetic sequence? Of a geometric sequence?

(A) $8, 2, 0.5, 0.125, \ldots$ (B) $-7, -2, 3, 8, \ldots$ (C) $1, 5, 25, 100, \ldots$

nth-Term Formulas

If $\{a_n\}$ is an arithmetic sequence with common difference d, then

$$a_2 = a_1 + d$$
$$a_3 = a_2 + d = a_1 + 2d$$
$$a_4 = a_3 + d = a_1 + 3d$$

This suggests that

THEOREM 1   nth Term of an Arithmetic Sequence

$$a_n = a_1 + (n - 1)d \quad \text{for all } n > 1 \tag{1}$$

Similarly, if $\{a_n\}$ is a geometric sequence with common ratio r, then

$$a_2 = a_1 r$$
$$a_3 = a_2 r = a_1 r^2$$
$$a_4 = a_3 r = a_1 r^3$$

This suggests that

THEOREM 2   nth Term of a Geometric Sequence

$$a_n = a_1 r^{n-1} \quad \text{for all } n > 1 \tag{2}$$

EXAMPLE 2   Finding Terms in Arithmetic and Geometric Sequences

(A) If the 1st and 10th terms of an arithmetic sequence are 3 and 30, respectively, find the 40th term of the sequence.

(B) If the 1st and 10th terms of a geometric sequence are 3 and 30, find the 40th term to three decimal places.

SOLUTION

(A) First use formula (1) with $a_1 = 3$ and $a_{10} = 30$ to find d:

$$a_n = a_1 + (n - 1)d$$
$$a_{10} = a_1 + (10 - 1)d$$
$$30 = 3 + 9d$$
$$d = 3$$

Now find a_{40}:

$$a_{40} = 3 + 39 \cdot 3 = 120$$

(B) First use formula (2) with $a_1 = 3$ and $a_{10} = 30$ to find r:

$$a_n = a_1 r^{n-1}$$
$$a_{10} = a_1 r^{10-1}$$
$$30 = 3r^9$$
$$r^9 = 10$$
$$r = 10^{1/9}$$

Now find a_{40}:

$$a_{40} = 3(10^{1/9})^{39} = 3(10^{39/9}) = 64{,}633.041$$

Matched Problem 2

(A) If the 1st and 15th terms of an arithmetic sequence are -5 and 23, respectively, find the 73rd term of the sequence.

(B) Find the 8th term of the geometric sequence

$$\frac{1}{64}, \frac{-1}{32}, \frac{1}{16}, \ldots$$

Sum Formulas for Finite Arithmetic Series

If $a_1, a_2, a_3, \ldots, a_n$ is a finite arithmetic sequence, then the corresponding series $a_1 + a_2 + a_3 + \cdots + a_n$ is called a *finite arithmetic series*. We will derive two simple and very useful formulas for the sum of a finite arithmetic series. Let d be the common difference of the arithmetic sequence $a_1, a_2, a_3, \ldots, a_n$ and let S_n denote the sum of the series $a_1 + a_2 + a_3 + \cdots + a_n$. Then

$$S_n = a_1 + (a_1 + d) + \cdots + [a_1 + (n-2)d] + [a_1 + (n-1)d]$$

Reversing the order of the sum, we obtain

$$S_n = [a_1 + (n-1)d] + [a_1 + (n-2)d] + \cdots + (a_1 + d) + a_1$$

Something interesting happens if we combine these last two equations by addition (adding corresponding terms on the right sides):

$$2S_n = [2a_1 + (n-1)d] + [2a_1 + (n-1)d] + \cdots + [2a_1 + (n-1)d] + [2a_1 + (n-1)d]$$

All the terms on the right side are the same, and there are n of them. Thus,

$$2S_n = n[2a_1 + (n-1)d]$$

and we have the following general formula:

THEOREM 3 Sum of a Finite Arithmetic Series: First Form

$$S_n = \frac{n}{2}[2a_1 + (n-1)d] \tag{3}$$

Replacing

$$[a_1 + (n-1)d] \quad \text{in} \quad \frac{n}{2}[a_1 + a_1 + (n-1)d]$$

by a_n from equation (1), we obtain a second useful formula for the sum:

THEOREM 4 Sum of a Finite Arithmetic Series: Second Form

$$S_n = \frac{n}{2}(a_1 + a_n) \tag{4}$$

EXAMPLE 3 Finding a Sum Find the sum of the first 30 terms in the arithmetic sequence:

$$3, 8, 13, 18, \ldots$$

SOLUTION Use formula (3) with $n = 30$, $a_1 = 3$, and $d = 5$:

$$S_{30} = \frac{30}{2}[2 \cdot 3 + (30-1)5] = 2{,}265$$

Matched Problem 3 Find the sum of the first 40 terms in the arithmetic sequence:

$$15, 13, 11, 9, \ldots$$

EXAMPLE 4 Finding a Sum Find the sum of all the even numbers between 31 and 87.

SOLUTION First, find n using equation (1):

$$a_n = a_1 + (n-1)d$$
$$86 = 32 + (n-1)2$$
$$n = 28$$

Now find S_{28} using formula (4):

$$S_n = \frac{n}{2}(a_1 + a_n)$$

$$S_{28} = \frac{28}{2}(32 + 86) = 1,652$$

Matched Problem 4 Find the sum of all the odd numbers between 24 and 208.

Sum Formulas for Finite Geometric Series

If $a_1, a_2, a_3, \ldots, a_n$ is a finite geometric sequence, then the corresponding series $a_1 + a_2 + a_3 + \cdots + a_n$ is called a *finite geometric series*. As with arithmetic series, we can derive two simple and very useful formulas for the sum of a finite geometric series. Let r be the common ratio of the geometric sequence $a_1, a_2, a_3, \ldots, a_n$ and let S_n denote the sum of the series $a_1 + a_2 + a_3 + \cdots + a_n$. Then

$$S_n = a_1 + a_1r + a_1r^2 + \cdots + a_1r^{n-2} + a_1r^{n-1}$$

If we multiply both sides by r, we obtain

$$rS_n = a_1r + a_1r^2 + a_1r^3 + \cdots + a_1r^{n-1} + a_1r^n$$

Now combine these last two equations by subtraction to obtain

$$rS_n - S_n = (a_1r + a_1r^2 + a_1r^3 + \cdots + a_1r^{n-1} + a_1r^n) - (a_1 + a_1r + a_1r^2 + \cdots + a_1r^{n-2} + a_1r^{n-1})$$
$$(r-1)S_n = a_1r^n - a_1$$

Notice how many terms drop out on the right side. Solving for S_n, we have

THEOREM 5 Sum of a Finite Geometric Series: First Form

$$S_n = \frac{a_1(r^n - 1)}{r - 1} \qquad r \neq 1 \tag{5}$$

Since $a_n = a_1r^{n-1}$, or $ra_n = a_1r^n$, formula (5) also can be written in the form

THEOREM 6 Sum of a Finite Geometric Series: Second Form

$$S_n = \frac{ra_n - a_1}{r - 1} \qquad r \neq 1 \tag{6}$$

EXAMPLE 5 Finding a Sum Find the sum (to 2 decimal places) of the first ten terms of the geometric sequence:

$$1, 1.05, 1.05^2, \ldots$$

SOLUTION Use formula (5) with $a_1 = 1$, $r = 1.05$, and $n = 10$:

$$S_n = \frac{a_1(r^n - 1)}{r - 1}$$

$$S_{10} = \frac{1(1.05^{10} - 1)}{1.05 - 1}$$

$$\approx \frac{0.6289}{0.05} \approx 12.58$$

Matched Problem 5 ⌋ Find the sum of the first eight terms of the geometric sequence:

$$100, 100(1.08), 100(1.08)^2, \ldots$$

Sum Formula for Infinite Geometric Series

Given a geometric series, what happens to the sum S_n of the first n terms as n increases without stopping? To answer this question, let us write formula (5) in the form

$$S_n = \frac{a_1 r^n}{r - 1} - \frac{a_1}{r - 1}$$

It is possible to show that if $-1 < r < 1$, then r^n will approach 0 as n increases. The first term above will approach 0 and S_n can be made as close as we please to the second term, $-a_1/(r - 1)$ [which can be written as $a_1/(1 - r)$], by taking n sufficiently large. So, if the common ratio r is between -1 and 1, we conclude that the sum of an infinite geometric series is

THEOREM 7 Sum of an Infinite Geometric Series

$$S_\infty = \frac{a_1}{1 - r} \qquad -1 < r < 1 \tag{7}$$

If $r \leq -1$ or $r \geq 1$, then an infinite geometric series has no sum.

Applications

EXAMPLE 6 Loan Repayment A person borrows \$3,600 and agrees to repay the loan in monthly installments over 3 years. The agreement is to pay 1% of the unpaid balance each month for using the money and \$100 each month to reduce the loan. What is the total cost of the loan over the 3 years?

SOLUTION Let us look at the problem relative to a time line:

\$3,600	\$3,500	\$3,400	$\cdots$	\$200	\$100	Unpaid balance
0	1	2	3 $\cdots$	34	35	36	Months
	0.01(3,600) = 36	0.01(3,500) = 35	0.01(3,400) = 34 $\cdots$	0.01(300) = 3	0.01(200) = 2	0.01(100) = 1	1% of unpaid balance

The total cost of the loan is

$$1 + 2 + \cdots + 34 + 35 + 36$$

The terms form a finite arithmetic series with $n = 36$, $a_1 = 1$, and $a_{36} = 36$, so we can use formula (4):

$$S_n = \frac{n}{2}(a_1 + a_n)$$

$$S_{36} = \frac{36}{2}(1 + 36) = \$666$$

We conclude that the total cost of the loan over 3 years is $666.

Matched Problem 6   Repeat Example 6 with a loan of $6,000 over 5 years.

EXAMPLE 7   Economy Stimulation   The government has decided on a tax rebate program to stimulate the economy. Suppose that you receive $1,200 and you spend 80% of this, and each of the people who receive what you spend also spend 80% of what they receive, and this process continues without end. According to the **multiplier principle** in economics, the effect of your $1,200 tax rebate on the economy is multiplied many times. What is the total amount spent if the process continues as indicated?

SOLUTION   We need to find the sum of an infinite geometric series with the first amount spent being $a_1 = (0.8)(\$1,200) = \$960$ and $r = 0.8$. Using formula (7), we obtain

$$S_\infty = \frac{a_1}{1 - r}$$

$$= \frac{\$960}{1 - 0.8} = \$4,800$$

Assuming the process continues as indicated, we would expect the $1,200 tax rebate to result in about $4,800 of spending.

Matched Problem 7   Repeat Example 7 with a tax rebate of $2,000.

Exercises B.2

In Problems 1 and 2, determine whether the indicated sequence can be the first three terms of an arithmetic or geometric sequence, and, if so, find the common difference or common ratio and the next two terms of the sequence.

1. (A) $-11, -16, -21, \ldots$ (B) $2, -4, 8, \ldots$

   (C) $1, 4, 9, \ldots$ (D) $\frac{1}{2}, \frac{1}{6}, \frac{1}{18}, \ldots$

2. (A) $5, 20, 100, \ldots$ (B) $-5, -5, -5, \ldots$

   (C) $7, 6.5, 6, \ldots$ (D) $512, 256, 128, \ldots$

In Problems 3–8, determine whether the finite series is arithmetic, geometric, both, or neither. If the series is arithmetic or geometric, find its sum.

3. $\sum_{k=1}^{101} (-1)^{k+1}$

4. $\sum_{k=1}^{200} 3$

5. $1 + \frac{1}{2} + \frac{1}{3} + \cdots + \frac{1}{50}$

6. $3 - 9 + 27 - \cdots - 3^{20}$

7. $5 + 4.9 + 4.8 + \cdots + 0.1$

8. $1 - \frac{1}{4} + \frac{1}{9} - \cdots - \frac{1}{100^2}$

Let $a_1, a_2, a_3, \ldots, a_n, \ldots$ be an arithmetic sequence. In Problems 9–14, find the indicated quantities.

9. $a_1 = 7$; $d = 4$; $a_2 = ?$; $a_3 = ?$

10. $a_1 = -2$; $d = -3$; $a_2 = ?$; $a_3 = ?$

11. $a_1 = 2$; $d = 4$; $a_{21} = ?$; $S_{31} = ?$

12. $a_1 = 8$; $d = -10$; $a_{15} = ?$; $S_{23} = ?$

13. $a_1 = 18$; $a_{20} = 75$; $S_{20} = ?$

14. $a_1 = 203$; $a_{30} = 261$; $S_{30} = ?$

Let $a_1, a_2, a_3, \ldots, a_n, \ldots$ be a geometric sequence. In Problems 15–24, find the indicated quantities.

15. $a_1 = 3$; $r = -2$; $a_2 = ?$; $a_3 = ?$; $a_4 = ?$

16. $a_1 = 32$; $r = -\frac{1}{2}$; $a_2 = ?$; $a_3 = ?$; $a_4 = ?$

17. $a_1 = 1; a_7 = 729; r = -3; S_7 = ?$

18. $a_1 = 3; a_7 = 2,187; r = 3; S_7 = ?$

19. $a_1 = 100; r = 1.08; a_{10} = ?$

20. $a_1 = 240; r = 1.06; a_{12} = ?$

21. $a_1 = 100; a_9 = 200; r = ?$

22. $a_1 = 100; a_{10} = 300; r = ?$

23. $a_1 = 500; r = 0.6; S_{10} = ?; S_\infty = ?$

24. $a_1 = 8,000; r = 0.4; S_{10} = ?; S_\infty = ?$

25. $S_{41} = \sum_{k=1}^{41} (3k + 3) = ?$ **26.** $S_{50} = \sum_{k=1}^{50} (2k - 3) = ?$

27. $S_8 = \sum_{k=1}^{8} (-2)^{k-1} = ?$ **28.** $S_8 = \sum_{k=1}^{8} 2^k = ?$

29. Find the sum of all the odd integers between 12 and 68.

30. Find the sum of all the even integers between 23 and 97.

31. Find the sum of each infinite geometric sequence (if it exists).

(A) $2, 4, 8, \ldots$ (B) $2, -\frac{1}{2}, \frac{1}{8}, \ldots$

32. Repeat Problem 31 for:

(A) $16, 4, 1, \ldots$ (B) $1, -3, 9, \ldots$

33. Find $f(1) + f(2) + f(3) + \cdots + f(50)$
if $f(x) = 2x - 3$.

34. Find $g(1) + g(2) + g(3) + \cdots + g(100)$
if $g(t) = 18 - 3t$.

35. Find $f(1) + f(2) + \cdots + f(10)$ if $f(x) = \left(\frac{1}{2}\right)^x$.

36. Find $g(1) + g(2) + \cdots + g(10)$ if $g(x) = 2^x$.

37. Show that the sum of the first n odd positive integers is n^2, using appropriate formulas from this section.

38. Show that the sum of the first n even positive integers is $n + n^2$, using formulas in this section.

39. If $r = 1$, neither the first form nor the second form for the sum of a finite geometric series is valid. Find a formula for the sum of a finite geometric series if $r = 1$.

40. If all of the terms of an infinite geometric series are less than 1, could the sum be greater than 1,000? Explain.

41. Does there exist a finite arithmetic series with $a_1 = 1$ and $a_n = 1.1$ that has sum equal to 100? Explain.

42. Does there exist a finite arithmetic series with $a_1 = 1$ and $a_n = 1.1$ that has sum equal to 105? Explain.

43. Does there exist an infinite geometric series with $a_1 = 10$ that has sum equal to 6? Explain.

44. Does there exist an infinite geometric series with $a_1 = 10$ that has sum equal to 5? Explain.

Applications

45. Loan repayment. If you borrow $4,800 and repay the loan by paying $200 per month to reduce the loan and 1% of the unpaid balance each month for the use of the money, what is the total cost of the loan over 24 months?

46. Loan repayment. If you borrow $5,400 and repay the loan by paying $300 per month to reduce the loan and 1.5% of the unpaid balance each month for the use of the money, what is the total cost of the loan over 18 months?

47. Economy stimulation. The government, through a subsidy program, distributes $5,000,000. If we assume that each person or agency spends 70% of what is received, and 70% of this is spent, and so on, how much total increase in spending results from this government action? (Let $a_1 = \$3,500,000$.)

48. Economy stimulation. Due to reduced taxes, a person has an extra $1,200 in spendable income. If we assume that the person spends 65% of this on consumer goods, and the producers of these goods in turn spend 65% on consumer goods, and that this process continues indefinitely, what is the total amount spent (to the nearest dollar) on consumer goods?

49. Compound interest. If $1,000 is invested at 5% compounded annually, the amount A present after n years forms a geometric sequence with common ratio $1 + 0.05 = 1.05$. Use a geometric sequence formula to find the amount A in the account (to the nearest cent) after 10 years. After 20 years. (*Hint*: Use a time line.)

50. Compound interest. If P is invested at $100r\%$ compounded annually, the amount A present after n years forms a geometric sequence with common ratio $1 + r$. Write a formula for the amount present after n years. (*Hint*: Use a time line.)

Answers to Matched Problems

1. (A) The sequence is geometric with $r = \frac{1}{4}$. It is not arithmetic.

(B) The sequence is arithmetic with $d = 5$. It is not geometric.

(C) The sequence is neither arithmetic nor geometric.

2. (A) 139 (B) -2

3. -960 **4.** 10,672 **5.** 1,063.66 **6.** $1,830 **7.** $8,000

B.3 Binomial Theorem

- Factorial
- Development of the Binomial Theorem

The binomial form

$$(a + b)^n$$

where n is a natural number, appears more frequently than you might expect. The coefficients in the expansion play an important role in probability studies. The *binomial formula*, which we will derive informally, enables us to expand $(a + b)^n$ directly for

n any natural number. Since the formula involves *factorials*, we digress for a moment here to introduce this important concept.

Factorial

For n a natural number, **n factorial**, denoted by $n!$, is the product of the first n natural numbers. **Zero factorial** is defined to be 1. That is,

---

DEFINITION n Factorial

$$n! = n \cdot (n - 1) \cdot \cdots \cdot 2 \cdot 1$$
$$1! = 1$$
$$0! = 1$$

It is also useful to note that $n!$ can be defined recursively.

DEFINITION n Factorial—Recursive Definition

$$n! = n \cdot (n - 1)! \quad n \geq 1$$

EXAMPLE 1   Factorial Forms   Evaluate.

(A) $5! = 5 \cdot 4 \cdot 3 \cdot 2 \cdot 1 = 120$

(B) $\dfrac{8!}{7!} = \dfrac{8 \cdot 7!}{7!} = 8$

(C) $\dfrac{10!}{7!} = \dfrac{10 \cdot 9 \cdot 8 \cdot 7!}{7!} = 720$

Matched Problem 1   Evaluate.

(A) $4!$ (B) $\dfrac{7!}{6!}$ (C) $\dfrac{8!}{5!}$

The following formula involving factorials has applications in many areas of mathematics and statistics. We will use this formula to provide a more concise form for the expressions encountered later in this discussion.

THEOREM 1   For n and r integers satisfying $0 \leq r \leq n$,

$$_nC_r = \frac{n!}{r!(n - r)!}$$

EXAMPLE 2   Evaluating $_nC_r$

(A) $_9C_2 = \dfrac{9!}{2!(9 - 2)!} = \dfrac{9!}{2!7!} = \dfrac{9 \cdot 8 \cdot 7!}{2 \cdot 7!} = 36$

(B) $_5C_5 = \dfrac{5!}{5!(5 - 5)!} = \dfrac{5!}{5!0!} = \dfrac{5!}{5!} = 1$

Matched Problem 2   Find

(A) $_5C_2$ (B) $_6C_0$

Development of the Binomial Theorem

Let us expand $(a + b)^n$ for several values of n to see if we can observe a pattern that leads to a general formula for the expansion for any natural number n:

$$(a + b)^1 = a + b$$
$$(a + b)^2 = a^2 + 2ab + b^2$$
$$(a + b)^3 = a^3 + 3a^2b + 3ab^2 + b^3$$
$$(a + b)^4 = a^4 + 4a^3b + 6a^2b^2 + 4ab^3 + b^4$$
$$(a + b)^5 = a^5 + 5a^4b + 10a^3b^2 + 10a^2b^3 + 5ab^4 + b^5$$

CONCEPTUAL INSIGHT

1. The expansion of $(a + b)^n$ has $(n + 1)$ terms.
2. The power of a decreases by 1 for each term as we move from left to right.
3. The power of b increases by 1 for each term as we move from left to right.
4. In each term, the sum of the powers of a and b always equals n.
5. Starting with a given term, we can get the coefficient of the next term by multiplying the coefficient of the given term by the exponent of a and dividing by the number that represents the position of the term in the series of terms. For example, in the expansion of $(a + b)^4$ above, the coefficient of the third term is found from the second term by multiplying 4 and 3, and then dividing by 2 [that is, the coefficient of the third term $= (4 \cdot 3)/2 = 6$].

We now postulate these same properties for the general case:

$$(a + b)^n = a^n + \frac{n}{1}a^{n-1}b + \frac{n(n-1)}{1 \cdot 2}a^{n-2}b^2 + \frac{n(n-1)(n-2)}{1 \cdot 2 \cdot 3}a^{n-3}b^3 + \cdots + b^n$$

$$= \frac{n!}{0!(n-0)!}a^n + \frac{n!}{1!(n-1)!}a^{n-1}b + \frac{n!}{2!(n-2)!}a^{n-2}b^2 + \frac{n!}{3!(n-3)!}a^{n-3}b^3 + \cdots + \frac{n!}{n!(n-n)!}b^n$$

$$= {}_nC_0a^n + {}_nC_1a^{n-1}b + {}_nC_2a^{n-2}b^2 + {}_nC_3a^{n-3}b^3 + \cdots + {}_nC_nb^n$$

And we are led to the formula in the binomial theorem:

THEOREM 2 Binomial Theorem

For all natural numbers n,

$$(a + b)^n = {}_nC_0a^n + {}_nC_1a^{n-1}b + {}_nC_2a^{n-2}b^2 + {}_nC_3a^{n-3}b^3 + \cdots + {}_nC_nb^n$$

EXAMPLE 3 Using the Binomial Theorem Use the binomial theorem to expand $(u + v)^6$.

SOLUTION

$$(u + v)^6 = {}_6C_0u^6 + {}_6C_1u^5v + {}_6C_2u^4v^2 + {}_6C_3u^3v^3 + {}_6C_4u^2v^4 + {}_6C_5uv^5 + {}_6C_6v^6$$
$$= u^6 + 6u^5v + 15u^4v^2 + 20u^3v^3 + 15u^2v^4 + 6uv^5 + v^6$$

Matched Problem 3 Use the binomial theorem to expand $(x + 2)^5$.

EXAMPLE 4   Using the Binomial Theorem   Use the binomial theorem to find the sixth term in the expansion of $(x - 1)^{18}$.

SOLUTION   Sixth term $= {}_{18}C_5 x^{13}(-1)^5 = \dfrac{18!}{5!(18 - 5)!} x^{13}(-1)$

$$= -8,568x^{13}$$

Matched Problem 4   Use the binomial theorem to find the fourth term in the expansion of $(x - 2)^{20}$.

Exercises B.3

In Problems 1–20, evaluate each expression.

1. $6!$

2. $7!$

3. $\dfrac{10!}{9!}$

4. $\dfrac{20!}{19!}$

5. $\dfrac{12!}{9!}$

6. $\dfrac{10!}{6!}$

7. $\dfrac{5!}{2!3!}$

8. $\dfrac{7!}{3!4!}$

9. $\dfrac{6!}{5!(6 - 5)!}$

10. $\dfrac{7!}{4!(7 - 4)!}$

11. $\dfrac{20!}{3!17!}$

12. $\dfrac{52!}{50!2!}$

13. ${}_5C_3$

14. ${}_7C_3$

15. ${}_6C_5$

16. ${}_7C_4$

17. ${}_5C_0$

18. ${}_5C_5$

19. ${}_{18}C_{15}$

20. ${}_{18}C_3$

Expand each expression in Problems 21–26 using the binomial theorem.

21. $(a + b)^4$

22. $(m + n)^5$

23. $(x - 1)^6$

24. $(u - 2)^5$

25. $(2a - b)^5$

26. $(x - 2y)^5$

Find the indicated term in each expansion in Problems 27–32.

27. $(x - 1)^{18}$; 5th term

28. $(x - 3)^{20}$; 3rd term

29. $(p + q)^{15}$; 7th term

30. $(p + q)^{15}$; 13th term

31. $(2x + y)^{12}$; 11th term

32. $(2x + y)^{12}$; 3rd term

33. Show that ${}_nC_0 = {}_nC_n$ for $n \geq 0$.

34. Show that ${}_nC_r = {}_nC_{n-r}$ for $n \geq r \geq 0$.

35. The triangle next is called **Pascal's triangle**. Can you guess what the next two rows at the bottom are? Compare these numbers with the coefficients of binomial expansions.

$$1$$
$$1 \quad 1$$
$$1 \quad 2 \quad 1$$
$$1 \quad 3 \quad 3 \quad 1$$
$$1 \quad 4 \quad 6 \quad 4 \quad 1$$

36. Explain why the sum of the entries in each row of Pascal's triangle is a power of 2. (*Hint:* Let $a = b = 1$ in the binomial theorem.)

37. Explain why the alternating sum of the entries in each row of Pascal's triangle (e.g., $1 - 4 + 6 - 4 + 1$) is equal to 0.

38. Show that ${}_nC_r = \frac{n - r + 1}{r}{}_nC_{r-1}$ for $n \geq r \geq 1$.

39. Show that ${}_nC_{r-1} + {}_nC_r = {}_{n+1}C_r$ for $n \geq r \geq 1$.

Answers to Matched Problems

1. (A) 24   (B) 7   (C) 336

2. (A) 10   (B) 1

3. $x^5 + 10x^4 + 40x^3 + 80x^2 + 80x + 32$

4. $-9,120x^{17}$

Appendix

Tables

Table I **Basic Geometric Formulas**

1. Similar Triangles

(A) Two triangles are similar if two angles of one triangle have the same measure as two angles of the other.

(B) If two triangles are similar, their corresponding sides are proportional:

$$\frac{a}{a'} = \frac{b}{b'} = \frac{c}{c'}$$

2. Pythagorean Theorem

$$c^2 = a^2 + b^2$$

3. Rectangle

$A = ab$ Area

$P = 2a + 2b$ Perimeter

4. Parallelogram

$h =$ height

$A = ah = ab \sin \theta$ Area

$P = 2a + 2b$ Perimeter

5. Triangle

$h =$ height

$A = \frac{1}{2}hc$ Area

$P = a + b + c$ Perimeter

$s = \frac{1}{2}(a + b + c)$ Semiperimeter

$A = \sqrt{s(s - a)(s - b)(s - c)}$ Area: Heron's formula

6. Trapezoid

Base a is parallel to base b.

$h =$ height

$A = \frac{1}{2}(a + b)h$ Area

7. Circle

$R =$ radius

$D =$ diameter

$D = 2R$

$A = \pi R^2 = \frac{1}{4}\pi D^2$ Area

$C = 2\pi R = \pi D$ Circumference

$\dfrac{C}{D} = \pi$ For all circles

$\pi \approx 3.14159$

Table I Continued

8. Rectangular Solid

$V = abc$ — Volume

$T = 2ab + 2ac + 2bc$ — Total surface area

9. Right Circular Cylinder

R = radius of base

h = height

$V = \pi R^2 h$ — Volume

$S = 2\pi R h$ — Lateral surface area

$T = 2\pi R(R + h)$ — Total surface area

10. Right Circular Cone

R = radius of base

h = height

s = slant height

$V = \frac{1}{3}\pi R^2 h$ — Volume

$S = \pi Rs = \pi R\sqrt{R^2 + h^2}$ — Lateral surface area

$T = \pi R(R + s) = \pi R(R + \sqrt{R^2 + h^2})$ — Total surface area

11. Sphere

R = radius

D = diameter

$D = 2R$

$V = \frac{4}{3}\pi R^3 = \frac{1}{6}\pi D^3$ — Volume

$S = 4\pi R^2 = \pi D^2$ — Surface area

Table II Integration Formulas

Integrals Involving u^n

1. $\displaystyle\int u^n \, du = \frac{u^{n+1}}{n + 1}, \quad n \neq -1$

2. $\displaystyle\int u^{-1} \, du = \int \frac{1}{u} \, du = \ln|u|$

Integrals Involving $a + bu, a \neq 0$ and $b \neq 0$

3. $\displaystyle\int \frac{1}{a + bu} \, du = \frac{1}{b} \ln|a + bu|$

4. $\displaystyle\int \frac{u}{a + bu} \, du = \frac{u}{b} - \frac{a}{b^2} \ln|a + bu|$

5. $\displaystyle\int \frac{u^2}{a + bu} \, du = \frac{(a + bu)^2}{2b^3} - \frac{2a(a + bu)}{b^3} + \frac{a^2}{b^3} \ln|a + bu|$

6. $\displaystyle\int \frac{u}{(a + bu)^2} \, du = \frac{1}{b^2}\left(\ln|a + bu| + \frac{a}{a + bu} \right)$

7. $\displaystyle\int \frac{u^2}{(a + bu)^2} \, du = \frac{(a + bu)}{b^3} - \frac{a^2}{b^3(a + bu)} - \frac{2a}{b^3} \ln|a + bu|$

8. $\displaystyle\int u(a + bu)^n \, du = \frac{(a + bu)^{n+2}}{(n + 2)b^2} - \frac{a(a + bu)^{n+1}}{(n + 1)b^2}, \quad n \neq -1, -2$

9. $\displaystyle\int \frac{1}{u(a + bu)} \, du = \frac{1}{a} \ln\left| \frac{u}{a + bu} \right|$

10. $\displaystyle\int \frac{1}{u^2(a + bu)} \, du = -\frac{1}{au} + \frac{b}{a^2} \ln\left| \frac{a + bu}{u} \right|$

11. $\displaystyle\int \frac{1}{u(a + bu)^2} \, du = \frac{1}{a(a + bu)} + \frac{1}{a^2} \ln\left| \frac{u}{a + bu} \right|$

12. $\displaystyle\int \frac{1}{u^2(a + bu)^2} \, du = -\frac{a + 2bu}{a^2 u(a + bu)} + \frac{2b}{a^3} \ln\left| \frac{a + bu}{u} \right|$

Table II **Continued**

Integrals Involving $a^2 - u^2, a > 0$

13. $\int \dfrac{1}{u^2 - a^2}\, du = \dfrac{1}{2a} \ln \left| \dfrac{u - a}{u + a} \right|$

14. $\int \dfrac{1}{a^2 - u^2}\, du = \dfrac{1}{2a} \ln \left| \dfrac{u + a}{u - a} \right|$

Integrals Involving $(a + bu)$ and $(c + du), b \neq 0, d \neq 0,$ and $ad - bc \neq 0$

15. $\int \dfrac{1}{(a + bu)(c + du)}\, du = \dfrac{1}{ad - bc} \ln \left| \dfrac{c + du}{a + bu} \right|$

16. $\int \dfrac{u}{(a + bu)(c + du)}\, du = \dfrac{1}{ad - bc} \left(\dfrac{a}{b} \ln |a + bu| - \dfrac{c}{d} \ln |c + du| \right)$

17. $\int \dfrac{u^2}{(a + bu)(c + du)}\, du = \dfrac{1}{bd} u - \dfrac{1}{ad - bc} \left(\dfrac{a^2}{b^2} \ln |a + bu| - \dfrac{c^2}{d^2} \ln |c + du| \right)$

18. $\int \dfrac{1}{(a + bu)^2 (c + du)}\, du = \dfrac{1}{ad - bc} \dfrac{1}{a + bu} + \dfrac{d}{(ad - bc)^2} \ln \left| \dfrac{c + du}{a + bu} \right|$

19. $\int \dfrac{u}{(a + bu)^2 (c + du)}\, du = -\dfrac{a}{b(ad - bc)} \dfrac{1}{a + bu} - \dfrac{c}{(ad - bc)^2} \ln \left| \dfrac{c + du}{a + bu} \right|$

20. $\int \dfrac{a + bu}{c + du}\, du = \dfrac{bu}{d} + \dfrac{ad - bc}{d^2} \ln |c + du|$

Integrals Involving $\sqrt{a + bu}, a \neq 0$ and $b \neq 0$

21. $\int \sqrt{a + bu}\, du = \dfrac{2\sqrt{(a + bu)^3}}{3b}$

22. $\int u\sqrt{a + bu}\, du = \dfrac{2(3bu - 2a)}{15b^2} \sqrt{(a + bu)^3}$

23. $\int u^2\sqrt{a + bu}\, du = \dfrac{2(15b^2u^2 - 12abu + 8a^2)}{105b^3} \sqrt{(a + bu)^3}$

24. $\int \dfrac{1}{\sqrt{a + bu}}\, du = \dfrac{2\sqrt{a + bu}}{b}$

25. $\int \dfrac{u}{\sqrt{a + bu}}\, du = \dfrac{2(bu - 2a)}{3b^2} \sqrt{a + bu}$

26. $\int \dfrac{u^2}{\sqrt{a + bu}}\, du = \dfrac{2(3b^2u^2 - 4abu + 8a^2)}{15b^3} \sqrt{a + bu}$

27. $\int \dfrac{1}{u\sqrt{a + bu}}\, du = \dfrac{1}{\sqrt{a}} \ln \left| \dfrac{\sqrt{a + bu} - \sqrt{a}}{\sqrt{a + bu} + \sqrt{a}} \right|, \quad a > 0$

28. $\int \dfrac{1}{u^2\sqrt{a + bu}}\, du = -\dfrac{\sqrt{a + bu}}{au} - \dfrac{b}{2a\sqrt{a}} \ln \left| \dfrac{\sqrt{a + bu} - \sqrt{a}}{\sqrt{a + bu} + \sqrt{a}} \right|, \quad a > 0$

Integrals Involving $\sqrt{a^2 - u^2}, a > 0$

29. $\int \dfrac{1}{u\sqrt{a^2 - u^2}}\, du = -\dfrac{1}{a} \ln \left| \dfrac{a + \sqrt{a^2 - u^2}}{u} \right|$

30. $\int \dfrac{1}{u^2\sqrt{a^2 - u^2}}\, du = -\dfrac{\sqrt{a^2 - u^2}}{a^2 u}$

31. $\int \dfrac{\sqrt{a^2 - u^2}}{u}\, du = \sqrt{a^2 - u^2} - a \ln \left| \dfrac{a + \sqrt{a^2 - u^2}}{u} \right|$

Integrals Involving $\sqrt{u^2 + a^2}, a > 0$

32. $\int \sqrt{u^2 + a^2}\, du = \dfrac{1}{2} \left(u\sqrt{u^2 + a^2} + a^2 \ln |u + \sqrt{u^2 + a^2}| \right)$

33. $\int u^2\sqrt{u^2 + a^2}\, du = \dfrac{1}{8} \left[u(2u^2 + a^2)\sqrt{u^2 + a^2} - a^4 \ln |u + \sqrt{u^2 + a^2}| \right]$

34. $\int \dfrac{\sqrt{u^2 + a^2}}{u}\, du = \sqrt{u^2 + a^2} - a \ln \left| \dfrac{a + \sqrt{u^2 + a^2}}{u} \right|$

35. $\int \dfrac{\sqrt{u^2 + a^2}}{u^2}\, du = -\dfrac{\sqrt{u^2 + a^2}}{u} + \ln |u + \sqrt{u^2 + a^2}|$

36. $\int \dfrac{1}{\sqrt{u^2 + a^2}}\, du = \ln |u + \sqrt{u^2 + a^2}|$

(continued)

Table II **Continued**

---

37. $\int \dfrac{1}{u\sqrt{u^2 + a^2}}\, du = \dfrac{1}{a}\ln\left|\dfrac{u}{a + \sqrt{u^2 + a^2}}\right|$

38. $\int \dfrac{u^2}{\sqrt{u^2 + a^2}}\, du = \dfrac{1}{2}\left(u\sqrt{u^2 + a^2} - a^2 \ln|u + \sqrt{u^2 + a^2}|\right)$

39. $\int \dfrac{1}{u^2\sqrt{u^2 + a^2}}\, du = -\dfrac{\sqrt{u^2 + a^2}}{a^2 u}$

Integrals Involving $\sqrt{u^2 - a^2}, a > 0$

40. $\int \sqrt{u^2 - a^2}\, du = \dfrac{1}{2}\left(u\sqrt{u^2 - a^2} - a^2 \ln|u + \sqrt{u^2 - a^2}|\right)$

41. $\int u^2 \sqrt{u^2 - a^2}\, du = \dfrac{1}{8}\left[u(2u^2 - a^2)\sqrt{u^2 - a^2} - a^4 \ln|u + \sqrt{u^2 - a^2}|\right]$

42. $\int \dfrac{\sqrt{u^2 - a^2}}{u^2}\, du = -\dfrac{\sqrt{u^2 - a^2}}{u} + \ln|u + \sqrt{u^2 - a^2}|$

43. $\int \dfrac{1}{\sqrt{u^2 - a^2}}\, du = \ln|u + \sqrt{u^2 - a^2}|$

44. $\int \dfrac{u^2}{\sqrt{u^2 - a^2}}\, du = \dfrac{1}{2}\left(u\sqrt{u^2 - a^2} + a^2 \ln|u + \sqrt{u^2 - a^2}|\right)$

45. $\int \dfrac{1}{u^2\sqrt{u^2 - a^2}}\, du = \dfrac{\sqrt{u^2 - a^2}}{a^2 u}$

Integrals Involving $e^{au}, a \neq 0$

46. $\int e^{au}\, du = \dfrac{e^{au}}{a}$

47. $\int u^n e^{au}\, du = \dfrac{u^n e^{au}}{a} - \dfrac{n}{a}\int u^{n-1} e^{au}\, du$

48. $\int \dfrac{1}{c + de^{au}}\, du = \dfrac{u}{c} - \dfrac{1}{ac}\ln|c + de^{au}|, \quad c \neq 0$

Integrals Involving $\ln u$

49. $\int \ln u\, du = u \ln u - u$

50. $\int \dfrac{\ln u}{u}\, du = \dfrac{1}{2}(\ln u)^2$

51. $\int u^n \ln u\, du = \dfrac{u^{n+1}}{n+1}\ln u - \dfrac{u^{n+1}}{(n+1)^2}, \quad n \neq -1$

52. $\int (\ln u)^n\, du = u(\ln u)^n - n\int (\ln u)^{n-1}\, du$

Integrals Involving Trigonometric Functions of $au, a \neq 0$

53. $\int \sin au\, du = -\dfrac{1}{a}\cos au$

54. $\int \cos au\, du = \dfrac{1}{a}\sin au$

55. $\int \tan au\, du = -\dfrac{1}{a}\ln|\cos au|$

56. $\int \cot au\, du = \dfrac{1}{a}\ln|\sin au|$

57. $\int \sec au\, du = \dfrac{1}{a}\ln|\sec au + \tan au|$

58. $\int \csc au\, du = \dfrac{1}{a}\ln|\csc au - \cot au|$

59. $\int (\sin au)^2\, du = \dfrac{u}{2} - \dfrac{1}{4a}\sin 2au$

60. $\int (\cos au)^2\, du = \dfrac{u}{2} + \dfrac{1}{4a}\sin 2au$

61. $\int (\sin au)^n\, du = -\dfrac{1}{an}(\sin au)^{n-1}\cos au + \dfrac{n-1}{n}\int (\sin au)^{n-2}\, du, \quad n \neq 0$

62. $\int (\cos au)^n\, du = \dfrac{1}{an}\sin au(\cos au)^{n-1} + \dfrac{n-1}{n}\int (\cos au)^{n-2}\, du, \quad n \neq 0$

[*Note:* **The constant of integration is omitted for each integral, but must be included in any particular application of a formula.** The variable u is the variable of integration; all other symbols represent constants.]

ANSWERS

Diagnostic Prerequisite Test

Section references are provided in parentheses following each answer to guide students to the specific content in the book where they can find help or remediation.

1. (A) $(y + z)x$ (B) $(2 + x) + y$ (C) $2x + 3x$ *(A.1)* **2.** $x^3 - 3x^2 + 4x + 8$ *(A.2)* **3.** $x^3 + 3x^2 - 2x + 12$ *(A.2)* **4.** $-3x^5 + 2x^3 - 24x^2 + 16$ *(A.2)*
5. (A) 1 (B) 1 (C) 2 (D) 3 *(A.2)* **6.** (A) 3 (B) 1 (C) -3 (D) 1 *(A.2)* **7.** $14x^2 - 30x$ *(A.2)* **8.** $6x^2 - 5xy - 4y^2$ *(A.2)* **9.** $(x + 2)(x + 5)$ *(A.3)*
10. $x(x + 3)(x - 5)$ *(A.3)* **11.** $7/20$ *(A.1)* **12.** 0.875 *(A.1)* **13.** (A) 4.065×10^{12} (B) 7.3×10^{-3} *(A.5)* **14.** (A) $255{,}000{,}000$ (B) $0{,}000\,406$ *(A.5)*
15. (A) T (B) F *(A.1)* **16.** 0 and -3 are two examples of infinitely many. *(A.1)* **17.** $6x^5y^{15}$ *(A.5)* **18.** $3u^4/v^2$ *(A.5)* **19.** 6×10^2 *(A.5)* **20.** x^6/y^4 *(A.5)*
21. $u^{7/3}$ *(A.6)* **22.** $3a^2/b$ *(A.6)* **23.** $\frac{5}{9}$ *(A.5)* **24.** $x + 2x^{1/2}y^{1/2} + y$ *(A.6)* **25.** $\dfrac{a^2 + b^2}{ab}$ *(A.4)* **26.** $\dfrac{a^2 - c^2}{abc}$ *(A.4)* **27.** $\dfrac{y^5}{x}$ *(A.4)* **28.** $\dfrac{1}{xy^2}$ *(A.4)*
29. $\dfrac{-1}{7(7 + h)}$ *(A.4)* **30.** $\dfrac{xy}{y - x}$ *(A.6)* **31.** (A) Subtraction (B) Commutative $(+)$ (C) Distributive (D) Associative $(\cdot)$ (E) Negatives
(F) Identity $(+)$ *(A.1)* **32.** (A) 6 (B) 0 *(A.1)* **33.** $4x = x - 4; x = -4/3$ *(1.1)* **34.** $-15/7$ *(1.2)* **35.** $(4/7, 0)$ *(1.2)* **36.** $(0, -4)$ *(1.2)*
37. $(x - 5y)(x + 2y)$ *(A.3)* **38.** $(3x - y)(2x - 5y)$ *(A.3)* **39.** $3x^{-1} + 4y^{1/2}$ *(A.6)* **40.** $8x^{-2} - 5y^{-4}$ *(A.5)*
41. $\dfrac{2}{5}x^{-3/4} - \dfrac{7}{6}y^{-2/3}$ *(A.6)* **42.** $\dfrac{1}{3}x^{-1/2} + 9y^{-1/3}$ *(A.6)* **43.** $\dfrac{2}{7} + \dfrac{1}{14}\sqrt{2}$ *(A.6)* **44.** $\dfrac{14}{11} - \dfrac{5}{11}\sqrt{3}$ *(A.6)* **45.** $x = 0, 5$ *(A.7)*
46. $x = \pm\sqrt{7}$ *(A.7)* **47.** $x = -4, 5$ *(A.7)* **48.** $x = 1, \dfrac{1}{6}$ *(A.7)* **49.** $x = -1 \pm \sqrt{2}$ *(A.7)* **50.** $x = \pm 1, \pm\sqrt{5}$ *(A.7)*

Chapter 1

Exercises 1.1

1. **3.** **5.** **7.** **9.** A function **11.** Not a function **13.** A function **15.** A function
17. Not a function **19.** A function **21.** Linear **23.** Neither
25. Constant **27.** Linear

29. **31.** **33.** **35.** **37.** **39.** $y = 0$ **41.** $y = 4$ **43.** $x = -5, 0, 4$
45. $x = -6$ **47.** All real numbers
49. All real numbers except -4
51. $x \le 7$ **53.** Yes; all real numbers
55. No; for example, when $x = 0, y = \pm 2$

57. Yes; all real numbers except 0 **59.** No; when $x = 1, y = \pm 1$ **61.** 12 **63.** $x^2 + 2x - 3$ **65.** $36x^2 - 4$ **67.** $x^6 - 4$ **69.** $h^2 - 4$ **71.** $4h + h^2$
73. $4h + h^2$ **75.** (A) $4x + 4h - 3$ (B) $4h$ (C) 4 **77.** (A) $4x^2 + 8xh + 4h^2 - 7x - 7h + 6$ (B) $8xh + 4h^2 - 7h$ (C) $8x + 4h - 7$

79. (A) $20x + 20h - x^2 - 2xh - h^2$ (B) $20h - 2xh - h^2$ (C) $20 - 2x - h$ **81.** $P(w) = 2w + \dfrac{50}{w}, w > 0$ **83.** $A(l) = l(50 - l), 0 < l < 50$

85. (A) $p(x)$ (B) $\$54; \$42$ **87.** (A) $R(x) = (75 - 3x)x, 1 \le x \le 20$ (B) (C) $R(x)$

x	$R(x)$
1	72
4	252
8	408
12	468
16	432
20	300

89. (A) $P(x) = 59x - 3x^2 - 125, 1 \le x \le 20$ (B) (C) $P(x)$

x	$P(x)$
1	-69
4	63
8	155
12	151
16	51
20	-145

91. (A) $V(x) = x(8 - 2x)(12 - 2x)$ (B) $0 < x < 4$
(C) (D) $V(x)$

x	$V(x)$
1	60
2	64
3	36

93. (A) The graph indicates that there is a value of x near 2 that will produce a volume of 65.
(B) The table shows $x = 1.9$ to one decimal place:

x	1.8	1.9	2
$V(x)$	66.5	65.4	64

(C) $x = 1.93$ to two decimal places **95.** $v = \dfrac{75 - w}{15 + w}$; 1.9032 cm/sec

Exercises 1.2   **1.** Domain: all real numbers; range: all real numbers   **3.** Domain: $[0, \infty)$; range: $(-\infty, 15]$

5. Domain: all real numbers; range: $[7, \infty)$ **7.** Domain: all real numbers; range: all real numbers

9.   **11.**   **13.**   **15.**   **17.**   **19.**   **21.**

23.   **25.** The graph of $g(x) = -|x + 3|$ is the   **27.** The graph of $f(x) = (x - 4)^2 - 3$
graph of $y = |x|$ reflected in the x axis   is the graph of $y = x^2$ shifted 4 units
and shifted 3 units to the left.   to the right and 3 units down.

29. The graph of $f(x) = 7 - \sqrt{x}$ **31.** The graph of $h(x) = -3|x|$ is   **33.** The graph of the basic function $y = x^2$
is the graph of $y = \sqrt{x}$ the graph of $y = |x|$ reflected in   is shifted 2 units to the left and 3 units
reflected in the x axis and   the x axis and vertically stretched   down. Equation: $y = (x + 2)^2 - 3$.
shifted 7 units up.   by a factor of 3.

35. The graph of the basic function $y = x^2$ is reflected in the x axis and shifted 3 units to the right and 2 units up. Equation: $y = 2 - (x - 3)^2$.   **37.** The graph of the basic function $y = \sqrt{x}$ is reflected in the x axis and shifted 4 units up. Equation: $y = 4 - \sqrt{x}$.   **39.** The graph of the basic function $y = x^3$ is shifted 2 units to the left and 1 unit down. Equation: $y = (x + 2)^3 - 1$.

41. $g(x) = \sqrt{x - 2} - 3$ **43.** $g(x) = -|x + 3|$ **45.** $g(x) = -(x - 2)^3 - 1$ **47.**   **49.**   **51.**

53. The graph of the basic function $y = |x|$ is reflected in the x axis and vertically shrunk by a factor of 0.5. Equation: $y = -0.5|x|$.   **55.** The graph of the basic function $y = x^2$ is reflected in the x axis and vertically stretched by a factor of 2. Equation: $y = -2x^2$.   **57.** The graph of the basic function $y = \sqrt[3]{x}$ is reflected in the x axis and vertically stretched by a factor of 3. Equation: $y = -3\sqrt[3]{x}$.   **59.** Reversing the order does not change the result.   **61.** Reversing the order can change the result.   **63.** Reversing the order can change the result.

65. (A) The graph of the basic function   (B)   **67.** (A) The graph of the basic function   (B)
$y = \sqrt{x}$ is reflected in the x axis, $y = x^3$ is vertically contracted by a
vertically expanded by a factor of 4,   factor of 0.000 48 and shifted right
and shifted up 115 units.   500 units and up 60,000 units.

69. (A) $S(x) = \begin{cases} 8.5 + 0.065x & \text{if } 0 \le x \le 700 \\ -9 + 0.09x & \text{if } x > 700 \end{cases}$ **71.** (A) $T(x) = \begin{cases} 0.035x & \text{if } 0 \le x \le 30{,}000 \\ 0.0625x - 825 & \text{if } 30{,}000 < x \le 60{,}000 \\ 0.0645x - 945 & \text{if } x > 60{,}000 \end{cases}$

(B)   (B)

(C) $1,675; $3,570

73. (A) The graph of the basic function $y = x$ is vertically stretched   **75.** (A) The graph of the basic function $y = \sqrt{x}$ is vertically stretched by
by a factor of 5.5 and shifted down 220 units.   a factor of 7.08.

(B)   (B)

Exercises 1.3   **1.**   **3.**   **5.** Slope = 5; y intercept = -7 **7.** Slope = $-\dfrac{5}{2}$; y intercept = -9 **9.** $y = 2x + 1$

11. $y = -\dfrac{1}{3}x + 6$ **13.** x int.: -1; y int.: -2; $y = -2x - 2$

15. x int.: -3; y int.: 1; $y = \dfrac{x}{3} + 1$ **17.** (A) m (B) g (C) f (D) n

19. (A) x int.: 1, 3; y int.: -3 (B) Vertex: $(2, 1)$ (C) Max.: 1   (D) Range: $y \le 1$ or $(-\infty, 1]$ **21.** (A) x int.: $-3, -1$; y int.: 3   (B) Vertex: $(-2, -1)$
(C) Min.: -1 (D) Range: $y \ge -1$ or $[-1, \infty)$ **23.** (A) x int.: $3 \pm \sqrt{2}$; y int.: -7 (B) Vertex: $(3, 2)$ (C) Max.: 2   (D) Range: $y \le 2$ or $(-\infty, 2]$

25. (A) x int.: $-1 \pm \sqrt{2}$; y int.: -1 (B) Vertex: $(-1, -2)$ (C) Min.: -2 (D) Range: $y \geq -2$ or $[-2, \infty)$ **27.** (A) $m = \dfrac{2}{3}$ (B) $y - 5 = \dfrac{2}{3}(x - 2)$

(C) $y = \dfrac{2}{3}x + \dfrac{11}{3}$ (D) $-2x + 3y = 11$ **29.** (A) $m = -\dfrac{5}{4}$ (B) $y + 1 = -\dfrac{5}{4}(x + 2)$ (C) $y = -\dfrac{5}{4}x - \dfrac{7}{2}$ (D) $5x + 4y = -14$ **31.** (A) Not defined

(B) None   (C) None   (D) $x = 5$ **33.** (A) $m = 0$ (B) $y - 5 = 0$ (C) $y = 5$ (D) $y = 5$ **35.** Vertex form: $(x - 4)^2 - 4$ (A) x int.: $2, 6$; y int.: 12

(B) Vertex: $(4, -4)$ (C) Min.: -4 (D) Range: $y \geq -4$ or $[-4, \infty)$ **37.** Vertex form: $-4(x - 2)^2 + 1$ (A) x int.: $1.5, 2.5$; y int.: -15 (B) Vertex: $(2, 1)$

(C) Max.: 1 (D) Range: $y \leq 1$ or $(-\infty, 1]$ **39.** Vertex form: $0.5(x - 2)^2 + 3$ (A) x int.: none; y int.: 5 (B) Vertex: $(2, 3)$ (C) Min.: 3

(D) Range: $y \geq 3$ or $[3, \infty)$ **41.** $\left(-\infty, -\dfrac{7}{2}\right]$ **43.** $\left(-\infty, -\dfrac{3}{5}\right]$ **45.** $(-\infty, 0) \cup (10, \infty)$ **47.** $\left[-10 - 5\sqrt{2}, -10 + 5\sqrt{2}\right]$

49.   **51.** (A)   (B) x int.: 3.5; y int.: -4.2 (C)   (D) x int.: 3.5; y int.: -4.2

53. (A) $-4.87, 8.21$ (B) $-3.44, 6.78$ (C) No solution   **55.** 651.0417 **59.** (A) $P = 0.44\overline{5}d + 14.7$ (B) The rate of change of pressure with respect to depth is

$0.44\overline{5}$ lb/in^2 per foot.   (C) 37 lb/in^2 (D) 99 ft   **61.** (A) $a = 2,880 - 24t$ (B) -24 ft/sec   (C) 24 ft/sec

63. (A) $C = 75x + 1,647$ **65.** (A) $V = -7,500t + 157,000$ **67.** (A) $T = 70 - 3.6A$ **69.** (A) $p = 0.000\,225x + 0.5925$

(B)   (B) $112,000$ (B) $10,000$ ft   (B) $p = -0.0009x + 9.39$

(C) During the 12th year   (C) $(7,820, 2.352)$

(D)   (D)

(C) The y intercept, $1,647$, is the   (D)

fixed cost and the slope, 75, is

the cost per club.

71. (A)   **73.** (A)

x	28	30	32	34	36
Mileage	45	52	55	51	47
$f(x)$	45.3	51.8	54.2	52.4	46.5

(B) y (C) $f(31) = 53.50$ thousand miles;

$f(35) = 49.95$ thousand miles

(B) $1,200,000$ (C) $1,000,000$

77. (A)   **79.** (A) The rate of change of height with respect to Dbh is 1.37 ft/in.   **85.** 10.6 mph

(B) Height increases by approximately 1.37 ft.   (C) 18 ft   (D) 20 in.

81. (A) The monthly price is increasing at a rate of $1.70 per

year.   (B) $71.70   **83.** Men: $y = -0.087x + 49.207$; women:

$y = -0.088x + 54.884$; yes

```
QuadReg
y=ax²+bx+c
a=1.4ε⁻6
b=⁻.00266
c=5.4
```

(B) 12.5 ($12,500,000$ chips);

$468,750,000   (C) $37.50

Exercises 1.4   **1.** (A) 1 (B) 10 (C) 50 **3.** (A) 5 (B) $0, 1$ (C) 0 **5.** (A) 2 (B) $-1, -2$ (C) 2 **7.** (A) 4 (B) $-1, 1, -3, 3$

(C) 9 **9.** (A) 9 (B) $-3/2, 5$ (C) $-253,125$ **11.** (A) 4 (B) Negative   **13.** (A) 5 (B) Negative   **15.** (A) 1 (B) Negative

17. (A) 6 (B) Positive   **19.** 10 **21.** 1 **23.** (A) x int.: -2; y int.: -1 (B) Domain: all real numbers except 2

(C) Vertical asymptote: $x = 2$; horizontal asymptote: $y = 1$ (D) $f(x)$ (E)

25. (A) x int.: 0; y int.: 0 **27.** (A) x int.: 2; y int.: -1

(B) Domain: all real numbers except -2 (B) Domain: all real numbers except 4

(C) Vertical asymptote: $x = -2$; horizontal asymptote: $y = 3$ (C) Vertical asymptote: $x = 4$; horizontal asymptote: $y = -2$

(D) $f(x)$ (E)   (D) $f(x)$ (E)

29. (A)

(B)

31. (A)

(B)

33. $y = \dfrac{5}{6}$ **35.** $y = \dfrac{1}{4}$ **37.** $y = 0$ **39.** None   **41.** $x = -1, x = 1, x = -3, x = 3$ **43.** $x = 5$ **45.** $x = -6, x = 6$

47. (A) x int.: 0; y int.: 0
   (B) Vertical asymptotes: $x = -2, x = 3$;
       horizontal asymptote: $y = 2$
   (C)   (D)

49. (A) x int.: $\pm\sqrt{3}$; y int.: $-\dfrac{2}{3}$
   (B) Vertical asymptotes: $x = -3, x = 3$;
       horizontal asymptote: $y = -2$
   (C)   (D)

51. (A) x int.: 6; y int.: -4
   (B) Vertical asymptotes: $x = -3, x = 2$;
       horizontal asymptote: $y = 0$
   (C)   (D)

53. $f(x) = x^2 - x - 2$ **55.** $f(x) = 4x - x^3$

57. (A) $C(x) = 180x + 200$ (B) $\overline{C}(x) = \dfrac{180x + 200}{x}$
   (C)   (D) \$180 per board

59. (A) $\overline{C}(n) = \dfrac{2{,}500 + 175n + 25n^2}{n}$ (C) 10 yr; \$675.00 per year
                                                              (D) 10 yr; \$675.00 per year
   (B)

61. (A) $\overline{C}(x) = \dfrac{0.00048(x - 500)^3 + 60{,}000}{x}$
   (B)   (C) 750 cases per month;
                  \$90 per case

63. (A)
```
CubicReg
y=ax³+bx²+cx+d
a=-2.666667E-4
b=.0096666667
c=-.2011904762
d=17.84761905
```
(B) 4.1 lb   **65.** (A) 0.06 cm/sec   (B)   **67.** (A)
```
CubicReg
y=ax³+bx²+cx+d
a=8.7037037E-5
b=-.0108492063
c=.2907407407
d=8.546031746
```
(B) 5.5

Exercises 1.5   **1.** (A) k **3.**   **5.**   **7.**   **9.**   **11.** The graph of g is the graph of f reflected
                        (B) g in the x axis.   **13.** The graph of g is the graph
                        (C) h of f shifted 1 unit to the left.   **15.** The graph
                        (D) f of g is the graph of f shifted 1 unit up.

17. The graph of g is the graph of f vertically stretched by a factor of 2 and shifted to the left 2 units.

19. (A) (B) (C) (D) **21.** $f(t)$ **23.**

25. **27.** $a = 1, -1$ **29.** $x = 1$ **43.** $h(x)$ **45.** N **47.** \$16,064.07 **49.** (A) \$2,633.56

31. $x = -1, 6$ **33.** $x = 3$ (B) \$7,079.54 **51.** \$10,706 **53.** (A) \$10,095.41

35. $x = -7$ **37.** $x = -2, 2$ (B) \$10,080.32 (C) \$10,085.27

39. $x = 1/4$ **41.** No solution

55. N approaches 2 as t increases without bound. **57.** (A) \$9,781,000

59. (A) 10% (B) 1%

61. (A) $P = 7.1e^{0.011t}$ (B) 2025: 8.1 billion; 2035: 9.0 billion

63. (A) 42,772,000,000

```
ExpReg
y=a*b^x
a=732.7877195
b=1.084347949
```

(B) The model gives an annual salary of \$1,647,000 in 2000.

```
ExpReg
y=a*b^x
a=5.729914723
b=1.375060902
```

Exercises 1.6 **1.** $27 = 3^3$ **3.** $10^0 = 1$ **5.** $8 = 4^{3/2}$ **7.** $\log_7 49 = 2$ **9.** $\log_4 8 = \dfrac{3}{2}$ **11.** $\log_b A = u$ **13.** 2 **15.** 4 **17.** -2 **19.** -4

21. $\log_b P - \log_b Q$ **23.** $5 \log_b L$ **25.** q^p **27.** $x = 9$ **29.** $y = 2$ **31.** $b = 10$ **33.** $x = 2$ **35.** False **37.** True **39.** True **41.** False **43.** $x = 2$

45. $x = 8$ **47.** $x = 7$ **49.** No solution **51.** y **53.** The graph of $y = \log_2 (x - 2)$ is the graph of $y = \log_2 x$ shifted to the right 2 units.

55. Domain: $(-1, \infty)$; range: all real numbers

57. (A) 3.547 43 (B) -2.160 32 (C) 5.626 29 (D) -3.197 04

59. (A) 13.4431 (B) 0.0089 (C) 16.0595 (D) 0.1514

61. 1.0792 **63.** 1.4595 **65.** 18.3559

67. Increasing: $(0, \infty)$ **69.** Decreasing: $(0, 1]$ **71.** Increasing: $(-2, \infty)$ **73.** Increasing: $(0, \infty)$ **75.** Because $b^0 = 1$ for any permissible base

Increasing: $[1, \infty)$ $b (b > 0, b \neq 1)$. **77.** $x > \sqrt{x} > \ln x$ for $1 < x \leq 16$

79. 4 yr **81.** 9.87 yr; 9.80 yr **83.** 7.51 yr

85. (A) 5,373 (B) 7,220 **89.** 168 bushels/acre **91.** 916 yr

```
LnReg
y=a+blnx
a=256.4659159
b=-24.03812068
```

```
LnReg
y=a+blnx
a=-127.8085281
b=20.01315349
```

```
LnReg
y=a+blnx
a=-551.2132518
b=149.1505358
```

Chapter 1 Review Exercises

1. y *(1.1)* **2.** y *(1.1)* **3.** y *(1.1)* **4.** (A) Not a function (B) A function (C) A function (D) Not a function *(1.1)*

5. (A) -2 (B) -8 (C) 0 (D) Not defined *(1.1)*

6. y *(1.3)* **7.** $2x + 3y = 12$ *(1.3)*

8. x intercept $= 9$; y intercept $= -6$; slope $= \dfrac{2}{3}$ *(1.3)* **9.** $y = -\dfrac{2}{3}x + 6$ *(1.3)* **10.** Vertical line: $x = -6$; horizontal line: $y = 5$ *(1.3)*

11. (A) $y = -\dfrac{2}{3}x$ (B) $y = 3$ *(1.3)* **12.** (A) $3x + 2y = 1$ (B) $y = 5$ (C) $x = -2$ *(1.3)*

13. $v = \ln u$ *(1.6)* **14.** $y = \log x$ *(1.6)* **15.** $M = e^N$ *(1.6)* **16.** $u = 10^v$ *(1.6)* **17.** $x = 9$ *(1.6)*

18. $x = 6$ *(1.6)* **19.** $x = 4$ *(1.6)* **20.** $x = 2.157$ *(1.6)* **21.** $x = 13.128$ *(1.6)* **22.** $x = 1,273.503$ *(1.6)*

23. $x = 0.318$ *(1.6)* **24.** (A) $y = 4$ (B) $x = 0$ (C) $y = 1$ (D) $x = -1$ or 1

(E) $y = -2$ (F) $x = -5$ or 5 *(1.1)*

25. (A) (B) (C) (D) *(1.2)* **26.** $f(x) = -(x - 2)^2 + 4$. The graph of $f(x)$ is the graph of $y = x^2$ reflected in the x axis, then shifted right 2 units and up 4 units. *(1.2)*   **27.** (A) g (B) m (C) n (D) f *(1.2, 1.3)*
28. (A) x int.: $-4, 0$; y int.: 0 (B) Vertex: $(-2, -4)$
(C) Min.: -4 (D) Range: $y \geq -4$ or $[-4, \infty)$ *(1.3)*

29. Quadratic *(1.3)*   **30.** Linear *(1.1)*   **31.** None *(1.1, 1.3)*   **32.** Constant *(1.1)*   **33.** $x = 8$ *(1.6)*   **34.** $x = 3$ *(1.6)*   **35.** $x = 0, \frac{3}{2}$ *(1.5)*   **36.** $x = -2$ *(1.6)*
37. $x = 1.4650$ *(1.6)*   **38.** $x = 92.1034$ *(1.6)*   **39.** $x = 9.0065$ *(1.6)*   **40.** $x = 2.1081$ *(1.6)*   **41.** (A) All real numbers except $x = -2$ and 3   (B) $x < 5$ *(1.1)*

42. Vertex form: $4\left(x + \frac{1}{2}\right)^2 - 4$; x int.: $-\frac{3}{2}$ and $\frac{1}{2}$; y int.: -3; vertex: $\left(-\frac{1}{2}, -4\right)$; min.: -4; range: $y \geq -4$ or $[-4, \infty)$ *(1.3)*

43. $(-1.54, -0.79)$; $(0.69, 0.99)$ *(1.5, 1.6)*   **44.** *(1.1)*   **45.** *(1.1)*   **46.** 6 *(1.1)*   **47.** -19 *(1.1)*   **48.** $10x - 4$ *(1.1)*
49. $21 - 5x$ *(1.1)*   **50.** (A) -1 (B) $-1 - 2h$
(C) $-2h$ (D) -2 *(1.1)*   **51.** The graph of function m is the graph of $y = |x|$ reflected in the x axis and shifted to the right 4 units. *(1.2)*

52. The graph of function g is the graph of $y = x^3$ vertically shrunk by a factor of 0.3 and shifted up 3 units. *(1.2)*   **53.** $y = 0$ *(1.4)*

54. $y = \frac{3}{4}$ *(1.4)*   **55.** None *(1.4)*   **56.** $x = -10, x = 10$ *(1.4)*   **57.** $x = -2$ *(1.4)*   **58.** True *(1.3)*   **59.** False *(1.3)*   **60.** False *(1.3)*   **61.** True *(1.3)*

62. *(1.2)*   **63.** *(1.2)*   **64.** $y = -(x - 4)^2 + 3$ *(1.2, 1.3)*
65. $f(x) = -0.4(x - 4)^2 + 7.6$
(A) x int.: $-0.4, 8.4$; y int.: 1.2 (B) Vertex: $(4.0, 7.6)$ (C) Max.: 7.6
(D) Range: $y \leq 7.6$ or $(-\infty, 7.6]$ *(1.3)*

66.   **67.** $\log 10^\pi = \pi$ and $10^{\log \sqrt{2}} = \sqrt{2}$; $\ln e^\pi = \pi$ and $e^{\ln \sqrt{2}} = \sqrt{2}$ *(1.6)*   **68.** $x = 2$ *(1.6)*   **69.** $x = 2$ *(1.6)*
70. $x = 1$ *(1.6)*   **71.** $x = 300$ *(1.6)*   **72.** $y = ce^{-5t}$ *(1.6)*   **73.** The function $y = 1^x$ is not one-to-one, so has no inverse. *(1.6)*   **74.** The graph of $y = \sqrt[3]{x}$ is vertically expanded by a factor of 2, reflected in the x axis, and shifted 1 unit left and 1 unit down. Equation: $y = -2\sqrt[3]{x + 1} - 1$. *(1.2)*   **75.** $G(x) = 0.3(x + 2)^2 - 8.1$ (A) x int.: $-7.2, 3.2$; y int.: -6.9 (B) Vertex: $(-2, -8.1)$ (C) Min.: -8.1 (D) Range: $y \geq -8.1$ or $[-8.1, \infty)$ *(1.3)*

(A) x int.: $-0.4, 8.4$; y int.: 1.2
(B) Vertex: $(4.0, 7.6)$ (C) Max.: 7.6
(D) Range: $y \leq 7.6$ or $(-\infty, 7.6]$ *(1.3)*

76.   (A) x int.: $-7.2, 3.2$; y int.: -6.9 (B) Vertex: $(-2, -8.1)$
(C) Min.: -8.1 (D) Range: $y \geq -8.1$ or $[-8.1, \infty)$ *(1.3)*

77. (A) $S(x) = \begin{cases} 3 & \text{if } 0 \leq x \leq 20 \\ 0.057x + 1.86 & \text{if } 20 < x \leq 200 \\ 0.0346x + 6.34 & \text{if } 200 < x \leq 1{,}000 \\ 0.0217x + 19.24 & \text{if } x > 1{,}000 \end{cases}$ (B) $S(x)$ *(1.2)*   **78.** $5{,}321.95$ *(1.5)*   **79.** $5{,}269.51$ *(1.5)*   **80.** 201 months $(\approx 16.7 \text{ years})$ *(1.5)*   **81.** 9.38 yr *(1.5)*
82. (A) $m = 132 - 0.6x$ (B) $M = 187 - 0.85x$
(C) Between 120 and 170 beats per minute   (D) Between 102 and 144.5 beats per minute *(1.3)*

83. (A) $V = 224{,}000 - 15{,}500t$ **84.** (A) The dropout rate is decreasing at a   (B)   (C) 2027 *(1.3)*
(B) $38{,}000$ *(1.3)*   rate of 0.198 percentage points per year.   **85.** (A) The CPI is increasing at a rate of 4.75 units per year.   (B) 285 *(1.3)*

Dropout rate (%)
Years since 1980

86. (A) $A(x) = -\frac{3}{2}x^2 + 420x$ (B) Domain: $0 \leq x \leq 280$ **87.** (A) 2,833 sets   (B) 4,836
(C) $A(x)$

```
QuadReg
y=ax²+bx+c
a=5.9477212E-6
b=-.1024018814
c=422.3467853
```

```
LinReg
y=ax+b
a=.0387421907
b=-7.364689544
```

(D) There are two solutions to the equation $A(x) = 25{,}000$, one near 90 and another near 190.
(E) 86 ft; 194 ft
(F) Maximum combined area is $29{,}400$ ft^2. This occurs for $x = 140$ ft and $y = 105$ ft. *(1.3)*

(C) Price is likely to decrease   (D) Equilibrium price: 131.59; equilibrium quantity: 3,587 cookware sets *(1.3)*

88. (A)
```
CubicReg
y=ax³+bx²+cx+d
a=.5813376005
b=-21.33512555
c=96.11031183
d=5571.799951
```
(B) 7,725 *(1.4)*   **89.** (A) $N = 2^{2t}$ or $N = 4^t$ **91.** (A) 6,134,000 *(1.6)*
```
LnReg
y=a+blnx
a=42400.65695
b=-8207.259234
```
92. 23.1 yr *(1.5)*

(B) 15 days *(1.5)*

90. $k = 0.009\ 42$; 489 ft *(1.6)*

93. (A) $1,203 billion
```
ExpReg
y=a*b^x
a=45.31715635
b=1.081196187
```
(B) 2028 *(1.5)*

Chapter 2

Exercises 2.1   **1.** $(x - 9)(x + 9)$ **3.** $(x - 7)(x + 3)$ **5.** $x(x - 3)(x - 4)$ **7.** $(2x - 1)(3x + 1)$ **9.** 2   **11.** 1.25   **13.** (A) 2   (B) 2
(C) 2   (D) 2   **15.** (A) 1   (B) 2   (C) Does not exist   (D) 2   (E) No   **17.** 2   **19.** 0.5   **21.** (A) 1   (B) 2   (C) Does not exist   (D) Does not exist   (E) No
23. (A) 1   (B) 1   (C) 1   (D) 3   (E) Yes, define $g(3) = 1$ **25.** (A) -2 (B) -2 (C) -2 (D) 1   (E) Yes, define $f(-3) = -2$ **27.** (A) 2   (B) 2   (C) 2
(D) Does not exist   (E) Yes, define $f(0) = 2$ **29.** 12   **31.** 1   **33.** -4 **35.** -1.5 **37.** 3   **39.** 15   **41.** -6 **43.** $\dfrac{7}{5}$ **45.** 3

47.   **49.**
f(x)   *f(x)*

51. (A) 1   (B) 1   (C) 1   (D) 1   **53.** (A) 2   (B) 1   (C) Does not exist   (D) Does not exist
55. (A) -6 (B) Does not exist   (C) 6   **57.** (A) 1   (B) -1 (C) Does not exist   (D) Does not exist
59. (A) Does not exist   (B) $\dfrac{1}{2}$ (C) $\dfrac{1}{4}$ **61.** (A) -5 (B) -3 (C) 0   **63.** (A) 0   (B) -1 (C) Does not exist
65. (A) 1   (B) $\dfrac{1}{3}$ (C) $\dfrac{3}{4}$ **67.** False   **69.** True   **71.** False   **73.** Yes; 0   **75.** No; 5/16   **77.** No; does not exist

79. Yes; 1/16   **89.** (A) $\lim_{x\to 1^-} f(x) = 2$ (B) $\lim_{x\to 1^-} f(x) = 3$ (C) $m = 1.5$ (D) The graph in (A) is broken when it jumps from $(1, 2)$ up to
81. 3 $\lim_{x\to 1^+} f(x) = 3$ $\lim_{x\to 1^+} f(x) = 2$ *f(x)* $(1, 3)$. The graph in (B) is also broken when it jumps down
83. 4   *f(x)*   *f(x)*   from $(1, 3)$ to $(1, 2)$. The graph in (C) is one continuous
85. -7 piece, with no breaks or jumps.
87. 1

91. (A) $F(x) = \begin{cases} 0.99 & \text{if } 0 < x \le 20 \\ 0.07x - 0.41 & \text{if } x \ge 20 \end{cases}$ **95.** (A) $D(x) = \begin{cases} x & \text{if } 0 \le x < 300 \\ 0.97x & \text{if } 300 \le x < 1{,}000 \\ 0.95x & \text{if } 1{,}000 \le x < 3{,}000 \\ 0.93x & \text{if } 3{,}000 \le x < 5{,}000 \\ 0.9x & \text{if } x \ge 5{,}000 \end{cases}$ **97.** $F(x) = \begin{cases} 20x & \text{if } 0 < x \le 4{,}000 \\ 80{,}000 & \text{if } x \ge 4{,}000 \end{cases}$

(B) *F(x)* $\lim_{x\to 4{,}000} F(x) = 80{,}000;$ $\lim_{x\to 8{,}000} F(x) = 80{,}000$

(B) $\lim_{x\to 1{,}000} D(x)$ does not exist because   **99.** $\lim_{x\to 5} f(x)$ does not exit; $\lim_{x\to 10} f(x) = 0;$
$\lim_{x\to 1{,}000^-} D(x) = 970$ and $\lim_{x\to 1{,}000^+} D(x) = 950;$ $\lim_{x\to 5} g(x) = 0;$ $\lim_{x\to 10} g(x) = 1$
$\lim_{x\to 3{,}000} D(x)$ does not exist because

(C) All 3 limits are 0.99. $\lim_{x\to 3{,}000^-} D(x) = 2{,}850$ and $\lim_{x\to 3{,}000^+} D(x) = 2{,}790$

Exercises 2.2   **1.** $y = 4$ **3.** $x = -6$ **5.** $2x - y = -13$ **7.** $7x + 9y = 63$ **9.** -2 **11.** $-\infty$ **13.** Does not exist   **15.** 0   **17.** (A) $-\infty$
(B) ∞ (C) Does not exist   **19.** (A) ∞ (B) ∞ (C) ∞ **21.** (A) 3   (B) 3   (C) 3   **23.** (A) $-\infty$ (B) ∞ (C) Does not exist   **25.** (A) $-5x^3$
(B) $-\infty$ (C) ∞ **27.** (A) $-6x^4$ (B) $-\infty$ (C) $-\infty$ **29.** (A) x^2 (B) ∞ (C) ∞ **31.** (A) $2x^5$ (B) ∞ (C) $-\infty$
33. $\lim_{x\to -3^-} f(x) = -\infty;$ $\lim_{x\to -3^+} f(x) = \infty;$ $x = -3$ is a vertical asymptote
35. $\lim_{x\to -2^-} h(x) = \infty;$ $\lim_{x\to -2^+} h(x) = -\infty;$ $\lim_{x\to 2^-} h(x) = -\infty;$ $\lim_{x\to 2^+} h(x) = \infty;$ $x = -2$ and $x = 2$ are a vertical asymptote
37. No zeros of denominator; no vertical asymptotes   **39.** $\lim_{x\to 1^-} H(x) = -\infty;$ $\lim_{x\to 1^+} H(x) = \infty;$ $\lim_{x\to 3} H(x) = 2;$ $x = 1$ is a vertical asymptote
41. $\lim_{x\to 0} T(x) = -\infty;$ $\lim_{x\to 4} T(x) = \infty;$ $x = 0$ and $x = 4$ are vertical asymptotes   **43.** (A) $\dfrac{47}{41} \approx 1.146$ (B) $\dfrac{407}{491} \approx 0.829$ (C) $\dfrac{4}{5} = 0.8$
45. (A) $\dfrac{2{,}011}{138} \approx 14.572$ (B) $\dfrac{12{,}511}{348} \approx 35.951$ (C) ∞ **47.** (A) $-\dfrac{8{,}568}{46{,}653} \approx -0.184$ (B) $-\dfrac{143{,}136}{1{,}492{,}989} \approx -0.096$ (C) 0   **49.** (A) $-\dfrac{7{,}010}{996} \approx -7.038$
(B) $-\dfrac{56{,}010}{7{,}996} \approx -7.005$ (C) -7 **51.** Horizontal asymptote: $y = 2$; vertical asymptote: $x = -2$ **53.** Horizontal asymptote: $y = 1$; vertical asymptotes:
$x = -1$ and $x = 1$ **55.** No horizontal asymptotes; no vertical asymptotes   **57.** Horizontal asymptote: $y = 0$; no vertical asymptotes   **59.** No horizontal
asymptotes; vertical asymptote: $x = 3$ **61.** Horizontal asymptote: $y = 2$; vertical asymptotes: $x = -1$ and $x = 2$ **63.** Horizontal asymptote: $y = 2$; vertical
asymptote: $x = -1$ **65.** $\lim_{x\to\infty} f(x) = 0$ **67.** $\lim_{x\to\infty} f(x) = \infty$ **69.** $\lim_{x\to -\infty} f(x) = -\dfrac{1}{4}$ **71.** $\lim_{x\to -\infty} f(x) = -\infty$ **73.** $\lim_{x\to\infty} f(x) = \infty,$ $\lim_{x\to -\infty} f(x) = -\infty$
75. $\lim_{x\to\infty} f(x) = -5,$ $\lim_{x\to -\infty} f(x) = -5$ **77.** False   **79.** False   **81.** True   **83.** If $n \ge 1$ and $a_n > 0$, then the limit is ∞. If $n \ge 1$ and $a_n < 0$, then the limit is $-\infty$.

85. (A) $C(x) = 180x + 200$ (C) $\overline{C}(x)$ (D) \$180 per board   **87.** (A) $C_e(x) - 950 + 56x$; $\overline{C}_e(x) = \dfrac{950}{x} + 56$ (B) $C_e(x) - 900 + 66x$;

(B) $\overline{C}(x) = \dfrac{180x + 200}{x}$

$\overline{C}_e(x) = \dfrac{900}{x} + 66$ (C) At $x = 5$ years   (D) At $x = 5$ years

(E) $\lim\limits_{x\to\infty} \overline{C}_e(x) = 56$; $\lim\limits_{x\to\infty} \overline{C}_e(x) = 66$ **89.** The long-term drug concentration is 5 mg/ml.   **91.** (A) \$18 million   (B) \$38 million   (C) $\lim\limits_{x\to1^-} P(x) = \infty$

93. (A) $V_{max} = 4$, $K_M = 20$ (B) $v(s) = \dfrac{4s}{20+s}$

(C) $v = \dfrac{12}{7}$ when $s = 15$; $s = 60$ when $v = 3$

95. (A) $C_{max} = 18$, $M = 150$

(B) $C(T) = \dfrac{18T}{150 + T}$

(C) $C = 14.4$ when $T = 600$ K; $T = 300$ K when $C = 12$

Exercises 2.3   **1.** $[-3, 5]$ **3.** $(-10, 100)$ **5.** $(-\infty, -5) \cup (5, \infty)$ **7.** $(-\infty, -1] \cup (2, \infty)$
9. f is continuous at $x = 1$, since $\lim_{x\to1} f(x) = f(1)$.   **11.** f is discontinuous at $x = 1$, since $\lim_{x\to1} f(x) \ne f(1)$.   **13.** f is discontinuous at $x = 1$, since $\lim_{x\to1} f(x)$ does not exist.   **15.** 1.9   **17.** 0.9   **19.** (A) 2   (B) 1   (C) Does not exist   (D) 1   (E) No
21. (A) 1   (B) 1   (C) 1   (D) 3   (E) No
23. 0.9   **25.** 2.05   **27.** (A) 1   (B) 1   (C) 1   (D) 3
(E) No   **29.** (A) 2   (B) -1 (C) Does not exist
(D) 2   (E) No   **31.** All x **33.** All x, except $x = -2$
35. All x, except $x = -4$ and $x = 1$ **37.** All x

39. All x, except $x = \pm\dfrac{3}{2}$ **41.** $-\dfrac{8}{3}, 4$ **43.** $-1, 1$ **45.** $-9, -6, 0, 5$ **47.** $-3 < x < 4$; $(-3, 4)$ **49.** $x < 3$ or $x > 7$; $(-\infty, 3) \cup (7, \infty)$

51. $x < -2$ or $0 < x < 2$; $(-\infty, -2) \cup (0, 2)$ **53.** $-5 < x < 0$ or $x > 3$; $(-5, 0) \cup (3, \infty)$ **55.** (A) $(-4, -2) \cup (0, 4, \infty)$
(B) $(-\infty, -4) \cup (-2, 0) \cup (2, 4)$ **57.** (A) $(-\infty, -2.5308) \cup (-0.7198, \infty)$ (B) $(-2.5308, -0.7198)$
59. (A) $(-\infty, -2.1451) \cup (-1, -0.5240) \cup (1, 2.6691)$ (B) $(-2.1451, -1) \cup (-0.5240, 1) \cup (2.6691, \infty)$ **61.** $[6, \infty)$ **63.** $(-\infty, \infty)$
65. $(-\infty, -3] \cup [3, \infty)$ **67.** $(-\infty, \infty)$
69. Since $\lim_{x\to1^-} f(x) = 2$ and   **71.** This function is   **73.** Since $\lim_{x\to0} f(x) = 0$ and   **75.** (A) Yes   (B) No   (C) Yes
$\lim_{x\to1^+} f(x) = 4$, $\lim_{x\to1} f(x)$ does not   continuous for all x. $f(0) = 1$, $\lim_{x\to0} f(x) \ne f(0)$ and f (D) No   (E) Yes   **77.** True
exist and f is not continuous at $x = 1$.   is not continuous at $x = 0$.   **79.** False   **81.** True
83. x int.: $-5, 2$

85. x int.: $x = -6, -1, 4$ **87.** No, but this does not contradict Theorem 2, since f is discontinuous at $x = 1$.

89. (A) $P(x) = \begin{cases} 0.44 & \text{if } 0 < x \le 1 \\ 0.61 & \text{if } 1 < x \le 2 \\ 0.78 & \text{if } 2 < x \le 3 \\ 0.95 & \text{if } 3 < x \le 3.5 \end{cases}$ (B) $P(x)$ (C) Yes; no

93. (A) $S(x) = \begin{cases} 5 + 0.63x & \text{if } 0 \le x \le 50 \\ 14 + 0.45x & \text{if } 50 < x \end{cases}$
(B) $S(x)$ (C) Yes

95. (A) $E(s)$

(B) $\lim_{x\to10,000} E(s) = \$1,000$; $E(10,000) = \$1,000$
(C) $\lim_{x\to20,000} E(s)$ does not exist; $E(20,000) = \$2,000$
(D) Yes; no

97. (A) t_2, t_3, t_4, t_6, t_7
(B) $\lim_{t\to t_5} N(t) = 7$; $N(t_5) = 7$
(C) $\lim_{t\to t_3} N(t)$ does not exist; $N(t_3) = 4$

Exercises 2.4   **1.** $\dfrac{9}{4} = 2.25$ **3.** $-\dfrac{27}{5} = -5.4$ **5.** $\dfrac{1}{3}\sqrt{3}$ **7.** $\dfrac{15}{2} - \dfrac{5}{2}\sqrt{7}$ **9.** (A) -3; slope of the secant line through $(1, f(1))$ and $(2, f(2))$
(B) $-2 - h$; slope of the secant line through $(1, f(1))$ and $(1 + h, f(1 + h))$ (C) -2; slope of the tangent line at $(1, f(1))$ **11.** (A) 15   (B) $6 + 3h$ (C) 6
13. (A) 40 km/hr   (B) 40   (C) $y - 80 = 45(x - 2)$ or $y = 45x - 10$ **15.** $y - \dfrac{1}{2} = -\dfrac{1}{2}(x - 1)$ or $y = -\dfrac{x}{2} + 1$ **17.** $y - 16 = -32(x + 2)$ or
$y = -32x - 48$ **19.** $f'(x) = 0$; $f'(1) = 0$, $f'(2) = 0$, $f'(3) = 0$ **21.** $f'(x) = 3$; $f'(1) = 3$, $f'(2) = 3$, $f'(3) = 3$ **23.** $f'(x) = -6x$; $f'(1) = -6$,
$f'(2) = -12$, $f'(3) = -18$ **25.** $f'(x) = 2x + 6$; $f'(1) = 8$, $f'(2) = 10$, $f'(3) = 12$ **27.** $f'(x) = 4x - 7$; $f'(1) = -3$, $f'(2) = 1$, $f'(3) = 5$

29. $f'(x) = -2x + 4$; $f'(1) = 2$, $f'(2) = 0$, $f'(3) = -2$ **31.** $f'(x) = 6x^2$; $f'(1) = 6$, $f'(2) = 24$, $f'(3) = 54$ **33.** $f'(x) = -\dfrac{4}{x^2}$; $f'(1) = -4$,

$f'(2) = -1$, $f'(3) = -\dfrac{4}{9}$ **35.** $f'(x) = \dfrac{3}{2\sqrt{x}}$; $f'(1) = \dfrac{3}{2}$, $f'(2) = \dfrac{3}{2\sqrt{2}}$ or $\dfrac{3\sqrt{2}}{4}$, $f'(3) = \dfrac{3}{2\sqrt{3}}$ or $\dfrac{\sqrt{3}}{2}$ **37.** $f'(x) = \dfrac{5}{\sqrt{x+5}}$; $f'(1) = \dfrac{5}{\sqrt{6}}$ or $\dfrac{5\sqrt{6}}{6}$,

$f'(2) = \dfrac{5}{\sqrt{7}}$ or $\dfrac{5\sqrt{7}}{7}$, $f'(3) = \dfrac{5}{2\sqrt{2}}$ or $\dfrac{5\sqrt{2}}{4}$ **39.** $f'(x) = -\dfrac{1}{(x-4)^2}$; $f'(1) = -\dfrac{1}{9}$, $f'(2) = -\dfrac{1}{4}$, $f'(3) = -1$ **41.** $f'(x) = \dfrac{1}{(x+1)^2}$; $f'(1) = \dfrac{1}{4}$;

$f'(2) = \dfrac{1}{9}$; $f'(3) = \dfrac{1}{16}$ **43.** (A) 5   (B) $3 + h$ (C) 3   (D) $y = 3x - 1$ **45.** (A) 5 m/s   (B) $3 + h$ m/s   (C) 3 m/s   **47.** Yes   **49.** No

51. Yes   **55.** (A) $f'(x) = 2x - 4$ **57.** $v = f'(x) = 8x - 2$; 6 ft/s, 22 ft/s, 38 ft/s   **67.** f is nondifferentiable at $x = 1$ **69.** f is differentiable for all

53. Yes   (B) -4, 0, 4   **59.** (A) The graphs of g and h are vertical   real numbers

(C)   translations of the graph of f. All three functions

should have the same derivative.   (B) $2x$

61. True   **63.** False   **65.** False

71. No   **73.** No   **75.** $f'(0) = 0$ **77.** 6 s; 192 ft/s   **79.** (A) \$8.75   (B) $R'(x) = 60 - 0.05x$ (C) $R(1,000) = 35,000$; $R'(1,000) = 10$; At a production
level of 1,000 car seats, the revenue is \$35,000 and is increasing at the rate of \$10 per seat.   **81.** (A) $S'(t) = 1/\sqrt{t + 10}$ (B) $S(15) = 10$; $S'(15) = 0.2$;
After 15 months, the total sales are \$10 million and are increasing at the rate of \$0.2 million, or \$200,000, per month.   (C) The estimated total sales are \$10.2
million after 16 months and \$10.4 million after 17 months.   **83.** (A) $p'(t) = 276t + 1,072$ (B) $p(10) = 39,437$, $p'(10) = 3,832$; In 2020, 39,437 metric
tons of tungsten are consumed and this quantity is increasing at the rate of 3,832 metric tons per year.

85. (A)   (B) $R(20) = 1650.7$ billion kilowatts, $R'(20) = 19.9$ billion kilowatts per year. In 2020, 1650.7 billion kilowatts will be
sold and the amount sold is increasing at the rate of 19.9 billion kilowatts per year.   **87.** (A) $P'(t) = 12 - 2t$
(B) $P(3) = 107$; $P'(3) = 6$. After 3 hours, the ozone level is 107 ppb and is increasing at the rate of 6 ppb per hour.

Exercises 2.5   **1.** $x^{1/2}$ **3.** x^{-5} **5.** x^{12} **7.** $x^{-1/4}$ **9.** 0   **11.** $9x^8$ **13.** $3x^2$ **15.** $-4x^{-5}$ **17.** $\dfrac{8}{3}x^{5/3}$ **19.** $-\dfrac{10}{x^{11}}$ **21.** $10x$ **23.** $2.8x^6$ **25.** $\dfrac{x^2}{6}$

27. 12   **29.** 2   **31.** 9   **33.** 2   **35.** $4t - 3$ **37.** $-10x^{-3} - 9x^{-2}$ **39.** $1.5u^{-0.7} - 8.8u^{1.2}$ **41.** $0.5 - 3.3t^2$ **43.** $-\dfrac{8}{5}x^{-5}$ **45.** $3x + \dfrac{14}{5}x^{-3}$

47. $-\dfrac{20}{9}w^{-5} + \dfrac{5}{3}w^{-2/3}$ **49.** $2u^{-1/3} - \dfrac{5}{3}u^{-2/3}$ **51.** $-\dfrac{9}{5}t^{-8/5} + 3t^{-3/2}$ **53.** $-\dfrac{1}{3}x^{-4/3}$ **55.** $-0.6x^{-3/2} + 6.4x^{-3} + 1$ **57.** (A) $f'(x) = 6 - 2x$

(B) $f'(2) = 2$; $f'(4) = -2$ (C) $y = 2x + 4$; $y = -2x + 16$ (D) $x = 3$ **59.** (A) $f'(x) = 12x^3 - 12x$ (B) $f'(2) = 72$; $f'(4) = 720$
(C) $y = 72x - 127$; $y = 720x - 2,215$ (D) $x = -1, 0, 1$ **61.** (A) $v = f'(x) = 176 - 32x$ (B) $f'(0) = 176$ ft/s; $f'(3) = 80$ ft/s   (C) 5.5 s
63. (A) $v = f'(x) = 3x^2 - 18x + 15$ (B) $f'(0) = 15$ ft/s; $f'(3) = -12$ ft/s   (C) $x = 1$ s, $x = 5$ s

65. $f'(x) = 2x - 3 - 2x^{-1/2} = 2x - 3 - \dfrac{2}{x^{1/2}}$; $x = 2.1777$ **67.** $f'(x) = 4\sqrt[3]{x} - 3x - 3$; $x = -2.9018$ **69.** $f'(x) = 0.2x^3 + 0.3x^2 - 3x - 1.6$;

$x = -4.4607, -0.5159, 3.4765$ **71.** $f'(x) = 0.8x^3 - 9.36x^2 + 32.5x - 28.25$; $x = 1.3050$ **77.** $8x - 4$ **79.** $-20x^{-2}$ **81.** $-\dfrac{1}{4}x^{-2} + \dfrac{2}{3}x^{-3}$

83. False   **85.** True   **89.** (A) $S'(t) = 0.09t^2 + t + 2$ (B) $S(5) = 29.25$, $S'(5) = 9.25$. After 5 months, sales are \$29.25 million and are increasing at the
rate of \$9.25 million per month.   (C) $S(10) = 103$, $S'(10) = 21$. After 10 months, sales are \$103 million and are increasing at the rate of \$21 million
per month.   **91.** (A) $N'(x) = 3,780/x^2$ (B) $N'(10) = 37.8$. At the \$10,000 level of advertising, sales are increasing at the rate of 37.8 boats per \$1,000 spent
on advertising. $N'(20) = 9.45$. At the \$20,000 level of advertising, sales are increasing at the rate of 9.45 boats per \$1,000 spent on advertising.

93. (A) CubicReg
y=ax³+bx²+cx+d
a=-8.083333ᴇ-4
b=.0624285714
c=-1.081309524
d=40.57571429

(B) In 2020, 41.5% of male high-school graduates enroll in
college and the percentage is decreasing at the rate of
0.9% per year.

95. (A) -1.37 beats/min   (B) -0.58 beats/min
97. (A) 25 items/hr   (B) 8.33 items/hr

Exercises 2.6   **1.** 3; 3.01   **3.** 2.8; 2.799   **5.** 0; 0.01   **7.** 100; 102.01   **9.** $\Delta x = 3$; $\Delta y = 45$; $\Delta y/\Delta x = 15$ **11.** 12   **13.** 12   **15.** $dy = (24x - 3x^2)dx$

17. $dy = \left(2x - \dfrac{x^2}{3}\right)dx$ **19.** $dy = -\dfrac{295}{x^{3/2}}dx$ **21.** (A) $12 + 3\Delta x$ (B) 12   **23.** $dy = (8x + 4)dx$ **25.** $dy = (1 - 9x^{-2})dx$ **27.** $dy = 1.4$; $\Delta y = 1.44$

29. $dy = -3$; $\Delta y = -\dfrac{10}{3}$ **31.** 120 in.³   **33.** (A) $\Delta y = \Delta x + (\Delta x)^2$; $dy = \Delta x$ (B)

(C)

Δx	Δy	dy
.1	.11	.1
.2	.24	.2
.3	.39	.3

35. (A) $\Delta y = -\Delta x + (\Delta x)^2 + (\Delta x)^3; dy = -\Delta x$

(B)

(C)

Δx	Δy	dy
.05	-.0474	-.05
.1	-.089	-.1
.15	-.1241	-.15

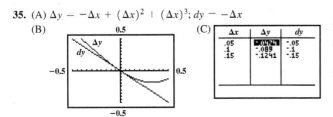

37. True   **39.** False   **41.** $dy = \left(\dfrac{2}{3}x^{1/3} - \dfrac{10}{3}x^{2/3}\right)dx$ **43.** $dy = 3.9; \Delta y = 3.83$

45. 40-unit increase; 20-unit increase   **47.** $-\$2.50; \$1.25$ **49.** -1.37 beats/min; -0.58 beats/min   **51.** 1.26 mm^2 **53.** 3 wpm   **55.** (A) 2,100 increase   (B) 4,800 increase   (C) 2,100 increase

Exercises 2.7   **1.** \$22,889.80   **3.** \$110.20   **5.** \$32,000.00   **7.** \$230.00   **9.** $C'(x) = 0.8$ **11.** $C'(x) = 4.6 - 0.02x$ **13.** $R'(x) = 4 - 0.02x$

15. $R'(x) = 12 - 0.08x$ **17.** $P'(x) = 3.2 - 0.02x$ **19.** $P'(x) = 7.4 - 0.06x$ **21.** $\overline{C}(x) = 1.1 + \dfrac{145}{x}$ **23.** $\overline{C}'(x) = -\dfrac{145}{x^2}$

25. $P(x) = 3.9x - 0.02x^2 - 145$ **27.** $\overline{P}(x) = 3.9 - 0.02x - \dfrac{145}{x}$ **29.** True   **31.** False   **33.** (A) \$29.50   (B) \$30   **35.** (A) \$420   (B) $\overline{C}'(500) = -0.24$. At a production level of 500 frames, average cost is decreasing at the rate of 24¢ per frame.   (C) Approximately \$419.76   **37.** (A) \$14.70   (B) \$15

39. (A) $P'(450) = 0.5$. At a production level of 450 DVDs, profit is increasing at the rate of 50¢ per DVD.   (B) $P'(750) = -2.5$. At a production level of 750 DVDs, profit is decreasing at the rate of \$2.50 per DVD.   **41.** (A) \$13.50   (B) $\overline{P}'(50) = \$0.27$. At a production level of 50 mowers, the average profit per mower is increasing at the rate of \$0.27 per mower.   (C) Approximately \$13.77   **43.** (A) $p = 100 - 0.025x$, domain: $0 \le x \le 4,000$

(B) $R(x) = 100x - 0.025x^2$, domain: $0 \le x \le 4,000$ (C) $R'(1,600) = 20$. At a production level of 1,600 pairs of running shoes, revenue is increasing at the rate of \$20 per pair.   (D) $R'(2,500) = -25$. At a production level of 2,500 pairs of running shoes, revenue is decreasing at the rate of \$25 per pair.

45. (A) $p = 200 - \dfrac{1}{30}x$, domain: $0 \le x \le 6,000$ (B) $C'(x) = 60$ (C) $R(x) = 200x - (x^2/30)$, domain: $0 \le x \le 6,000$

(D) $R'(x) = 200 - (x/15)$ (E) $R'(1,500) = 100$. At a production level of 1,500 saws, revenue is increasing at the rate of \$100 per saw. $R'(4,500) = -100$. At a production level of 4,500 saws, revenue is decreasing at the rate of \$100 per saw.

(F) Break-even points: $(600, 108,000)$ and $(3,600, 288,000)$ (G) $P(x) = -(x^2/30) + 140x - 72,000$

(H) $P'(x) = -(x/15) + 140$

(I) $P'(1,500) = 40$. At a production level of 1,500 saws, profit is increasing at the rate of \$40 per saw. $P'(3,000) = -60$. At a production level of 3,000 saws, profit is decreasing at the rate of \$60 per saw.

47. (A) $p = 20 - 0.02x$, domain: $0 \le x \le 1,000$

(B) $R(x) = 20x - 0.02x^2$, domain: $0 \le x \le 1,000$ (C) $C(x) = 4x + 1,400$ (D) Break-even points: $(100, 1,800)$ and $(700, 4,200)$

(E) $P(x) = 16x - 0.02x^2 - 1,400$

(F) $P'(250) = 6$. At a production level of 250 toasters, profit is increasing at the rate of \$6 per toaster.

$P'(475) = -3$. At a production level of 475 toasters, profit is decreasing at the rate of \$3 per toaster.

49. (A) $x = 500$
(B) $P(x) = 176x - 0.2x^2 - 21,900$
(C) $x = 440$
(D) Break-even points: $(150, 25,500)$ and $(730, 39,420)$; x intercepts for $P(x)$: $x = 150$ and $x = 730$

51. (A) $R(x) = 20x - x^{3/2}$
(B) Break-even points: $(44, 588)$, $(258, 1,016)$

53. (A)
```
QuadReg
y=ax²+bx+c
a=1.4101002E-5
b=-.2732556676
c=1320.924694
```

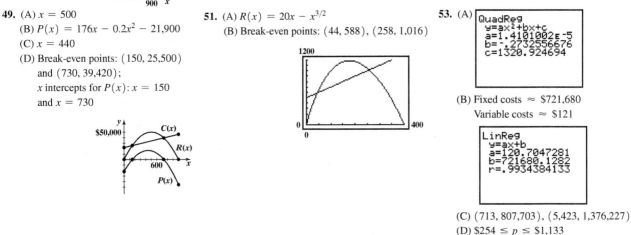

(B) Fixed costs $\approx$ \$721,680
Variable costs $\approx$ \$121

```
LinReg
y=ax+b
a=120.7047281
b=721680.1282
r=.9934384133
```

(C) $(713, 807,703)$, $(5,423, 1,376,227)$
(D) $\$254 \le p \le \$1,133$

Chapter 2 Review Exercises   **1.** (A) 16   (B) 8   (C) 8   (D) 4   (E) 4   (F) 4 *(2.2)*   **2.** $f'(x) = -3$ *(2.2)*   **3.** (A) 22   (B) 8   (C) 2   (D) -5 *(2.1)*
4. 1.5 *(2.1)*   **5.** 3.5 *(2.1)*   **6.** 3.75 *(2.1)*   **7.** 3.75 *(2.1)*   **8.** (A) 1   (B) 1   (C) 1   (D) 1 *(2.1)*   **9.** (A) 2   (B) 3   (C) Does not exist   (D) 3 *(2.1)*   **10.** (A) 4
(B) 4   (C) 4   (D) Does not exist *(2.1)*   **11.** (A) Does not exist   (B) 3   (C) No *(2.3)*   **12.** (A) 2   (B) Not defined   (C) No *(2.3)*   **13.** (A) 1   (B) 1
(C) Yes *(2.3)*   **14.** 5 *(2.2)*   **15.** 5 *(2.2)*   **16.** ∞ *(2.2)*   **17.** $-\infty$ *(2.2)*   **18.** 0 *(2.1)*   **19.** 0 *(2.1)*   **20.** 0 *(2.1)*   **21.** Vertical asymptote: $x = 2$ *(2.3)*
22. Horizontal asymptote: $y = 5$ *(2.2)*   **23.** $x = 2$ *(2.3)*   **24.** $f'(x) = 10x$ *(2.4)*   **25.** (A) -3 (B) 6   (C) -2 (D) 3   (E) -11 **26.** $x^2 - 10x$ *(2.5)*
27. $x^{-1/2} - 3 - \dfrac{1}{x^{1/2}} - 3$ *(2.5)*   **28.** 0 *(2.5)*   **29.** $-\dfrac{3}{2}x^{-2} + \dfrac{15}{4}x^2 = \dfrac{-3}{2x^2} + \dfrac{15x^2}{4}$ *(2.5)*   **30.** $-2x^{-5} + x^3 = \dfrac{-2}{x^5} + x^3$ *(2.5)*
31. $f'(x) = 12x^3 + 9x^2 - 2$ *(2.5)*   **32.** $\Delta x = 2$, $\Delta y = 10$, $\Delta y/\Delta x = 5$ *(2.6)*   **33.** 5 *(2.6)*   **34.** 6 *(2.6)*   **35.** $\Delta y = 0.64; dy = 0.6$ *(2.6)*   **36.** (A) 4

(B) 6   (C) Does not exist   (D) 6   (E) No *(2.3)*   **37.** (A) 3   (B) 3   (C) 3   (D) 3   (E) Yes *(2.3)*   **38.** (A) $(8, \infty)$ (B) $[0, 8]$ *(2.3)*   **39.** $(-3, 4)$ *(2.3)*
40. $(-3, 0) \cup (5, \infty)$ *(2.3)*   **41.** $(-2.3429, -0.4707) \cup (1.8136, \infty)$ *(2.3)*   **42.** (A) 3   (B) $2 + 0.5h$ (C) 2 *(2.4)*   **43.** $-x^{-4} + 10x^{-3}$ *(2.4)*
44. $\dfrac{3}{4}x^{-1/2} - \dfrac{5}{6}x^{-3/2} = \dfrac{3}{4\sqrt{x}} - \dfrac{5}{6\sqrt{x^3}}$ *(2.5)*   **45.** $0.6x^{-2/3} - 0.3x^{-4/3} = \dfrac{0.6}{x^{2/3}} - \dfrac{0.3}{x^{4/3}}$ *(2.4)*   **46.** $-\dfrac{3}{5}(-3)x^{-4} = \dfrac{9}{5x^4}$ *(2.5)*   **47.** (A) $m = f'(1) = 2$
(B) $y = 2x + 3$ *(2.4, 2.5)*   **48.** $x = 5$ *(2.4)*   **49.** $x = -5, x = 3$ *(2.5)*   **50.** $x = -1.3401, 0.5771, 2.2630$ *(2.4)*   **51.** ± 2.4824 *(2.5)*
52. (A) $v = f'(x) = 16x - 4$ (B) 44 ft/sec *(2.5)*   **53.** (A) $v = f'(x) = -10x + 16$ (B) $x = 1.6$ sec *(2.5)*
54. (A) The graph of g is the graph of f (B) The graph of g' is the graph   **55.** $(-\infty, \infty)$ *(2.3)*

shifted 4 units to the right, and   of f' shifted 4 units to the   **56.** $(-\infty, 2) \cup (2, \infty)$ *(2.3)*
the graph of h is the graph of f right, and the graph of h' **57.** $(-\infty, -4) \cup (-4, 1) \cup (1, \infty)$ *(2.3)*
shifted 3 units to the left: is the graph of f' shifted 3   **58.** $(-\infty, \infty)$ *(2.3)*   **59.** $[-2, 2]$ *(2.3)*
units to the left:

60. (A) -1 (B) Does not exist   (C) $-\dfrac{2}{3}$ *(2.1)*

61. (A) $\dfrac{1}{2}$ (B) 0   (C) Does not exist *(2.1)*   **62.** (A) -1 (B) 1   (C) Does not exist *(2.1)*   **63.** (A) $-\dfrac{1}{6}$ (B) Does not exist   (C) $-\dfrac{1}{3}$ *(2.1)*   **64.** (A) 0   (B) -1
(C) Does not exist *(2.1)*   **65.** (A) $\dfrac{2}{3}$ (B) $\dfrac{2}{3}$ (C) Does not exist *(2.3)*   **66.** (A) ∞ (B) $-\infty$ (C) ∞ *(2.3)*   **67.** (A) 0   (B) 0   (C) Does not exist *(2.2)*
68. 4 *(2.1)*   **69.** $\dfrac{-1}{(x + 2)^2}$ *(2.1)*   **70.** $2x - 1$ *(2.4)*   **71.** $1/(2\sqrt{x})$ *(2.4)*   **72.** Yes *(2.4)*   **73.** No *(2.4)*   **74.** No *(2.4)*   **75.** No *(2.4)*   **76.** Yes *(2.4)*
77. Yes *(2.4)*   **78.** Horizontal asymptote: $y = 5$; vertical asymptote: $x = 7$ *(2.2)*   **79.** Horizontal asymptote: $y = 0$; vertical asymptote: $x = 4$ *(2.2)*
80. No horizontal asymptote; vertical asymptote: $x = 3$ *(2.2)*   **81.** Horizontal asymptote: $y = 1$; vertical asymptotes: $x = -2, x = 1$ *(2.2)*   **82.** Horizontal
asymptote: $y = 1$; vertical asymptotes: $x = -1, x = 1$ *(2.2)*   **83.** The domain of $f'(x)$ is all real numbers except $x = 0$. At $x = 0$, the graph of $y = f(x)$ is
smooth, but it has a vertical tangent. *(2.4)*
84. (A) $\lim_{x \to 1^-} f(x) = 1$;   (B) $\lim_{x \to 1^-} f(x) = -1$;   (C) $m = 1$ (D) The graphs in (A) and (B) have   **85.** (A) 1   (B) -1 (C) Does not exist
$\lim_{x \to 1^+} f(x) = -1$ $\lim_{x \to 1^+} f(x) = 1$ discontinuities at $x = 1$; the graph in   (D) No *(2.4)*
(C) does not. *(2.2)*

86. (A) $S(x) = \begin{cases} 7.47 + 0.4x & \text{if } 0 \le x \le 90 \\ 24.786 + 0.2076x & \text{if } 90 < x \end{cases}$ **87.** (A) \$179.90   (B) \$180 *(2.7)*   **88.** (A) $C(100) = 9,500; C'(100) = 50$. At a production level of
100 bicycles, the total cost is \$9,500, and cost is increasing at the rate of \$50 per bicycle.
(B) $\overline{C}(100) = 95; \overline{C}'(100) = -0.45$. At a production level of 100 bicycles, the average cost is \$95,
and average cost is decreasing at a rate of \$0.45 per bicycle. *(2.7)*   **89.** The approximate cost of
producing the 201st printer is greater than that of the 601st printer. Since these marginal costs are
decreasing, the manufacturing process is becoming more efficient. *(2.7)*

(B)   (C) Yes *(2.2)*

90. (A) $C'(x) = 2; \overline{C}(x) = 2 + \dfrac{9,000}{x}; \overline{C}'(x) = \dfrac{-9,000}{x^2}$ (B) $R(x) = xp = 25x - 0.01x^2; R'(x) = 25 - 0.02x; \overline{R}(x) = 25 - 0.01x; \overline{R}'(x) = -0.01$

(C) $P(x) = R(x) - C(x) = 23x - 0.01x^2 - 9,000; P'(x) = 23 - 0.02x; \overline{P}(x) = 23 - 0.01x - \dfrac{9,000}{x}; \overline{P}'(x) = -0.01 + \dfrac{9,000}{x^2}$

(D) (500, 10,000) and (1,800, 12,600)   (E) $P'(1,000) = 3$. Profit is increasing at   (F)   **91.** (A) 8   (B) 20 *(2.5)*
the rate of \$3 per umbrella.   **92.** $N(9) = 27; N'(t) = 3.5$; After
$P'(1,150) = 0$. Profit is flat.   9 months, 27,000 pools have been sold
$P'(1,400) = -5$. Profit is decreasing   and the total sales are increasing at the
at the rate of \$5 per umbrella.   rate of 3,500 pools per month. *(2.5)*

93. (A)
```
CubicReg
y=ax³+bx²+cx+d
a=5.5277778E-4
b=-.0444761905
c=1.084484127
d=12.5452381
```
94. (A)
```
LinReg
y=ax+b
a=-.0384180791
b=13.59887006
r=-.9897782666
```
(B) Fixed costs: \$484.21; variable   (C) (51, 591.15), (248, 1,007.62)
costs per kringle: \$2.11   (D) \$4.07 $< p <$ \$11.64 *(2.7)*
```
LinReg
y=ax+b
a=2.107344633
b=484.2090395
r=.9939318704
```

(B) $N(60) = 36.9; N'(60) = 1.7$.
In 2020, natural-gas consumption is 36.9 trillion cubic feet and
is increasing at the rate of 1.7
trillion cubic feet per year *(2.4)*
95. $C'(10) = -1; C'(100) = -0.001$ *(2.5)*   **98.** (A)   (B) $C(T) = \dfrac{12T}{150 + T}$
96. $F(4) = 98.16; F'(4) = -0.32$; After 4 hours the
patient's temperature is 98.16°F and is decreasing at the rate   (C) $C = 9.6$ at $T = 600$ K,
of 0.32°F per hour. *(2.5)* $T = 750$ K when $C = 10$ *(2.3)*
97. (A) 10 items/h   (B) 5 items/h *(2.5)*

Chapter 3

Exercises 3.1   **1.** $A = 1,465.68$ **3.** $P = 9,117.21$ **5.** $t = 5.61$ **7.** $r = 0.04$ **9.** $\$1,221.40; \$1,648.72; \$2,225.54$

11.   **13.** 11.55   **19.**   **21.** $\lim_{n \to \infty}(1 + n)^{1/n} = 1$

15. 10.99   **23.**

17. 0.14

n	$[1 + (1/n)]^n$
10	2.593 74
100	2.704 81
1,000	2.716 92
10,000	2.718 15
100,000	2.718 27
1,000,000	2.718 28
10,000,000	2.718 28
↓	↓
∞	$e = 2.718\,281\,828\,459\ldots$

25. (A) $\$12,398.62$ (B) 27.34 yr   **31.** (A)   (B) $\lim_{t \to \infty} 10,000e^{-0.08t} = 0$ **33.** 17.33 yr   **35.** 8.66%   **37.** 7.3 yr
27. $\$11,890.41$ **29.** 8.11%

39. (A) $A = Pe^{rt}$ (B)   Although r could be any positive number, the restrictions on   **41.** $t = -(\ln 0.5)/0.000\,433\,2 \approx 1,600$ yr
$2P = Pe^{rt}$ $t = \frac{\ln 2}{r}$ r are reasonable in the sense that most investments would be   **43.** $r = (\ln 0.5)/30 \approx -0.0231$
$2 = e^{rt}$ expected to earn a return of between 2% and 30%.   **45.** 53.3 yr
$rt = \ln 2$ (C) The doubling times (in years) are 13.86, 6.93, 4.62,   **47.** 1.39%
$t = \frac{\ln 2}{r}$ 3.47, 2.77, and 2.31, respectively.

Exercises 3.2   **1.** $y = 7$ **3.** $x = 81$ **5.** $b = 8$ **7.** $y = \frac{1}{2}$ **9.** $5e^x + 3$ **11.** $-\frac{2}{x} + 2x$ **13.** $3x^2 - 6e^x$ **15.** $e^x + 1 - \frac{1}{x}$ **17.** $\frac{3}{x}$ **19.** $5 - \frac{5}{x}$

21. $\frac{2}{x} + 4e^x$ **23.** $f'(x) = e^x + exe^{-1}$ **25.** $f'(x) = (e + 1)x^e$ **27.** $f'(x) = \frac{1}{x}; y = x + 2$ **29.** $f'(x) = 3e^x; y = 3x + 3$ **31.** $f'(x) = \frac{3}{x}; y = \frac{3x}{e}$

33. $f'(x) = e^x; y = ex + 2$ **35.** Yes; yes   **37.** No; no   **39.** $f(x) = 10x + \ln 10 + \ln x;\ f'(x) = 10 + \frac{1}{x}$ **41.** $f(x) = \ln 4 - 3 \ln x; f'(x) = -\frac{3}{x}$

43. $\frac{1}{x \ln 2}$ **45.** $3^x \ln 3$ **47.** $2 - \frac{1}{x \ln 10}$ **49.** $1 + 10^x \ln 10$ **51.** $\frac{3}{x} + \frac{2}{x \ln 3}$ **53.** $2^x \ln 2$ **55.** $(-0.82, 0.44), (1.43, 4.18), (8.61, 5503.66)$

57. $(0.49, 0.49)$ **59.** $(3.65, 1.30), (332,105.11, 12.71)$ **63.** $\$28,447/yr; \$18,664/yr; \$11,021/yr$ **65.** $A'(t) = 5,000(\ln 4)4^t; A'(1) = 27,726$ bacteria/hr (rate of change at the end of the first hour); $A'(5) = 7,097,827$ bacteria/hr (rate of change at the end of the fifth hour)   **67.** At the 40-lb weight level, blood pressure would increase at the rate of 0.44 mm of mercury per pound of weight gain. At the 90-lb weight level, blood pressure would increase at the rate of 0.19 mm of mercury per pound of weight gain.   **69.** $dR/dS = k/S$ **71.** (A) $\$808.41$ per year   (B) $\$937.50$ per year

Exercises 3.3   **1.** One answer is: $F(x) = x^3, S(x) = 5 - 4 \ln x$ **3.** One answer is: $F(x) = x^3 + 3, S(x) = e^x + 2$ **5.** One answer is:
$T(x) = 9x^2, B(x) = e^{5x}$ **7.** One answer is: $T(x) = 3x^2 + e^x, B(x) = x^4$ **9.** $2x^3(2x) + (x^2 - 2)(6x^2) = 10x^4 - 12x^2$

11. $(x - 3)(2) + (2x - 1)(1) = 4x - 7$ **13.** $\frac{(x - 3)(1) - x(1)}{(x - 3)^2} = \frac{-3}{(x - 3)^2}$ **15.** $\frac{(x - 2)(2) - (2x + 3)(1)}{(x - 2)^2} = \frac{-7}{(x - 2)^2}$

17. $3xe^x + 3e^x = 3(x + 1)e^x$ **19.** $x^3\left(\frac{1}{x}\right) + 3x^2 \ln x = x^2(1 + 3 \ln x)$ **21.** $(x^2 + 1)(2) + (2x - 3)(2x) = 6x^2 - 6x + 2$

23. $(0.4x + 2)(0.5) + (0.5x - 5)(0.4) = 0.4x - 1$ **25.** $\frac{(2x - 3)(2x) - (x^2 + 1)(2)}{(2x - 3)^2} = \frac{2x^2 - 6x - 2}{(2x - 3)^2}$ **27.** $(x^2 + 2)2x + (x^2 - 3)2x = 4x^3 - 2x$

29. $\frac{(x^2 - 3)2x - (x^2 + 2)2x}{(x^2 - 3)^2} = \frac{-10x}{(x^2 - 3)^2}$ **31.** $\frac{(x^2 + 1)e^x - e^x(2x)}{(x^2 + 1)^2} = \frac{(x - 1)^2 e^x}{(x^2 + 1)^2}$ **33.** $\frac{(1 + x)\left(\frac{1}{x}\right) - \ln x}{(1 + x)^2} = \frac{1 + x - x \ln x}{x(1 + x)^2}$ **35.** $xf'(x) + f(x)$

37. $x^3 f'(x) + 3x^2 f(x)$ **39.** $\frac{x^2 f'(x) - 2xf(x)}{x^4}$ **41.** $\frac{f(x) - xf'(x)}{[f(x)]^2}$ **43.** $e^x f'(x) + f(x)e^x = e^x[f'(x) + f(x)]$

45. $\frac{f(x)\left(\frac{1}{x}\right) - (\ln x)f'(x)}{f(x)^2} = \frac{f(x) - (x \ln x)f'(x)}{xf(x)^2}$ **47.** $(2x + 1)(2x - 3) + (x^2 - 3x)(2) = 6x^2 - 10x - 3$

49. $(2.5t - t^2)(4) + (4t + 1.4)(2.5 - 2t) = -12t^2 + 17.2t + 3.5$ **51.** $\frac{(x^2 + 2x)(5) - (5x - 3)(2x + 2)}{(x^2 + 2x)^2} = \frac{-5x^2 + 6x + 6}{(x^2 + 2x)^2}$

53. $\frac{(w^2 - 1)(2w - 3) - (w^2 - 3w + 1)(2w)}{(w^2 - 1)^2} = \frac{3w^2 - 4w + 3}{(w^2 - 1)^2}$ **55.** $(1 + x - x^2)e^x + e^x(1 - 2x) = (2 - x - x^2)e^x$

57. (A) $f'(x) = \dfrac{x \cdot 0 - 1 \cdot 1}{x^2} = -\dfrac{1}{x^2}$ (B) Note that $f(x) = x^{-1}$ and use the power rule: $f'(x) = -x^{-2} = -\dfrac{1}{x^2}$ **59.** (A) $f'(x) = \dfrac{x^4 \cdot 0 - (-3) \cdot 4x^3}{x^8} = \dfrac{12}{x^5}$

(B) Note that $f(x) = -3x^{-4}$ and use the power rule: $f'(x) = 12x^{-5} = \dfrac{12}{x^5}$ **61.** $f'(x) = (1 + 3x)(-2) + (5 - 2x)(3); y = -11x + 29$

63. $f'(x) = \dfrac{(3x - 4)(1) - (x - 8)(3)}{(3x - 4)^2}; y = 5x - 13$ **65.** $f'(x) = \dfrac{2^x - x(2^x \ln 2)}{2^{2x}}; y = \left(\dfrac{1 - 2 \ln 2}{4}\right)x + \ln 2$

67. $f'(x) = (2x - 15)(2x) + (x^2 + 18)(2) = 6(x - 2)(x - 3); x = 2, x = 3$ **69.** $f'(x) = \dfrac{(x^2 + 1)(1) - x(2x)}{(x^2 + 1)^2} = \dfrac{1 - x^2}{(x^2 + 1)^2}; x = -1, x = 1$

71. $7x^6 - 3x^2$ **73.** $-27x^{-4} = -\dfrac{27}{x^4}$ **75.** $(w + 1)2^w \ln 2 + 2^w = [(w + 1) \ln 2 + 1]2^w$ **77.** $9x^{1/3}(3x^2) + (x^3 + 5)(3x^{-2/3}) = \dfrac{30x^3 + 15}{x^{2/3}}$

79. $\dfrac{(1 + x^2)\dfrac{1}{x \ln 2} - 2x \log_2 x}{(1 + x^2)^2} = \dfrac{1 + x^2 - 2x^2 \ln x}{x(1 + x^2)^2 \ln 2}$ **81.** $\dfrac{(x^2 - 3)(2x^{-2/3}) - 6x^{1/3}(2x)}{(x^2 - 3)^2} = \dfrac{-10x^2 - 6}{(x^2 - 3)^2 x^{2/3}}$

83. $g'(t) = \dfrac{(3t^2 - 1)(0.2) - (0.2t)(6t)}{(3t^2 - 1)^2} = \dfrac{-0.6t^2 - 0.2}{(3t^2 - 1)^2}$ **85.** $(20x)\dfrac{1}{x \ln 10} + 20 \log x = \dfrac{20(1 + \ln x)}{\ln 10}$

87. $x^{-2/3}(3x^2 - 4x) + (x^3 - 2x^2)(-\tfrac{2}{3}x^{-5/3}) = -\tfrac{8}{3}x^{1/3} + \tfrac{7}{3}x^{4/3}$

89. $\dfrac{(x^2 + 1)[(2x^2 - 1)(2x) + (x^2 + 3)(4x)] - (2x^2 - 1)(x^2 + 3)(2x)}{(x^2 + 1)^2} = \dfrac{4x^5 + 8x^3 + 16x}{(x^2 + 1)^2}$ **91.** $\dfrac{e^t(1 + \ln t) - (t \ln t)e^t}{e^{2t}} = \dfrac{1 + \ln t - t \ln t}{e^t}$

93. (A) $S'(t) = \dfrac{(t^2 + 50)(180t) - 90t^2(2t)}{(t^2 + 50)^2} = \dfrac{9{,}000t}{(t^2 + 50)^2}$ (B) $S(10) = 60; S'(10) = 4.$ After 10 months, the total sales are 60,000 DVDs and sales are

increasing at the rate of 4,000 DVDs per month. (C) Approximately 64,000 DVDs

95. (A) $\dfrac{dx}{dp} = \dfrac{(0.1p + 1)(0) - 4{,}000(0.1)}{(0.1p + 1)^2} = \dfrac{-400}{(0.1p + 1)^2}$ (B) $x = 800; dx/dp = -16.$ At a price level of \$40, the demand is 800 DVD players per week

and demand is decreasing at the rate of 16 players per dollar. (C) Approximately 784 DVD players

97. (A) $C'(t) = \dfrac{(t^2 + 1)(0.14) - 0.14t(2t)}{(t^2 + 1)^2} = \dfrac{0.14 - 0.14t^2}{(t^2 + 1)^2}$ (B) $C'(0.5) = 0.0672.$ After 0.5 hr, concentration is increasing at the rate of

0.0672 mg/cm^3 per hour. $C'(3) = -0.0112.$ After 3 hr, concentration is decreasing at the rate of 0.0112 mg/cm^3 per hour.

Exercises 3.4 **1.** $3x^3 + 5$ **3.** $2x^2e^x + \ln x^2 e^x$ **5.** $E(u) = \ln u, I(x) = x^3 - 6x + 10$ is one answer. **7.** $E(u) = \sqrt{u}, I(x) = x^2 + 4$ is one answer.
9. 3 **11.** $(-4x)$ **13.** $2x$ **15.** $4x^3$ **17.** $-8(5 - 2x)^3$ **19.** $5(4 + 0.2x)^4(0.2) = (4 + 0.2x)^4$ **21.** $30x(3x^2 + 5)^4$ **23.** $5e^x$ **25.** $5e^{5x}$ **27.** $-18e^{-6x}$

29. $(2x - 5)^{-1/2} = \dfrac{1}{(2x - 5)^{1/2}}$ **31.** $-8x^3(x^4 + 1)^{-3} = \dfrac{-8x^3}{(x^4 + 1)^3}$ **33.** $-\dfrac{2}{x}$ **35.** $\dfrac{6x}{1 + x^2}$ **37.** $\dfrac{3(1 + \ln x)^2}{x}$ **39.** $f'(x) = 6(2x - 1)^2; y = 6x - 5; x = \tfrac{1}{2}$

41. $f'(x) = 2(4x - 3)^{-1/2} = \dfrac{2}{(4x - 3)^{1/2}}; y = \dfrac{2}{3}x + 1;$ none **43.** $f'(x) = 10(x - 2)e^{x^2 - 4x + 1}; y = -20ex + 5e; x = 2$

45. $12(x^2 - 2)^3(2x) = 24x(x^2 - 2)^3$ **47.** $-6(t^2 + 3t)^{-4}(2t + 3) = \dfrac{-6(2t + 3)}{(t^2 + 3t)^4}$ **49.** $\dfrac{1}{2}(w^2 + 8)^{-1/2}(2w) = \dfrac{w}{\sqrt{w^2 + 8}}$

51. $12xe^{3x} + 4e^{3x} = 4(3x + 1)e^{3x}$ **53.** $\dfrac{x^3\left(\dfrac{1}{1 + x}\right) - 3x^2 \ln (1 + x)}{x^6} = \dfrac{x - 3(1 + x) \ln (1 + x)}{x^4(1 + x)}$ **55.** $6te^{3(t^2 + 1)}$ **57.** $\dfrac{3x}{x^2 + 3}$

59. $-5(w^3 + 4)^{-6}(3w^2) = \dfrac{-15w^2}{(w^3 + 4)^6}$ **61.** $f'(x) = (4 - x)^3 - 3x(4 - x)^2 = 4(4 - x)^2(1 - x); y = -16x + 48$

63. $f'(x) = \dfrac{(2x - 5)^3 - 6x(2x - 5)^2}{(2x - 5)^6} = \dfrac{-4x - 5}{(2x - 5)^4}; y = -17x + 54$ **65.** $f'(x) = \dfrac{1}{2x\sqrt{\ln x}}; y = \dfrac{x}{2e} + \dfrac{1}{2}$

67. $f'(x) = 2x(x - 5)^3 + 3x^2(x - 5)^2 = 5x(x - 5)^2(x - 2); x = 0, 2, 5$ **69.** $f'(x) = \dfrac{(2x + 5)^2 - 4x(2x + 5)}{(2x + 5)^4} = \dfrac{5 - 2x}{(2x + 5)^3}; x = \tfrac{5}{2}$

71. $f'(x) = (x^2 - 8x + 20)^{-1/2}(x - 4) = \dfrac{x - 4}{(x^2 - 8x + 20)^{1/2}}; x = 4$ **73.** No; yes **75.** Domain of f: $(0, \infty)$; domain of g: $(-\infty, \infty)$; domain of m: $(-2, 2)$

77. Domain of f: all real numbers except ± 1; domain of g: $(0, \infty)$; domain of m: all positive real numbers except e and $\tfrac{1}{e}$

79. $18x^2(x^2 + 1)^2 + 3(x^2 + 1)^3 = 3(x^2 + 1)^2(7x^2 + 1)$ **81.** $\dfrac{24x^5(x^3 - 7)^3 - (x^3 - 7)^4 6x^2}{4x^6} = \dfrac{3(x^3 - 7)^3(3x^3 + 7)}{2x^4}$ **83.** $\dfrac{1}{\ln 2}\left(\dfrac{6x}{3x^2 - 1}\right)$

85. $(2x + 1)(10^{x^2 + x})(\ln 10)$ **87.** $\dfrac{12x^2 + 5}{(4x^3 + 5x + 7) \ln 3}$ **89.** $2^{x^3 - x^2 + 4x + 1}(3x^2 - 2x + 4) \ln 2$ **91.** (A) $C'(x) = (2x + 16)^{-1/2} = \dfrac{1}{(2x + 16)^{1/2}}$

(B) $C'(24) = \tfrac{1}{8},$ or \$12.50. At a production level of 24 cell phones, total cost is increasing at the rate of \$12.50 per cell phone and the cost of producing the 25th

cell phone is approximately \$12.50. $C'(42) = \tfrac{1}{10},$ or \$10.00. At a production level of 42 cell phones, total cost is increasing at the rate of \$10.00 per cell phone

and the cost of producing the 43rd cell phone is approximately \$10.00. **93.** (A) $\dfrac{dx}{dp} = 40(p + 25)^{-1/2} = \dfrac{40}{(p + 25)^{1/2}}$ (B) $x = 400$ and $dx/dp = 4.$

At a price of \$75, the supply is 400 bicycle helmets per week and supply is increasing at
the rate of 4 bicycle helmets per dollar.

95. (A) After 1 hr, the concentration is decreasing at the rate of 1.60 mg/mL per hour; after 4 hr, the concentration is decreasing at the rate of 0.08 mg/mL per hour.

(B) $C(t)$

97. 2.27 mm of mercury/yr; 0.81 mm of mercury/yr; 0.41 mm of mercury/yr

---

Exercises 3.5   **1.** $y = -\dfrac{3}{2}x + 10$ **3.** $y = \pm\dfrac{4}{3}\sqrt{9 - x^2}$ **5.** $y = \dfrac{-x \pm \sqrt{4 - 3x^2}}{2}$ **7.** Impossible **9.** $y' = -\dfrac{3}{5}$ **11.** $y' = \dfrac{3x}{2}$ **13.** $y' = 10x$; 10

15. $y' = \dfrac{2x}{3y^2}$; $\dfrac{4}{3}$ **17.** $y' = -\dfrac{3}{2y + 2}$; $-\dfrac{3}{4}$ **19.** $y' = -\dfrac{y}{x}$; $-\dfrac{3}{2}$ **21.** $y' = -\dfrac{2y}{2x + 1}$; 4 **23.** $y' = \dfrac{6 - 2y}{x}$; -1 **25.** $y' = \dfrac{2x}{e^y - 2y}$; 2 **27.** $y' = \dfrac{3x^2 y}{y + 1}$; $\dfrac{3}{2}$

29. $y' = \dfrac{6x^2 y - y \ln y}{x + 2y}$; 2 **31.** $x' = \dfrac{2tx - 3t^2}{2x - t^2}$; 8 **33.** $y'|_{(1.6,1.8)} = -\dfrac{3}{4}$; $y'|_{(1.6,0.2)} = \dfrac{3}{4}$ **35.** $y = -x + 5$ **37.** $y = \dfrac{2}{5}x - \dfrac{12}{5}$; $y = \dfrac{3}{5}x + \dfrac{12}{5}$

39. $y' = -\dfrac{1}{x}$ **41.** $y' = \dfrac{1}{3(1 + y)^2 + 1}$; $\dfrac{1}{13}$ **43.** $y' = \dfrac{3(x - 2y)^2}{6(x - 2y)^2 + 4y}$; $\dfrac{3}{10}$ **45.** $y' = \dfrac{3x^2(7 + y^2)^{1/2}}{y}$; 16 **47.** $y' = \dfrac{y}{2xy^2 - x}$; 1

49. $y = 0.63x + 1.04$ **51.** $p' = \dfrac{1}{2p - 2}$ **53.** $p' = -\dfrac{x}{p} = -\dfrac{\sqrt{10,000 - p^2}}{p}$ **55.** $\dfrac{dL}{dV} = \dfrac{-(L + m)}{V + n}$ **57.** $\dfrac{dT}{dv} = \dfrac{2}{k}\sqrt{T}$ **59.** $\dfrac{dv}{dT} = \dfrac{k}{2\sqrt{T}}$

Exercises 3.6   **1.** 19.5 ft **3.** 46 m **5.** 34.5 ft **7.** 32 ft **9.** 30 **11.** $-\dfrac{16}{3}$ **13.** $-\dfrac{16}{7}$ **15.** Decreasing at 9 units/sec **17.** Approx. -3.03 ft/sec
19. $dA/dt \approx 126$ ft²/sec **21.** 3,770 cm³/min **23.** 6 lb/in.²/hr **25.** $\dfrac{9}{4}$ ft/sec **27.** $\dfrac{20}{3}$ ft/sec **29.** 0.0214 ft/sec; 0.0135 ft/sec; yes, at $t = 0.000\ 19$ sec
31. 3.835 units/sec **33.** (A) $dC/dt = \$15,000/\text{wk}$ (B) $dR/dt = -\$50,000/\text{wk}$ (C) $dP/dt = -\$65,000/\text{wk}$ **35.** $ds/dt = \$2,207/\text{wk}$
37. (A) $dx/dt = -12.73$ units/month (B) $dp/dt = \$1.53/\text{month}$ **39.** Approximately 100 ft³/min

---

Exercises 3.7   **1.** $x = f(p) = 105 - 2.5p, 0 \le p \le 42$ **3.** $x = f(p) = \sqrt{100 - 2p}, 0 \le p \le 50$

5. $x = f(p) = 20(\ln 25 - \ln p), 25/e \approx 9.2 \le p \le 25$ **7.** $x = f(p) = e^{8 - 0.1p}, 80 - 10 \ln 30 \approx 46.0 \le p \le 80$ **9.** $\dfrac{35 - 0.8x}{35x - 0.4x^2}$ **11.** $-\dfrac{4e^{-x}}{7 + 4e^{-x}}$

13. $\dfrac{5}{x(12 + 5 \ln x)}$ **15.** 0 **17.** -0.017 **19.** -0.034 **21.** 1.013 **23.** 0.405 **25.** 11.8% **27.** 5.4% **29.** -14.7% **31.** -431.6%

33. $E(p) = \dfrac{450p}{25,000 - 450p}$ **35.** $E(p) = \dfrac{8p^2}{4,800 - 4p^2}$ **37.** $E(p) = \dfrac{0.6pe^p}{98 - 0.6e^p}$ **39.** 0.07 **41.** 0.15 **43.** $\dfrac{x + 1}{x}$ **45.** $\dfrac{1}{x \ln x}$ **47.** (A) Inelastic

(B) Unit elasticity (C) Elastic **49.** (A) Inelastic (B) Unit elasticity (C) Elastic **51.** (A) $x = 6,000 - 200p$ $0 \le p \le 30$ (B) $E(p) = \dfrac{p}{30 - p}$

(C) $E(10) = 0.5$; 5% decrease (D) $E(25) = 5$; 50% decrease (E) $E(15) = 1$; 10% decrease **53.** (A) $x = 3,000 - 50p$ $0 \le p \le 60$

(B) $R(p) = 3,000p - 50p^2$ (C) $E(p) = \dfrac{p}{60 - p}$ (D) Elastic on $(30, 60)$; inelastic on $(0, 30)$ (E) Increasing on $(0, 30)$; decreasing on $(30, 60)$

(F) Decrease (G) Increase
55. Elastic on $(3.5, 7)$; inelastic on $(0, 3.5)$
57. Elastic on $(25/\sqrt{3}, 25)$; inelastic on $(0, 25/\sqrt{3})$
59. Elastic on $(48, 72)$; inelastic on $(0, 48)$
61. Elastic on $(25, 25\sqrt{2})$; inelastic on $(0, 25)$

63. $R(p) = 20p(10 - p)$ **65.** $R(p) = 40p(p - 15)^2$ **67.** $R(p) = 30p - 10p\sqrt{p}$

69. $\dfrac{3}{2}$ **71.** $\dfrac{1}{2}$ **73.** Elastic on $(0, 300)$; inelastic on $(300, 600)$ **75.** Elastic on $(0, 10\sqrt{3})$; inelastic on $(10\sqrt{3}, 30)$ **77.** k **79.** \$75 per day

81. Increase **83.** Decrease **85.** \$3.75 **87.** $p(t) = \dfrac{31}{0.31t + 18.5}$

89. -0.025

Chapter 3 Review Exercises   **1.** \$3,136.62; \$4,919.21; \$12,099.29 (3.1) **2.** $E(u) = u^{3/2}, I(x) = 6x + 5$ is one answer. (3.4)

3. $E(u) = \ln u, I(x) = x^2 + 4$ is one answer. (3.4) **4.** $E(u) = e^u, I(x) = 0.02x$ is one answer. (3.4) **5.** $\dfrac{2}{x} + 3e^x$ (3.2) **6.** $2e^{2x - 3}$ (3.4) **7.** $\dfrac{2}{2x + 7}$ (3.4)

8. $\dfrac{e^x}{3 + e^x}$ (3.4) **9.** $y' = \dfrac{9x^2}{4y}$; $\dfrac{9}{8}$ (3.5) **10.** $dy/dt = 216$ (3.6) **11.** (A) $x = 1,000 - 25p$ (B) $\dfrac{p}{40 - p}$ (C) 0.6; demand is inelastic and insensitive to

small changes in price. (D) $1,000p - 25p^2$ (E) Revenue increases (3.7) **12.** -10 (3.2) **13.** $\displaystyle\lim_{n \to \infty}\left(1 + \dfrac{2}{n}\right)^n = e^2 \approx 7.389\ 06$ (3.1)

14. $\dfrac{7[(\ln z)^6 + 1]}{z}$ (3.4) **15.** $x^5(1 + 6 \ln x)$ (3.3) **16.** $\dfrac{e^x(x - 6)}{x^7}$ (3.3) **17.** $\dfrac{6x^2 - 3}{2x^3 - 3x}$ (3.4) **18.** $(3x^2 - 2x)e^{x^3 - x^2}$ (3.4) **19.** $\dfrac{1 - 2x \ln 5x}{xe^{2x}}$ (3.4)

20. $y = -x + 2$; $y = -ex + 1$ (3.4) **21.** $y' = \dfrac{3y - 2x}{8y - 3x}$; $\dfrac{8}{19}$ (3.5) **22.** $x' = \dfrac{4tx}{3x^2 - 2t^2}$; -4 (3.5) **23.** $y' = \dfrac{1}{e^y + 2y}$; 1 (3.5)

24. $y' = \dfrac{2xy}{1 + 2y^2}; \dfrac{2}{3}$ *(3.5)*   **25.** 0.049 *(3.7)*   **26.** $-\dfrac{3}{100 - 3p}$ *(3.7)*   **27.** $\dfrac{2x}{1 + x^2}$ *(3.7)*   **28.** $dy/dt = -2$ units/sec *(3.6)*   **29.** 0.27 ft/sec *(3.6)*

30. $dR/dt = 1/\pi \approx 0.318$ in./min *(3.6)*   **31.** Elastic for $5 < p < 15$; inelastic for $0 < p < 5$ *(3.7)*

32.

33. (A) $y = [\ln(4 - e^x)]^3$ (B) $\dfrac{dy}{dx} = \dfrac{-3e^x[\ln(4 - e^x)]^2}{4 - e^x}$ *(3.4)*   **34.** $2x(5^{x^2-1})(\ln 5)$ *(3.4)*   **35.** $\left(\dfrac{1}{\ln 5}\right)\dfrac{2x - 1}{x^2 - x}$ *(3.4)*

36. $\dfrac{2x + 1}{2(x^2 + x)\sqrt{\ln(x^2 + x)}}$ *(3.4)*   **37.** $y' = \dfrac{2x - e^{xy}y}{xe^{xy} - 1}; 0$ *(3.5)*   **38.** The rate of increase of area is proportional to the radius R, so the rate is smallest when $R = 0$, and has no largest value. *(3.6)*   **39.** Yes, for $-\sqrt{3}/3 < x < \sqrt{3}/3$ *(3.6)*

40. (A) 15 yr   (B) 13.9 yr *(3.1)*   **41.** $A'(t) = 10e^{0.1t}$; $A'(1) = \$11.05/\text{yr}$; $A'(10) = \$27.18/\text{yr}$ *(3.1)*   **42.** \$987.50/yr *(3.2)*

43. $R'(x) = (1{,}000 - 20x)e^{-0.02x}$ *(3.4)*   **44.** $p' = -\dfrac{x}{3p^2} = \dfrac{-(5{,}000 - 2p^3)^{1/2}}{3p^2}$ *(3.5)*   **45.** $dR/dt = \$2{,}242/\text{day}$ *(3.6)*   **46.** Decrease price *(3.7)*   **47.** 0.02125 *(3.7)*

48. -1.111 mg/mL per hour; -0.335 mg/mL per hour *(3.4)*   **49.** $dR/dt = -3/(2\pi)$; approx. 0.477 mm/day *(3.6)*   **50.** (A) Increasing at the rate of 2.68 units/day at the end of 1 day of training; increasing at the rate of 0.54 unit/day after 5 days of training   (B) 7 days *(3.4)*   **51.** $dT/dt = -1/27 \approx -0.037$ min/hr *(3.6)*

Chapter 4

Exercises 4.1   **1.** Decreasing   **3.** Increasing   **5.** Increasing   **7.** Decreasing   **9.** $(a, b); (d, f); (g, h)$ **11.** $(b, c); (c, d); (f, g)$ **13.** c, d, f
15. b, f **17.** Local maximum at $x = a$; local minimum at $x = c$; no local extrema at $x = b$ and $x = d$ **19.** $f(3) = 5$ is a local maximum; e
21. No local extremum; d   **23.** $f(3) = 5$ is a local maximum; f   **25.** No local extremum; c   **27.** (A) $f'(x) = 3x^2 - 12$ (B) $-2, 2$ (C) $-2, 2$
29. (A) $f'(x) = -\dfrac{6}{(x + 2)^2}$ (B) -2 (C) None   **31.** (A) $f'(x) = \begin{cases} -1 \text{ if } x < 0 \\ 1 \text{ if } x > 0 \end{cases}$ (B) 0   (C) 0   **33.** Decreasing on $(-\infty, 1)$; increasing on
$(1, \infty); f(1) = -2$ is a local minimum   **35.** Increasing on $(-\infty, -4)$; decreasing on $(-4, \infty); f(-4) = 7$ is a local maximum   **37.** Increasing for all x; no local extrema   **39.** Increasing on $(-\infty, -2)$ and $(3, \infty)$; decreasing on $(-2, 3); f(-2) = 44$ is a local maximum, $f(3) = -81$ is a local minimum
41. Decreasing on $(-\infty, 1)$; increasing on $(1, \infty); f(1) = 4$ is a local minimum   **43.** Increasing on $(-\infty, 2)$; decreasing on $(2, \infty); f(2) = e^{-2} \approx 0.135$ is a local maximum   **45.** Increasing on $(-\infty, 8)$; decreasing on $(8, \infty); f(8) = 4$ is a local maximum   **47.** Critical numbers: $x = -0.77, 1.08, 2.69$; decreasing on $(-\infty, -0.77)$ and $(1.08, 2.69)$; increasing on $(-0.77, 1.08)$ and $(2.69, \infty)$; $f(-0.77) = -4.75$ and $f(2.69) = -1.29$ are local minima; $f(1.08) = 6.04$ is a local maximum   **49.** Critical numbers: $x = 1.34, 2.82$; decreasing on $(0, 1.34)$ and $(2.82, \infty)$; increasing on $(1.34, 2.82)$; $f(1.34) = 0.68$ is a local minimum; $f(2.82) = 2.37$ is a local maximum   **51.** Critical numbers: $0.36, 2.15$; increasing on $(-\infty, 0.36)$ and $(2.15, \infty)$; decreasing on $(0.36, 2.15)$; $f(0.36) = 1.17$ is a local maximum; $f(2.15) = -0.66$ is a local minimum

53. Increasing on $(-\infty, 4)$
Decreasing on $(4, \infty)$
Horizontal tangent at $x = 4$

55. Increasing on $(-\infty, -1), (1, \infty)$
Decreasing on $(-1, 1)$
Horizontal tangents at $x = -1, 1$

57. Decreasing for all x
Horizontal tangent at $x = 2$

59. Decreasing on $(-\infty, -3)$ and $(0, 3)$;
increasing on $(-3, 0)$ and $(3, \infty)$
Horizontal tangents at $x = -3, 0, 3$

61.   **63.**   **65.**   **67.**   **69.** g_4 **71.** g_6 **73.** g_2

75. Increasing on $(-1, 2)$; decreasing on $(-\infty, -1)$ and $(2, \infty)$; local minimum at $x = -1$; local maximum at $x = 2$

77. Increasing on $(-1, 2)$ and $(2, \infty)$; decreasing on $(-\infty, -1)$; local minimum at $x = -1$

79. Increasing on $(-2, 0)$ and $(3, \infty)$; decreasing on $(-\infty, -2)$ and $(0, 3)$; local minima at $x = -2$ and $x = 3$; local maximum at $x = 0$

81. $f'(x) > 0$ on $(-\infty, -1)$ and $(3, \infty); f'(x) < 0$ on $(-1, 3); f'(x) = 0$ at $x = -1$ and $x = 3$

83. $f'(x) > 0$ on $(-2, 1)$ and $(3, \infty); f'(x) < 0$ on $(-\infty, -2)$ and $(1, 3); f'(x) = 0$ at $x = -2, x = 1$, and $x = 3$

85. Critical numbers: $x = -2, x = 2$; increasing on $(-\infty, -2)$ and $(2, \infty)$; decreasing on $(-2, 0)$ and $(0, 2); f(-2) = -4$ is a local maximum; $f(2) = 4$ is a local minimum
87. Critical numbers: $x = -2$; increasing on $(-2, 0)$; decreasing on $(-\infty, -2)$ and $(0, \infty); f(-2) = 0.75$ is a local minimum
89. Critical numbers: $x = 0, x = 4$; increasing on $(-\infty, 0)$ and $(4, \infty)$; decreasing on $(0, 2)$ and $(2, 4); f(0) = 0$ is a local maximum; $f(4) = 8$ is a local minimum

91. (A) The marginal profit is positive on $(0, 600)$, 0 (B) $P'(x)$
at $x = 600$, and negative on $(600, 1,000)$.

93. (A) The price decreases for the first 15 months to a local minimum, increases for the next 40 months to a local maximum, and then decreases for the remaining 15 months.   (B) $B(t)$

95. (A) $\overline{C}(x) = 0.05x + 20 + \dfrac{320}{x}$ (B) Critical number: $x = 80$; decreasing for $0 < x < 80$; increasing for $80 < x < 150$; $\overline{C}(80) = 28$ is a local minimum

97. Critical number: $t = 2$; increasing on $(0, 2)$; decreasing on $(2, 24)$; $C(2) = 0.07$ is a local maximum.

Exercises 4.2   **1.** Concave up   **3.** Concave down   **5.** Concave down   **7.** Neither   **9.** (A) $(a, c), (c, d), (e, g)$ (B) $(d, e), (g, h)$ (C) $(d, e), (g, h)$
(D) $(a, c), (c, d), (e, g)$ (E) $(a, c), (c, d), (e, g)$ (F) $(d, e), (g, h)$ **11.** (A) $f(-2) = 3$ is a local maximum of f; $f(2) = -1$ is a local minimum of f.

(B) $(0, 1)$ (C) 0 **13.** (C)   **15.** (D)   **17.** $12x - 8$ **19.** $4x^{-3} - 18x^{-4}$ **21.** $2 + \dfrac{9}{2}x^{-3/2}$ **23.** $8(x^2 + 9)^3 + 48x^2(x^2 + 9)^2 = 8(x^2 + 9)^2(7x^2 + 9)$

25. $(-10, 2{,}000)$ **27.** $(0, 2)$ **29.** None   **31.** Concave upward for all x; no inflection points   **33.** Concave downward on $(-\infty, \frac{4}{3})$; concave upward
on $(\frac{4}{3}, \infty)$; inflection point at $x = \frac{4}{3}$ **35.** Concave downward on $(-\infty, 0)$ and $(6, \infty)$; concave upward on $(0, 6)$; inflection points at $x = 0$ and $x = 6$
37. Concave upward on $(-2, 4)$; concave downward on $(-\infty, -2)$ and $(4, \infty)$; inflection points at $x = -2$ and $x = 4$ **39.** Concave upward on $(-\infty, \ln 2)$;
concave downward on $(\ln 2, \infty)$; inflection point at $x = \ln 2$

41. $f(x)$

43. $f(x)$

45. $f(x)$

47. $f(x)$

49. Domain: All real numbers
y int.: 16; x int.: $2 - 2\sqrt{3}, 2, 2 + 2\sqrt{3}$
Increasing on $(-\infty, 0)$ and $(4, \infty)$
Decreasing on $(0, 4)$
Local maximum: $f(0) = 16$;
local minimum: $f(4) = -16$
Concave downward on $(-\infty, 2)$
Concave upward on $(2, \infty)$
Inflection point: $(2, 0)$
$f(x)$

51. Domain: All real numbers
y int.: 2; x int.: -1
Increasing on $(-\infty, \infty)$
Concave downward on $(-\infty, 0)$
Concave upward on $(0, \infty)$
Inflection point: $(0, 2)$
$f(x)$

53. Domain: All real numbers
y int.: 0; x int.: 0, 4
Increasing on $(-\infty, 3)$
Decreasing on $(3, \infty)$
Local maximum: $f(3) = 6.75$
Concave upward on $(0, 2)$
Concave downward on $(-\infty, 0)$ and $(2, \infty)$
Inflection points: $(0, 0), (2, 4)$
$f(x)$

55. Domain: All real numbers
y int.: 0; x int.: 0, 1
Increasing on $(0.25, \infty)$
Decreasing on $(-\infty, 0.25)$
Local minimum: $f(0.25) = -1.6875$
Concave upward on $(-\infty, 0.5)$ and $(1, \infty)$
Concave downward on $(0.5, 1)$
Inflection points: $(0.5, -1), (1, 0)$
$f(x)$

57. Domain: All real numbers
y int.: 27; x int.: $-3, 3$
Increasing on $(-\infty, -\sqrt{3})$ and $(0, \sqrt{3})$
Decreasing on $(-\sqrt{3}, 0)$ and $(\sqrt{3}, \infty)$
Local maxima: $f(-\sqrt{3}) = 36, f(\sqrt{3}) = 36$
Local minimum: $f(0) = 27$
Concave upward on $(-1, 1)$
Concave downward on $(-\infty, -1)$ and $(1, \infty)$
Inflection points: $(-1, 32), (1, 32)$
$f(x)$

59. Domain: All real numbers
y int.: 16; x int.: $-2, 2$
Decreasing on $(-\infty, -2)$ and $(0, 2)$
Increasing on $(-2, 0)$ and $(2, \infty)$
Local minima: $f(-2) = 0, f(2) = 0$
Local maximum: $f(0) = 16$
Concave upward on $(-\infty, -2\sqrt{3}/3)$ and $(2\sqrt{3}/3, \infty)$
Concave downward on $(-2\sqrt{3}/3, 2\sqrt{3}/3)$
Inflection points: $(-1.15, 7.11), (1.15, 7.11)$
$f(x)$

61. Domain: All real numbers
y int.: 0; int.: 0, 1.5
Decreasing on $(-\infty, 0)$ and $(0, 1.25)$
Increasing on $(1.25, \infty)$
Local minimum: $f(1.25) = -1.53$
Concave upward on $(-\infty, 0)$ and $(1, \infty)$
Concave downward on $(0, 1)$
Inflection points: $(0, 0), (1, -1)$
$f(x)$

63. Domain: All real numbers
y int.: 0; x int.: 0
Increasing on $(-\infty, \infty)$
Concave downward on $(-\infty, \infty)$
$f(x)$

65. Domain: All real numbers
y int.: 5
Decreasing on $(-\infty, \ln 4)$
Increasing on $(\ln 4, \infty)$
Local minimum: $f(\ln 4) = 4$
Concave upward on $(-\infty, \infty)$
$f(x)$

67. Domain: $(0, \infty)$
  x int.: e^2
  Increasing on $(-\infty, \infty)$
  Concave downward on $(-\infty, \infty)$

69. Domain: $(-4, \infty)$
  y int.: $-2 + \ln 4$; x int.: $e^2 - 4$
  Increasing on $(-4, \infty)$
  Concave downward on $(-4, \infty)$

71.

x	$f'(x)$	$f(x)$
$-\infty < x < -1$	Positive and decreasing	Increasing and concave downward
$x = -1$	x intercept	Local maximum
$-1 < x < 0$	Negative and decreasing	Decreasing and concave downward
$x = 0$	Local minimum	Inflection point
$0 < x < 2$	Negative and increasing	Decreasing and concave upward
$x = 2$	Local max., x intercept	Inflection point, horiz. tangent
$2 < x < \infty$	Negative and decreasing	Decreasing and concave downward

73.

x	$f'(x)$	$f(x)$
$-\infty < x < -2$	Negative and increasing	Decreasing and concave upward
$x = -2$	Local max., x intercept	Inflection point, horiz. tangent
$-2 < x < 0$	Negative and decreasing	Decreasing and concave downward
$x = 0$	Local minimum	Inflection point
$0 < x < 2$	Negative and increasing	Decreasing and concave upward
$x = 2$	Local max., x intercept	Inflection point, horiz. tangent
$2 < x < \infty$	Negative and decreasing	Decreasing and concave downward

75. Domain: All real numbers
  x int.: $-1.18, 0.61, 1.87, 3.71$
  y int.: -5
  Decreasing on $(-\infty, -0.53)$ and $(1.24, 3.04)$
  Increasing on $(-0.53, 1.24)$ and $(3.04, \infty)$
  Local minima: $f(-0.53) = -7.57$, $f(3.04) = -8.02$
  Local maximum: $f(1.24) = 2.36$
  Concave upward on $(-\infty, 0.22)$ and $(2.28, \infty)$
  Concave downward on $(0.22, 2.28)$
  Inflection points: $(0.22, -3.15)$, $(2.28, -3.41)$

77. Domain: All real numbers
  y int.: 100; x int.: $8.01, 13.36$
  Increasing on $(-0.10, 4.57)$ and $(11.28, \infty)$
  Decreasing on $(-\infty, -0.10)$ and $(4.57, 11.28)$
  Local minima: $f(-0.10) = 99.02$, $f(11.28) = -901.18$
  Local maximum: $f(4.57) = 711.75$
  Concave upward on $(-\infty, 1.95)$ and $(8.55, \infty)$
  Concave downward on $(1.95, 8.55)$
  Inflection points: $(1.95, 377.82)$, $(8.55, -200.66)$

79. Domain: All real numbers
  x int.: $-2.40, 1.16$; y int.: 3
  Increasing on $(-\infty, -1.58)$
  Decreasing on $(-1.58, \infty)$
  Local maximum: $f(-1.58) = 8.87$
  Concave downward on $(-\infty, -0.88)$ and $(0.38, \infty)$
  Concave upward on $(-0.88, 0.38)$
  Inflection points: $(-0.88, 6.39)$, $(0.38, 2.45)$

81. Domain: All real numbers
  x int.: $-6.68, -3.64, -0.72$; y int.: 30
  Decreasing on $(-5.59, -2.27)$ and $(1.65, 3.82)$
  Increasing on $(-\infty, -5.59)$, $(-2.27, 1.65)$, and $(3.82, \infty)$
  Local minima: $f(-2.27) = -37.84$, $f(3.82) = 32.09$
  Local maxima: $f(-5.59) = 95.97$, $f(1.65) = 67.87$
  Concave upward on $(-4.31, -0.40)$ and $(2.91, \infty)$
  Concave downward on $(-\infty, -4.31)$ and $(-0.40, 2.91)$
  Inflection points: $(-4.31, 39.98)$, $(-0.40, 13.54)$, $(2.91, 47.83)$

83. The graph of the CPI is concave upward.   **85.** The graph of $y = C'(x)$ is positive and decreasing. Since marginal costs are decreasing, the production process is becoming more efficient as production increases.   **87.** (A) Local maximum at $x = 60$ (B) Concave downward on the whole interval $(0, 80)$ **89.** (A) Local maximum at $x = 1$ (B) Concave downward on $(-\infty, 2)$; concave upward on $(2, \infty)$

91. Increasing on $(0, 10)$; decreasing on $(10, 15)$; point of diminishing returns is $x = 10$, max $T'(x) = T'(10) = 500$

93. Increasing on $(24, 36)$; decreasing on $(36, 45)$; point of diminishing returns is $x = 36$, max $N'(x) = N'(36) = 3,888$

95. (A)

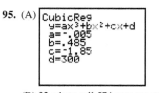

  (B) 32 ads to sell 574 cars per month

97. (A) Increasing on $(0, 10)$; decreasing on $(10, 20)$
  (B) Inflection point: $(10, 3000)$
  (C)

  (D) $N'(10) = 300$

99. (A) Increasing on $(5, \infty)$; decreasing on $(0, 5)$
  (B) Inflection point: $(5, 10)$
  (C)

  (D) $T'(5) = 0$

Exercises 4.3   **1.** 500   **3.** 0   **5.** 50   **7.** 0   **9.** 6   **11.** $-\frac{1}{10}$ **13.** 7   **15.** $-\frac{1}{5}$ **17.** $\frac{2}{5}$ **19.** 0   **21.** $-\infty$ **23.** $\frac{2}{3}$ **25.** $\frac{1}{2}$ **27.** 1   **29.** 0   **31.** 4
33. 5   **35.** ∞ **37.** 8   **39.** 0   **41.** ∞ **43.** ∞ **45.** $\frac{1}{3}$ **47.** -2 **49.** $-\infty$ **51.** 0   **53.** 0   **55.** 0   **57.** $\frac{1}{4}$ **59.** $\frac{1}{3}$ **61.** 0   **63.** 0   **65.** ∞ **67.** 1   **69.** 1

Exercises 4.4   **1.** Domain: All real numbers; x int.: -12; y int.: 36   **3.** Domain: $(-\infty, 25]$; x int.: 25; y int.: 5   **5.** Domain: All real
numbers except 2; x int.: -1; y int.: $-\frac{1}{2}$ **7.** Domain: All real numbers except -1 and 1; No x intercept; y int.: -3 **9.** (A) $(-\infty, b)$, $(0, e)$, (e, g)
(B) (b, d), $(d, 0)$, (g, ∞) (C) (b, d), $(d, 0)$, (g, ∞) (D) $(-\infty, b)$, $(0, e)$, (e, g) (E) $x = 0$ (F) $x = b, x = g$ (G) $(-\infty, a)$, (d, e), (h, ∞)
(H) (a, d), (e, h) (I) (a, d), (e, h) (J) $(-\infty, a)$, (d, e), (h, ∞) (K) $x = a, x = h$ (L) $y = L$ (M) $x = d, x = e$

11.   **13.**   **15.**   **17.**

19. Domain: All real numbers, except 3
    y int.: -1; x int.: -3
    Horizontal asymptote: $y = 1$
    Vertical asymptote: $x = 3$
    Decreasing on $(-\infty, 3)$ and $(3, \infty)$
    Concave upward on $(3, \infty)$
    Concave downward on $(-\infty, 3)$

21. Domain: All real numbers, except 2
    y int.: 0; x int.: 0
    Horizontal asymptote: $y = 1$
    Vertical asymptote: $x = 2$
    Decreasing on $(-\infty, 2)$ and $(2, \infty)$
    Concave downward on $(-\infty, 2)$
    Concave upward on $(2, \infty)$

23. Domain: $(-\infty, \infty)$
    y int.: 10
    Horizontal asymptote: $y = 5$
    Decreasing on $(-\infty, \infty)$
    Concave upward on $(-\infty, \infty)$

25. Domain: $(-\infty, \infty)$
    y int.: 0; x int.: 0
    Horizontal asymptote: $y = 0$
    Increasing on $(-\infty, 5)$
    Decreasing on $(5, \infty)$
    Local maximum: $f(5) = 9.20$
    Concave upward on $(10, \infty)$
    Concave downward on $(-\infty, 10)$
    Inflection point: $(10, 6.77)$

27. Domain: $(-\infty, 1)$
    y int.: 0; x int.: 0
    Vertical asymptote: $x = 1$
    Decreasing on $(-\infty, 1)$
    Concave downward on $(-\infty, 1)$

29. Domain: $(0, \infty)$
    Vertical asymptote: $x - 0$
    Increasing on $(1, \infty)$
    Decreasing on $(0, 1)$
    Local minimum: $f(1) = 1$
    Concave upward on $(0, \infty)$

31. Domain: All real numbers, except ± 2
    y int.: 0; x int.: 0
    Horizontal asymptote: $y = 0$
    Vertical asymptotes: $x = -2, x = 2$
    Decreasing on $(-\infty, -2)$, $(-2, 2)$, and $(2, \infty)$
    Concave upward on $(-2, 0)$ and $(2, \infty)$
    Concave downward on $(-\infty, -2)$ and $(0, 2)$
    Inflection point: $(0, 0)$

33. Domain: All real numbers
    y int.: 1
    Horizontal asymptote: $y = 0$
    Increasing on $(-\infty, 0)$
    Decreasing on $(0, \infty)$
    Local maximum: $f(0) = 1$
    Concave upward on $(-\infty, -\sqrt{3}/3)$ and $(\sqrt{3}/3, \infty)$
    Concave downward on $(-\sqrt{3}/3, \sqrt{3}/3)$
    Inflection points: $(-\sqrt{3}/3, 0.75)$, $(\sqrt{3}/3, 0.75)$

35. Domain: All real numbers except -1 and 1
    y int.: 0; x int.: 0
    Horizontal asymptote: $y = 0$
    Vertical asymptote: $x = -1$ and $x = 1$
    Increasing on $(-\infty, -1)$, $(-1, 1)$, and $(1, \infty)$
    Concave upward on $(-\infty, -1)$ and $(0, 1)$
    Concave downward on $(-1, 0)$ and $(1, \infty)$
    Inflection point: $(0, 0)$

37. Domain: All real numbers except 1
    y int.: 0; x int.: 0
    Horizontal asymptote: $y = 0$
    Vertical asymptote: $x = 1$
    Increasing on $(-\infty, -1)$ and $(1, \infty)$
    Decreasing on $(-1, 1)$
    Local maximum: $f(-1) = 1.25$
    Concave upward on $(-\infty, -2)$
    Concave downward on $(-2, 1)$ and $(1, \infty)$
    Inflection point: $(-2, 1.11)$

39. Domain: All real numbers except 0
    Horizontal asymptote: $y = 1$
    Vertical asymptote: $x = 0$
    Increasing on $(0, 4)$
    Decreasing on $(-\infty, 0)$ and $(4, \infty)$
    Local maximum: $f(4) = 1.125$
    Concave upward on $(6, \infty)$
    Concave downward on $(-\infty, 0)$ and $(0, 6)$
    Inflection point: $(6, 1.11)$

41. Domain: All real numbers except 1
    y int.: 0; x int.: 0
    Vertical asymptote: $x = 1$
    Oblique asymptote: $y = x + 1$
    Increasing on $(-\infty, 0)$ and $(2, \infty)$
    Decreasing on $(0, 1)$ and $(1, 2)$
    Local maximum: $f(0) = 0$
    Local minimum: $f(2) = 4$
    Concave upward on $(1, \infty)$
    Concave downward on $(-\infty, 1)$

43. Domain: All real numbers except $-3, 3$
y int.: $-\frac{2}{9}$
Horizontal asymptote: $y = 3$
Vertical asymptotes: $x = -3, x = 3$
Increasing on $(-\infty, -3)$ and $(-3, 0)$
Decreasing on $(0, 3)$ and $(3, \infty)$
Local maximum: $f(0) = -0.22$
Concave upward on $(-\infty, -3)$ and $(3, \infty)$
Concave downward on $(-3, 3)$

47. Domain: All real numbers
y int.: 3; x int.: 3
Horizontal asymptote: $y = 0$
Increasing on $(-\infty, 2)$
Decreasing on $(2, \infty)$
Local maximum: $f(2) = 7.39$
Concave upward on $(-\infty, 1)$
Concave downward on $(1, \infty)$
Inflection point: $(1, 5.44)$

51. Domain: $(0, \infty)$
x int.: 1
Increasing on $(e^{-1/2}, \infty)$
Decreasing on $(0, e^{-1/2})$
Local minimum: $f(e^{-1/2}) = -0.18$
Concave upward on $(e^{-3/2}, \infty)$
Concave downward on $(0, e^{-3/2})$
Inflection point: $(e^{-3/2}, -0.07)$

55. Domain: All real numbers except $-4, 2$
y int.: $-\frac{1}{8}$
Horizontal asymptote: $y = 0$
Vertical asymptote: $x = -4, x = 2$
Increasing on $(-\infty, -4)$ and $(-4, -1)$
Decreasing on $(-1, 2)$ and $(2, \infty)$
Local maximum: $f(-1) = -0.11$
Concave upward on $(-\infty, -4)$ and $(2, \infty)$
Concave downward on $(-4, 2)$

59. Domain: All real numbers except 0
Vertical asymptote: $x = 0$
Oblique asymptote: $y = x$
Increasing on $(-\infty, -2)$ and $(2, \infty)$
Decreasing on $(-2, 0)$ and $(0, 2)$
Local maximum: $f(-2) = -4$
Local minimum: $f(2) = 4$
Concave upward on $(0, \infty)$
Concave downward on $(-\infty, 0)$

63. Domain: All real numbers except 0
x int.: $-\sqrt{3}, \sqrt{3}$
Vertical asymptote: $x = 0$
Oblique asymptote: $y = x$
Increasing on $(-\infty, 0)$ and $(0, \infty)$
Concave upward on $(-\infty, 0)$
Concave downward on $(0, \infty)$

45. Domain: All real numbers except 2
y int.: 0; x int.: 0
Vertical asymptote: $x = 2$
Increasing on $(3, \infty)$
Decreasing on $(-\infty, 2)$ and $(2, 3)$
Local minimum: $f(3) = 27$
Concave upward on $(-\infty, 0)$ and $(2, \infty)$
Concave downward on $(0, 2)$
Inflection point: $(0, 0)$

49. Domain: $(-\infty, \infty)$
y int.: 1
Horizontal asymptote: $y = 0$
Increasing on $(-\infty, 0)$
Decreasing on $(0, \infty)$
Local maximum: $f(0) = 1$
Concave upward on $(-\infty, -1)$ and $(1, \infty)$
Concave downward on $(-1, 1)$
Inflection points: $(-1, 0.61), (1, 0.61)$

53. Domain: $(0, \infty)$
x int.: 1
Vertical asymptote: $x = 0$
Increasing on $(1, \infty)$
Decreasing on $(0, 1)$
Local minimum: $f(1) = 0$
Concave upward on $(0, e)$
Concave downward on (e, ∞)
Inflection point: $(e, 1)$

57. Domain: All real numbers except $-\sqrt{3}, \sqrt{3}$
y int.: 0; x int.: 0
Vertical asymptote: $x = -\sqrt{3}, x = \sqrt{3}$
Oblique asymptote: $y = -x$
Increasing on $(-3, -\sqrt{3}), (-\sqrt{3}, \sqrt{3})$, and $(\sqrt{3}, 3)$
Decreasing on $(-\infty, -3)$ and $(3, \infty)$
Local maximum: $f(3) = -4.5$
Local minimum: $f(-3) = 4.5$
Concave upward on $(-\infty, -\sqrt{3})$ and $(0, \sqrt{3})$
Concave downward on $(-\sqrt{3}, 0)$ and $(\sqrt{3}, \infty)$
Inflection point: $(0, 0)$

61. Domain: All real numbers except 0
x int.: $\sqrt[3]{4}$
Vertical asymptote: $x = 0$
Oblique asymptote: $y = x$
Increasing on $(-\infty, -2)$ and $(0, \infty)$
Local maximum: $f(-2) = -3$
Decreasing on $(-2, 0)$
Concave downward on $(-\infty, 0)$ and $(0, \infty)$

65. Domain: All real numbers except 0
Vertical asymptote: $x = 0$
Oblique asymptote: $y = x$
Increasing on $(-\infty, -2)$ and $(2, \infty)$
Decreasing on $(-2, 0)$ and $(0, 2)$
Local maximum: $f(-2) = -3$
Local minimum: $f(2) = 3$
Concave upward on $(0, \infty)$
Concave downward on $(-\infty, 0)$

67. $y = 90 + 0.02x$ **69.** $y = 210 + 0.1x$
71. Domain: All real numbers except 2, 4
   y int.: $-3/4$; x int.: -3
   Vertical asymptote: $x = 4$
   Horizontal asymptote: $y = 1$
   Decreasing on $(-\infty, 2)$, $(2, 4)$, and $(4, \infty)$
   Concave upward on $(4, \infty)$
   Concave downward on $(-\infty, 2)$ and $(2, 4)$
75. Domain: All real numbers except $-1, 2$
   y int.: 0; x int.: 0, 3
   Vertical asymptote: $x = -1$
   Oblique asymptote: $y = x - 4$
   Increasing on $(-\infty, -3)$, $(1, 2)$, and $(2, \infty)$
   Decreasing on $(-3, -1)$ and $(-1, 1)$
   Local maximum: $f(-3) = -9$
   Local minimum: $f(1) = -1$
   Concave upward on $(-1, 2)$ and $(2, \infty)$
   Concave downward on $(-\infty, -1)$

73. Domain: All real numbers except $-3, 3$
   y int.: 5/3; x int.: 2.5
   Vertical asymptote: $x = 3$
   Horizontal asymptote: $y = 2$
   Decreasing on $(-\infty, -3)$, $(-3, 3)$, and $(3, \infty)$
   Concave upward on $(3, \infty)$
   Concave downward on $(-\infty, -3)$ and $(-3, 3)$
77. Domain: All real numbers except 1
   y int.: -2; x int.: -2
   Vertical asymptote: $x = 1$
   Horizontal asymptote: $y = 1$
   Decreasing on $(-\infty, 1)$ and $(1, \infty)$
   Concave upward on $(1, \infty)$
   Concave downward on $(-\infty, 1)$

79. $R(x)$, 60,000, 80 x

81. (A) Increasing on $(0, 1)$
   (B) Concave upward on $(0, 1)$
   (C) $x = 1$ is a vertical asymptote
   (D) The origin is both an x and a y intercept
   (E) $P(x)$, Million dollars, 40.00, 1.00 x

83. (A) $\overline{C}(n) = \dfrac{3{,}200}{n} + 250 + 50n$
   (B) $\overline{C}(n)$, 3,500, 20 n
   (C) 8 yr

85. (A) y, $\overline{C}(x)$, 50, $C'(x)$, $y = 5 + 0.1x$, 150 x
   (B) \$25 at $x = 100$

87. (A) QuadReg
   y=ax²+bx+c
   a=.0100714286
   b=.7835714286
   c=316

   (B) Minimum average cost is \$4.35 when 177 pizzas are produced daily.

89. $C(t)$, 0.07, 12 t

91. $N(t)$, 25, 30 t

Exercise 4.5   **1.** Max $f(x) = f(3) = 3$; Min $f(x) = f(-2) = -2$ **3.** Max $h(x) = h(-5) = 25$; Min $h(x) = h(0) = 0$
5. Max $n(x) = n(4) = 2$; Min $n(x) = n(3) = \sqrt{3}$ **7.** Max $q(x) = q(27) = -3$; Min $q(x) = q(64) = -4$
9. Min $f(x) = f(0) = 0$; Max $f(x) = f(10) = 14$ **11.** Min $f(x) = f(0) = 0$; Max $f(x) = f(3) = 9$
13. Min $f(x) = f(1) = f(7) = 5$; Max $f(x) = f(10) = 14$ **15.** Min $f(x) = f(1) = f(7) = 5$; Max $f(x) = f(3) = f(9) = 9$
17. Min $f(x) = f(5) = 7$; Max $f(x) = f(3) = 9$ **19.** (A) Max $f(x) = f(4) = 3$; Min $f(x) = f(0) = -5$
(B) Max $f(x) = f(10) = 15$; Min $f(x) = f(0) = -5$ (C) Max $f(x) = f(10) = 15$; Min $f(x) = f(-5) = -15$
21. (A) Max $f(x) = f(-1) = f(1) = 1$; Min $f(x) = f(0) = 0$ (B) Max $f(x) = f(5) = 25$; Min $f(x) = f(1) = 1$
(C) Max $f(x) = f(-5) = f(5) = 25$; Min $f(x) = f(0) = 0$ **23.** Max $f(x) = f(-1) = e \approx 2.718$; Min $f(x) = e^{-1} \approx 0.368$
25. Max $f(x) = f(0) = 9$; Min $f(x) = f(\pm 4) = -7$ **27.** Min $f(x) = f(1) = 2$; no maximum   **29.** Max $f(x) = f(-3) = 18$; no minimum
31. No absolute extrema   **33.** Max $f(x) = f(3) = 54$; no minimum   **35.** No absolute extrema   **37.** Min $f(x) = f(0) = 0$; no maximum
39. Max $f(x) = f(1) = 1$; Min $f(x) = f(-1) = -1$ **41.** Min $f(x) = f(0) = -1$; no maximum   **43.** Min $f(x) = f(2) = -2$
45. Max $f(x) = f(2) = 4$ **47.** Min $f(x) = f(2) = 0$ **49.** No maximum   **51.** Max $f(x) = f(2) = 8$ **53.** Min $f(x) = f(4) = 22$
55. Min $f(x) = f(\sqrt{10}) = 14/\sqrt{10}$ **57.** Min $f(x) = f(2) = \dfrac{e^2}{4} \approx 1.847$ **59.** Max $f(x) = f(3) = \dfrac{27}{e^3} \approx 1.344$
61. Max $f(x) = f(e^{1.5}) = 2e^{1.5} \approx 8.963$ **63.** Max $f(x) = f(e^{2.5}) = \dfrac{e^5}{2} \approx 74.207$ **65.** Max $f(x) = f(1) = -1$
67. (A) Max $f(x) = f(5) = 14$; Min $f(x) = f(-1) = -22$ (B) Max $f(x) = f(1) = -2$; Min $f(x) = f(-1) = -22$
(C) Max $f(x) = f(5) = 14$; Min $f(x) = f(3) = -6$ **69.** (A) Max $f(x) = f(0) = 126$; Min $f(x) = f(2) = -26$
(B) Max $f(x) = f(7) = 49$; Min $f(x) = f(2) = -26$ (C) Max $f(x) = f(6) = 6$; Min $f(x) = f(3) = -15$
71. (A) Max $f(x) = f(-1) = 10$; Min $f(x) = f(2) = -11$ (B) Max $f(x) = f(0) = f(4) = 5$; Min $f(x) = f(3) = -22$
(C) Max $f(x) = f(-1) = 10$; Min $f(x) = f(1) = 2$ **73.** Local minimum   **75.** Unable to determine   **77.** Neither   **79.** Local maximum

Exercises 4.6   **1.** $f(x) = x(28 - x)$ **3.** $f(x) = \pi x^2/4$ **5.** $f(x) = \pi x^3$ **7.** $f(x) = x(60 - x)$ **9.** 7.5 and 7.5   **11.** 7.5 and -7.5
13. $\sqrt{15}$ and $\sqrt{15}$ **15.** $10\sqrt{2}$ ft by $10\sqrt{2}$ ft   **17.** 37 ft by 37 ft   **19.** (A) Maximum revenue is \$125,000 when 500 phones are produced and sold for
\$250 each.   (B) Maximum profit is \$46,612.50 when 365 phones are produced and sold for \$317.50 each.   **21.** (A) Max $R(x) = R(3{,}000) = \$300{,}000$
(B) Maximum profit is \$75,000 when 2,100 sets are manufactured and sold for \$130 each.   (C) Maximum profit is \$64,687.50 when 2,025 sets are manufactured
and sold for \$132.50 each.

23. (A)

```
QuadReg
y=ax²+bx+c
a=-2.352941E-5
b=-.0325964781
c=288.9535407
```

(B)

```
LinReg
y=ax+b
a=53.50318471
b=82245.22293
```

(C) The maximum profit is \$118,996 when the price per sleeping bag is \$195.
25. (A) \$4.80 (B) \$8 **27.** \$35; \$6,125 **29.** 40 trees; 1,600 lb
31. $(10 - 2\sqrt{7})/3 = 1.57$ in. squares **33.** 20 ft by 40 ft (with the expensive side being one of the short sides) **35.** (A) 70 ft by 100 ft (B) 125 ft by 125 ft **37.** 8 production runs per year **39.** 10,000 books in 5 printings **41.** 34.64 mph

43. (A) $x = 5.1$ mi (B) $x = 10$ mi **45.** 4 days; 20 bacteria/cm^3 **47.** 1 month; 2 ft **49.** 4 yr from now

Chapter 4 Review Exercises
1. $(a, c_1), (c_3, c_6)$ *(4.1, 4.2)* **2.** $(c_1, c_3), (c_6, b)$ *(4.1, 4.2)* **3.** $(a, c_2), (c_4, c_5), (c_7, b)$ *(4.1, 4.2)* **4.** c_3 *(4.1)*
5. c_1, c_6 *(4.1)* **6.** c_1, c_3, c_5 *(4.1)* **7.** c_4, c_6 *(4.1)* **8.** c_2, c_4, c_5, c_7 *(4.2)*
9. *(4.2)* **10.** *(4.2)* **11.** $f''(x) = 12x^2 + 30x$ *(4.2)* **12.** $y'' = 8/x^3$ *(4.2)* **13.** Domain: All real numbers, except 4 y int.: $\frac{5}{4}$; x int.: -5 *(4.2)* **14.** Domain: $(-2, \infty)$ y int.: $\ln 2$; x int.: -1 *(4.2)*
15. Horizontal asymptote: $y = 0$; Vertical asymptotes: $x = -2, x = 2$ *(4.4)* **16.** Horizontal asymptote: $y = \frac{2}{3}$; Vertical asymptote: $x = -\frac{10}{3}$ *(4.4)* **17.** $(-\sqrt{2}, -20), (\sqrt{2}, -20)$ *(4.2)*
18. $\left(-\frac{1}{2}, -6\right)$ *(4.2)* **19.** (A) $f'(x) = \frac{1}{5}x^{-4/5}$ (B) 0 (C) 0 *(4.1)* **20.** (A) $f'(x) = -\frac{1}{5}x^{-6/5}$ (B) 0 (C) None *(4.1)*

21. Domain: All real numbers
y int.: 0; x int.: 0, 9
Increasing on $(-\infty, 3)$ and $(9, \infty)$
Decreasing on $(3, 9)$
Local maximum: $f(3) = 108$
Local minimum: $f(9) = 0$
Concave upward on $(6, \infty)$
Concave downward on $(-\infty, 6)$
Inflection point: $(6, 54)$ *(4.4)*

22. Domain: All real numbers
y int.: 16; x int.: $-4, 2$
Increasing on $(-\infty, -2)$ and $(2, \infty)$
Decreasing on $(-2, 2)$
Local maximum: $f(-2) = 32$
Local minimum: $f(2) = 0$
Concave upward on $(0, \infty)$
Concave downward on $(-\infty, 0)$
Inflection point: $(0, 16)$ *(4.4)*

23. Domain: All real numbers
y int.: 0; x int.: 0, 4
Increasing on $(-\infty, 3)$
Decreasing on $(3, \infty)$
Local maximum: $f(3) = 54$
Concave upward on $(0, 2)$
Concave downward on $(-\infty, 0)$ and $(2, \infty)$
Inflection points: $(0, 0), (2, 32)$ *(4.4)*

24. Domain: all real numbers
y int.: -3; x int.: $-3, 1$
No vertical or horizontal asymptotes
Increasing on $(-2, \infty)$
Decreasing on $(-\infty, -2)$
Local minimum: $f(-2) = -27$
Concave upward on $(-\infty, -1)$ and $(1, \infty)$
Concave downward on $(-1, 1)$
Inflection points: $(-1, -16), (1, 0)$ *(4.4)*

25. Domain: All real numbers, except -2
y int.: 0; x int.: 0
Horizontal asymptote: $y = 3$
Vertical asymptote: $x = -2$
Increasing on $(-\infty, -2)$ and $(-2, \infty)$
Concave upward on $(-\infty, -2)$
Concave downward on $(-2, \infty)$ *(4.4)*

26. Domain: All real numbers
y int.: 0; x int.: 0
Horizontal asymptote: $y = 1$
Increasing on $(0, \infty)$
Decreasing on $(-\infty, 0)$
Local minimum: $f(0) = 0$
Concave upward on $(-3, 3)$
Concave downward on $(-\infty, -3)$ and $(3, \infty)$
Inflection points: $(-3, 0.25), (3, 0.25)$ *(4.4)*

27. Domain: All real numbers except $x = -2$
y int.: 0; x int.: 0
Horizontal asymptote: $y = 0$
Vertical asymptote: $x = -2$
Increasing on $(-2, 2)$
Decreasing on $(-\infty, -2)$ and $(2, \infty)$
Local maximum: $f(2) = 0.125$
Concave upward on $(4, \infty)$
Concave downward on $(-\infty, -2)$ and $(-2, 4)$
Inflection point: $(4, 0.111)$ *(4.4)*

28. Domain: All real numbers
y int.: 0; x int.: 0
Oblique asymptote: $y = x$
Increasing on $(-\infty, \infty)$
Concave upward on $(-\infty, -3)$ and $(0, 3)$
Concave downward on $(-3, 0)$ and $(3, \infty)$
Inflection points: $(-3, -2.25), (0, 0), (3, 2.25)$ *(4.4)*

29. Domain: All real numbers
y int.: 0; x int.: 0
Horizontal asymptote: $y = 5$
Increasing on $(-\infty, \infty)$
Concave downward on $(-\infty, \infty)$ *(4.4)*

30. Domain: $(0, \infty)$
x int.: 1
Increasing on $(e^{-1/3}, \infty)$
Decreasing on $(0, e^{-1/3})$
Local minimum: $f(e^{-1/3}) = -0.123$
Concave upward on $(e^{-5/6}, \infty)$
Concave downward on $(0, e^{-5/6})$
Inflection point: $(e^{-5/6}, -0.068)$ *(4.4)*

31. 3 *(4.3)*   **32.** $-\dfrac{1}{5}$ *(4.3)*   **33.** $-\infty$ *(4.3)*   **34.** 0 *(4.3)*   **35.** ∞ *(4.3)*   **36.** 1 *(4.3)*   **37.** 0 *(4.3)*   **38.** 0 *(4.3)*   **39.** 1 *(4.3)*   **40.** 2 *(4.3)*

41.

x	$f'(x)$	$f(x)$
$-\infty < x < -2$	Negative and increasing	Decreasing and concave upward
$x = -2$	x intercept	Local minimum
$-2 < x < -1$	Positive and increasing	Increasing and concave upward
$x = -1$	Local maximum	Inflection point
$-1 < x < 1$	Positive and decreasing	Increasing and concave downward
$x = 1$	Local min., x intercept	Inflection point, horiz. tangent
$1 < x < \infty$	Positive and increasing	Increasing and concave upward

 (4.2)

42. (C) *(4.2)*   **43.** Local maximum: $f(-1) = 20$; local minimum $f(5) = -88$ *(4.5)*
44. Min $f(x) = f(2) = -4$; Max $f(x) = f(5) = 77$ *(4.5)*
45. Min $f(x) = f(2) = 8$ *(4.5)*
46. Max $f(x) = f(e^{4.5}) = 2e^{4.5} \approx 180.03$ *(4.5)*
47. Max $f(x) = f(0.5) = 5e^{-1} \approx 1.84$ *(4.5)*
48. Yes. Since f is continuous on $[a, b]$, f has an absolute maximum on $[a, b]$. But neither $f(a)$ nor $f(b)$ is an absolute maximum, so the absolute maximum must occur between a and b. *(4.5)*

49. No, increasing/decreasing properties apply to intervals in the domain of f. It is correct to say that $f(x)$ is decreasing on $(-\infty, 0)$ and $(0, \infty)$. *(4.1)*
50. A critical number of $f(x)$ is a partition number for $f'(x)$ that is also in the domain of f. For example, if $f(x) = x^{-1}$, then 0 is a partition number for $f'(x) = -x^{-2}$, but 0 is not a critical number of $f(x)$ since 0 is not in the domain of f. *(4.1)*
51. Max $f'(x) = f'(2) = 12$ *(4.2, 4.5)*

52. Each number is 20; minimum sum is 40 *(4.6)*

53. Domain: All real numbers
x int.: 0.79, 1.64; y int.: 4
Increasing on $(-1.68, -0.35)$ and $(1.28, \infty)$
Decreasing on $(-\infty, -1.68)$ and $(-0.35, 1.28)$
Local minima: $f(-1.68) = 0.97$, $f(1.28) = -1.61$
Local maximum: $f(-0.35) = 4.53$
Concave downward on $(-1.10, 0.60)$
Concave upward on $(-\infty, -1.10)$ and $(0.60, \infty)$
Inflection points: $(-1.10, 2.58)$, $(0.60, 1.08)$

54. Domain: All real numbers
x intercepts; 0, 11.10; y int.: 0
Increasing on $(1.87, 4.19)$ and $(8.94, \infty)$
Decreasing on $(-\infty, 1.87)$ and $(4.19, 8.94)$
Local maximum: $f(4.19) = -39.81$
Local minima: $f(1.87) = -52.14$, $f(8.94) = -123.81$
Concave upward on $(-\infty, 2.92)$ and $(7.08, \infty)$
Concave downward on $(2.92, 7.08)$
Inflection points: $(2.92, -46.41)$, $(7.08, -88.04)$ *(4.4)*

55. Max $f(x) = f(1.373) = 2.487$ *(4.5)*   **56.** Max $f(x) = f(1.763) = 0.097$ *(4.5)*

57. (A) For the first 15 months, the graph of the price is increasing and concave downward, with a local maximum at $t = 15$.
For the next 15 months, the graph of the price is decreasing and concave downward, with an inflection point at $t = 30$.
For the next 15 months, the graph of the price is decreasing and concave upward, with a local minimum at $t = 45$.
For the remaining 15 months, the graph of the price is increasing and concave upward.

(B) *(4.2)*

58. (A) Max $R(x) = R(10,000) = \$2,500,000$
(B) Maximum profit is $175,000 when 3,000 readers are manufactured and sold for $425 each.
(C) Maximum profit is $119,000 when 2,600 readers are manufactured and sold for $435 each. *(4.6)*
59. (A) The expensive side is 50 ft; the other side is 100 ft.   (B) The expensive side is 75 ft; the other side is 150 ft. *(4.6)*   **60.** $49; $6,724 *(4.6)*
61. 12 orders/yr *(4.6)*

62. Min $\overline{C}(x) = \overline{C}(200) = \$50$ *(4.4)*

63. Min $\overline{C}(x) = \overline{C}(e^5) \approx \$49.66$ *(4.4)*
64. A maximum revenue of $18,394 is realized at a production level of 50 units at $367.88 each. *(4.6)*

65. *(4.6)*

66. $549.15; $9,864 *(4.6)*
67. $1.52 *(4.6)*
68. 20.39 feet *(4.6)*
69. (A)

(B) Min $\overline{C}(x) = \overline{C}(129) = \$1.71$ *(4.4)*

70. Increasing on $(0, 18)$; decreasing on $(18, 24)$; point of diminishing returns is $x = 18$, max $N'(x) = N'(18) = 972$ *(4.2)*

71. (A)
```
CubicReg
y=ax³+bx²+cx+d
a=-.01
b=.83
c=-2.3
d=221
```

(B) 28 ads to sell 588 refrigerators per month *(4.2)*
72. 3 days *(4.1)*
73. 2 yr from now *(4.1)*

Chapter 5

Exercises 5.1   **1.** $f(x) = 5x^{-4}$ **3.** $f(x) = 3x^{-4} - 2x^{-5}$ **5.** $f(x) = x^{1/2} + 5x^{-1/2}$ **7.** $f(x) = 4x^{1/3} + x^{4/3} - 3x^{7/3}$ **9.** $7x + C$ **11.** $4x^2 + C$
13. $3x^3 + C$ **15.** $(x^6/6) + C$ **17.** $(-x^{-2}/2) + C$ **19.** $4x^{5/2} + C$ **21.** $3 \ln|z| + C$ **23.** $16e^u + C$ **25.** Yes   **27.** Yes   **29.** No   **31.** No
33. True   **35.** False   **37.** True   **39.** No, since one graph cannot be obtained from another by a vertical translation.   **41.** Yes, since one graph can be obtained from another by a vertical translation.   **43.** $(5x^2/2) - (5x^3/3) + C$ **45.** $2\sqrt{u} + C$ **47.** $-(x^{-2}/8) + C$ **49.** $4 \ln|u| + u + C$ **51.** $5e^z + 4z + C$
53. $x^3 + 2x^{-1} + C$ **55.** $C(x) = 2x^3 - 2x^2 + 3,000$ **57.** $x - 40\sqrt{t}$ **59.** $y = -2x^{-1} + 3 \ln|x| - x + 3$ **61.** $x = 4e^t - 2t - 3$
63. $y = 2x^2 - 3x + 1$ **65.** $x^2 + x^{-1} + C$ **67.** $\frac{1}{2}x^2 + x^{-2} + C$ **69.** $e^x - 2 \ln|x| + C$ **71.** x^3 **73.** $x^4 + 3x^2 + C$

81. $\overline{C}(x) = 15 + \dfrac{1,000}{x}$; $C(x) = 15x + 1,000$; $C(0) = \$1,000$ **83.** (A) The cost function increases from 0 to 8, is concave downward from 0 to 4, and is concave upward from 4 to 8. There is an inflection point at $x = 4$.   (B) $C(x) = x^3 - 12x^2 + 53x + 30$; $C(4) = \$114,000$; $C(8) = \$198,000$
(C)

(D) Manufacturing plants are often inefficient at low and high levels of production.
85. $S(t) = 1,200 - 18t^{4/3}$; $50^{3/4} \approx 19$ mo   **87.** $S(t) = 1,200 - 18t^{4/3} - 70t$; $t \approx 8.44$ mo
89. $L(x) = 4,800x^{1/2}$; 24,000 labor-hours   **91.** $W(h) = 0.0005h^3$; 171.5 lb   **93.** 19,400

Exercises 5.2   **1.** $f'(x) = 50(5x + 1)^9$ **3.** $f'(x) = 14x(x^2 + 1)^6$ **5.** $f'(x) = 2xe^{x^2}$ **7.** $f'(x) = \dfrac{4x^3}{x^4 - 10}$ **9.** $\frac{1}{3}(3x + 5)^3 + C$

11. $\frac{1}{6}(x^2 - 1)^6 + C$ **13.** $-\frac{1}{2}(5x^3 + 1)^{-2} + C$ **15.** $e^{5x} + C$ **17.** $\ln|1 + x^2| + C$ **19.** $\frac{2}{3}(1 + x^4)^{3/2} + C$ **21.** $\frac{1}{11}(x + 3)^{11} + C$

23. $-\frac{1}{6}(6t - 7)^{-1} + C$ **25.** $\frac{1}{12}(t^2 + 1)^6 + C$ **27.** $\frac{1}{2}e^{x^2} + C$ **29.** $\frac{1}{5}\ln|5x + 4| + C$ **31.** $-e^{1-t} + C$ **33.** $-\frac{1}{18}(3t^2 + 1)^{-3} + C$

35. $\frac{2}{5}(x + 4)^{5/2} - \frac{8}{3}(x + 4)^{3/2} + C$ **37.** $\frac{2}{3}(x - 3)^{3/2} + 6(x - 3)^{1/2} + C$ **39.** $\frac{1}{11}(x - 4)^{11} + \frac{2}{5}(x - 4)^{10} + C$ **41.** $\frac{1}{8}(1 + e^{2x})^4 + C$

43. $\frac{1}{2}\ln|4 + 2x + x^2| + C$ **45.** $\frac{1}{2}(5x + 3)^2 + C$ **47.** $\frac{1}{2}(x^2 - 1)^2 + C$ **49.** $\frac{1}{5}(x^5)^5 + C$ **51.** No   **53.** Yes   **55.** No   **57.** Yes

59. $\frac{1}{9}(3x^2 + 7)^{3/2} + C$ **61.** $\frac{1}{8}x^8 + \frac{4}{5}x^5 + 2x^2 + C$ **63.** $\frac{1}{9}(x^3 + 2)^3 + C$ **65.** $\frac{1}{4}(2x^4 + 3)^{1/2} + C$ **67.** $\frac{1}{4}(\ln x)^4 + C$ **69.** $e^{-1/x} + C$

71. $x = \frac{1}{3}(t^3 + 5)^7 + C$ **73.** $y = 3(t^2 - 4)^{1/2} + C$ **75.** $p = -(e^x - e^{-x})^{-1} + C$ **77.** $p(x) = \dfrac{2,000}{3x + 50} + 4$; 250 bottles

79. $C(x) = 12x + 500 \ln(x + 1) + 2,000$; $\overline{C}(1,000) = \$17.45$ **81.** (A) $S(t) = 10t + 100e^{-0.1t} - 100, 0 \le t \le 24$ (B) $50 million   (C) 18.41 mo
83. $Q(t) = 100 \ln(t + 1) + 5t, 0 \le t \le 20$; 275 thousand barrels   **85.** $W(t) = 2e^{0.1t}$; 4.45 g   **87.** (A) $-1,000$ bacteria/mL per day
(B) $N(t) = 5,000 - 1,000 \ln(1 + t^2)$; 385 bacteria/mL   (C) 7.32 days   **89.** $N(t) = 100 - 60e^{-0.1t}, 0 \le t \le 15$; 87 words/min
91. $E(t) = 12,000 - 10,000(t + 1)^{-1/2}$; 9,500 students

Exercises 5.3   **1.** The derivative of $f(x)$ is 5 times $f(x)$; $y' = 5y$ **3.** The derivative of $f(x)$ is -1 times $f(x)$; $y' = -y$
5. The derivative of $f(x)$ is $2x$ times $f(x)$; $y' = 2xy$ **7.** The derivative of $f(x)$ is 1 minus $f(x)$; $y' = 1 - y$ **9.** $y = 3x^2 + C$ **11.** $y = 7 \ln|x| + C$

13. $y = 50e^{0.02x} + C$ **15.** $y = \dfrac{x^3}{3} - \dfrac{x^2}{2}$ **17.** $y = e^{-x^2} + 2$ **19.** $y = 2 \ln|1 + x| + 5$ **21.** Second-order   **23.** Third-order   **25.** Yes

27. Yes   **29.** Yes   **31.** Yes   **33.** Figure B. When $x = 1$, the slope $dy/dx = 1 - 1 = 0$ for any y. When $x = 0$, the slope $dy/dx = 0 - 1 = -1$

for any y. Both are consistent with the slope field shown in Figure B.   **35.** $y = \dfrac{x^2}{2} - x + C$; $y = \dfrac{x^2}{2} - x - 2$

37.   **39.** $y = Ce^{2t}$ **41.** $y = 100e^{-0.5x}$ **43.** $x = Ce^{-5t}$ **45.** $x = -(5t^2/2) + C$ **47.** Logistic growth   **49.** Unlimited growth
51. Figure A. When $y = 1$, the slope $dy/dx = 1 - 1 = 0$ for any x. When $y = 2$, the slope $dy/dx = 1 - 2 = -1$ for any x. Both are consistent with the slope field shown in Figure A.   **53.** $y = 1 - e^{-x}$

55.   **57.**   **59.** $y = \sqrt{25 - x^2}$ **65.**   **67.**
61. $y = -3x$
63. $y = 1/(1 - 2e^{-t})$

69.   **71.**   **73.** Apply the second-derivative test to $f(y) = ky(M - y)$.   **75.** 2009
77. $A = 1,000e^{0.03t}$ **79.** $A = 8,000e^{0.016t}$ **81.** (A) $p(x) = 100e^{-0.05x}$
(B) $60.65 per unit   (C)

83. (A) $N = L(1 - e^{-0.051t})$ **85.** $I = I_0e^{-0.00942x}$; $x \approx 74$ ft   **89.** 0.023 117   **91.** Approx. 24,200 yr   **93.** 104 times; 67 times
(B) 22.5%   **87.** (A) $Q = 3e^{-0.04t}$ **95.** (A) 7 people; 353 people   (B) 400   (C)
(C) 32 days   (B) $Q(10) = 2.01$ mL
(D)   (C) 27.47 hr
(D)

Exercises 5.4   **1.** 80 in.² **3.** 36 m² **5.** No, $\pi - 2 > 1$ m² **7.** C, E **9.** B **11.** H, I **13.** H

15.

17. Figure A: $L_3 = 13$, $R_3 = 20$; Figure B: $L_3 = 14$, $R_3 = 7$

19. $L_3 \le \int_1^4 f(x)\,dx \le R_3$; $R_3 \le \int_1^4 g(x)\,dx \le L_3$; since $f(x)$ is increasing, L_3 underestimates the area and R_3 overestimates the area; since $g(x)$ is decreasing, the reverse is true. **21.** In both figures, the error bound for L_3 and R_3 is 7. **23.** $S_5 = -260$ **25.** $S_4 = -1{,}194$ **27.** $S_3 = -33.01$ **29.** $S_6 = -38$ **31.** -2.475

33. 4.266 **35.** 2.474 **37.** -5.333 **39.** 1.067 **41.** -1.066 **43.** 15 **45.** 58.5 **47.** -54 **49.** 248 **51.** 0 **53.** -183 **55.** False **57.** False
59. False **61.** $L_{10} = 286{,}100$ ft²; error bound is 50,000 ft²; $n \ge 200$ **63.** $L_6 = -3.53$, $R_6 = -0.91$; error bound for L_6 and R_6 is 2.63. Geometrically, the definite integral over the interval [2, 5] is the sum of the areas between the curve and the x axis from $x = 2$ to $x = 5$, with the areas below the x axis counted negatively and those above the x axis counted positively. **65.** Increasing on $(-\infty, 0]$; decreasing on $[0, \infty)$ **67.** Increasing on $[-1, 0]$ and $[1, \infty)$; decreasing on $(-\infty, -1]$ and $[0, 1]$ **69.** $n \ge 22$ **71.** $n \ge 104$ **73.** $L_3 = 2{,}580$, $R_3 = 3{,}900$; error bound for L_3 and R_3 is 1,320

75. (A) $L_5 = 3.72$; $R_5 = 3.37$ (B) $R_5 = 3.37 \le \int_0^5 A'(t)\,dt \le 3.72 = L_5$ **77.** $L_3 = 114$, $R_3 = 102$; error bound for L_3 and R_3 is 12

Exercises 5.5   **1.** 500 **3.** 28 **5.** 48 **7.** $4.5\pi \approx 14.14$ **9.** (A) $F(15) - F(10) = 375$ **11.** (A) $F(15) - F(10) = 85$ **13.** 40 **15.** 72 **17.** 46.5
19. $e - 1 \approx 1.718$
21. $\ln 2 \approx 0.693$
23. 0 **25.** 48
27. -48 **29.** -10.25
31. 0 **33.** -2 **35.** 14

37. $5^6 = 15{,}625$ **39.** $\ln 4 \approx 1.386$ **41.** $20(e^{0.25} - e^{-0.5}) \approx 13.550$ **43.** $\frac{1}{2}$ **45.** $\frac{1}{2}(1 - e^{-1}) \approx 0.316$ **47.** 0
49. (A) Average $f(x) = 250$ **51.** (A) Average $f(t) = 2$ **53.** (A) Average $f(x) = \frac{45}{28} \approx 1.61$ **55.** (A) Average $f(x) = 2(1 - e^{-2}) \approx 1.73$
(B)   (B)   (B)   (B)

57. $\frac{1}{6}(15^{3/2} - 5^{3/2}) \approx 7.819$ **59.** $\frac{1}{2}(\ln 2 - \ln 3) \approx -0.203$ **61.** 0 **63.** 4.566 **65.** 2.214 **69.** $\int_{300}^{900} \left(500 - \frac{x}{3}\right) dx = \$180{,}000$

71. $\int_0^5 500(t - 12)\,dt = -\$23{,}750$; $\int_5^{10} 500(t - 12)\,dt = -\$11{,}250$

73. (A)

(B) 6,505

75. Useful life $= \sqrt{\ln 55} \approx 2$ yr; total profit $= \frac{51}{22} - \frac{5}{2}e^{-4} \approx 2.272$ or $\$2{,}272$
77. (A) $\$420$ (B) $\$135{,}000$

79. (A)

81. $50e^{0.6} - 50e^{0.4} - 10 \approx \$6.51$ **83.** 4,800 labor-hours **85.** (A) $I = -200t + 600$
(B) $\frac{1}{3}\int_0^3 (-200t + 600)\,dt = 300$ **87.** $100 \ln 11 + 50 \approx 290$ thousand barrels;
$100 \ln 21 - 100 \ln 11 + 50 \approx 115$ thousand barrels
89. $2e^{0.8} - 2 \approx 2.45$ g; $2e^{1.6} - 2e^{0.8} \approx 5.45$ g
91. $10°C$ **93.** $0.6 \ln 2 + 0.1 \approx 0.516$; $(4.2 \ln 625 + 2.4 - 4.2 \ln 49)/24 \approx 0.546$

(B) $\$100{,}505$

Chapter 5 Review Exercises   **1.** $3x^2 + 3x + C$ (5.1) **2.** 50 (5.5) **3.** -207 (5.5) **4.** $-\frac{1}{8}(1 - t^2)^4 + C$ (5.2) **5.** $\ln|u| + \frac{1}{4}u^4 + C$ (5.1)
6. 0.216 (5.5) **7.** No (5.1) **8.** Yes (5.1) **9.** No (5.1) **10.** Yes (5.1) **11.** Yes (5.3) **12.** Yes (5.3) **13.** e^{-x^2} (5.1) **14.** $\sqrt{4 + 5x} + C$ (5.1)
15. $y = f(x) = x^3 - 2x + 4$ (5.3) **16.** (A) $2x^4 - 2x^2 - x + C$ (B) $e^t - 4\ln|t| + C$ (5.1) **17.** $R_2 = 72$; error bound for R_2 is 48 (5.4)
18. $\int_1^5 (x^2 + 1)\,dx = \frac{136}{3} \approx 45.33$; actual error is $\frac{80}{3} \approx 26.67$ (5.5) **19.** $L_4 = 30.8$ (5.4) **20.** 7 (5.5) **21.** Width $= 2 - (-1) = 3$;
height $=$ average $f(x) = 7$ (5.5) **22.** $S_4 = 368$ (5.4) **23.** $S_5 = 906$ (5.4) **24.** -10 (5.4) **25.** 0.4 (5.4) **26.** 1.4 (5.4) **27.** 0 (5.4) **28.** 0.4 (5.4)
29. 2 (5.4) **30.** -2 (5.4) **31.** -0.4 (5.4) **32.** (A) 1; 1 (B) 4; 4 (5.3) **33.** $dy/dx = (2y)/x$; at points on the x axis ($y = 0$) the slopes are 0. (5.3)
35. $y = \frac{1}{4}x^2$; $y = -\frac{1}{4}x^2$ (5.3)

36. *(5.3)*   **37.** *(5.3)*

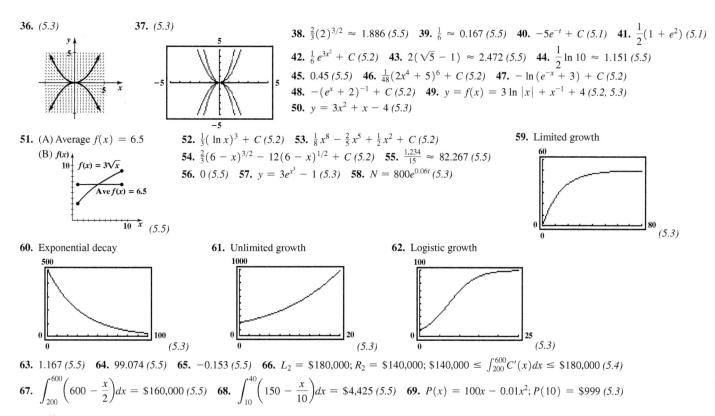

38. $\frac{2}{3}(2)^{3/2} \approx 1.886$ *(5.5)*   **39.** $\frac{1}{6} \approx 0.167$ *(5.5)*   **40.** $-5e^{-t} + C$ *(5.1)*   **41.** $\frac{1}{2}(1 + e^2)$ *(5.1)*

42. $\frac{1}{6}e^{3x^2} + C$ *(5.2)*   **43.** $2(\sqrt{5} - 1) \approx 2.472$ *(5.5)*   **44.** $\frac{1}{2}\ln 10 \approx 1.151$ *(5.5)*

45. 0.45 *(5.5)*   **46.** $\frac{1}{48}(2x^4 + 5)^6 + C$ *(5.2)*   **47.** $-\ln(e^{-x} + 3) + C$ *(5.2)*

48. $-(e^x + 2)^{-1} + C$ *(5.2)*   **49.** $y = f(x) = 3\ln|x| + x^{-1} + 4$ *(5.2, 5.3)*

50. $y = 3x^2 + x - 4$ *(5.3)*

51. (A) Average $f(x) = 6.5$ **52.** $\frac{1}{3}(\ln x)^3 + C$ *(5.2)*   **53.** $\frac{1}{8}x^8 - \frac{2}{5}x^5 + \frac{1}{2}x^2 + C$ *(5.2)*   **59.** Limited growth

(B) **54.** $\frac{2}{3}(6 - x)^{3/2} - 12(6 - x)^{1/2} + C$ *(5.2)*   **55.** $\frac{1,234}{15} \approx 82.267$ *(5.5)*

56. 0 *(5.5)*   **57.** $y = 3e^{x^3} - 1$ *(5.3)*   **58.** $N = 800e^{0.06t}$ *(5.3)*

60. Exponential decay   **61.** Unlimited growth   **62.** Logistic growth

63. 1.167 *(5.5)*   **64.** 99.074 *(5.5)*   **65.** -0.153 *(5.5)*   **66.** $L_2 = \$180,000; R_2 = \$140,000; \$140,000 \le \int_{200}^{600} C'(x)\,dx \le \$180,000$ *(5.4)*

67. $\int_{200}^{600}\left(600 - \frac{x}{2}\right)dx = \$160,000$ *(5.5)*   **68.** $\int_{10}^{40}\left(150 - \frac{x}{10}\right)dx = \$4,425$ *(5.5)*   **69.** $P(x) = 100x - 0.01x^2; P(10) = \$999$ *(5.3)*

70. $\int_0^{15}(60 - 4t)\,dt = 450$ thousand barrels *(5.5)*   **71.** 109 items *(5.5)*   **72.** $16e^{2.5} - 16e^2 - 8 \approx \$68.70$ *(5.5)*   **73.** Useful life $= 10\ln\frac{20}{3} \approx 19$ yr;
total profit $= 143 - 200e^{-1.9} \approx 113.086$ or $\$113,086$ *(5.5)*   **74.** $S(t) = 50 - 50e^{-0.08t}; 50 - 50e^{-0.96} \approx \$31$ million; $-(\ln 0.2)/0.08 \approx 20$ mo *(5.3)*

75. 1 cm^2 *(5.3)*   **76.** 800 gal *(5.5)*   **77.** (A) 132 million   (B) About 65 years *(5.5)*   **78.** $\dfrac{-\ln 0.04}{0.000\ 123\ 8} \approx 26,000$ yr *(5.3)*

79. $N(t) = 95 - 70e^{-0.1t}; N(15) \approx 79$ words/min *(5.3)*

Chapter 6

Exercises 6.1   **1.** 150 **3.** 37.5 **5.** 25.5 **7.** $\pi/2$ **9.** $\int_a^b g(x)\,dx$ **11.** $\int_a^b[-h(x)]\,dx$ **13.** Since the shaded region in Figure C is below the x axis,
$h(x) \le 0$; so, $\int_a^b h(x)\,dx$ represents the negative of the area.   **15.** 24 **17.** 51 **19.** 42 **21.** 6 **23.** 0.833 **25.** 2.350 **27.** 1 **29.** Canada; Mexico
31. India; Brazil   **33.** $\int_a^b[-f(x)]\,dx$ **35.** $\int_b^c f(x)\,dx + \int_c^d[-f(x)]\,dx$ **37.** $\int_c^d[f(x) - g(x)]\,dx$ **39.** $\int_a^b[f(x) - g(x)]\,dx + \int_b^c[g(x) - f(x)]\,dx$
41. Find the intersection points by solving $f(x) = g(x)$ on the interval $[a, d]$ to determine b and c.
Then observe that $f(x) \ge g(x)$ over $[a, b], g(x) \ge f(x)$ over $[b, c]$, and $f(x) \ge g(x)$ over $[c, d]$.
Area $= \int_a^b[f(x) - g(x)]\,dx + \int_b^c[g(x) - f(x)]\,dx + \int_c^d[f(x) - g(x)]\,dx$.
43. 2.5 **45.** 7.667 **47.** 12 **49.** 15 **51.** 32 **53.** 36 **55.** 9 **57.** 2.832 **59.** $\int_{-3}^3\sqrt{9 - x^2}\,dx; 14.137$ **61.** $\int_0^4\sqrt{16 - x^2}\,dx; 12.566$
63. $\int_{-2}^2 2\sqrt{4 - x^2}\,dx; 12.566$ **65.** 52.616 **67.** 8 **69.** 101.75 **71.** 17.979 **73.** 5.113 **75.** 8.290 **77.** 3.166 **79.** 1.385 **81.** 3.17 **83.** 1.82
85. Total production from the end of the fifth year to the end of the 10th year is $50 + 100\ln 20 - 100\ln 15 \approx 79$ thousand barrels.   **87.** Total profit over the
5-yr useful life of the game is $20 - 30e^{-1.5} \approx 13.306$, or $\$13,306$.   **89.** 1935: 0.412; 1947: 0.231; income was more equality distributed in 1947.
91. 1963: 0.818; 1983: 0.846; total assets were less equally distributed in 1983.   **93.** (A) $f(x) = 0.3125x^2 + 0.7175x - 0.015$ (B) 0.104
95. Total weight gain during the first 10 hr is $3e - 3 \approx 5.15$ g.   **97.** Average number of words learned from $t = 2$ hr to $t = 4$ hr is $15\ln 4 - 15\ln 2 \approx 10$.

Exercises 6.2   **1.** $b = 20; c = -5$ **3.** $b = 0.32; c = -0.04$ **5.** $b = 1.6; c = -0.03$ **7.** $b = 1.75; c = 0.02$ **9.** 10.27 **11.** 151.75
13. $93,268.66$ **15.** (A) 10.72 (B) 3.28 (C) 10.72
17.   **19.**   **21.** (A) 0.6827 (B) 0.9545 (C) 0.9973
23. (A) 0.6827 (B) 0.9545 (C) 0.9973
25. (A) $.75$ (B) $.11$ (C)

27. 8 yr   **29.** (A) $.11$ (B) $.10$ **31.** $P(t \ge 12) = 1 - P(0 \le t \le 12) = .89$ **33.** $\$12,500$

35. If $f(t)$ is the rate of flow of a continuous income stream, then the total income produced from 0 to 5 yr is the area under the graph of $y = f(t)$ from $t = 0$ to $t = 5$.

37. $8{,}000(e^{0.15} - 1) \approx \$1{,}295$

39. If $f(t)$ is the rate of flow of a continuous income stream, then the total income produced from 0 to 3 yr is the area under the graph of $y = f(t)$ from $t = 0$ to $t = 3$.

41. $\$255{,}562;\ \$175{,}562$ **43.** $\$6{,}780$ **45.** $\$437$ **47.** Clothing store: $\$66{,}421$; computer store: $\$62{,}623$; the clothing store is the better investment.

49. Bond: $\$12{,}062$ business: $\$11{,}824$; the bond is the better investment.   **51.** $\$55{,}230$ **53.** $\dfrac{k}{r}(e^{rT} - 1)$ **55.** $\$625{,}000$

57. The shaded area is the consumers' surplus and represents the total savings to consumers who are willing to pay more than \$150 for a product but are still able to buy the product for \$150.

59. $\$9{,}900$

61. The area of the region PS is the producers' surplus and represents the total gain to producers who are willing to supply units at a lower price than \$67 but are still able to supply the product at \$67.

63. $CS = \$3{,}380;\ PS = \$1{,}690$

65. $CS = \$6{,}980;\ PS = \$5{,}041$

67. $CS = \$7{,}810;\ PS = \$8{,}336$

69. $CS = \$8{,}544;\ PS = \$11{,}507$

71. (A) $\bar{x} = 21.457;\ \bar{p} = \$6.51$ (B) $CS = 1.774$ or \$1,774; $PS = 1.087$ or \$1,087

Exercises 6.3   **1.** $f'(x) = 5;\ \displaystyle\int g(x)\,dx = \dfrac{x^4}{4} + C$ **3.** $f'(x) = 3x^2;\ \displaystyle\int g(x)\,dx = \dfrac{5x^2}{2} + C$ **5.** $f'(x) = 4e^{4x};\ \displaystyle\int g(x)\,dx = \ln|x| + C$

7. $f'(x) = -x^{-2};\ \displaystyle\int g(x)\,dx = \dfrac{1}{4}e^{4x} + C$ **9.** $\frac{1}{3}xe^{3x} - \frac{1}{9}e^{3x} + C$ **11.** $\dfrac{x^3}{3}\ln x - \dfrac{x^3}{9} + C$ **13.** $u = x + 2;\ \dfrac{(x+2)(x+1)^6}{6} - \dfrac{(x+1)^7}{42} + C$

15. $-xe^{-x} - e^{-x} + C$ **17.** $\frac{1}{2}e^{x^2} + C$ **19.** $(xe^x - 4e^x)\big|_0^1 = -3e + 4 \approx -4.1548$ **21.** $(x\ln 2x - x)\big|_1^3 = (3\ln 6 - 3) - (\ln 2 - 1) \approx 2.6821$

23. $\ln(x^2 + 1) + C$ **25.** $(\ln x)^2/2 + C$ **27.** $\frac{2}{3}x^{3/2}\ln x - \frac{4}{9}x^{3/2} + C$ **29.** $\dfrac{(x-3)(x+1)^3}{3} - \dfrac{(x+1)^4}{12} + C$ or $\dfrac{x^4}{4} - \dfrac{x^3}{3} - \dfrac{5x^2}{2} - 3x + C$

31. $\dfrac{(2x+1)(x-2)^3}{3} - \dfrac{(x-2)^4}{6} + C$ or $\dfrac{x^4}{2} - \dfrac{7x^3}{3} + 2x^2 + 4x + C$

33. The integral represents the negative of the area between the graph of $y = (x-3)e^x$ and the x axis from $x = 0$ to $x = 1$.

y = (x − 3)e^x

35. The integral represents the area between the graph of $y = \ln 2x$ and the x axis from $x = 1$ to $x = 3$.

y = ln 2x

37. $(x^2 - 2x + 2)e^x + C$

39. $\dfrac{xe^{ax}}{a} - \dfrac{e^{ax}}{a^2} + C$

41. $\left(-\dfrac{\ln x}{x} - \dfrac{1}{x}\right)\Big|_1^e = -\dfrac{2}{e} + 1 \approx 0.2642$

43. $6\ln 6 - 4\ln 4 - 2 \approx 3.205$

45. $xe^{x-2} - e^{x-2} + C$

47. $\frac{1}{2}(1 + x^2)\ln(1 + x^2) - \frac{1}{2}(1 + x^2) + C$ **49.** $(1 + e^x)\ln(1 + e^x) - (1 + e^x) + C$ **51.** $x(\ln x)^2 - 2x\ln x + 2x + C$

53. $x(\ln x)^3 - 3x(\ln x)^2 + 6x\ln x - 6x + C$ **55.** 2   **57.** $\dfrac{1}{3}$ **59.** 1.56   **61.** 34.98   **63.** $\int_0^5 (2t - te^{-t})\,dt = \$24$ million

65. The total profit for the first 5 yr (in millions of dollars) is the same as the area under the marginal profit function, $P'(t) = 2t - te^{-t}$, from $t = 0$ to $t = 5$.

$P'(t) = 2t - te^{-t}$

67. $\$2{,}854.88$ **69.** 0.264

71. The area bounded by $y = x$ and the Lorenz curve $y = xe^{x-1}$, divided by the area under the graph of $y = x$ from $x = 0$ to $x = 1$, is the Gini index of income concentration. The closer this index is to 0, the more equally distributed the income; the closer the index is to 1, the more concentrated the income in a few hands.

$y = x$

$y = xe^{x-1}$

73. $S(t) = 1,600 + 400e^{0.1t} - 40te^{0.1t}$; 15 mo   **75.** $977

77. The area bounded by the price–demand equation,
$p = 9 - \ln(x + 4)$, and the price equation, $y = \bar{p} = 2.089$, from
$x = 0$ to $x = \bar{x} = 1,000$, represents the consumers' surplus. This is
the amount consumers who are willing to pay more than \$2.089 save.

79. 2.1388 ppm   **81.** $N(t) = -4te^{-0.25t} - 40e^{-0.25t} + 80$; 8 wk; 78 words/min

83. 20,980

Exercises 6.4   **1.** 77.32   **3.** 74.15   **5.** 0.47   **7.** 0.46   **9.** $\ln\left|\dfrac{x}{1+x}\right| + C$ **11.** $\dfrac{1}{3+x} + 2\ln\left|\dfrac{5+2x}{3+x}\right| + C$ **13.** $\dfrac{2(x-32)}{3}\sqrt{16+x} + C$

15. $-\ln\left|\dfrac{1+\sqrt{1-x^2}}{x}\right| + C$ **17.** $\dfrac{1}{2}\ln\left|\dfrac{x}{2+\sqrt{x^2+4}}\right| + C$ **19.** $\frac{1}{3}x^3 \ln x - \frac{1}{9}x^3 + C$ **21.** $x - \ln|1+e^x| + C$ **23.** $9\ln\frac{3}{2} - 2 \approx 1.6492$

25. $\frac{1}{2}\ln\frac{12}{5} \approx 0.4377$ **27.** $\ln 3 \approx 1.0986$ **29.** $730; 723\frac{1}{3}$ **31.** $1.61; \ln 5 \approx 1.61$ **33.** 69; 69   **35.** 756; 756

37. $-\dfrac{\sqrt{4x^2+1}}{x} + 2\ln|2x + \sqrt{4x^2+1}| + C$ **39.** $\frac{1}{2}\ln|x^2 + \sqrt{x^4-16}| + C$ **41.** $\frac{1}{6}(x^3\sqrt{x^6+4} + 4\ln|x^3 + \sqrt{x^6+4}|) + C$

43. $-\dfrac{\sqrt{4-x^4}}{8x^2} + C$ **45.** $\dfrac{1}{5}\ln\left|\dfrac{3+4e^x}{2+e^x}\right| + C$ **47.** $\frac{2}{3}(\ln x - 8)\sqrt{4 + \ln x} + C$ **49.** $\frac{1}{5}x^2e^{5x} - \frac{2}{25}xe^{5x} + \frac{2}{125}e^{5x} + C$

51. $-x^3e^{-x} - 3x^2e^{-x} - 6xe^{-x} - 6e^{-x} + C$ **53.** $x(\ln x)^3 - 3x(\ln x)^2 + 6x\ln x - 6x + C$ **55.** $\frac{64}{3}$ **57.** $\frac{1}{2}\ln\frac{9}{5} \approx 0.2939$ **59.** $\dfrac{-1 - \ln x}{x} + C$

61. $\sqrt{x^2 - 1} + C$ **65.** 31.38   **67.** 5.48   **69.** $3,000 + 1,500\ln\dfrac{1}{3} \approx \$1,352$

71.

73. $C(x) = 200x + 1,000\ln(1 + 0.05x) + 25,000$; 608; \$198,773   **75.** \$18,673.95   **77.** 0.1407

79. As the area bounded by the two curves gets smaller, the Lorenz
curve approaches $y = x$ and the distribution of income approaches
perfect equality—all persons share equally in the income available.

81. $S(t) = 1 + t - \dfrac{1}{1+t} - 2\ln|1 + t|$; $24.96 - 2\ln 25 \approx \$18.5$ million

83. The total sales (in millions of dollars) over the first 2 yr (24 mo) is the area
under the graph of $y = S'(t)$ from $t = 0$ to $t = 24$.

85. $p(x) = \dfrac{2(9x-4)}{135}(2+3x)^{3/2} - 2,000.83$; 54; \$37,932   **87.** $100\ln 3 \approx 110$ ft   **89.** $60\ln 5 \approx 97$ items

91. The area under the graph of $y = N'(t)$ from
$t = 0$ to $t = 12$ represents the total number of
items learned in that time interval.

Chapter 6 Review Exercises

1. $\int_a^b f(x)\,dx$ (6.1)   **2.** $\int_b^c [-f(x)]\,dx$ (6.1)   **3.** $\int_a^b f(x)\,dx + \int_b^c [-f(x)]\,dx$ (6.1)

4. Area $= 1.153$ (6.1)   **5.** $\frac{1}{4}xe^{4x} - \frac{1}{16}e^{4x} + C$ (6.3, 6.4)   **6.** $\frac{1}{2}x^2 \ln x - \frac{1}{4}x^2 + C$ (6.3, 6.4)   **7.** $\dfrac{(\ln x)^2}{2} + C$ (5.2)   **8.** $\dfrac{\ln(1+x^2)}{2} + C$ (6.2)

9. $\dfrac{1}{1+x} + \ln\left|\dfrac{x}{1+x}\right| + C$ (6.4)   **10.** $-\dfrac{\sqrt{1+x}}{x} - \dfrac{1}{2}\ln\left|\dfrac{\sqrt{1+x}-1}{\sqrt{1+x}+1}\right| + C$ (6.4)   **11.** 12 (6.1)   **12.** 40 (6.1)   **13.** 34.167 (6.1)

14. 0.926 (6.1)   **15.** 12 (6.1)   **16.** 18.133 (6.1)   **17.** Indonesia (6.1)   **18.** Vietnam (6.1)   **19.** $\int_a^b [f(x) - g(x)]\,dx$ (6.1)

20. $\int_b^c [g(x) - f(x)]\,dx$ (6.1)   **21.** $\int_b^c [g(x) - f(x)]\,dx + \int_c^d [f(x) - g(x)]\,dx$ (6.1)

22. $\int_a^b [f(x) - g(x)]dx + \int_b^c [g(x) - f(x)]dx + \int_c^d [f(x) - g(x)]dx$ *(6.1)*

23. Area $= 20.833$ *(6.1)*   **24.** 1 *(6.3, 6.4)*   **25.** $\frac{15}{2} - 8\ln 8 + 8\ln 4 \approx 1.955$ *(6.4)*   **26.** $\frac{1}{6}(3x\sqrt{9x^2 - 49} - 49\ln|3x + \sqrt{9x^2 - 49}|) + C$ *(6.4)*

$y = x^2 - 6x + 9$
$(0, 9)$
5
$(5, 4)$
$y = 9 - x$

27. $-2te^{-0.5t} - 4e^{-0.5t} + C$ *(6.3, 6.4)*   **28.** $\frac{1}{3}x^3 \ln x - \frac{1}{9}x^3 + C$ *(6.3, 6.4)*   **29.** $x - \ln|1 + 2e^x| + C$ *(6.4)*

30. (A) Area $= 8$ (B) Area $= 8.38$ *(6.1)*

$y = x^3 - 6x^2 + 9x$
$(2, 2)$ $y = x$
4 $(4, 4)$
$(0, 0)$ 4

$y = x^3 - 6x^2 + 9x$
6 $(1.75, 2.75)$ $y = x + 1$
$(4.11, 5.11)$
$(0.14, 1.14)$
4

31. $4{,}109.36$ *(6.4)*   **32.** $2{,}640.35$ *(6.4)*   **33.** 4.87 *(6.4)*   **34.** 4.86 *(6.4)*   **35.** $\frac{1}{3}(\ln x)^3 + C$ *(5.2)*

36. $\frac{1}{2}x^2(\ln x)^2 - \frac{1}{2}x^2 \ln x + \frac{1}{4}x^2 + C$ *(6.3, 6.4)*   **37.** $\sqrt{x^2 - 36} + C$ *(5.2)*

38. $\frac{1}{2}\ln|x^2 + \sqrt{x^4 - 36}| + C$ *(6.4)*   **39.** $50\ln 10 - 42\ln 6 - 24 \approx 15.875$ *(6.3, 6.4)*

40. $x(\ln x)^2 - 2x\ln x + 2x + C$ *(6.3, 6.4)*   **41.** $-\frac{1}{4}e^{-2x^2} + C$ *(5.2)*

42. $-\frac{1}{2}x^2 e^{-2x} - \frac{1}{2}xe^{-2x} - \frac{1}{4}e^{-2x} + C$ *(6.3, 6.4)*   **43.** 1.703 *(6.1)*   **44.** (A) $.189$ (B) $.154$ *(6.2)*

45. The probability that the product will fail during the second year of warranty is the area under the probability density function $y = f(t)$ from $t = 1$ to $t = 2$. *(6.2)*

46. $R(x) = 65x - 6[(x + 1)\ln(x + 1) - x]$; 618/wk; $29,506 *(6.3)*

47. (A)
$y = f(t)$
$3{,}000$
Total income
5 t
    (B) $8,507 *(6.2)*

0.2
$y = f(t)$
3 t

48. (A) $15,656   (B) $1,454 *(6.2)*   **49.** (A)
1 CURRENT
$y = x$
$y = f(x)$
1 x

1 PROJECTED
$y = x$
$y = g(x)$
1 x

(B) More equitably distributed, since the area bounded by the two curves will have decreased.
(C) Current $= 0.3$; Projected $= 0.2$; income will be more equitably distributed 10 years from now *(6.1)*

50. (A) $CS = $2,250;   (B) $CS = $2,890;$ *(6.2)*
$PS = $2,700$ $PS = $2,278$

51. (A) 25.403 or $25{,}403$ lb   (B) $PS = 121.6$ or $1,216 *(6.2)*   **52.** 4.522 mL; 1.899 mL *(5.5, 6.4)*

53.
8
$y = R(t)$
6 t *(5.5, 6.1)*

54. $.667; .333$ *(6.2)*

p
70 $p = D(x)$
CS
$\bar{p} = 40$
PS
$p = S(x)$
200 x
$\bar{x} = 150$

p
70 $p = D(x)$
CS
$\bar{p} = 36$
PS
$p = S(x)$
200 x
$\bar{x} = 170$

55. The probability that the doctor will spend more than an hour with a randomly selected patient is the area under the probability density function $y = f(t)$ from $t = 1$ to $t = 3$. *(6.2)*

1.5
$y = f(t)$
3 x

56. 45 thousand *(5.5, 6.1)*   **57.** $.368$ *(6.2)*

Chapter 7

Exercises 7.1   **1.** 19.5 ft^2 **3.** 240 in.^{3} **5.** $32\pi \approx 100.5$ m^3 **7.** $1{,}440\pi \approx 4{,}523.9$ cm^2 **9.** -4 **11.** 11 **13.** 4 **15.** Not defined   **17.** -1
19. -64 **21.** $154{,}440$ **23.** $192\pi \approx 603.2$ **25.** $3\pi\sqrt{109} \approx 98.4$ **27.** 118 **29.** $36{,}095.07$ **31.** $f(x) = x^2 - 7$ **33.** $f(y) = 38y + 20$

35. $f(y) = -2y^3 + 5$ **37.** $y = 2$ **39.** $x = -\frac{1}{2}, 1$ **41.** $-1.926, 0.599$ **43.** $2x + h$ **45.** $2y^2$ **47.** $E(0, 0, 3); F(2, 0, 3)$ **49.** (A) In the plane $y = c$,

c any constant, $z = x^2$.   (B) The y axis; the line parallel to the y axis and passing through the point $(1, 0, 1)$; the line parallel to the y axis and passing through the point $(2, 0, 4)$ (C) A parabolic "trough" lying on top of the y axis   **51.** (A) Upper semicircles whose centers lie on the y axis   (B) Upper semicircles whose centers lie on the x axis   (C) The upper hemisphere of radius 6 with center at the origin   **53.** (A) $a^2 + b^2$ and $c^2 + d^2$ both equal the square of the radius of the circle.   (B) Bell-shaped curves with maximum values of 1 at the origin   (C) A bell, with maximum value 1 at the origin, extending infinitely far in all directions.
55. $13,200; $18,000; $21,300   **57.** $R(p, q) = -5p^2 + 6pq - 4q^2 + 200p + 300q; R(2, 3) = $1,280; R(3, 2) = $1,175   **59.** $30,065$ units
61. (A) $237,877.08   (B) 4.4% **63.** $T(70, 47) \approx 29$ min; $T(60, 27) = 33$ min   **65.** $C(6, 8) = 75; C(8.1, 9) = 90$ **67.** $Q(12, 10) = 120; Q(10, 12) \approx 83$

Exercises 7.2   **1.** $f'(x) = 3\pi x^2 + \pi^3$ **3.** $f'(x) = exe^{-1} + e^x$ **5.** $\dfrac{dz}{dx} = \dfrac{1}{e} - \dfrac{e}{x^2}$ **7.** $\dfrac{dz}{dx} = \dfrac{2x}{x^2 + e^2}$ **9.** $f_x(x, y) = 4$ **11.** $f_y(x, y) = -3x + 4y$

13. $\dfrac{\partial z}{\partial x} = 3x^2 + 8xy$ **15.** $\dfrac{\partial z}{\partial y} = 20(5x + 2y)^9$ **17.** 9   **19.** 3   **21.** -4 **23.** 0   **25.** 45.6 mpg; mileage is 45.6 mpg at a tire pressure of 32 psi and a speed of

40 mph   **27.** 37.6 mpg; mileage is 37.6 mpg at a tire pressure of 32 psi and a speed of 50 mph   **29.** 0.3 mpg per psi; mileage increases at a rate of

0.3 mpg per psi of tire pressure   **31.** $f_{xx}(x, y) = 0$ **33.** $f_{xy}(x, y) = 0$ **35.** $f_{xy}(x, y) = y^2 e^{xy^2}(2xy) + e^{xy^2}(2y) = 2y(1 + xy^2)e^{xy^2}$ **37.** $f_{yy}(x, y) = \dfrac{2\ln x}{y^3}$

39. $f_{xx}(x, y) = 80(2x + y)^3$ **41.** $f_{xy}(x, y) = 720xy^3(x^2 + y^4)^8$ **43.** $C_x(x, y) = 6x + 10y + 4$ **45.** 2   **47.** $C_{xx}(x, y) = 6$ **49.** $C_{xy}(x, y) = 10$

51. 6   **53.** \$3,000; daily sales are \$3,000 when the temperature is 60° and the rainfall is 2 in.   **55.** $-2,500$ \$/in.; daily sales decrease at a rate of \$2,500 per inch

of rain when the temperature is 90° and rainfall is 1 in.   **57.** -50 \$/in. per °F; S_r decreases at a rate of 50 \$/in. per degree of temperature

61. $f_{xx}(x, y) = 2y^2 + 6x; f_{xy}(x, y) = 4xy = f_{yx}(x, y); f_{yy}(x, y) = 2x^2$ **63.** $f_{xx}(x, y) = -2y/x^3; f_{xy}(x, y) = (-1/y^2) + (1/x^2) = f_{yx}(x, y); f_{yy}(x, y) = 2x/y^3$

65. $f_{xx}(x, y) = (2y + xy^2)e^{xy}; f_{xy}(x, y) = (2x + x^2y)e^{xy} = f_{yx}(x, y); f_{yy}(x, y) = x^3 e^{xy}$ **67.** $x = 2$ and $y = 4$ **69.** $x = 1.200$ and $y = -0.695$

71. (A) $-\frac{13}{3}$ (B) The function $f(0, y)$, for example, has values less than $-\frac{3}{13}$.   **73.** (A) $c = 1.145$ (B) $f_x(c, 2) = 0; f_y(c, 2) = 92.021$ **75.** (A) $2x$ (B) $4y$

77. $P_x(1,200, 1,800) = 24$; profit will increase approx. \$24 per unit increase in production of type A calculators at the (1,200, 1,800) output level;

$P_y(1,200, 1,800) = -48$; profit will decrease approx. \$48 per unit increase in production of type B calculators at the (1,200, 1,800) output level

79. $\partial x/\partial p = -5$: a \$1 increase in the price of brand A will decrease the demand for brand A by 5 lb at any price level (p, q); $\partial y/\partial p = 2$: a \$1 increase in the price

of brand A will increase the demand for brand B by 2 lb at any price level (p, q) **81.** (A) $f_x(x, y) = 7.5x^{-0.25}y^{0.25}; f_y(x, y) = 2.5x^{0.75}y^{-0.75}$ (B) Marginal

productivity of labor $= f_x(600, 100) \approx 4.79$; marginal productivity of capital $= f_y(600, 100) \approx 9.58$ (C) Capital   **83.** Competitive   **85.** Complementary

87. (A) $f_w(w, h) = 6.65w^{-0.575}h^{0.725}; f_h(w, h) = 11.34w^{0.425}h^{-0.275}$ (B) $f_w(65, 57) = 11.31$: for a 65-lb child 57 in. tall, the rate of change in surface area

is 11.31 in.^{2} for each pound gained in weight (height is held fixed); $f_h(65, 57) = 21.99$: for a child 57 in. tall, the rate of change in surface area is 21.99 in.^{2}

for each inch gained in height (weight is held fixed)   **89.** $C_W(6, 8) = 12.5$: index increases approx. 12.5 units for a 1-in. increase in width of head (length held

fixed) when $W = 6$ and $L = 8$; $C_L(6, 8) = -9.38$: index decreases approx. 9.38 units for a 1-in. increase in length (width held fixed) when $W = 6$ and $L = 8$.

Exercises 7.3   **1.** $f'(0) = 0; f''(0) = -18$; local maximum   **3.** $f'(0) = 0; f''(0) = 2$; local minimum   **5.** $f'(0) = 0; f''(0) = -2$; local maximum

7. $f'(0) = 1; f''(0) = -2$; neither   **9.** $f_x(x, y) = 4; f_y(x, y) = 5$; the functions $f_x(x, y)$ and $f_y(x, y)$ never have the value 0.   **11.** $f_x(x, y) = -1.2 + 4x^3$;

$f_y(x, y) = 6.8 + 0.6y^2$; the function $f_y(x, y)$ never has the value 0.   **13.** $f(-2, 0) = 10$ is a local maximum.   **15.** $f(-1, 3) = 4$ is a local minimum.

17. f has a saddle point at $(3, -2)$.   **19.** $f(3, 2) = 33$ is a local maximum.   **21.** $f(2, 2) = 8$ is a local minimum.   **23.** f has a saddle point at $(0, 0)$.

25. f has a saddle point at $(0, 0); f(1, 1) = -1$ is a local minimum.   **27.** f has a saddle point at $(0, 0); f(3, 18) = -162$ and $f(-3, -18) = -162$ are

local minima.   **29.** The test fails at $(0, 0); f$ has saddle points at $(2, 2)$ and $(2, -2)$.   **31.** f has a saddle point at $(0.614, -1.105)$.   **33.** $f(x, y)$ is nonnegative

and equals 0 when $x = 0$, so f has the local minimum 0 at each point of the y axis.   **35.** (B) Local minimum   **37.** 2,000 type A and 4,000 type B; max $P =$

$P(2, 4) = \$15$ million   **39.** (A) When $p = \$100$ and $q = \$120$, $x = 80$ and $y = 40$; when $p = \$110$ and $q = \$110$, $x = 40$ and $y = 70$ (B) A maximum

weekly profit of \$4,800 is realized for $p = \$100$ and $q = \$120$.   **41.** $P(x, y) = P(4, 2)$ **43.** 8 in. by 4 in. by 2 in.   **45.** 20 in. by 20 in. by 40 in.

Exercises 7.4   **1.** Min $f(x, y) = f(-2, 4) = 12$ **3.** Min $f(x, y) = f(1, -1) = -4$ **5.** Max $f(x, y) = f(1, 0) = 2$

7. Max $f(x, y) = f(3, 3) = 18$ **9.** Min $f(x, y) = f(3, 4) = 25$ **11.** $F_x = -3 + 2\lambda = 0$ and $F_y = 4 + 5\lambda = 0$ have no simultaneous solution.

13. Max $f(x, y) = f(3, 3) = f(-3, -3) = 18$; min $f(x, y) = f(3, -3) = f(-3, 3) = -18$ **15.** Maximum product is 25 when each number is 5.

17. Min $f(x, y, z) = f(-4, 2, -6) = 56$ **19.** Max $f(x, y, z) = f(2, 2, 2) = 6$; min $f(x, y, z) = f(-2, -2, -2) = -6$

21. Max $f(x, y) = f(0.217, 0.885) = 1.055$ **23.** $F_x = e^x + \lambda = 0$ and $F_y = 3e^y - 2\lambda = 0$ have no simultaneous solution.   **25.** Maximize $f(x, 5)$, a

function of just one independent variable.   **27.** (A) Max $f(x, y) = f(0.707, 0.5) = f(-0.707, 0.5) = 0.47$ **29.** 60 of model A and 30 of model B will yield a

minimum cost of \$32,400 per week.   **31.** (A) 8,000 units of labor and 1,000 units of capital; max $N(x, y) = N(8,000, 1,000) \approx 263,902$ units   (B) Marginal

productivity of money ≈ 0.6598; increase in production $\approx 32,990$ units   **33.** 8 in. by 8 in. by $\frac{8}{3}$ in.   **35.** $x = 50$ ft and $y = 200$ ft; maximum area is 10,000 ft^2

Exercises 7.5   **1.** 10   **3.** 98   **5.** 380   **7.** $y = 0.7x + 1$ **9.** $y = -2.5x + 10.5$ **11.** $y = x + 2$

13. $y = -1.5x + 4.5$; $y = 0.75$ when $x = 2.5$

15. $y = 2.12x + 10.8$; $y = 63.8$ when $x = 25$

17. $y = -1.2x + 12.6$; $y = 10.2$ when $x = 2$

19. $y = -1.53x + 26.67$; $y = 14.4$ when $x = 8$

21. $y = 0.75x^2 - 3.45x + 4.75$ **27.** (A) $y = 1.52x - 0.16$; $y = 0.73x^2 - 1.39x + 1.30$ (B) The quadratic function   **29.** The normal equations form a

system of 4 linear equations in the 4 variables a, b, c, and d, which can be solved by Gauss–Jordan elimination.

31. (A) $y = -79.36x + 3793.6$ (B) 1,889 crimes per 100,000 population   **33.** (A) $y = -0.48x + 4.38$

(B) \$6.56 per bottle   **35.** (A) $y = 0.0222x + 18.94$ (B) 19.92 ft   **37.** (A) $y = 0.0121x + 56.35$ (B) 58.77°F

Exercises 7.6   **1.** $\pi x + \dfrac{x^2}{2} + C$ **3.** $x + \pi \ln |x| + C$ **5.** $\dfrac{e^{\pi x}}{\pi} + C$ **7.** (A) $3x^2y^4 + C(x)$ (B) $3x^2$ **9.** (A) $2x^2 + 6xy + 5x + E(y)$ (B) $35 + 30y$

11. (A) $\sqrt{y + x^2} + E(y)$ (B) $\sqrt{y + 4} - \sqrt{y}$ **13.** (A) $\dfrac{\ln x \ln y}{x} + C(x)$ (B) $\dfrac{2\ln x}{x}$ **15.** 9   **17.** 330   **19.** $(56 - 20\sqrt{5})/3$ **21.** 1   **23.** 16

25. 49   **27.** $\frac{1}{8}\int_1^5 \int_{-1}^1 (x + y)^2 dy\, dx = \frac{32}{3}$ **29.** $\frac{1}{15}\int_1^4 \int_2^7 (x/y)\, dy\, dx = \frac{1}{2}\ln \frac{7}{2} \approx 0.6264$ **31.** $\frac{4}{3}$ cubic units   **33.** $\frac{32}{3}$ cubic units

35. $\int_0^1 \int_1^2 xe^{xy}\, dy\, dx = \frac{1}{2} + \frac{1}{2}e^2 - e$ **37.** $\int_0^1 \int_{-1}^1 \dfrac{2y + 3xy^2}{1 + x^2}\, dy\, dx = \ln 2$ **41. (A)** $\dfrac{1}{3} + \dfrac{1}{4}e^{-2} - \dfrac{1}{4}e^2$ **(B)**

(C) Points to the right of the graph in part (B) are greater than 0; points to the left of the graph are less than 0.

43. $\dfrac{1}{0.4}\int_{0.6}^{0.8}\int_5^7 \dfrac{y}{1-x}\, dy\, dx = 30 \ln 2 \approx \$20.8$ billion   **45.** $\frac{1}{10}\int_{10}^{20}\int_1^2 x^{0.75}y^{0.25}\, dy\, dx = \frac{8}{175}(2^{1.25} - 1)(20^{1.75} - 10^{1.75}) \approx 8.375$ or 8,375 units

47. $\dfrac{1}{192}\int_{-8}^8\int_{-6}^6 [10 - \frac{1}{10}(x^2 + y^2)]\, dy\, dx = \frac{20}{3}$ insects/ft^2 **49.** $\frac{1}{8}\int_{-2}^2\int_{-1}^1 [100 - 15(x^2 + y^2)]\, dy\, dx = 75$ ppm

51. $\dfrac{1}{10,000}\int_{2,000}^{3,000}\int_{50}^{60} 0.000\,013\,3xy^2\, dy\, dx \approx 100.86$ ft   **53.** $\frac{1}{16}\int_8^{16}\int_{10}^{12} 100\dfrac{x}{y}\, dy\, dx = 600 \ln 1.2 \approx 109.4$

Exercises 7.7
1. $R = \{(x, y)\,|\, 0 \le y \le 4 - x^2, 0 \le x \le 2\}$
$R = \{(x, y)\,|\, 0 \le x \le \sqrt{4 - y}, 0 \le y \le 4\}$ **3.** R is a regular x region:
$R = \{(x, y)\,|\, x^3 \le y \le 12 - 2x, 0 \le x \le 2\}$ **5.** R is a regular y region:
$R = \{(x, y)\,|\, \frac{1}{2}y^2 \le x \le y + 4, -2 \le y \le 4\}$

7. $\frac{1}{2}$ **9.** $\frac{39}{70}$ **11.** R consists of the points on or inside the rectangle with corners $(\pm 2, \pm 3)$; both   **13.** R is the arch-shaped region consisting of the points on or inside the rectangle with corners $(\pm 2, 0)$ and $(\pm 2, 2)$ that are not inside the circle of radius 1 centered at the origin; regular x region   **15.** $\frac{56}{3}$ **17.** $-\frac{3}{4}$
19. $\frac{1}{2}e^4 - \frac{5}{2}$ **21.** $R = \{(x, y)\,|\, 0 \le y \le x + 1, 0 \le x \le 1\}$ **23.** $R = \{(x, y)\,|\, 0 \le y \le 4x - x^2, 0 \le x \le 4\}$
$\int_0^1 \int_0^{x+1} \sqrt{1 + x + y}\, dy\, dx = (68 - 24\sqrt{2})/15$ $\int_0^4 \int_0^{4x-x^2} \sqrt{y + x^2}\, dy\, dx = \frac{128}{5}$

25. $R = \{(x, y)\,|\, 1 - \sqrt{x} \le y \le 1 + \sqrt{x}, 0 \le x \le 4\}$ **27.** $\int_0^3 \int_0^{3-y}(x + 2y)\, dx\, dy = \frac{27}{2}$ **29.** $\int_0^1 \int_0^{\sqrt{1-y}} x\sqrt{y}\, dx\, dy = \frac{2}{15}$ **31.** $\int_0^1 \int_{4y^2}^{4y} x\, dx\, dy = \frac{16}{15}$

$\int_0^4 \int_{1-\sqrt{x}}^{1+\sqrt{x}} x(y - 1)^2\, dy\, dx = \frac{512}{21}$

33. $\int_0^4 \int_0^{4-x}(4 - x - y)\, dy\, dx = \frac{32}{3}$ **35.** $\int_0^1 \int_0^{1-x^2} 4\, dy\, dx = \frac{8}{3}$ **37.** $\int_0^4 \int_0^{\sqrt{y}} \dfrac{4x}{1 + y^2}\, dx\, dy = \ln 17$ **39.** $\int_0^1 \int_0^{\sqrt{x}} 4ye^{x^2}\, dy\, dx = e - 1$

41. $R = \{(x, y)\,|\, x^2 \le y \le 1 + \sqrt{x}, 0 \le x \le 1.49\}$ **43.** $R = \{(x, y)\,|\, y^3 \le x \le 1 - y, 0 \le y \le 0.68\}$

$\int_0^{1.49} \int_{x^2}^{1+\sqrt{x}} x\, dy\, dx \approx 0.96$ $\int_0^{0.68} \int_{y^3}^{1-y} 24xy\, dx\, dy \approx 0.83$

45. $R = \{(x, y) \mid e^{-x} \leq y \leq 3 - x, -1.51 \leq x \leq 2.95\}$ Regular x region

$R = \{(x, y) \mid -\ln y \leq x \leq 3 - y, 0.05 \leq y \leq 4.51\}$ Regular y region

$\int_{-1.51}^{2.95} \int_{e^{-x}}^{3-x} 4y \, dy \, dx = \int_{0.05}^{4.51} \int_{-\ln y}^{3-y} 4y \, dx \, dy \approx 40.67$

Chapter 7 Review Exercises   **1.** $f(5, 10) = 2{,}900; f_x(x, y) = 40; f_y(x, y) = 70$ *(7.1, 7.2)*   **2.** $\partial^2 z/\partial x^2 = 6xy^2; \partial^2 z/\partial x \, \partial y = 6x^2 y$ *(7.2)*
3. $2xy^3 + 2y^2 + C(x)$ *(7.6)*   **4.** $3x^2 y^2 + 4xy + E(y)$ *(7.6)*   **5.** 1 *(7.6)*   **6.** $f_x(x, y) = 5 + 6x + 3x^2; f_y(x, y) = -2$; the function $f_y(x, y)$ never has the
value 0. *(7.3)*   **7.** $f(2, 3) = 7; f_y(x, y) = -2x + 2y + 3; f_y(2, 3) = 5$ *(7.1, 7.2)*   **8.** $(-8)(-6) - (4)^2 = 32$ *(7.2)*   **9.** $(1, 3, -\frac{1}{2}), (-1, -3, \frac{1}{2})$ *(7.4)*
10. $y = -1.5x + 15.5; y = 0.5$ when $x = 10$ *(7.5)*   **11.** 18 *(7.6)*   **12.** $\frac{8}{5}$ *(7.7)*   **13.** $f_x(x, y) = 2xe^{x^2 + 2y}; f_y(x, y) = 2e^{x^2 + 2y}; f_{xy}(x, y) = 4xe^{x^2 + 2y}$ *(7.2)*
14. $f_x(x, y) = 10x(x^2 + y^2)^4; f_{xy}(x, y) = 80xy(x^2 + y^2)^3$ *(7.2)*   **15.** $f(2, 3) = -25$ is a local minimum; f has a saddle point at $(-2, 3)$. *(7.3)*
16. Max $f(x, y) = f(6, 4) = 24$ *(7.4)*   **17.** Min $f(x, y, z) = f(2, 1, 2) = 9$ *(7.4)*   **18.** $y = \frac{116}{165}x + \frac{100}{3}$ *(7.5)*   **19.** $\frac{27}{5}$ *(7.6)*   **20.** 4 cubic units *(7.6)*
21. 0 *(7.6)*   **22.** (A) 12.56 (B) No *(7.6)*   **23.** $F_x = 12x^2 + 3\lambda = 0, F_y = -15y^2 + 2\lambda = 0,$ and $F_\lambda = 3x + 2y - 7 = 0$ have no simultaneous solution. *(7.4)*
24. 1 *(7.7)*   **25.** (A) $P_x(1, 3) = 8$; profit will increase $\$8{,}000$ for a 100-unit increase in product A if the production of product B is held fixed at an output level
of $(1, 3)$.   (B) For 200 units of A and 300 units of B, $P(2, 3) = \$100$ thousand is a local maximum. *(7.2, 7.3)*   **26.** $x = 6$ in., $y = 8$ in., $z = 2$ in. *(7.3)*
27. $y = 0.63x + 1.33$; profit in sixth year is $\$5.11$ million *(7.4)*   **28.** (A) Marginal productivity of labor ≈ 8.37; marginal productivity of capital ≈ 1.67;
management should encourage increased use of labor.   (B) 80 units of labor and 40 units of capital; max $N(x, y) = N(80, 40) \approx 696$ units; marginal productiv-

ity of money ≈ 0.0696; increase in production ≈ 139 units   (C) $\dfrac{1}{1{,}000} \int_{50}^{100} \int_{20}^{40} 10x^{0.8} y^{0.2} \, dy \, dx = \dfrac{(40^{1.2} - 20^{1.2})(100^{1.8} - 50^{1.8})}{216} = 621$ items *(7.4)*

29. $T_x(70, 17) = -0.924$ min/ft increase in depth when $V = 70$ ft^3 and $x = 17$ ft *(7.2)*   **30.** $\frac{1}{16} \int_{-2}^{2} \int_{-2}^{2} [100 - 24(x^2 + y^2)] \, dy \, dx = 36$ ppm *(7.6)*
31. $50{,}000$ *(7.1)*   **32.** $y = \frac{1}{2}x + 48; y = 68$ when $x = 40$ *(7.5)*   **33.** (A) $y = 0.734x + 49.93$ (B) 97.64 people/mi^2 (C) 101.10 people/mi^2;
103.70 people/mi^2 *(7.5)*   **34.** (A) $y = 1.069x + 0.522$ (B) 64.68 yr   (C) 64.78 yr; 64.80 yr *(7.5)*

Chapter 8

Exercises 8.1   **1.** $\dfrac{\pi}{3}$ rad   **3.** $\dfrac{3\pi}{4}$ rad   **5.** $-45°$ **7.** $270°$ **9.** $\sqrt{3}/2$ **11.** $-1/\sqrt{2}$ **13.** 1 **15.** 0 **17.** $-1/\sqrt{2}$ **19.** $-1/2$ **21.** -1 **23.** $\sqrt{3}/2$
27. -1 **29.** $2/\sqrt{3}$ **31.** Not defined   **33.** $\sqrt{3}$ **35.** -2 **37.** -1 **39.** $-\sqrt{3}$ **41.** -1 **43.** 0.1736 **45.** 0.6157 **47.** 1.5574 **49.** 92.6259 **51.** 57.2987
53. 3.0777 **55.**

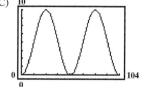

57.

59. $\left\{ x \mid x \neq \pm\dfrac{\pi}{2}, \pm\dfrac{3\pi}{2}, \pm\dfrac{5\pi}{2}, \ldots \right\}$ **61.** $\left\{ x \mid x \neq \pm\dfrac{\pi}{2}, \pm\dfrac{3\pi}{2}, \pm\dfrac{5\pi}{2}, \ldots \right\}$

67. (A) $P(13) = 5, P(26) = 10, P(39) = 5, P(52) = 0$ **69.** (A) $V(0) = 0.10, V(1) = 0.45, V(2) = 0.80, V(3) = 0.45,$ **71.** (A) $-5.6°$
(B) $P(30) \approx 9.43, P(100) \approx 0.57$; 30 weeks after $V(7) = 0.45$ (B) $-4.7°$
January 1 the profit on a week's sales of bathing suits   (B) $V(3.5) \approx 0.20, V(5.7) \approx 0.76$; the volume of air in the lungs of
is $\$943$, and 100 weeks after January 1 the profit on a   a normal seated adult 3.5 sec after exhaling is approximately 0.20 L
week's sales of bathing suits is $\$57$.   and 5.7 sec after exhaling is approx. 0.76 L.

(C)   (C)

Exercises 8.2   **1.** Decreasing   **3.** Increasing   **5.** Concave down   **7.** Concave down   **9.** $-5 \sin x$ **11.** $-5 \sin(5x)$ **13.** $2x \cos(x^2 + 1)$

15. $\cos(w + \pi)$ **17.** $t \cos t + \sin t$ **19.** $(\cos x)^2 - (\sin x)^2$ **21.** $5(\sin x)^4 \cos x$ **23.** $\dfrac{\cos x}{2\sqrt{\sin x}}$ **25.** $-\dfrac{x^{-1/2}}{2} \sin \sqrt{x} = \dfrac{-\sin \sqrt{x}}{2\sqrt{x}}$

27. $f'\left(\dfrac{\pi}{6}\right) = \cos \dfrac{\pi}{6} = \dfrac{\sqrt{3}}{2}$

29. Increasing on $[-\pi, 0]$; decreasing on $[0, \pi]$; concave upward on $[-\pi, -\pi/2]$ and $[\pi/2, \pi]$; concave downward on $[-\pi/2, \pi/2]$; local maximum at $x = 0$; $f(x) = \cos x$; $f'(x) = -\sin x$

31. $-\pi \csc(\pi x)\cot(\pi x)$ **33.** $-\dfrac{\pi}{2}\csc^2\!\left(\dfrac{\pi x}{2}\right)$ **35.** $-(x+1)e^x\sin(xe^x)$ **37.** $2x\sec^2(x^2)$

39. $2e^x\cos x$ **41.**

43.

45.

47. (A) $P'(t) = \dfrac{5\pi}{26}\sin\dfrac{\pi t}{26}$, $0 < t < 104$ (B) $P'(8) = \$0.50$ hundred, or \$50 per week; $P'(26) = \$0$ per week; $P'(50) = -\$0.14$ hundred, or $-\$14$ per week

(C)

t	$P(t)$	
26	\$1,000	Local maximum
52	\$0	Local minimum
78	\$1,000	Local maximum

(D)

t	$P(t)$	
0	\$0	Absolute minimum
26	\$1,000	Absolute maximum
52	\$0	Absolute minimum
78	\$1,000	Absolute maximum
104	\$0	Absolute minimum

(E) Same answer as for part (C)

49. (A) $V'(t) = \dfrac{0.35\pi}{2}\sin\dfrac{\pi t}{2}$, $0 \le t \le 8$ (B) $V'(3) = -0.55$ L/sec; $V'(4) = 0.00$ L/sec; $V'(5) = 0.55$ L/sec

(C)

t	$V(t)$	
2	0.80	Local maximum
4	0.10	Local minimum
6	0.80	Local maximum

(D)

t	$V(t)$	
0	0.10	Absolute minimum
2	0.80	Absolute maximum
4	0.10	Absolute minimum
6	0.80	Absolute maximum
8	0.10	Absolute minimum

(E) Same answer as for part (C)

Exercises 8.3   **1.** $[0, \pi]$ **3.** $[0, \pi/3) \cup (5\pi/3, 2\pi]$ **5.** $\{\pi/4, 3\pi/4, 5\pi/4, 7\pi/4\}$ **7.** $(-\pi/2, \pi/4]$ **9.** $-\cos t + C$ **11.** $\frac{1}{3}\sin 3x + C$

13. $\frac{1}{13}(\sin x)^{13} + C$ **15.** $-\frac{3}{4}(\cos x)^{4/3} + C$ **17.** $\frac{1}{3}\sin x^3 + C$ **19.** 1   **21.** 1   **23.** $\sqrt{3}/2 - \frac{1}{2} \approx 0.366$ **25.** 1.4161   **27.** 0.0678   **29.** $e^{\sin x} + C$

31. $\ln|\sin x| + C$ **33.** $-\ln|\cos x| + C$ **35.** (A) $f(x)$

(B) $L_6 \approx 0.498$ **37.** (A) \$520 hundred, or \$52,000   (B) \$106.38 hundred, or \$10,638

(C) $P(t)$

39. (A) 104 tons   (B) 31 tons   (C) $P(n)$

Chapter 8 Review Exercises   **1.** (A) $\pi/6$ (B) $\pi/4$ (C) $\pi/3$ (D) $\pi/2$ (8.1)   **2.** (A) -1 (B) 0   (C) 1 (8.1)   **3.** $-\sin m$ (8.2)   **4.** $\cos u$ (8.2)
5. $(2x-2)\cos(x^2 - 2x + 1)$ (8.2)   **6.** $-\frac{1}{3}\cos 3t + C$ (8.3)   **7.** (A) $30°$ (B) $45°$ (C) $60°$ (D) $90°$ (8.1)   **8.** (A) $\frac{1}{2}$ (B) $\sqrt{2}/2$ (C) $\sqrt{3}/2$ (8.1)
9. (A) -0.6543 (B) 0.8308 (8.1)   **10.** $(x^2 - 1)\cos x + 2x\sin x$ (8.2)   **11.** $6(\sin x)^5\cos x$ (8.2)   **12.** $(\cos x)/[3(\sin x)^{2/3}]$ (8.2)
13. $\frac{1}{2}\sin(t^2 - 1) + C$ (8.3)   **14.** 2 (8.3)   **15.** $\sqrt{3}/2$ (8.3)   **16.** -0.243 (8.3)   **17.** $-\sqrt{2}/2$ (8.2)   **18.** $\sqrt{2}$ (8.3)
19. (A) $f(x)$

20. $\pi/12$ (8.1)   **21.** (A) -1 (B) $-\sqrt{3}/2$ (C) $-\frac{1}{2}$ (8.1)
22. $1/(\cos u)^2 = (\sec u)^2$ (8.2)   **23.** $-2x(\sin x^2)e^{\cos x^2}$ (8.2)
24. $e^{\sin x} + C$ (8.3)   **25.** $-\ln|\cos x| + C$ (8.3)   **26.** 15.2128 (8.3)

(B) $R_4 \approx 0.121$ (5.4, 8.3)

27. *(8.2, 8.3)*   **28.** *(8.2, 8.3)*   **29.** *(8.2, 8.3)*

30. (A) $R(0) =$ \$5 thousand; $R(2) =$ \$4 thousand; $R(3) =$ \$3 thousand; $R(6) =$ \$1 thousand   (B) $R(1) =$ \$4.732 thousand; $R(22) =$ \$4 thousand; the revenue is \$4,732 for a month of sweater sales 1 month after January 1, and \$4,000 for a month of sweater sales 22 months after January 1. *(8.1)*

31. (A) $R'(t) = -\dfrac{\pi}{3}\sin\dfrac{\pi t}{6}, 0 \le t \le 24$ (B) $R'(3) = -$\$1.047 thousand, or $-$\$1.047/mo; $R'(10) =$ \$0.907 thousand, or \$907/mo; $R'(18) =$ \$0.000 thousand

(C)

t	$R(t)$	
6	\$1,000	Local minimum
12	\$5,000	Local maximum
18	\$1,000	Local minimum

(D)

t	$R(t)$	
0	\$5,000	Absolute maximum
6	\$1,000	Absolute minimum
12	\$5,000	Absolute maximum
18	\$1,000	Absolute minimum
24	\$5,000	Absolute maximum

(E) Same answer as for part (C) *(8.2)*

32. (A) \$72 thousand, or \$72,000   (B) \$6.270 thousand, or \$6,270   (C) $R(t)$ *(8.3)*

Appendix A

Exercises A.1   **1.** vu **3.** $(3 + 7) + y$ **5.** $u + v$ **7.** T   **9.** T   **11.** F   **13.** T   **15.** T   **17.** T   **19.** T   **21.** F   **23.** T   **25.** T   **27.** No
29. (A) F   (B) T   (C) T   **31.** $\sqrt{2}$ and π are two examples of infinitely many.   **33.** (A) N, Z, Q, R (B) R (C) Q, R (D) Q, R
35. (A) F, since, for example, $2(3 - 1) \ne 2 \cdot 3 - 1$ (B) F, since, for example, $(8 - 4) - 2 \ne 8 - (4 - 2)$ (C) T   (D) F, since, for example,
$(8 \div 4) \div 2 \ne 8 \div (4 \div 2)$.   **37.** $\dfrac{1}{11}$ **39.** (A) 2.166 666 666 . . .   (B) 4.582 575 69 . . .   (C) 0.437 500 000 . . .   (D) 0.261 261 261 . . .   **41.** (A) 3   (B) 2
43. (A) 2   (B) 6   **45.** \$16.42   **47.** 2.8%

Exercises A.2   **1.** 3   **3.** $x^3 + 4x^2 - 2x + 5$ **5.** $x^3 + 1$ **7.** $2x^5 + 3x^4 - 2x^3 + 11x^2 - 5x + 6$ **9.** $-5u + 2$ **11.** $6a^2 + 6a$ **13.** $a^2 - b^2$
15. $6x^2 - 7x - 5$ **17.** $2x^2 + xy - 6y^2$ **19.** $9y^2 - 4$ **21.** $-4x^2 + 12x - 9$ **23.** $16m^2 - 9n^2$ **25.** $9u^2 + 24uv + 16v^2$ **27.** $a^3 - b^3$
29. $x^2 - 2xy + y^2 - 9z^2$ **31.** 1   **33.** $x^4 - 2x^2y^2 + y^4$ **35.** $-40ab$ **37.** $-4m + 8$ **39.** $-6xy$ **41.** $u^3 + 3u^2v + 3uv^2 + v^3$
43. $x^3 - 6x^2y + 12xy^2 - 8y^3$ **45.** $2x^2 - 2xy + 3y^2$ **47.** $x^4 - 10x^3 + 27x^2 - 10x + 1$ **49.** $4x^3 - 14x^2 + 8x - 6$ **51.** $m + n$ **53.** No change
55. $(1 + 1)^2 \ne 1^2 + 1^2$; either a or b must be 0   **57.** $0.09x + 0.12(10{,}000 - x) = 1{,}200 - 0.03x$
59. $20x + 30(3x) + 50(4{,}000 - x - 3x) = 200{,}000 - 90x$ **61.** $0.02x + 0.06(10 - x) = 0.6 - 0.04x$

Exercises A.3   **1.** $3m^2(2m^2 - 3m - 1)$ **3.** $2uv(4u^2 - 3uv + 2v^2)$ **5.** $(7m + 5)(2m - 3)$ **7.** $(4ab - 1)(2c + d)$ **9.** $(2x - 1)(x + 2)$
11. $(y - 1)(3y + 2)$ **13.** $(x + 4)(2x - 1)$ **15.** $(w + x)(y - z)$ **17.** $(a - 3b)(m + 2n)$ **19.** $(3y + 2)(y - 1)$ **21.** $(u - 5v)(u + 3v)$
23. Not factorable   **25.** $(wx - y)(wx + y)$ **27.** $(3m - n)^2$ **29.** Not factorable   **31.** $4(z - 3)(z - 4)$ **33.** $2x^2(x - 2)(x - 10)$ **35.** $x(2y - 3)^2$
37. $(2m - 3n)(3m + 4n)$ **39.** $uv(2u - v)(2u + v)$ **41.** $2x(x^2 - x + 4)$ **43.** $(2x - 3y)(4x^2 + 6xy + 9y^2)$ **45.** $xy(x + 2)(x^2 - 2x + 4)$
47. $[(x + 2) - 3y][(x + 2) + 3y]$ **49.** Not factorable   **51.** $(6x - 6y - 1)(x - y + 4)$ **53.** $(y - 2)(y + 2)(y^2 + 1)$
55. $3(x - y)^2(5xy - 5y^2 + 4x)$ **57.** True   **59.** False

Exercises A.4   **1.** 39/7   **3.** 495   **5.** $8d^6$ **7.** $\dfrac{15x^2 + 10x - 6}{180}$ **9.** $\dfrac{15m^2 + 14m - 6}{36m^3}$ **11.** $\dfrac{1}{x(x - 4)}$ **13.** $\dfrac{x - 6}{x(x - 3)}$ **15.** $\dfrac{-3x - 9}{(x - 2)(x + 1)^2}$
17. $\dfrac{2}{x - 1}$ **19.** $\dfrac{5}{a - 1}$ **21.** $\dfrac{x^2 + 8x - 16}{x(x - 4)(x + 4)}$ **23.** $\dfrac{7x^2 - 2x - 3}{6(x + 1)^2}$ **25.** $\dfrac{x(y - x)}{y(2x - y)}$ **27.** $\dfrac{-17c + 16}{15(c - 1)}$ **29.** $\dfrac{1}{x - 3}$ **31.** $\dfrac{-1}{2x(x + h)}$ **33.** $\dfrac{x - y}{x + y}$
35. (A) Incorrect   (B) $x + 1$ **37.** (A) Incorrect   (B) $2x + h$ **39.** (A) Incorrect   (B) $\dfrac{x^2 - x - 3}{x + 1}$ **41.** (A) Correct   **43.** $\dfrac{-2x - h}{3(x + h)^2 x^2}$ **45.** $\dfrac{x(x - 3)}{x - 1}$

Exercises A.5   **1.** $2/x^9$ **3.** $3w^7/2$ **5.** $2/x^3$ **7.** $1/w^5$ **9.** $4/a^6$ **11.** $1/a^6$ **13.** $1/8x^{12}$ **15.** 8.23×10^{10} **17.** 7.83×10^{-1} **19.** 3.4×10^{-5}
21. 40,000   **23.** 0.007   **25.** 61,710,000   **27.** 0.000 808   **29.** 1   **31.** 10^{14} **33.** $y^6/25x^4$ **35.** $4x^6/25$ **37.** $4y^3/3x^5$ **39.** $\dfrac{7}{4} - \dfrac{1}{4}x^{-3}$
41. $\dfrac{5}{2}x^2 - \dfrac{3}{2} + 4x^{-2}$ **43.** $\dfrac{x^2(x - 3)}{(x - 1)^3}$ **45.** $\dfrac{2(x - 1)}{x^3}$ **47.** 2.4×10^{10}; 24,000,000,000   **49.** 3.125×10^4; 31,250   **51.** 64   **55.** uv **57.** $\dfrac{bc(c + b)}{c^2 + bc + b^2}$
59. (A) \$51,329   (B) \$1,150   (C) 2.24%   **61.** (A) 9×10^{-6} (B) 0.000 009   (C) 0.0009%   **63.** 1,248,000

Exercises A.6   **1.** $6\sqrt[5]{x^3}$ **3.** $\sqrt[5]{(32x^2y^3)^3}$ **5.** $\sqrt{x^2 + y^2}$ (not $x + y$)   **7.** $5x^{3/4}$ **9.** $(2x^2y)^{3/5}$ **11.** $x^{1/3} + y^{1/3}$ **13.** 5   **15.** 64   **17.** -7

19. -16 **21.** $\dfrac{8}{125}$ **23.** $\dfrac{1}{27}$ **25.** $x^{2/5}$ **27.** m **29.** $2x/y^2$ **31.** $xy^2/2$ **33.** $1/(24x^{7/12})$ **35.** $2x + 3$ **37.** $30x^5\sqrt{3x}$ **39.** 2   **41.** $12x - 6x^{35/4}$

43. $3u - 13u^{1/2}v^{1/2} + 4v$ **45.** $36m^{3/2} - \dfrac{6m^{1/2}}{n^{1/2}} + \dfrac{6m}{n^{1/2}} - \dfrac{1}{n}$ **47.** $9x - 6x^{1/2}y^{1/2} + y$ **49.** $\dfrac{1}{2}x^{1/3} + x^{-1/3}$ **51.** $\dfrac{2}{3}x^{-1/4} + \dfrac{1}{3}x^{-2/3}$ **53.** $\dfrac{1}{2}x^{-1/6} - \dfrac{1}{4}$

55. $4n\sqrt{3mn}$ **57.** $\dfrac{2(x + 3)\sqrt{x - 2}}{x - 2}$ **59.** $7(x - y)(\sqrt{x} + \sqrt{y})$ **61.** $\dfrac{1}{xy\sqrt{5xy}}$ **63.** $\dfrac{1}{\sqrt{x + h} + \sqrt{x}}$ **65.** $\dfrac{1}{(t + x)(\sqrt{t} + \sqrt{x})}$

67. $x = y = 1$ is one of many choices.   **69.** $x = y = 1$ is one of many choices.   **71.** False   **73.** False   **75.** False   **77.** True   **79.** True   **81.** False

83. $\dfrac{x + 8}{2(x + 3)^{3/2}}$ **85.** $\dfrac{x - 2}{2(x - 1)^{3/2}}$ **87.** $\dfrac{x + 6}{3(x + 2)^{5/3}}$ **89.** 103.2   **91.** 0.0805   **93.** 4,588   **95.** (A) and (E); (B) and (F); (C) and (D)

Exercises A.7   **1.** $\pm\sqrt{11}$ **3.** $-\dfrac{4}{3}, 2$ **5.** $-2, 6$ **7.** $0, 2$ **9.** $3 \pm 2\sqrt{3}$ **11.** $-2 \pm \sqrt{2}$ **13.** $0, \dfrac{15}{2}$ **15.** $\pm\dfrac{3}{2}$ **17.** $\dfrac{1}{2}, -3$ **19.** $(-1 \pm \sqrt{5})/2$

21. $(3 \pm \sqrt{3})/2$ **23.** No real solution   **25.** $(-3 \pm \sqrt{11})/2$ **27.** $\pm\sqrt{3}$ **29.** $-\dfrac{1}{2}, 2$ **31.** $(x - 2)(x + 42)$ **33.** Not factorable in the integers
35. $(2x - 9)(x + 12)$ **37.** $(4x - 7)(x + 62)$ **39.** $r = \sqrt{A/P} - 1$ **41.** If $c < 4$, there are two distinct real roots; if $c = 4$, there is one real double root; and if $c > 4$, there are no real roots.   **43.** -2 **45.** $\pm\sqrt{10}$ **47.** $\pm\sqrt{3}, \pm\sqrt{5}$ **49.** 1,575 bottles at \$4 each   **51.** 13.64%   **53.** 8 ft/sec; $4\sqrt{2}$ or 5.66 ft/sec

Appendix B

Exercises B.1   **1.** 5, 7, 9, 11   **3.** $\dfrac{3}{2}, \dfrac{4}{3}, \dfrac{5}{4}, \dfrac{6}{5}$ **5.** $9, -27, 81, -243$ **7.** 23   **9.** $\dfrac{101}{100}$ **11.** $1 + 2 + 3 + 4 + 5 + 6 = 21$ **13.** $5 + 7 + 9 + 11 = 32$

15. $1 + \dfrac{1}{10} + \dfrac{1}{100} + \dfrac{1}{1,000} = \dfrac{1,111}{1,000}$ **17.** 3.6   **19.** 82.5   **21.** $\dfrac{1}{2}, -\dfrac{1}{4}, \dfrac{1}{8}, -\dfrac{1}{16}, \dfrac{1}{32}$ **23.** $0, 4, 0, 8, 0$ **25.** $1, -\dfrac{3}{2}, \dfrac{9}{4}, -\dfrac{27}{8}, \dfrac{81}{16}$ **27.** $a_n = n - 3$

29. $a_n = 4n$ **31.** $a_n = (2n - 1)/2n$ **33.** $a_n = (-1)^{n+1}n$ **35.** $a_n = (-1)^{n+1}(2n - 1)$ **37.** $a_n = \left(\dfrac{2}{5}\right)^{n-1}$ **39.** $a_n = x^n$ **41.** $a_n = (-1)^{n+1}x^{2n-1}$

43. $1 - 9 + 25 - 49 + 81$ **45.** $\dfrac{4}{7} + \dfrac{8}{9} + \dfrac{16}{11} + \dfrac{32}{13}$ **47.** $1 + x + x^2 + x^3 + x^4$ **49.** $x - \dfrac{x^3}{3} + \dfrac{x^5}{5} - \dfrac{x^7}{7} + \dfrac{x^9}{9}$ **51.** (A) $\displaystyle\sum_{k=1}^{5}(k + 1)$ (B) $\displaystyle\sum_{j=0}^{4}(j + 2)$

53. (A) $\displaystyle\sum_{k=1}^{4}\dfrac{(-1)^{k+1}}{k}$ (B) $\displaystyle\sum_{j=0}^{3}\dfrac{(-1)^j}{j + 1}$ **55.** $\displaystyle\sum_{k=1}^{n}\dfrac{k + 1}{k}$ **57.** $\displaystyle\sum_{k=1}^{n}\dfrac{(-1)^{k+1}}{2^k}$ **59.** False   **61.** True   **63.** 2, 8, 26, 80, 242   **65.** 1, 2, 4, 8, 16

67. $1, \dfrac{3}{2}, \dfrac{17}{12}, \dfrac{577}{408}; a_4 = \dfrac{577}{408} \approx 1.414\,216, \sqrt{2} \approx 1.414\,214$ **69.** 1, 1, 2, 3, 5, 8, 13, 21, 34, 55

Exercises B.2   **1.** (A) Arithmetic, with $d = -5; -26, -31$ (B) Geometric, with $r = -2; -16, 32$ (C) Neither   (D) Geometric, with $r = \dfrac{1}{3}; \dfrac{1}{54}, \dfrac{1}{162}$

3. Geometric; 1   **5.** Neither   **7.** Arithmetic; 127.5   **9.** $a_2 = 11, a_3 = 15$ **11.** $a_{21} = 82, S_{31} = 1,922$ **13.** $S_{20} = 930$ **15.** $a_2 = -6, a_3 = 12, a_4 = -24$

17. $S_7 = 547$ **19.** $a_{10} = 199.90$ **21.** $r = 1.09$ or -1.09 **23.** $S_{10} = 1,242, S_\infty = 1,250$ **25.** 2,706   **27.** -85 **29.** 1,120   **31.** (A) Does not exist

(B) $S_\infty = \dfrac{8}{5} = 1.6$ **33.** 2,400   **35.** 0.999   **37.** Use $a_1 = 1$ and $d = 2$ in $S_n = (n/2)[2a_1 + (n - 1)d]$.   **39.** $S_n = na_1$ **41.** No   **43.** Yes

45. $\$48 + \$46 + \cdots + \$4 + \$2 = \$600$ **47.** About \$11,670,000   **49.** \$1,628.89; \$2,653.30

Exercises B.3   **1.** 720   **3.** 10   **5.** 1,320   **7.** 10   **9.** 6   **11.** 1,140   **13.** 10   **15.** 6   **17.** 1   **19.** 816
21. $_4C_0a^4 + {}_4C_1a^3b + {}_4C_2a^2b^2 + {}_4C_3ab^3 + {}_4C_4b^4 = a^4 + 4a^3b + 6a^2b^2 + 4ab^3 + b^4$ **23.** $x^6 - 6x^5 + 15x^4 - 20x^3 + 15x^2 - 6x + 1$

25. $32a^5 - 80a^4b + 80a^3b^2 - 40a^2b^3 + 10ab^4 - b^5$ **27.** $3,060x^{14}$ **29.** $5,005p^9q^6$ **31.** $264x^2y^{10}$ **33.** $_nC_0 = \dfrac{n!}{0!\,n!} = 1; {}_nC_n = \dfrac{n!}{n!\,0!} = 1$
35. 1 5 10 10 5 1; 1 6 15 20 15 6 1

INDEX

INDEX OF APPLICATIONS

The following text is taken from *Additional Calculus Topics, To Accompany Calculus*, 13E
and *College Math*, 13E
by Barnett, Ziegler and Byleen

Differential Equations

CHAPTER

1

INTRODUCTION

Mathematical models for many processes in nature and society are best developed by understanding the *rate* at which the process occurs. For example, the rate of growth of a population may be proportional to the size of the population, proportional to the difference between the size and a fixed limit, or proportional to both the size and the difference between the size and a fixed limit. These descriptions of the rate may be expressed succinctly by *differential equations* such as

$$\frac{dy}{dt} = ky \qquad \frac{dy}{dt} = k(M - y) \qquad \frac{dy}{dt} = ky(M - y)$$

Solutions to these differential equations provide models for several types of exponential growth—unlimited, limited, and logistic (see Table 1, page 20). Unfortunately, there is no single method that will solve all the differential equations that may be encountered—even in very simple applications. In this chapter, after discussing some basic concepts in the first section, we will consider methods for solving several types of differential equations that have significant applications.

577

Section 1.1 BASIC CONCEPTS

- ■ Solutions of Differential Equations
- ■ Implicit Solutions
- ■ Application

In this section we review the basic concepts introduced in Section 5.3 of *Calculus* 13/e or Section 13.3 of *College Mathematics* 13/e and discuss in more detail what is meant by a solution to a differential equation, including explicit and implicit representations. Specific techniques for solving differential equations will be discussed in the next two sections.

■ Solutions of Differential Equations

A **differential equation** is an equation involving an unknown function, usually denoted by y, and one or more of its derivatives. For example,

$$y' = 0.2xy \tag{1}$$

is a differential equation. Since only the first derivative of the unknown function y appears in this equation, it is called a **first-order** differential equation. In general, the **order** of a differential equation is the highest derivative of the unknown function present in the equation.

Notice that we used y' rather than dy/dx to represent the derivative of y with respect to x in equation (1). This is customary practice in the study of differential equations. Unless indicated otherwise, we will assume that y is a function of the independent variable x and that y' refers to the derivative of y with respect to x.

Explore & Discuss **1**

Consider the differential equation

$$y' = 2x \tag{2}$$

(A) Which of the following functions satisfy this equation?

$$y = x^2 \qquad y = 2x^2 \qquad y = x^2 + 2$$

(B) Can you find other functions that satisfy equation (2)? What form do all these functions have?

(C) Discuss possible solution methods for any differential equation of the form

$$y' = f(x)$$

Figure 1A shows a *slope field* for equation (1). Recall from Section 5.3 of *Calculus* 13/e or Section 13.3 of *College Mathematics* 13/e that the **slope field** for a differential equation is obtained by drawing tangent line segments determined by the equation at each point in a grid. This provides a geometric interpretation of the equation that indicates the general shape of solutions to the equation. Due to the large number of line segments, slope fields are usually generated by a graphing utility. Figure 1B shows the slope field for $y' = 0.2xy$ on a TI-83 Plus.

Now consider the function

$$y = 2e^{0.1x^2}$$

whose derivative is

$$y' = 2e^{0.1x^2}(0.2x) = 0.4xe^{0.1x^2}$$

Substituting for y and y' in equation (1) gives

$$y' = 0.2xy \tag{1}$$

$$0.4xe^{0.1x^2} = 0.2x(2e^{0.1x^2})$$

$$0.4xe^{0.1x^2} = 0.4xe^{0.1x^2}$$

which is certainly true for all values of x. This shows that the function $y = 2e^{0.1x^2}$ is a **solution** of equation (1). But this function is not the only solution.

(A)

(B)

FIGURE 1 Slope field for
$y' = 0.2xy$

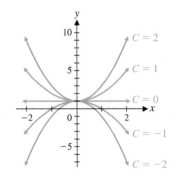

FIGURE 2 Particular solutions of $y' = 0.2xy$

In fact, if C is any constant, substituting $y = Ce^{0.1x^2}$ and $y' = 0.2xCe^{0.1x^2}$ in equation (1) yields the identity

$$y' = 0.2xy$$
$$0.2xCe^{0.1x^2} = 0.2xCe^{0.1x^2}$$

It turns out that all solutions of $y' = 0.2xy$ can be obtained from $y = Ce^{0.1x^2}$ by assigning C appropriate values; hence, $y = Ce^{0.1x^2}$ is called the **general solution** of equation (1). The collection of all functions of the form $y = Ce^{0.1x^2}$ is called the **family of solutions** of equation (1). The function $y = 2e^{0.1x^2}$, obtained by letting $C = 2$ in the general solution, is called a **particular solution** of equation (1). Other particular solutions are

$$y = -2e^{0.1x^2} \qquad C = -2$$
$$y = -e^{0.1x^2} \qquad C = -1$$
$$y = 0 \qquad C = 0$$
$$y = e^{0.1x^2} \qquad C = 1$$

These particular solutions are graphed in Figure 2, along with the slope field for equation (1). Notice how the particular solutions conform to the shapes indicated by the slope field.

INSIGHT

Most, but not all, first-order differential equations have general solutions that involve one arbitrary constant. Whenever we find a function, such as $y = Ce^{0.1x^2}$, that satisfies a given differential equation for any value of the constant C, we will assume this function is the general solution.

EXAMPLE 1   Verifying the Solution of a Differential Equation   Show that

$$y = Cx^2 + 1$$

is the general solution of the differential equation

$$xy' = 2y - 2$$

On the same set of axes, graph the particular solutions obtained by letting $C = -2, -1, 0, 1,$ and 2.

SOLUTION   Substituting $y = Cx^2 + 1$ and $y' = 2Cx$ in the differential equation, we have

$$xy' = 2y - 2$$
$$x(2Cx) = 2(Cx^2 + 1) - 2$$
$$2Cx^2 = 2Cx^2 + 2 - 2$$
$$2Cx^2 = 2Cx^2$$

which shows that $y = Cx^2 + 1$ is the general solution. The particular solutions corresponding to $C = -2, -1, 0, 1,$ and 2 are graphed in Figure 3.

FIGURE 3 Particular solutions of $xy' = 2y - 2$

MATCHED PROBLEM 1 | Show that

$$y = Cx + 1$$

is the general solution of the differential equation

$$xy' = y - 1$$

On the same set of axes, graph the particular solutions obtained by letting $C = -2, -1, 0, 1,$ and 2.

In many applications, we will be interested in finding a particular solution $y(x)$ that satisfies an **initial condition** of the form $y(x_0) = y_0$. The value of the constant C in the general solution must then be selected so that this initial condition is satisfied; that is, so that the solution curve (from the family of solution curves) passes through (x_0, y_0).

EXAMPLE 2 | **Finding a Particular Solution** Using the general solution in Example 1, find a particular solution of the differential equation $xy' = 2y - 2$ that satisfies the indicated initial condition, if such a solution exists.

(A) $y(1) = 3$ (B) $y(0) = 3$ (C) $y(0) = 1$

SOLUTION (A) *Initial condition* $y(1) = 3$. From Example 1, the general solution of the differential equation is

$$y = Cx^2 + 1$$

Substituting $x = 1$ and $y = 3$ in this general solution yields

$$3 = C(1)^2 + 1$$
$$= C + 1$$
$$C = 2$$

Thus, the particular solution satisfying the initial condition $y(1) = 3$ is

$$y = 2x^2 + 1$$

See the graph labeled $C = 2$ in Figure 3.

(B) *Initial condition* $y(0) = 3$. Substituting $x = 0$ and $y = 3$ in the general solution yields

$$3 = C(0)^2 + 1$$

No matter what value of C we select, $C(0)^2 = 0$ and this equation reduces to

$$3 = 1$$

which is *never* valid. Thus, we must conclude that there is no particular solution of this differential equation that will satisfy the initial condition $y(0) = 3$.

(C) *Initial condition* $y(0) = 1$. Substituting $x = 0$ and $y = 1$ in the general solution, we have

$$1 = C(0)^2 + 1$$
$$1 = 1$$

This equation is valid for *all* values of C. Thus, all solutions of this differential equation satisfy the initial condition $y(0) = 1$ (see Fig. 3).

INSIGHT

Example 2 shows that there may be exactly one particular solution, no particular solution, or many particular solutions that satisfy a given initial condition. The situation illustrated in Example 2A is the most common. Most first-order differential equations you will encounter will have exactly one particular solution that satisfies a given initial condition. However, we must always be aware of the possibility that a differential equation may not have any particular solutions that satisfy a given initial condition, or the possibility that it may have many particular solutions satisfying a given initial condition.

MATCHED PROBLEM 2   Using the general solution in Matched Problem 1, find a particular solution of the differential equation $xy' = y - 1$ that satisfies the indicated initial condition, if such a solution exists.

(A) $y(1) = 2$ (B) $y(0) = 2$ (C) $y(0) = 1$

◼ Implicit Solutions

The solution method we will discuss in the next section always produces an implicitly defined solution of a differential equation. In most of the differential equations we will consider, an explicit form of the solution can then be found by solving this implicit equation for the dependent variable in terms of the independent variable.

Explore & Discuss **2**   Let y be a function defined implicitly by the equation

$$xy = C \qquad \text{where } C \text{ is a constant} \qquad (3)$$

(A) Differentiate equation (3) implicitly to obtain a differential equation involving y and y'.

(B) Solve equation (3) for y, and verify that the resulting function satisfies the differential equation you found in part (A).

EXAMPLE 3   **Verifying an Implicit Solution** If y is defined implicitly by the equation

$$y^3 + e^y - x^4 = C \qquad (4)$$

show that y satisfies the differential equation

$$(3y^2 + e^y)y' = 4x^3$$

SOLUTION   We use implicit differentiation to show that y satisfies the given differential equation:

$$y^3 + e^y - x^4 = C$$

$$\frac{d}{dx}(y^3 + e^y - x^4) = \frac{d}{dx}C \quad \text{Remember, } \frac{d}{dx}x^n = nx^{n-1} \text{ and } \frac{d}{dx}e^x = e^x,$$

$$\boxed{\frac{d}{dx}y^3 + \frac{d}{dx}e^y - \frac{d}{dx}x^4 = 0} \qquad \text{but } \frac{d}{dx}y^n = ny^{n-1}y' \text{ and } \frac{d}{dx}e^y = e^y y'$$

$$\text{since } y \text{ is a function of } x.$$

$$3y^2y' + e^yy' - 4x^3 = 0$$

$$(3y^2 + e^y)y' = 4x^3$$

Since the last equation is the given differential equation, our calculations show that any function y defined implicitly by equation (4) is a solution of this differential equation. We cannot find an explicit formula for y, since none exists in terms of finite combinations of elementary functions.   ◼

MATCHED PROBLEM 3   If y is defined implicitly by the equation

$$y + e^{y^2} - x^2 = C$$

show that y satisfies the differential equation

$$(1 + 2ye^{y^2})y' = 2x$$

EXAMPLE 4   **Finding an Explicit Solution** If y is defined implicitly by the equation

$$y^2 - x^2 = C$$

show that y satisfies the differential equation

$$yy' = x$$

Find an explicit expression for the particular solution that satisfies the initial condition $y(0) = 2$.

SOLUTION   Using implicit differentiation, we have

$$y^2 - x^2 = C$$
$$\frac{d}{dx}(y^2 - x^2) = \frac{d}{dx}C$$
$$2yy' - 2x = 0$$
$$2yy' = 2x$$
$$yy' = x$$

which shows that y satisfies the given differential equation. Substituting $x = 0$ and $y = 2$ in $y^2 - x^2 = C$, we have

$$y^2 - x^2 = C$$
$$(2)^2 - (0)^2 = C$$
$$4 = C$$

Thus, the particular solution satisfying $y(0) = 2$ is a solution of the equation

$$y^2 - x^2 = 4$$

or

$$y^2 = 4 + x^2$$

Solving the last equation for y yields two explicit solutions,

$$y_1(x) = \sqrt{4 + x^2} \quad \text{and} \quad y_2(x) = -\sqrt{4 + x^2}$$

The first of these two solutions satisfies

$$y_1(0) = \sqrt{4 + (0)^2} = \sqrt{4} = 2$$

whereas the second satisfies

$$y_2(0) = -\sqrt{4 + (0)^2} = -\sqrt{4} = -2$$

Thus, the particular solution of the differential equation $yy' = x$ that satisfies the initial condition $y(0) = 2$ is

$$y(x) = \sqrt{4 + x^2}$$

Check:

$$y'(x) = \frac{1}{2}(4 + x^2)^{-1/2}2x \qquad\qquad yy' = x$$

$$= \frac{x}{\sqrt{4 + x^2}} \qquad\qquad \sqrt{4 + x^2}\left(\frac{x}{\sqrt{4 + x^2}}\right) \overset{?}{=} x$$

$$x \overset{\checkmark}{=} x$$

■

MATCHED PROBLEM 4   If y is defined implicitly by the equation

$$y^2 - x = C$$

show that y satisfies the differential equation

$$2yy' = 1$$

Find an explicit expression for the particular solution that satisfies the initial condition $y(0) = 3$.

APPLICATION

In economics, the price of a product is often studied over time, and so it is natural to view price as a function of time. Let $p(t)$ be the price of a particular product at time t. If $p(t)$ approaches a limiting value $\bar{p}$ as t approaches infinity, then the price for this product is said to be **dynamically stable** and $\bar{p}$ is referred to as the **equilibrium price.** (Later in this chapter, this definition of equilibrium price will be related to the one given in Section 6.2 of *Calculus* 13/e or Section 14.2 of *College Mathematics* 13/e.) In order to study the behavior of price as a function of time, economists often assume that the price satisfies a differential equation. This approach is illustrated in the next example.

EXAMPLE 5   **Dynamic Price Stability**   The price $p(t)$ of a product is assumed to satisfy the differential equation

$$\frac{dp}{dt} = 10 - 0.5p \qquad t \geq 0$$

(A) Show that

$$p(t) = 20 - Ce^{-0.5t}$$

is the general solution of this differential equation, and evaluate

$$\bar{p} = \lim_{t \to \infty} p(t)$$

(B) On the same set of axes, graph the three particular solutions that satisfy the initial conditions $p(0) = 40$, $p(0) = 10$, and $p(0) = 20$.

(C) Discuss the long-term behavior of the price of this product.

SOLUTION   (A) $p(t) = 20 - Ce^{-0.5t}$
$p'(t) = 0.5Ce^{-0.5t}$

Substituting in the given differential equation, we have

$$\frac{dp}{dt} = 10 - 0.5p$$

$$0.5Ce^{-0.5t} = 10 - 0.5(20 - Ce^{-0.5t})$$

$$= 10 - 10 + 0.5Ce^{-0.5t}$$

$$= 0.5Ce^{-0.5t}$$

which shows that $p(t) = 20 - Ce^{-0.5t}$ is the general solution of this differential equation. To find the equilibrium price, we must evaluate $\lim_{t \to \infty} p(t)$.

$$\bar{p} = \lim_{t \to \infty} p(t)$$

$$= \lim_{t \to \infty} (20 - Ce^{-0.5t})$$

$$= 20 - C \lim_{t \to \infty} e^{-0.5t} \qquad \lim_{t \to \infty} e^{-0.5t} = 0$$

$$= 20 - C \cdot 0$$

$$= 20$$

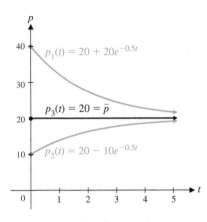

FIGURE 4 Particular solutions of

$$\frac{dp}{dt} = 10 - 0.5p$$

(B) Before we can graph the three particular solutions, we must evaluate the constant C for each of the indicated initial conditions. In each case, we will make use of the equation

$$p(0) = 20 - Ce^0 = 20 - C$$

Case 1	**Case 2**	**Case 3**
$p(0) = 40$	$p(0) = 10$	$p(0) = 20$
$20 - C = 40$	$20 - C = 10$	$20 - C = 20$
$C = -20$	$C = 10$	$C = 0$
$p_1(t) = 20 + 20e^{-0.5t}$	$p_2(t) = 20 - 10e^{-0.5t}$	$p_3(t) = 20$

The graphs are shown in Figure 4.

(C) From part (A), we know that $p'(t) = 0.5Ce^{-0.5t}$ and that the equilibrium price is $\bar{p} = 20$. If

$$p(0) = 20 - C > \bar{p} = 20 \qquad \boxed{\text{Add } -20 \text{ to both sides.}}$$
$$-C > 0 \qquad \text{or} \qquad C < 0$$

then $p'(t)$ is negative and the price decreases and approaches $\bar{p}$ as $t \to \infty$ [See the graph of $p_1(t)$ in Fig. 4]. On the other hand, if

$$p(0) = 20 - C < \bar{p} = 20 \qquad \boxed{\text{Add } -20 \text{ to both sides.}}$$
$$-C < 0 \qquad \text{or} \qquad C > 0$$

then $p'(t)$ is positive and the price increases and approaches $\bar{p}$ as $t \to \infty$ [See the graph of $p_2(t)$ in Fig. 4]. Finally, if

$$p(0) = 20 - C = \bar{p} = 20 \qquad \boxed{\text{Add } -20 \text{ to both sides.}}$$
$$-C = 0 \qquad \text{or} \qquad C = 0$$

then $p'(t) = 0$ and the price is constant for all t [See the graph of $p_3(t)$ in Fig. 4]. ▬

MATCHED PROBLEM 5 (A) Show that the price function

$$p(t) = 25 - Ce^{-0.2t}$$

is the general solution of the differential equation

$$\frac{dp}{dt} = 5 - 0.2p \qquad t \geq 0$$

Find the equilibrium price $\bar{p}$.

(B) On the same set of axes, graph the three particular solutions that satisfy the initial conditions $p(0) = 40, p(0) = 5$, and $p(0) = 25$.

(C) Discuss the long-term behavior of the price of this product. ▬▬

Answers to Matched Problems **1.**

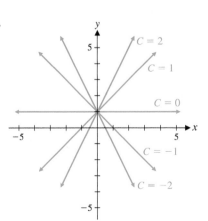

2. (A) $y = x + 1$

(B) No particular solution exists.

(C) $y = Cx + 1$ for any C

3. $\dfrac{d}{dx}y + \dfrac{d}{dx}e^{y^2} - \dfrac{d}{dx}x^2 = \dfrac{d}{dx}C$

$y' + e^{y^2}2yy' - 2x = 0$

$(1 + 2ye^{y^2})y' = 2x$

4. $y(x) = \sqrt{9 + x}$

5. (A) $\bar{p} = 25$

(B)

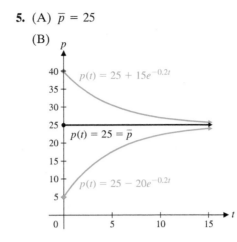

$p(t) = 25 + 15e^{-0.2t}$

$p(t) = 25 = \bar{p}$

$p(t) = 25 - 20e^{-0.2t}$

(C) If $p(0) > \bar{p}$, then the price decreases and approaches $\bar{p}$ as a limit. If $p(0) < \bar{p}$, then the price increases and approaches $\bar{p}$ as a limit. If $p(0) = \bar{p}$, then the price remains constant for all t.

Exercise 1.1

A In Problems 1–10, show that the given function is the general solution of the indicated differential equation.

1. $y = Cx^2$; $xy' = 2y$

2. $y = Cx^3$; $xy' = 3y$

3. $y = \dfrac{C}{x}$; $xy' = -y$

4. $y = \dfrac{C}{x^2}$; $xy' = -2y$

5. $y = C(x - 1)^2$; $(x - 1)y' = -y$

6. $y = \dfrac{C}{x + 1}$; $(x + 1)y' = -y$

7. $y = Ce^{x^2}$; $y' = 2xy$

8. $y = Ce^{-x^3}$; $y' = -3x^2y$

9. $y = 4 + Ce^x$; $y' = y - 4$

10. $y = 1.5 + Ce^{-2x}$; $y' = 3 - 2y$

In Problems 11–14, determine which of the slope fields (A)–(D) is associated with the indicated differential equation. Briefly justify your answer.

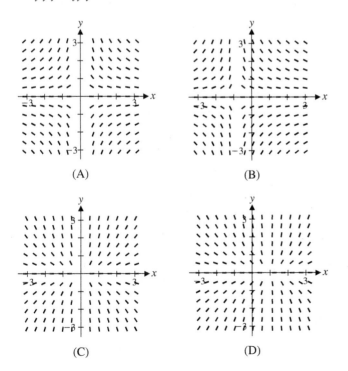

(A)

(B)

(C)

(D)

11. $xy' = 2y$ (From Problem 1)

12. $(x - 1)y' = -y$ (From Problem 5)

13. $xy' = -y$ (From Problem 3)

14. $(x + 1)y' = -y$ (From Problem 6)

In Problems 15–18, use the appropriate slope field—(A), (B), (C), or (D), given for Problems 11–14 (or a copy)—to graph the particular solutions obtained by letting C = −2, −1, 0, 1, and 2.

15. $y = Cx^2$ (From Problem 1)

16. $y = C(x - 1)^2$ (From Problem 5)

17. $y = \dfrac{C}{x}$ (From Problem 3)

18. $y = \dfrac{C}{x + 1}$ (From Problem 6)

B In Problems 19–28, show that the given function y is the general solution of the indicated differential equation. Find a particular solution satisfying the given initial condition.

19. $y = 3 + 3x + Ce^x$; $y' = y - 3x$; $y(0) = 4$

20. $y = -4 - 4x + Ce^x$; $y' = y + 4x$; $y(0) = 1$

21. $y = xe^{-x} + Ce^{-x}$; $y' = -y + e^{-x}$; $y(0) = 0$

22. $y = xe^{2x} + Ce^{2x}$; $y' = 2y + e^{2x}$; $y(0) = 0$

23. $y = 2x + \dfrac{C}{x}$; $xy' = 4x - y$; $y(1) = 1$

24. $y = -3x + \dfrac{C}{x}$; $xy' + y = -6x$; $y(1) = 2$

25. $y = 2 + Cx^{-3}$; $xy' + 3y = 6$; $y(1) = 3$

26. $y = 2 + Cx^{-4}$; $xy' + 4y = 8$; $y(1) = -2$

27. $y = x + Cx^{1/2}$; $2xy' - y = x$; $y(1) = 0$

28. $y = x^2 + Cx^{1/2}$; $2xy' - y = 3x^2$; $y(1) = 1$

If y is defined implicitly by the given equation, use implicit differentiation in Problems 29–32 to show that y satisfies the indicated differential equation.

29. $y^3 + xy - x^3 = C$; $(3y^2 + x)y' = 3x^2 - y$

30. $y + x^3y^3 - 2x = C$; $(1 + 3x^3y^2)y' = 2 - 3x^2y^3$

31. $xy + e^{y^2} - x^2 = C; (x + 2ye^{y^2})y' = 2x - y$

32. $y + e^{xy} - x = C; (1 + xe^{xy})y' = 1 - ye^{xy}$

If y is defined implicitly by the given equation, use implicit differentiation in Problems 33–36 to show that y satisfies the indicated differential equation. Find an explicit expression for the particular solution that satisfies the given initial condition.

33. $y^2 + x^2 = C; yy' = -x; y(0) = 3$

34. $y^2 + 2x^2 = C; yy' = -2x; y(0) = -4$

35. $\ln(2 - y) = x + C; y' = y - 2; y(0) = 1$

36. $\ln(5 - y) = 2x + C; y' = 2(y - 5); y(0) = 2$

In Problems 37–40, use the general solution y of the differential equation to find a particular solution that satisfies the indicated initial condition. Graph the particular solutions for $x \geq 0$.

37. $y = 2 + Ce^{-x}; y' = 2 - y$

    (A) $y(0) = 1$ (B) $y(0) = 2$ (C) $y(0) = 3$

38. $y = 4 + Ce^{-x}; y' = 4 - y$

    (A) $y(0) = 2$ (B) $y(0) = 4$ (C) $y(0) = 5$

39. $y = 2 + Ce^x; y' = y - 2$

    (A) $y(0) = 1$ (B) $y(0) = 2$ (C) $y(0) = 3$

40. $y = 4 + Ce^x; y' = y - 4$

    (A) $y(0) = 2$ (B) $y(0) = 4$ (C) $y(0) = 5$

In Problems 41–44, write a differential equation that expresses the given description of a rate. Explain what each symbol in your differential equation represents.

41. The number of employees of a corporation increases at a rate of 650 employees per year.

42. The blood pressure in the aorta decreases between heartbeats at a rate proportional to the blood pressure.

43. When a pizza is taken out of a hot oven, it cools off at a rate proportional to the difference between the temperature of the pizza and the room temperature of 72°F.

44. When a gallon of milk is taken out of a refrigerator, it warms up at a rate proportional to the difference between the room temperature of 75°F and the temperature of the milk.

C *In Problems 45 and 46, use the general solution y of the differential equation to find a particular solution that satisfies the indicated initial condition. Graph the particular solutions for $x \geq 0$.*

45. $y = \dfrac{10}{1 + Ce^{-x}}; y' = 0.1y(10 - y)$

    (A) $y(0) = 1$ (B) $y(0) = 10$ (C) $y(0) = 20$

    [*Hint:* The particular solution in part (A) has an inflection point at $x = \ln 9$.]

46. $y = \dfrac{5}{1 + Ce^{-x}}; y' = 0.2y(5 - y)$

    (A) $y(0) = 1$ (B) $y(0) = 5$ (C) $y(0) = 10$

    [*Hint:* The particular solution in part (A) has an inflection point at $x = \ln 4$.]

In Problems 47 and 48, use the general solution y of the differential equation to find a particular solution that satisfies the indicated initial condition.

47. $y = Cx^3 + 2; xy' = 3y - 6$

    (A) $y(0) = 2$ (B) $y(0) = 0$ (C) $y(1) = 1$

48. $y = Cx^4 + 1; xy' = 4y - 4$

    (A) $y(0) = 1$ (B) $y(0) = 0$ (C) $y(1) = 2$

In Problems 49 and 50, use window dimensions $Xmin = -5, Xmax = 5, Ymin = -5,$ and $Ymax = 5$.

49. Given that $y = x + Ce^{-x}$ is the general solution of the differential equation $y' + y = 1 + x$:

    (A) In the same viewing window, graph the particular solutions obtained by letting $C = 0, 1, 2,$ and 3.

    (B) What do the graphs of the solutions for $C > 0$ have in common?

    (C) In the same viewing window, graph the particular solutions obtained by letting $C = 0, -1, -2,$ and -3.

    (D) What do the graphs of the solutions for $C < 0$ have in common?

50. Repeat Problem 49, given that $y = x + (C/x)$ is the general solution of the differential equation $xy' = 2x - y$.

Applications

51. *Price stability.* The price $p(t)$ of a product is assumed to satisfy the differential equation

$$\frac{dp}{dt} = 0.5 - 0.1p$$

    (A) Show that

$$p(t) = 5 - Ce^{-0.1t}$$

    is the general solution of this differential equation, and evaluate

$$\bar{p} = \lim_{t \to \infty} p(t)$$

    (B) Graph the particular solutions that satisfy the initial conditions $p(0) = 1$ and $p(0) = 10$.

    (C) Discuss the long-term behavior of the price of this product.

52. *Price stability.* The price $p(t)$ of a product is assumed to satisfy the differential equation

$$\frac{dp}{dt} = 0.8 - 0.2p$$

    (A) Show that

$$p(t) = 4 - Ce^{-0.2t}$$

is the general solution of this differential equation, and evaluate

$$\bar{p} = \lim_{t \to \infty} p(t)$$

(B) Graph the particular solutions that satisfy the initial conditions $p(0) = 2$ and $p(0) = 8$.

(C) Discuss the long-term behavior of the price of this product.

53. *Continuous compound interest.* If money is deposited at the continuous rate of $200 per year into an account earning 8% compounded continuously, then the amount A in the account after t years satisfies the differential equation

$$\frac{dA}{dt} = 0.08A + 200$$

(A) Show that

$$A = Ce^{0.08t} - 2{,}500$$

is the general solution of this differential equation.

(B) Graph the particular solutions satisfying $A(0) = 0$ and $A(0) = 1{,}000$.

(C) Compare the long-term behavior of the two particular solutions in part (B). Discuss the effect of the value of $A(0)$ on the amount in the account.

54. *Continuous compound interest.* If money is withdrawn at the continuous rate of $500 per year from an account earning 10% compounded continuously, then the amount A in the account after t years satisfies the differential equation

$$\frac{dA}{dt} = 0.1A - 500$$

(A) Show that

$$A = 5{,}000 + Ce^{0.1t}$$

is the general solution of this differential equation.

(B) Graph the particular solutions satisfying $A(0) = 4{,}000$ and $A(0) = 6{,}000$.

(C) Compare the long-term behavior of the two particular solutions in part (B). Discuss the effect of the value of $A(0)$ on the amount in the account.

55. *Population growth—Verhulst growth model.* The number $N(t)$ of bacteria in a culture at time t is assumed to satisfy the Verhulst growth model

$$\frac{dN}{dt} = 100 - 0.5N$$

(A) Show that

$$N(t) = 200 - Ce^{-0.5t}$$

is the general solution of this differential equation, and evaluate

$$\bar{N} = \lim_{t \to \infty} N(t)$$

where $\bar{N}$ is the equilibrium size of the population.

(B) Graph the particular solutions that satisfy $N(0) = 50$ and $N(0) = 300$.

(C) Discuss the long-term behavior of this population.

56. *Population growth—logistic growth model.* The population $N(t)$ of a certain species of animal in a controlled habitat at time t is assumed to satisfy the logistic growth model

$$\frac{dN}{dt} = \frac{1}{500}N(1{,}000 - N)$$

(A) Show that

$$N(t) = \frac{1{,}000}{1 + Ce^{-2t}}$$

is the general solution of this differential equation, and evaluate $\bar{N} = \lim_{t \to \infty} N(t)$.

(B) Graph the particular solutions that satisfy $N(0) = 200$ and $N(0) = 2{,}000$.

(C) Discuss the long-term behavior of this population.

57. *Rumor spread—Gompertz growth model.* The rate of propagation of a rumor is assumed to satisfy the Gompertz growth model

$$\frac{dN}{dt} = Ne^{-0.5t}$$

where $N(t)$ is the number of individuals who have heard the rumor at time t.

(A) Show that $N(t) = Ce^{-2e^{-0.5t}}$ is the general solution of this differential equation, and evaluate $\bar{N} = \lim_{t \to \infty} N(t)$.

(B) Graph the particular solutions that satisfy $N(0) = 100$ and $N(0) = 200$.

(C) Discuss the effect of the value of $N(0)$ on the long-term propagation of this rumor.

Section 1.2   SEPARATION OF VARIABLES

- Separation of Variables
- Exponential Growth
- Limited Growth
- Logistic Growth
- Comparison of Exponential Growth Phenomena

■ Separation of Variables

In this section we will develop a technique called *separation of variables,* which can be used to solve differential equations that can be expressed in the form

$$f(y)y' = g(x) \tag{1}$$

We have already used this technique informally in Section 5.3 of *Calculus* 13/e or in Section 13.3 of *College Mathematics* 13/e to derive some important exponential growth laws. We will now present a more formal development of this method.

Explore & Discuss 1

Use algebraic manipulation to express each of the following equations in the form $f(y)y' = g(x)$, or explain why it is not possible to do so.

(A) $y' = x^2y$

(B) $y' = x^2 + xy$

(C) $y' = x^2y + xy$

The solution of differential equations by the method of separating the variables is based on the substitution formula for indefinite integrals. If $y = y(x)$ is a differentiable function of x, then

$$\int f(y)\, dy = \int f[y(x)]y'(x)\, dx \qquad \text{Substitution formula} \tag{2}$$
$$\text{for indefinite integrals}$$

If $y(x)$ is also the solution of (1), then $y(x)$ and $y'(x)$ must satisfy (1). That is,

$$f[y(x)]y'(x) = g(x)$$

Substituting $g(x)$ for $f[y(x)]y'(x)$ in (2), we have

$$\int f(y)\, dy = \int g(x)\, dx \tag{3}$$

Thus, the solution $y(x)$ of (1) is given implicitly by this equation. If both indefinite integrals can be evaluated, and if the resulting equation can be solved for y in terms of x, then we have an explicit solution of the differential equation (1).

This discussion is summarized in Theorem 1:

THEOREM 1   SEPARATION OF VARIABLES

The solution of the differential equation

$$f(y)y' = g(x) \tag{1}$$

is given implicitly by the equation

$$\int f(y)\, dy = \int g(x)\, dx \tag{3}$$

> ### INSIGHT
>
> Differentials can be used to make the connection between equations (1) and (3) in Theorem 1:
>
> $$f(y)y' = g(x) \qquad \text{Substitute } y' = \frac{dy}{dx} \text{ in equation (1).}$$
>
> $$f(y)\frac{dy}{dx} = g(x) \qquad \text{Multiply both sides by } dx.$$
>
> $$f(y)\,dy = g(x)\,dx \qquad \text{Integrate both sides.}$$
>
> $$\int f(y)\,dy = \int g(x)\,dx \qquad \text{Equation (3)}$$

Some prefer to go directly from equation (1) to equation (3). Others may want to switch to differential notation and multiply both sides by dx. The choice is up to you. We will illustrate both approaches in the following examples.

EXAMPLE 1   Using Separation of Variables, Solve: $y' = 2xy^2$.

SOLUTION   We choose to introduce differentials:

$$y' = 2xy^2 \qquad \text{Multiply by } 1/y^2 \text{ to separate the variables.}$$

$$\frac{1}{y^2}y' = 2x \qquad \text{Substitute } y' = \frac{dy}{dx}.$$

$$\frac{1}{y^2}\frac{dy}{dx} = 2x \qquad \text{Multiply both sides by } dx \text{ and write } 1/y^2 \text{ as a power form.}$$

$$y^{-2}\,dy = 2x\,dx \qquad \text{Integrate both sides.}$$

$$\int y^{-2}\,dy = \int 2x\,dx \qquad \text{Use the power rule to evaluate each integral.}$$

$$\frac{y^{-1}}{-1} + C_1 = 2\frac{x^2}{2} + C_2 \qquad \begin{array}{l}\text{Simplify each side algebraically and combine } C_1 \text{ and } C_2 \\ \text{into a single arbitrary constant.}\end{array}$$

$$-\frac{1}{y} = x^2 + C \qquad \text{Solve for } y.$$

$$y = -\frac{1}{x^2 + C} \qquad \text{General solution of } y' = 2xy^2.$$

Check:

$$y' = \frac{d}{dx}\left(-\frac{1}{x^2 + C}\right) = \frac{2x}{(x^2 + C)^2}$$

$$y' = 2xy^2 \qquad \begin{array}{l}\text{Substitute } y' = 2x/(x^2 + C)^2 \text{ and} \\ y = -1/(x^2 + C).\end{array}$$

$$\frac{2x}{(x^2 + C)^2} \overset{?}{=} 2x\left(-\frac{1}{x^2 + C}\right)^2$$

$$\frac{2x}{(x^2 + C)^2} \overset{\checkmark}{=} \frac{2x}{(x^2 + C)^2}$$

This verifies that our general solution is correct. (You should develop the habit of checking the solution of each differential equation you solve, as we have done here. From now on, we leave it to you to check most of the examples worked in the text.)

MATCHED PROBLEM 1   Solve: $y' = 4x^3y^2$.

In some cases the general solution obtained by the technique of separation of variables does not include all the solutions to a differential equation. For example, the constant function $y = 0$ also satisfies the differential equation in Example 1. (Verify this.) Yet the solution $y = 0$ cannot be obtained from the expression

$$y = -\frac{1}{x^2 + C}$$

for any choice of the constant C. Solutions of this type are referred to as **singular solutions** and are usually discussed in more advanced courses. We will not attempt to find the singular solutions of any of the differential equations we consider.

EXAMPLE 2

Using Separation of Variables Find the general solution of

$$(1 + x^2)y' = 2x(y - 1)$$

Then find the particular solution that satisfies the initial condition $y(0) = 3$.

SOLUTION   First, we find the general solution:

$$(1 + x^2)y' = 2x(y - 1)$$ *Multiply by $1/(1 + x^2)$ and $1/(y - 1)$ to separate the variables.*

$$\frac{y'}{y - 1} = \frac{2x}{1 + x^2}$$ *Convert to an equation involving indefinite integrals (Theorem 1).*

$$\int \frac{dy}{y - 1} = \int \frac{2x \, dx}{1 + x^2}$$ *Evaluate each indefinite integral.*

$$\ln|y - 1| = \ln(1 + x^2) + C$$

where C is an arbitrary constant. Notice that the two constants of integration always can be combined to form a single arbitrary constant. Also note that we can use $1 + x^2$ instead of $|1 + x^2|$, since $1 + x^2$ is always positive. In order to solve for y, we convert this last equation to exponential form:

$$|y - 1| = e^{\ln(1+x^2)+C}$$
$$= e^C e^{\ln(1+x^2)}$$ *Use the property $e^{\ln r} = r$.*
$$= e^C(1 + x^2)$$

It can be shown that if we replace e^C with an arbitrary constant K, then we can omit the absolute value signs on the left side of the last equation.* The resulting equation can then be used to find the general solution to the original differential equation. Thus,

$$y - 1 = K(1 + x^2)$$
$$y = 1 + K(1 + x^2)$$ *General solution*

To find the particular solution that satisfies $y(0) = 3$, we substitute $x = 0$ and $y = 3$ in the general solution and solve for K:

$$3 = 1 + K(1 + 0)$$
$$K = 2$$
$$y = 1 + 2(1 + x^2) = 3 + 2x^2$$ *Particular solution*

---

*In any problem involving separation of variables, you may assume that the equations

$$e^{\ln|f(y)|} = e^C g(x) \qquad \text{and} \qquad f(y) = Kg(x)$$

are equivalent (both C and K are arbitrary constants). Justification of this assumption involves properties of the absolute value and exponential functions.

MATCHED PROBLEM 2 | Find the general solution of

$$(2 + x^4)y' = 4x^3(y - 3)$$

Then find the particular solution that satisfies the initial condition $y(0) = 5$.

Explore & Discuss 2

Let y be a positive quantity that is changing with respect to time t, such as the price of a product, the amount of a drug in the bloodstream, or the population of a country. If y satisfies the differential equation

$$\frac{dy}{dt} = ky \qquad k \text{ a constant}$$

then we say that the rate of change of y with respect to time t is proportional to y. If $k > 0$, y is increasing (growing); if $k = 0$, y is constant; and if $k < 0$, y is decreasing (declining or decaying). For each of the following differential equations, write a brief verbal description of the rate of change of y and discuss the possible increasing/decreasing properties of y.

(A) $\dfrac{dy}{dt} = k$ (B) $\dfrac{dy}{dt} = k(100 - y)$ (C) $\dfrac{dy}{dt} = ky(100 - y)$

■ Exponential Growth

We now return to the study of exponential growth models first begun in Section 5.3 of *Calculus* 13/e or Section 13.3 of *College Mathematics* 13/e. This time we will place more emphasis on determining the relevant model for a particular application and on using separation of variables to solve the corresponding differential equation in each problem. We begin with the familiar exponential growth model.

DEFINITION   Exponential Growth Model

If the rate of change with respect to time t of a quantity y is proportional to the amount present, then y satisfies the differential equation

$$\frac{dy}{dt} = ky$$

Exponential growth includes both the case where y is increasing and the case where y is decreasing (or decaying).

EXAMPLE 3

Product Analysis Mothballs of a certain brand evaporate at a rate proportional to their volume, losing half their volume every 4 weeks. If the volume of each mothball is initially 15 cubic centimeters and a mothball becomes ineffective when its volume reaches 1 cubic centimeter, how long will these mothballs be effective?

SOLUTION

The volume of each mothball is decaying at a rate proportional to its volume. This indicates that an exponential growth model is appropriate for this problem. If V is the volume of a mothball after t weeks, then

$$\frac{dV}{dt} = kV \qquad \text{Exponential growth model}$$

Since the initial volume is 15 cubic centimeters, we know that $V(0) = 15$. After 4 weeks, the volume will be half the original volume, so $V(4) = 7.5$. Summarizing these requirements, we have the following exponential decay model:

$$\frac{dV}{dt} = kV$$

$$V(0) = 15 \qquad V(4) = 7.5$$

We want to determine the value of t that satisfies the equation $V(t) = 1$. First, we use separation of variables to find the general solution of the differential equation:

$$\frac{dV}{dt} = kV$$

$$\frac{1}{V}\frac{dV}{dt} = k$$

$$\int \frac{dV}{V} = \int k\,dt$$

$$\ln V = kt + C \qquad \text{\textit{We can write ln V in place of ln |V|, since V > 0.}}$$
$$V = e^{kt+C} = e^C e^{kt} = Ae^{kt} \qquad \text{\textit{General solution}}$$

where $A = e^C$ is a positive constant. Now we use the initial condition to determine the value of the constant A:

$$V(0) = Ae^0 = A = 15$$
$$V(t) = 15e^{kt}$$

Next, we apply the condition $V(4) = 7.5$ to determine the constant k:

$$V(4) = 15e^{4k} = 7.5$$
$$e^{4k} = \frac{7.5}{15} = 0.5$$
$$4k = \ln 0.5$$
$$k = \frac{\ln 0.5}{4} \approx -0.1733$$
$$V(t) = 15e^{(t/4)\ln 0.5} \qquad \text{\textit{Particular solution}}$$

The graph of $V(t)$ is shown in Figure 1. To determine how long the mothballs will be effective, we find t when $V = 1$:

$$V(t) = 1$$
$$15e^{(t/4)\ln 0.5} = 1$$
$$e^{(t/4)\ln 0.5} = \frac{1}{15}$$
$$\frac{t}{4}\ln 0.5 = \ln \frac{1}{15}$$
$$t = \frac{4 \ln \frac{1}{15}}{\ln 0.5} \approx 15.6 \text{ weeks}$$

V

15

$V(t) = 15e^{(t/4)\ln 0.5}$

7.5

1

0   4   15.6 t

FIGURE 1 Exponential decay

MATCHED PROBLEM 3   Repeat Example 3 if the mothballs lose half their volume every 5 weeks.

Limited Growth

In certain situations there is an upper limit (or a lower limit), say M, on the values a variable can assume. This limiting value leads to the *limited growth model*.

DEFINITION Limited Growth Model

If the rate of change with respect to time t of a quantity y is proportional to the difference between y and a limiting value M, then y satisfies the differential equation

$$\frac{dy}{dt} = k(M - y)$$

When we speak of limited growth, we will include both the case where y increases and approaches M from below and the case where y decreases and approaches M from above.

EXAMPLE 4

Sales Growth   The annual sales S of a new company are expected to grow at a rate proportional to the difference between the sales and an upper limit of $20 million. The sales are 0 initially and $4 million for the second year of operation.

(A) Find the sales S during year t.

(B) Find $S(10)$ and $S'(10)$ and interpret.

(C) In what year should the sales be expected to reach $15 million?

SOLUTION

(A) The description of the sales growth indicates that a limited growth model is appropriate for this problem. That is,

$$\frac{dS}{dt} = k(20 - S) \qquad \text{Limited growth model}$$

$$S(0) = 0 \qquad S(2) = 4$$

Separating the variables in the limited growth model, we have

$$\frac{dS}{dt} = k(20 - S) \qquad \text{Multiply both sides by } dt \text{ and } 1/(20 - S).$$

$$\frac{1}{20 - S}\, dS = k\, dt \qquad \text{Integrate both sides.}$$

$$\int \frac{1}{20 - S}\, dS = \int k\, dt \qquad \text{Evaluate both integrals.}$$

$$-\ln(20 - S) = kt + C \qquad \text{We can write } -\ln(20 - S) \text{ in place}$$

$$\ln(20 - S) = -kt - C \qquad \text{of } -\ln|20 - S|, \text{ since } 0 < S < 20.$$

$$20 - S = e^{-kt-C} = e^{-C}e^{-kt} = Ae^{-kt} \qquad A = e^{-C}$$

$$S = 20 - Ae^{-kt} \qquad \text{General solution}$$

Now we use the conditions $S(0) = 0$ and $S(2) = 4$ to determine the constants A and k:

$$S(0) = 20 - Ae^{0}$$

$$= 20 - A = 0$$

$$A = 20$$

$$S(t) = 20 - 20e^{-kt}$$

$$S(2) = 20 - 20e^{-2k} = 4$$

$$20e^{-2k} = 16$$

$$e^{-2k} = \frac{16}{20} = 0.8$$

$$-2k = \ln 0.8$$

$$k = -\frac{\ln 0.8}{2} \approx 0.1116$$

$$S(t) = 20 - 20e^{(t/2)\ln 0.8} \qquad \text{Particular solution}$$

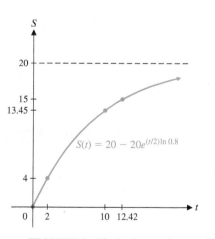

S

20

15
13.45

$S(t) = 20 - 20e^{(t/2)\ln 0.8}$

4

0   2   10   12.42 t

FIGURE 2 Limited growth

The graph of $S(t)$ is shown in Figure 2. Notice that the upper limit of $20 million is a horizontal asymptote.

(B) $S'(t) = -20\left(\frac{1}{2}\ln 0.8\right)e^{(t/2)\ln 0.8}$

$S(10) = 20 - 20e^{5\ln 0.8} \approx \$13.45$ million

$S'(10) = -20\left(\frac{1}{2}\ln 0.8\right)e^{5\ln 0.8} \approx \$0.7312$ million

During the tenth year, the sales are approximately \$13.45 million and are increasing at the rate of \$0.7312 million per year.

(C) $S(t) = 20 - 20e^{(t/2)\ln 0.8} = 15$

$20e^{(t/2)\ln 0.8} = 5$

$e^{(t/2)\ln 0.8} = \frac{5}{20} = 0.25$

$\frac{t}{2}\ln 0.8 = \ln 0.25$

$t = \frac{2\ln 0.25}{\ln 0.8} \approx 12.43$ years

The annual sales will exceed \$15 million in the thirteenth year.   ▬

MATCHED PROBLEM 4   Repeat Example 4 if the sales during the second year are \$3 million.

Logistic Growth

If a quantity first begins to grow exponentially but then starts to approach a limiting value, it is said to exhibit *logistic growth*. More formally, we have:

DEFINITION   Logistic Growth Model

If the rate of change with respect to time t of a quantity y is proportional to both the amount present and the difference between y and a limiting value M, then y satisfies the differential equation

$$\frac{dy}{dt} = ky(M - y)$$

Theoretically, functions satisfying logistic growth models can be increasing or decreasing, just as was the case for the exponential and limited growth models. However, decreasing functions are seldom encountered in actual practice.

EXAMPLE 5   **Population Growth** In a study of ciliate protozoans, it has been shown that the rate of growth of the number of *Paramecium caudatum* in a medium with fixed volume is proportional to the product of the number present and the difference between an upper limit of 375 and the number present. Suppose the medium initially contains 25 paramecia. After 1 hour there are 125 paramecia. How many paramecia are present after 2 hours?

SOLUTION   If P is the number of paramecia in the medium at time t, then the model for this problem is the following logistic growth model:

$$\frac{dP}{dt} = kP(375 - P)$$

$$P(0) = 25 \qquad P(1) = 125$$

We want to find $P(2)$. First, we separate the variables and convert to an equation involving indefinite integrals:

$$\frac{1}{P(375 - P)}\frac{dP}{dt} = k$$

$$\int \frac{1}{P(375 - P)}\,dP = \int k\,dt \qquad (4)$$

The integral on the left side of (4) can be evaluated either by using an algebraic identity* or by using formula 9 in Table II in *Calculus* 13/e or in *College Mathematics* 13/e. We will use formula 9 with $u = P$, $a = 375$, and $b = -1$:

$$\int \frac{1}{u(a + bu)}\,du = \frac{1}{a}\ln\left|\frac{u}{a + bu}\right| \qquad \text{Formula 9}$$

$$\int \frac{1}{P(375 - P)}\,dP = \frac{1}{375}\ln\left|\frac{P}{375 - P}\right| \qquad \text{Since } 0 < P < 375, \text{ the absolute value}$$
$$\text{signs can be omitted.}$$

$$= \frac{1}{375}\ln\left(\frac{P}{375 - P}\right)$$

Returning to equation (4), we have

$$\frac{1}{375}\ln\left(\frac{P}{375 - P}\right) = \int k\,dt = kt + D \qquad \text{D is a constant.}$$

$$\ln\left(\frac{P}{375 - P}\right) = 375kt + 375D$$

$$\frac{P}{375 - P} = e^{375kt + 375D} = e^{Bt}e^{C} \qquad B = 375k,\ C = 375D$$

$$P = 375e^{Bt}e^{C} - Pe^{Bt}e^{C}$$

$$P(e^{Bt}e^{C} + 1) = 375e^{Bt}e^{C}$$

$$P = \frac{375e^{Bt}e^{C}}{e^{Bt}e^{C} + 1} \qquad \text{Multiply numerator and denominator}$$
$$\text{by } e^{-Bt}e^{-C} \text{ and let } A = e^{-C}.$$

$$= \frac{375}{1 + Ae^{-Bt}} \qquad \text{General solution}$$

Now we use the conditions $P(0) = 25$ and $P(1) = 125$ to evaluate the constants A and B:

$$P(0) = \frac{375}{1 + A} = 25$$

$$375 = 25 + 25A$$

$$A = 14$$

$$P(t) = \frac{375}{1 + 14e^{-Bt}}$$

$$P(1) = \frac{375}{1 + 14e^{-B}} = 125$$

$$375 = 125 + 1{,}750e^{-B}$$

$$e^{-B} = \frac{250}{1{,}750} = \frac{1}{7}$$

$$-B = \ln\frac{1}{7} = -\ln 7$$

$$B = \ln 7$$

$$P(t) = \frac{375}{1 + 14e^{-t\ln 7}} \qquad \text{Particular solution}$$

---

*If you do not wish to use Table II to evaluate integrals, you can use the algebraic identity

$$\frac{1}{x(a - x)} = \frac{1}{a}\left[\frac{(a - x) + x}{x(a - x)}\right] = \frac{1}{a}\left(\frac{1}{x} + \frac{1}{a - x}\right)$$

to evaluate this integral and in all logistic growth problems in Exercise 1-2.

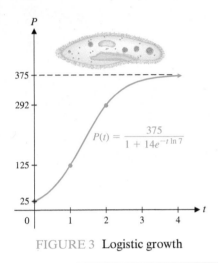

$$P(t) = \frac{375}{1 + 14e^{-t \ln 7}}$$

FIGURE 3 Logistic growth

To determine the population after 2 hours, we evaluate $P(2)$:

$$P(2) = \frac{375}{1 + 14e^{-2 \ln 7}} \approx 292 \text{ paramecia}$$

The graph of $P(t)$ is shown in Figure 3. This S-shaped curve is typical of logistic growth functions. Notice that the upper limit of 375 is a horizontal asymptote. ▬

Comparison of Exponential Growth Phenomena

The graphs and equations given in Table 1 compare several widely used growth models. These are divided basically into two groups: unlimited growth and limited growth. Following each equation and graph is a short (and necessarily incomplete) list of areas in which each model is used.

MATCHED PROBLEM 5 Repeat Example 5 for 15 paramecia initially and 150 paramecia after 1 hour.

Answers to Matched Problems

1. $y = -1/(x^4 + C)$
2. General solution: $y = 3 + K(2 + x^4)$; particular solution: $y = 5 + x^4$
3. 19.5 weeks
4. (A) $S(t) = 20 - 20e^{(t/2)\ln 0.8}$
   (B) $S(10) = \$11.13$ million; $S'(10) = \$0.7211$ million; during the tenth year, the sales are approximately $11.13 million and are increasing at the rate of $0.72211 million per year.
   (C) $t \approx 17.06$ yr; annual sales will exceed $15 million near the beginning of the eighteenth year.
5. 343 paramecia

TABLE 1 Exponential Growth

Description	Model	Solution	Graph	Uses
Unlimited growth: Rate of growth is proportional to the amount present	$\dfrac{dy}{dt} = ky$ $k, t > 0$ $y(0) = c$	$y = ce^{kt}$		• Short-term population growth (people, bacteria, etc.) • Growth of money at continuous compound interest • Price–supply curves
Exponential decay: Rate of growth is proportional to the amount present	$\dfrac{dy}{dt} = -ky$ $k, t > 0$ $y(0) = c$	$y = ce^{-kt}$		• Depletion of natural resources • Radioactive decay • Light absorption in water • Price–demand curves • Atmospheric pressure (t is altitude)
Limited growth: Rate of growth is proportional to the difference between the amount present and a fixed limit	$\dfrac{dy}{dt} = k(M - y)$ $k, t > 0$ $y(0) = 0$	$y = M(1 - e^{-kt})$		• Sales fads (for example, skateboards) • Depreciation of equipment • Company growth • Learning
Logistic growth: Rate of growth is proportional to the amount present and to the difference between the amount present and a fixed limit	$\dfrac{dy}{dt} = ky(M - y)$ $k, t > 0$ $y(0) = \dfrac{M}{1 + c}$	$y = \dfrac{M}{1 + ce^{-kMt}}$		• Long-term population growth • Epidemics • Sales of new products • Rumor spread • Company growth

Exercise 1.2

A *In Problems 1–4, write a differential equation that describes the rate of change of the indicated quantity.*

1. The annual sales y of a company are increasing at the rate of $100,000 per year.

2. The annual sales y of a company are increasing at a rate proportional to the annual sales.

3. The fish population y in a lake is growing at a rate proportional to the difference between the population and an upper limit of 10,000 fish.

4. In a community of 100,000, the number of people y who have contracted an infectious disease is growing at a rate proportional to the product of the number of people who have contracted the disease and the number who have not.

In Problems 5–8, write a verbal description of the rate of change of the given quantity satisfying the indicated differential equation, and discuss the increasing/decreasing properties of the quantity.

5. The annual sales y (in millions of dollars) of a company satisfy $dy/dt = 0.1y$ and $y(0) = 2$.

6. The annual sales y (in millions of dollars) of a company satisfy $dy/dt = 0.1(8 - y)$ and $y(0) = 2$.

7. The number of people y who have heard a rumor satisfies $dy/dt = 0.2y(5,000 - y)$ and $y(0) = 1$.

8. The amount of a drug y (in milliliters) in a patient's bloodstream satisfies $dy/dt = -0.2y$ and $y(0) = 5$.

In Problems 9–12, show that the technique of separation of variables is applicable by writing each differential equation in the form $f(y)y' = g(x)$.

9. $xy' = y^2$

10. $y' + xy = 2x$

11. $xy' + xy = 3y$

12. $y' + \dfrac{x}{y} = \dfrac{2}{y}$

In Problems 13–22, find the general solution for each differential equation. Then find the particular solution satisfying the initial condition.

13. $y' = 3x^2$; $y(0) = -1$

14. $y' = 2e^{2x}$; $y(0) = 5$

15. $y' = \dfrac{2}{x}$; $y(1) = 2$

16. $y' = \dfrac{2}{\sqrt[3]{x}}$; $y(1) = 2$

17. $y' = y$; $y(0) = 10$

18. $y' = y - 10$; $y(0) = 15$

19. $y' = 25 - y$; $y(0) = 5$

20. $y' = 3x^2y$; $y(0) = \dfrac{1}{2}$

21. $y' = \dfrac{y}{x}$; $y(1) = 5$; $x > 0$

22. $y' = \dfrac{y}{x^2}$; $y(-1) = 2e$

B *In Problems 23–32, find the general solution for each differential equation. Then find the particular solution satisfying the initial condition.*

23. $y' = \dfrac{1}{y^2}$; $y(1) = 3$

24. $y' = \dfrac{x^2}{y^2}$; $y(0) = 2$

25. $y' = ye^x$; $y(0) = 3e$

26. $y' = -y^2e^x$; $y(0) = \dfrac{1}{2}$

27. $y' = \dfrac{e^x}{e^y}$; $y(0) = \ln 2$

28. $y' = y^2(2x + 1)$; $y(0) = -\dfrac{1}{5}$

29. $y' = xy + x$; $y(0) = 2$

30. $y' = (2x + 4)(y - 3)$; $y(0) = 2$

31. $y' = (2 - y)^2e^x$; $y(0) = 1$

32. $y' = \dfrac{x^{1/2}}{(y - 5)^2}$; $y(1) = 7$

In Problems 33–38, find the general solution for each differential equation. Do not attempt to find an explicit expression for the solution.

33. $y' = \dfrac{1 + x^2}{1 + y^2}$

34. $y' = \dfrac{6x - 9x^2}{2y + 4}$

35. $xyy' = (1 + x^2)(1 + y^2)$

36. $(xy^2 - x)y' = x^2y - x^2$

37. $x^2e^yy' = x^3 + x^3e^y$

38. $y' = \dfrac{xe^x}{\ln y}$

C *In Problems 39–44, find an explicit expression for the particular solution for each differential equation.*

39. $xyy' = \ln x$; $y(1) = 1$

40. $y' = \dfrac{xe^{x^2}}{y}$; $y(0) = 2$

41. $xy' = x\sqrt{y} + 2\sqrt{y}$; $y(1) = 4$

42. $y' = x(x - 1)^{1/2}(y - 1)^{1/2}$; $y(1) = 1$

43. $yy' = xe^{-y^2}$; $y(0) = 1$

44. $yy' = x(1 + y^2)$; $y(0) = 1$

In Problems 45–48, discuss why the technique of separation of variables does not produce an explicit solution $y = h(x)$ of the differential equation.

45. $y' + xy = 2$

46. $y' - 5x^2y = e^x$

47. $3yy' = e^{x^2} + y$

48. $y' = \dfrac{9x^2 + 2}{5y^4 - 6}$

49. In many applications involving limited growth, the limiting value M is not known in advance and must be determined from data. Suppose that the rate of change with respect to time t of a quantity y is proportional to the difference between y and an unknown upper limit M, and that $y = 0$ when $t = 0$. Using the limited growth model, it follows that

$$y = M(1 - e^{-kt}) \qquad M > 0, k > 0$$

(A)   Using the data given in the table, find two equations that M and k must satisfy, and solve each equation for M.

t	1	1.5
y	3	4

(B)   Use a graphing utility and the equations from part (A) to approximate M to one decimal place.

50.   Refer to Problem 49. Suppose that the rate of change with respect to time of a quantity y is proportional to the difference between y and an unknown lower limit M,

and that $y = 10$ when $t = 0$. Using the limited growth model, it follows that

$$y = M + (10 - M)e^{-kt} \qquad M > 0, k > 0$$

(A)   Using the data given in the table, find two equations that M and k must satisfy, and solve each equation for M.

t	1	5
y	9	7

(B)   Use a graphing utility and the equations from part (A) to approximate M to one decimal place.

Applications

51.   *Continuous compound interest.* Provident Bank offers a CD (certificate of deposit) that earns 5.5% compounded continuously. How much will a $5,000 investment be worth in 5 years?

52.   *Continuous compound interest.* Equitable Federal offers a CD that earns 4.9% compounded continuously. How much will a $10,000 investment be worth in 4 years?

53.   *Advertising.* A company is using radio advertising to introduce a new product to a community of 100,000 people. Suppose the rate at which people learn about the new product is proportional to the number who have not yet heard of it.

(A)   If no one is aware of the product at the start of the advertising campaign and after 7 days 20,000 people are aware of the product, how long will it take for 50,000 people to become aware of the product?

(B)   Suppose the company is dissatisfied with the result in part (A) and wants to decrease to 14 days the amount of time it takes for 50,000 people to become aware of their product. For this to happen, how many people must become aware of the product during the first 7 days?

54.   *Advertising.* Prior to the beginning of an advertising campaign, 10% of the potential users of a certain brand are aware of the brand name. After the first week of the campaign, 20% of the consumers are aware of the brand name. Assume that the percentage of informed consumers is growing at a rate proportional to the product of the percentage of informed consumers and the percentage of uninformed consumers.

(A)   What percentage of consumers will be aware of the brand name after 5 weeks of advertising?

(B)   Suppose the company is dissatisfied with the result in part (A) and increases the intensity of the advertising campaign so that 25% of the consumers are aware of the brand name after the first week. What effect does this have on the percentage of consumers that will be aware of the brand name after 5 weeks of advertising?

55.   *Product analysis.* A company wishes to analyze a new room deodorizer. The active ingredient evaporates at a

rate proportional to the amount present. Half of the ingredient evaporates in the first 30 days after the deodorizer is installed. If the deodorizer becomes ineffective after 90% of the active ingredient has evaporated, how long will one of these deodorizers remain effective?

56.   *Product analysis.* A chlorine-based pool disinfectant contains an active ingredient with a half-life of 4 days. How often should this disinfectant be added to a pool to ensure that at least 30% of the active ingredient is present?

57.   *Personal income.* According to the U.S. Census Bureau, total personal income was $6,201 billion in 1995 and $8,407 billion in 2000. If personal income is increasing at a rate proportional to total personal income, find the total personal income and the rate of change of total personal income in 2010 and interpret.

58.   *Corporate profits.* According to the U.S. Bureau of Economic Analysis, total corporate profits in domestic industries were $576.8 billion in 1995 and $946.2 billion in 2000. If corporate profits are increasing at a rate proportional to total corporate profits, find the total corporate profits and the rate of change of total corporate profits in 2010 and interpret.

59.   *Sales analysis.* The annual sales of a new company are expected to grow at a rate proportional to the difference between the sales and an upper limit of $5 million. If the sales are 0 initially and $1 million during the fourth year of operation, find the sales and the rate of change of the sales during the fifteenth year and interpret. How long (to the nearest year) will it take for the sales to grow to $4 million?

60.   *Sales analysis.* The annual sales of a company have declined from $8 million 2 years ago to $6 million today. If the annual sales continue to decline at a rate proportional to the difference between the annual sales and a lower limit of $3 million, find the sales and the rate of change of the sales 3 years from now and interpret. How long (to the nearest year) will it take for the sales to decline to $3.5 million?

61.   *Sales analysis.* A new company has 0 sales initially, sales of $2 million during the first year, and sales of $5 million during the third year. If the annual sales S are assumed to be growing at a rate proportional to the difference between the sales and an unknown upper limit M, then by the limited growth model,

$$S(t) = M(1 - e^{-kt}) \qquad M > 0, k > 0$$

where t is time (in years) and $S(t)$ represents sales (in millions of dollars). Use approximation techniques to find k to one decimal place and M to the nearest million. (See Problem 49.)

62. *Sales analysis.* Refer to Problem 61. Approximate k to one decimal place and M to the nearest million if the sales during the third year are $4 million and all other information is unchanged.

Newton's law of cooling states that the rate of change of the temperature of an object is proportional to the difference between the temperature of the object and the temperature of the surrounding medium. Use this law to formulate models for Problems 63–66, and then solve using the techniques discussed in this section.

63. *Manufacturing.* As part of a manufacturing process, a metal bar is to be heated in an oven until its temperature reaches 500°F. The oven is maintained at a constant temperature of 800°F. The temperature of the bar before it is placed in the oven is 80°F. After 2 minutes in the oven, the temperature of the bar is 200°F. How long should the bar be left in the oven?

64. *Manufacturing.* The next step in the manufacturing process described in Problem 63 calls for the heated bar to be cooled in a vat of water until its temperature reaches 100°F. The water in the vat is maintained at a constant temperature of 50°F. If the temperature of the bar is 500°F when it is first placed in the water and the bar has cooled to 400°F after 5 minutes in the water, how long should the bar be left in the water?

65. *Food preparation.* A pie is removed from an oven where the temperature is 325°F and placed in a freezer with a constant temperature of 25°F. After 1 hour in the freezer, the temperature of the pie is 225°F. What is the temperature of the pie after 4 hours in the freezer?

66. *Food preparation.* A roast is taken from a freezer where the temperature is 20°F and placed in an oven with a constant temperature of 350°F. After 1 hour in the oven, the temperature of the roast is 185°F. What is the temperature of the roast after 3 hours in the oven?

67. *Population growth.* A culture of bacteria is growing at a rate proportional to the number present. The culture initially contains 100 bacteria. After 1 hour there are 140 bacteria in the culture.

(A)   How many bacteria will be present after 5 hours?

(B)   When will the culture contain 1,000 bacteria?

68. *Population growth.* A culture of bacteria is growing in a medium that can support a maximum of 1,100 bacteria. The rate of change of the number of bacteria is proportional to the product of the number present and the difference between 1,100 and the number present. The culture initially contains 100 bacteria. After 1 hour there are 140 bacteria.

(A)   How many bacteria are present after 5 hours?

(B)   When will the culture contain 1,000 bacteria?

69. *Simple epidemic.* An influenza epidemic has spread throughout a community of 50,000 people at a rate proportional to the product of the number of people who have been infected and the number who have not been infected. If 100 individuals were infected initially and 500 were infected 10 days later:

(A)   How many people will be infected after 20 days?

(B)   When will half the community be infected?

70. *Ecology.* A fish population in a large lake is declining at a rate proportional to the difference between the population and a lower limit of 5,000 fish.

(A)   If the population has declined from 15,000 fish 3 years ago to 10,000 today, find the population 6 years from now.

(B)   Suppose the fish population 6 years from now turns out to be 8,000, indicating that the lake might be able to support more than the original lower limit of 5,000 fish. Assuming that the rate of change of the population is still proportional to the difference between the population and an unknown lower limit M, approximate M to the nearest hundred.

Body temperature is one factor that crime scene investigators use to estimate time of death. Use Newton's law of cooling in Problems 71 and 72 and assume that the body temperature at the time of death is 98.6°F.

71. *Crime scene investigation.* A body was found in an alley at 1:00 A.M. The temperature that night was a constant 50°F and the temperature of the body at the time of discovery was 75°F. The investigator left the body in the alley while she looked for other evidence. She checked the body temperature again at 2:00 A.M. and found that the temperature of the body had dropped to 70°F. What was the time of death (to the nearest hour)?

72. *Crime scene investigation.* A body was found stashed in a freezer at 3:00 P.M. The temperature in the freezer was a constant 0°F. A crime scene investigator determined that the temperature of the body at the time of discovery was 55°F. Evidence suggested that death occurred in the freezer. Leaving the body in the freezer, the investigator checked the body temperature again at 4:00 P.M. and found that the temperature had dropped to 50°F. What was the time of death (to the nearest hour)?

73. *Sensory perception.* A person is subjected to a physical stimulus that has a measurable magnitude, but the intensity of the resulting sensation is difficult to measure. If s is the magnitude of the stimulus and $I(s)$ is the intensity of sensation, experimental evidence suggests that

$$\frac{dI}{ds} = k\frac{I}{s}$$

for some constant k. Express I as a function of s.

74. *Learning.* The number of words per minute, N, a person can type increases with practice. Suppose the rate of change of N is proportional to the difference between N and an upper limit of 140. It is reasonable to assume that a beginner cannot type at all. Thus, $N = 0$ when $t = 0$. If a person can type 35 words per minute after 10 hours of practice:

(A)   How many words per minute can that individual type after 20 hours of practice?

(B)   How many hours must that individual practice to be able to type 105 words per minute?

75.   *Rumor spread.* A rumor spreads through a population of 1,000 people at a rate proportional to the product of

the number who have heard it and the number who have not heard it. If 5 people initiated a rumor and 10 people had heard it after 1 day:

(A)   How many people will have heard the rumor after 7 days?

(B)   How long will it take for 850 people to hear the rumor?

Section 1.3   FIRST-ORDER LINEAR DIFFERENTIAL EQUATIONS

- The Product Rule Revisited
- Solution of First-Order Linear Differential Equations
- Applications

The Product Rule Revisited

The solution method we will discuss in this section is based in part on the product rule. Recall that if F and S are two differentiable functions, then

$$(FS)' = FS' + F'S$$

In Chapter 2 of *Calculus* 13/e or Chapter 10 of *College Mathematics* 13/e, we started with F and S and used the product rule to find $(FS)'$. Now we want to use the rule in the reverse direction. That is, we want to be able to recognize when a sum of two terms is the derivative of a product.

Explore & Discuss **1**   Match each sum on the left with the derivative of a product on the right, where y is an unknown differentiable function of x.

(A) $x^2y' + 2xy$ (1) $(e^{x^2}y)'$

(B) $e^{-2x}y' - 2e^{-2x}y$ (2) $\left(\dfrac{1}{x^2}\, y\right)'$

(C) $\dfrac{1}{x^2}\, y' - \dfrac{2}{x^3}\, y$ (3) $(e^{-2x}y)'$

(D) $e^{x^2}y' + 2xe^{x^2}y$ (4) $(x^2y)'$

    In general, if $m(x)y' + n(x)y$ is the derivative of a product, how must $m(x)$ and $n(x)$ be related?

Solution of First-Order Linear Differential Equations

A differential equation that can be expressed in the form

$$y' + f(x)y = g(x)$$

is called a **first-order linear differential equation.**
    For example,

$$y' + \frac{2}{x}\, y = x \tag{1}$$

is a first-order linear differential equation with $f(x) = 2/x$ and $g(x) = x$. This equation cannot be solved by the method of separation of variables. (Try to separate the variables to convince yourself that this is true.) Instead, we will change the form of the equation by multiplying both sides by x^2:

$$x^2y' + 2xy = x^3 \tag{2}$$

How was x^2 chosen? We will discuss that shortly. Let us first see how this choice leads to a solution of the problem.

Since $(x^2)' = 2x$, the left side of (2) is the derivative of a product:

$$x^2y' + 2xy = (x^2y)'$$

Thus, we can write equation (2) as

$$(x^2y)' = x^3$$

Now we can integrate both sides:

$$\int (x^2y)'\,dx = \int x^3\,dx$$

$$x^2y = \frac{x^4}{4} + C$$

Solving for y, we obtain the general solution

$$y = \frac{x^2}{4} + \frac{C}{x^2}$$

The function x^2, which we used to transform the original equation into one we could solve as illustrated, is called an *integrating factor*. It turns out that there is a specific formula for determining the integrating factor for any first-order linear differential equation. Furthermore, this integrating factor can then be used to find the solution of the differential equation, just as we used x^2 to find the solution to (1). The formula for the integrating factor and a step-by-step summary of the solution process are given in the box that follows.

PROCEDURE   **Solving First-Order Linear Differential Equations**

Step 1. Write the equation in the **standard form:**

$$y' + f(x)y = g(x)$$

Step 2. Compute the **integrating factor:**

$$I(x) = e^{\int f(x)\,dx}$$

[When evaluating $\int f(x)\,dx$, choose 0 for the constant of integration.]

Step 3. Multiply both sides of the standard form by the integrating factor $I(x)$. The left side should now be in the form $[I(x)y]'$:

$$[I(x)y]' = I(x)g(x)$$

Step 4. Integrate both sides:

$$I(x)y = \int I(x)g(x)\,dx$$

[When evaluating $\int I(x)g(x)\,dx$, include an arbitrary constant of integration.]

Step 5. Solve for y to obtain the **general solution:**

$$y = \frac{1}{I(x)} \int I(x)g(x)\,dx$$

EXAMPLE 1   **Using an Integrating Factor**   Solve: $2xy' + y = 10x^2$.

SOLUTION   **Step 1.** Multiply both sides by $1/(2x)$ to obtain the standard form:

$$y' + \frac{1}{2x}y = 5x \qquad f(x) = \frac{1}{2x} \text{ and } g(x) = 5x$$

Step 2. Find the integrating factor:

$$I(x) = e^{\int f(x)\,dx}$$

$$= e^{\int [1/(2x)]\,dx} \qquad \text{Assume } x > 0 \text{ and choose } 0$$
$$\text{for the constant of integration.}$$

$$= e^{(1/2)\ln x} \qquad r\ln t = \ln t^r$$

$$= e^{\ln x^{1/2}} \qquad e^{\ln r} = r, r > 0$$

$$= x^{1/2} \qquad \text{Integrating factor}$$

Step 3. Multiply both sides of the standard form by the integrating factor:

$$x^{1/2}\left(y' + \frac{1}{2x}y\right) = x^{1/2}(5x)$$

$$x^{1/2}y' + \tfrac{1}{2}x^{-1/2}y = 5x^{3/2} \qquad \text{The left side should have}$$
$$\text{the form } [I(x)y]'.$$

$$(x^{1/2}y)' = 5x^{3/2}$$

Step 4. Integrate both sides:

$$\int (x^{1/2}y)'\,dx = \int 5x^{3/2}\,dx \qquad \text{Include an arbitrary constant}$$
$$\text{of integration on the right side.}$$

$$x^{1/2}y = 2x^{5/2} + C$$

Step 5. Solve for y:

$$y = \frac{1}{x^{1/2}}(2x^{5/2} + C)$$

$$= 2x^2 + \frac{C}{x^{1/2}} \qquad \text{General solution} \qquad \blacksquare$$

MATCHED PROBLEM 1

Solve: $xy' + 3y = 4x$.

INSIGHT

The requirement that a differential equation be written in standard form is essential. To see why, consider the following equation, which is not written in standard form:

$$2y' + 4y = 8 \tag{3}$$

If we proceed without first converting (3) to standard form, the integrating factor formula gives us

$$I(x) = e^{\int 4\,dx} = e^{4x}$$

Notice that we chose 0 for the constant of integration when computing $I(x)$. This is not a requirement but a recommendation. Ignoring this recommendation will not result in an error, but will complicate the subsequent calculations.

Returning to the differential equation in (3) and multiplying both sides by $I(x)$, we have:

$$2e^{4x}y' + 4e^{4x}y = 8e^{4x} \tag{4}$$

The left side of (4) is supposed to be $[e^{4x}y]'$. But

$$[e^{4x}y]' = e^{4x}y' + 4e^{4x}y \tag{5}$$

Since the left side of (4) does not equal $[e^{4x}y]'$ (the coefficients of the y' terms are different), we cannot integrate both sides of (4) to find the solution to (3). In other words, $I(x) = e^{4x}$ is not an integrating factor for (3).

Whenever you use an integrating factor, you should check that

$$[I(x)y]' = I(x)y' + I'(x)y$$

as we did in (5), before proceeding to solve for y.

As an exercise, you should provide a correct solution to equation (3).

In Example 1, notice that we assumed $x > 0$ to avoid introducing absolute value signs in the integrating factor. Many of the problems in this section will require the evaluation of expressions of the form $e^{\int [h'(x)/h(x)]dx}$. In order to avoid the complications caused by the introduction of absolute value signs, we will assume that the domain of $h(x)$ has been restricted so that $h(x) > 0$. This will simplify the solution process. We state the following familiar formulas for convenient reference (in the first formula the constant of integration is 0, in accordance with Step 2):

SUMMARY **BASIC FORMULAS INVOLVING THE NATURAL LOGARITHM FUNCTION**

If the domain of $h(x)$ is restricted so that $h(x) > 0$, then

$$\int \frac{h'(x)}{h(x)}\, dx = \ln h(x) \quad \text{and} \quad e^{\ln h(x)} = h(x)$$

INSIGHT

If a first-order linear differential equation is written in standard form, then multiplying both sides of the equation by its integrating factor will always convert the left side of the equation into the derivative of $I(x)y$. Thus, it is possible to omit Steps 3 and 4, and proceed directly to Step 5. This approach is illustrated in the next example. You decide which is easier to use—the step-by-step procedure or the formula in Step 5.

EXAMPLE 2 **Using an Integrating Factor** Find the particular solution of the equation

$$y' + 2xy = 4x$$

satisfying the initial condition $y(0) = 5$.

SOLUTION Since the equation is already in standard form, we begin by finding the integrating factor:

$$I(x) = e^{\int 2x\, dx} = e^{x^2} \quad f(x) = 2x$$

Proceeding directly to Step 5, we have

$$y = \frac{1}{I(x)} \int I(x)g(x)\, dx \quad g(x) = 4x$$

$$= \frac{1}{e^{x^2}} \int e^{x^2}(4x)\, dx$$

$$= e^{-x^2} \int 4xe^{x^2}\, dx \qquad \text{Let } u = x^2, du = 2x\, dx.$$

$$= e^{-x^2}(2e^{x^2} + C)$$

$$= 2 + Ce^{-x^2} \qquad \text{General solution}$$

Substituting $x = 0$ and $y = 5$ in the general solution, we have

$$5 = 2 + C$$

$$C = 3$$

$$y = 2 + 3e^{-x^2} \quad \text{Particular solution}$$

MATCHED PROBLEM 2 Find the particular solution of $y' + 3x^2y = 9x^2$ satisfying the initial condition $y(0) = 7$.

⚠ CAUTION:

1. When integrating both sides of an equation such as

$$(x^{1/2}y)' = 5x^{3/2}$$

remember that

$$x^{1/2}y = \int 5x^{3/2}\, dx \neq 2x^{5/2} \quad \text{"4 C" is missing in the antiderivative.}$$

Remember: A constant of integration must be included when evaluating

$$\int I(x)g(x)\, dx.$$

If you omit this constant, you will not be able to find the general solution of the differential equation. See Step 4 of Example 1 for the correct procedure.

2. $\dfrac{1}{e^{x^2}} \int 4xe^{x^2}\, dx \neq \dfrac{1}{e^{x^2}} \int 4xe^{x^2}\, dx = \int 4x\, dx$

Just as a variable factor cannot be moved across the integral sign, a variable factor outside the integral sign cannot be used to cancel a factor inside the integral sign. See Example 2 for the correct procedure.

APPLICATIONS

If P is the initial amount deposited into an account earning $100r\%$ compounded continuously, and A is the amount in the account after t years, then we saw in Section 5.3 of *Calculus* 13/e or in Section 13.3 of *College Mathematics* 13/e that A satisfies the exponential growth equation

$$\frac{dA}{dt} = rA \qquad A(0) = P$$

Now suppose that money is continuously withdrawn from this account at a rate of $\$m$ per year. Then the amount A in the account at time t must satisfy

$$\begin{pmatrix} \text{Rate of change} \\ \text{of amount } A \end{pmatrix} = \begin{pmatrix} \text{Rate of growth} \\ \text{from continuous} \\ \text{compounding} \end{pmatrix} - \begin{pmatrix} \text{Rate of} \\ \text{withdrawal} \end{pmatrix}$$

$$\frac{dA}{dt} \qquad = \qquad rA \qquad - \qquad m$$

or

$$\frac{dA}{dt} - rA = -m \tag{6}$$

Explore & Discuss 2   How does equation (6) change if instead of making continuous withdrawals, money is continuously deposited into the account at the rate of $\$m$ per year?

EXAMPLE 3   **Continuous Compound Interest** An initial deposit of $10,000 is made into an account earning 8% compounded continuously. Money is then continuously withdrawn at a constant rate of $1,000 a year until the account is depleted. Find the amount in the account at any time t. When will the amount be 0? What is the total amount withdrawn from this account?

SOLUTION   The amount A in the account at any time t must satisfy [see equation (6)]

$$\frac{dA}{dt} - 0.08A = -1,000 \qquad A(0) = 10,000$$

The integrating factor for this equation is

$$I(t) = e^{\int -0.08\, dt} = e^{-0.08t} \quad f(t) = -0.08$$

Multiplying both sides of the differential equation by $I(t)$ and following the step-by-step procedure, we have

$$e^{-0.08t} \frac{dA}{dt} - 0.08e^{-0.08t} A = -1{,}000e^{-0.08t}$$

$$(e^{-0.08t} A)' = -1{,}000e^{-0.08t}$$

$$e^{-0.08t} A = \int -1{,}000e^{-0.08t}\, dt$$

$$= 12{,}500e^{-0.08t} + C$$

$$A = 12{,}500 + Ce^{0.08t} \quad \textit{General solution}$$

Applying the initial condition $A(0) = 10{,}000$ yields

$$A(0) = 12{,}500 + C = 10{,}000$$

$$C = -2{,}500$$

$$A(t) = 12{,}500 - 2{,}500e^{0.08t} \quad \textit{Amount in the account at any time } t$$

To determine when the amount in the account is 0, we solve $A(t) = 0$ for t:

$$A(t) = 0$$

$$12{,}500 - 2{,}500e^{0.08t} = 0$$

$$12{,}500 = 2{,}500e^{0.08t}$$

$$5 = e^{0.08t}$$

$$t = \frac{\ln 5}{0.08} \approx 20.118 \text{ years}$$

Thus, the account is depleted after 20.118 years.

MATCHED PROBLEM 3   Repeat Example 3 if the account earns 5% compounded continuously.

EXAMPLE 4   **Equilibrium Price**   In economics, the supply S and the demand D for a commodity often can be considered as functions of both the price, $p(t)$, and the rate of change of the price, $p'(t)$. (Thus, S and D are ultimately functions of time t.) The **equilibrium price at time** t is the solution of the equation $S = D$. If $p(t)$ is the solution of this equation, then the **long-range equilibrium price** is

$$\bar{p} = \lim_{t \to \infty} p(t)$$

For example, if

$$D = 50 - 2p(t) + 2p'(t) \qquad S = 20 + 4p(t) + 5p'(t)$$

and $p(0) = 15$, then the equilibrium price at time t is the solution of the equation

$$50 - 2p(t) + 2p'(t) = 20 + 4p(t) + 5p'(t)$$

This simplifies to

$$p'(t) + 2p(t) = 10 \quad f(t) = 2 \text{ and } g(t) = 10$$

which is a first-order linear equation with integrating factor

$$I(t) = e^{\int 2\, dt} = e^{2t}$$

$p(t)$

15

$p(t) = 5 + 10e^{-2t}$

10

$\bar{p} = 5$

1   2 t

FIGURE 1

Proceeding directly to Step 5, we have

$$p(t) = \frac{1}{e^{2t}} \int 10e^{2t}\, dt$$

$$= e^{-2t}(5e^{2t} + C)$$

$$p(t) = 5 + Ce^{-2t} \qquad \textit{General solution}$$

$$p(0) = 5 + C = 15$$

$$C = 10$$

$$p(t) = 5 + 10e^{-2t} \qquad \textit{Equilibrium price at time } t \text{ (see Fig. 1)}$$

$$\bar{p} = \lim_{t\to\infty}(5 + 10e^{-2t}) = 5 \quad \textit{Long-range equilibrium price}$$

MATCHED PROBLEM 4 If $D = 70 + 2p(t) + 2p'(t)$, $S = 30 + 6p(t) + 3p'(t)$, and $p(0) = 25$, find the equilibrium price at time t, and find the long-range equilibrium price.

EXAMPLE 5 **Pollution Control** A company has a 1,000-gallon holding tank that is used to control the release of pollutants into a sewage system. Initially, the tank contains 500 gallons of water. Each gallon of water contains 2 pounds of pollutants. Additional polluted water containing 5 pounds of pollutants per gallon is pumped into the tank at the rate of 100 gallons per hour and is thoroughly mixed with the water already present in the tank. At the same time, the uniformly mixed water in the tank is released into the sewage system at a rate of 50 gallons per hour (Fig. 2). This process continues for 5 hours. At the end of this 5-hour period, determine

(A) The total amount of pollutants in the tank

(B) The rate (in pounds per gallon) at which pollutants are being released into the sewage system

SOLUTION Let $p(t)$ be the total amount (in pounds) of pollutants in the tank t hours after this process begins. Since the tank initially contains 500 gallons of water and each gallon of water contains 2 pounds of pollutants,

$$p(0) = 2 \cdot 500 = 1{,}000 \quad \textit{Initial amount of pollutants in the tank}$$

Since polluted water is entering and leaving the tank at different rates and with different concentrations of pollutants, the rate of change of the amount of pollutants in the tank will depend on the rate at which pollutants enter the tank and the rate at which they leave the tank:

$$\begin{pmatrix} \text{Rate of change} \\ \text{of pollutants} \end{pmatrix} = \begin{pmatrix} \text{Rate pollutants} \\ \text{enter the tank} \end{pmatrix} - \begin{pmatrix} \text{Rate pollutants} \\ \text{leave the tank} \end{pmatrix}$$

Finding expressions for the two rates on the right side of this equation will produce a differential equation involving $p'(t)$.

Since water containing 5 pounds of pollutants per gallon is entering the tank at a constant rate of 100 gallons per hour, pollutants are entering the tank at a constant rate of

$$\begin{pmatrix} 5 \text{ pounds} \\ \text{per gallon} \end{pmatrix} \times \begin{pmatrix} 100 \text{ gallons} \\ \text{per hour} \end{pmatrix} = 500 \text{ pounds per hour}$$

How fast are the pollutants leaving the tank? Since the total amount of pollutants in the tank is increasing, the rate at which the pollutants leave the tank will depend on the amount of pollutants in the tank at time t and the amount of water in the tank at time t. Since 100 gallons of water enter the tank each hour and only 50 gallons

Water enters tank at 100 gallons per hour

Water level is rising

Water leaves tank at 50 gallons per hour

FIGURE 2

leave each hour, the amount of water in the tank increases at the rate of 50 gallons per hour. Thus, the amount of water in the tank at time t is

$$\left(\begin{array}{c}\text{Initial amount}\\\text{of water}\end{array}\right) + \left(\begin{array}{c}\text{Gallons}\\\text{per hour}\end{array}\right) \times \left(\begin{array}{c}\text{Number}\\\text{of hours}\end{array}\right)$$

$$500 \qquad + \qquad 50t$$

The amount of pollutants in each gallon of water at any time t is

$$\frac{p(t)}{500 + 50t} \qquad \frac{\left(\begin{array}{c}\text{Total amount}\\\text{of pollutants}\end{array}\right)}{\left(\begin{array}{c}\text{Total amount}\\\text{of water}\end{array}\right)} = \text{Pollutants per gallon}$$

Since water is leaving the tank at the rate of 50 gallons per hour, the rate at which the pollutants are leaving the tank is

$$\frac{50p(t)}{500 + 50t} = \frac{p(t)}{10 + t}$$

Thus, the rate of change of $p(t)$ must satisfy

$$\left(\begin{array}{c}\text{Rate of change}\\\text{of pollutants}\end{array}\right) = \left(\begin{array}{c}\text{Rate pollutants}\\\text{enter the tank}\end{array}\right) - \left(\begin{array}{c}\text{Rate pollutants}\\\text{leave the tank}\end{array}\right)$$

$$p'(t) \qquad = \qquad 500 \qquad - \qquad \frac{p(t)}{10 + t}$$

This gives the following model for this problem:

$$p'(t) = 500 - \frac{p(t)}{10 + t} \qquad p(0) = 1{,}000$$

or

$$p'(t) + \frac{1}{10 + t} p(t) = 500 \qquad \text{First-order linear equation with } f(t) = 1/(10 + t) \text{ and } g(t) = 500$$

$$I(t) = e^{\int dt/(10+t)} = e^{\ln(10+t)} = 10 + t \qquad \text{Integrating factor}$$

$$p(t) = \frac{1}{10 + t} \int 500(10 + t)\, dt \qquad \text{Proceeding directly to Step 5}$$

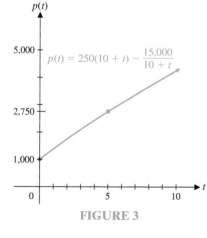

$$= \frac{1}{10 + t} [250(10 + t)^2 + C]$$

$$p(t) = 250(10 + t) + \frac{C}{10 + t} \qquad \text{General solution}$$

$$1{,}000 = 250(10) + \frac{C}{10} \qquad \text{Initial condition: } p(0) = 1{,}000$$

$$\frac{C}{10} = -1{,}500$$

$$C = -15{,}000$$

$$p(t) = 250(10 + t) - \frac{15{,}000}{10 + t} \qquad \text{Particular solution (see Fig. 3)}$$

FIGURE 3

(A) To find the total amount of pollutants after 5 hours, we evaluate $p(5)$:

$$p(5) = 250(15) - \frac{15{,}000}{15} = 2{,}750 \text{ pounds}$$

(B) After 5 hours, the tank contains 750 gallons of water. The rate at which pollutants are being released into the sewage system is

$$\frac{2,750}{750} \approx 3.67 \text{ pounds per gallon}$$

MATCHED PROBLEM 5 Repeat Example 5 if water is released from the tank at the rate of 75 gallons per hour.

Answers to Matched Problems

1. $I(x) = x^3; y = x + (C/x^3)$
2. $I(x) = e^{x^3}; y = 3 + 4e^{-x^3}$
3. $A(t) = 20,000 - 10,000e^{0.05t}; A = 0$ when $t = (\ln 2)/0.05 \approx 13.863$ yr; total withdrawals = $13,863
4. $p(t) = 10 + 15e^{-4t}; \overline{p} = 10$
5. $p(t) = 125(20 + t) - \dfrac{12,000,000}{(20 + t)^3}$ (A) 2,357 lb (B) Approx. 3.77 lb/gal

Exercise 1.3

In all problems, assume $h(x) > 0$ whenever $\ln h(x)$ is involved.

A *In Problems 1–4, is the differential equation first-order linear? If so, find $f(x)$ and $g(x)$ so that the equation can be expressed in the form $y' + f(x)y = g(x)$.*

1. $y' = ky$
2. $y' = k(M - y)$
3. $y' = ky(M - y)$
4. $y' = kx^2(M - y)$

In Problems 5–12, replace each ? with a function of x that will make the integrand equal to the derivative of a product, and then find the antiderivative. Choose 0 for the constant of integration.

5. $\int (x^3 y' + ?y)\, dx$
6. $\int (e^{2x}y' + ?y)\, dx$
7. $\int (e^{-3x}y' + ?y)\, dx$
8. $\int (x^{1/2}y' + ?y)\, dx$
9. $\int (?y' + 4x^3y)\, dx$
10. $\int (?y' + 0.2e^{0.2x}y)\, dx$
11. $\int (?y' - 0.5e^{-0.5x}y)\, dx$
12. $\int \left(?y' - \dfrac{1}{x^2}y \right) dx$

In Problems 13–24, find the integrating factor, the general solution, and the particular solution satisfying the given initial condition.

13. $y' + 2y = 4; y(0) = 1$
14. $y' - 3y = 3; y(0) = -1$
15. $y' + y = e^{-2x}; y(0) = 3$
16. $y' - 2y = e^{3x}; y(0) = 2$
17. $y' - y = 2e^x; y(0) = -4$
18. $y' + 4y = 3e^{-4x}; y(0) = 5$
19. $y' + y = 9x^2e^{-x}; y(0) = 2$

20. $y' - 3y = 6\sqrt{x}\, e^{3x}; y(0) = -2$
21. $xy' + y = 2x; y(1) = 1$
22. $xy' - 3y = 4x; y(1) = 1$
23. $xy' + 2y = 10x^3; y(2) = 8$
24. $xy' - y = \dfrac{9}{x^2}; y(2) = 3$

B *In Problems 25–34, find the integrating factor $I(x)$ for each equation, and then find the general solution.*

25. $y' + xy = 5x$
26. $y' - 2xy = 6x$
27. $y' - 2y = 4x$
28. $y' + y = x^2$
29. $xy' + y = xe^x$
30. $xy' + 2y = xe^{3x}$
31. $xy' + y = x \ln x$
32. $xy' - y = x \ln x$
33. $2xy' + 3y = 20x$
34. $2xy' - y = 6x^2$

In Problems 35–38, suppose that the indicated "solutions" were given to you by a student whom you are tutoring in this class.

(A) *How would you have the student check each solution?*

(B) *Is the solution right or wrong? If the solution is wrong, explain what is wrong and how it can be corrected.*

(C) *Show a correct solution for each incorrect solution, and check the result.*

35. Equation: $y' + \dfrac{1}{x} y = (x + 1)^2$

Solution: $y = \dfrac{1}{x} \displaystyle\int x(x + 1)^2 \, dx$

$\qquad\quad = \dfrac{1}{3}(x + 1)^3 + C$

36. Equation: $y' + \dfrac{2}{x} y = x - 1$

Solution: $y = \dfrac{1}{x^2} \displaystyle\int x^2(x - 1) \, dx$

$\qquad\quad = \dfrac{1}{2}(x - 1)^2 + C$

37. Equation: $y' + 3y = e^{-x}$

Solution: $y = \dfrac{1}{e^{3x}} \displaystyle\int e^{2x} \, dx$

$\qquad\quad = \dfrac{1}{2} e^{-x}$

38. Equation: $y' - 2y = e^x$

Solution: $y = e^{2x} \displaystyle\int e^{-x} \, dx$

$\qquad\quad = -e^x$

C *In Problems 39–44, find the general solution two ways. First use an integrating factor and then use separation of variables.*

39. $y' = \dfrac{1 - y}{x}$

40. $y' = \dfrac{y + 2}{x + 1}$

41. $y' = \dfrac{2x + 2xy}{1 + x^2}$

42. $y' = \dfrac{4x + 2xy}{4 + x^2}$

43. $y' = 2x(y + 1)$

44. $y' = 3x^2(y + 2)$

45. Use an integrating factor to find the general solution of the unlimited growth model,

$$\frac{dy}{dt} = ky$$

[*Hint:* Remember, the antiderivative of the constant function 0 is an arbitrary constant C.]

46. Use an integrating factor to find the general solution of the limited growth model,

$$\frac{dy}{dt} = k(L - y)$$

47. Discuss how the solution process for

$$y' + f(x)y = g(x)$$

simplifies if $f(x)$ and $g(x)$ are constants $a \neq 0$ and b, respectively, and find the general solution.

48. Discuss how the solution process for

$$y' + f(x)y = g(x)$$

simplifies if $g(x) = 0$ for all x, and find the general solution.

Applications

49. *Continuous compound interest.* An initial deposit of $20,000 is made into an account that earns 4.8% compounded continuously. Money is then withdrawn at a constant rate of $3,000 a year until the amount in the account is 0. Find the amount in the account at any time t. When is the amount 0? What is the total amount withdrawn from the account?

50. *Continuous compound interest.* An initial deposit of $50,000 is made into an account that earns 4.5% compounded continuously. Money is then withdrawn at a constant rate of $5,400 a year until the amount in the account is 0. Find the amount in the account at any time t. When is the amount 0? What is the total amount withdrawn from the account?

51. *Continuous compound interest.* An initial deposit of $P is made into an account that earns 4.75% compounded continuously. Money is then withdrawn at a constant rate of $1,900 a year. After 10 years of continuous withdrawals, the amount in the account is 0. Find the initial deposit P.

52. *Continuous compound interest.* An initial deposit of $P is made into an account that earns 4.25% compounded continuously. Money is then withdrawn at a constant rate of $3,400 a year. After 5 years of continuous withdrawals, the amount in the account is 0. Find the initial deposit P.

53. *Continuous compound interest.* An initial deposit of $5,000 is made into an account earning 7% compounded continuously. Thereafter, money is deposited into the account at a constant rate of $2,100 per year. Find the amount in this account at any time t. How much is in this account after 5 years?

54. *Continuous compound interest.* An initial deposit of $10,000 is made into an account earning 6.25% compounded continuously. Thereafter, money is deposited into the account at a constant rate of $5,000 per year. Find the amount in this account at any time t. How much is in this account after 10 years?

55. *Continuous compound interest.* An initial investment of $10,000 is made in a mutual fund. Additional investments are made at the rate of $1,000 per year. After 10 years the fund has a value of $30,000. What continuous compound rate of interest has this fund earned over this 10 year period? Express the answer as a percentage, correct to two decimal places.

56. *Continuous compound interest.* A trust fund is established by depositing $100,000 into an account. Withdrawals are made at the rate of $20,000 per year. After 5 years, the trust fund contains $15,000. What continuous compound rate of interest has this fund earned over this 5 year period? Express the answer as a percentage, correct to two decimal places.

57. *Supply–demand.* The supply S and demand D for a certain commodity satisfy the equations

$$S = 35 - 2p(t) + 3p'(t) \quad \text{and}$$

$$D = 95 - 5p(t) + 2p'(t)$$

If $p(0) = 30$, find the equilibrium price at time t and the long-range equilibrium price.

58. *Supply–demand.* The supply S and demand D for a certain commodity satisfy the equations

$$S = 70 - 3p(t) + 2p'(t) \quad \text{and}$$

$$D = 100 - 5p(t) + p'(t)$$

If $p(0) = 5$, find the equilibrium price at time t and the long-range equilibrium price.

59. *Pollution.* A 1,000-gallon holding tank contains 200 gallons of water. Initially, each gallon of water in the tank contains 2 pounds of pollutants. Water containing 3 pounds of pollutants per gallon enters the tank at a rate of 75 gallons per hour, and the uniformly mixed water is released from the tank at a rate of 50 gallons per hour. How many pounds of pollutants are in the tank after 2 hours? At what rate (in pounds per gallon) are the pollutants being released after 2 hours?

Water enters tank at 75 gallons per hour

Water leaves tank at 50 gallons per hour

60. *Pollution.* Rework Problem 59 if water is entering the tank at the rate of 100 gallons per hour.

61. *Pollution.* Rework Problem 59 if water is entering the tank at the rate of 50 gallons per hour.

62. *Pollution.* Rework Problem 59 if water is entering the tank at the rate of 150 gallons per hour.

63. *Pollution.* Refer to Problem 59. When will the tank contain 1,000 pounds of pollutants? Round answer to one decimal place.

64. *Pollution.* Refer to Problem 62. When will the tank contain 1,500 pounds of pollutants? Round answer to one decimal place.

In an article in the College Mathematics Journal *(Jan. 1987, 18:1)*, Arthur Segal proposed the following model for weight loss or gain:

$$\frac{dw}{dt} + 0.005w = \frac{1}{3,500}C$$

where $w(t)$ is a person's weight (in pounds) after t days of consuming exactly C calories per day. Use this model to solve Problems 65–68.

65. *Weight loss.* A person weighing 160 pounds goes on a diet of 2,100 calories per day. How much will this person weigh after 30 days on this diet? How long will it take this person to lose 10 pounds? Find $\lim_{t \to \infty} w(t)$ and interpret the results.

66. *Weight loss.* A person weighing 200 pounds goes on a diet of 2,800 calories per day. How much will this person weigh after 90 days on this diet? How long will it take this person to lose 25 pounds? Find $\lim_{t \to \infty} w(t)$ and interpret the results.

67. *Weight loss.* A person weighing 130 pounds would like to lose 5 pounds during a 30 day period. How many calories per day should this person consume to reach this goal?

68. *Weight loss.* A person weighing 175 pounds would like to lose 10 pounds during a 45 day period. How many calories per day should this person consume to reach this goal?

In 1960, William K. Estes proposed the following model for measuring a student's performance in the classroom:

$$\frac{dk}{dt} + \ell k = \lambda \ell$$

where $k(t)$ is the student's knowledge after t weeks (expressed as a percentage and measured by performance on examinations), ℓ is a constant called the coefficient of learning and representing the student's ability to learn (expressed as a percentage and determined by IQ or some similar general intelligence predictor), and λ is a constant representing the fraction of available time the student spends performing helpful acts that should increase knowledge of the subject (studying, going to class, and so on). Use this model to solve Problems 69 and 70.

69. *Learning theory.* Students enrolled in a beginning Spanish class are given a pretest the first day of class to determine their knowledge of the subject. The results of the pretest, the coefficient of learning, and the fraction of time spent performing helpful acts for two students in the class are given in the table. Use the Estes model to predict the knowledge of each student after 6 weeks in the class.

	Score on Pretest	Coefficient of Learning	Fraction of Helpful Acts
Student A	0.1 (10%)	0.8	0.9
Student B	0.4 (40%)	0.8	0.7

70. *Learning theory.* Refer to Problem 69. When will both students have the same level of knowledge? Round answer to one decimal place.

CHAPTER 1 REVIEW

Important Terms, Symbols, and Concepts

1.1 Basic Concepts

A **differential equation** is an equation involving an unknown function, usually denoted by y, and one or more of its derivatives. The **order** of a differential equation is the highest derivative of the unknown function present in the equation. We only consider **first-order** differential equations. The **slope field** for a differential equation is obtained by drawing tangent line segments determined by the equation at each point in a grid. The **solution** of a differential equation is a function y with the property that substituting y and y' into the equation produces a statement that is true for all values of x. A solution of a differential equation that involves an arbitrary constant is called the **general solution,** and collectively, is referred to as the **family of solutions.** Each member of the family of solutions is called a **particular solution.** A condition of the form $y(x_0) = y_0$ is called an **initial condition** and is often used to specify a particular solution.

1.2 Separation of Variables

The solution of a differential equation that can be written in the form

$$f(y)y' = g(x)$$

is given implicitly by the equation

$$\int f(y)\, dy = \int g(x)\, dx$$

If both integrals can be evaluated and if the resulting equation can be solved for y in terms of x, then we have an explicit solution for the differential equation. A solution to a differential equation that cannot be obtained from the general solution is referred to as a singular solution. The basic exponential growth models and their solutions are as follows:

Exponential Growth		
Description	**Model**	**Solution**
Unlimited growth: Rate of growth is proportional to the amount present	$\dfrac{dy}{dt} = ky$ $k, t > 0$ $y(0) = c$	$y = ce^{kt}$
Exponential decay: Rate of growth is proportional to the amount present	$\dfrac{dy}{dt} = -ky$ $k, t > 0$ $y(0) = c$	$y = ce^{-kt}$
Limited growth: Rate of growth is proportional to the difference between the amount present and a fixed limit	$\dfrac{dy}{dt} = k(M - y)$ $k, t > 0$ $y(0) = 0$	$y = M(1 - e^{-kt})$
Logistic growth: Rate of growth is proportional to the amount present and to the difference between the amount present and a fixed limit	$\dfrac{dy}{dt} = ky(M - y)$ $k, t > 0$ $y(0) = \dfrac{M}{1 + c}$	$y = \dfrac{M}{1 + ce^{-kMt}}$

1.3 First-Order Linear Differential Equations

A differential equation that can be expressed in the form

$$y' + f(x)y = g(x)$$

is called a **first-order linear differential equation.**

Equations in this form can be solved by the following procedure:

PROCEDURE

Solving First-Order Linear Differential Equations

Step 1. Write the equation in the **standard form:**

$$y' + f(x)y = g(x)$$

Step 2. Compute the **integrating factor:**

$$I(x) = e^{\int f(x)\,dx}$$

[When evaluating $\int f(x)\,dx$, choose 0 for the constant of integration.]

Step 3. Multiply both sides of the standard form by the integrating factor $I(x)$. The left side should now be in the form $[I(x)y]'$:

$$[I(x)y]' = I(x)g(x)$$

Step 4. Integrate both sides:

$$I(x)y = \int I(x)g(x)\,dx$$

[When evaluating $\int I(x)g(x)\,dx$, include an arbitrary constant of integration.]

Step 5. Solve for y to obtain the **general solution:**

$$y = \frac{1}{I(x)}\int I(x)g(x)\,dx$$

REVIEW EXERCISE

Work through all the problems in this chapter review and check your answers in the back of this supplement. Answers to all review problems are there along with section numbers in italics to indicate where each type of problem is discussed. Where weaknesses show up, review appropriate sections in the text.

A In Problems 1 and 2, show that the given function is the general solution of the indicated differential equation.

1. $y = C\sqrt{x}$; $2xy' = y$

2. $y = 1 + Ce^{-x/3}$; $3y' + y = 1$

In Problems 3 and 4, determine which of the following slope fields is associated with the indicated differential equation. Briefly justify your answer.

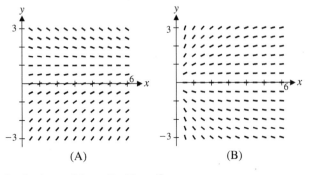

(A)   (B)

3. $2xy' = y$ (From Problem 1)

4. $3y' + y = 1$ (From Problem 2)

In Problems 5 and 6, use the appropriate slope field—(A) or (B), given for Problems 3 and 4 (or a copy)—to graph the particular solutions obtained by letting $C = -2, -1, 0, 1,$ and 2.

5. $y = C\sqrt{x}$ (From Problem 1)

6. $y = 1 + Ce^{-x/3}$ (From Problem 2)

In Problems 7 and 8, write a differential equation that describes the rate of change of the indicated quantity.

7. The price y of a product is decreasing at a rate proportional to the difference between the price and a lower limit of \$5.

8. The price y of a product is increasing at a rate proportional to the price.

In Problems 9 and 10, write a verbal description of the rate of change of the given quantity satisfying the indicated differential equation and discuss the increasing/decreasing properties of the quantity.

9. The number of people y who have contracted an infectious disease satisfies $dy/dt = 0.2y(50{,}000 - y)$ and $y(0) = 1$.

10. The amount of radioactive material y (in grams) at the site of a nuclear accident satisfies $dy/dt = -0.001y$ and $y(0) = 100$.

In Problems 11–14, determine whether the differential equation can be written in the separation of variables form

$f(y)y' = g(x)$, *the first-order linear form* $y' + f(x)y = g(x)$, *both forms, or neither form.*

11. $y' + 3x^2y + 9 = e^x(1 - x + y)$

12. $y' + 10y + 25 = 5xy^2$

13. $y' + 3y = xy + 2x - 6$

14. $y^2y' = 4xe^{x-y}$

In Problems 15–20, find the general solution.

15. $y' = -\dfrac{4y}{x}$

16. $y' = -\dfrac{4y}{x} + x$

17. $y' = 3x^2y^2$

18. $y' = 2y - e^x$

19. $y' = \dfrac{5}{x}y + x^6$

20. $y' = \dfrac{3 + y}{2 + x}, \; x > -2$

B *In Problems 21–28, find the particular solution that satisfies the given condition.*

21. $y' = 10 - y; y(0) = 0$

22. $y' + y = x; y(0) = 0$

23. $y' = 2ye^{-x}; y(0) = 1$

24. $y' = \dfrac{2x - y}{x + 4}; y(0) = 1$

25. $y' = \dfrac{x}{y + 4}; y(0) = 0$

26. $y' + \dfrac{2}{x}y = \ln x; y(1) = 2$

27. $yy' = \dfrac{x(1 + y^2)}{1 + x^2}; y(0) = 1$

28. $y' + 2xy = 2e^{-x^2}; y(0) = 1$

C

29. Solve the following differential equation two ways. First use an integrating factor and then use separation of variables.

$$xy' - 4y = 8$$

30. Give an example of an equation that can be solved using an integrating factor but cannot be solved using separation of variables. Solve the equation.

31. Give an example of an equation that can be solved using separation of variables but cannot be solved using an integrating factor. Solve the equation.

32. Find the general solution of the following differential equation and then find the particular solutions satisfying the indicated initial conditions.

$$xy' - 5y = -10$$

   (A) $y(0) = 2$ (B) $y(0) = 0$ (C) $y(1) = 1$

33. Find an explicit expression for the particular solution of the differential equation $yy' = x$ satisfying the initial condition $y(0) = 4$.

34. Given that $y = x^3 + Cx$ is the general solution of the differential equation $xy' - y = 2x^3$:

   (A) In the same viewing window, graph the particular solutions obtained by letting $C = 0, 1, 2$, and 3.

   (B) What do the graphs of the solutions for $C > 0$ have in common?

   (C) In the same viewing window, graph the particular solutions obtained by letting $C = 0, -1, -2$, and -3.

   (D) What do the graphs of the solutions for $C < 0$ have in common?

35. The rate of change with respect to time t of a quantity y is proportional to the difference between y and an unknown upper limit M, and $y = 0$ when $t = 0$. Using the limited growth law, it follows that

$$y = M(1 - e^{-kt}) \qquad M > 0, k > 0$$

   (A) Using the data given in the table, find two equations that M and k must satisfy, and solve each equation for M.

t	2	5
y	4	7

   (B) Use a graphing utility and the equations from part (A) to approximate M to one decimal place.

APPLICATIONS

36. *Depreciation.* A refrigerator costs $500 when it is new. The value of the refrigerator depreciates to $25 over a 20-year period. If the rate of change of the value is proportional to the value, find the value of the refrigerator 5 years after it was purchased.

37. *Sales growth.* The rate of growth of the annual sales of a new company is proportional to the difference between the annual sales S and an upper limit of $200,000. Assume that $S(0) = 0$.

   (A) If the sales are $50,000 for the first year, how long will it take for the annual sales to reach $150,000? Round answer to the nearest year.

   (B) Suppose the company is dissatisfied with the results in part (A) and wants the annual sales to reach $150,000 after just 3 years. In order for this to happen, what must the sales be for the first year? Round answer to the nearest thousand dollars.

38. *Price stability.* The supply S and the demand D for a certain commodity satisfy the equations

$$S = 100 + p + p' \quad \text{and} \quad D = 200 - p - p'$$

(A) Find the equilibrium price p at any time t.

(B) Find the long-range equilibrium price $\bar{p}$.

(C) Graph the particular solutions that satisfy the initial conditions $p(0) = 75$ and $p(0) = 25$.

(D) Discuss the long-term behavior of the price of this commodity.

39. *Continuous compound interest.* An initial deposit of $60,000 is made into an account that earns 5% compounded continuously. Money is then withdrawn at a constant rate of $5,000 per year until the amount in the account is 0. Find the amount in the account at any time t. When is the amount 0? What is the total amount withdrawn from the account?

40. *Continuous compound interest.* An initial investment of $15,000 is made in a mutual fund. Additional investments are made at the rate of $2,000 per year. After 10 years the fund has a value of $50,000. What continuous compound rate of interest has this fund earned over this 10-year period? Express the answer as a percentage, correct to two decimal places.

41. *Crop yield.* The yield $y(t)$ (in bushels per acre) of a corn crop satisfies the equation

$$\frac{dy}{dt} = 100 + e^{-t} - y$$

If $y(0) = 0$, find y at any time t.

42. *Pollution.* A 1,000-gallon holding tank contains 100 gallons of unpolluted water. Water containing 2 pounds of pollutant per gallon is pumped into the tank at the rate of 75 gallons per hour. The uniformly mixed water is released from the tank at 50 gallons per hour.

(A) Find the total amount of pollutants in the tank after 2 hours. Round answer to one decimal place.

(B) When will the tank contain 700 pounds of pollutants? Round answer to one decimal place.

43. *Ecology.* A bird population on an island is declining at a rate proportional to the difference between the population and a lower limit of 200 birds.

(A) If the population has declined from 1,000 birds 5 years ago to 500 today, find the population 4 years from now.

(B) Suppose the bird population 4 years from now turns out to be 400, indicating that the island might be able to support more than the original lower limit of 200 birds. Assuming that the rate of change of the population is still proportional to the difference between the population and an unknown lower limit M, approximate M to the nearest integer.

44. *Rumor spread.* A single individual starts a rumor in a community of 200 people. The rumor spreads at a rate proportional to the number of people who have not yet heard the rumor. After 2 days, 10 people have heard the rumor.

(A) How many people will have heard the rumor after 5 days?

(B) How long will it take for the rumor to spread to 100 people?

Taylor Polynomials and Infinite Series

INTRODUCTION

The circuits inside a calculator are capable only of performing the basic operations of addition, subtraction, multiplication, and division. Yet, many calculators have keys that allow you to evaluate functions such as e^x, ln x, and sin x. How is this done? In most cases, the values of these functions are *approximated* by using a carefully selected polynomial, and, of course, polynomials can be evaluated by using the basic arithmetic operations. Thus, the approximating polynomials give the calculator the capability of evaluating nonpolynomial functions. In this chapter we will study one type of approximating polynomial, called a *Taylor polynomial* after the English mathematician Brook Taylor (1685–1731). For a given function f, we will determine the coefficients of the Taylor polynomial, the values of x where the Taylor polynomial approximates $f(x)$, and the accuracy of this approximation. We will also consider various applications involving Taylor polynomials, including the approximation of definite integrals.

Section 2.1 TAYLOR POLYNOMIALS

- Higher-Order Derivatives
- Approximating e^x with Polynomials
- Taylor Polynomials at 0
- Taylor Polynomials at a
- Application

Higher-Order Derivatives

Up to this point, we have considered only the first and second derivatives of a function. In the work that follows, we will need to find higher-order derivatives. For example, if we start with the function f defined by

$$f(x) = x^{-1}$$

then the first derivative of f is

$$f'(x) = -x^{-2}$$

and the second derivative of f is

$$f''(x) = \frac{d}{dx}f'(x) = \frac{d}{dx}(-x^{-2}) = 2x^{-3}$$

Additional higher-order derivatives are found by successive differentiation. Thus, the third derivative is

$$f^{(3)}(x) = \frac{d}{dx}f''(x) = \frac{d}{dx}(2x^{-3}) = -6x^{-4}$$

the fourth derivative is

$$f^{(4)}(x) = \frac{d}{dx}f^{(3)}(x) = \frac{d}{dx}(-6x^{-4}) = 24x^{-5}$$

and so on.

In general, the symbol $f^{(n)}$ is used to represent the **nth derivative of the function** f. When stating formulas involving a function and its higher-order derivatives, it is convenient to let $f^{(0)}$ represent the function f (that is, the zeroth derivative of a function is just the function itself).

The order of the derivative must be enclosed in parentheses, because in most contexts, $f^n(x)$ is interpreted to mean the nth power of f, not the nth derivative. Thus, $f^2(x) = [f(x)]^2 = f(x)f(x)$, while $f^{(2)}(x) = f''(x)$.

Finding a particular higher-order derivative is a routine calculation. However, finding a formula for the nth derivative for arbitrary n requires careful observation of the patterns that develop as each successive derivative is found. Study the next example carefully. Many problems in this chapter will involve similar concepts.

EXAMPLE 1   Finding *nth* Derivatives   Find the nth derivative of

$$f(x) = \frac{1}{1+x} = (1+x)^{-1}$$

SOLUTION   We begin by finding the first four derivatives of f:

$$f(x) = (1+x)^{-1}$$
$$f'(x) = (-1)(1+x)^{-2}$$
$$f''(x) = (-1)(-2)(1+x)^{-3}$$
$$f^{(3)}(x) = (-1)(-2)(-3)(1+x)^{-4}$$
$$f^{(4)}(x) = (-1)(-2)(-3)(-4)(1+x)^{-5}$$

Notice that we did not multiply out the coefficient of $(1 + x)^{-k}$ in each derivative. Our objective is to look for a pattern in the form of each derivative. Multiplying out these coefficients would tend to obscure any pattern that is developing. Instead, we observe that each coefficient is a product of successive negative integers that can be written as follows:

$$(-1) = (-1)^1(1)$$
$$(-1)(-2) = (-1)^2(1)(2)$$
$$(-1)(-2)(-3) = (-1)^3(1)(2)(3)$$
$$(-1)(-2)(-3)(-4) = (-1)^4(1)(2)(3)(4)$$

Next we note that the product of natural numbers in each expression on the right can be written in terms of a factorial:*

$$(-1) = (-1)^1 1! \qquad 1! = 1$$
$$(-1)(-2) = (-1)^2 2! \qquad 2! = 1 \cdot 2$$
$$(-1)(-2)(-3) = (-1)^3 3! \qquad 3! = 1 \cdot 2 \cdot 3$$
$$(-1)(-2)(-3)(-4) = (-1)^4 4! \qquad 4! = 1 \cdot 2 \cdot 3 \cdot 4$$

Substituting these last expressions in the derivatives of f, we have

$$f'(x) = (-1)^1 1!(1 + x)^{-2} \qquad n = 1$$
$$f''(x) = (-1)^2 2!(1 + x)^{-3} \qquad n = 2$$
$$f^{(3)}(x) = (-1)^3 3!(1 + x)^{-4} \qquad n = 3$$
$$f^{(4)}(x) = (-1)^4 4!(1 + x)^{-5} \qquad n = 4$$

This suggests that

$$f^{(n)}(x) = (-1)^n n!(1 + x)^{-(n+1)} \qquad \text{Arbitrary } n$$

■

MATCHED PROBLEM 1   Find the nth derivative of $f(x) = \ln x$.

Explore & Discuss **1**

(A) Compute the first six derivatives of the polynomial function $p(x) = 7x^3 - 9x^2 + 4x - 15$.

(B) Let $q(x)$ be a polynomial of degree n. For which orders are the higher-order derivatives of $q(x)$ equal to the constant function $f(x) = 0$?

■ Approximating e^x with Polynomials

We have already seen that the irrational number e and the exponential function e^x play important roles in many applications, including continuous compound interest, population growth, and exponential decay, to name a few. Now, given the function

$$f(x) = e^x$$

we would like to construct a polynomial function p whose values are close to the values of f, at least for some values of x. If we are successful, then we can use the values of p (which are easily computed) to approximate the values of f. We begin by trying to approximate f for values of x near 0 with a first-degree polynomial of the form

$$p_1(x) = a_0 + a_1 x \tag{1}$$

We want to place conditions on p_1 that will enable us to determine the unknown coefficients a_0 and a_1. Since we want to approximate f for values near 0, it is reasonable to require that f and p_1 agree at 0. Thus,

$$a_0 = p_1(0) = f(0) = e^0 = 1$$

---

*For n a natural number, $n! = n(n - 1)! = n(n - 1)(n - 2) \cdots 2 \cdot 1$ and $0! = 1$.

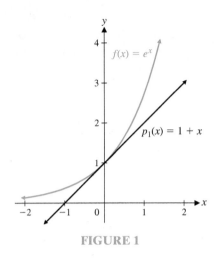

FIGURE 1

This determines the value of a_0. To determine the value of a_1, we require that both functions have the same slope at 0. Since $p_1'(x) = a_1$ and $f'(x) = e^x$, this implies that

$$a_1 = p_1'(0) = f'(0) = e^0 = 1$$

Thus, after substituting $a_0 = 1$ and $a_1 = 1$ into (1), we obtain

$$p_1(x) = 1 + x$$

which is a first-degree polynomial satisfying

$$p_1(0) = f(0) \qquad \text{and} \qquad p_1'(0) = f'(0)$$

How well does $1 + x$ approximate e^x? Examining the graph in Figure 1, it appears that $1 + x$ is a good approximation to e^x for x very close to 0. However, as x moves away from 0, in either direction, the distance between the values of $1 + x$ and e^x increases and the accuracy of the approximation decreases.

Now we will try to improve this approximation by using a second-degree polynomial of the form

$$p_2(x) = a_0 + a_1 x + a_2 x^2 \tag{2}$$

We need three conditions to determine the coefficients a_0, a_1, and a_2. We still require that $p_2(0) = f(0)$ and $p_2'(0) = f'(0)$, and add the condition that $p_2''(0) = f''(0)$. This ensures that the graphs of p_2 and f have the same concavity at $x = 0$. Proceeding as before, we compute the first and second derivatives of p_2 and f and apply these conditions:

$$
\begin{array}{ll}
p_2(x) = a_0 + a_1 x + a_2 x^2 & f(x) = e^x \\
p_2'(x) = \qquad\quad a_1 + 2a_2 x & f'(x) = e^x \\
p_2''(x) = \qquad\qquad\quad 2a_2 & f''(x) = e^x
\end{array}
$$

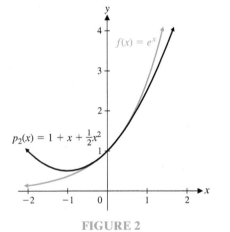

$p_2(x) = 1 + x + \frac{1}{2}x^2$

FIGURE 2

Thus,

$$
\begin{array}{llll}
a_0 = p_2(0) = f(0) = e^0 = 1 & \text{implies} & a_0 = 1 \\
a_1 = p_2'(0) = f'(0) = e^0 = 1 & \text{implies} & a_1 = 1 \\
2a_2 = p_2''(0) = f''(0) = e^0 = 1 & \text{implies} & a_2 = \frac{1}{2}
\end{array}
$$

and, substituting in (2), we obtain

$$p_2(x) = 1 + x + \frac{1}{2}x^2$$

The graph is shown in Figure 2.

Comparing Figures 1 and 2, we see that for values of x near 0, the graph of $p_2(x) = 1 + x + \frac{1}{2}x^2$ is closer to the graph of $f(x) = e^x$ than was the graph of $p_1(x) = 1 + x$. Thus, the polynomial $1 + x + \frac{1}{2}x^2$ can be used to approximate e^x over a larger range of x values than the polynomial $1 + x$.

It seems reasonable to assume that a third-degree polynomial would yield a still better approximation. Using the notation for higher-order derivatives discussed earlier in this section, we can state the required condition as

Find

$$p_3(x) = a_0 + a_1 x + a_2 x^2 + a_3 x^3 \tag{3}$$

Satisfying

$$p_3^{(k)}(0) = f^{(k)}(0) \qquad k = 0, 1, 2, 3$$

As before, we obtain the value of the additional coefficient a_3 by adding the requirement that

$$p_3^{(3)}(0) = f^{(3)}(0)$$

Thus,

$$
\begin{array}{llll}
p_3(x) = a_0 + a_1x + a_2x^2 + a_3x^3 & f(x) = e^x \\
p_3'(x) = \quad\quad a_1 + 2a_2x + 3a_3x^2 & f'(x) = e^x \\
p_3''(x) = \quad\quad\quad\quad 2a_2 + 6a_3x & f''(x) = e^x \\
p_3^{(3)}(x) = \quad\quad\quad\quad\quad 6a_3 & f^{(3)}(x) = e^x
\end{array}
$$

Applying the conditions $p_3^{(k)}(0) = f^{(k)}(0)$, we have

$$
\begin{array}{lllll}
a_0 = p_3(0) & = f(0) & = e^0 = 1 & \text{implies} & a_0 = 1 \\
a_1 = p_3'(0) & = f'(0) & = e^0 = 1 & \text{implies} & a_1 = 1 \\
2a_2 = p_3''(0) & = f''(0) & = e^0 = 1 & \text{implies} & a_2 = \tfrac{1}{2} \\
6a_3 = p_3^{(3)}(0) & = f^{(3)}(0) & = e^0 = 1 & \text{implies} & a_3 = \tfrac{1}{6}
\end{array}
$$

Substituting in (3), we obtain

$$
p_3(x) = 1 + x + \tfrac{1}{2}x^2 + \tfrac{1}{6}x^3
$$

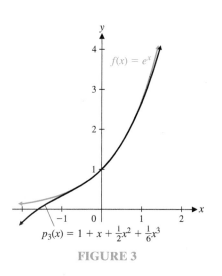

$p_3(x) = 1 + x + \tfrac{1}{2}x^2 + \tfrac{1}{6}x^3$

FIGURE 3

Figure 3 indicates that the approximations provided by p_3 are an improvement over those provided by p_2 and p_1.

In order to compare all three approximations, Table 1 lists the values of p_1, p_2, p_3, and e^x at selected values of x, and Table 2 lists the absolute value of the difference between these polynomials and e^x for the same x values. The values of e^x were obtained by using a calculator and are rounded to six decimal places. Comparing the columns in Table 2, we see that increasing the degree of the approximating polynomial decreases the difference between the polynomial and e^x. Thus, p_2 provides a better approximation than p_1, and p_3 provides a better approximation than p_2. We will have more to say about the accuracy of these approximations later in this chapter.

TABLE 1 $p_1(x) = 1 + x$, $p_2(x) = 1 + x + \tfrac{1}{2}x^2$, $p_3(x) = 1 + x + \tfrac{1}{2}x^2 + \tfrac{1}{6}x^3$

x	$p_1(x)$	$p_2(x)$	$p_3(x)$	e^x
-0.2	0.8	0.820	0.818 667	0.818 731
-0.1	0.9	0.905	0.904 833	0.904 837
0	1	1	1	1
0.1	1.1	1.105	1.105 167	1.105 171
0.2	1.2	1.220	1.221 333	1.221 403

TABLE 2

x	$\lvert p_1(x) - e^x \rvert$	$\lvert p_2(x) - e^x \rvert$	$\lvert p_3(x) - e^x \rvert$
-0.2	0.018 731	0.001 269	0.000 064
-0.1	0.004 837	0.000 163	0.000 004
0	0	0	0
0.1	0.005 171	0.000 171	0.000 004
0.2	0.021 403	0.001 403	0.000 069

Explore & Discuss 2

(A) Let $p(x)$ be a polynomial of degree $n \geq 1$. Explain why each of the following is true:

   (1) The graph of $p(x)$ intersects any vertical line in exactly one point.

   (2) The graph of $p(x)$ intersects any horizontal line in at most n points.

   (3) The graph of $p(x)$ has neither horizontal nor vertical asymptotes.

(B) Discuss the graphs of

$$
f(x) = e^x \quad g(x) = \frac{5x^2 - 3x + 1}{2x^2 + 3} \quad h(x) = \frac{1}{x - 2} \quad k(x) = e^{-x^2}
$$

Use part (A) to explain why none of the graphs of f, g, h, or k is the graph of a polynomial function.

■ Taylor Polynomials at 0

The process we have used to determine $p_1, p_2,$ and p_3 can be continued. Given any positive integer n, we define

$$p_n(x) = a_0 + a_1 x + a_2 x^2 + \cdots + a_n x^n$$

and require that

$$p_n^{(k)}(0) = f^{(k)}(0) \qquad k = 0, 1, 2, \ldots, n$$

The polynomial p_n is called a *Taylor polynomial*. Before determining p_n for $f(x) = e^x$, it will be convenient to make some general statements concerning the relationship between $a_k, p_n^{(k)}(0),$ and $f^{(k)}(0)$ for an arbitrary function f. First, $p_n(x)$ is differentiated n times to obtain the following relationships:

$$
\begin{aligned}
p_n(x) &= a_0 + a_1 x + a_2 x^2 + a_3 x^3 + \cdots + a_n x^n \\
p_n'(x) &= a_1 + 2a_2 x + 3a_3 x^2 + \cdots + n a_n x^{n-1} \\
p_n''(x) &= 2a_2 + (3)(2)a_3 x + \cdots + n(n-1)a_n x^{n-2} \\
p_n^{(3)}(x) &= (3)(2)a_3 + \cdots + n(n-1)(n-2)a_n x^{n-3} \\
&\ \ \vdots \\
p_n^{(n)}(x) &= n(n-1)(n-2) \cdot \cdots \cdot (1)a_n = n! a_n
\end{aligned}
$$

Evaluating each derivative at 0 and applying the requirement that $p_n^{(k)}(0) = f^{(k)}(0)$ leads to the following equations:

$$
\begin{aligned}
a_0 &= p_n(0) &= f(0) \\
a_1 &= p_n'(0) &= f'(0) \\
2a_2 &= p_n''(0) &= f''(0) \\
(3)(2)a_3 &= p_n^{(3)}(0) &= f^{(3)}(0) \\
&\ \ \vdots & \vdots \\
n! a_n &= p_n^{(n)}(0) &= f^{(n)}(0)
\end{aligned}
$$

Solving each equation for a_k, we have

$$a_k = \frac{p_n^{(k)}(0)}{k!} = \frac{f^{(k)}(0)}{k!}$$

This relationship enables us to state the general definition of a Taylor polynomial.

DEFINITION **Taylor Polynomial at 0***

If f has n derivatives at 0, then the **nth-degree Taylor polynomial for f at 0** is

$$p_n(x) = a_0 + a_1 x + a_2 x^2 + \cdots + a_n x^n = \sum_{k=0}^{n} a_k x^k$$

where

$$p_n^{(k)}(0) = f^{(k)}(0) \qquad \text{and} \qquad a_k = \frac{f^{(k)}(0)}{k!} \qquad k = 0, 1, 2, \ldots, n$$

---

* Taylor polynomials at 0 are also often referred to as *Maclaurin polynomials*, but we will not use this terminology.

This result can be stated in a form that is more readily remembered as follows:

DEFINITION   **Taylor Polynomial at 0: Concise Form**

The nth-degree Taylor polynomial for f at 0 is

$$p_n(x) = f(0) + f'(0)x + \frac{f''(0)}{2!}x^2 + \cdots + \frac{f^{(n)}(0)}{n!}x^n = \sum_{k=0}^{n} \frac{f^{(k)}(0)}{k!}x^k$$

provided f has n derivatives at 0.

In each of the preceding definitions, notice that we have used both the **expanded notation**

$$p_n(x) = a_0 + a_1 x + a_2 x^2 + \cdots + a_n x^n$$

$$= f(0) + f'(0)x + \frac{f''(0)}{2!}x^2 + \cdots + \frac{f^{(n)}(0)}{n!}x^n$$

and the more compact **summation notation**

$$p_n(x) = \sum_{k=0}^{n} a_k x^k = \sum_{k=0}^{n} \frac{f^{(k)}(0)}{k!}x^k$$

to represent a finite sum. Recall that we used summation notation earlier in Chapters 5 and 6 of *Calculus* 13/e or Chapters 13 and 14 of *College Mathematics* 13/e. In this chapter we will place more emphasis on the expanded notation, since it is usually easier to visualize a polynomial written in this notation, but we will continue to include the summation notation where appropriate.

INSIGHT

The nth-degree Taylor polynomial for f at 0 is always a polynomial, but it does not necessarily have degree n, because it is possible that $f^{(n)}(0) = 0$. For example, if $g(x) = x^3 + 2x + 1$, then $g'(x) = 3x^2 + 2$ and $g''(x) = 6x$, so $g(0) = 1$, $g'(0) = 2$, and $g''(0) = 0$. Therefore, for this function g at 0, the second-degree Taylor polynomial is $p_2(x) = 1 + 2x$, which actually has degree 1, not 2.

Returning to our original function $f(x) = e^x$, it is now an easy matter to find the nth-degree Taylor polynomial for this function. Since $(d/dx)e^x = e^x$, it follows that

$$f^{(k)}(x) = e^x \qquad f^{(k)}(0) = e^0 = 1 \qquad a_k = \frac{f^{(k)}(0)}{k!} = \frac{1}{k!}$$

for all values of k. Thus, for any n, the nth-degree Taylor polynomial for e^x is

$$p_n(x) = 1 + x + \frac{1}{2!}x^2 + \frac{1}{3!}x^3 + \cdots + \frac{1}{n!}x^n = \sum_{k=0}^{n} \frac{1}{k!}x^k$$

EXAMPLE 2   **Approximation Using a Taylor Polynomial** Find the third-degree Taylor polynomial at 0 for $f(x) = \sqrt{x + 4}$. Use p_3 to approximate $\sqrt{5}$.

SOLUTION   Step 1.   *Find the derivatives:*

$$f(x) = (x + 4)^{1/2}$$
$$f'(x) = \tfrac{1}{2}(x + 4)^{-1/2}$$
$$f''(x) = -\tfrac{1}{4}(x + 4)^{-3/2}$$
$$f^{(3)}(x) = \tfrac{3}{8}(x + 4)^{-5/2}$$

Step 2. *Evaluate the derivatives at 0:*

$$f(0) = 4^{1/2} = 2$$
$$f'(0) = \tfrac{1}{2}(4^{-1/2}) = \tfrac{1}{4}$$
$$f''(0) = -\tfrac{1}{4}(4^{-3/2}) = -\tfrac{1}{32}$$
$$f^{(3)}(0) = \tfrac{3}{8}(4^{-5/2}) = \tfrac{3}{256}$$

Step 3. *Find the coefficients of the Taylor polynomial:*

$$a_0 = \frac{f(0)}{0!} = f(0) = 2$$

$$a_1 = \frac{f'(0)}{1!} = f'(0) = \frac{1}{4}$$

$$a_2 = \frac{f''(0)}{2!} = \frac{-\frac{1}{32}}{2} = -\frac{1}{64}$$

$$a_3 = \frac{f^{(3)}(0)}{3!} = \frac{\frac{3}{256}}{6} = \frac{1}{512}$$

Step 4. *Write down the Taylor polynomial:*

$$p_3(x) = 2 + \tfrac{1}{4}x - \tfrac{1}{64}x^2 + \tfrac{1}{512}x^3 \quad \text{Taylor polynomial.}$$

To use p_3 to approximate $\sqrt{5}$, we must first determine the appropriate value of x:

$$f(x) = \sqrt{x+4} = \sqrt{5} \quad \text{Square both sides.}$$
$$x + 4 = 5 \quad \text{Solve for } x.$$
$$x = 1$$

Thus,

$$\sqrt{5} = f(1) \approx p_3(1) = 2 + \tfrac{1}{4} - \tfrac{1}{64} + \tfrac{1}{512} \approx 2.236\ 328\ 1$$

[*Note:* The value of $\sqrt{5}$ obtained by using a calculator is, to six decimal places, 2.236 068.] ▬

FIGURE 4 Graphs of $f(x) = \sqrt{x+4}$ and $p_3(x)$

Compare the evaluation of $p_3(1)$ shown in Figure 4 to the value obtained in Example 2. The figure illustrates graphically that $p_3(x)$ is a good approximation to $f(x)$ for values of x near 0.

MATCHED PROBLEM 2   Find the second-degree Taylor polynomial at 0 for $f(x) = \sqrt{x+9}$. Use $p_2(x)$ to approximate $\sqrt{10}$.

Many of the problems in this section involve approximating the values of functions that also can be evaluated with the use of a calculator. In such problems you should compare the Taylor polynomial approximation with the calculator value (which is also an approximation). This will give you some indication of the accuracy of the Taylor polynomial approximation. Later in this chapter we will discuss methods for determining the accuracy of any Taylor polynomial approximation.

EXAMPLE 3   **Taylor Polynomials at 0** Find the nth-degree Taylor polynomial at 0 for $f(x) = e^{2x}$.

SOLUTION

Step 1	Step 2	Step 3
$f(x) = e^{2x}$	$f(0) = 1$	$a_0 = f(0) = 1$
$f'(x) = 2e^{2x}$	$f'(0) = 2$	$a_1 = f'(0) = 2$

$$f''(x) = 2^2 e^{2x} \qquad f''(0) = 2^2 \qquad a_2 = \frac{f''(0)}{2!} = \frac{2^2}{2!}$$

$$f^{(3)}(x) = 2^3 e^{2x} \qquad f^{(3)}(0) = 2^3 \qquad a_3 = \frac{f^{(3)}(0)}{3!} = \frac{2^3}{3!}$$

$$\vdots \qquad\qquad \vdots \qquad\qquad \vdots \qquad \vdots$$

$$f^{(n)}(x) = 2^n e^{2x} \qquad f^{(n)}(0) = 2^n \qquad a_n = \frac{f^{(n)}(0)}{n!} = \frac{2^n}{n!}$$

Step 4. *Write down the Taylor polynomial:*

$$p_n(x) = 1 + 2x + \frac{2^2}{2!}x^2 + \frac{2^3}{3!}x^3 + \cdots + \frac{2^n}{n!}x^n = \sum_{k=0}^{n} \frac{2^k}{k!}x^k$$

MATCHED PROBLEM 3 Find the *n*th-degree Taylor polynomial at 0 for $f(x) = e^{x/3}$.

◼ Taylor Polynomials at *a*

Suppose we want to approximate the function $f(x) = \sqrt[4]{x}$ with a polynomial. Since $f^{(k)}(0)$ is undefined for $k = 1, 2, \ldots$, this function does not have a Taylor polynomial at 0. However, all the derivatives of f exist at any $x > 0$. How can we generalize the definition of the Taylor polynomial to approximate functions such as this one? Before answering this question, we need to review a basic property of polynomials.

We are used to expressing polynomials in powers of x. However, it is also possible to express any polynomial in powers of $x - a$ for an arbitrary number a. For example, the following three expressions all represent the same polynomial:

$$
\begin{aligned}
p(x) &= 3 + 2x \qquad\quad + x^2 && \text{Powers of } x. \\
&= 6 + 4(x - 1) + (x - 1)^2 && \text{Powers of } x - 1. \\
&= 3 - 2(x + 2) + (x + 2)^2 && \text{Powers of } x + 2.
\end{aligned}
$$

To verify this statement, we expand the second and third expressions:

$$
\begin{aligned}
6 + 4(x - 1) + (x - 1)^2 &= 6 + 4x - 4 + x^2 - 2x + 1 \\
&= 3 + 2x + x^2 \\
3 - 2(x + 2) + (x + 2)^2 &= 3 - 2x - 4 + x^2 + 4x + 4 \\
&= 3 + 2x + x^2
\end{aligned}
$$

Now we return to the problem of generalizing the definition of the Taylor polynomial. Proceeding as we did before, given a function f with n derivatives at a number a, we want to find an nth-degree polynomial p_n with the property that

$$p^{(k)}(a) = f^{(k)}(a) \qquad k = 0, 1, \ldots, n$$

That is, we require that p_n and its first n derivatives agree with f and its first n derivatives at the number a. It turns out that it is much easier to find p_n when it is expressed in powers of $x - a$. The general expression for an nth-degree polynomial in powers of $x - a$ and its first n derivatives are as follows:

$$
\begin{aligned}
p_n(x) &= a_0 + a_1(x - a) + a_2(x - a)^2 + a_3(x - a)^3 + \cdots + a_n(x - a)^n \\
p_n'(x) &= \qquad\quad a_1 \qquad + 2a_2(x - a) + 3a_3(x - a)^2 + \cdots + na_n(x - a)^{n-1} \\
p_n''(x) &= \qquad\qquad\qquad\qquad 2a_2 \qquad + (3)(2)a_3(x - a) + \cdots + n(n - 1)a_n(x - a)^{n-2} \\
p_n^{(3)}(x) &= \qquad\qquad\qquad\qquad\qquad\qquad\quad (3)(2)(1)a_3 \qquad + \cdots + n(n - 1)(n - 2)a_n(x - a)^{n-3} \\
&\;\;\vdots \\
p_n^{(n)}(x) &= n(n - 1) \cdots \cdot (1)a_n = n!a_n
\end{aligned}
$$

Now we evaluate each function at a and apply the appropriate condition:

$$a_0 = p_n(a) = f(a) \qquad k = 0$$
$$a_1 = p'_n(a) = f'(a) \qquad k = 1$$
$$2a_2 = p''_n(a) = f''(a) \qquad k = 2$$
$$(3)(2)(1)a_3 = p^{(3)}_n(a) = f^{(3)}(a) \qquad k = 3$$
$$\vdots \qquad \vdots \qquad \vdots$$
$$n!a_n = p^{(n)}_n(a) = f^{(n)}(a) \qquad k = n$$

Thus, each coefficient of p_n satisfies

$$a_k = \frac{f^{(k)}(a)}{k!} \qquad k = 0, 1, 2, \ldots, n$$

DEFINITION   **Taylor Polynomial at a**

The ***nth-degree Taylor polynomial at a*** for a function f is

$$p_n(x) = f(a) + f'(a)(x - a) + \frac{f''(a)}{2!}(x - a)^2 + \cdots + \frac{f^{(n)}(a)}{n!}(x - a)^n$$

$$= \sum_{k=0}^{n} \frac{f^{(k)}(a)}{k!}(x - a)^k$$

provided f has n derivatives at a.

Theoretically, a function f has an nth-degree Taylor polynomial at any value a where it has n derivatives. In practice, we usually choose a so that f and its derivatives are easy to evaluate at $x = a$. For example, if $f(x) = \sqrt{x}$, then good choices for a are 1, 4, 9, 16, and so on.

EXAMPLE 4   **Taylor Polynomials at a**   Find the third-degree Taylor polynomial at $a = 1$ for $f(x) = \sqrt[4]{x}$. Use $p_3(x)$ to approximate $\sqrt[4]{2}$.

SOLUTION   **Step 1.**   *Find the derivatives:*

$$f(x) = x^{1/4}$$
$$f'(x) = \tfrac{1}{4}x^{-3/4}$$
$$f''(x) = -\tfrac{3}{16}x^{-7/4}$$
$$f^{(3)}(x) = \tfrac{21}{64}x^{-11/4}$$

Step 2.   *Evaluate the derivatives at $a = 1$:*

$$f(1) = 1$$
$$f'(1) = \tfrac{1}{4}$$
$$f''(1) = -\tfrac{3}{16}$$
$$f^{(3)}(1) = \tfrac{21}{64}$$

Step 3.   *Find the coefficients of the Taylor polynomial:*

$$a_0 = f(1) = 1$$
$$a_1 = f'(1) = \tfrac{1}{4}$$
$$a_2 = \frac{f''(1)}{2!} = \frac{-\tfrac{3}{16}}{2} = -\frac{3}{32}$$
$$a_3 = \frac{f^{(3)}(1)}{3!} = \frac{\tfrac{21}{64}}{6} = \frac{7}{128}$$

Step 4.   *Write down the Taylor polynomial:*

$$p_3(x) = 1 + \tfrac{1}{4}(x-1) - \tfrac{3}{32}(x-1)^2 + \tfrac{7}{128}(x-1)^3$$

Now we use the Taylor polynomial to approximate $\sqrt[4]{2}$:

$$\sqrt[4]{2} = f(2) \approx p_3(2) = 1 + \tfrac{1}{4} - \tfrac{3}{32} + \tfrac{7}{128} = 1.2109375$$

[*Note:* The value obtained by using a calculator is $\sqrt[4]{2} \approx 1.1892071.$]

MATCHED PROBLEM 4   Find the second-degree Taylor polynomial at $a = 8$ for $f(x) = \sqrt[3]{x}$. Use $p_2(x)$ to approximate $\sqrt[3]{9}$.

APPLICATIONS

EXAMPLE 5   **Average Price** Given the demand function

$$p = D(x) = \sqrt{2,500 - x^2}$$

use the second-degree Taylor polynomial at 0 to approximate the average price (in dollars) over the demand interval $[10, 40]$.

SOLUTION   The average price over the demand interval $[10, 40]$ is given by

$$\text{Average price} = \frac{1}{30}\int_{10}^{40} \sqrt{2,500 - x^2}\, dx$$

This integral cannot be evaluated by any of the techniques we have discussed. However, we can use a Taylor polynomial to approximate the value of the integral. Omitting the details (which you should supply), the second-degree Taylor polynomial at 0 for $D(x) = \sqrt{2,500 - x^2}$ is

$$p_2(x) = 50 - \tfrac{1}{100}x^2$$

Assuming that $D(x) \approx p_2(x)$ for $10 \le x \le 40$ (see Fig. 5), we have

$$\text{Average price} \approx \frac{1}{30}\int_{10}^{40}\left(50 - \frac{1}{100}x^2\right)dx$$

$$= \frac{1}{30}\left(50x - \frac{1}{300}x^3\right)\Big|_{10}^{40}$$

$$= \$43$$

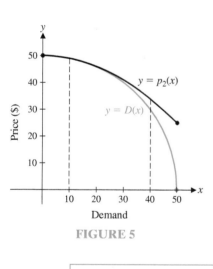

FIGURE 5

MATCHED PROBLEM 5   Given the demand function

$$p = D(x) = \sqrt{400 - x^2}$$

use the second-degree Taylor polynomial at 0 to approximate the average price (in dollars) over the demand interval $[5, 15]$.

Example 5 illustrates the convenience of using Taylor polynomials to approximate more complicated functions, but it also raises several important questions. First, how can we determine whether it is reasonable to use the Taylor polynomial to approximate a function on a given interval? Second, is it possible to find the Taylor polynomial without resorting to successive differentiation of the function? Finally, can we determine the accuracy of an approximation such as the approximate average price found in Example 5? These questions will be discussed in the next three sections.

1. $f^{(n)}(x) = (-1)^{n-1}(n-1)! \, x^{-n}$

2. $p_2(x) = 3 + \frac{1}{6}x - \frac{1}{216}x^2$; $\sqrt{10} \approx 3.162\,037$

3. $p_n(x) = 1 + \frac{1}{3}x + \frac{1}{3^2}\frac{1}{2!}x^2 + \frac{1}{3^3}\frac{1}{3!}x^3 + \cdots + \frac{1}{3^n}\frac{1}{n!}x^n = \sum_{k=0}^{n} \frac{1}{3^k}\frac{1}{k!}x^k$

4. $p_2(x) = 2 + \frac{1}{12}(x - 8) - \frac{1}{288}(x - 8)^2$; $\sqrt[3]{9} \approx 2.079\,861\,1$

5. $\frac{1}{10}\int_5^{15}\left(20 - \frac{x^2}{40}\right)dx = \frac{415}{24} \approx \$17.29$

Exercise 2.1

A *In Problems 1–4, find $f^{(3)}(x)$.*

1. $f(x) = \dfrac{1}{x}$

2. $f(x) = \ln(1 + x)$

3. $f(x) = e^{-x}$

4. $f(x) = \sqrt{x}$

In Problems 5–8, find $f^{(4)}(x)$.

5. $f(x) = \ln(1 + 3x)$

6. $f(x) = e^{5x}$

7. $f(x) = \sqrt{1 + x}$

8. $f(x) = \dfrac{1}{2 + x}$

In Problems 9–16, find the indicated Taylor polynomial at 0.

9. $f(x) = e^{-x}$; $p_4(x)$

10. $f(x) = e^{4x}$; $p_3(x)$

11. $f(x) = (x + 1)^3$; $p_4(x)$

12. $f(x) = (1 - x)^4$; $p_3(x)$

13. $f(x) = \ln(1 + 2x)$; $p_3(x)$

14. $f(x) = \ln(1 + \frac{1}{2}x)$; $p_4(x)$

15. $f(x) = \sqrt[3]{x + 1}$; $p_3(x)$

16. $f(x) = \sqrt[4]{x + 16}$; $p_2(x)$

17. (A) Find the third-degree Taylor polynomial $p_3(x)$ for $f(x) = x^4 - 1$ at 0. For which values of x is $|p_3(x) - f(x)| < 0.1$?

(B) Find the fourth-degree Taylor polynomial $p_4(x)$ for $f(x) = x^4 - 1$ at 0. For which values of x is $|p_4(x) - f(x)| < 0.1$?

18. (A) Find the fourth-degree Taylor polynomial $p_4(x)$ for $f(x) = x^5$ at 0. For which values of x is $|p_4(x) - f(x)| < 0.01$?

(B) Find the fifth-degree Taylor polynomial $p_5(x)$ for $f(x) = x^5$ at 0. For which values of x is $|p_5(x) - f(x)| < 0.01$?

In Problems 19–24, find the indicated Taylor polynomial at the given value of a.

19. $f(x) = e^{x-1}$; $p_4(x)$ at 1

20. $f(x) = e^{2x}$; $p_3(x)$ at $\frac{1}{2}$

21. $f(x) = x^3$; $p_3(x)$ at 1

22. $f(x) = x^2 - 6x + 10$; $p_2(x)$ at $x = 3$

23. $f(x) = \ln(3x)$; $p_3(x)$ at $\frac{1}{3}$

24. $f(x) = \ln(2 - x)$; $p_4(x)$ at 1

25. Use the third-degree Taylor polynomial at 0 for $f(x) = e^{-2x}$ and $x = 0.25$ to approximate $e^{-0.5}$.

26. Use the fourth-degree Taylor polynomial at 0 for $f(x) = \ln(1 - x)$ and $x = 0.1$ to approximate $\ln 0.9$.

27. Use the second-degree Taylor polynomial at 0 for $f(x) = \sqrt{x + 16}$ and $x = 1$ to approximate $\sqrt{17}$.

28. Use the third-degree Taylor polynomial at 0 for $f(x) = \sqrt{(x + 4)^3}$ and $x = 1$ to approximate $\sqrt{125}$.

29. Use the fourth-degree Taylor polynomial at 1 for $f(x) = \sqrt{x}$ and $x = 1.2$ to approximate $\sqrt{1.2}$.

30. Use the third-degree Taylor polynomial at 4 for $f(x) = \sqrt{x}$ and $x = 3.95$ to approximate $\sqrt{3.95}$.

B *In Problems 31–36, find $f^{(n)}(x)$.*

31. $f(x) = \dfrac{1}{4 - x}$

32. $f(x) = \dfrac{4}{1 + x}$

33. $f(x) = e^{3x}$

34. $f(x) = \ln(2x + 1)$

35. $f(x) = \ln(6 - x)$

36. $f(x) = e^{x/2}$

In Problems 37–42, find the nth-degree Taylor polynomial at 0. Write the answer in expanded notation.

37. $f(x) = \dfrac{1}{4 - x}$

38. $f(x) = \dfrac{4}{1 + x}$

39. $f(x) = e^{3x}$

40. $f(x) = \ln(2x + 1)$

41. $f(x) = \ln(6 - x)$

42. $f(x) = e^{x/2}$

In Problems 43–50, find the nth-degree Taylor polynomial at the indicated value of a. Write the answer in expanded notation.

43. $f(x) = \dfrac{1}{x}$; at -1

44. $f(x) = \dfrac{2}{x}$; at 1

45. $f(x) = \ln x$; at 1

46. $f(x) = e^x$; at -2

47. $f(x) = e^{-x}$; at 2

48. $f(x) = \ln(2 - x)$; at -1

49. $f(x) = x \ln x$; at 3

50. $f(x) = xe^x$; at 1

51. Let $f(x) = x^4 + 5x^2 + 1$.

(A) Find the third-degree Taylor polynomial $p_3(x)$ for f at 0.

(B) What is the degree of the polynomial $p_3(x)$?

52. Let $f(x) = x^5 + 2x^3 + 8x^2 + 1$.

   (A) Find the fourth-degree Taylor polynomial $p_4(x)$ for f at 0.

   (B) What is the degree of the polynomial $p_4(x)$?

53. Let $f(x) = x^6 + 2x^3 + 1$. For which values of n does $p_n(x)$, the nth-degree Taylor polynomial for f at 0, have degree n?

54. Let $f(x) = x^4 - 1$. For which values of n does $p_n(x)$, the nth-degree Taylor polynomial for f at 0, have degree n?

55. Find the first three Taylor polynomials at 0 for $f(x) = \ln(1 + x)$, and use these polynomials to complete the following two tables. Round all table entries to six decimal places.

x	$p_1(x)$	$p_2(x)$	$p_3(x)$	$f(x)$
−0.2				
−0.1				
0				
0.1				
0.2				

x	$|p_1(x) - f(x)|$	$|p_2(x) - f(x)|$	$|p_3(x) - f(x)|$
−0.2			
−0.1			
0			
0.1			
0.2			

56. Repeat Problem 55 for $f(x) = \sqrt{1 + x}$.

57. Refer to Problem 55. Graph $f(x) = \ln(1 + x)$ and its first three Taylor polynomials in the same viewing window. Use $[-3, 3]$ for both the x range and the y range.

58. Refer to Problem 56. Graph $f(x) = \sqrt{1 + x}$ and its first three Taylor polynomials in the same viewing window. Use $[-3, 3]$ for both the x range and the y range.

59. Consider $f(x) = e^x$ and its third-degree Taylor polynomial $p_3(x)$ at 0. Use graphical approximation techniques to find all values of x such that $|p_3(x) - e^x| < 0.1$.

60. Consider $f(x) = \ln(1 + x)$ and its third-degree Taylor polynomial $p_3(x)$ at 0. Use graphical approximation techniques to find all values of x such that
$$|p_3(x) - \ln(1 + x)| < 0.1$$

In Problems 61–64, write the answer in both expanded notation and summation notation.

61. Find the nth-degree Taylor polynomial for $f(x) = e^x$ at any point a.

62. Find the nth-degree Taylor polynomial for $f(x) = \ln x$ at any $a > 0$.

63. Find the nth-degree Taylor polynomial for $f(x) = 1/x$ at any $a \neq 0$.

64. Find the nth-degree Taylor polynomial at 0 for $f(x) = (x + c)^n$, where c is a constant.

65. Let $f(x)$ be a polynomial. For which values of n is the nth-degree Taylor polynomial for f at 0 equal to $f(x)$? Explain.

66. Explain how any polynomial expressed in powers of x may be rewritten in powers of $x - 1$ using Taylor polynomials. Illustrate your method for $f(x) = 1 + x^2 + x^4$.

67. Let $p_{10}(x)$ be the tenth-degree Taylor polynomial for $f(x) = e^x$ at 0. Do values of x exist for which $|p_{10}(x) - f(x)| \geq 100$? Explain.

68. Let $p_{12}(x)$ be the twelfth-degree Taylor polynomial for $f(x) = 1/x$ at 1. Do values of $x \neq 0$ exist for which $|p_{12}(x) - f(x)| \geq 100$? Explain.

Applications

69. *Average price.* Given the demand equation
$$p = D(x) = \tfrac{1}{10}\sqrt{10,000 - x^2}$$
use the second-degree Taylor polynomial at 0 to approximate the average price (in dollars) over the demand interval $[0, 30]$.

70. *Average price.* Given the demand equation
$$p = D(x) = \tfrac{1}{5}\sqrt{1,600 - x^2}$$
use the second-degree Taylor polynomial at 0 to approximate the average price (in dollars) over the demand interval $[0, 15]$.

71. *Average price.* Refer to Problem 69. Use the second-degree Taylor polynomial at $a = 60$ to approximate the average price over the demand interval $[60, 80]$.

72. *Average price.* Refer to Problem 70. Use the second-degree Taylor polynomial at $a = 24$ to approximate the average price over the demand interval $[24, 32]$.

73. *Production.* The rate of production of a mine (in millions of dollars per year) is given by
$$R(t) = 2 + 8e^{-0.1t^2}$$
Use the second-degree Taylor polynomial at 0 to approximate the total production during the first 2 years of operation of the mine.

74. *Production.* The rate of production of an oil well (in millions of dollars per year) is given by
$$R(t) = 5 + 10e^{-0.05t^2}$$
Use the second-degree Taylor polynomial at 0 to approximate the total production during the first 3 years of operation of the well.

75. *Medicine.* The rate of healing for a skin wound (in square centimeters per day) is given by
$$A'(t) = \frac{-75}{t^2 + 25}$$

The initial wound has an area of 12 square centimeters. Use the second-degree Taylor polynomial at 0 for $A'(t)$ to approximate the area of the wound after 2 days.

76. *Medicine.* Rework Problem 75 for $A'(t) = \dfrac{-60}{t^2 + 20}$.

77. *Pollution.* On an average summer day in a particular large city the air pollution level (in parts per million) is given by

$$P(x) = 20\sqrt{3x^2 + 25} - 80$$

where x is the number of hours elapsed since 8:00 A.M. Use the second-degree Taylor polynomial for $P(x)$ at $a = 5$ to approximate the average pollution level during the 10-hour period from 8:00 A.M. to 6:00 P.M.

78. *Pollution.* On an average summer day in another large city the air pollution level (in parts per million) is given by

$$P(x) = 10\sqrt{4x^2 + 36} - 50$$

where x is the number of hours elapsed since 8:00 A.M. Use the second-degree Taylor polynomial for $P(x)$ at $a = 4$ to approximate the average pollution level during the 8-hour period from 8:00 A.M. to 4:00 P.M.

79. *Learning.* In a particular business college, it was found that an average student enrolled in an advanced typing class progresses at a rate of $N'(t) = 6e^{-0.01t^2}$ words per minute per week, t weeks after enrolling in a 15-week course. At the beginning of the course an average student could type 40 words per minute. Use the second-degree Taylor polynomial at 0 for $N'(t)$ to approximate the improvement in typing after 5 weeks in the course.

80. *Learning.* In the same business college, it was also found that an average student enrolled in a beginning shorthand class progressed at a rate of $N'(t) = 12e^{-0.005t^2}$ words per minute per week, t weeks after enrolling in a 15-week course. At the beginning of the course none of the students could take any dictation by shorthand. Use the second-degree Taylor polynomial at 0 for $N'(t)$ to approximate the improvement after 5 weeks in the course.

In Problems 81–88, use a graphing utility to graph the given function and its second-degree Taylor polynomial at a in the indicated viewing window.

81. *Average price.* From Problem 69,

$$p = D(x) = \tfrac{1}{10}\sqrt{10,000 - x^2}$$

$a = 0$

x range: $[0, 100]$

p range: $[0, 10]$

82. *Average price.* From Problem 70,

$$p = D(x) = \tfrac{1}{5}\sqrt{1,600 - x^2}$$

$a = 0$

x range: $[0, 40]$

p range: $[0, 8]$

83. *Production.* From Problem 73,

$$y = R(t) = 2 + 8e^{-0.1t^2}$$

$a = 0$

t range: $[0, 5]$

y range: $[0, 10]$

84. *Production.* From Problem 74,

$$y = R(t) = 5 + 10e^{-0.05t^2}$$

$a = 0$

t range: $[0, 5]$

y range: $[0, 15]$

85. *Pollution.* From Problem 77,

$$y = P(x) = 20\sqrt{3x^2 + 25} - 80$$

$a = 5$

x range: $[0, 10]$

y range: $[0, 300]$

86. *Pollution.* From Problem 78,

$$y = P(x) = 10\sqrt{4x^2 + 36} - 50$$

$a = 4$

x range: $[0, 10]$

y range: $[0, 200]$

87. *Learning.* From Problem 79,

$$y = N'(t) = 6e^{-0.01t^2}$$

$a = 0$

t range: $[0, 10]$

y range: $[0, 6]$

88. *Learning.* From Problem 80,

$$y = N'(t) = 12e^{-0.005t^2}$$

$a = 0$

t range: $[0, 15]$

y range: $[0, 12]$

Section 2.2 TAYLOR SERIES

- Introduction
- Taylor Series
- Representation of Functions by Taylor Series

Introduction

If f is a function with derivatives of all order at a point a, then we can construct the Taylor polynomial p_n at a for any integer n. Now we are interested in the relationship between the original function f and the corresponding Taylor polynomial p_n as n assumes larger and larger values. If the Taylor polynomial is to be a useful tool for approximating functions, then the accuracy of the approximation should improve as we increase the size of n. Indeed, Figures 1, 2, and 3 and Tables 1 and 2 in the preceding section indicate that this is the case for the function e^x.

For a given value of x, we would like to know whether we can make $p_n(x)$ arbitrarily close to $f(x)$ by making n sufficiently large. In other words, we want to know whether

$$\lim_{n \to \infty} p_n(x) = f(x) \tag{1}$$

It turns out that for most functions with derivatives of all order at a point, there is a set of values of x for which equation (1) is valid. We will begin by considering a specific example to illustrate this.

Let

$$f(x) = \frac{1}{1-x} \quad \text{and} \quad a = 0$$

First, we find p_n:

Step 1

$$f(x) = (1-x)^{-1}$$

$$f'(x) = (-1)(1-x)^{-2}(-1) = (1-x)^{-2}$$

$$f''(x) = (-2)(1-x)^{-3}(-1) = 2(1-x)^{-3}$$

$$f^{(3)}(x) = (-3)(2)(1-x)^{-4}(-1) = 3!(1-x)^{-4}$$

$$\vdots$$

$$f^{(n)}(x) = n!(1-x)^{-n-1}$$

Step 2

$$f(0) = 1$$

$$f'(0) = 1$$

$$f''(0) = 2$$

$$f^{(3)}(0) = 3!$$

$$\vdots$$

$$f^{(n)}(0) = n!$$

Step 3

$$a_0 = f(0) = 1$$

$$a_1 = f'(0) = 1$$

$$a_2 = \frac{f''(0)}{2!} = \frac{2}{2!} = 1$$

$$a_3 = \frac{f^{(3)}(0)}{3!} = \frac{3!}{3!} = 1$$

$$\vdots$$

$$a_n = \frac{f^{(n)}(0)}{n!} = \frac{n!}{n!} = 1$$

Step 4. *Write down the Taylor polynomial:*

$$p_n(x) = 1 + x + x^2 + x^3 + \cdots + x^n \tag{2}$$

$$= \sum_{k=0}^{n} x^k$$

Now we want to evaluate

$$\lim_{n \to \infty} p_n(x) = \lim_{n \to \infty} \sum_{k=0}^{n} x^k$$

As we saw in Chapter 5 of *Calculus* 13/e or Chapter 13 of *College Mathematics* 13/e, it is not possible to evaluate limits written in this form. The difficulty lies in the fact that the number of terms is increasing as n increases. First, we must find a closed form for the summation that does not involve a sum of n terms. [You may recognize that $p_n(x)$ is a finite geometric series with common ratio x. See Appendix B-2 of *Calculus* 13/e or *College Mathematics* 13/e].

If we multiply both sides of (2) by x and subtract this new equation from the original, we obtain an equation that we can solve for $p_n(x)$. Notice how many terms drop out when the subtraction is performed.

$$p_n(x) = 1 + x + x^2 + \cdots + x^{n-1} + x^n$$
$$xp_n(x) = x + x^2 + \cdots + x^{n-1} + x^n + x^{n+1}$$
$$\overline{p_n(x) - xp_n(x) = 1 \phantom{+ x + x^2 + \cdots + x^{n-1} + x^n} - x^{n+1}}$$
$$p_n(x)(1 - x) = 1 - x^{n+1}$$
$$p_n(x) = \frac{1 - x^{n+1}}{1 - x} \qquad x \neq 1$$

Since we had to exclude the value $x = 1$ to avoid division by 0, we must consider $x = 1$ as a special case:

$$p_n(1) = \overbrace{1 + 1 + 1^2 + \cdots + 1^n}^{n + 1 \text{ terms}}$$
$$= n + 1$$

Thus,

$$p_n(x) = \begin{cases} \dfrac{1 - x^{n+1}}{1 - x} & \text{if } x \neq 1 \\ n + 1 & \text{if } x = 1 \end{cases}$$

If $x = 1$, it is clear that

$$\lim_{n \to \infty} p_n(1) = \lim_{n \to \infty} (n + 1) = \infty$$

That is, $\lim_{n \to \infty} p_n(1)$ does not exist. What happens to this limit for other values of x? It can be shown that

$$\lim_{n \to \infty} x^{n+1} = \begin{cases} 0 & \text{if } -1 < x < 1 \\ 1 & \text{if } x = 1 \\ \text{Does not exist} & \text{if } x \leq -1 \text{ or } x > 1 \end{cases}$$

Experimenting with a calculator for various values of x and large values of n should convince you that this statement is valid.

Thus,

$$\lim_{n \to \infty} p_n(x) = \begin{cases} \dfrac{1}{1 - x} & \text{if } -1 < x < 1 \\ \text{Does not exist} & \text{if } x = 1 \\ \text{Does not exist} & \text{if } x \leq -1 \text{ or } x > 1 \end{cases}$$

$$\lim_{n \to \infty} x^{n+1} = 0$$
$$\lim_{n \to \infty} (n + 1) \text{ does not exist}$$
$$\lim_{n \to \infty} x^{n+1} \text{ does not exist}$$

Explore & Discuss **1**

(A) Construct a table with eight rows labeled with values of n from 1 to 8, and seven columns labeled with the following values of x: $-1.5, -1, -0.5, 0, 0.5,$ 1 and 1.5. Complete the table by computing each entry $p_n(x)$.

(B) Explain how the table from part (A) provides supporting evidence for the statement that $\lim_{n \to \infty} p_n(x)$ equals $1/(1 - x)$ if $-1 < x < 1$, but does not exist if $x \leq -1$ or $x \geq 1$.

We can now conclude that

$$f(x) = \frac{1}{1 - x}$$
$$= \lim_{n \to \infty} p_n(x) \qquad -1 < x < 1$$
$$= \lim_{n \to \infty} \sum_{k=0}^{n} x^k$$

and that the limit does not exist for any other values of x. This is often abbreviated by writing

$$\frac{1}{1-x} = 1 + x + x^2 + \cdots + x^n + \cdots \qquad -1 < x < 1 \qquad (3)$$

$$= \sum_{k=0}^{\infty} x^k$$

INSIGHT

Equation (3) is often described in words as follows: The sum of an infinite geometric series, having first term 1 and common ratio x, is equal to $1/(1 - x)$, provided that the absolute value of the common ratio is less than 1.

The expression $\sum_{k=0}^{\infty} x^k$ is called the *Taylor series for f at 0*, and the expanded notation

$$1 + x + x^2 + \cdots + x^n + \cdots$$

is just another way to write this series. The Taylor series is said to *converge at x* if $\lim_{n \to \infty} p_n(x)$ exists and to *diverge at x* if this limit fails to exist. Thus, $\sum_{k=0}^{\infty} x^k$ converges for $-1 < x < 1$ and diverges for $x \le -1$ or $x \ge 1$. The set of values $\{x \mid -1 < x < 1\} = (-1, 1)$ where this Taylor series converges is called the *interval of convergence*. Since $f(x)$ is equal to the Taylor series for any x in the interval of convergence, we say that f is represented by its Taylor series throughout this interval. That is,

$$f(x) = \frac{1}{1-x}$$
$$= 1 + x + x^2 + \cdots + x^n + \cdots \qquad -1 < x < 1$$

There can be no relationship between f and its Taylor series outside the interval of convergence since the series is not defined there (see Fig. 1).

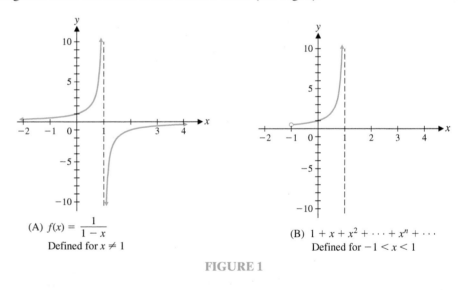

(A) $f(x) = \dfrac{1}{1-x}$

Defined for $x \ne 1$

(B) $1 + x + x^2 + \cdots + x^n + \cdots$

Defined for $-1 < x < 1$

FIGURE 1

Explore & Discuss **2**

FIGURE 2

(A) The six functions $p_n(x) = 1 + x + \cdots + x^n, n = 1, 2, \ldots, 6$, are graphed in Figure 2. Which graph belongs to which function?

(B) Based solely on the graphs, would you conjecture that the interval of convergence of the Taylor series representation

$$\frac{1}{1-x} = 1 + x + x^2 + \cdots + x^n + \cdots$$

is $-1 < x < 1$? Explain.

■ Taylor Series

We now generalize the concepts introduced in the preceding discussion to arbitrary functions.

DEFINITION **Taylor Series**

If f is a function with derivatives of all order at a point a, $p_n(x)$ is the nth-degree Taylor polynomial for f at a, and $a_n = f^{(n)}(a)/n!$, $n = 0, 1, 2, \ldots$, then

$$\sum_{k=0}^{\infty} a_k(x - a)^k = a_0 + a_1(x - a) + a_2(x - a)^2 + \cdots + a_n(x - a)^n + \cdots$$

is the **Taylor series for f at a.** The Taylor series **converges at x** if

$$\lim_{n \to \infty} p_n(x) = \lim_{n \to \infty} \sum_{k=0}^{n} a_k(x - a)^k$$

exists and **diverges at x** if this limit does not exist. The set of values of x for which this limit exists is called the **interval of convergence.**

We must emphasize that we are not really adding up an infinite number of terms in a Taylor series, nor is a Taylor series an "infinite" polynomial. Rather, for x in the interval of convergence,

$$\sum_{k=0}^{\infty} a_k(x - a)^k = \lim_{n \to \infty} \sum_{k=0}^{n} a_k(x - a)^k$$

Thus, when we write

$$\frac{1}{1 - x} = 1 + x + x^2 + \cdots + x^n + \cdots \qquad -1 < x < 1$$

we mean

$$\frac{1}{1 - x} = \lim_{n \to \infty} (1 + x + x^2 + \cdots + x^n) \qquad -1 < x < 1$$

In general, it is very difficult to find the interval of convergence by directly evaluating

$$\lim_{n \to \infty} \sum_{k=0}^{n} a_k(x - a)^k$$

For many Taylor series, the following theorem can be used to find the interval of convergence.

THEOREM 1 **INTERVAL OF CONVERGENCE**

Let f be a function with derivatives of all order at a point a, let $a_n = f^{(n)}(a)/n!$, $n = 0, 1, 2, \ldots$, and let

$$\sum_{k=0}^{\infty} a_k(x - a)^k = a_0 + a_1(x - a) + a_2(x - a)^2 + \cdots + a_n(x - a)^n + \cdots$$

be the Taylor series for f at a. If $a_n \neq 0$ for $n \geq n_0$, then:

Case 1. If

$$\lim_{n \to \infty} \left| \frac{a_{n+1}}{a_n} \right| = L > 0 \qquad \text{and} \qquad R = \frac{1}{L}$$

then the series converges for $|x - a| < R$ and diverges for $|x - a| > R$.

Case 2. If

$$\lim_{n \to \infty} \left| \frac{a_{n+1}}{a_n} \right| = 0$$

then the series converges for all values of x.

Case 3. If

$$\lim_{n \to \infty} \left| \frac{a_{n+1}}{a_n} \right| = \infty$$

then the series converges only at $x = a$.

The various possibilities for the interval of convergence are illustrated in Figure 3. In case 1, the series may or may not converge at the end points $x = a - R$ and $x = a + R$. (Determination of the behavior of a series at the end points of the interval of convergence requires techniques that we will not discuss.)

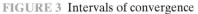

FIGURE 3 Intervals of convergence

Notice that the set of values where a series converges can be expressed in interval notation as $(a - R, a + R)$ in case 1 and as $(-\infty, \infty)$ in case 2. We were anticipating this result when we used the term *interval of convergence* to describe the set of points where a Taylor series converges.

Finally, the requirement that all the coefficients be nonzero from some point on ensures that the ratio a_{n+1}/a_n is well defined.

REMARK

It is possible that

$$\lim_{n \to \infty} \left| \frac{a_{n+1}}{a_n} \right|$$

fails to exist so that none of the cases in Theorem 1 hold. In that event, the interval of convergence will still have one of the forms illustrated by Figure 3, but other techniques are required to determine which one.

INSIGHT

Assume that $a_n \neq 0$ for $n \geq n_0$ and consider case 1 of Theorem 1. The ratio of consecutive terms of the Taylor series is equal to

$$\frac{a_{n+1}(x - a)^{n+1}}{a_n(x - a)^n}$$

The absolute value of this ratio for large n, by the limit in case 1, is approximately $L|x - a|$. Therefore, the Taylor series is approximately an infinite geometric series with common ratio having absolute value $L|x - a|$. Such a series converges if $L|x - a| < 1$, or equivalently, if $|x - a| < 1/L = R$.

The next two examples illustrate the application of Theorem 1. The details of finding the Taylor series are omitted. In the next section we will discuss methods that greatly simplify the process of finding Taylor series. For now, we want to concentrate on understanding the significance of the interval of convergence.

EXAMPLE 1   **Finding the Interval of Convergence** The Taylor series at 0 for $f(x) = e^{2x}$ is

$$1 + 2x + \frac{2^2}{2!}x^2 + \cdots + \frac{2^n}{n!}x^n + \cdots$$

Find the interval of convergence.

SOLUTION

$$a_n = \frac{2^n}{n!} \qquad \text{\textit{Notice that } } a_n > 0 \text{ \textit{for } } n \geq 0.$$

$$a_{n+1} = \frac{2^{n+1}}{(n+1)!}$$

$$\frac{a_{n+1}}{a_n} = \frac{\dfrac{2^{n+1}}{(n+1)!}}{\dfrac{2^n}{n!}} \qquad \text{\textit{Form the ratio } } a_{n-1}/a_n \text{ \textit{and simplify.}}$$

$$= \frac{2^{n+1}}{(n+1)!} \cdot \frac{n!}{2^n} \qquad \frac{n!}{(n+1)!} = \frac{n!}{(n+1)n!} = \frac{1}{n+1}$$

$$= \frac{2}{n+1}$$

$$\lim_{n \to \infty} \left| \frac{a_{n+1}}{a_n} \right| = \lim_{n \to \infty} \left| \frac{2}{n+1} \right| \qquad \text{\textit{Absolute value signs can be dropped since}}$$
$$\qquad\qquad\qquad\qquad\qquad\qquad a_{n+1}/a_n > 0.$$

$$= \lim_{n \to \infty} \frac{2}{n+1} = 0*$$

Case 2 in Theorem 1 applies, and the series converges for all values of x.   ▬

MATCHED PROBLEM 1   The Taylor series at 0 for $f(x) = e^{x/3}$ is

$$1 + \frac{1}{3}x + \frac{1}{3^2 2!}x^2 + \cdots + \frac{1}{3^n n!}x^n + \cdots$$

Find the interval of convergence.

EXAMPLE 2   **Finding the Interval of Convergence** The Taylor series at 0 for $f(x) = 1/(1+5x)^2$ is

$$1 - 2 \cdot 5x + 3 \cdot 5^2 x^2 - \cdots + (-1)^n (n+1)5^n x^n + \cdots$$

Find the interval of convergence.

---

*The limit expressions $\lim_{x \to \infty} g(x)$ and $\lim_{n \to \infty} g(n)$ are very similar. If $\lim_{x \to \infty} g(x) = L$ [that is, $g(x)$ can be made arbitrarily close to L by making the *real number* x sufficiently large], then $\lim_{n \to \infty} g(n) = L$ [that is, $g(n)$ can be made arbitrarily close to L by making the *integer* n sufficiently large]. In particular,

$$\lim_{n \to \infty} \frac{2}{n+1} = \lim_{x \to \infty} \frac{2}{x+1} = 0$$

Thus, the results of Section 2.2 of *Calculus* 13/e or Section 12.3 of *College Mathematics* 13/e on limits at infinity for rational functions can be helpful in evaluating limits of the form $\lim_{n \to \infty} g(n)$.

SOLUTION

$$a_n = (-1)^n(n + 1)5^n \qquad \text{\textit{Notice that }} a_n \neq 0 \text{ \textit{for }} n \geq 0.$$

$$a_{n+1} = (-1)^{n+1}(n + 2)5^{n+1}$$

$$\frac{a_{n+1}}{a_n} = \frac{(-1)^{n+1}(n + 2)5^{n+1}}{(-1)^n(n + 1)5^n}$$

$$= \frac{-5(n + 2)}{n + 1}$$

$$\lim_{n \to \infty} \left| \frac{a_{n+1}}{a_n} \right| = \lim_{n \to \infty} \left| \frac{-5(n + 2)}{n + 1} \right|$$

$$= \lim_{n \to \infty} \frac{5(n + 2)}{n + 1}$$

$$= \lim_{n \to \infty} \frac{5n + 10}{n + 1} \qquad \text{\textit{Divide numerator and denominator by }} n.$$

$$= \lim_{n \to \infty} \frac{5 + \dfrac{10}{n}}{1 + \dfrac{1}{n}} = 5$$

Applying case 1 in Theorem 1, we have $L = 5$, $R = \frac{1}{5}$, and the series converges for $-\frac{1}{5} < x < \frac{1}{5}$.

■

MATCHED PROBLEM 2

The Taylor series at 0 for $f(x) = 4/(2 + x)^2$ is

$$1 - \frac{2}{2}x + \frac{3}{2^2}x^2 - \cdots + \frac{(-1)^n(n + 1)}{2^n}x^n + \cdots$$

Find the interval of convergence.

■ Representation of Functions by Taylor Series

Referring to the function $f(x) = 1/(1 - x)$ discussed earlier in this section, our calculations showed that the Taylor series at 0 for f is

$$\lim_{n \to \infty} p_n(x) = 1 + x + x^2 + \cdots + x^n + \cdots$$

with interval of convergence $(-1, 1)$. Furthermore, we showed that f is represented by its Taylor series throughout the interval of convergence. That is,

$$f(x) = \frac{1}{1 - x} = \lim_{n \to \infty} p_n(x)$$

$$= 1 + x + x^2 + \cdots + x^n + \cdots \qquad -1 < x < 1$$

A similar statement can be made for most functions that have derivatives of all order at a point a, but not for all. For example, the absolute value function $g(x) = |x|$ has Taylor series (verify this)

$$1 + (x - 1) = x$$

at the point $a = 1$. Clearly, this very simple Taylor series converges for all x, but $g(x) = x$ only for $x \geq 0$. So g is not represented by its Taylor series throughout the interval of convergence of the series. The problem with g is that it is not differentiable at 0. Even if we require that a function f has derivatives of all order at every point in the interval of convergence of its Taylor series, it is still possible that f is not represented by its Taylor series. Since we will not consider such functions, we will make the following assumption.

AGREEMENT

Assumption on the Representation of Functions by Taylor Series

If f is a function with derivatives of all order throughout the interval of convergence of its Taylor series at a, then f **is represented by its Taylor series throughout the interval of convergence.** Thus, if $p_n(x)$ is the nth-degree Taylor polynomial at a for f and $a_n = f^{(n)}(a)/n!$, $n = 0, 1, 2, \ldots$, then

$$f(x) = \lim_{n \to \infty} p_n(x) = \sum_{k=0}^{\infty} a_k(x - a)^k$$

for any x in the interval of convergence of the Taylor series at a for f.

Consequently, the interval of convergence determines the values of x for which the Taylor polynomials $p_n(x)$ can be used to approximate the values of the function f.

Referring to Examples 1 and 2, we can now write

$$e^{2x} = 1 + 2x + \frac{2^2}{2!}x^2 + \cdots + \frac{2^n}{n!}x^n + \cdots \qquad -\infty < x < \infty$$

and

$$\frac{1}{(1 + 5x)^2} = 1 - 2 \cdot 5x + 3 \cdot 5^2x^2 - \cdots + (-1)^n(n + 1)5^nx^n + \cdots \qquad -\tfrac{1}{5} < x < \tfrac{1}{5}$$

EXAMPLE 3   RepresentationofaFunctionbyItsTaylorSeries   Let $f(x) = \ln x$.

(A) Find the nth-degree Taylor polynomial at $a = 1$ for f.

(B) Find the Taylor series at $a = 1$ for f.

(C) Determine the values of x for which $f(x) = \lim_{n \to \infty} p_n(x)$.

SOLUTION   (A) We use the four-step process from the preceding section to find the nth-degree Taylor polynomial:

Step 1	Step 2	Step 3
$f(x) = \ln x$	$f(1) = \ln 1 = 0$	$a_0 = f(1) \quad = 0$
$f'(x) = \dfrac{1}{x} = x^{-1}$	$f'(1) = 1$	$a_1 = f'(1) \quad = 1$
$f''(x) = (-1)x^{-2}$	$f''(1) = -1$	$a_2 = \dfrac{f''(1)}{2!} = -\dfrac{1}{2}$
$f^{(3)}(x) = (-1)(-2)x^{-3}$ $= (-1)^2 2! x^{-3}$	$f^{(3)}(1) = (-1)^2 2!$	$a_3 = \dfrac{f^{(3)}(1)}{3!} = \dfrac{(-1)^2 2!}{3!} = \dfrac{1}{3}$
$f^{(4)}(x) = (-1)(-2)(-3)x^{-4}$ $= (-1)^3 3! x^{-4}$	$f^{(4)}(1) = (-1)^3 3!$	$a_4 = \dfrac{f^{(4)}(1)}{4!} = \dfrac{(-1)^3 3!}{4!} = \dfrac{-1}{4}$
$\vdots$	$\vdots$	$\vdots$
$f^{(n)}(x) = (-1)^{n-1}(n-1)! x^{-n}$	$f^{(n)}(1) = (-1)^{n-1}(n-1)!$	$a_n = \dfrac{f^{(n)}(1)}{n!} = \dfrac{(-1)^{n-1}(n-1)!}{n!} = \dfrac{(-1)^{n-1}}{n}$

Step 4. The nth-degree Taylor polynomial at $a = 1$ for $f(x) = \ln x$ is

$$p_n(x) = (x - 1) - \frac{1}{2}(x - 1)^2 + \frac{1}{3}(x - 1)^3 - \cdots + \frac{(-1)^{n-1}}{n}(x - 1)^n$$

(B) Once the nth-degree Taylor polynomial for a function has been determined, finding the Taylor series is simply a matter of using the notation correctly. Using the Taylor polynomial from part (A), the Taylor series at $a = 1$ for $f(x) = \ln x$ can be written as

$$\lim_{n \to \infty} p_n(x) = (x - 1) - \frac{1}{2}(x - 1)^2 + \frac{1}{3}(x - 1)^3 - \cdots + \frac{(-1)^{n-1}}{n}(x - 1)^n + \cdots$$

or, using summation notation,* as

$$\lim_{n \to \infty} p_n(x) = \sum_{k=0}^{\infty} \frac{(-1)^{k-1}}{k}(x - 1)^k$$

(C) To determine the values for which $f(x) = \lim_{n \to \infty} p_n(x)$, we use Theorem 1 to find the interval of convergence of the Taylor series in part (B):

$$a_n = \frac{(-1)^{n-1}}{n}$$

$$a_{n+1} = \frac{(-1)^n}{n + 1}$$

$$\frac{a_{n+1}}{a_n} = \frac{\dfrac{(-1)^n}{n + 1}}{\dfrac{(-1)^{n-1}}{n}} = \frac{(-1)^n}{n + 1} \cdot \frac{n}{(-1)^{n-1}} = \frac{-n}{n + 1}$$

$$\lim_{n \to \infty} \left| \frac{a_{n+1}}{a_n} \right| = \lim_{n \to \infty} \left| \frac{-n}{n + 1} \right|$$

$$= \lim_{n \to \infty} \frac{n}{n + 1} \qquad \textit{Divide numerator and denominator by n.}$$

$$= \lim_{n \to \infty} \frac{1}{1 + \dfrac{1}{n}} = 1$$

From case 1 of Theorem 1, $L = 1$, $R = 1/L = 1$, and the series converges for $|x - 1| < 1$. Converting this to double inequalities, we have

$$|x - 1| < 1 \qquad \textit{|y| < c is equivalent to} -c < y < c.$$
$$-1 < x - 1 < 1 \qquad \textit{Add 1 to each side.}$$
$$0 < \quad x \quad < 2 \qquad \textit{Interval of convergence.}$$

Thus, $f(x) = \lim_{n \to \infty} p_n(x)$ for $0 < x < 2$ or, equivalently,

$$\ln x = (x - 1) - \frac{1}{2}(x - 1)^2 + \frac{1}{3}(x - 1)^3 - \cdots + \frac{(-1)^{n-1}}{n}(x - 1)^n + \cdots \qquad 0 < x < 2$$

---

*From this point on, we will use the expanded notation exclusively when writing Taylor series.

MATCHED PROBLEM 3 Repeat Example 3 for $f(x) = 1/x$.

Table 1 displays the values of the Taylor polynomials for $f(x) = \ln x$ at $x = 1.5$ and at $x = 3$ for $n = 1, 2, \ldots, 10$ (see Example 3). Notice that $x = 1.5$ is in the interval of convergence of the Taylor series at 1 for $f(x)$ and that the values of $p_n(1.5)$ are approaching $\ln 1.5$ as n increases. On the other hand, $x = 3$ is *not* in the interval of convergence and the values of $p_n(3)$ do not approach $\ln 3$. These calculations illustrate the importance of the interval of convergence.

The values of x must be in the interval of convergence in order to use Taylor polynomials to approximate the values of a function.

TABLE 1

$f(x) = \ln x$

$$p_n(x) = (x - 1) - \frac{1}{2}(x - 1)^2 + \frac{1}{3}(x - 1)^3 - \cdots + \frac{(-1)^{n-1}}{n}(x - 1)^n$$

n	$p_n(1.5)$	$p_n(3)$
1	0.5	2
2	0.375	0
3	0.416 667	2.666 667
4	0.401 042	−1.333 333
5	0.407 292	5.066 667
6	0.404 688	−5.6
7	0.405 804	12.685 714
8	0.405 315	−19.314 286
9	0.405 532	37.574 603
10	0.405 435	−64.825 397
	$\ln 1.5 = 0.405\ 465$	$\ln 3 = 1.098\ 612$

Answers to Matched Problems

1. $-\infty < x < \infty$

2. $-2 < x < 2$

3. (A) $1 - (x - 1) + (x - 1)^2 - \cdots + (-1)^n(x - 1)^n$

    (B) $1 - (x - 1) + (x - 1)^2 - \cdots + (-1)^n(x - 1)^n + \cdots$

    (C) $0 < x < 2$

Exercise 2.2

A   *In Problems 1–12, find the interval of convergence of the given Taylor series representation.*

1. $\dfrac{4}{1 - x} = 4 + 4x + 4x^2 + \cdots + 4x^n + \cdots$

2. $\dfrac{3}{1 - x} = 3 + 3x + 3x^2 + \cdots + 3x^n + \cdots$

3. $\dfrac{1}{1 + 7x} = 1 - 7x + 7^2x^2 - \cdots + (-1)^n 7^n x^n + \cdots$

4. $\dfrac{1}{1 + 2x} = 1 - 2x + 2^2x^2 - \cdots + (-1)^n 2^n x^n + \cdots$

5. $\dfrac{1}{6 - x} = \dfrac{1}{6} + \dfrac{1}{6^2}x + \dfrac{1}{6^3}x^2 + \cdots + \dfrac{1}{6^{n+1}}x^n + \cdots$

6. $\dfrac{2}{3 + x} = \dfrac{2}{3} - \dfrac{2}{3^2}x + \dfrac{2}{3^3}x^2 - \cdots + \dfrac{2(-1)^n}{3^{n+1}}x^n + \cdots$

7. $\ln(1 + x) = x - \dfrac{1}{2}x^2 + \dfrac{1}{3}x^3 - \cdots + \dfrac{(-1)^{n-1}}{n}x^n + \cdots$

8. $\ln(1 - x) = -x - \dfrac{1}{2}x^2 - \dfrac{1}{3}x^3 - \cdots - \dfrac{1}{n}x^n - \cdots$

9. $\dfrac{1}{(1 + x)^2} = 1 - 2x + 3x^2 - \cdots$
                      $+ (-1)^n(n + 1)x^n + \cdots$

10. $\dfrac{x}{(1 - x)^2} = x + 2x^2 + 3x^3 + \cdots + nx^n + \cdots$

11. $e^x = 1 + x + \dfrac{1}{2!}x^2 + \cdots + \dfrac{1}{n!}x^n + \cdots$

12. $e^{-x} = 1 - x + \dfrac{1}{2!}x^2 - \cdots + \dfrac{(-1)^n}{n!}x^n + \cdots$

13. The Taylor series for e^x at 0 is

    $e^x = 1 + x + \dfrac{1}{2!}x^2 + \dfrac{1}{3!}x^3 + \cdots + \dfrac{1}{n!}x^n + \cdots$

(A) Find the smallest value of n such that
$$|p_n(2) - e^2| < 0.1$$

(B) Does a value of n exist such that
$$|p_n(100) - e^{100}| < 0.1? \text{ Explain.}$$

14. Suppose the function f has the following Taylor series representation at 0:
$$f(x) = 1 + x + 2!x^2 + 3!x^3 + \cdots + n!x^n + \cdots$$

(A) Find the interval of convergence.

(B) Compute $p_n(0.2)$ for $n = 1, 2, 3, \ldots, 10$, where $p_n(x)$ is the nth-degree Taylor polynomial for f at 0. Explain why your computations are consistent with your answer to part (A).

B *In Problems 15–22, find the interval of convergence of the given Taylor series representation.*

15. $\ln(4 + x) = (x + 3) - \dfrac{1}{2}(x + 3)^2$
$$+ \frac{1}{3}(x + 3)^3 - \cdots + \frac{(-1)^{n+1}}{n}(x + 3)^n + \cdots$$

16. $\ln(9 - 2x) = -2(x - 4) - \dfrac{2^2}{2}(x - 4)^2$
$$- \frac{2^3}{3}(x - 4)^3 - \cdots - \frac{2^n}{n}(x - 4)^n - \cdots$$

17. $e^{2x} = 1 + 2x + \dfrac{2^2}{2!}x^2 + \cdots + \dfrac{2^n}{n!}x^n + \cdots$

18. $e^{-x/3} = 1 - \dfrac{1}{3}x + \dfrac{1}{2!3^2}x^2 - \cdots + \dfrac{(-1)^n}{n!3^n}x^n + \cdots$

19. $\dfrac{1}{6 - x} = \dfrac{1}{4} + \dfrac{1}{4^2}(x - 2) + \dfrac{1}{4^3}(x - 2)^2 + \cdots$
$$+ \frac{1}{4^{n+1}}(x - 2)^n + \cdots$$

20. $\dfrac{3}{2 + 3x} = -3 - 3^2(x + 1) - 3^3(x + 1)^2 - \cdots$
$$- 3^{n+1}(x + 1)^n - \cdots$$

21. $\dfrac{1}{6 - x} = -\dfrac{1}{2} + \dfrac{1}{2^2}(x - 8) - \dfrac{1}{2^3}(x - 8)^2$
$$+ \cdots + \frac{(-1)^n}{2^{n+1}}(x - 8)^n + \cdots$$

22. $\dfrac{3}{2 + 3x} = \dfrac{3}{5} - \dfrac{3^2}{5^2}(x - 1) + \dfrac{3^3}{5^3}(x - 1)^2 - \cdots$
$$+ \frac{(-1)^n 3^{n+1}}{5^{n+1}}(x - 1)^n + \cdots$$

23. (A) Graph the nth-degree Taylor polynomials at 0 for $f(x) = e^x, n = 1, 2, 3, 4, 5$. Use the viewing window Xmin = -3, Xmax = 3, Ymin = -5, and Ymax = 15. Based solely on the graphs, what would you conjecture the interval of convergence to be? Explain.

(B) What is the actual interval of convergence?

24. (A) Graph the nth-degree Taylor polynomials at 0 for $f(x) = \ln(1 + x), n = 1, 2, 3, 4, 5$. Use the viewing window Xmin = -3, Xmax = 3, Ymin = -15, and Ymax = 15. Based solely on the graphs, what would you conjecture the interval of convergence to be? Explain.

(B) What is the actual interval of convergence?

C *In Problems 25–30, find the nth-degree Taylor polynomial at 0 for f, find the Taylor series at 0 for f, and determine the values of x for which $f(x) = \lim\limits_{n \to \infty} p_n(x)$.*

25. $f(x) = e^{4x}$

26. $f(x) = e^{-x/2}$

27. $f(x) = \ln(1 + 2x)$

28. $f(x) = \ln(1 - 4x)$

29. $f(x) = \dfrac{2}{2 - x}$

30. $f(x) = \dfrac{3}{3 + x}$

In Problems 31–34, find the nth-degree Taylor polynomial at the indicated value of a for f, find the Taylor series at a for f, and determine the values of x for which $f(x) = \lim\limits_{n \to \infty} p_n(x)$.

31. $f(x) = \ln(2 - x); a = 1$

32. $f(x) = \ln(2 + x); a = -1$

33. $f(x) = \dfrac{1}{1 - x}; a = 2$

34. $f(x) = \dfrac{1}{4 - x}; a = 3$

35. (A) Find the interval of convergence of the Taylor series representation
$$\frac{1}{4 - x} = \frac{1}{4} + \frac{1}{4^2}x + \frac{1}{4^3}x^2 + \cdots + \frac{1}{4^{n+1}}x^n + \cdots$$

(B) Explain why Theorem 1 is not directly applicable to the Taylor series representation
$$\frac{1}{4 - x^2} = \frac{1}{4} + \frac{1}{4^2}x^2 + \frac{1}{4^3}x^4 + \cdots + \frac{1}{4^{n+1}}x^{2n} + \cdots$$

(C) Use part (A) to find the interval of convergence of the Taylor series of part (B).

36. (A) Explain why Theorem 1 is not directly applicable to the Taylor series representation
$$e^{x^2} = 1 + x^2 + \frac{1}{2!}x^4 + \frac{1}{3!}x^6 + \cdots + \frac{1}{n!}x^{2n} + \cdots$$

(B) Use the Taylor series for e^x at 0 to find the interval of convergence of the Taylor series of part (A).

37. (A) Explain why the interval of convergence of the Taylor series
$$\frac{1}{1 - x} + \frac{1}{1 - x^2} = 2 + x + 2x^2 + x^3$$
$$+ 2x^4 + x^5 + \cdots$$
cannot be determined by applying Theorem 1.

(B) If two Taylor series have the same interval of convergence, then so does their term-by-term sum. Use this fact to find the interval of convergence of the Taylor series of part (A).

38. (A) Explain why the interval of convergence of the Taylor series
$$e^x - e^{x^2} = x + \left(\frac{1}{2!} - 1\right)x^2 + \frac{1}{3!}x^3$$
$$+ \left(\frac{1}{4!} - \frac{1}{2!}\right)x^4 + \frac{1}{5!}x^5 + \cdots$$
cannot be determined by applying Theorem 1.

(B) If two Taylor series have the same interval of convergence, then so does their term-by-term difference. Use this fact to find the interval of convergence of the Taylor series of part (A).

Section 2.3 OPERATIONS ON TAYLOR SERIES

- Basic Taylor Series
- Addition and Multiplication
- Differentiation and Integration
- Substitution

Basic Taylor Series

In the preceding sections, we used repeated differentiation and the formula $a_n = f^{(n)}(a)/n!$ to find Taylor polynomials and Taylor series for a variety of simple functions. In this section we will see how to use the series for these simple functions and some basic properties of Taylor series to find the Taylor series for more complicated functions. Table 1 lists the series we will use in this process for convenient reference.

Most of the discussion in this section involves Taylor series at 0. At the end of the section we will see that Taylor series at points other than 0 can be obtained from Taylor series at 0 by using a simple substitution process.

TABLE 1 Basic Taylor Series

Function $f(x)$	Taylor Series at 0	Interval of Convergence
$\dfrac{1}{1-x}$	$= 1 + x + x^2 + \cdots + x^n + \cdots$	$-1 < x < 1$
$\dfrac{1}{1+x}$	$= 1 - x + x^2 - \cdots + (-1)^n x^n + \cdots$	$-1 < x < 1$
$\ln(1-x)$	$= -x - \dfrac{1}{2}x^2 - \dfrac{1}{3}x^3 - \cdots - \dfrac{1}{n}x^n - \cdots$	$-1 < x < 1$
$\ln(1+x)$	$= x - \dfrac{1}{2}x^2 + \dfrac{1}{3}x^3 - \cdots + \dfrac{(-1)^{n-1}}{n}x^n + \cdots$	$-1 < x < 1$
e^x	$= 1 + x + \dfrac{1}{2!}x^2 + \cdots + \dfrac{1}{n!}x^n + \cdots$	$-\infty < x < \infty$
e^{-x}	$= 1 - x + \dfrac{1}{2!}x^2 - \cdots + \dfrac{(-1)^n}{n!}x^n + \cdots$	$-\infty < x < \infty$

Addition and Multiplication

PROPERTY 1   **Addition**

Two Taylor series at 0 can be added term by term:

If

$$f(x) = a_0 + a_1 x + a_2 x^2 + \cdots + a_n x^n + \cdots$$

and

$$g(x) = b_0 + b_1 x + b_2 x^2 + \cdots + b_n x^n + \cdots$$

then

$$f(x) + g(x) = (a_0 + b_0) + (a_1 + b_1)x + (a_2 + b_2)x^2 + \cdots$$
$$+ (a_n + b_n)x^n + \cdots$$

This operation is valid in the intersection of the intervals of convergence of the series for f and g.

EXAMPLE 1   **Addition of Taylor Series** Find the Taylor series at 0 for $f(x) = e^x + \ln(1+x)$, and find the interval of convergence.

SOLUTION From Table 1,

$$e^x = 1 + x + \frac{1}{2!}x^2 + \frac{1}{3!}x^3 + \cdots + \frac{1}{n!}x^n + \cdots \qquad -\infty < x < \infty$$

and

$$\ln(1 + x) = x - \frac{1}{2}x^2 + \frac{1}{3}x^3 - \cdots + \frac{(-1)^{n-1}}{n}x^n + \cdots \qquad -1 < x < 1$$

Adding the coefficients of corresponding powers of x, we have

$$f(x) = e^x + \ln(1 + x)$$

$$= 1 + 2x + \left(\frac{1}{2!} - \frac{1}{2}\right)x^2 + \left(\frac{1}{3!} + \frac{1}{3}\right)x^3 + \cdots$$

$$+ \left[\frac{1}{n!} + \frac{(-1)^{n-1}}{n}\right]x^n + \cdots$$

The series for e^x converges for all x; however, the series for $\ln(1 + x)$ converges only for $-1 < x < 1$. Thus, the combined series converges for $-1 < x < 1$, the intersection of these two intervals of convergence.　■

MATCHED PROBLEM 1 Find the Taylor series at 0 for $f(x) = e^x + 1/(1 - x)$, and find the interval of convergence.

PROPERTY 2 **Multiplication**

A Taylor series at 0 can be multiplied term by term by an expression of the form cx^r, where c is a nonzero constant and r is a non-negative integer:

If

$$f(x) = a_0 + a_1x + a_2x^2 + \cdots + a_nx^n + \cdots$$

then

$$cx^r f(x) = ca_0x^r + ca_1x^{r+1} + ca_2x^{r+2} + \cdots + ca_nx^{r+n} + \cdots$$

The Taylor series for $cx^r f(x)$ has the same interval of convergence as the Taylor series for f.

EXAMPLE 2 **Multiplication of Taylor Series** Find the Taylor series at 0 for $f(x) = 2x^2e^{-x}$, and find the interval of convergence.

SOLUTION From Table 1,

$$e^{-x} = 1 - x + \frac{1}{2!}x^2 - \cdots + \frac{(-1)^n}{n!}x^n + \cdots \qquad -\infty < x < \infty$$

Multiplying each term of this series by $2x^2$, the series for $f(x)$ is

$$f(x) = 2x^2e^{-x}$$

$$= 2x^2\left[1 - x + \frac{1}{2!}x^2 - \cdots + \frac{(-1)^n}{n!}x^n + \cdots\right]$$

$$= 2x^2 - 2x^3 + \frac{2}{2!}x^4 - \cdots + \frac{2(-1)^n}{n!}x^{n+2} + \cdots$$

Since the series for e^{-x} converges for all x, the series for $f(x)$ also converges for $-\infty < x < \infty$.　■

MATCHED PROBLEM 2 | Find the Taylor series at 0 for $f(x) = 3x^3 \ln(1 - x)$, and find the interval of convergence.

■ Differentiation and Integration

PROPERTY 3 **Differentiation**

A Taylor series at 0 can be differentiated term by term:
If

$$f(x) = a_0 + a_1 x + a_2 x^2 + a_3 x^3 + \cdots + a_n x^n + \cdots$$

then

$$f'(x) = a_1 + 2a_2 x + 3a_3 x^2 + \cdots + n a_n x^{n-1} + \cdots$$

The Taylor series for f' has the same interval of convergence as the Taylor series for f.

INSIGHT

Assume that $a_n \neq 0$ for $n \geq n_0$. Then the ratio of consecutive coefficients in the Taylor series for f' is

$$\frac{(n + 1)a_{n+1}}{na_n}$$

and

$$\lim_{n \to \infty} \left| \frac{(n + 1)a_{n+1}}{na_n} \right| = \lim_{n \to \infty} \left| \frac{a_{n+1}}{a_n} \right| \qquad \lim_{n \to \infty} \frac{n + 1}{n} = 1$$

Therefore, by Theorem 1 of the preceding section, the Taylor series for f and f' have the same interval of convergence.

EXAMPLE 3 | **Differentiation of Taylor Series** Find the Taylor series at 0 for $f(x) = 1/(1 - x)^2$, and find the interval of convergence.

SOLUTION | We want to relate f to the derivative of one of the functions in Table 1, so that we can apply property 3. Since

$$\frac{d}{dx}\left(\frac{1}{1 - x}\right) = \frac{d}{dx}(1 - x)^{-1}$$
$$= -(1 - x)^{-2}(-1)$$
$$= \frac{1}{(1 - x)^2}$$
$$= f(x)$$

we can apply property 3 to the series for $1/(1 - x)$. From Table 1,

$$\frac{1}{1 - x} = 1 + x + x^2 + x^3 + \cdots + x^n + \cdots \qquad -1 < x < 1$$

Differentiating both sides of this equation,

$$\frac{d}{dx}\left(\frac{1}{1 - x}\right) = \frac{d}{dx}(1 + x + x^2 + x^3 + \cdots + x^n + \cdots)$$

$$\frac{1}{(1 - x)^2} = \frac{d}{dx}1 + \frac{d}{dx}x + \frac{d}{dx}x^2 + \frac{d}{dx}x^3 + \cdots + \frac{d}{dx}x^n + \cdots$$

$$f(x) = 1 + 2x + 3x^2 + \cdots + nx^{n-1} + \cdots$$

Since the series for $1/(1 - x)$ converges for $-1 < x < 1$, the series for $f(x)$ also converges for $-1 < x < 1$. [Verify this statement by applying Theorem 1 in the preceding section to the series for $f(x)$.] ▬

MATCHED PROBLEM 3	Find the Taylor series at 0 for $f(x) = 1/(1 + x)^2$, and find the interval of convergence.

Explore & Discuss **1**   The Taylor series representation for a function f at 0 is

$$f(x) = x - \frac{1}{3!}x^3 + \frac{1}{5!}x^5 - \frac{1}{7!}x^7 + \cdots$$

$$+ \frac{(-1)^n}{(2n + 1)!}x^{2n+1} + \cdots \qquad -\infty < x < \infty$$

(A) Find the Taylor series for $f'(x)$.
(B) Find the Taylor series for $f''(x)$. How are f and f'' related?

PROPERTY4   Integration

A Taylor series at 0 can be integrated term by term:
If

$$f(x) = a_0 + a_1x + a_2x^2 + \cdots + a_nx^n + \cdots$$

then

$$\int f(x)\, dx = C + a_0x + \frac{1}{2}a_1x^2 + \frac{1}{3}a_2x^3 + \cdots + \frac{1}{n + 1}a_nx^{n+1} + \cdots$$

where C is the constant of integration. The Taylor series for $\int f(x)\, dx$ has the same interval of convergence as the Taylor series for f.

EXAMPLE 4   **Integration of Taylor Series** If f is a function that satisfies $f'(x) = x^2e^x$ and $f(0) = 2$, find the Taylor series at 0 for f. Find the interval of convergence.

SOLUTION   Using the series for e^x from Table 1 and property 2, the series for f' is

$$f'(x) = x^2e^x$$

$$= x^2\left(1 + x + \frac{1}{2!}x^2 + \cdots + \frac{1}{n!}x^n + \cdots\right) \qquad -\infty < x < \infty$$

$$= x^2 + x^3 + \frac{1}{2!}x^4 + \cdots + \frac{1}{n!}x^{n+2} + \cdots$$

Integrating term by term produces a series for f:

$$f(x) = \int f'(x)\, dx$$

$$= \int\left(x^2 + x^3 + \frac{1}{2!}x^4 + \cdots + \frac{1}{n!}x^{n+2} + \cdots\right) dx$$

$$= \int x^2\, dx + \int x^3\, dx + \frac{1}{2!}\int x^4\, dx + \cdots + \frac{1}{n!}\int x^{n+2}\, dx + \cdots$$

$$= C + \frac{1}{3}x^3 + \frac{1}{4}x^4 + \frac{1}{(5)2!}x^5 + \cdots + \frac{1}{(n + 3)n!}x^{n+3} + \cdots$$

Now we use the condition $f(0) = 2$ to evaluate the constant of integration C:

$$2 = f(0)$$
$$= C + 0 + 0 + \cdots + 0 + \cdots$$
$$= C$$

Thus,

$$f(x) = 2 + \frac{1}{3}x^3 + \frac{1}{4}x^4 + \cdots + \frac{1}{(n+3)n!}x^{n+3} + \cdots$$

Since the series for f' converges for $-\infty < x < \infty$, the series for f also converges for $-\infty < x < \infty$.

MATCHED PROBLEM 4 · If f is a function that satisfies $f'(x) = x \ln(1 + x)$ and $f(0) = 4$, find the Taylor series at 0 for f. Find the interval of convergence.

■ Substitution

EXAMPLE 5 · **Using Substitution to Find Taylor Series** Find the Taylor series at 0 for $f(x) = e^{-x^2}$, and find the interval of convergence.

SOLUTION · Suppose we try to solve this problem by finding the general form of the nth derivative of f:

$$f(x) = e^{-x^2}$$
$$f'(x) = -2xe^{-x^2}$$
$$f''(x) = -2e^{-x^2} + 4x^2e^{-x^2}$$
$$f^{(3)}(x) = 4xe^{-x^2} + 8xe^{-x^2} - 8x^3e^{-x^2}$$
$$= 12xe^{-x^2} - 8x^3e^{-x^2}$$
$$f^{(4)}(x) = 12e^{-x^2} - 24x^2e^{-x^2} - 24x^2e^{-x^2} + 16x^4e^{-x^2}$$
$$= 12e^{-x^2} - 48x^2e^{-x^2} + 16x^4e^{-x^2}$$

Since the higher-order derivatives are becoming very complicated and no general pattern is emerging, we will try another approach. How can we relate f to one of the functions in Table 1? If we let $g(x) = e^{-x}$, then f and g are related by

$$f(x) = e^{-x^2} = g(x^2)$$

From Table 1,

$$g(x) = e^{-x}$$
$$= 1 - x + \frac{1}{2!}x^2 - \frac{1}{3!}x^3 + \cdots + \frac{(-1)^n}{n!}x^n + \cdots \qquad -\infty < x < \infty$$

Substituting x^2 for x in the series for g, we have

$$f(x) = g(x^2)$$
$$= 1 - x^2 + \frac{1}{2!}(x^2)^2 - \frac{1}{3!}(x^2)^3 + \cdots + \frac{(-1)^n}{n!}(x^2)^n + \cdots$$
$$= 1 - x^2 + \frac{1}{2!}x^4 - \frac{1}{3!}x^6 + \cdots + \frac{(-1)^n}{n!}x^{2n} + \cdots$$

Since the series for g converges for all values of x, the series for f must also converge for all values of x.

Explore & Discuss 2

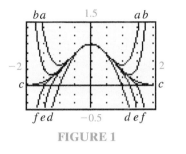

FIGURE 1

(A) The function $f(x) = e^{-x^2}$ and the Taylor polynomials

$$1 - x^2 + \frac{1}{2!}x^4 - \cdots + \frac{(-1)^n}{n!}x^{2n}$$

are graphed for $n = 1, 2, 3, 4, 5$ in Figure 1. Which curve belongs to which function?

(B) Does Figure 1 provide supporting evidence for the statement that the Taylor series for f at 0 converges for all values of x? Explain.

MATCHED PROBLEM 5   Find the Taylor series at 0 for $f(x) = e^{x^3}$, and find the interval of convergence.

Making a substitution in a known Taylor series to obtain a new series is a very useful technique. Since there are many different substitutions that can be used, it is difficult to make a general statement concerning the effect of a substitution on the interval of convergence. The following examples illustrate some of the possibilities that may occur.

EXAMPLE 6   **Using Substitution to Find Taylor Series** Find the Taylor series at 0 for $f(x) = 1/(4 - x)$, and find the interval of convergence.

SOLUTION   If we factor a 4 out of the denominator of f, we can establish a relationship between $f(x)$ and $g(x) = 1/(1 - x)$. Thus,

$$f(x) = \frac{1}{4 - x}$$

$$= \left(\frac{1}{4}\right)\frac{1}{1 - (x/4)} \qquad g(x) = \frac{1}{1 - x}$$

$$= \frac{1}{4}g\left(\frac{x}{4}\right)$$

From Table 1,

$$g(x) = \frac{1}{1 - x}$$

$$= 1 + x + x^2 + \cdots + x^n + \cdots \qquad -1 < x < 1$$

Substituting $x/4$ for x in this series and multiplying by $\frac{1}{4}$, we have

$$f(x) = \frac{1}{4}g\left(\frac{x}{4}\right)$$

$$= \frac{1}{4}\left[1 + \left(\frac{x}{4}\right) + \left(\frac{x}{4}\right)^2 + \cdots + \left(\frac{x}{4}\right)^n + \cdots\right]$$

$$= \frac{1}{4} + \frac{1}{4^2}x + \frac{1}{4^3}x^2 + \cdots + \frac{1}{4^{n+1}}x^n + \cdots$$

Since the original series for g converges for $-1 < x < 1$ and we substituted $x/4$ for x in that series, the series for f converges for

$$-1 < \frac{x}{4} < 1 \quad \text{Multiply each member by 4.}$$

$$-4 < x < 4$$

MATCHED PROBLEM 6   Find the Taylor series at 0 for $f(x) = 1/(3 + x)$, and find the interval of convergence.

EXAMPLE 7   **Using Substitution to Find Taylor Series** Find the Taylor series at 0 for $f(x) = \ln(1 + 4x^2)$, and find the interval of convergence.

SOLUTION   If we let $g(x) = \ln(1 + x)$, then

$$f(x) = \ln(1 + 4x^2)$$
$$= g(4x^2)$$

From Table 1, the series for g is

$$g(x) = x - \frac{1}{2}x^2 + \frac{1}{3}x^3 - \cdots + \frac{(-1)^{n-1}}{n}x^n + \cdots \qquad -1 < x < 1$$

Substituting $4x^2$ for x in this series, we have

$$f(x) = g(4x^2)$$
$$= 4x^2 - \frac{1}{2}(4x^2)^2 + \frac{1}{3}(4x^2)^3 - \cdots + \frac{(-1)^{n-1}}{n}(4x^2)^n + \cdots$$
$$= 4x^2 - \frac{4^2}{2}x^4 + \frac{4^3}{3}x^6 - \cdots + \frac{(-1)^{n-1}4^n}{n}x^{2n} + \cdots$$

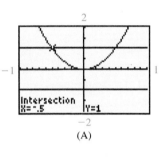

(A)

The series for g converges for $-1 < x < 1$. Since we substituted $4x^2$ for x, the series for f converges for

$$-1 < 4x^2 < 1$$

Inequalities of this type are easier to solve if we use absolute value notation:

(B)

FIGURE 2 Graphical solution of $-1 < 4x^2 < 1$

$$-1 < 4x^2 < 1 \qquad \textit{Change to absolute value notation.}$$
$$|4x^2| < 1 \qquad \textit{Multiply by } \frac{1}{4}.$$
$$|x^2| < \frac{1}{4}$$
$$|x|^2 < \frac{1}{4}$$
$$|x| < \frac{1}{2} \qquad \textit{Convert to double inequalities.}$$
$$-\frac{1}{2} < x < \frac{1}{2} \qquad \textit{See Figure 2 for a graphical solution.}$$

Thus, the series for f converges for $-\frac{1}{2} < x < \frac{1}{2}$.

MATCHED PROBLEM 7   Find the Taylor series at 0 for $f(x) = 1/(1 + 9x^2)$, and find the interval of convergence.

Up to this point in this section we have restricted our attention to Taylor series at 0. How can we use the techniques discussed to find a Taylor series at a point $a \neq 0$? Properties 1–4 could be stated in terms of Taylor series at an arbitrary point a; however, there is an easier way to proceed. The method of substitution allows us to use Taylor series at 0 to find Taylor series at other points. The following example illustrates this technique.

EXAMPLE 8   **Using Substitution to Find Taylor Series** Find the Taylor series at 1 for $f(x) = 1/(2 - x)$, and find the interval of convergence.

SOLUTION　In order to find a Taylor series for f in powers of $x - 1$, we will use the substitution $t = x - 1$ to express f as a function of t. If we find the Taylor series at 0 for this new function and then replace t with $x - 1$, we will have obtained the Taylor series at 1 for f.

$$t = x - 1 \qquad \text{Solve for x.}$$
$$x = t + 1 \qquad \text{Substitute for x in } f(x) = 1/(2 - x).$$

$$\frac{1}{2 - x} = \frac{1}{2 - (t + 1)}$$

$$= \frac{1}{1 - t} \qquad \text{Find the Taylor series at 0}$$
$$\text{for this function of t.}$$

$$= 1 + t + t^2 + \cdots + t^n + \cdots \qquad \text{Substitute x} - 1 \text{ for t.}$$
$$-1 < t < 1$$

$$= 1 + (x - 1) + (x - 1)^2 + \cdots + (x - 1)^n + \cdots$$

Since $t = x - 1$ and the series in powers of t converges for $-1 < t < 1$, the series in powers of $x - 1$ converges for

$$-1 < x - 1 < 1 \qquad \text{Add 1 to each member.}$$
$$0 < \quad x \quad < 2$$

MATCHED PROBLEM 8　Find the Taylor series at 1 for $f(x) = 1/x$, and find the interval of convergence.

Answers to Matched Problems

1. $2 + 2x + \left(\dfrac{1}{2!} + 1\right)x^2 + \cdots + \left(\dfrac{1}{n!} + 1\right)x^n + \cdots, -1 < x < 1$

2. $-3x^4 - \dfrac{3}{2}x^5 - x^6 - \cdots - \dfrac{3}{n}x^{n+3} - \cdots, -1 < x < 1$

3. $1 - 2x + 3x^2 - \cdots + (-1)^{n+1}nx^{n-1} + \cdots, -1 < x < 1$

4. $4 + \dfrac{1}{3}x^3 - \dfrac{1}{8}x^4 + \dfrac{1}{15}x^5 - \cdots + \dfrac{(-1)^{n-1}}{n(n+2)}x^{n+2} + \cdots, -1 < x < 1$

5. $1 + x^3 + \dfrac{1}{2!}x^6 + \cdots + \dfrac{1}{n!}x^{3n} + \cdots, -\infty < x < \infty$

6. $\dfrac{1}{3} - \dfrac{1}{3^2}x + \dfrac{1}{3^3}x^2 - \cdots + \dfrac{(-1)^n}{3^{n+1}}x^n + \cdots, -3 < x < 3$

7. $1 - 9x^2 + 9^2x^4 - \cdots + (-1)^n 9^n x^{2n} + \cdots, -\frac{1}{3} < x < \frac{1}{3}$

8. $1 - (x - 1) + (x - 1)^2 - \cdots + (-1)^n(x - 1)^n + \cdots, 0 < x < 2$

Exercise 2.3

Solve all the problems in this exercise by performing operations on the Taylor series in Table 1. State the interval of convergence for each series you find.

A　*In Problems 1–12, find the Taylor series at 0.*

1. $f(x) = \dfrac{1}{1 - x} + \dfrac{1}{1 + x}$

2. $f(x) = e^x + e^{-x}$

3. $f(x) = \dfrac{1}{1 - x} + e^{-x}$

4. $f(x) = \dfrac{1}{1 + x} + \ln(1 + x)$

5. $f(x) = \dfrac{x^3}{1 + x}$

6. $f(x) = xe^x$

7. $f(x) = x^2 \ln(1 - x)$

8. $f(x) = \dfrac{5x^4}{1 - x}$

9. $f(x) = e^{x^2}$

10. $f(x) = \ln(1 - x^3)$

11. $f(x) = \ln(1 + 3x)$

12. $f(x) = \dfrac{x}{1 + x^2}$

B   *In Problems 13–20, find the Taylor series at 0.*

13. $f(x) = \dfrac{1}{2 - x}$

14. $f(x) = \dfrac{1}{5 + x}$

15. $f(x) = \dfrac{1}{1 - 8x^3}$

16. $f(x) = \ln(1 + 16x^2)$

17. $f(x) = 10^x$

18. $f(x) = \log(1 + x)$

19. $f(x) = \log_2(1 - x)$

20. $f(x) = 3^x$

21. $f(x) = \dfrac{1}{4 + x^2}$

22. $f(x) = \dfrac{1}{9 - x^2}$

23. Substituting $\sqrt{x}$ for x in the Taylor series at 0 for e^x gives the formula

$$e^{\sqrt{x}} = 1 + x^{1/2} + \frac{1}{2!}x + \frac{1}{3!}x^{3/2} + \cdots + \frac{1}{n!}x^{n/2} + \cdots$$

(A) For which values of x is the formula valid?

(B) Is the formula a Taylor series at 0 for $e^{\sqrt{x}}$? Explain.

24. Substituting $1/x$ for x in the Taylor series at 0 for $1/(1 - x)$ gives the formula

$$\frac{1}{1 - \dfrac{1}{x}} = 1 + x^{-1} + x^{-2} + \cdots + x^{-n} + \cdots$$

(A) For which values of x is the formula valid?

(B) Explain why the formula is not a Taylor series at 0 for

$$f(x) = \frac{1}{1 - \dfrac{1}{x}}$$

(C) Find a Taylor series at 0 that equals

$$\frac{1}{1 - \dfrac{1}{x}}$$

for all $x \neq 0$ in the interval $-1 < x < 1$.

25. Find the Taylor series at 0 for

(A) $f(x) = \dfrac{1}{1 - x^2}$

(B) $g(x) = \dfrac{2x}{(1 - x^2)^2}$

[*Hint:* Compare $f'(x)$ and $g(x)$.]

26. Find the Taylor series at 0 for

(A) $f(x) = \dfrac{x}{1 - x^2}$

(B) $g(x) = \dfrac{1 + x^2}{(1 - x^2)^2}$

[*Hint:* Compare $f'(x)$ and $g(x)$.]

27. If $f(x)$ satisfies $f'(x) = 1/(1 + x^2)$ and $f(0) = 0$, find the Taylor series at 0 for $f(x)$.

28. If $f(x)$ satisfies $f'(x) = \ln(1 + x^2)$ and $f(0) = 1$, find the Taylor series at 0 for $f(x)$.

29. If $f(x)$ satisfies $f'(x) = x^2 \ln(1 - x)$ and $f(0) = 5$, find the Taylor series at 0 for $f(x)$.

30. If $f(x)$ satisfies $f'(x) = xe^x$ and $f(0) = -3$, find the Taylor series at 0 for $f(x)$.

31. Most graphing calculators include the hyperbolic sine function, $f(x) = \sinh x$, as a built-in function. The Taylor series for the hyperbolic sine at 0 is

$$\sinh x = x + \frac{1}{3!}x^3 + \frac{1}{5!}x^5 + \cdots$$

$$+ \frac{1}{(2n + 1)!}x^{2n+1} + \cdots \qquad -\infty < x < \infty$$

(A) Graph f and its Taylor polynomials $p_1(x)$, $p_3(x)$, and $p_5(x)$ in the viewing window $-5 \le x \le 5$, $-30 \le y \le 30$.

(B) Explain why $\dfrac{d^2}{dx^2}(\sinh x) = \sinh x$.

32. Most graphing calculators include the hyperbolic cosine function, $g(x) = \cosh x$, as a built-in function. The Taylor series for the hyperbolic cosine at 0 is

$$\cosh x = 1 + \frac{1}{2!}x^2 + \frac{1}{4!}x^4 + \frac{1}{6!}x^6 + \cdots$$

$$+ \frac{1}{(2n)!}x^{2n} + \cdots \qquad -\infty < x < \infty$$

(A) Graph g and its Taylor polynomials $p_2(x)$, $p_4(x)$, and $p_6(x)$ in the viewing window $-5 \le x \le 5, 0 \le y \le 60$.

(B) Explain why $\dfrac{d^2}{dx^2}(\cosh x) = \cosh x$.

In Problems 33–38, use the substitution $t = x - a$ to find the Taylor series at the indicated value of a.

33. $f(x) = \dfrac{1}{4 - x}$; at 3

34. $f(x) = \dfrac{1}{3 + x}$; at -2

35. $f(x) = \ln x$; at 1

36. $f(x) = \ln(3 - x)$; at 2

37. $f(x) = \dfrac{1}{4 - 3x}$; at 1

38. $f(x) = \dfrac{1}{5 - 2x}$; at 2

C

39. Use the Taylor series at 0 for $1/(1 - x)$ and repeated applications of property 3 to find the Taylor series at 0 for

$$f(x) = \frac{1}{(1 - x)^3}$$

40. Use the Taylor series at 0 for $1/(1 + x)$ and repeated applications of property 3 to find the Taylor series at 0 for

$$f(x) = \frac{1}{(1 + x)^4}$$

41. Suppose that the Taylor series for f at 0 is

$$f(x) = x + \frac{1}{3}x^3 + \frac{1}{5}x^5 + \cdots$$

$$+ \frac{1}{2n + 1}x^{2n+1} + \cdots \qquad -1 < x < 1$$

(A) Find the Taylor series for f'.

(B) Explain why $f'(x) = \dfrac{1}{1 - x^2}$ for $-1 < x < 1$.

42. Suppose that the Taylor series for g at 0 is

$$g(x) = x - \frac{1}{3}x^3 + \frac{1}{5}x^5 - \cdots$$

$$+ \frac{(-1)^n}{2n + 1}x^{2n+1} + \cdots \qquad -1 < x < 1$$

(A) Find the Taylor series for g'.

(B) Explain why $g'(x) = \dfrac{1}{1 + x^2}$ for $-1 < x < 1$.

43. Find the Taylor series at 0 for $f(x) = \dfrac{1 + x}{1 - x}$.

$$\left[\textit{Note:} \ \frac{1 + x}{1 - x} = \frac{1}{1 - x} + \frac{x}{1 - x} \right]$$

44. Find the Taylor series at 0 for $f(x) = \dfrac{1 - 2x}{1 + x}$.

$$\left[\textit{Note:} \ \frac{1 - 2x}{1 + x} = \frac{1}{1 + x} - \frac{2x}{1 + x} \right]$$

45. Find the Taylor series at 0 for $f(x) = \dfrac{1}{2} \ln\!\left(\dfrac{1 + x}{1 - x}\right)$.

$$\left[\textit{Note:} \ \ln\!\left(\frac{1 + x}{1 - x}\right) = \ln(1 + x) - \ln(1 - x) \right]$$

46. Find the Taylor series at 0 for
$f(x) = \ln(1 - 2x + x^2)$.

47. Find the Taylor series at 0 for $f(x) = \dfrac{e^x + e^{-x}}{2}$.

48. Find the Taylor series at 0 for $f(x) = \dfrac{e^x - e^{-x}}{2}$.

49. If $f(x)$ satisfies $f''(x) = \ln(1 + x)$, $f'(0) = 3$, and $f(0) = -2$, find the Taylor series at 0 for $f(x)$.

50. If $f(x)$ satisfies $f''(x) = \dfrac{1}{1 - x^2}$, $f'(0) = 4$, and $f(0) = 5$, find the Taylor series at 0 for $f(x)$.

51. Find the Taylor series at any $a > 0$ for $f(x) = \ln x$.

52. Find the Taylor series at any a for $f(x) = e^x$.

53. If a and b are constants $(b \neq 0, a \neq b^{-1})$, find the Taylor series at a for

$$f(x) = \frac{1}{1 - bx}$$

54. If a and b are constants $(a \neq b)$, find the Taylor series at a for

$$f(x) = \frac{1}{b - x}$$

Section 2.4   APPROXIMATIONS USING TAYLOR SERIES

- The Remainder
- Taylor's Formula for the Remainder
- Taylor Series with Alternating Terms
- Approximating Definite Integrals

■ The Remainder

Now that we can find Taylor series for a variety of functions, we return to our original goal: approximating the values of a function.

If x is in the interval of convergence of the Taylor series for a function f and $p_n(x)$ is the nth-degree Taylor polynomial, then

$$f(x) = \lim_{n \to \infty} p_n(x)$$

and $p_n(x)$ can be used to approximate $f(x)$. We want to consider two questions:

1. If we select a particular value of n, how accurate is the approximation $f(x) \approx p_n(x)$?
2. If we want the approximation $f(x) \approx p_n(x)$ to have a specified accuracy, how do we select the proper value of n?

It turns out that both of these questions can be answered by examining the difference between $f(x)$ and $p_n(x)$. This difference is called the *remainder* and is defined in the following box.

The Remainder of a Taylor Series

If p_n is the nth-degree Taylor polynomial for f, then the **remainder** is

$$R_n(x) = f(x) - p_n(x)$$

The **error** in the approximation $f(x) \approx p_n(x)$ is

$$|f(x) - p_n(x)| = |R_n(x)|$$

If the Taylor series at 0 for f is

$$f(x) = \overbrace{a_0 + a_1x + a_2x^2 + \cdots + a_nx^n}^{p_n(x)} + \overbrace{a_{n+1}x^{n-1} + \cdots}^{R_n(x)}$$

then

$$p_n(x) = a_0 + a_1x + a_2x^2 + \cdots + a_nx^n$$

and

$$R_n(x) = a_{n+1}x^{n+1} + a_{n+2}x^{n+2} + \cdots$$

Similar statements can be made for Taylor series at a.

It follows from our basic assumption (see page 71) for the functions we consider that

$$\lim_{n\to\infty} R_n(x) = \lim_{n\to\infty}[f(x) - p_n(x)] = f(x) - f(x) = 0$$

if and only if x is in the interval of convergence of f.*

In general, it is difficult to find the exact value of $R_n(x)$. In fact, since $f(x) = p_n(x) + R_n(x)$, this is equivalent to finding the exact value of $f(x)$. Instead, we will discuss two methods for *estimating* the value of $R_n(x)$. The first method works in all cases, but can be difficult to apply, while the second method is easy to apply, but does not work in all cases.

Explore & Discuss **1**

Let $p_1(x), p_2(x)$, and $p_3(x)$ be Taylor polynomials for $f(x) = e^x$ at 0. The corresponding remainder functions $R_1(x), R_2(x)$, and $R_3(x)$ are graphed in Figure 1.

(A) Which curve belongs to which function?

(B) Use graphical approximation techniques to estimate those values of x for which the error in each of the approximations $f(x) \approx p_n(x)$ is less than 0.01.

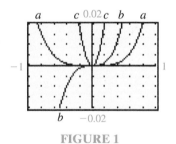

FIGURE 1

■ Taylor's Formula for the Remainder

The first method for estimating the remainder of a Taylor series is based on *Taylor's formula for the remainder*.

Taylor's Formula for the Remainder

If f has derivatives of all order at 0, then

$$R_n(x) = \frac{f^{(n+1)}(t)x^{n+1}}{(n+1)!}$$

for some number t between 0 and x.

---

* In more advanced texts, the statement $\lim_{n\to\infty} R_n(x) = 0$ for x in the interval of convergence is actually proved for functions such as e^x, making our basic assumption unnecessary.

A similar formula can be stated for the remainder of a Taylor series at an arbitrary point a. (We will not use this formula in this text.)

In most applications of the remainder formula, it is not possible to find the value of t. However, if we can find a number M satisfying

$$|f^{(n+1)}(t)| < M \qquad \text{for all } t \text{ between } 0 \text{ and } x$$

then we can estimate $R_n(x)$ as follows:

$$|R_n(x)| = \left| \frac{f^{(n+1)}(t)x^{n+1}}{(n+1)!} \right| < \frac{M|x|^{n+1}}{(n+1)!}$$

This technique is illustrated in the next example.

EXAMPLE 1   **Taylor's Formula for the Remainder**   Use the second-degree Taylor polynomial at 0 for $f(x) = e^x$ to approximate $e^{0.1}$. Use Taylor's formula for the remainder to estimate the error in this approximation.

SOLUTION   Since $f^{(n)}(x) = e^x$ for any n, we can write

$$f(x) = e^x = p_2(x) + R_2(x)$$

$$= \underbrace{1 + x + \frac{1}{2!}x^2}_{p_2(x)} + \underbrace{\frac{e^t x^3}{3!}}_{R_2(x)} \quad f^{(3)}(t) = e^t$$

for some number t between 0 and x. Thus,

$$
\begin{aligned}
f(0.1) &= e^{0.1} \\
&= p_2(0.1) + R_2(0.1) \\
&\approx p_2(0.1) \\
&= 1 + 0.1 + \tfrac{1}{2}(0.1)^2 \\
&= 1.105
\end{aligned}
$$

To estimate the error in this approximation, we must estimate

$$|R_2(0.1)| = \left| \frac{e^t (0.1)^3}{3!} \right| = \frac{e^t}{6,000}$$

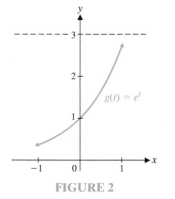

FIGURE 2

where $0 \le t \le 0.1$. In order to estimate $|R_2(0.1)|$, we must estimate $g(t) = e^t$ for $0 \le t \le 0.1$. Since e^t is always increasing, $e^t \le e^{0.1}$ for $0 \le t \le 0.1$. However, $e^{0.1}$ is the number we are trying to approximate. We do not want to use this number in our estimate of the error. (This situation occurs frequently in approximation problems involving the exponential function.) Instead, we will use the following rough estimate for e^t (see Fig. 2):

$$\text{If} \quad t \le 1, \quad \text{then} \quad e^t \le 3. \tag{1}$$

Since estimate (1) holds for $t \le 1$, it certainly holds for $0 \le t \le 0.1$. Thus,

$$|R_2(0.1)| = \frac{e^t}{6,000} \le \frac{3}{6,000} = 0.0005$$

and we can conclude that the approximate value 1.105 is within ± 0.0005 of the exact value of $e^{0.1}$.   ▬

MATCHED PROBLEM 1   Use the second-degree Taylor polynomial at 0 for $f(x) = e^x$ to approximate $e^{0.2}$. Use Taylor's formula for the remainder to estimate the error in the approximation.

If f is a polynomial of degree n and $k \geq n$, then $f^{(k+1)}(t) = 0$ for all t. So by Taylor's formula for the remainder, $R_k(x) = 0$. Therefore, in the special case in which f is a polynomial of degree n, each Taylor polynomial p_k, for $k \geq n$, is equal to f.

■ Taylor Series with Alternating Terms

Taylor's formula for the remainder can be difficult to apply for large values of n. For most functions, the formula for the nth derivative becomes very complicated as n increases. For a certain type of problem, there is another method that does not require estimation of the nth derivative. If the series of numbers that is formed by evaluating a Taylor series at a given number x_0 *alternates in sign and decreases in absolute value*, then the remainder can be estimated by simply examining the numbers in the series. Series of numbers whose terms alternate in sign are called **alternating series.** The estimate for the remainder in an alternating series is given in Theorem 1.

THEOREM 1   **ERROR ESTIMATION FOR ALTERNATING SERIES**

If x_0 is a number in the interval of convergence for

$$f(x) = a_0 + a_1 x + a_2 x^2 + \cdots + a_k x^k + \cdots$$

and the terms in the series

$$f(x_0) = a_0 + a_1 x_0 + a_2 x_0^2 + \cdots + a_k x_0^k + \cdots$$

are alternating in sign and decreasing in absolute value, then the error in the approximation

$$f(x_0) \approx a_0 + a_1 x_0 + a_2 x_0^2 + \cdots + a_n x_0^n$$

is strictly less than the absolute value of the next term. That is,

$$|R_n(x_0)| < |a_{n+1} x_0^{n+1}|$$

EXAMPLE 2   **Estimating the Remainder for Alternating Series**   Use the Taylor series at 0 for $f(x) = e^{-x}$ to approximate $e^{-0.3}$ with an error of no more than 0.0005.

SOLUTION   From Table 1 in Section 2-3, the Taylor series at 0 for $f(x) = e^{-x}$ is

$$e^{-x} = 1 - x + \frac{1}{2!}x^2 - \frac{1}{3!}x^3 + \cdots + \frac{(-1)^k}{k!}x^k + \cdots \qquad -\infty < x < \infty$$

If we substitute $x = 0.3$ in this series, we obtain

$$
\begin{aligned}
f(0.3) &= e^{-0.3} \\
&= 1 - 0.3 + \tfrac{1}{2}(0.3)^2 - \tfrac{1}{6}(0.3)^3 + \tfrac{1}{24}(0.3)^4 - \cdots \\
&= 1 - 0.3 + 0.045 - 0.0045 + 0.000\,337\,5 - \cdots
\end{aligned}
$$

Since the terms in this series are alternating in sign and decreasing in absolute value, Theorem 1 applies. If we use the first four terms in this series to approximate $e^{-0.3}$, then the error in this approximation is less than the absolute value of the fifth term. That is,

$$|R_3(0.3)| < 0.000\,337\,5 < 0.0005$$

Thus,

$$e^{-0.3} \approx 1 - 0.3 + 0.045 - 0.0045 = 0.7405$$

and the error in this approximation is less than the specified accuracy of 0.0005.

MATCHED PROBLEM 2   Use the Taylor series at 0 for $f(x) = e^{-x}$ to approximate $e^{-0.1}$ with an error of no more than 0.0005.

As Example 2 illustrates, Theorem 1 is much easier to use than Taylor's formula for the remainder. Notice that we did not have to find an estimate for $f^{(n+1)}(t)$. However, it is very important to understand that Theorem 1 can be applied only if the terms in the series *alternate in sign after they have been evaluated at* x_0. For example, if we try to use the series for e^{-x} to approximate $e^{0.3}$ by substituting $x_0 = -0.3$, we have

$$e^{0.3} = 1 - (-0.3) + \tfrac{1}{2}(-0.3)^2 - \tfrac{1}{6}(-0.3)^3 + \cdots$$
$$= 1 + 0.3 + \tfrac{1}{2}(0.3)^2 + \tfrac{1}{6}(0.3)^3 + \cdots$$

Since these numbers do not alternate in sign, Theorem 1 does not apply. Taylor's formula for the remainder would have to be used to estimate the error in approximations obtained from this series.

■ Approximating Definite Integrals

In order to find the exact value of a definite intergral $\int_a^b f(x)\,dx$, we must first find an antiderivative of the function f. But suppose we cannot find an anti-derivative of f (it may not even exist in a convenient form). In Section 5.5 of *Calculus* 13/e or Section 13.5 of *College Mathematics* 13/e we saw that Riemann sums can be used to approximate definite integrals. Taylor series techniques provide an alternative method for approximating definite integrals that is often more efficient, and, in the case of alternating series, automatically determines the accuracy of the approximation.

EXAMPLE 3   **Using Taylor Series to Approximate Definite Integrals**   Approximate $\int_0^1 e^{-x^2}\,dx$ with a maximum error of 0.005.

SOLUTION   If $F(x)$ is an antiderivative of e^{-x^2}, then

$$\int_0^1 e^{-x^2}\,dx = F(1) - F(0)$$

It is not possible to express $F(x)$ as a finite combination of simple functions; however, it is possible to find a Taylor series for F. This series can be used to approximate the values of F and, consequently, of the definite integral.

Step 1. *Find a Taylor series for the integrand:* From Table 1 in Section 2-3,

$$e^x = 1 + x + \frac{1}{2!}x^2 + \cdots + \frac{1}{n!}x^n + \cdots \qquad -\infty < x < \infty$$

Thus,

$$e^{-x^2} = 1 + (-x^2) + \frac{1}{2!}(-x^2)^2 + \cdots + \frac{1}{n!}(-x^2)^n + \cdots$$

$$= 1 - x^2 + \frac{1}{2!}x^4 - \cdots + \frac{(-1)^n}{n!}x^{2n} + \cdots \qquad -\infty < x < \infty$$

Step 2. *Find the Taylor series for the antiderivative:* Integrating term by term, we have

$$F(x) = \int e^{-x^2}\,dx$$

$$= \int \left[1 - x^2 + \frac{1}{2!}x^4 - \cdots + \frac{(-1)^n}{n!}x^{2n} + \cdots\right]dx$$

$$= C + x - \frac{1}{3}x^3 + \frac{1}{10}x^5 - \cdots + \frac{(-1)^n}{n!(2n+1)}x^{2n+1} + \cdots \qquad -\infty < x < \infty$$

Step 3. *Approximate the definite integral:* If we choose $C = 0$, then $F(0) = 0$ and

$$\int_0^1 e^{-x^2}\,dx = F(1) - F(0)$$

$$= \left[x - \frac{1}{3}x^3 + \frac{1}{10}x^5 - \cdots + \frac{(-1)^n}{n!(2n+1)}x^{2n+1} + \cdots \right]\Big|_0^1$$

$$= \left[1 - \frac{1}{3} + \frac{1}{10} - \cdots + \frac{(-1)^n}{n!(2n+1)} + \cdots \right] - 0$$

$$= 1 - \frac{1}{3} + \frac{1}{10} - \frac{1}{42} + \frac{1}{216} - \cdots$$

$$= 1 - 0.333\,333 + 0.1 - 0.023\,809 + 0.004\,630 - \cdots$$

Since the Taylor series for $F(x)$ converges for all values of x, we can use this last series of numbers to approximate $F(1)$. Notice that the terms in this series are alternating in sign and decreasing in absolute value. Applying Theorem 1, we conclude that the error introduced by approximating $F(1)$ with the first four terms of this series will be no more than $0.004\,630$, the absolute value of the fifth term. Since this is less than the specified error of 0.005, we have

$$\int_0^1 e^{-x^2}\,dx = F(1) - F(0)$$

$$\approx 1 - 0.333\,333 + 0.1 - 0.023\,809$$

$$\approx 0.743 \quad \text{\textit{Rounded to three decimal places.}}$$

MATCHED PROBLEM 3   Approximate $\int_0^{0.5} e^{-x^2}$ with a maximum error of 0.005.

Explore & Discuss **2**   Suppose you wish to use a Taylor series for

$$f(x) = \frac{1}{1-x^2} \quad \text{to approximate} \quad \int_2^3 \frac{dx}{1-x^2}$$

(A) Explain why you would not use the Taylor series for f at 0.

(B) If you use the Taylor series for f at a, which value of a would you expect to yield the best approximation to the integral? Explain.

EXAMPLE 4   **Income Distribution** Approximate the index of income concentration for the Lorenz curve given by

$$f(x) = \frac{11x^4}{10 + x^2}$$

with an error of no more than 0.005.

SOLUTION   Referring to Section 6.1 of *Calculus* 13/e or Section 14.1 of *College Mathematics* 13/e, the index of income concentration for a Lorenz curve is twice the area between the graph of the Lorenz curve and the graph of the line $y = x$ (see Fig. 3). Thus, we must evaluate the integral

$$2\int_0^1 [x - f(x)]\,dx = 2\int_0^1 x\,dx - 2\int_0^1 f(x)\,dx$$

$$= \int_0^1 2x\,dx - \int_0^1 \frac{22x^4}{10 + x^2}\,dx \tag{2}$$

FIGURE 3

The first integral in (2) is easy to evaluate:

$$\int_0^1 2x \, dx = x^2 \Big|_0^1 = 1 - 0 = 1$$

Since the second integral in (2) cannot be evaluated by any of the techniques we have discussed, we will use a Taylor series to approximate this integral.

Step 1.   *Find a Taylor series for the integrand:*

$$\frac{22x^4}{10 + x^2} = \frac{22x^4}{10}\left[\frac{1}{1 + (x^2/10)}\right] \quad \text{Substitute } x^2/10 \text{ for } x \text{ in the series for } 1/(1+x).$$

$$= 2.2x^4\left[1 - \frac{x^2}{10} + \left(\frac{x^2}{10}\right)^2 - \cdots + (-1)^n\left(\frac{x^2}{10}\right)^n + \cdots\right] \quad -1 < \frac{x^2}{10} < 1$$

$$= 2.2x^4 - \frac{2.2}{10}x^6 + \frac{2.2}{10^2}x^8 - \cdots + \frac{2.2(-1)^n}{10^n}x^{2n+4} + \cdots$$

To find the interval of convergence, we solve $-1 < x^2/10 < 1$ for x:

$$-1 < \frac{x^2}{10} < 1 \qquad \text{Change to absolute value notation.}$$

$$\left|\frac{x^2}{10}\right| < 1 \qquad \text{Multiply by 10.}$$

$$|x^2| < 10 \qquad \text{Take the square root of both sides.}$$

$$|x| < \sqrt{10} \qquad \text{Convert to double inequalities.}$$

$$-\sqrt{10} < x < \sqrt{10} \qquad \text{Interval of convergence.}$$

Step 2.   *Find the Taylor series for the antiderivative:* Using property 4,

$$\int \frac{22x^4}{10 + x^2} \, dx = \int\left[2.2\, x^4 - \frac{2.2}{10}x^6 + \frac{2.2}{10^2}x^8 - \cdots + \frac{2.2(-1)^n}{10^n}x^{2n+4} + \cdots\right] dx$$

$$= C + \frac{2.2}{5}x^5 - \frac{2.2}{7 \cdot 10}x^7 + \frac{2.2}{9 \cdot 10^2}x^9 - \cdots$$

$$+ \frac{2.2(-1)^n}{(2n+5)10^n}x^{2n+5} + \cdots$$

This series also converges for $-\sqrt{10} < x < \sqrt{10}$.

Step 3.   *Approximate the definite integral:* Choosing $C = 0$ in the antiderivative, we have

$$\int_0^1 \frac{22x^4}{10 + x^2} \, dx = \left[\frac{2.2}{5}x^5 - \frac{2.2}{7 \cdot 10}x^7 + \frac{2.2}{9 \cdot 10^2}x^9 - \cdots\right.$$

$$\left.+ \frac{2.2(-1)^n}{(2n+5)10^n}x^{2n+5} + \cdots\right]\Big|_0^1$$

$$= \left[\frac{2.2}{5} - \frac{2.2}{7 \cdot 10} + \frac{2.2}{9 \cdot 10^2} - \cdots + \frac{2.2(-1)^n}{(2n+5)10^n} + \cdots\right] - 0$$

$$= 0.44 - 0.031\,429 + 0.002\,444 - \cdots$$

Since the limits of integration, 0 and 1, are within the interval of convergence of the Taylor series for the antiderivative, we can use this series to approximate the value of the definite integral. Notice that the numbers in this series are alternating in sign and decreasing in absolute value. Since the absolute value of the third term is less than 0.005, Theorem 1 implies that we can use the first two terms of this series to approximate the definite integral to the specified accuracy. Thus,

$$\int_0^1 \frac{22x^4}{10 + x^2} \, dx \approx 0.44 - 0.031\,429$$

$$\approx 0.409 \qquad \text{Rounded to three decimal places.}$$

Returning to (2), we have

$$2 \int_0^1 [x - f(x)]\, dx = 2 \int_0^1 x\, dx - 2 \int_0^1 f(x)\, dx$$

$$\approx 1 - 0.409$$

$$= 0.591 \quad \text{Index of income concentration.}$$

MATCHED PROBLEM 4 Repeat Example 4 for $f(x) = \dfrac{11x^5}{10 + x^2}$.

Answers to Matched Problems

1. $e^{0.2} \approx 1 + 0.2 + \frac{1}{2}(0.2)^2 = 1.22;\ |R_2(0.2)| < 0.004$

2. $e^{-0.1} \approx 1 - 0.1 + 0.005 = 0.905$ within $\pm 0.000\,167$

3. $\displaystyle\int_0^{0.5} e^{-x^2}\, dx \approx 0.5 - \frac{1}{3}(0.5)^3 \approx 0.458$ within $\pm 0.003\,125$

4. $\displaystyle\int_0^1 \frac{22x^5}{10 + x^2}\, dx \approx \frac{2.2}{6} - \frac{2.2}{80} \approx 0.339$ within $\pm 0.0022;$
index of income concentration ≈ 0.661

Exercise 2.4

In Problems 1–30, use Theorem 1 to perform the indicated error estimations.

A *Evaluating the Taylor series at 0 for $f(x) = e^{-x}$ at $x = 0.6$ produces the following series:*

$$e^{-0.6} = 1 - 0.6 + 0.18 - 0.036 + 0.0054$$
$$- 0.000\,648 + \cdots$$

In Problems 1–4, use the indicated number of terms in this series to approximate $e^{-0.6}$, and then estimate the error in this approximation.

1. Two terms   **2.** Three terms

3. Four terms   **4.** Five terms

Evaluating the Taylor series at 0 for $f(x) = \ln(1 + x)$ at $x = 0.3$ produces the following series:

$$\ln 1.3 = 0.3 - 0.045 + 0.009 - 0.002\,025 + 0.000\,486$$
$$- 0.000\,121\,5 + \cdots$$

In Problems 5–8, use the indicated number of terms in this series to approximate $\ln 1.3$, and then estimate the error in this approximation.

5. Two terms   **6.** Three terms

7. Four terms   **8.** Five terms

In Problems 9–12, use the third-degree Taylor polynomial at 0 for $f(x) = e^{-x}$ to approximate each expression, and then estimate the error in the approximation.

9. $e^{-0.2}$ **10.** $e^{-0.5}$

11. $e^{-0.03}$ **12.** $e^{-0.06}$

In Problems 13–16, use the third-degree Taylor polynomial at 0 for $f(x) = \ln(1 + x)$ to approximate each expression, and then estimate the error in the approximation.

13. $\ln 1.6$ **14.** $\ln 1.8$

15. $\ln 1.06$ **16.** $\ln 1.08$

B *In Problems 17–24, use a Taylor polynomial at 0 to approximate each expression with an error of no more than 0.000 005. Select the polynomial of lowest degree that can be used to obtain this accuracy and state the degree of this polynomial.*

17. $e^{-0.1}$ **18.** $e^{-0.2}$

19. $e^{-0.01}$ **20.** $e^{-0.02}$

21. $\ln 1.2$ **22.** $\ln 1.1$

23. $\ln 1.02$ **24.** $\ln 1.01$

In Problems 25–30, use a Taylor series at 0 to approximate each integral with an error of no more than 0.0005.

25. $\displaystyle\int_0^{0.2} \frac{1}{1 + x^2}\, dx$ **26.** $\displaystyle\int_0^{0.5} \frac{x}{1 + x^4}\, dx$

27. $\displaystyle\int_0^{0.6} \ln(1 + x^2)\, dx$ **28.** $\displaystyle\int_0^{0.7} x \ln(1 + x^4)\, dx$

29. $\displaystyle\int_0^{0.4} x^2 e^{-x^2}\, dx$ **30.** $\displaystyle\int_0^{0.8} x^4 e^{-x^2}\, dx$

In Problems 31–34, assume that f(x) is a function such that
$|f^{(n)}(x)| \leq 1$ *for all n and all x [the trigonometric functions*
$f(x) = \sin x$ *and* $f(x) = \cos x$, *for example, satisfy that proper-*
ty] and let $p_n(x)$ *be the nth-degree Taylor polynomial for f at 0.*

31. Use Taylor's formula for the remainder to find the small-est value of n such that the error in the approximation of $f(2)$ by $p_n(2)$ is guaranteed to be less than 0.001.

32. Use Taylor's formula for the remainder to find the small-est value of n such that the error in the approximation of $f(10)$ by $p_n(10)$ is guaranteed to be less than 0.001.

33. Use Taylor's formula for the remainder to determine the values of x such that the error in the approximation of $f(x)$ by $p_5(x)$ is guaranteed to be less than 0.05.

34. Use Taylor's formula for the remainder to determine the values of x such that the error in the approximation of $f(x)$ by $p_{10}(x)$ is guaranteed to be less than 0.05.

35. Let $f(x) = xe^x$ and consider the third-degree Taylor poly-nomial $p_3(x)$ for f at 0. Use graphical approximation tech-niques to determine those values of x for which the error in the approximation $f(x) \approx p_3(x)$ is less than 0.005.

36. Let $f(x) = 1/(4 - x^2)$ and consider the fourth-degree Taylor polynomial $p_4(x)$ for f at 0. Use graphical approx-imation techniques to determine those values of x for which the error in the approximation $f(x) \approx p_4(x)$ is less than 0.0001.

C *In Problems 37–40, use the second-degree Taylor polynomial*
at 0 for $f(x) = e^x$ *to approximate the given number. Use*
Taylor's formula for the remainder to estimate the error in
each approximation.

37. $e^{-0.3}$ **38.** $e^{-0.4}$ **39.** $e^{0.05}$ **40.** $e^{0.01}$

41. The Taylor series at 0 for $f(x) = \sqrt{16 + x}$ converges for $-16 < x < 16$. Use the second-degree Taylor poly-nomial at 0 to approximate $\sqrt{17}$. Use Taylor's formula for the remainder to estimate the error in this approxi-mation.

42. The Taylor series at 0 for $f(x) = \sqrt{(4 + x)^3}$ converges for $-4 < x < 4$. Use the third-degree Taylor polynomial at 0 to approximate $\sqrt{125}$. Use Taylor's formula for the remainder to estimate the error in this approximation.

43. To estimate

$$\int_{-2}^{0} \frac{1}{1 - x} \, dx$$

a student takes the first five terms of the Taylor series for $f(x) = 1/(1 - x)$ at 0 and integrates term by term. He obtains the estimate 5.067. A second student estimates the integral by noting that $F(x) = -\ln(1 - x)$ is an anti-derivative for $f(x)$. She evaluates $F(x)$ between -2 and 0 to obtain the estimate 1.099. Is either computation cor-rect? How do you account for the large discrepancy be-tween the two estimates?

44. To estimate

$$\int_{0}^{1.5} \frac{1}{1 + x^2} \, dx$$

a student takes the first five nonzero terms of the Taylor series for $f(x) = 1/(1 + x^2)$ at 0 and integrates term by term. He obtains the estimate 3.724. A second student doubts the estimate. She claims that since $1/(1 + x^2) \leq 1$ for $0 \leq x \leq 1.5$, the value of the integral must be less than 1.5. Is either student correct? How do you account for the large discrepancy between their estimates?

There are different ways to approximate a function f by poly-
nomials. If, for example, $f(a)$, $f'(a)$, *and* $f''(a)$ *are known,*
then we can construct the second-degree Taylor polynomial
$p_2(x)$ *at a for* $f(x)$; $p_2(x)$ *and* $f(x)$ *will have the same value at*
a and the same first and second derivatives at a. If, on the other
hand, $f(x_1)$, $f(x_2)$, *and* $f(x_3)$ *are known, then we can compute*
the quadratic regression polynomial $q_2(x)$ *for the points*
$(x_1, f(x_1))$, $(x_2, f(x_2))$, $(x_3, f(x_3))$; $q_2(x)$ *and* $f(x)$ *will have the*
same values at x_1, x_2, x_3. *Problems 45 and 46 concern these*
contrasting methods of approximation by polynomials.

45. (A) Find the second-degree Taylor polynomial $p_2(x)$ at 0 for $f(x) = e^x$, and use a graphing utility to com-pute the quadratic regression polynomial $q_2(x)$ for the points $(-0.1, e^{-0.1})$, $(0, e^0)$, and $(0.1, e^{0.1})$.

   (B) Use graphical approximation techniques to find the maximum error for $-0.1 \leq x \leq 0.1$ in approximat-ing $f(x) = e^x$ by $p_2(x)$ and by $q_2(x)$.

   (C) Which polynomial, $p_2(x)$ or $q_2(x)$, gives the better approximation to

$$\int_{-0.1}^{0.1} e^x dx?$$

46. (A) Find the fourth-degree Taylor polynomial $p_4(x)$ at 0 for $f(x) = \ln(1 + x)$, and use a graphing utility to compute the quartic regression polynomial $q_4(x)$ for the points $(0, \ln 1)$,

$$\left(-\tfrac{1}{2}, \ln(1 - \tfrac{1}{2})\right), \left(-\tfrac{3}{4}, \ln(1 - \tfrac{3}{4})\right),$$
$$\left(-\tfrac{7}{8}, \ln(1 - \tfrac{7}{8})\right), \left(-\tfrac{15}{16}, \ln(1 - \tfrac{15}{16})\right).$$

   (B) Use graphical approximation techniques to find the maximum error for $-\tfrac{15}{16} \leq x \leq 0$ in approximating $f(x) = \ln(1 + x)$ by $p_4(x)$ and by $q_4(x)$.

   (C) Which polynomial, $p_4(x)$ or $q_4(x)$, gives the better approximation to

$$\int_{-15/16}^{0} \ln(1 + x) \, dx?$$

Applications

In Problems 47–58, use Theorem 1 to perform the indicated error estimations.

47. *Income distribution.* The income distribution for a certain country is represented by the Lorenz curve with the equation

$$f(x) = \frac{5x^6}{4 + x^2}$$

Approximate the index of income concentration to within ± 0.005.

48. *Income distribution.* Repeat Problem 47 for

$$f(x) = \frac{10x^4}{9 + x^2}$$

49. *Marketing.* A soft drink manufacturer is ready to introduce a new diet soda by a national sales campaign. After test marketing the soda in a carefully selected city, the market research department estimates that sales (in millions of dollars) will increase at the monthly rate of

$$S'(t) = 10 - 10e^{-0.01t^2} \qquad 0 \le t \le 12$$

t months after the national campaign is started. Use the fourth-degree Taylor polynomial at 0 for $S'(t)$ to approximate the total sales during the first 4 months of the campaign, and estimate the error in this approximation.

50. *Marketing.* Repeat Problem 49 if the monthly rate of increase in sales is given by

$$S'(t) = 10 - 10e^{-0.005t^2} \qquad 0 \le t \le 12$$

51. *Useful life.* A computer store rents time on desktop publishing systems. The total accumulated costs $C(t)$ and revenues $R(t)$ (in thousands of dollars) from a particular system satisfy

$$C'(t) = 4 \quad \text{and} \quad R'(t) = \frac{80}{16 + t^2}$$

where t is the time in years that the system has been available for rental. Find the useful life of the system, and approximate the total profit during the useful life to within ± 0.005.

52. *Average price.* Given the demand equation

$$p = D(x) = 10 - 20\ln\left(1 + \frac{x^2}{2{,}500}\right) \qquad 0 \le x \le 40$$

approximate the average price (in dollars) over the demand interval $[0, 20]$ to within ± 0.005.

53. *Temperature.* The temperature (in degrees Celsius) in an artificial habitat is made to change according to the equation

$$C(t) = 20 + 800\ln\left(1 + \frac{t^2}{100}\right) \qquad 0 \le t \le 2$$

Use a Taylor series at 0 to approximate the average temperature over the time interval $[0, 2]$ to within ± 0.005.

54. *Temperature.* Repeat Problem 53 for

$$C(t) = 10 + 200\ln\left(1 + \frac{t^2}{50}\right) \qquad 0 \le t \le 2$$

55. *Medicine.* The rate of healing for a skin wound (in square centimeters per day) is given by

$$A'(t) = \frac{-75}{t^2 + 25}$$

The initial wound has an area of 12 square centimeters. Use the second-degree Taylor polynomial at 0 for $A'(t)$ to approximate the area of the wound after 2 days, and estimate the error in this approximation.

56. *Medicine.* Repeat Problem 55 for

$$A'(t) = \frac{-60}{t^2 + 20}$$

57. *Learning.* In a particular business college, it was found that an average student enrolled in an advanced typing class progresses at a rate of $N'(t) = 6e^{-0.01t^2}$ words per minute per week, t weeks after enrolling in a 15-week course. At the beginning of the course an average student could type 40 words per minute. Use the second-degree Taylor polynomial at 0 for $N'(t)$ to approximate the improvement in typing after 5 weeks in the course, and estimate the error in this approximation.

58. *Learning.* In the same business college, it was found that an average student in a beginning shorthand class progressed at a rate of $N'(t) = 12e^{-0.005t^2}$ words per minute per week, t weeks after enrolling in a 15-week course. At the beginning of the course none of the students could take any dictation by shorthand. Use the second-degree Taylor polynomial at 0 for $N'(t)$ to approximate the improvement after 5 weeks in the course, and estimate the error in this approximation.

CHAPTER 2 REVIEW

Important Terms, Symbols, and Concepts

2.1 Taylor Polynomials

If f is a function that has n derivatives at 0, then the **nth-degree Taylor polynomial for f at 0** is

$$p_n(x) = f(0) + f'(0)x + \frac{f''(0)}{2!}x^2 + \cdots + \frac{f^{(n)}(0)}{n!}x^n$$

If f has n derivatives at a, then the **nth-degree Taylor polynomial for f at a** is

$$p_n(x) = f(a) + f'(a)(x - a) + \frac{f''(a)}{2!}(x - a)^2 + \cdots$$
$$+ \frac{f^{(n)}(a)}{n!}(x - a)^n$$

2.2 Taylor Series

If f is a function that has derivatives of all order at a point a and $p_n(x)$ is the nth-degree Taylor polynomial for f at a, then the **Taylor series for f at a** is

$$f(a) + f'(a)(x - a) + \frac{f''(a)}{2!}(x - a)^2 + \cdots$$
$$+ \frac{f^{(n)}(a)}{n!}(x - a)^n + \cdots$$

The Taylor series **converges at x** if $\lim\limits_{n \to \infty} p_n(x)$ exists, and **diverges at x** if the limit does not exist. The set of values of x for which this limit exists is called the **interval of convergence.**

• **Theorem 1 Interval of Convergence**

Let f be a function with derivatives of all order at a point a, let $a_n = f^{(n)}(a)/n!$ for $n = 0, 1, 2, \ldots$, and let $a_0 + a_1(x - a) + a_2(x - a)^2 + \cdots + a_n(x - a)^n + \cdots$ be the Taylor series for f at a. If $a_n \neq 0$ for $n \geq n_0$, then:

Case 1. If $\lim\limits_{n \to \infty} \left| \dfrac{a_{n+1}}{a_n} \right| = L > 0$ and $R = \dfrac{1}{L}$ then the series converges for $|x - a| < R$ and diverges for $|x - a| > R$.

Case 2. If $\lim\limits_{n \to \infty} \left| \dfrac{a_{n+1}}{a_n} \right| = 0$, then the series converges for all values of x.

Case 3. If $\lim\limits_{n \to \infty} \left| \dfrac{a_{n+1}}{a_n} \right| = \infty$, then the series converges only at $x = a$.

We assume that functions are represented by their Taylor series throughout the interval of convergence (there exist functions that do not satisfy this condition, but they are not considered in this supplement).

2.3 Operations on Taylor Series

Property 1. Two Taylor series can be added term by term. This operation is valid in the intersection of the intervals of convergence of the series for f and g.

Property 2. A Taylor series for f at 0 can be multiplied term by term by an expression of the form cx^r, where c is a nonzero constant and r is a non-negative integer. The resulting series has the same interval of convergence as the Taylor series for f.

Property 3. A Taylor series for f at 0 can be differentiated term by term to obtain a Taylor series for f'. Both series have the same interval of convergence.

Property 4. A Taylor series at 0 can be integrated term by term to obtain a Taylor series for $\int f(x)\, dx$. Both series have the same interval of convergence.

Making a substitution in a known Taylor series to obtain a new series is a useful technique. A series for e^{x^2}, for example, can be obtained by substituting x^2 for x in the Taylor series for e^x at 0.

2.4 Approximations Using Taylor Series

If $p_n(x)$ is the nth-degree Taylor polynomial for f, then the **remainder** is $R_n(x) = f(x) - p_n(x)$. The **error** in the approximation $f(x) \approx p_n(x)$ is $|f(x) - p_n(x)| = |R_n(x)|$.

• *Taylor's Formula for the Remainder*

If f has derivatives of all order at 0, then

$$R_n(x) = \frac{f^{(n+1)}(t)\, x^{n+1}}{(n+1)!} \text{ for some number } t \text{ between 0 and } x.$$

THEOREM 1   **ERROR ESTIMATION FOR ALTERNATING SERIES**

If x_0 is a number in the interval of convergence for

$$f(x) = a_0 + a_1 x + a_2 x^2 + \cdots + a_k x^k + \cdots$$

and the terms in the series

$$f(x_0) = a_0 + a_1 x_0 + a_2 x_0^2 + \cdots + a_k x_0^k + \cdots$$

are alternating in sign and decreasing in absolute value, then

$$|R_n(x_0)| < |a_{n+1} x_0^{n+1}|$$

Taylor series techniques provide a method for approximating definite integrals which, in the case of alternating series, automatically determines the accuracy of the approximation.

REVIEW EXERCISE

Work through all the problems in this chapter review and check your answers in the back of this supplement. Answers to all review problems are there along with section numbers in italics to indicate where each type of problem is discussed. Where weaknesses show up, review appropriate sections in the text.

Unless directed otherwise, use Theorem 1 of Section 2-4 in all problems involving error estimation.

A

1. Find $f^{(4)}(x)$ for $f(x) = \ln(x + 5)$.
2. Use the third-degree Taylor polynomial at 0 for
   $f(x) = \sqrt[3]{1 + x}$ and $x = 0.01$ to approximate $\sqrt[3]{1.01}$.
3. Use the third-degree Taylor polynomial at $a = 3$ for
   $f(x) = \sqrt{1 + x}$ and $x = 2.9$ to approximate $\sqrt{3.9}$.
4. Use the second-degree Taylor polynomial at 0 for
   $f(x) = \sqrt{9 + x^2}$ and $x = 0.1$ to approximate $\sqrt{9.01}$.

Use Theorem 1 of Section 2-2 to find the interval of convergence of each Taylor series representation given in Problems 5–8.

5. $\dfrac{1}{1 - 4x} = 1 + 4x + 4^2 x^2 + \cdots + 4^n x^n + \cdots$

6. $\dfrac{5}{x - 1} = 1 - \dfrac{1}{5}(x - 6) + \dfrac{1}{5^2}(x - 6)^2 - \cdots$
   $\qquad\qquad + \dfrac{(-1)^n}{5^n}(x - 6)^n + \cdots$

7. $\dfrac{2x}{(1 - x)^3} = 1 \cdot 2x + 2 \cdot 3x^2 + 3 \cdot 4x^3 + \cdots$
   $\qquad\qquad + n(n + 1)x^n + \cdots$

8. $e^{10x} = 1 + 10x + \dfrac{10^2}{2!}x^2 + \cdots + \dfrac{10^n}{n!}x^n + \cdots$

9. Find the nth derivative of $f(x) = e^{-9x}$.

B *In Problems 10 and 11, use the formula $a_n = f^{(n)}(a)/n!$ to find the Taylor series at the indicated value of a. Use Theorem 1 of Section 2-2 to find the interval of convergence.*

10. $f(x) = \dfrac{1}{7 - x}$; at 0   11. $f(x) = \ln x$; at 2

In Problems 12–16, use Table 1 of Section 2-3 and the properties of Taylor series to find the Taylor series of each function at the indicated value of a. Find the interval of convergence.

12. $f(x) = \dfrac{1}{10 + x}$; at 0   13. $f(x) = \dfrac{x^2}{4 - x^2}$; at 0

14. $f(x) = x^2 e^{3x}$; at 0   15. $f(x) = x \ln(e + x)$; at 0

16. $f(x) = \dfrac{1}{4 - x}$; at 2

17. (A) Explain why Theorem 1 of Section 2-2 is not directly applicable to the Taylor series representation
    $$\ln(1 - 5x^2) = -5x^2 - \frac{5^2}{2}x^4 - \frac{5^3}{3}x^6 - \cdots - \frac{5^n}{n}x^{2n} - \cdots$$
    (B) Use another method to find the interval of convergence of the Taylor series in part (A).

18. Substituting $\sqrt{x}$ for x in the Taylor series at 0 for $1/(1 + x)$ gives the formula
    $$\frac{1}{1 + \sqrt{x}} = 1 - x^{1/2} + x - x^{3/2} + \cdots + (-1)^n x^{n/2} + \cdots$$
    (A) For which values of x is the formula valid?
    (B) Is the formula a Taylor series at 0 for $1/(1 + \sqrt{x})$? Explain.

In Problems 19 and 20, find the Taylor series at 0 for $f(x)$ and use the relationship $g(x) = f'(x)$ to find the Taylor series at 0 for $g(x)$. Find the interval of convergence for both series.

19. $f(x) = \dfrac{1}{2-x}$; $g(x) = \dfrac{1}{(2-x)^2}$

20. $f(x) = \dfrac{x^2}{1+x^2}$; $g(x) = \dfrac{2x}{(1+x^2)^2}$

In Problems 21 and 22, find the Taylor series at 0, and find the interval of convergence.

21. $f(x) = \displaystyle\int_0^x \dfrac{t^2}{9+t^2}\, dt$ **22.** $f(x) = \displaystyle\int_0^x \dfrac{t^4}{16-t^2}\, dt$

23. (A) Compute the Taylor series for
$f(x) = x^3 - 3x^2 + 4$ at $a = 1$ and at $a = -1$.

  (B) Explain how the two series are related.

24. (A) Explain why $f(x) = |x|$ does not have any Taylor polynomials at 0.

  (B) If $a \neq 0$, find the Taylor polynomials for $f(x) = |x|$ at a.

In Problems 25 and 26, use the second-degree Taylor polynomial at 0 for $f(x) = e^x$ to approximate the indicated quantity. Use Taylor's formula for the remainder to estimate the error in the approximation.

25. $e^{0.6}$

26. $e^{0.06}$

In Problems 27 and 28, use a Taylor polynomial at 0 for $f(x) = \ln(1+x)$ to estimate the indicated quantity to within ± 0.0005. Give the degree of the Taylor polynomial of lowest degree that will provide this accuracy.

27. $\ln 1.3$

28. $\ln 1.03$

29. If $f(x)$ satisfies $f'(x) = x \ln(1-x)$ and $f(0) = 5$, find the Taylor series at 0 for $f(x)$.

30. If $f(x)$ satisfies $f''(x) = xe^{-x}$, $f'(0) = -4$, and $f(0) = 3$, find the Taylor series at 0 for $f(x)$.

C *In Problems 31 and 32, approximate the integral to within ± 0.0005.*

31. $\displaystyle\int_0^1 \dfrac{1}{16+x^2}\, dx$ **32.** $\displaystyle\int_0^1 x^2 e^{-0.1x^2}\, dx$

In Problems 33 and 34, assume that $f(x)$ is a function such that $|f^{(n)}(x)| \leq 10$ for all n and all x, and let $p_n(x)$ be the nth-degree Taylor polynomial for f at 0.

33. Use Taylor's formula for the remainder to find the smallest value of n such that the error in the approximation of $f(0.5)$ by $p_n(0.5)$ is guaranteed to be less than 10^{-6}.

34. Use Taylor's formula for the remainder to determine the values of x such that the error in the approximation of $f(x)$ by $p_8(x)$ is guaranteed to be less than 10^{-6}.

35. Let $f(x) = e^{x^2}$ and consider the fourth-degree Taylor polynomial $p_4(x)$ for f at 0. Use graphical approximation techniques to determine those values of x for which the error in the approximation $f(x) \approx p_4(x)$ is less than 0.01.

36. Let $f(x) = \ln(1-x^2)$ and consider the sixth-degree Taylor polynomial $p_6(x)$ for f at 0. Use graphical approximation techniques to determine those values of x for which the error in the approximation $f(x) \approx p_6(x)$ is less than 0.001.

APPLICATIONS

37. *Average price.* Given the demand equation
$$p = D(x) = \tfrac{1}{10}\sqrt{2{,}500 - x^2}$$
use the second-degree Taylor polynomial at 0 to approximate the average price (in dollars) over the demand interval $[0, 15]$.

38. *Production.* The rate of production of an oil well (in thousands of dollars per year) is given by
$$R(t) = 6 + 3e^{-0.01t^2}$$
Use the second-degree Taylor polynomial at 0 to approximate the total production during the first 10 years of operation of the well.

39. *Income distribution.* The income distribution for a certain country is represented by the Lorenz curve with the equation
$$f(x) = \dfrac{9x^3}{8+x^2}$$
Approximate the index of income concentration to within ± 0.005.

40. *Marketing.* A cereal manufacturer is ready to introduce a new high-fiber cereal by a national sales campaign. After test-marketing the cereal in a carefully selected city, the market research department estimates that sales (in millions of dollars) will increase at the monthly rate of
$$S'(t) = 20 - 20e^{-0.001t^2}\qquad 0 \leq t \leq 12$$
t months after the national campaign is started. Use the fourth-degree Taylor polynomial at 0 for $S'(t)$ to approximate the total sales during the first 8 months of the campaign, and estimate the error in this approximation.

41. *Medicine.* The rate of healing for a skin wound (in square centimeters per day) is given by
$$A'(t) = \dfrac{-100}{t^2+40}$$
The initial wound has an area of 15 square centimeters. Use the second-degree Taylor polynomial at 0 for $A'(t)$ to approximate the area of the wound after 2 days, and estimate the error in this approximation.

42. *Medicine.* A large injection of insulin is administered to a patient. The level of insulin in the blood-stream t minutes after the injection is given approximately by

$$L(t) = \frac{5{,}000t^2}{10{,}000 + t^4}$$

Express the average insulin level over the time interval $[0, 5]$ as a definite integral, and use a Taylor series at 0 to approximate this integral to within ± 0.005.

43. *Politics.* In a newly incorporated city, the number of voters (in thousands) t years after incorporation is given by

$$N(t) = 10 + 2t - 5e^{-0.01t^2} \qquad 0 \le t \le 5$$

Express the average number of voters over the time interval $[0, 5]$ as a definite integral, and use a Taylor series at 0 to approximate this integral to within ± 0.05.

APPENDIX C   Tables

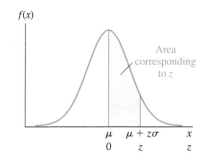

f(x)

Area corresponding to z

μ $\mu + z\sigma$ x
0   z z

TABLE III Area Under the Standard Normal Curve

(Table Entries Represent the Area Under the Standard Normal Curve from 0 to z, z ≥ 0)

z	.00	.01	.02	.03	.04	.05	.06	.07	.08	.09
0.0	0.0000	0.0040	0.0080	0.0120	0.0160	0.0199	0.0239	0.0279	0.0319	0.0359
0.1	0.0398	0.0438	0.0478	0.0517	0.0557	0.0596	0.0636	0.0675	0.0714	0.0753
0.2	0.0793	0.0832	0.0871	0.0910	0.0948	0.0987	0.1026	0.1064	0.1103	0.1141
0.3	0.1179	0.1217	0.1255	0.1293	0.1331	0.1368	0.1406	0.1443	0.1480	0.1517
0.4	0.1554	0.1591	0.1628	0.1664	0.1700	0.1736	0.1772	0.1808	0.1844	0.1879
0.5	0.1915	0.1950	0.1985	0.2019	0.2054	0.2088	0.2123	0.2157	0.2190	0.2224
0.6	0.2257	0.2291	0.2324	0.2357	0.2389	0.2422	0.2454	0.2486	0.2517	0.2549
0.7	0.2580	0.2611	0.2642	0.2673	0.2704	0.2734	0.2764	0.2794	0.2823	0.2852
0.8	0.2881	0.2910	0.2939	0.2967	0.2995	0.3023	0.3051	0.3078	0.3106	0.3133
0.9	0.3159	0.3186	0.3212	0.3238	0.3264	0.3289	0.3315	0.3340	0.3365	0.3389
1.0	0.3413	0.3438	0.3461	0.3485	0.3508	0.3531	0.3554	0.3577	0.3599	0.3621
1.1	0.3643	0.3665	0.3686	0.3708	0.3729	0.3749	0.3770	0.3790	0.3810	0.3830
1.2	0.3849	0.3869	0.3888	0.3907	0.3925	0.3944	0.3962	0.3980	0.3997	0.4015
1.3	0.4032	0.4049	0.4066	0.4082	0.4099	0.4115	0.4131	0.4147	0.4162	0.4177
1.4	0.4192	0.4207	0.4222	0.4236	0.4251	0.4265	0.4279	0.4292	0.4306	0.4319
1.5	0.4332	0.4345	0.4357	0.4370	0.4382	0.4394	0.4406	0.4418	0.4429	0.4441
1.6	0.4452	0.4463	0.4474	0.4484	0.4495	0.4505	0.4515	0.4525	0.4535	0.4545
1.7	0.4554	0.4564	0.4573	0.4582	0.4591	0.4599	0.4608	0.4616	0.4625	0.4633
1.8	0.4641	0.4649	0.4656	0.4664	0.4671	0.4678	0.4686	0.4693	0.4699	0.4706
1.9	0.4713	0.4719	0.4726	0.4732	0.4738	0.4744	0.4750	0.4756	0.4761	0.4767
2.0	0.4772	0.4778	0.4783	0.4788	0.4793	0.4798	0.4803	0.4808	0.4812	0.4817
2.1	0.4821	0.4826	0.4830	0.4834	0.4838	0.4842	0.4846	0.4850	0.4854	0.4857
2.2	0.4861	0.4864	0.4868	0.4871	0.4875	0.4878	0.4881	0.4884	0.4887	0.4890
2.3	0.4893	0.4896	0.4898	0.4901	0.4904	0.4906	0.4909	0.4911	0.4913	0.4916
2.4	0.4918	0.4920	0.4922	0.4925	0.4927	0.4929	0.4931	0.4932	0.4934	0.4936
2.5	0.4938	0.4940	0.4941	0.4943	0.4945	0.4946	0.4948	0.4949	0.4951	0.4952
2.6	0.4953	0.4955	0.4956	0.4957	0.4959	0.4960	0.4961	0.4962	0.4963	0.4964
2.7	0.4965	0.4966	0.4967	0.4968	0.4969	0.4970	0.4971	0.4972	0.4973	0.4974
2.8	0.4974	0.4975	0.4976	0.4977	0.4977	0.4978	0.4979	0.4979	0.4980	0.4981
2.9	0.4981	0.4982	0.4982	0.4983	0.4984	0.4984	0.4985	0.4985	0.4986	0.4986
3.0	0.4987	0.4987	0.4987	0.4988	0.4988	0.4989	0.4989	0.4989	0.4990	0.4990
3.1	0.4990	0.4991	0.4991	0.4991	0.4992	0.4992	0.4992	0.4992	0.4993	0.4993
3.2	0.4993	0.4993	0.4994	0.4994	0.4994	0.4994	0.4994	0.4995	0.4995	0.4995
3.3	0.4995	0.4995	0.4995	0.4996	0.4996	0.4996	0.4996	0.4996	0.4996	0.4997
3.4	0.4997	0.4997	0.4997	0.4997	0.4997	0.4997	0.4997	0.4997	0.4997	0.4998
3.5	0.4998	0.4998	0.4998	0.4998	0.4998	0.4998	0.4998	0.4998	0.4998	0.4998
3.6	0.4998	0.4998	0.4999	0.4999	0.4999	0.4999	0.4999	0.4999	0.4999	0.4999
3.7	0.4999	0.4999	0.4999	0.4999	0.4999	0.4999	0.4999	0.4999	0.4999	0.4999
3.8	0.4999	0.4999	0.4999	0.4999	0.4999	0.4999	0.4999	0.4999	0.4999	0.4999
3.9	0.5000	0.5000	0.5000	0.5000	0.5000	0.5000	0.5000	0.5000	0.5000	0.5000

APPENDIX D   Special Calculus Topic

Section D.1   INTERPOLATING POLYNOMIALS AND DIVIDED DIFFERENCES

- Introduction
- The Interpolating Polynomial
- Divided Difference Tables
- Application

Given two points in the plane with distinct x coordinates, we can use the point-slope form of the equation of a line to find a polynomial whose graph passes through these two points. If we are given a set of three, four, or more points with distinct x coordinates, is there a polynomial whose graph will pass through all the given points? In this section, we will see that the answer to this question is yes, and we will discuss several methods for finding this polynomial, called the *interpolating polynomial*. The principal use of interpolating polynomials is to approximate y coordinates for points not in the given set. For example, a retail sales firm may have obtained a table of prices at various demands by examining past sales records. Prices for demands not in the table can be approximated by an interpolating polynomial. Interpolating polynomials also have applications to computer graphics. If a computer user selects a set of points on a drawing, the interpolating polynomial can be used to produce a smooth curve that passes through the selected points.

■ Introduction

We usually write polynomials in standard form using either increasing or decreasing powers of x. Both of the following polynomials are written in standard form:

$$p(x) = 1 + x^2 - 2x^3 \qquad q(x) = -3x^5 + 2x^4 - 5x$$

In this section, we will find it convenient to write polynomials in a different form. The following activity will give you some experience with this new form.

Explore & Discuss 1

Consider the points in Table 1.

(A) Let $p_1(x) = a_0 + a_1(x - 1)$. Determine a_0 and a_1 so that the graph of $y = p_1(x)$ passes through the first two points in Table 1.

(B) Let $p_2(x) = a_0 + a_1(x - 1) + a_2(x - 1)(x - 2)$. Determine $a_0, a_1,$ and a_2 so that the graph of $y = p_2(x)$ passes through the first three points in Table 1.

(C) Let

$$p_3(x) = a_0 + a_1(x - 1) + a_2(x - 1)(x - 2) + a_3(x - 1)(x - 2)(x - 3).$$

Determine $a_0, a_1, a_2,$ and a_3 so that the graph of $y = p_3(x)$ passes through all four points in Table 1.

TABLE 1

x	1	2	3	4
y	4	7	4	1

The following example will illustrate basic concepts.

EXAMPLE 1   **Approximating Revenue** A manufacturing company has defined the revenue function for one of its products by examining past records and listing the revenue (in thousands of dollars) for certain levels of production (in thousands of units). Use the revenue function defined by Table 2 to estimate the revenue if 3,000 units are produced and if 7,000 units are produced.

665

SOLUTION One way to approximate values of a function defined by a table is to use a **piecewise linear approximation.** To form the piecewise linear approximation for Table 2, we simply use the point-slope formula to find the equation of the line joining each successive pair of points in the table (see Fig. 1).

TABLE 2	Revenue R Defined as a Function of Production x by a Table		
x	1	4	6	8
$R(x)$	65	80	40	16

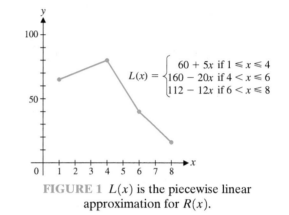

$$L(x) = \begin{cases} 60 + 5x & \text{if } 1 \leq x \leq 4 \\ 160 - 20x & \text{if } 4 < x \leq 6 \\ 112 - 12x & \text{if } 6 < x \leq 8 \end{cases}$$

FIGURE 1 $L(x)$ is the piecewise linear approximation for $R(x)$.

This type of approximation is very useful in certain applications, but it has several disadvantages. First, the piecewise linear approximation usually has a sharp corner at each point in the table and thus is not differentiable at these points. Second, the piecewise linear approximation requires the use of a different formula between each successive pair of points in the table (see Fig. 1).

Instead of using the piecewise linear approximation, we will outline a method that will produce a polynomial whose values agree with $R(x)$ at each point in Table 2. This will provide us with a differentiable function given by a single formula that can be used to approximate $R(x)$ for any value of x between 1 and 8.

Suppose $p(x)$ is a polynomial whose values agree with the values of $R(x)$ at the four x values given in Table 2. Instead of expressing $p(x)$ in terms of powers of x, the standard method for writing polynomial forms, we use the first three x values in the table to write

$$p(x) = a_0 + a_1(x - 1) + a_2(x - 1)(x - 4) + a_3(x - 1)(x - 4)(x - 6)$$

As we will see, writing $p(x)$ in this special form will greatly simplify our work.

Since $p(x)$ is to agree with $R(x)$ at each x value in Table 2, we can write the following equations involving the coefficients a_0, a_1, a_2, and a_3:

$$65 = R(1) = p(1) = a_0 \tag{1}$$

$$80 = R(4) = p(4) = a_0 + 3a_1 \tag{2}$$

$$40 = R(6) = p(6) = a_0 + 5a_1 + 10a_2 \tag{3}$$

$$16 = R(8) = p(8) = a_0 + 7a_1 + 28a_2 + 56a_3 \tag{4}$$

From equation (1), we see that $a_0 = 65$. Solving equation (2) for a_1 and substituting for a_0, we have

$$a_1 = \frac{1}{3}(80 - a_0) = \frac{1}{3}(80 - 65) = 5$$

Proceeding the same way with equations (3) and (4), we have

$$a_2 = \frac{1}{10}(40 - a_0 - 5a_1) = \frac{1}{10}(40 - 65 - 25) = -5$$

$$a_3 = \frac{1}{56}(16 - a_0 - 7a_1 - 28a_2) = \frac{1}{56}(16 - 65 - 35 + 140) = 1$$

Thus,

$$p(x) = 65 + 5(x - 1) - 5(x - 1)(x - 4) + (x - 1)(x - 4)(x - 6)$$

The polynomial $p(x)$ agrees with $R(x)$ at each x value in Table 2 (verify this) and can be used to approximate $R(x)$ for values of x between 1 and 8 (see Fig. 2).

If 3,000 units are produced, then the revenue can be approximated by evaluating $p(3)$:

$$R(3) \approx p(3) = 65 + 5(2) - 5(2)(-1) + (2)(-1)(-3)$$
$$= 91 \text{ or } \$91,000$$

If 7,000 units are produced, then

$$R(7) \approx p(7) = 65 + 5(6) - 5(6)(3) + (6)(3)(1)$$
$$= 23 \text{ or } \$23,000$$

TABLE 2			
x	1	4	6	8
$R(x)$	65	80	40	16

FIGURE 2 $p(x) = 65 + 5(x - 1) - 5(x - 1)(x - 4) + (x - 1)(x - 4)(x - 6)$

MATCHED PROBLEM 1 Refer to Example 1. Approximate the revenue if 2,000 units are produced and if 5,000 units are produced.

Since the revenue function in Example 1 was defined by a table, we have no information about this function for any value of x other than those listed in the table. Thus, we cannot say anything about the accuracy of the approximations obtained by using $p(x)$. As we mentioned earlier, the piecewise linear approximation might provide a better approximation in some cases. The primary advantage of using $p(x)$ is that we have a differentiable function that is defined by a single equation and agrees with the revenue function at every value of x in the table.

■ The Interpolating Polynomial

The procedure we used to find a polynomial approximation for the revenue function in Example 1 can be applied to any function that is defined by a table. The polynomial that is obtained in this way is referred to as the *interpolating polynomial*. The basic concepts are summarized in the next box.

DEFINITION **The Interpolating Polynomial**

If $f(x)$ is the function defined by the following table of $n + 1$ points,

x	x_0	x_1	$\ldots$	x_n
$f(x)$	y_0	y_1	$\ldots$	y_n

then the **interpolating polynomial** for $f(x)$ is the polynomial $p(x)$ of degree less than or equal to n that satisfies

$$p(x_0) = y_0 = f(x_0)$$

$$p(x_1) = y_1 = f(x_1)$$

$$\vdots \qquad \vdots$$

$$p(x_n) = y_n = f(x_n)$$

Newton's form for the interpolating polynomial is

$$p(x) = a_0 + a_1(x - x_0) + a_2(x - x_0)(x - x_1) + \cdots$$
$$+ a_n(x - x_0)(x - x_1)\cdots(x - x_{n-1})$$

Notice that if we graph the points in the defining table and the interpolating polynomial $p(x)$ on the same set of axes, then the graph of $p(x)$ will pass through every point given in the table (see Fig. 2). Is it possible to find a polynomial that is different from $p(x)$ and also has a graph that passes through all the points in the table? In more advanced texts, it is shown that

The interpolating polynomial is the only polynomial of degree less than or equal to n whose graph will pass through every point in the table.

Any other polynomial whose graph goes through all these points must be of degree greater than n. The steps we used in finding the interpolating polynomial are summarized in the following box.

PROCEDURE | **Steps for Finding the Interpolating Polynomial**

Step 1. Write Newton's form for $p(x)$.

Step 2. Use the conditions $p(x_i) = y_i, i = 0, 1, \ldots, n$ to write $n + 1$ linear equations for the coefficients. Do not change the order of these equations. This system of equations is called a **lower triangular system.**

Step 3. Starting with the first and proceeding down the list, solve each equation for the coefficient with the largest subscript and substitute all the previously determined coefficients. This method of solving for the coefficients is called **forward substitution.**

EXAMPLE 2 | **Finding the Interpolating Polynomial** Find the interpolating polynomial for the function defined by the following table:

x	0	1	2	3
$f(x)$	5	4	−3	−4

SOLUTION | Step 1. Newton's form for $p(x)$ is

$$p(x) = a_0 + a_1 x + a_2 x(x - 1) + a_3 x(x - 1)(x - 2)$$

Step 2. The lower triangular system is

$$a_0 \qquad\qquad\qquad = 5 \quad p(0) = f(0) = 5$$
$$a_0 + a_1 \qquad\qquad = 4 \quad p(1) = f(1) = 4$$
$$a_0 + 2a_1 + 2a_2 \qquad = -3 \quad p(2) = f(2) = -3$$
$$a_0 + 3a_1 + 6a_2 + 6a_3 = -4 \quad p(3) = f(3) = -4$$

Step 3.   Solving this system by forward substitution, we have

$$a_0 = 5$$

$$a_1 = 4 - a_0 = 4 - 5 = -1$$

$$a_2 = \frac{1}{2}(-3 - a_0 - 2a_1) = \frac{1}{2}(-3 - 5 + 2) = -3$$

$$a_3 = \frac{1}{6}(-4 - a_0 - 3a_1 - 6a_2) = \frac{1}{6}(-4 - 5 + 3 + 18) = 2$$

Thus, Newton's form for this interpolating polynomial is

$$p(x) = 5 - x - 3x(x - 1) + 2x(x - 1)(x - 2)$$

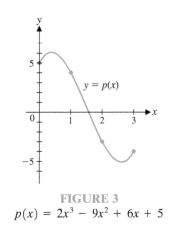

FIGURE 3

$$p(x) = 2x^3 - 9x^2 + 6x + 5$$

This form of $p(x)$ is suitable for evaluating the polynomial. For other operations, such as differentiation, integration, or graphing, it may be preferable to perform the indicated operations, collect like terms, and express $p(x)$ in the standard polynomial form

$$p(x) = 2x^3 - 9x^2 + 6x + 5$$

The graph of $p(x)$ is shown in Figure 3.

MATCHED PROBLEM 2   Find the interpolating polynomial for the function defined by the following table:

x	−1	0	1	2
$f(x)$	5	3	3	11

Explore & Discuss **2**   Given the following polynomial and table,

$$p(x) = x^3 - 10x^2 + 29x - 17$$

x	1	3	6
y	3	7	13

(A) Show that the graph of $p(x)$ passes through each point in the table.

(B) Is $p(x)$ the interpolating polynomial for this table? If not, what is the interpolating polynomial for this table?

(C) Discuss the relationship between the number of points in a table and the degree of the interpolating polynomial for that table.

■ Divided Difference Tables

We now present a simple computational procedure for finding the coefficients $a_0, a_1, \ldots, a_n$ in Newton's form for an interpolating polynomial. To introduce this method, we return to Table 2 in Example 1, which we restate here.

TABLE 2

x	1	4	6	8
$f(x)$	65	80	40	16

The coefficients in Newton's form for the interpolating polynomial for this table were $a_0 = 65$, $a_1 = 5$, $a_2 = -5$, and $a_3 = 1$. We will now construct a table, called a *divided difference table,* which will produce these coefficients with a minimum of computation. To begin, we place the x and y values in the first two columns of a new table. Then we compute the ratio of the change in y to the change in x for each successive pair of points in the table, and place the result on the line between the two points (see Table 3). These ratios are called the **first divided differences.**

To form the next column in the table, we repeat this process, using the change in the first divided differences in the numerator and the change in *two* successive values of x in the denominator. These ratios are called the **second divided differences** and are placed on the line between the corresponding first divided differences (see Table 4).

TABLE 3 First Divided Differences

x_k	y_k	First Divided Difference
1	65	
		$\dfrac{80 - 65}{4 - 1} = \dfrac{15}{3} = 5$
4	80	
		$\dfrac{40 - 80}{6 - 4} = \dfrac{-40}{2} = -20$
6	40	
		$\dfrac{16 - 40}{8 - 6} = \dfrac{-24}{2} = -12$
8	16	

TABLE 4 Second Divided Differences

x_k	y_k	First Divided Difference	Second Divided Difference
1	65		
		5	
4	80		$\dfrac{-20 - 5}{6 - 1} = \dfrac{-25}{5} = -5$
		-20	
6	40		$\dfrac{-12 - (-20)}{8 - 4} = \dfrac{8}{4} = 2$
		-12	
8	16		

To form the next column of the table, we form the ratio of the change in the second divided differences to the change in *three* successive values of x. These ratios are called the **third divided differences** and are placed on the line between the corresponding second divided differences (see Table 5). Since our table has only two second divided differences, there is only one third divided difference and this process is now complete.

TABLE 5 Third Divided Differences

x_k	y_k	First Divided Difference	Second Divided Difference	Third Divided Difference
1	65			
		5		
4	80		-5	
		-20		$\dfrac{2 - (-5)}{8 - 1} = \dfrac{7}{7} = 1$
6	40		2	
		-12		
8	16			

We have presented each step in constructing the divided difference table here in a separate table to clearly illustrate this process. In applications of this technique, these steps are combined into a single table. With a little practice, you should be able to proceed quickly from the defining table for the function (Table 2) to the final form of the divided difference table (Table 6 on the next page).

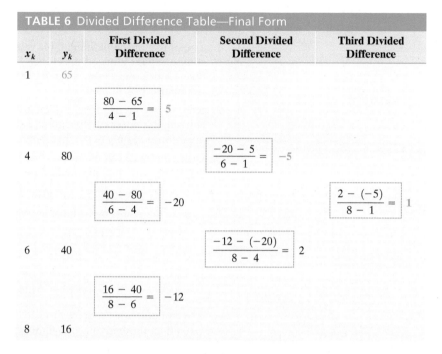

TABLE 6 Divided Difference Table—Final Form

x_k	y_k	First Divided Difference	Second Divided Difference	Third Divided Difference
1	65			
		$\dfrac{80-65}{4-1}=5$		
4	80		$\dfrac{-20-5}{6-1}=-5$	
		$\dfrac{40-80}{6-4}=-20$		$\dfrac{2-(-5)}{8-1}=1$
6	40		$\dfrac{-12-(-20)}{8-4}=2$	
		$\dfrac{16-40}{8-6}=-12$		
8	16			

Now that we have computed the divided difference table, how do we use it? If we write the first number from each column of the divided difference table, beginning with the second column:

$$65 \quad 5 \quad -5 \quad 1$$

we see that these numbers are the coefficients of the interpolating polynomial for Table 2 (see Example 1). Thus, Table 6 contains all the information we need to write the interpolating polynomial:

$$p(x) = 65 + 5(x-1) - 5(x-1)(x-4) + (x-1)(x-4)(x-6)$$

The divided difference table provides an alternate method for finding interpolating polynomials that generally requires fewer computations and can be implemented easily on a computer. The ideas introduced in the preceding discussion are summarized in the following box.

PROCEDURE

> **Divided Difference Tables and Interpolating Polynomials**
>
> Given the defining table for a function $f(x)$ with $n+1$ points,
>
> | x | x_0 | x_1 | $\cdots$ | x_n |
> |---|---|---|---|---|
> | $f(x)$ | y_0 | y_1 | $\cdots$ | y_n |
>
> where $x_0 < x_1 < \cdots < x_n$, then the **divided difference table** is computed as follows:
>
> *Column 1*: x values from the defining table
> *Column 2*: y values from the defining table
> *Column 3*: First divided differences computed using columns 1 and 2
> *Column 4*: Second divided differences computed using columns 1 and 3
> ⋮
> *Column $n+2$*: nth divided differences computed using columns 1 and $n+1$
>
> The coefficients in Newton's form for the interpolating polynomial,
>
> $$p(x) = a_0 + a_1(x-x_0) + a_2(x-x_0)(x-x_1) + \cdots$$
> $$+ a_n(x-x_0)(x-x_1)\cdots(x-x_{n-1})$$
>
> are the first numbers in each column of the divided difference table, beginning with column 2.

INSIGHT

1. The points in the defining table must be arranged with increasing x values before computing the divided difference table. If the x values are out of order, then the divided difference table will not contain the coefficients of Newton's form for the interpolating polynomial.

2. Since each column in the divided difference table uses all the values in the preceding column, it is necessary to compute all the numbers in every column, even though we are interested only in the first number in each column.

3. Other methods can be used to find interpolating polynomials. Referring to Table 1, we could write $p(x)$ in standard polynomial notation

$$p(x) = b_3 x^3 + b_2 x^2 + b_1 x + b_0$$

and use the points in the table to write the following system of linear equations:

$$
\begin{aligned}
p(1) &= & b_3 + & b_2 + & b_1 + b_0 &= 65 \\
p(4) &= & 64b_3 + & 16b_2 + & 4b_1 + b_0 &= 80 \\
p(6) &= & 216b_3 + & 36b_2 + & 6b_1 + b_0 &= 40 \\
p(8) &= & 512b_3 + & 64b_2 + & 8b_1 + b_0 &= 16
\end{aligned}
$$

The computations required to solve this system of equations are far more complicated than those involved in finding the divided difference table.

EXAMPLE 3   Using a Divided Difference Table

TABLE 7

x	0	1	2	3	4
$f(x)$	35	25	19	−7	−29

(A) Find the divided difference table for the points in Table 7.

(B) Use the divided difference table to find the interpolating polynomial.

SOLUTION   (A) The divided difference table is as follows.

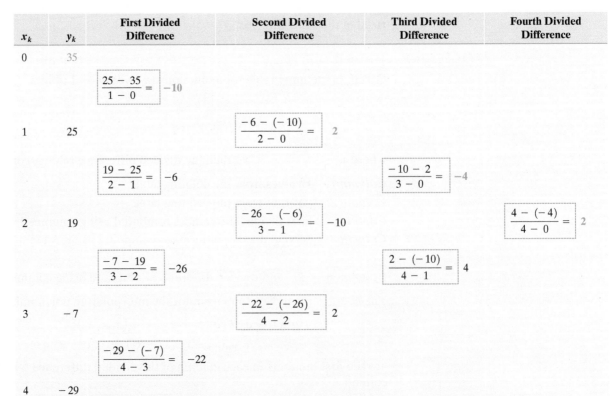

(B) Newton's form for the interpolating polynomial is

$$p(x) = a_0 + a_1x + a_2x(x - 1) + a_3x(x - 1)(x - 2)$$
$$+ a_4x(x - 1)(x - 2)(x - 3)$$

Substituting the values from the divided difference table for the coefficients in Newton's form, we have

$$p(x) = 35 - 10x + 2x(x - 1) - 4x(x - 1)(x - 2)$$
$$+ 2x(x - 1)(x - 2)(x - 3)$$
$$= 35 - 32x + 36x^2 - 16x^3 + 2x^4 \quad \text{Standard form}$$

Multiplication details for the standard form are omitted. Figure 4 verifies that the values of the interpolating polynomial agree with the values in Table 7. ▬▬

FIGURE 4

MATCHED PROBLEM 3

TABLE 8					
x	0	1	2	3	4
$f(x)$	5	1	−1	−7	1

(A) Find the divided difference table for the points in Table 8.

(B) Use the divided difference table to find the interpolating polynomial.

Explore & Discuss 3

A graphing utility can be used to calculate a divided difference table. Figure 5A shows a program on a TI-83 that calculates divided difference tables and Figure 5B shows the input and output generated when we use this program to solve Example 3.

(A) Program

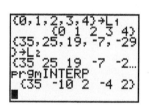

(B) Input and output

FIGURE 5

Enter this program into your TI-83 and use it to solve Matched Problem 3. If you have a different graphing utility, consult the manual for the correct format for each statement in the program.

APPLICATION

EXAMPLE 4 **Inventory** A store orders 8,000 units of a new product. The inventory I on hand t weeks after the order arrived is given in the following table:

Inventory					
t	0	2	4	6	8
$I(t)$	8,000	5,952	3,744	1,568	0

Use the interpolating polynomial to approximate the inventory after 5 weeks and the average inventory during the first 5 weeks after the order arrived.

SOLUTION The divided difference table is as follows:

t_k	y_k	First Divided Difference	Second Divided Difference	Third Divided Difference	Fourth Divided Difference
0	8,000				
		$-1,024$			
2	5,952		-20		
		$-1,104$		4	
4	3,744		4		1
		$-1,088$		12	
6	1,568		76		
		-784			
8	0				

The interpolating polynomial is

$$p(t) = 8,000 - 1,024t - 20t(t - 2) + 4t(t - 2)(t - 4)$$
$$+ t(t - 2)(t - 4)(t - 6)$$

or, after simplifying,

$$p(t) = t^4 - 8t^3 - 1,000t + 8,000$$

The inventory after 5 weeks is given approximately by

$$p(5) = 5^4 - 8(5^3) - 1,000(5) + 8,000 = 2,625 \text{ units}$$

The average inventory during the first 5 weeks is given approximately by

$$\frac{1}{5}\int_0^5 p(t)\, dt = \frac{1}{5}\int_0^5 (t^4 - 8t^3 - 1,000t + 8,000)\, dt$$

$$= \frac{1}{5}\left(\frac{1}{5}t^5 - 2t^4 - 500t^2 + 8,000t\right)\Big|_0^5$$

$$= \frac{1}{5}(625 - 1,250 - 12,500 + 40,000) - \frac{1}{5}(0)$$

$$= 5,375 \text{ units}$$

MATCHED PROBLEM 4 Refer to Example 4. Approximate the inventory after 7 weeks and the average inventory during the first 7 weeks.

Answers to Matched Problems **1.** $p(2) = 88$ or \$88,000; $p(5) = 61$ or \$61,000

2. $p(x) = 5 - 2(x + 1) + (x + 1)x + (x + 1)x(x - 1)$

3. (A)

x_k	y_k	First Divided Difference	Second Divided Difference	Third Divided Difference	Fourth Divided Difference
0	5				
		-4			
1	1		1		
		-2		-1	
2	-1		-2		1
		-6		3	
3	-7		7		
		8			
4	1				

(B) $p(x) = 5 - 4x + x(x - 1) - x(x - 1)(x - 2)$
$\qquad + x(x - 1)(x - 2)(x - 3)$
$\qquad = 5 - 13x + 15x^2 - 7x^3 + x^4$

4. 657 units; 4,294.2 units

Exercise D.1

A   *In Problems 1–4,*

(A) *Write Newton's form for the interpolating polynomial.*
(B) *Write the associated lower triangular system for the coefficients.*
(C) *Use forward substitution to find the interpolating polynomial.*

1.

x	1	3	4
$f(x)$	2	6	11

2.

x	-1	1	2
$f(x)$	1	3	7

3.

x	-1	0	2	4
$f(x)$	6	5	15	-39

4.

x	-1	0	2	3
$f(x)$	5	1	5	1

In Problems 5–10, find the divided difference table and then find the interpolating polynomial.

5.

x	1	2	3
$f(x)$	4	8	14

6.

x	1	2	3
$f(x)$	1	3	7

7.

x	-1	0	1	2
$f(x)$	-3	1	3	9

8.

x	-1	0	1	2
$f(x)$	5	6	3	2

9.

x	-2	1	2	4
$f(x)$	25	10	17	13

10.

x	-1	0	3	5
$f(x)$	17	10	25	5

B

11. Can a table with three points have a linear interpolating polynomial? A quadratic interpolating polynomial? A cubic interpolating polynomial? Explain.

12. Can a table with four points have a linear interpolating polynomial? A quadratic interpolating polynomial? A cubic interpolating polynomial? A quartic interpolating polynomial? Explain.

In Problems 13–20, use the interpolating polynomial to approximate the value of the function defined by the table at the indicated values of x.

13.

x	−4	0	4	8
f(x)	−64	32	0	224

(A) f(2) ≈ ?   (B) f(6) ≈ ?

14.

x	−5	0	5	10
f(x)	250	50	100	−350

(A) f(−3) ≈ ?   (B) f(8) ≈ ?

15.

x	−1	0	1	4
f(x)	0	0	0	15

(A) f(2) ≈ ?   (B) f(3) ≈ ?

16.

x	−2	0	2	6
f(x)	0	0	0	−96

(A) f(1) ≈ ?   (B) f(4) ≈ ?

17.

x	−4	−2	0	2	4
f(x)	24	2	0	−6	8

(A) f(−3) ≈ ?   (B) f(1) ≈ ?

18.

x	−6	−2	0	2	6
f(x)	19	3	10	3	19

(A) f(1) ≈ ?   (B) f(5) ≈ ?

19.

x	−3	−2	−1	1	2	3
f(x)	−24	−6	0	0	6	24

(A) f(−0.5) ≈ ?   (B) f(2.5) ≈ ?

20.

x	−3	−2	−1	0	1	2	3
f(x)	40	0	0	4	0	0	40

(A) f(−2.5) ≈ ?   (B) f(1.5) ≈ ?

In Problems 21–30, find the interpolating polynomial. Graph the interpolating polynomial and the points in the given table on the same set of axes.

21.

x	−2	0	2
f(x)	2	0	2

22.

x	−2	0	2
f(x)	2	0	−2

23.

x	0	1	2
f(x)	−4	−2	0

24.

x	0	1	2
f(x)	−4	−3	0

25.

x	−1	0	2	3
f(x)	0	2	0	−4

26.

x	−3	−1	0	1
f(x)	0	4	3	0

27.

x	−2	−1	0	1	2
f(x)	1	5	3	1	5

28.

x	−2	−1	0	1	2
f(x)	−8	0	2	4	12

29.

x	−2	−1	0	1	2
f(x)	−3	0	5	0	−3

30.

x	−1	0	1	2	3
f(x)	6	2	0	−6	2

In problems 31–34, use the quartic regression routine on a graphing utility to fit a fourth degree polynomial to the tables in the indicated problems. Compare this polynomial with the interpolating polynomial.

31. Problem 27   **32.** Problem 28

33. Problem 29   **34.** Problem 30

35. The following table was obtained from the function $f(x) = \sqrt{x}$:

x	1	4	9
f(x)	1	2	3

Find the interpolating polynomial for this table. Compare the values of the interpolating polynomial $p(x)$ and the original function $f(x) = \sqrt{x}$ by completing the table below. Use a calculator to evaluate $\sqrt{x}$ and round each value to one decimal place.

x	1	2	3	4	5	6	7	8	9
p(x)	1			2					3
$\sqrt{x}$	1			2					3

36. The following table was obtained from the function $f(x) = 6/\sqrt{x}$:

x	1	4	9
f(x)	6	3	2

Find the interpolating polynomial for this table. Compare the values of the interpolating polynomial $p(x)$ and the original function $f(x) = 6/\sqrt{x}$ by completing the table below. Use a calculator to evaluate $6/\sqrt{x}$ and round each value to one decimal place.

x	1	2	3	4	5	6	7	8	9
$p(x)$	6			3					2
$6/\sqrt{x}$	6			3					2

37. The following table was obtained from the function $f(x) = 10x/(1 + x^2)$:

x	-2	-1	0	1	2
$f(x)$	-4	-5	0	5	4

Find the interpolating polynomial $p(x)$ for this table. Graph $p(x)$ and $f(x)$ on the same set of axes.

38. The following table was obtained from the function $f(x) = (9 - x^2)/(1 + x^2)$:

x	-2	-1	0	1	2
$f(x)$	1	4	9	4	1

Find the interpolating polynomial $p(x)$ for this table. Graph $p(x)$ and $f(x)$ on the same set of axes.

39. Find the equation of the parabola whose graph passes through the points $(-x_1, y_1)$, $(0, y_2)$, and (x_1, y_1), where $x_1 > 0$ and $y_1 \neq y_2$.

40. Find the equation of the parabola whose graph passes through the points $(0, 0)$, (x_1, y_1), and $(2x_1, 0)$, where $x_1 > 0$ and $y_1 \neq 0$.

Applications

41. *Cash reserves.* Suppose the cash reserves C (in thousands of dollars) for a small business are given by the following table, where t is the number of months after the first of the year.

t	0	4	8	12
$C(t)$	2	32	38	20

(A) Find the interpolating polynomial for this table.

(B) Use the interpolating polynomial to approximate (to the nearest thousand dollars) the cash reserves after 6 months.

(C) Use the interpolating polynomial to approximate (to the nearest hundred dollars) the average cash reserves for the first quarter.

42. *Inventory.* A hardware store orders 147 lawn mowers. The inventory I of lawn mowers on hand t months after the order arrived is given in the table.

t	0	1	2	3
$I(t)$	147	66	19	0

(A) Find the interpolating polynomial for this table.

(B) Use the interpolating polynomial to approximate (to the nearest integer) the average number of lawn mowers on hand for this three-month period.

43. *Income distribution.* The income distribution for the United States in 1999 is represented by the Lorenz curve $y = f(x)$, where $f(x)$ is given in the table.

x	0	0.2	0.8	1
$f(x)$	0	0.04	0.52	1

(A) Find the interpolating polynomial for this table.

(B) Use the interpolating polynomial to approximate (to four decimal places) the index of income concentration.

44. *Income distribution.* Refer to Problem 43. After making a series of adjustments for things like taxes, fringe benefits, and returns on home equity, the income distribution for the United States in 1999 is represented by the Lorenz curve $y = g(x)$, where $g(x)$ is given in the table.

x	0	0.2	0.8	1
$g(x)$	0	0.06	0.54	1

(A) Find the interpolating polynomial for this table.

(B) Use the interpolating polynomial to approximate (to four decimal places) the index of income concentration.

45. *Maximum revenue.* The revenue R (in thousands of dollars) from the sale of x thousand table lamps is given in the table.

x	2	4	6
$R(x)$	24.4	36	34.8

(A) Find the interpolating polynomial for this table.

(B) Use the interpolating polynomial to approximate (to the nearest thousand dollars) the revenue if 5,000 table lamps are produced.

(C) Use the interpolating polynomial to approximate (to the nearest integer) the production level that will maximize the revenue.

46. *Minimum average cost.* The cost C (in thousands of dollars) of producing x thousand microwave ovens is given in the table.

x	1	3	5
$C(x)$	215	535	1,055

(A) Find the interpolating polynomial for this table.

(B) Use the interpolating polynomial to approximate (to the nearest thousand dollars) the cost of producing 4,000 ovens.

(C) Use the interpolating polynomial to approximate (to the nearest integer) the production level that will minimize the average cost.

47. *Temperature.* The temperature C (in degrees celsius) in an artificial habitat after t hours is given in the table.

t	0	1	2	3	4
$C(t)$	14	13	16	17	10

(A) Find the interpolating polynomial for this table.

(B) Use the interpolating polynomial to approximate (to the nearest tenth of a degree) the average temperature over this 4-hour period.

48. *Drug concentration.* The concentration C (in milligrams per cubic centimeter) of a particular drug in a patient's bloodstream t hours after the drug is taken is given in the table.

t	0	1	2	3	4
$C(t)$	0	0.032	0.036	0.024	0.008

(A) Find the interpolating polynomial for this table.

(B) Use the interpolating polynomial to approximate (to two decimal places) the number of hours it will take for the drug concentration to reach its maximum level.

49. *Bacteria control.* A lake that is used for recreational swimming is treated periodically to control harmful bacteria growth. The concentration C (in bacteria per cubic centimeter) t days after a treatment is given in the table.

t	0	2	4	6
$C(t)$	450	190	90	150

(A) Find the interpolating polynomial for this table.

(B) Use the interpolating polynomial to approximate (to two decimal places) the number of days it will take for the bacteria concentration to reach its minimum level.

50. *Medicine-respiration.* Physiologists use a machine called a pneumotachograph to produce a graph of the rate of

flow R on air into the lungs (inspiration) and out (expiration). The figure gives the graph of the inspiration phase of the breathing cycle of an individual at rest.

(A) Use the values given by the graph at $t = 0, 1, 2,$ and 3 to find the interpolating polynomial for R.

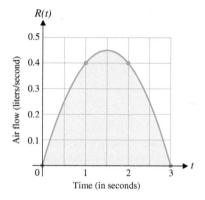

(B) Use the interpolating polynomial to approximate (to one decimal place) the total volume of air inhaled.

51. *Voter registration.* The number N of registered voters in a precinct over a 30-year period is given in the table.

t	0	10	20	30
$N(t)$	10,000	13,500	20,000	23,500

(A) Find the interpolating polynomial for this table.

(B) Use the interpolating polynomial to approximate (to the nearest thousand) the average number of voters over the first 20 years of this period.

52. *Voter registration.* The number N of registered voters in a precinct over a 10-year period is given in the table.

t	0	4	6	10
$N(t)$	15,000	18,800	22,200	26,000

(A) Find the interpolating polynomial for this table.

(B) Use the interpolating polynomial to approximate (to the nearest integer) the year t in which the rate of increase in the number of voters is most rapid.

ANSWERS

CHAPTER 1

11. (C)   **13.** (A)   **15.**

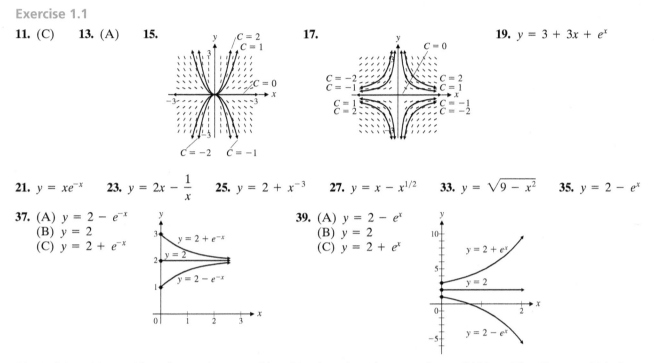

17.

19. $y = 3 + 3x + e^x$

21. $y = xe^{-x}$ **23.** $y = 2x - \dfrac{1}{x}$ **25.** $y = 2 + x^{-3}$ **27.** $y = x - x^{1/2}$ **33.** $y = \sqrt{9 - x^2}$ **35.** $y = 2 - e^x$

37. (A) $y = 2 - e^{-x}$
   (B) $y = 2$
   (C) $y = 2 + e^{-x}$

39. (A) $y = 2 - e^x$
   (B) $y = 2$
   (C) $y = 2 + e^x$

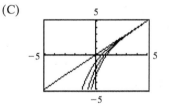

41. $dN/dt = 650$; $t =$ Time (in years), $N = N(t) =$ Number of employees at time t, $dN/dt = N' =$ Rate at which the number of employees is changing

43. $dT/dt = -k(T - 72)$; $t =$ Time, $T = T(t) =$ Temperature of pizza at time t, $k =$ Positive constant of proportionality, $dT/dt = T' =$ Rate at which the temperature of the pizza is changing (dT/dt is negative because the temperature of the pizza is decreasing)

45. (A) $y = \dfrac{10}{1 + 9e^{-x}}$

   (B) $y = 10$

   (C) $y = \dfrac{10}{1 - 0.5e^{-x}}$

47. (A) $y = Cx^3 + 2$ for any C
   (B) No particular solution exists.
   (C) $y = 2 - x^3$

49. (A)

   (B) Each graph decreases to a local minimum and then increases, approaching the line $y = x$ as x approaches ∞.

   (C)

   (D) Each graph is increasing for all x and approaches the line $y = x$ as x approaches ∞.

51. (A) $\bar{p} = 5$
(B) $p(t) = 5 - 4e^{-0.1t}$
$p(t) = 5 + 5e^{-0.1t}$

53. (B) $A(t) = 2{,}500e^{0.08t} - 2{,}500$
$A(t) = 3{,}500e^{0.08t} - 2{,}500$

55. (A) $\bar{N} = 200$
(B) $N(t) = 200 - 150e^{-0.5t}$
$N(t) = 200 + 100e^{-0.5t}$

57. (A) $\bar{N} = C$
(B) $N(t) = 100e^{2-2e^{-0.5t}}$
$N(t) = 200e^{2-2e^{-0.5t}}$

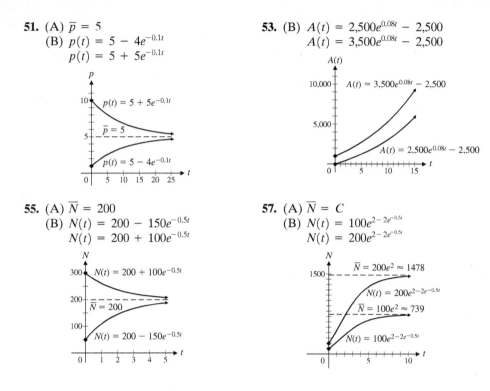

Exercise 1.2

1. $dy/dt = 100{,}000$ **3.** $dy/dt = k(10{,}000 - y)$

5. The annual sales now are $2 million, and sales are increasing at a rate proportional to the annual sales.

7. In a community of 5,000 people, a single person began the spread of a rumor that is spreading at a rate proportional to the product of the number of people who have heard the rumor and the number who have not.

9. $\dfrac{1}{y^2} y' = \dfrac{1}{x}$ **11.** $\dfrac{1}{y} y' = \dfrac{3-x}{x}$

13. General solution: $y = x^3 + C$; particular solution: $y = x^3 - 1$

15. General solution: $y = 2\ln x + C$; particular solution: $y = 2\ln x + 2$

17. General solution: $y = Ce^x$; particular solution: $y = 10e^x$

19. General solution: $y = 25 - Ce^{-x}$; particular solution: $y = 25 - 20e^{-x}$

21. General solution: $y = Cx$; particular solution: $y = 5x$

23. General solution: $y = (3x + C)^{1/3}$; particular solution: $y = (3x + 24)^{1/3}$

25. General solution: $y = Ce^{e^x}$; particular solution: $y = 3e^{e^x}$

27. General solution: $y = \ln(e^x + C)$; particular solution: $y = \ln(e^x + 1)$

29. General solution: $y = Ce^{x^2/2} - 1$; particular solution: $y = 3e^{x^2/2} - 1$

31. General solution: $y = 2 - 1/(e^x + C)$; particular solution: $y = 2 - e^{-x}$

33. $y + \frac{1}{3}y^3 = x + \frac{1}{3}x^3 + C$ **35.** $\frac{1}{2}\ln|1 + y^2| = \ln|x| + (x^2/2) + C$ or $\ln(1 + y^2) = \ln(x^2) + x^2 + C$

37. $\ln(1 + e^y) = \frac{1}{2}x^2 + C$ **39.** $y = \sqrt{1 + (\ln x)^2}$ **41.** $y = \frac{1}{4}[x + \ln(x^2) + 3]^2$ **43.** $y = \sqrt{\ln(x^2 + e)}$

45. The differential equation cannot be written in the form $f(y)y' = g(x)$.

47. The integrand e^{x^2} does not have an elementary antiderivative.

49. (A) $M = 3/(1 - e^{-k})$; $M = 4/(1 - e^{-1.5k})$ (B) 7.3   **51.** $5{,}000 \, e^{0.275} \approx \$6{,}582.65$

53. (A) $\dfrac{7 \ln 0.5}{\ln 0.8} \approx 22$ days (B) $100{,}000(1 - e^{0.5 \ln 0.5}) \approx 29{,}300$ people

55. $\dfrac{30 \ln 0.1}{\ln 0.5} \approx 100$ days

57. In 2010, total personal income is about $15,452 billion and this amount is increasing at the rate of $940.6 billion per year.

59. After 15 years, the total sales are about $2.8 million and this amount is increasing at the rate of $0.12 million per year. It will take 29 years for the sales to grow to $4 million.

61. $k = 0.2$; $M = \$11$ million   **63.** $\dfrac{2 \ln(5/12)}{\ln(5/6)} \approx 9.6$ min   **65.** $25 + 300e^{4 \ln(2/3)} \approx 84.26°F$

67. (A) $100e^{5 \ln 1.4} \approx 538$ bacteria (B) $\dfrac{\ln 10}{\ln 1.4} \approx 6.8$ hr

69. (A) $\dfrac{50{,}000}{1 + 499e^{2\ln(99/499)}} \approx 2{,}422$ people   (B) $\dfrac{10\ln(1/499)}{\ln(99/499)} \approx 38.4$ days

71. 10 P.M.   **73.** $I = As^k$ **75.** (A) $\dfrac{1{,}000}{1 + 199e^{7\ln(99/199)}} \approx 400$ people   (B) $\dfrac{\ln(3/3{,}383)}{\ln(99/199)} \approx 10$ days

Exercise 1.3

1. Yes; $f(x) = -k, g(x) = 0$

3. No; the equation has a y^2 term, so it is not first-order linear.

5. $\int (x^3 y' + 3x^2 y)\, dx = x^3 y$ **7.** $\int (e^{-3x} y' - 3e^{-3x} y)\, dx = e^{-3x} y$ **9.** $\int (x^4 y' + 4x^3 y)\, dx = x^4 y$

11. $\int (e^{-0.5x} y' - 0.5e^{-0.5x} y)\, dx = e^{-0.5x} y$ **13.** $I(x) = e^{2x}; y = 2 + Ce^{-2x}; y = 2 - e^{-2x}$

15. $I(x) = e^x; y = -e^{-2x} + Ce^{-x}; y = -e^{-2x} + 4e^{-x}$ **17.** $I(x) = e^{-x}; y = 2xe^x + Ce^x; y = 2xe^x - 4e^x$

19. $I(x) = e^x; y = 3x^3 e^{-x} + Ce^{-x}; y = 3x^3 e^{-x} + 2e^{-x}$ **21.** $I(x) = x; y = x + (C/x); y = x$

23. $I(x) = x^2; y = 2x^3 + (C/x^2); y = 2x^3 - (32/x^2)$ **25.** $I(x) = e^{x^2/2}; y = 5 + Ce^{-x^2/2}$

27. $I(x) = e^{-2x}; y = -2x - 1 + Ce^{2x}$ **29.** $I(x) = x; y = e^x - (e^x/x) + (C/x)$

31. $I(x) = x; y = \tfrac{1}{2}x \ln x - \tfrac{1}{4}x + (C/x)$ **33.** $I(x) = x^{3/2}; y = 4x + Cx^{-3/2}$

35. (B) The solution is wrong. The term $1/x$ in front of the integral and the term x inside the integral cannot be canceled.

(C) $y = \tfrac{1}{4}x^3 + \tfrac{2}{3}x^2 + \tfrac{1}{2}x + (C/x)$

37. (B) The solution is wrong. A constant of integration is omitted.

(C) $y = \tfrac{1}{2}e^{-x} + Ce^{-3x}$

39. $y = 1 + (C/x)$ **41.** $y = C(1 + x^2) - 1$ **43.** $y = Ce^{x^2} - 1$ **45.** $y = Ce^{kt}$ **47.** $y = (b/a) + Ce^{-ax}$

49. $A(t) = 62{,}500 - 42{,}500e^{0.048t}$; 8.035 years, \$24,105   **51.** \$15,124.60

53. $A(t) = 35{,}000e^{0.07t} - 30{,}000$; \$19,667.36   **55.** 5.23%   **57.** $p(t) = 20 + 10e^{-3t}; \bar{p} = 20$

59. 622 lb; $\dfrac{622}{250} \approx 2.5$ lb/gal

61. $600 - 200e^{-0.5} \approx 479$ lb; $3 - e^{-0.5} \approx 2.4$ lb/gal   **63.** 6.2 hr

65. $120 + 40e^{-0.15} \approx 154$ lb; $-(\ln\tfrac{3}{4})/0.005 \approx 58$ days; weight will approach 120 lb if the diet is maintained for a long period of time

67. $17.5\left(\dfrac{125 - 130e^{-0.15}}{1 - e^{-0.15}}\right) \approx 1{,}647$ cal

69. Student A: $0.9 - 0.8e^{-4.8} \approx 0.8934$ or 89.34%; student B: $0.7 - 0.3e^{-4.8} \approx 0.6975$ or 69.75%

Chapter 1 Review Exercise

3. (B) *(1-1)*   **4.** (A) *(1-1)*

5.

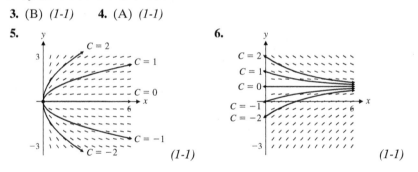

(1-1)   *(1-1)*

7. $dy/dt = -k(y - 5), k > 0$ *(1-2)*   **8.** $dy/dt = ky, k > 0$ *(1-2)*

9. A single person began the spread of a disease that is spreading at a rate proportional to the product of the number of people who have contracted the disease and the number who have not. *(1-2)*

10. The amount of radioactive material now is 100 g, and the amount is decreasing at a rate proportional to the amount present. *(1-2)*

11. First-order linear form: $y' + (3x^2 - e^x)y = (1 - x)e^x - 9$ *(1-2, 1-3)*

12. Neither form *(1-2, 1-3)*

13. Separation of variables form: $(y + 2)^{-1}y' = x - 3$; first-order linear form: $y' + (3 - x)y = 2x - 6$ *(1-2, 1-3)*

14. Separation of variables form: $y^2 e^y y' = 4xe^x$ *(1-2, 1-3)*

15. $y = C/x^4$ *(1-2)*   **16.** $y = \tfrac{1}{6}x^2 + (C/x^4)$ *(1-3)*   **17.** $y = -1/(x^3 + C)$ *(1-2)*   **18.** $y = e^x + Ce^{2x}$ *(1-3)*

19. $y = \tfrac{1}{2}x^7 + Cx^5$ *(1-3)*   **20.** $y = C(2 + x) - 3$ *(1-2)*   **21.** $y = 10 - 10e^{-x}$ *(1-2, 1-3)*

22. $y = x - 1 + e^{-x}$ *(1-3)*   **23.** $y = e^2 e^{-2e^{-x}}$ *(1-2)*   **24.** $y = (x^2 + 4)/(x + 4)$ *(1-3)*

25. $y = \sqrt{x^2 + 16} - 4$ *(1-2)*   **26.** $y = \tfrac{1}{3}x \ln x - \tfrac{1}{9}x + \tfrac{19}{9}(1/x^2)$ *(1-3)*   **27.** $y = \sqrt{1 + 2x^2}$ *(1-2)*

28. $y = (2x + 1)e^{-x}$ *(1-3)*   **29.** $y = -2 + Cx^4$ *(1-2, 1-3)*

32. $y = 2 + Cx^5$

   (A) $y = 2 + Cx^5$ for any constant C
   (B) No particular solution exists.
   (C) $y = 2 - x^5$ *(1-3)*

33. $y = \sqrt{x^2 + 16}$ *(1-2)*

34. (A)

   (B) The graphs are increasing and cross the x axis only at $x = 0$.

   (C)

   (D) Each graph has a local maximum, a local minimum, and crosses the x axis three times. *(1-1)*

35. (A) $M = 7/(1 - e^{-5k})$, $M = 4/(1 - e^{-2k})$ (B) 9.2 *(1-2)*

36. $500e^{-0.25 \ln 20} \approx \$236.44$ *(1-2)*   **37.** (A) 5 yr   (B) \$74,000 *(1-2)*

38. (A) $p = 50 + Ae^{-t}$ (B) $\bar{p} = 50$

   (C)

   (1-1, 1-2)

39. $A(t) = 100,000 - 40,000e^{0.05t}$; $(\ln 2.5)/0.05 \approx 18.326$ yr; \$91,630 *(1-3)*   **40.** 4.82% *(1-3)*

41. $y = 100 + te^{-t} - 100e^{-t}$ *(1-3)*   **42.** (A) 211.1 lb   (B) 10.3 hr *(1-3)*

43. (A) 337 birds   (B) 357 birds *(1-2)*

44. (A) $200 - 199e^{(5/2)\ln(190/199)} \approx 23$ people   (B) $\dfrac{2\ln(100/199)}{\ln(190/199)} \approx 30$ days *(1-2)*

CHAPTER 2

Exercise 2.1

1. $-6/x^4$ **3.** $-e^{-x}$ **5.** $-486/(1 + 3x)^4$ **7.** $\dfrac{-15}{16}(1 + x)^{-7/2}$

9. $1 - x + \frac{1}{2}x^2 - \frac{1}{6}x^3 + \frac{1}{24}x^4$ **11.** $1 + 3x + 3x^2 + x^3$ **13.** $2x - 2x^2 + \frac{8}{3}x^3$ **15.** $1 + \frac{1}{3}x - \frac{1}{9}x^2 + \frac{5}{81}x^3$

17. (A) $p_3(x) = -1$; $-0.562 < x < 0.562$ (B) $p_4(x) = x^4 - 1$; for all x

19. $1 + (x - 1) + \frac{1}{2}(x - 1)^2 + \frac{1}{6}(x - 1)^3 + \frac{1}{24}(x - 1)^4$

21. $1 + 3(x - 1) + 3(x - 1)^2 + (x - 1)^3$ **23.** $3(x - \frac{1}{3}) - \frac{9}{2}(x - \frac{1}{3})^2 + 9(x - \frac{1}{3})^3$

25. $1 - 2x + 2x^2 - \frac{4}{3}x^3$; 0.604 166 67   **27.** $4 + \frac{1}{8}x - \frac{1}{512}x^2$; 4.123 046 9

29. $1 + \frac{1}{2}(x - 1) - \frac{1}{8}(x - 1)^2 + \frac{1}{16}(x - 1)^3 - \frac{5}{128}(x - 1)^4$; 1.095 437 5   **31.** $n!\,(4 - x)^{-(n+1)}$

33. $3^n e^{3x}$ **35.** $-(n - 1)!(6 - x)^{-n}$

37. $\dfrac{1}{4} + \dfrac{1}{4^2}x + \dfrac{1}{4^3}x^2 + \dfrac{1}{4^4}x^3 + \cdots + \dfrac{1}{4^{n+1}}x^n$ **39.** $1 + 3x + \dfrac{3^2}{2!}x^2 + \dfrac{3^3}{3!}x^3 + \cdots + \dfrac{3^n}{n!}x^n$

41. $-\dfrac{1}{6}x - \dfrac{1}{6^2 2}x^2 - \dfrac{1}{6^3 3}x^3 - \cdots - \dfrac{1}{6^n n}x^n$ **43.** $-1 - (x + 1) - (x + 1)^2 - (x + 1)^3 - \cdots - (x + 1)^n$

45. $(x - 1) - \dfrac{1}{2}(x - 1)^2 + \dfrac{1}{3}(x - 1)^3 - \dfrac{1}{4}(x - 1)^4 + \cdots + \dfrac{(-1)^{n+1}}{n}(x - 1)^n$

47. $\dfrac{1}{e^2} - \dfrac{1}{e^2}(x - 2) + \dfrac{1}{2!e^2}(x - 2)^2 - \dfrac{1}{3!e^2}(x - 2)^3 + \cdots + \dfrac{(-1)^n}{n!e^2}(x - 2)^n$

49. $3 \ln 3 + (1 + \ln 3)(x - 3) + \dfrac{1}{3 \cdot 2}(x - 3)^2 - \dfrac{1}{3^2 \, 2 \cdot 3}(x - 3)^3$

$+ \dfrac{1}{3^3 \, 3 \cdot 4}(x - 3)^4 - \dfrac{1}{3^4 \, 4 \cdot 5}(x - 3)^5 + \cdots + \dfrac{(-1)^n}{3^{n-1}(n-1) \cdot n}(x - 3)^n$

51. (A) $p_3(x) = 5x^2 + 1$ (B) 2   **53.** $n = 0, 3, 6$

55. $p_1(x) = x, p_2(x) = x - \frac{1}{2}x^2, p_3(x) = x - \frac{1}{2}x^2 + \frac{1}{3}x^3$

x	$p_1(x)$	$p_2(x)$	$p_3(x)$	$f(x)$
-0.2	-0.2	-0.22	$-0.222\,667$	$-0.223\,144$
-0.1	-0.1	-0.105	$-0.105\,333$	$-0.105\,361$
0	0	0	0	0
0.1	0.1	0.095	$0.095\,333$	$0.095\,31$
0.2	0.2	0.18	$0.182\,667$	$0.182\,322$

x	$|p_1(x) - f(x)|$	$|p_2(x) - f(x)|$	$|p_3(x) - f(x)|$
-0.2	$0.023\,144$	$0.003\,144$	$0.000\,477$
-0.1	$0.005\,361$	$0.000\,361$	$0.000\,028$
0	0	0	0
0.1	$0.004\,69$	$0.000\,31$	$0.000\,023$
0.2	$0.017\,678$	$0.002\,322$	$0.000\,345$

57.

59. $-1.323 < x < 1.168$

61. $e^a \left[1 + (x - a) + \dfrac{1}{2!}(x - a)^2 + \dfrac{1}{3!}(x - a)^3 + \cdots + \dfrac{1}{n!}(x - a)^n \right] = e^a \displaystyle\sum_{k=0}^{n} \dfrac{1}{k!}(x - a)^k$

63. $\dfrac{1}{a} - \dfrac{1}{a^2}(x - a) + \dfrac{1}{a^3}(x - a)^2 - \dfrac{1}{a^4}(x - a)^3 + \cdots + \dfrac{(-1)^n}{a^{n+1}}(x - a)^n = \displaystyle\sum_{k=0}^{n} \dfrac{(-1)^k}{a^{k+1}}(x - a)^k$

65. $n \geq$ degree of f **67.** Yes   **69.** $p_2(x) = 10 - 0.0005x^2$; \$9.85

71. $p_2(x) = 8 - \frac{3}{40}(x - 60) - \frac{1}{1024}(x - 60)^2$; \$7.12   **73.** $p_2(t) = 10 - 0.8t^2$; approx. \$18 million

75. $p_2(t) = -3 + \frac{3}{25}t^2$; 6.32 cm^2 **77.** $p_2(x) = 120 + 30(x - 5) + \frac{3}{4}(x - 5)^2$; 126.25 ppm

79. $p_2(t) = 6 - 0.06t^2$; 27.5 wpm

81.

83.   **85.**   **87.**

Exercise 2.2

1. $|x| < 1$ or $-1 < x < 1$ **3.** $|x| < \frac{1}{7}$ or $-\frac{1}{7} < x < \frac{1}{7}$ **5.** $|x| < 6$ or $-6 < x < 6$ **7.** $|x| < 1$ or $-1 < x < 1$

9. $|x| < 1$ or $-1 < x < 1$ **11.** $-\infty < x < \infty$ **13.** (A) 6 (B) Yes   **15.** $|x + 3| < 1$ or $-4 < x < -2$

17. $-\infty < x < \infty$ **19.** $|x - 2| < 4$ or $-2 < x < 6$ **21.** $|x - 8| < 2$ or $6 < x < 10$

23. (A)

(B) $-\infty < x < \infty$

25. $p_n(x) = 1 + 4x + \dfrac{4^2}{2!}x^2 + \cdots + \dfrac{4^n}{n!}x^n$; $1 + 4x + \dfrac{4^2}{2!}x^2 + \cdots + \dfrac{4^n}{n!}x^n + \cdots$; $-\infty < x < \infty$

27. $p_n(x) = 2x - \dfrac{2^2}{2}x^2 + \dfrac{2^3}{3}x^3 - \cdots + \dfrac{(-1)^{n-1}2^n}{n}x^n$; $2x - \dfrac{2^2}{2}x^2 + \dfrac{2^3}{3}x^3 - \cdots + \dfrac{(-1)^{n-1}2^n}{n}x^n + \cdots$; $|x| < \frac{1}{2}$ or $-\frac{1}{2} < x < \frac{1}{2}$

29. $p_n(x) = 1 + \dfrac{1}{2}x + \dfrac{1}{2^2}x^2 + \cdots + \dfrac{1}{2^n}x^n$; $1 + \dfrac{1}{2}x + \dfrac{1}{2^2}x^2 + \cdots + \dfrac{1}{2^n}x^n + \cdots$; $|x| < 2$ or $-2 < x < 2$

31. $p_n(x) = -(x-1) - \dfrac{1}{2}(x-1)^2 - \dfrac{1}{3}(x-1)^3 - \cdots - \dfrac{1}{n}(x-1)^n;$

$\qquad -(x-1) - \dfrac{1}{2}(x-1)^2 - \dfrac{1}{3}(x-1)^3 - \cdots - \dfrac{1}{n}(x-1)^n - \cdots; |x-1| < 1 \text{ or } 0 < x < 2$

33. $p_n(x) = -1 + (x-2) - (x-2)^2 + \cdots + (-1)^{n-1}(x-2)^n;$

$\qquad -1 + (x-2) - (x-2)^2 + \cdots + (-1)^{n-1}(x-2)^n + \cdots; |x-2| < 1 \text{ or } 1 < x < 3$

35. (A) $|x| < 4$ or $-4 < x < 4$

(B) The coefficients of the odd powers of x are 0.

(C) $|x| < 2$ or $-2 < x < 2$

37. (A) $\displaystyle\lim_{n \to \infty} \left| \dfrac{a_{n+1}}{a_n} \right|$ does not exist   (B) $|x| < 1$ or $-1 < x < 1$

Exercise 2.3

1. $2 + 2x^2 + 2x^4 + \cdots + 2x^{2n} + \cdots; \; -1 < x < 1$

3. $2 + \dfrac{3}{2}x^2 + \dfrac{5}{6}x^3 + \cdots + \left[1 + \dfrac{(-1)^n}{n!} \right] x^n + \cdots; \; -1 < x < 1$

5. $x^3 - x^4 + x^5 - \cdots + (-1)^n x^{n+3} + \cdots; \; -1 < x < 1$

7. $-x^3 - \dfrac{1}{2}x^4 - \dfrac{1}{3}x^5 - \cdots - \dfrac{1}{n}x^{n+2} - \cdots; \; -1 < x < 1$

9. $1 + x^2 + \dfrac{1}{2}x^4 + \cdots + \dfrac{1}{n!}x^{2n} + \cdots; \; -\infty < x < \infty$

11. $3x - \dfrac{9}{2}x^2 + 9x^3 - \cdots + (-1)^{n-1}\dfrac{3^n}{n}x^n + \cdots; -\dfrac{1}{3} < x < \dfrac{1}{3}$

13. $\dfrac{1}{2} + \dfrac{1}{2^2}x + \dfrac{1}{2^3}x^2 + \cdots + \dfrac{1}{2^{n+1}}x^n + \cdots, -2 < x < 2$

15. $1 + 8x^3 + 8^2 x^6 + \cdots + 8^n x^{3n} + \cdots, -\frac{1}{2} < x < \frac{1}{2}$

17. $10^x = 1 + (\ln 10)x + \dfrac{(\ln 10)^2}{2!}x^2 + \dfrac{(\ln 10)^3}{3!}x^3 + \cdots + \dfrac{(\ln 10)^n}{n!}x^n + \cdots; -\infty < x < \infty$

19. $-\dfrac{1}{\ln 2}x - \dfrac{1}{2 \ln 2}x^2 - \dfrac{1}{3 \ln 2}x^3 - \cdots - \dfrac{1}{n \ln 2}x^n - \cdots; -1 < x < 1$

21. $\dfrac{1}{4} - \dfrac{1}{4^2}x^2 + \dfrac{1}{4^3}x^4 - \cdots + \dfrac{(-1)^n}{4^{n+1}}x^{2n} + \cdots, -2 < x < 2$

23. (A) $x \geq 0$ (B) No; some powers of x are not non-negative integers.

25. (A) $1 + x^2 + x^4 + x^6 + \cdots + x^{2n} + \cdots, -1 < x < 1$

(B) $2x + 4x^3 + 6x^5 + \cdots + 2nx^{2n-1} + \cdots, -1 < x < 1$

27. $x - \dfrac{1}{3}x^3 + \dfrac{1}{5}x^5 - \cdots + \dfrac{(-1)^n}{2n+1}x^{2n+1} + \cdots, -1 < x < 1$

29. $5 - \dfrac{1}{4}x^4 - \dfrac{1}{10}x^5 - \cdots - \dfrac{1}{n(n-3)}x^n - \cdots; -1 < x < 1$

31. (A)

(B) Differentiating the Taylor series for sinh x twice yields the series for sinh x.

33. $1 + (x-3) + (x-3)^2 + \cdots + (x-3)^n + \cdots, 2 < x < 4$

35. $(x-1) - \dfrac{1}{2}(x-1)^2 + \dfrac{1}{3}(x-1)^3 - \cdots + \dfrac{(-1)^{n-1}}{n}(x-1)^n + \cdots, 0 < x < 2$

37. $1 + 3(x-1) + 3^2(x-1)^2 + \cdots + 3^n(x-1)^n + \cdots, \frac{2}{3} < x < \frac{4}{3}$

39. $1 + 3x + 6x^2 + \cdots + \dfrac{n(n-1)}{2}x^{n-2} + \cdots, -1 < x < 1$

41. (A) $1 + x^2 + x^4 + \cdots + x^{2n} + \cdots, -1 < x < 1$

(B) f' and $\dfrac{1}{1-x^2}$ have identical Taylor series at 0.

43. $1 + 2x + 2x^2 + \cdots + 2x^n + \cdots, -1 < x < 1$

45. $x + \dfrac{1}{3}x^3 + \dfrac{1}{5}x^5 + \cdots + \dfrac{1}{2n+1}x^{2n+1} + \cdots, -1 < x < 1$

47. $1 + \dfrac{1}{2!}x^2 + \dfrac{1}{4!}x^4 + \cdots + \dfrac{1}{(2n)!}x^{2n} + \cdots, -\infty < x < \infty$

49. $-2 + 3x + \dfrac{1}{6}x^3 - \dfrac{1}{24}x^4 + \cdots + \dfrac{(-1)^{n+1}}{n(n-1)(n-2)}x^n + \cdots; -1 < x < 1$

51. $\ln a + \dfrac{1}{a}(x - a) - \dfrac{1}{2a^2}(x - a)^2 + \cdots + \dfrac{(-1)^{n-1}}{na^n}(x - a)^n + \cdots, 0 < x < 2a$

53. $\dfrac{1}{1 - ab} + \dfrac{b}{(1 - ab)^2}(x - a) + \dfrac{b^2}{(1 - ab)^3}(x - a)^2 + \cdots + \dfrac{b^n}{(1 - ab)^{n+1}}(x - a)^n + \cdots; |x - a| < \left|\dfrac{1 - ab}{b}\right|$

Exercise 2.4

1. $0.4; |R_1(0.6)| \le 0.18$ **3.** $0.544; |R_3(0.6)| \le 0.0054$ **5.** $0.255; |R_2(0.3)| < 0.009$

7. $0.261\,975; |R_4(0.3)| \le 0.000\,486$ **9.** $0.818\,667; |R_3(0.2)| \le 0.000\,067$

11. $0.970\,446; |R_3(0.03)| \le 0.000\,000\,033$ **13.** $0.492; |R_3(0.6)| \le 0.0324$

15. $0.058\,272; |R_3(0.06)| \le 0.000\,003\,24$ **17.** $0.904\,833; n = 3$ **19.** $0.990\,050; n = 2$ **21.** $0.182\,320; n = 6$

23. $0.019\,800; n = 2$ **25.** 0.1973 **27.** 0.0656 **29.** 0.0193 **31.** $n = 9$ **33.** $|x| < 1.817$

35. $-0.427 < x < 0.405$ **37.** $0.745; |R_2(0.3)| \le 0.0135$ **39.** $1.051\,25; |R_2(0.05)| \le 0.000\,063$

41. $4.123\,047; |R_2(1)| \le 0.000\,061$

43. The second computation is correct. The use of the Taylor series for f at 0 is invalid because the lower limit of integration lies outside the interval of convergence of the series.

45. (A) $p_2(x) = 1 + x + \dfrac{1}{2!}x^2$

```
QuadReg
y=ax²+bx+c
a=.5004168056
b=1.0016675
c=1
R²=1
```

(B) Max $|f(x) - p_2(x)| = 0.000\,171$

Max $|f(x) - q_2(x)| = 0.000\,065$

(C) $q_2(x)$

47. $\displaystyle\int_0^1 \dfrac{10x^6}{4 + x^2}\,dx \approx 0.302$; index of income concentration ≈ 0.698

49. $S(4) \approx 2.031$ within ± 0.004, or \$2,031,000 within $\pm$\$4,000   **51.** 2 yr; \$1,270   **53.** $30.539°C$

55. $A(2) \approx 6.32$ cm^2 within ± 0.031 **57.** $N(5) \approx 27.5$ wpm within ± 0.1875

Chapter 2 Review Exercise

1. $-6/(x + 5)^4$ *(2-1)*   **2.** $1 + \frac{1}{3}x - \frac{1}{9}x^2 + \frac{5}{81}x^3; 1.003\,322$ *(2-1)*

3. $2 + \frac{1}{4}(x - 3) - \frac{1}{64}(x - 3)^2 + \frac{1}{512}(x - 3)^3; 1.974\,842$ *(2-1)*

4. $3 + \frac{1}{6}x^2; 3.001\,667$ *(2-1)*   **5.** $-\frac{1}{4} < x < \frac{1}{4}$ *(2-2)*   **6.** $1 < x < 11$ *(2-2)*

7. $-1 < x < 1$ *(2-2)*   **8.** $-\infty < x < \infty$ *(2-2)*   **9.** $(-1)^n 9^n e^{-9x}$ *(2-1)*

10. $\dfrac{1}{7} + \dfrac{1}{7^2}x + \dfrac{1}{7^3}x^2 + \cdots + \dfrac{1}{7^{n+1}}x^n + \cdots, -7 < x < 7$ *(2-2)*

11. $\ln 2 + \dfrac{1}{2}(x - 2) - \dfrac{1}{8}(x - 2)^2 + \cdots + \dfrac{(-1)^{n-1}}{n2^n}(x - 2)^n + \cdots, 0 < x < 4$ *(2-2)*

12. $\dfrac{1}{10} - \dfrac{1}{10^2}x + \dfrac{1}{10^3}x^2 - \cdots + \dfrac{(-1)^n}{10^{n+1}}x^n + \cdots, -10 < x < 10$ *(2-3)*

13. $\dfrac{1}{4}x^2 + \dfrac{1}{4^2}x^4 + \dfrac{1}{4^3}x^6 + \cdots + \dfrac{1}{4^{n+1}}x^{2n+2} + \cdots, -2 < x < 2$ *(2-3)*

14. $x^2 + 3x^3 + \dfrac{3^2}{2!}x^4 + \cdots + \dfrac{3^n}{n!}x^{n+2} + \cdots, -\infty < x < \infty$ *(2-3)*

15. $x + \dfrac{1}{e}x^2 - \dfrac{1}{2e^2}x^3 + \cdots + \dfrac{(-1)^{n-1}}{ne^n}x^{n+1} + \cdots, -e < x < e$ *(2-3)*

16. $\dfrac{1}{2} + \dfrac{1}{2^2}(x - 2) + \dfrac{1}{2^3}(x - 2)^2 + \cdots + \dfrac{1}{2^{n+1}}(x - 2)^n + \cdots, 0 < x < 4$ *(2-3)*

17. (A) The coefficients of the odd powers of x are 0.   (B) $-\sqrt{5}/5 < x < \sqrt{5}/5$ *(2-2, 2-3)*

18. (A) $0 \le x < 1$ (B) No; some powers of x are not non-negative integers. *(2-2, 2-3)*

19. $f(x) = \dfrac{1}{2} + \dfrac{1}{2^2}x + \dfrac{1}{2^3}x^2 + \dfrac{1}{2^4}x^3 + \cdots + \dfrac{1}{2^{n+1}}x^n + \cdots, -2 < x < 2$

$g(x) = \dfrac{1}{2^2} + \dfrac{1}{2^2}x + \dfrac{3}{2^4}x^2 + \cdots + \dfrac{n}{2^{n+1}}x^{n-1} + \cdots, -2 < x < 2$ (2-3)

20. $f(x) = x^2 - x^4 + x^6 - \cdots + (-1)^n x^{2n+2} + \cdots, -1 < x < 1;$

$g(x) = 2x - 4x^3 + 6x^5 - \cdots + (2n+2)(-1)^n x^{2n+1} + \cdots, -1 < x < 1$ (2-3)

21. $\dfrac{1}{3\cdot 9}x^3 - \dfrac{1}{5\cdot 9^2}x^5 + \dfrac{1}{7\cdot 9^3}x^7 - \cdots + \dfrac{(-1)^n}{(2n+3)9^{n+1}}x^{2n+3} + \cdots; -3 < x < 3$ (2-3)

22. $\dfrac{1}{5\cdot 16}x^5 + \dfrac{1}{7\cdot 16^2}x^7 + \dfrac{1}{9\cdot 16^3}x^9 + \cdots + \dfrac{1}{(2n+5)16^{n+1}}x^{2n+5} + \cdots; -4 < x < 4$ (2-3)

23. (A) $g(x) = 2 - 3(x-1) + (x-1)^3; h(x) = 9(x+1) - 6(x+1)^2 + (x+1)^3$
(B) The two series represent the same polynomial function for $-\infty < x < \infty$. (2-2)

24. (A) f is not differentiable at 0.
(B) If $a > 0, p_n(x) = x$ for $n \geq 1$. If $a < 0, p_n(x) = -x$ for $n \geq 1$. (2-2)

25. $1.78; |R_2(0.6)| \leq 0.108$ (2-4)   **26.** $1.0618; |R_2(0.06)| \leq 0.000\,108$ (2-4)

27. $0.261\,975; n = 4$ (2-4)   **28.** $0.03; n = 1$ (2-4)

29. $5 - \dfrac{1}{3}x^3 - \dfrac{1}{8}x^4 - \cdots - \dfrac{1}{n(n-2)}x^n - \cdots; -1 < x < 1$ (2-3)

30. $3 - 4x + \dfrac{1}{6}x^3 - \dfrac{1}{12}x^4 + \cdots + \dfrac{(-1)^{n+1}}{(n-3)!(n-1)n}x^n + \cdots; -\infty < x < \infty$ (2-3)

31. 0.0612 (2-4)   **32.** 0.314 (2-4)   **33.** $n = 7$ (2-4)   **34.** $|x| < 0.6918$ (2-4)   **35.** $-0.616 < x < 0.616$ (2-4)

36. $-0.488 < x < 0.488$ (2-4)   **37.** $p_2(x) = 5 - \frac{1}{1,000}x^2; \$4.93$ (2-4)   **38.** $p_2(t) = 9 - 0.03t^2; \$80,000$ (2-4)

39. $\displaystyle\int_0^1 \dfrac{18x^3}{8 + x^2}\,dx \approx 0.516;$ index of income concentration ≈ 0.484 (2-4)

40. $S(8) \approx 3.348$ within ± 0.001, or \$3,348,000 within $\pm\$1,000$ (2-4)

41. $A(2) \approx 10.17$ cm^2 within ± 0.01 (2-4)   **42.** $\dfrac{1}{5}\displaystyle\int_0^5 \dfrac{5,000t^2}{10,000 + t^4}\,dt \approx 4.06$ (2-4)

43. $\dfrac{1}{5}\displaystyle\int_0^5 (10 + 2t - 5e^{-0.01t^2})\,dt \approx 10.4$ (2-4)

APPENDIX D

Exercise D.1

1. (A) $p(x) = a_0 + a_1(x-1) + a_2(x-1)(x-3)$
(B) $a_0 = 2, a_1 = 2, a_2 = 1$
(C) $p(x) = 2 + 2(x-1) + (x-1)(x-3)$

3. (A) $p(x) = a_0 + a_1(x+1) + a_2(x+1)x + a_3(x+1)x(x-2)$
(B) $a_0 = 6, a_1 = -1, a_2 = 2, a_3 = -2$
(C) $p(x) = 6 - (x+1) + 2(x+1)x - 2(x+1)x(x-2)$

5.

x_k	y_k	1st D.D.	2nd D.D.
1	4		
		4	
2	8		1
		6	
3	14		

$p(x) = 4 + 4(x-1) + (x-1)(x-2)$

7.

x_k	y_k	1st D.D.	2nd D.D.	3rd D.D.
-1	-3			
		4		
0	1		-1	
		2		1
1	3		2	
		6		
2	9			

$p(x) = -3 + 4(x+1) - (x+1)x + (x+1)x(x-1)$

9.

x_k	y_k	1st D.D.	2nd D.D.	3rd D.D.
−2	25			
		−5		
1	10		3	
		7		−1
2	17		−3	
		−2		
4	13			

$$p(x) = 25 - 5(x + 2) + 3(x + 2)(x - 1) - (x + 2)(x - 1)(x - 2)$$

13. $p(x) = -64 + 24(x + 4) - 4(x + 4)x + (x + 4)x(x - 4);$ (A) 8 (B) 56

15. $p(x) = \frac{1}{4}(x + 1)x(x - 1);$ (A) 1.5 (B) 6

17. $p(x) = 24 - 11(x + 4) + \frac{5}{2}(x + 4)(x + 2) - \frac{1}{2}(x + 4)(x + 2)x + \frac{1}{8}(x + 4)(x + 2)x(x - 2);$
(A) $\frac{57}{8} = 7.125$ (B) $-\frac{23}{8} = -2.875$

19. $p(x) = -24 + 18(x + 3) - 6(x + 3)(x + 2) + (x + 3)(x + 2)(x + 1);$ (A) $\frac{3}{8} = 0.375$ (B) $\frac{105}{8} = 13.125$

21. $p(x) = 2 - (x + 2) + \frac{1}{2}(x + 2)x = \frac{1}{2}x^2$ **23.** $p(x) = -4 + 2x$

25. $p(x) = 2(x + 1) - (x + 1)x = 2 + x - x^2$

27. $p(x) = 1 + 4(x + 2) - 3(x + 2)(x + 1) + (x + 2)(x + 1)x = x^3 - 3x + 3$

29. $p(x) = -3 + 3(x + 2) + (x + 2)(x + 1) - 2(x + 2)(x + 1)x + (x + 2)(x + 1)x(x - 1) = 5 - 6x^2 + x^4$

31. $p(x) = x^3 - 3x + 3;$ the two polynomials are identical.

33. $p(x) = x^4 - 6x^2 + 5;$ the two polynomials are identical.

35. $p(x) = 1 + \frac{1}{3}(x - 1) - \frac{1}{60}(x - 1)(x - 4)$

x	1	2	3	4	5	6	7	8	9
$p(x)$	1	1.4	1.7	2	2.3	2.5	2.7	2.9	3
$\sqrt{x}$	1	1.4	1.7	2	2.2	2.4	2.6	2.8	3

37. $p(x) = -4 - (x + 2) + 3(x + 2)(x + 1) - (x + 2)(x + 1)x = 6x - x^3$ **39.** $y = y_2 + (y_1 - y_2)x^2/x_1^2$

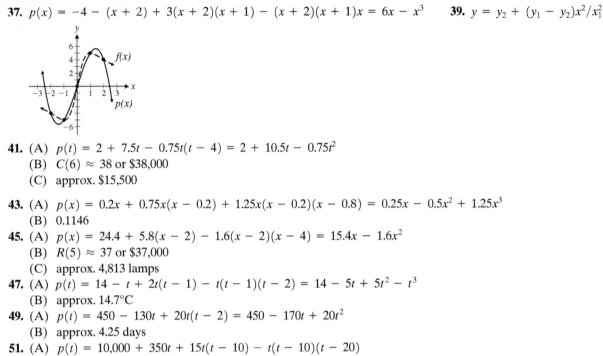

41. (A) $p(t) = 2 + 7.5t - 0.75t(t - 4) = 2 + 10.5t - 0.75t^2$
(B) $C(6) \approx 38$ or \$38,000
(C) approx. \$15,500

43. (A) $p(x) = 0.2x + 0.75x(x - 0.2) + 1.25x(x - 0.2)(x - 0.8) = 0.25x - 0.5x^2 + 1.25x^3$
(B) 0.1146

45. (A) $p(x) = 24.4 + 5.8(x - 2) - 1.6(x - 2)(x - 4) = 15.4x - 1.6x^2$
(B) $R(5) \approx 37$ or \$37,000
(C) approx. 4,813 lamps

47. (A) $p(t) = 14 - t + 2t(t - 1) - t(t - 1)(t - 2) = 14 - 5t + 5t^2 - t^3$
(B) approx. 14.7°C

49. (A) $p(t) = 450 - 130t + 20t(t - 2) = 450 - 170t + 20t^2$
(B) approx. 4.25 days

51. (A) $p(t) = 10,000 + 350t + 15t(t - 10) - t(t - 10)(t - 20)$
$= 10,000 + 45t^2 - t^3$
(B) approx. 14,000 registered voters

1 DIFFERENTIAL EQUATIONS

1. Substitute $y = Cx^2$, $y' = 2Cx$ into the given differential equation:
$$x(2Cx) = 2(Cx^2)$$
$$2Cx^2 = 2Cx^2$$
Thus, $y = Cx^2$ is the general solution.

3. Substitute $y = \dfrac{C}{x}$, $y' = -\dfrac{C}{x^2}$ into the given differential equation:
$$x\left(-\frac{C}{x^2}\right) = -\frac{C}{x}$$
$$-\frac{C}{x} = -\frac{C}{x}$$
Thus, $y = \dfrac{C}{x}$ is the general solution.

7. $y = ce^{x^2}$; $y' = 2xy$
$$y = ce^{x^2}$$
$$y' = c(2x)e^{x^2} = 2cxe^{x^2}$$
$$2xy = (2x)ce^{x^2} = 2cxe^{x^2}$$
Thus, $y = ce^{x^2}$ satisfies $y' = 2xy$.

9. Substituting $y = 4 + Ce^t$, $y' = Ce^t$ into the differential equation, we have
$$y' = y - 4$$
$$Ce^t = (4 + Ce^t) - 4$$
$$Ce^t = Ce^t$$

11. (C)

13. (A)

15.

17.

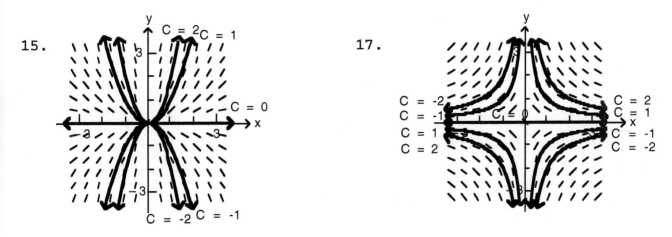

19. $y' = y - 3x$; $y(0) = 4$

Substituting $y = 3 + 3x + Ce^x$, $y' = 3 + Ce^x$ in the differential equation, we have

$$3 + Ce^x = 3 + 3x + Ce^x - 3x$$
$$3 + Ce^x = 3 + Ce^x$$

Thus, $y = 3 + 3x + Ce^x$ is the general solution.
Letting $x = 0$ and $y = 4$ in the general solution yields
$$4 = 3 + C$$
$$C = 1$$
Therefore, the particular solution satisfying $y(0) = 4$ is
$$y = 3 + 3x + e^x$$

21. $y' = -y + e^{-x}$; $y(0) = 0$

Substituting $y = xe^{-x} + Ce^{-x}$, $y' = e^{-x} - xe^{-x} - Ce^{-x}$ into the differential equation, we have

$$e^{-x} - xe^{-x} - Ce^{-x} = -(xe^{-x} + Ce^{-x}) + e^{-x}$$
$$e^{-x} - xe^{-x} - Ce^{-x} = -xe^{-x} - Ce^{-x} + e^{-x}$$

Thus, $y = xe^{-x} + Ce^{-x}$ is the general solution.
Letting $x = 0$ and $y = 0$ in the general solution yields
$$0 = 0 + C$$
$$C = 0$$
Therefore, the particular solution satisfying $y(0) = 0$ is
$$y = xe^{-x}$$

23. $xy' = 4x - y$; $y(1) = 1$

Substituting $y = 2x + \dfrac{C}{x}$, $y' = 2 - \dfrac{C}{x^2}$ into the differential equation, we have

$$x\left[2 - \frac{C}{x^2}\right] = 4x - \left[2x + \frac{C}{x}\right]$$
$$2x - \frac{C}{x} = 2x - \frac{C}{x}$$

Thus, $y = 2x + \dfrac{C}{x}$ is the general solution.

Letting $x = 1$ and $y = 1$ in the general solution yields
$$1 = 2 + C$$
$$C = -1$$

Therefore, the particular solution satisfying $y(1) = 1$ is
$$y = 2x - \frac{1}{x}$$

25. $y = 2 + Cx^{-3}$; $xy' + 3y = 6$; $y(1) = 3$

$y' = C(-3)x^{-4} = -3Cx^{-4}$, $xy' = -3Cx^{-3}$

$xy' + 3y = -3Cx^{-3} + 3(2 + Cx^{-3}) = -3Cx^{-3} + 6 + 3Cx^{-3} = 6$

Thus, $y = 2 + Cx^{-3}$ is the general solution of the first order differential equation $xy' + 3y = 6$.

$y(1) = 2 + C(1)^{-3} = 2 + C = 3$ or $C = 1$ and the particular solution is $y = 2 + x^{-3}$.

27. $y = x + Cx^{1/2}$; $2xy' - y = x$; $y(1) = 0$

$y' = 1 + C\left(\dfrac{1}{2}\right)x^{-1/2} = 1 + \dfrac{C}{2}x^{-1/2}$

$2xy' - y = 2x\left(1 + \dfrac{C}{2}x^{-1/2}\right) - (x + Cx^{1/2})$

$\qquad = 2x + Cx^{1/2} - x - Cx^{1/2} = x$

Thus, $y = x + Cx^{1/2}$ is the general solution of the first order differential equation $2xy' - y = x$.
$y(1) = 1 + C = 0$ or $C = -1$ and the particular solution is $y = x - x^{1/2}$.

29. Differentiating $y^3 + xy - x^3 = C$ implicitly, we have

$\qquad D_x(y^3 + xy - x^3) = D_x C$

$\qquad D_x y^3 + D_x(xy) - D_x x^3 = 0$

$\qquad 3y^2 y' + xy' + y - 3x^2 = 0$

$\qquad\qquad (3y^2 + x)y' = 3x^2 - y.$

Thus, y is a solution of the given differential equation.

31. Differentiating $xy + e^{y^2} - x^2 = C$ implicitly, we have

$\qquad D_x(xy + e^{y^2} - x^2) = D_x C$

$\qquad D_x(xy) + D_x e^{y^2} - D_x x^2 = 0$

$\qquad xy' + y + e^{y^2} D_x y^2 - 2x = 0$

$\qquad xy' + y + 2yy' e^{y^2} - 2x = 0$

$\qquad\qquad (x + 2ye^{y^2})y' = 2x - y.$

Thus, y is a solution of the given differential equation.

33. Differentiating $y^2 + x^2 = C$ implicitly, we have

$\qquad D_x(y^2 + x^2) = D_x C$

$\qquad D_x y^2 + D_x x^2 = 0$

$\qquad 2yy' + 2x = 0$

$\qquad\qquad yy' = -x$

Thus, y is a solution of the given differential equation. Substituting $x = 0$ and $y = 3$ in $y^2 + x^2 = C$ yields

$\qquad 3^2 + 0^2 = C$ or $C = 9$.

Therefore, the particular solution satisfying $y(0) = 3$ is a solution of the equation

$\qquad y^2 + x^2 = 9$ or $y^2 = 9 - x^2$.

This equation has two continuous solutions

$\qquad y_1(x) = \sqrt{9 - x^2}$ and $y_2(x) = -\sqrt{9 - x^2}$.

Clearly, $y_1(x) = \sqrt{9 - x^2}$ is the solution that satisfies the initial condition $y(0) = 3$.

35. Differentiating $\ln(2 - y) = x + C$ implicitly, we have

$$D_x [\ln(2 - y)] = D_x(x + C)$$

$$\frac{1}{2 - y}(-y') = 1$$

$$-y' = 2 - y$$

$$y' = y - 2.$$

Thus, y is a solution of the given differential equation. Substituting $x = 0$ and $y = 1$ in $\ln(2 - y) = x + C$ yields

$$\ln(2 - 1) = 0 + C \quad \text{or} \quad \ln 1 = C \quad \text{and} \quad C = 0.$$

Therefore, the particular solution satisfying $y(0) = 1$ is a solution of the equation

$$\ln(2 - y) = x.$$

We can solve this equation for y by taking the exponential of both sides. We have

$$e^{\ln(2-y)} = e^x \quad \text{or} \quad 2 - y = e^x \quad \text{and} \quad y = 2 - e^x.$$

37. Given the general solution $y = 2 + Ce^{-x}$.

(A) Substituting $x = 0$ and $y = 1$ in the general solution yields

$$1 = 2 + Ce^0$$

$$C = -1.$$

Thus, the particular solution satisfying $y(0) = 1$ is $y_a = 2 - e^{-x}$.

(B) Substituting $x = 0$ and $y = 2$ in the general solution yields

$$2 = 2 + Ce^0$$

$$C = 0.$$

Thus, the particular solution satisfying $y(0) = 2$ is $y_b = 2$.

(C) Substituting $x = 0$ and $y = 3$ in the general solution yields

$$3 = 2 + Ce^0$$

$$C = 1.$$

Thus, the particular solution satisfying $y(0) = 3$ is $y_c = 2 + e^{-x}$.

The graphs of the particular solutions for $x \geq 0$ are shown at the right.

39. Given the general solution $y = 2 + Ce^x$.

(A) Substituting $x = 0$ and $y = 1$ in the general solution yields

$$1 = 2 + Ce^0$$

$$C = -1$$

Thus, the particular solution satisfying $y(0) = 1$ is $y_a = 2 - e^x$.

(B) Substituting $x = 0$ and $y = 2$ in the general solution yields
$$2 = 2 + Ce^0$$
$$C = 0.$$
Thus, the particular solution satisfying $y(0) = 2$ is $y_b = 2$.

(C) Substituting $x = 0$ and $y = 3$ in the general solution yields
$$3 = 2 + Ce^0$$
$$C = 1.$$
Thus, the particular solution satisfying $y(0) = 3$ is $y_c = 2 + e^x$.

The graphs of these solutions for $x \geq 0$ are shown above.

41. $\dfrac{dN}{dt} = 650$

t = Time (in years)
$N = N(t)$ = Number of employees at time t
$\dfrac{dN}{dt} = N'$ = Rate at which the number of employees is changing.

43. $\dfrac{dT}{dt} = -k(T - 72)$

t = Time
$T = T(t)$ = Temperature of pizza at time t
k = Positive constant of proportionality
$\dfrac{dT}{dt} = T'$ = Rate at which the temperature of the pizza is changing;
$\dfrac{dT}{dt}$ is negative because the temperature of the pizza is decreasing.

45. Given the general solution $y = \dfrac{10}{1 + Ce^{-x}}$.

(A) Substituting $x = 0$ and $y = 1$ in the general solution yields
$$1 = \frac{10}{1 + Ce^0} = \frac{10}{1 + C}.$$
Therefore, $1 + C = 10$ or $C = 9$.
Thus, the particular solution satisfying $y(0) = 1$ is $y_a = \dfrac{10}{1 + 9e^{-x}}$.

(B) Substituting $x = 0$ and $y = 10$ in the general solution yields
$$10 = \frac{10}{1 + Ce^0} = \frac{10}{1 + C}.$$
Therefore, $10 + 10C = 10$ and $C = 0$.
Thus, the particular solution satisfying $y(0) = 10$ is $y_b = 10$.

(C) Substituting $x = 0$ and $y = 20$ in the general solution yields

$$20 = \frac{10}{1 + Ce^0} = \frac{10}{1 + C}.$$

Therefore, $20 + 20C = 10$ and $C = -0.5$.
Thus, the particular solution satisfying
$y(0) = 20$ is

$$y_c = \frac{10}{1 - 0.5e^{-x}}.$$

The graphs of these solutions for $x \geq 0$ are
shown at the right.

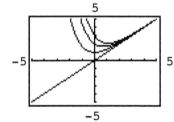

47. Given the general solution $y = Cx^3 + 2$.
   (A) Substituting $x = 0$, $y = 2$ in the general solution yields

   $2 = C \cdot 0 + 2$

   This equation is satisfied for all values of C. Thus, $y = Cx^3 + 2$
   satisfies the initial condition $y(0) = 2$ for any C.

   (B) Substituting $x = 0$, $y = 0$ in the general solution yields

   $0 = C \cdot 0 + 2$ or $0 = 2$.

   This equation is <u>not</u> satisfied for any value of C. There is <u>no</u>
   particular solution of the differential equation which satisfies
   the initial condition $y(0) = 0$.

   (C) Substituting $x = 1$, $y = 1$ in the general solution yields

   $1 = C \cdot 1 + 2$ and $C = -1$

   Thus, $y = 2 - x^3$ is the particular solution of the differential
   equation which satisfies the initial condition $y(1) = 1$.

49. (A) The graphs of $y = x + e^{-x}$, $y = x + 2e^{-x}$,
   $y = x + 3e^{-x}$ and the graph of $y = x$ are
   shown at the right.

   (B) Each of the graphs $y = x + Ce^{-x}$, $C = 1, 2, 3$,
   lies above the line $y = x$, each decreases to
   a local minimum and then increases,
   approaching $y = x$ as x approaches ∞.

   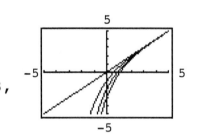

   (C) The graphs of $y = x - e^{-x}$, $y = x - 2e^{-x}$,
   $y = x - 3e^{-x}$ and the graph of $y = x$ are
   shown at the right.

   (D) Each of the graphs $y = x - Ce^{-x}$, $C = 1, 2, 3$,
   is increasing and approaches $y = x$ as
   x approaches ∞.

51. (A) Substitute $p = 5 - Ce^{-0.1t}$, $\dfrac{dp}{dt} = 0.1Ce^{-0.1t}$ into the differential equation:

$$
\begin{aligned}
0.1Ce^{-0.1t} &= 0.5 - 0.1(5 - Ce^{-0.1t}) \\
&= 0.5 - 0.5 + 0.1Ce^{-0.1t} \\
&= 0.1Ce^{-0.1t}
\end{aligned}
$$

Thus, $p = 5 - Ce^{-0.1t}$ is the general solution and

$$
\bar{p} = \lim_{t \to \infty} p(t) = \lim_{t \to \infty} (5 - Ce^{-0.1t}) = 5
$$

(B) Setting $t = 0$ and $p = 1$ in the general solution yields:

$$
1 = 5 - Ce^0 = 5 - C
$$

and $C = 4$

Thus, the particular solution satisfying the initial condition $p(0) = 1$ is:

$$
p(t) = 5 - 4e^{-0.1t}
$$

Setting $t = 0$ and $p = 10$ in the general solution yields:

$$
10 = 5 - Ce^0 = 5 - C
$$

and $C = -5$

Thus, the particular solution satisfying the initial condition $p(0) = 10$ is:

$$
p(t) = 5 + 5e^{-0.1t}
$$

The graphs of these solutions are shown above.

(C) From part (A), the equilibrium price $\bar{p} = 5$.

If $p(0) < 5$, then the price increases and approaches 5 as a limit.
If $p(0) > 5$, then the price decreases and approaches 5 as a limit.
If $p(0) = 5$, then $C = 0$ and $p(t) = 5$ for all t.

53. (A) Substitute $A(t) = Ce^{0.08t} - 2{,}500$, $\dfrac{dA}{dt} = 0.08Ce^{0.08t}$ into the differential equation:

$$
\begin{aligned}
0.08Ce^{0.08t} &= 0.08(Ce^{0.08t} - 2{,}500) + 200 \\
&= 0.08Ce^{0.08t} - 200 + 200 \\
&= 0.08Ce^{0.08t}
\end{aligned}
$$

Thus, $A(t) = Ce^{0.08t} - 2{,}500$ is the general solution.

(B) Setting $t = 0$ and $A = 0$ in the general solution yields:

$$
0 = Ce^0 - 2{,}500 = C - 2{,}500
$$

and $C = 2{,}500$

Thus, the particular solution satisfying $A(0) = 0$ is:

$$A_0(t) = 2,500e^{0.08t} - 2,500$$

Setting $t = 0$ and $A = 1,000$ in the general solution yields:
$$1000 = Ce^0 - 2,500 = C - 2,500$$
and $\quad C = 3,500$

Thus, the particular solution satisfying $A(0) = 1,000$ is:
$$A_1(t) = 3,500e^{0.08t} - 2,500$$

The graphs of these solutions are shown above.

(C) Each of the particular solutions, $A_0(t)$, $A_1(t)$, in part (B) approaches infinity as t approaches infinity. Also, the difference between $A_0(t)$ and $A_1(t)$:
$$A_1(t) - A_0(t) = 1,000e^{0.08t}$$
grows exponentially. Thus, the larger $A(0)$ is, the greater the amount in the account.

55. (A) Substitute $N(t) = 200 - Ce^{-0.5t}$, $\dfrac{dN}{dt} = 0.5Ce^{-0.5t}$ into the differential equation:
$$\begin{aligned}0.5Ce^{-0.5t} &= 100 - 0.5(200 - Ce^{-0.5t})\\ &= 100 - 100 + 0.5Ce^{-0.5t}\\ &= 0.5Ce^{-0.5t}\end{aligned}$$

Thus, $N(t) = 200 - Ce^{-0.5t}$ is the general solution.
Now, $\overline{N} = \lim\limits_{t \to \infty}(200 - Ce^{-0.5t}) = 200 - C\lim\limits_{t \to \infty}e^{-0.5t} = 200$

The equilibrium size of the population is: $\overline{N} = 200$.

(B) Setting $t = 0$ and $N = 50$ in the general solution yields
$$50 = 200 - Ce^0 = 200 - C$$
and $\quad C = 150$

Thus, the particular solution satisfying $N(0) = 50$ is:
$$N(t) = 200 - 150e^{-0.5t}$$

Setting $t = 0$ and $N = 300$ in the general solution yields:
$$300 = 200 - Ce^0 = 200 - C$$
and $\quad C = -100$

Thus, the particular solution satisfying $N(0) = 300$ is:
$$N(t) = 200 + 100e^{-0.5t}$$

The graphs of these solutions are shown at the right.

(C) If $N(0) < 200$, then number $N(t)$ of bacteria increases and approaches 200 as a limit; if $N(0) > 200$, then the number of bacteria decreases and approaches 200 as a limit. If $N(0) = 200$, then the number of bacteria remains constant for all t.

57. (A) Substitute $N(t) = Ce^{-2e^{-0.5t}}$, $\dfrac{dN}{dt} = Ce^{-2e^{-0.5t}}(-2e^{-0.5t})(-0.5) =$

$Ce^{-0.5t}e^{-2e^{-0.5t}}$ into the differential equation:

$$Ce^{-0.5t}e^{-2e^{-0.5t}} = (Ce^{-2e^{-0.5t}})e^{-0.5t}$$
$$= Ce^{-0.5t}e^{-2e^{-0.5t}}$$

Thus, $N(t) = Ce^{-2e^{-0.5t}}$ is the general solution.

Now, $\bar{N} = \lim\limits_{t \to \infty} Ce^{-2e^{-0.5t}} = C \lim\limits_{t \to \infty} e^{-2e^{-0.5t}}$

$$= C \lim\limits_{t \to \infty} e^{-2/e^{0.5t}} = Ce^0 = C$$

(B) Setting $t = 0$ and $N = 100$ in the general solution yields:

$$100 = Ce^{-2e^0} = Ce^{-2}$$

and $C = 100e^2$

Thus, the particular solution satisfying $N(0) = 100$ is:

$$N(t) = 100e^{2-2e^{-0.5t}}$$

Setting $t = 0$ and $N = 200$ in the general solution yields:

$$200 = Ce^{-2e^0} = Ce^{-2}$$

and $C = 200e^2$

Thus, the particular solution satisfying $N(0) = 200$ is:

$$N(t) = 200e^{2-2e^{-0.5t}}$$

The graphs of these solutions are shown at the right.

(C) As t approaches infinity, the number $N(t)$ of individuals who have heard the rumor approaches

$$\bar{N} = N(0)e^2$$

EXERCISE 1.2

1. $\dfrac{dy}{dt} = 100{,}000$

3. $\dfrac{dy}{dt} = k(10{,}000 - y)$, $k > 0$ constant

5. The annual sales of a company are $2 million initially, and are increasing at a rate (10%) proportional to the annual sales.

7. In a community of 5,000 people, one person started a rumor that is spreading at a rate proportional to the product of the number of people who have heard the rumor and the number who have not.

9. $xy' = y^2$

$\dfrac{1}{y^2}y' = \dfrac{1}{x}$ $\left(\text{multiply by } \dfrac{1}{xy^2}\right)$

11. $xy' + xy = 3y$

$\quad xy' = 3y - xy$

$\quad xy' = y(3 - x)$

$\quad \dfrac{1}{y}y' = \dfrac{3 - x}{x}$ $\left(\text{multiply by } \dfrac{1}{xy}\right)$

13. $y' = 3x^2$

$\int dy = \int 3x^2\,dx$

$\quad y = x^3 + C$ *General solution*

Applying the initial condition $y(0) = -1$, we have

$\quad -1 = 0 + C$ which implies $C = -1$

Thus, $y = x^3 - 1$ *Particular solution*

15. $y' = \dfrac{2}{x}$

$\int dy = \int \dfrac{2}{x}\,dx$

$\quad y = 2\ln|x| + C$ *General solution*

Applying the initial condition $y(1) = 2$, we have

$\quad 2 = 2\ln 1 + C = 2\cdot 0 + C = C$

so $C = 2$

Thus,

$\quad y = 2\ln|x| + 2$ *Particular solution*

17. $y' = y;\ y(0) = 10$.

$\dfrac{y'}{y} = 1$. Separate the variables

$\int \dfrac{dy}{y} = \int dx$

$\ln|y| = x + C$

$\quad y = e^{x+C}$

$\quad\quad = e^C e^x$ (put $K = e^C$)

$\quad\quad = Ke^x$. *General solution* Applying the initial condition $y(0) = 10$, we have

$\quad 10 = Ke^0$ or $K = 10$.

Thus,

$\quad y = 10e^x$. *Particular solution*

19. $y' = 25 - y;\ y(0) = 5$.

$\dfrac{y'}{25 - y} = 1$. Separate the variables

$\int \dfrac{dy}{25 - y} = \int dx$

$-\ln|25 - y| = x + C$

$\ln|25 - y| = -(x + C)$

$\quad 25 - y = e^{-x-C}$

$\quad 25 - y = e^{-C}e^{-x}$

$\quad 25 - y = Ke^{-x}$ (put $K = e^{-C}$)

$\quad\quad y = 25 - Ke^{-x}$.

General solution

Applying the initial condition $y(0) = 5$, we have

$\quad 5 = 25 - Ke^0$ or $K = 20$.

Thus,

$\quad y = 25 - 20e^{-x}$.

Particular solution

21. $y' = \dfrac{y}{x}$; $y(1) = 5$, $x > 0$.

$\dfrac{y'}{y} = \dfrac{1}{x}$ Separate the variables

$\displaystyle\int \dfrac{dy}{y} = \int \dfrac{dx}{x}$

$\ln|y| = \ln x + C$

(Note: $x > 0$, so $|x| = x$.)

$\qquad y = e^{\ln x + C} = e^C e^{\ln x}$

$\qquad\quad = Kx.$

(Note: $e^{\ln x} = x$, put $K = e^C$.)

Thus, $\quad y = Kx$. *General solution*

Applying the initial condition
$y(1) = 5$, we have

$\qquad 5 = K(1) \quad$ or $\quad K = 5$.

Therefore,

$\qquad y = 5x$. *Particular solution*

23. $y' = \dfrac{1}{y^2}$; $y(1) = 3$.

$y^2 y' = 1$

$\displaystyle\int y^2 dy = \int dx$

$\qquad \dfrac{y^3}{3} = x + C$

$\qquad y^3 = 3x + 3C$

$\qquad\quad = 3x + A$. (put $A = 3C$)

Thus, $y = (3x + A)^{1/3}$. *General
solution*

Applying the initial condition
$y(1) = 3$, we have

$\qquad 3 = (3 + A)^{1/3}$

$\qquad 27 = 3 + A \quad$ and $\quad A = 24$.

Therefore,

$\qquad y = (3x + 24)^{1/3}$. *Particular
solution*

25. $y' = ye^x$; $y(0) = 3e$

$\dfrac{y'}{y} = e^x$

$\displaystyle\int \dfrac{dy}{y} = \int e^x dx$

$\ln|y| = e^x + C$

$\qquad y = e^{e^x + C}$

$\qquad\quad = e^C e^{e^x}$

$\qquad\quad = Ke^{e^x}$. *General solution*

Applying the initial
condition $y(0) = 3e$, we have

$\qquad 3e = Ke^{e^0}$

$\qquad\quad = Ke \quad$ and $\quad K = 3$.

Thus,

$\qquad y = 3e^{e^x}$. *Particular
solution*

27. $y' = \dfrac{e^x}{e^y}$; $y(0) = \ln 2$.

$e^y y' = e^x$

$\displaystyle\int e^y dy = \int e^x dx$

$\qquad e^y = e^x + C$

$\qquad y = \ln(e^x + C)$ *General
solution*

Applying the initial condition
$y(0) = \ln 2$, we have

$\qquad \ln 2 = \ln(e^0 + C)$

$\qquad\quad = \ln(1 + C)$.

Therefore,

$\qquad 1 + C = 2 \quad$ and $\quad C = 1$.

Thus,

$\qquad y = \ln(e^x + 1)$. *Particular
solution*

29. $y' = xy + x$; $y(0) = 2$

$y' = x(y + 1)$

$$\int \frac{dy}{y + 1} = \int x \ dx$$

$$\ln|y + 1| = \frac{x^2}{2} + C$$

$$y + 1 = e^{x^2/2 + C}$$

$$y + 1 = e^C e^{x^2/2}$$

$$y + 1 = K e^{x^2/2}$$

$$y = K e^{x^2/2} - 1. \ \textit{General solution}$$

Applying the initial condition
$y(0) = 2$, we have

$2 = K e^0 - 1 = K - 1$ and $K = 3$.

Thus,

$$y = 3 e^{x^2/2} - 1$$

Particular solution

31. $y' = (2 - y)^2 e^x$; $y(0) = 1$.

$$\frac{y'}{(2 - y)^2} = e^x$$

$$\int \frac{dy}{(2 - y)^2} = \int e^x \ dx$$

$$\frac{1}{2 - y} = e^x + C$$

$$2 - y = \frac{1}{e^x + C}$$

$$y = 2 - \frac{1}{e^x + C} \cdot \ \textit{General solution}$$

Applying the initial condition
$y(0) = 1$, we have

$$1 = 2 - \frac{1}{e^0 + C}$$

$$\frac{1}{1 + C} = 1$$

$1 + C = 1$ and $C = 0$.

Thus,

$$y = 2 - \frac{1}{e^x} \quad \text{or} \quad y = 2 - e^{-x}$$

Particular solution

33. $y' = \dfrac{1 + x^2}{1 + y^2}$

$(1 + y^2)y' = 1 + x^2$ Separate the variables

$\int (1 + y^2)dy = \int (1 + x^2)dx$

$$y + \frac{y^3}{3} = x + \frac{x^3}{3} + C. \qquad \textit{General solution}$$

35. $xyy' = (1 + x^2)(1 + y^2)$

$$\frac{yy'}{1 + y^2} = \frac{1 + x^2}{x} \qquad \text{Separate the variables}$$

$$\int \frac{y \ dy}{1 + y^2} = \int \left(\frac{1}{x} + x\right) dx$$

$$\frac{1}{2} \int \frac{2y \ dy}{1 + y^2} = \ln|x| + \frac{x^2}{2} + C$$

$$\frac{1}{2} \ln(1 + y^2) = \ln|x| + \frac{x^2}{2} + C, \quad \textit{General solution}$$

or $\ln(1 + y^2) = \ln(x^2) + x^2 + C$.

37. $x^2 e^y y' = x^3 + x^3 e^y$

$\quad\ x^2 e^y y' = x^3(1 + e^y)$

$\quad\ \dfrac{e^y y'}{1 + e^y} = x \qquad$ Separate the variables

$\quad\ \displaystyle\int \dfrac{e^y y'}{1 + e^y} = \int x \, dx \qquad$ (<u>Note</u>: Put $u = 1 + e^y$, $du = e^y dy$.)

$\quad\ \ln(1 + e^y) = \dfrac{x^2}{2} + C. \quad$ *General solution*

39. $xyy' = \ln x; \ y(1) = 1$

$\quad\ yy' = \dfrac{\ln x}{x}$

$\quad\ \displaystyle\int y \, dy = \frac{1}{x}\int \dfrac{\ln x}{x \cdot x} \, dx \qquad$ (<u>Note</u>: Put $u = \ln x$,

$\quad\ \dfrac{y^2}{2} = \dfrac{[\ln x]^2}{2} + C$

$\quad\ y^2 = [\ln x]^2 + 2C$ or $y^2 = [\ln x]^2 + A$. $\quad$ *General solution.*

Solving this equation for y, we have

$\quad\ y = \pm\sqrt{[\ln x]^2 + A}$

Applying the initial condition $y(1) = 1$, we choose the function

$\qquad\ y = \sqrt{[\ln x]^2 + A} \quad$ and get

$\qquad\ 1 = \sqrt{[\ln x]^2 + A}$

$\qquad\ 1 = \sqrt{0 + A} \quad$ and $\quad A = 1$.

Thus, $y = \sqrt{[\ln x]^2 + 1}$. *Particular solution*

41. $xy' = x\sqrt{y} + 2\sqrt{y}; \ y(1) = 4$

$\quad\ xy' = \sqrt{y}(x + 2$

$\quad\ \dfrac{y'}{\sqrt{y}} = \dfrac{x + 2}{x} \quad$ Separate the variables

$\quad\ \displaystyle\int \dfrac{dy}{\sqrt{y}} = \int \left(1 + \dfrac{2}{x}\right) dx$

$\quad\ 2y^{1/2} = x + 2\ln|x| + C$

$\quad\ y^{1/2} = \dfrac{1}{2}(x + 2\ln|x| + C)$

$\qquad\ y = \dfrac{1}{4}(x + 2\ln|x| + C)^2$ or

$\qquad\ y = \dfrac{1}{4}[x + \ln(x^2) + C]^2.$

$\qquad\quad$ *General solution*

Applying the initial condition $y(1) = 4$, we have

$\qquad\ 4 = \dfrac{1}{4}[1 + \ln(1^2) + C]^2$

$\qquad\ 16 = (1 + C)^2$

$\quad\ 1 + C = 4$

$\qquad\ C = 3.$

Thus,

$\qquad\ y = \dfrac{1}{4}[x + \ln(x^2) + 3]^2.$

$\qquad\quad$ *Particular solution*

43. $yy' = xe^{-y^2}; \ y(0) = 1$

$ye^{y^2}y' = x$

$\int ye^{y^2} \, dy = \int x \, dx$ (<u>Note</u>: Put $u = y^2$, $dy = 2y \, dy$.)

$$\frac{1}{2}e^{y^2} = \frac{x^2}{2} + C$$

$$e^{y^2} = x^2 + 2C$$

$$e^{y^2} = x^2 + A$$

$$y^2 = \ln(x^2 + A). \ \textit{General}$$
$$\textit{solution}$$

Solving this equation for y, we have $y = \pm\sqrt{\ln(x^2 + A)}$.

We choose the function $y = \sqrt{\ln(x^2 + A)}$ and apply the initial condition $y(0) = 1$ to obtain

$$1 = \sqrt{\ln(0 + A)}$$
$$\ln A = 1$$
$$A = e$$

Thus, $y = \sqrt{\ln(x^2 + e)}$.   *Particular solution*

45. $y' + xy = 2$
This differential equation cannot be written in the form $f(y)y' = g(x)$.

47. $3yy' = e^{x^2+y} = e^{x^2}e^y$

$3ye^{-y}y' = e^{x^2}$; $f(y) = 3ye^{-y}$, $g(x) = e^{x^2}$

$\int 3ye^{-y} \, dy = \int ex^2 \, dx$

The integrand $g(x) = e^{x^2}$ does not have an elementary antiderivative.

49. $y = M(1 - e^{-kt})$, $M > 0$, $k > 0$ constants.

(A) At $t = 1$, $y = 3$:

$$3 = M(1 - e^{-k}) \quad \text{so} \quad M = \frac{3}{1 - e^{-k}}$$

At $t = 1.5$, $y = 4$

$$4 = M(1 - e^{1.5k}) \quad \text{so} \quad M = \frac{4}{1 - e^{-1.5k}}$$

(B) Using a graphing utility to graph the two equations in part (A), we find that $M \approx 7.3$ (and $k \approx 0.53$).

51. The model for this problem is $\dfrac{dA}{dt} = 0.055A$; $A(0) = 5000$.

$$\frac{dA}{A} = 0.055dt$$

$$\int \frac{dA}{A} = \int 0.055dt$$

$$\ln|A| = 0.055t + C$$

$$\begin{aligned} A &= e^{0.055t+C} \\ &= A^C e^{0.055t} \\ &= Ke^{0.055t}. \qquad \textit{General solution} \end{aligned}$$

Applying the initial condition $A(0) = 5000$, we have
$$5000 = Ke^0, \quad K = 5000.$$

Thus, $A(t) = 5000e^{0.055t}$ is the particular solution.

When $t = 5$ years,
$$A(5) = 5000e^{0.055(5)} = 5000e^{0.275} \approx \$6,582.65.$$

53. (A) Let $s(t)$ denote the number of people who have heard about the new product. Then the model for this problem is
$$\frac{ds}{dt} = k(100,000 - s); \quad s(0) = 0, \; s(7) = 20,000, \; k > 0.$$

$$\frac{ds}{(100,000 - s)} = k\,dt$$

$$\int \frac{ds}{100,000 - s} = \int k\,dt$$

$$-\ln|100,000 - s| = kt + C \qquad (0 < s < 100,000)$$

$$\ln|100,000 - s| = -kt - C$$

$$100,000 - s = e^{-kt-C}$$

$$100,000 - s = e^{-C}e^{-kt}$$

$$= Ae^{-kt}.$$

Thus,

$$s(t) = 100,000 - Ae^{-kt}. \quad (\textit{General solution})$$

We use the conditions $s(0) = 0$, $s(7) = 20,000$ to determine the constants A and k.
$$s(0) = 0 = 100,000 - Ae^0, \quad A = 100,000.$$

Thus, $s(t) = 100,000 - 100,000e^{-kt}$.
$$s(7) = 20,000 = 100,000 - 100,000e^{-7k}$$

$$100,000e^{-7k} = 80,000$$

$$e^{-7k} = 0.8$$

$$-7k = \ln(0.8)$$

$$k = \frac{-\ln(0.8)}{7}.$$

Therefore, the particular solution is
$$s(t) = 100,000 - 100,000e^{[\ln(0.8)/7]t}.$$

Finally, we want to find time t such that $s(t) = 50,000$:
$$50,000 = 100,000 - 100,000e^{[\ln(0.8)/7]t}$$
$$e^{[\ln(0.8)/7]t} = 0.5$$
$$\frac{\ln 0.8}{7}t = \ln(0.5).$$
Thus, $t = \dfrac{7\ln(0.5)}{\ln(0.8)} \approx 22$ days.

(B) From part (A), we know that
$$s(t) = 100,000(1 - e^{-kt})$$

Since we want 50,000 people to be aware of the product after 14 days, we have
$$50,000 = 100,000(1 - e^{-14k})$$
$$1 - e^{-14k} = \frac{1}{2}$$
$$e^{-14k} = \frac{1}{2}$$
$$-14k = \ln(0.5)$$
$$k = -\frac{1}{14}\ln(0.5)$$

Thus, $s(t) = 100,000[1 - e^{(t/14)\ln(0.5)}]$

Now, $s(7) = 100,000[1 - e^{(7/14)\ln(0.5)}]$
$$= 100,000[1 - e^{0.5\,\ln(0.5)}] \approx 29,300$$

Therefore, approximately 29,300 people must become aware of the product during the first 7 days in order to ensure that 50,000 will be aware of the product after 14 days.

55. Let $s(t)$ denote the percentage of the deodorizer that is present at time t. Then the model for this problem is
$$\frac{ds}{dt} = ks;\ s(0) = 1,\ s(30) = 0.5,\ k < 0.$$
Separating the variables, we have
$$\frac{ds}{s} = k\ dt$$
$$\int\frac{ds}{s} = \int k\ dt$$
$$\ln|s| = kt + C$$
$$s = e^{kt+C}$$
$$s = Ae^{kt}.\quad \textit{General solution}$$

We use the conditions $s(0) = 1$, $s(30) = 0.5$, to evaluate the constants A and k.
$$s(0) = 1 = Ae^0,\ A = 1.$$

Thus, $s(t) = e^{kt}$

$$s(30) = 0.5 = e^{30k}$$
$$30k = \ln(0.5)$$
$$k = \frac{\ln(0.5)}{30}.$$

Therefore, $s(t) = e^{[\ln(0.5)/30]t}$ *Particular solution*

Now, we want to find time t such that $s(t) = 0.1$:

$$0.1 = e^{[\ln(0.5)/30]t}$$
$$\frac{\ln(0.5)}{30} t = \ln(0.1)$$
$$t = \frac{30 \ln(0.1)}{\ln(0.5)} \approx 100 \text{ days}.$$

57. Let y be the total personal income and take 1995 as the base year (0), then $y(0) = 6{,}201$ billion, $y(5) = 8{,}407$ billion and $\dfrac{dy}{dt} = ky$.

From the last equation we have

$$\frac{dy}{y} = k \, dt \quad \text{or} \quad \ln y = kt + C \quad \text{or}$$
$$y = e^{kt+C} = e^C e^{kt} = A e^{kt}$$
$$y(0) = A = 6{,}201 \text{ and hence } y(t) = 6{,}201 e^{kt}$$
$$y(5) = 8{,}407 = 6{,}201 e^{k(5)} \quad \text{or} \quad e^{5k} = \frac{8{,}407}{6{,}201} \quad \text{or} \quad k = \frac{1}{5} \ln\left(\frac{8{,}407}{6{,}201}\right).$$

Thus, $y(t) = 6{,}201 e^{\frac{1}{5} \ln\left(\frac{8{,}407}{6{,}201}\right)t}$

Now, for $t = 15$, we have

$$y(15) = 6{,}201 e^{\frac{1}{5} \ln\left(\frac{8{,}407}{6{,}201}\right)(15)} \approx 15{,}452 \text{ billion}$$

Note that $\dfrac{dy}{dt} = 6{,}201 \left[\dfrac{1}{5} \ln\left(\dfrac{8{,}407}{6{,}201}\right)\right] e^{\frac{1}{5}t \ln\left(\frac{8{,}407}{6{,}201}\right)}$ and

$$\left.\frac{dy}{dt}\right|_{15} \approx 940.6 \text{ billion per year increase.}$$

59. Let y be the annual sales of the company, then $y(0) = 0$, $y(4) = 1$ million and

$$\frac{dy}{dt} = k(5 - y).$$

From this equation we have

$$\frac{dy}{5 - y} = k \, dt \quad \text{or} \quad \ln(5 - y)^{-1} = kt + C \quad \text{or}$$
$$5 - y = e^{-(kt+C)} \quad \text{or} \quad y = 5 - A e^{-kt}.$$
$$y(0) = 5 - A = 0, \text{ so } A = 5 \text{ and hence}$$
$$y = 5(1 - e^{-kt}).$$
$$y(4) = 5(1 - e^{-4k}) = 1 \text{ or } 1 - e^{-4k} = 0.2 \quad \text{or}$$
$$e^{-4k} = 0.8 \quad \text{and} \quad k = -\frac{1}{4} \ln(0.8) = -0.25 \ln(0.8).$$

Thus,
$$y(t) = 5(1 - e^{0.25t \ln(0.8)})$$

For $t = 15$, $y(15) = 5(1 - e^{0.25(15)\ln(0.8)}) = 2.8$ million.
$$\frac{dy}{dt} = -5(0.25)\ln(0.8)e^{0.25t \ln(0.8)} \quad \text{and}$$
$$\left.\frac{dy}{dt}\right|_{15} \approx 0.12 \text{ million per year increase.}$$

In order for the sales to grow to $4 million, we have to solve the following equation for t:
$$4 = 5(1 - e^{0.25t \ln(0.8)})$$
From this equation we have:
$$5e^{0.25t \ln(0.8)} = 1$$
or
$$0.25t \ln(0.8) = \ln(0.2)$$
or
$$t = \frac{\ln(0.2)}{0.25 \ln(0.8)} \approx 29 \text{ years.}$$

61. $S(t) = M(1 - e^{-kt})$, $M > 0$, $k > 0$ constant
We have:
$$S(1) = M(1 - e^{-k}) = 2$$
and $\qquad S(3) = M(1 - e^{-3k}) = 5$

From the first equation, $M = \dfrac{2}{1 - e^{-k}}$. Substituting this in the second equation yields:
$$\frac{2}{1 - e^{-k}}(1 - e^{-3k}) = 5$$
$$2 - 2e^{-3k} = 5 - 5e^{-k}$$
and $\qquad 2e^{-3k} - 5e^{-k} + 3 = 0 \qquad\qquad (1)$

Now let $t = e^{-k}$ ($k = -\ln t$). Then equation (1) becomes
$$2t^3 - 5t + 3 = 0$$
which factors into
$$(t - 1)(2t^2 + 2t - 3) = 0$$
The solutions are $t = 1$, $t \approx 0.82$ and $t \approx -1.82$.
Since $\ln(-1.82)$ is undefined and $\ln(1)$ implies $k = 0$, it follows that $k = -\ln(0.82) \approx 0.2$.
Now, $M = \dfrac{2}{(1 - e^{-0.2})} \approx 11$.
Thus, $k \approx 0.2$ and $M \approx \$11$ million.

63. Let $T(t)$ denote the temperature of the bar at time t. Then the model for this problem is

$$\frac{dT}{dt} = k(T - 800), \quad k < 0; \quad T(0) = 80, \quad T(2) = 200.$$

Separating the variables, we have

$$\frac{dT}{T - 800} = k \, dt$$

$$\int \frac{dT}{T - 800} = \int k \, dt$$

$$\ln|T - 800| = kt + C$$

$$T - 800 = e^{kt+C}$$

$$T = 800 + Ae^{kt} \quad \textit{General solution}$$

Using the conditions $T(0) = 80$ and $T(2) = 200$ to evaluate the constants A and k, we have

$$T(0) = 80 = 800 + Ae^0, \quad A = -720.$$

Thus, $T(t) = 800 - 720e^{kt}$.

$$T(2) = 200 = 800 - 720e^{2k}$$

$$720e^{2k} = 600$$

$$e^{2k} = \frac{5}{6}$$

$$2k = \ln\left(\frac{5}{6}\right)$$

$$k = \frac{1}{2}\ln\left(\frac{5}{6}\right)$$

Therefore, $T(t) = 800 - 720e^{1/2 \, \ln(5/6)t}$.

Finally, we want to find t such that $T(t) = 500$. Thus,

$$500 = 800 - 720e^{1/2 \, \ln(5/6)t}$$

$$720e^{1/2 \, \ln(5/6)t} = 300$$

$$e^{1/2 \, \ln(5/6)t} = \frac{5}{12}$$

$$\frac{1}{2}\ln\left(\frac{5}{6}\right)t = \ln\left(\frac{5}{12}\right)$$

$$t = \frac{2\ln\left(\frac{5}{12}\right)}{\ln\left(\frac{5}{6}\right)} \approx 9.6 \text{ minutes.}$$

65. Let $T(t)$ denote the temperature of the pie at time t. Then the model for this problem is:

$$\frac{dT}{dt} = k(T - 25), \ k < 0; \ T(0) = 325, \ T(1) = 225.$$

Separating the variables, we have $\dfrac{dT}{T - 25} = k \ dt$

$$\int \frac{dT}{T - 25} = \int k \ dt$$
$$\ln|T - 25| = kt + C$$
$$T - 25 = e^{kt+C}$$
$$T = 25 + Ae^{kt}$$

Using the initial conditions $T(0) = 325$ and $T(1) = 225$ to evaluate the constants A and k, we have:

$$T(0) = 325 = 25 + Ae^0, \ A = 300$$

Thus, $T(t) = 25 + 300e^{kt}$.

$$T(1) = 225 = 25 + 300e^k$$
$$300e^k = 200$$
$$e^k = \frac{2}{3}$$
$$k = \ln\left(\frac{2}{3}\right)$$

Therefore, $T(t) = 25 + 300e^{t \ \ln(2/3)}$.

Finally, we want to determine $T(4)$: $T(4) = 25 + 300e^{4 \ \ln(2/3)}$

$$= 25 + 300e^{\ln(2/3)^4}$$
$$= 25 + 300\left(\frac{2}{3}\right)^4 \approx 84.26°F$$

67. If $P(t)$ is the number of bacteria present at time t, then the model for this problem is:

$$\frac{dP}{dt} = kP; \ P(0) = 100, \ P(1) = 140, \ k > 0.$$
$$\frac{dP}{P} = k \ dt$$
$$\int \frac{dP}{P} = \int k \ dt$$
$$\ln|P| = kt + C$$
$$P = e^{kt+C}$$
$$P = Ae^{kt}. \quad \textit{General solution}$$

We use the conditions $P(0) = 100$ and $P(1) = 140$ to evaluate the constants A and k.

$$P(0) = 100 = Ae^0, \ A = 100.$$

Thus, $P(t) = 100e^{kt}$

$$P(1) = 140 = 100e^k$$
$$e^k = 1.4$$
$$k = \ln(1.4).$$

Therefore,
$$P(t) = 100e^{(\ln 1.4)t}. \quad \textit{Particular solution}$$

(A) When $t = 5$,
$$P(5) = 100e^{\ln(1.4)5}$$
$$\approx 538 \text{ bacteria.}$$

(B) When $P = 1000$,
$$1000 = 100e^{\ln(1.4)t}$$
$$e^{\ln(1.4)t} = 10$$
$$\ln(1.4)t = \ln 10$$
$$t = \frac{\ln 10}{\ln(1.4)} \approx 6.8 \text{ hours.}$$

69. If $P(t)$ is the number of people infected at time t, then the model for this problem is:
$$\frac{dP}{dt} = kP(50,000 - P); \ P(0) = 100, \ P(10) = 500.$$

$$\frac{dP}{P(50,000 - P)} = k \ dt$$

$$\int \frac{dP}{P(50,000 - P)} = \int k \ dt$$

$$\frac{1}{50,000} \int \left[\frac{1}{P} + \frac{1}{50,000 - P} \right] dP = kt + C$$

$$\frac{1}{50,000} [\ln P - \ln(50,000 - P)] = kt + C$$

$$\ln \left[\frac{P}{50,000 - P} \right] = 50,000(kt + C)$$

$$\frac{P}{50,000 - P} = e^{50,000kt + 50,000C}$$

$$= e^{50,000C} e^{50,000kt}$$

$$= Ae^{50,000kt}$$

Solving this equation for P, we obtain
$$P = (50,000 - P)Ae^{50,000kt}$$

$$P = \frac{50,000Ae^{50,000kt}}{1 + Ae^{50,000kt}},$$

which can be written
$$P(t) = \frac{50,000}{1 + Be^{-50,000kt}}, \quad B = \frac{1}{A}.$$

Using the conditions $P(0) = 100$ and $P(10) = 500$ to evaluate the constants B and k, we obtain
$$P(0) = 100 = \frac{50,000}{1 + Be^0}$$

$$100(1 + B) = 50,000$$

$$1 + B = 500$$

$$B = 499.$$

$$P(t) = \frac{50,000}{1 + 499e^{-50,000kt}} \cdot$$

$$P(10) = 500 = \frac{50,000}{1 + 499e^{-500,000k}}$$

$$1 + 499e^{-500,000k} = 100$$

$$499e^{-500,000k} = 99$$

$$-500,000k = \ln\left(\frac{99}{499}\right)$$

$$k = -\frac{1}{500,000}\ln\left(\frac{99}{499}\right) \cdot$$

Therefore, $P(t) = \dfrac{50,000}{1 + 499e^{0.1\ln(99/499)t}} \cdot$ *Particular solution*

(A) When $t = 20$,

$$P(20) = \frac{50,000}{1 + 499e^{2\ln(99/499)}}$$

$$\approx 2422 \text{ people.}$$

(B) When $P = 25,000$,

$$25,000 = \frac{50,000}{1 + 499e^{0.1\ln(99/499)t}}$$

$$1 + 499e^{0.1\ln(99/499)t} = 2$$

$$e^{0.1\ln(99/499)t} = \frac{1}{499}$$

$$0.1\ln\left(\frac{99}{499}\right)t = \ln\left(\frac{1}{499}\right)$$

$$t = \frac{10\ln\left(\frac{1}{499}\right)}{\ln\left(\frac{99}{499}\right)} \approx 38.4 \text{ days.}$$

71. Let y be the body temperature and let us assume that the time body was found (1:00 a.m.) as 0. Then $y(0) = 75°$ and $y(1) = 70°$ (2:00 a.m. is 1 hour after body was found).
Note that

$$\frac{dy}{dt} = k(y - C) = k(y - 50)$$

or

$$\frac{dy}{y - 50} = kt$$

or

$$\ln(y - 50) = kt + C_1$$

or

$y = 50 + Ae^{kt}$, where A and k are constants.

$y(0) = 75 = 50 + Ae^{k(0)} = 50 + A$ or $A = 25$

$y(1) = 70 = 50 + 25e^{k(1)}$ or $e^k = \dfrac{20}{25} = 0.8$ or $k = \ln(0.8)$.

Thus, $y(t) = 50 + 25e^{t\ln(0.8)}$.

To find the time of death we have to solve the following equation for t:

$$98.6 = 50 + 25e^{t \ln(0.8)}$$

Observe that

$$e^{t \ln(0.8)} = \frac{98.6 - 50}{25}$$

or

$$t = \frac{\ln\left(\frac{48.6}{25}\right)}{\ln(0.8)} \approx -3;\ \text{i.e. 3 hours before body was found.}$$

So, the time of death will be 10:00 p.m. since the body was found at 1:00 a.m.

73. $\dfrac{dI}{ds} = k\dfrac{I}{s},\ I > 0,\ s > 0.$

$$\frac{dI}{I} = \frac{k}{s}\,ds$$

$$\int \frac{dI}{I} = \int \frac{k}{s}\,ds$$

$$\ln I = k \ln s + C$$
$$= \ln s^k + C \qquad (k \ln s = \ln s^k)$$
$$I = e^{\ln s^k + C}$$
$$= e^C e^{\ln s^k}.$$

Therefore,

$$I = As^k. \qquad (\underline{\text{Note}}\colon e^{\ln s^k} = s^k.)$$

75. If $P(t)$ is the number of people who have heard the rumor at time t, then the model for this problem is:

$$\frac{dP}{dt} = kP(1000 - P);\ P(0) = 5,\ P(1) = 10.$$

$$\frac{dP}{P(1000 - P)} = k\,dt$$

$$\int \frac{dP}{P(1000 - P)} = \int k\,dt$$

$$\frac{1}{1000}\int \left[\frac{1}{P} + \frac{1}{1000 - P}\right] dP = kt + C$$

$$\frac{1}{1000}[\ln P - \ln(1000 - P)] = kt + C$$

$$\ln\left(\frac{P}{1000 - P}\right) = 1000(kt + C)$$

$$\frac{P}{1000 - P} = e^{1000kt + 1000C}$$

$$= e^{1000C}e^{1000kt}$$

$$= Ae^{1000kt}$$

Solving this equation for P, we obtain

$$P = \frac{1000Ae^{1000kt}}{1 + Ae^{1000kt}} \quad \text{or} \quad P = \frac{1000}{1 + Be^{-1000kt}} \left(B = \frac{1}{A}\right). \quad \textit{General solution}$$

Using the conditions $P(0) = 5$ and $P(1) = 10$ to evaluate the constants B and k, we have

$$P(0) = 5 = \frac{1000}{1 + Be^0}$$

$$5(1 + B) = 1000$$

$$1 + B = 200$$

$$B = 199.$$

Thus,

$$P(t) = \frac{1000}{1 + 199e^{-1000kt}}$$

$$P(1) = 10 = \frac{1000}{1 + 199e^{-1000k}}$$

$$1 + 199e^{-1000k} = 100$$

$$199e^{-1000k} = 99$$

$$e^{-1000k} = \frac{99}{199}$$

$$-1000k = \ln\left(\frac{99}{199}\right)$$

$$k = -\frac{1}{1000}\ln\left(\frac{99}{199}\right).$$

Therefore,

$$P(t) = \frac{1000}{1 + 199e^{\ln(99/199)t}}. \quad \textit{Particular solution}$$

(A) When $t = 7$,

$$P(7) = \frac{1000}{1 + 199e^{\ln(99/199)7}} \approx 400 \text{ people.}$$

(B) When $P = 850$,

$$850 = \frac{1000}{1 + 199e^{\ln(99/199)t}}$$

$$1 + 199e^{\ln(99/199)t} = \frac{1000}{850} = \frac{20}{17}$$

$$e^{\ln(99/199)t} = \frac{3}{3383}$$

$$\ln\left(\frac{99}{199}\right)t = \ln\left(\frac{3}{3383}\right)$$

$$t = \frac{\ln\left(\dfrac{3}{3383}\right)}{\ln\left(\dfrac{99}{199}\right)} \approx 10 \text{ days.}$$

1. $y' = ky$
   $y' - ky = 0$; $f(x) = -k$, $g(x) = 0$
   The differential equation is first-order linear.

3. $y' = ky(M - y) = kMy - ky^2$
   The equation has a y^2 term so it is **not** first-order linear.

5. $3x^2$; $\int(x^3y' + 3x^2y)\,dx = x^3y$

7. $-3e^{-3x}$; $\int(e^{-3x}y' - 3e^{-3x}y)\,dx = e^{-3x}y$

9. x^4; $\int(x^4y' + 4x^3y)\,dx = x^4y$

11. $e^{-0.5x}$; $\int(e^{-0.5x}y' - 0.5e^{-0.5x}y)\,dx = e^{-0.5x}y$

13. $y' + 2y = 4$; $y(0) = 1$

   Step 1: The equation is in standard form.

   Step 2: Find the integrating factor.
   $$f(x) = 2 \quad \text{and} \quad I(x) = e^{\int f(x)\,dx} = e^{\int 2\,dx} = e^{2x}$$

   Step 3: Multiply both sides of the standard form by the integrating factor.
   $$e^{2x}(y' + 2y) = e^{2x}(4)$$
   $$e^{2x}y' + 2e^{2x}y = 4e^{2x}$$
   $$[e^{2x}y]' = 4e^{2x}$$

   Step 4: Integrate both sides.
   $$\int[e^{2x}y]'\,dx = \int 4e^{2x}\,dx$$
   $$e^{2x}y = 2e^{2x} + C$$

   Step 5: Solve for y.
   $$y = \frac{1}{e^{2x}}(2e^{2x} + C) = 2 + Ce^{-2x} \quad \textit{General solution}$$

   To find the particular solution satisfying the initial condition $y(0) = 1$, substitute $x = 0$, $y = 1$ in the general solution:
   $$1 = 2 + Ce^0 = 2 + C.$$
   Thus, $C = -1$ and the particular solution is
   $$y = 2 - e^{-2x}$$

15. $y' + y = e^{-2x}$; $y(0) = 3$

   Step 1: The equation is in standard form.

   Step 2: Find the integrating factor.
   $$f(x) = 1 \quad \text{and} \quad I(x) = e^{\int f(x)\,dx} = e^{\int 1\,dx} = e^x$$

Step 3: Multiply both sides of the standard form by the integrating factor.

$$e^x \, [y' + y] = e^x \cdot e^{-2x}$$
$$e^x y' + e^x y = e^{-x}$$
$$[e^x y]' = e^{-x}$$

Step 4: Integrate both sides.

$$\int [e^x y]' \, dx = \int e^{-x} \, dx$$
$$e^x y = \frac{e^{-x}}{-1} + C = -e^{-x} + C$$

Step 5: Solve for y.

$$y = \frac{1}{e^x} [-e^{-x} + C] = -e^{-2x} + Ce^{-x} \qquad \textit{General solution}$$

To find the particular solution satisfying the initial condition $y(0) = 3$, substitute $x = 0$, $y = 3$ in the general solution:

$$3 = -e^0 + Ce^0 = -1 + C$$

Thus, $C = 4$ and the particular solution is

$$y = -e^{-2x} + 4e^{-x}$$

17. $y' - y = 2e^x$; $y(0) = -4$

Step 1: The equation is in standard form.

Step 2: Find the integrating factor.

$$f(x) = -1 \quad \text{and} \quad I(x) = e^{\int f(x)\,dx} = e^{\int (-1)\,dx} = e^{-x}$$

Step 3: Multiply both sides of the standard form by the integrating factor.

$$e^{-x} \, [y' - y] = e^{-x}(2e^x)$$
$$e^{-x} y' - e^{-x} y = 2$$
$$[e^{-x} y]' = 2$$

Step 4: Integrate both sides.

$$\int [e^{-x} y]' \, dx = \int 2 \, dx$$
$$e^{-x} y = 2x + C$$

Step 5: Solve for y.

$$y = \frac{1}{e^{-x}} [2x + C] = 2xe^x + Ce^x \qquad \textit{General solution}$$

To find the particular solution satisfying the initial condition $y(0) = -4$, substitute $x = 0$, $y = -4$ in the general solution:

$$-4 = 2(0)e^0 + Ce^0 = C$$

Thus, $C = -4$ and the particular solution is

$$y = 2xe^x - 4e^x$$

19. $y' + y = 9x^2 e^{-x}$; $y(0) = 2$

Step 1: The equation is in standard form.

Step 2: Find the integrating factor.
$$f(x) = 1 \quad \text{and} \quad I(x) = e^{\int f(x)\,dx} = e^{\int 1\,dx} = e^x$$

Step 3: Multiply both sides of the standard form by the integrating factor.
$$e^x\,[y' + y] = e^x(9x^2 e^{-x})$$
$$e^x y' + e^x y = 9x^2$$
$$[e^x y]' = 9x^2$$

Step 4: Integrate both sides.
$$\int [e^x y]'\,dx = \int 9x^2\,dx$$
$$e^x y = 3x^3 + C$$

Step 5: Solve for y.
$$y = \frac{1}{e^x}(3x^3 + C) = 3x^3 e^{-x} + Ce^{-x} \quad \textit{General solution}$$

To find the particular solution satisfying the initial condition $y(0) = 2$, substitute $x = 0$, $y = 2$ in the general solution:
$$2 = 3(0)^3 e^0 + Ce^0 = C$$

Thus, $C = 2$ and the particular solution is
$$y = 3x^3 e^{-x} + 2e^{-x}$$

21. $xy' + y = 2x$; $y(1) = 1$

Step 1: Write the differential equation in standard form.
Multiply both sides by $\frac{1}{x}$ to obtain:
$$y' + \frac{1}{x}y = 2$$

Step 2: Find the integrating factor.
$$f(x) = \frac{1}{x} \quad \text{and} \quad I(x) = e^{\int f(x)\,dx} = e^{\int (1/x)\,dx} = e^{\ln x} = x$$

Step 3: Multiply both sides of the standard form by the integrating factor.
$$x\left(y' + \frac{1}{x}\,y\right) = x(2)$$
$$xy' + y = 2x$$
$$[xy]' = 2x$$

Step 4: Integrate both sides.
$$\int [xy]'\,dx = \int 2x\,dx$$
$$xy = x^2 + C$$

Step 5: Solve for y.
$$y = \frac{1}{x}(x^2 + C) = x + \frac{C}{x} \qquad \textit{General solution}$$

To find the particular solution satisfying the initial condition $y(1) = 1$, substitute $x = 1$, $y = 1$ in the general solution:
$$1 = 1 + \frac{C}{1} = 1 + C$$
Thus, $C = 0$ and the particular solution is
$$y = x$$

23. $xy' + 2y = 10x^3; \quad y(2) = 8$

Step 1: Write the differential equation in standard form.
Multiply both sides by $\frac{1}{x}$ to obtain:
$$y' + \frac{2}{x}y = 10x^2$$

Step 2: Find the integrating factor.
$$f(x) = \frac{2}{x} \quad \text{and} \quad I(x) = e^{\int f(x)\,dx} = e^{\int (2/x)\,dx} = e^{2 \ln x} = e^{\ln x^2} = x^2$$

Step 3: Multiply both sides of the standard form by the integrating factor.
$$x^2\left(y' + \frac{2}{x}\, y\right) = x^2(10x^2)$$
$$x^2 y' + 2xy = 10x^4$$
$$[x^2 y]' = 10x^4$$

Step 4: Integrate both sides.
$$\int [x^2 y]'\, dx = \int 10x^4\, dx$$
$$x^2 y = 2x^5 + C$$

Step 5: Solve for y.
$$y = \frac{1}{x^2}(2x^5 + C) = 2x^3 + \frac{C}{x^2} \qquad \textit{General solution}$$

To find the particular solution satisfying the initial condition $y(2) = 8$, substitute $x = 2$, $y = 8$ in the general solution:
$$8 = 2(2)^3 + \frac{C}{2^2} = 16 + \frac{C}{4}$$
and $\quad -8 = \frac{C}{4}$.

Thus, $C = -32$ and the particular solution is
$$y = 2x^3 - \frac{32}{x^2}$$

25. $y' + xy = 5x$

$I(x) = e^{\int f(x)\,dx} = e^{\int x\,dx} = e^{x^2/2}$ *Integrating factor*

$y = \dfrac{1}{I(x)}\int I(x)\,g(x)\,dx$

$\quad = \dfrac{1}{e^{x^2/2}}\int e^{x^2/2}5x\,dx$

$\quad = 5e^{-x^2/2}\int xe^{x^2/2}\,dx \qquad \left(u = \dfrac{x^2}{2},\ du = x\,dx\right)$

$\quad = 5e^{-x^2/2}[e^{x^2/2} + C] = 5 + 5Ce^{-x^2/2}$

$y = 5 + Ae^{-x^2/2}.$ *General solution*

27. $y' - 2y = 4x$

$I(x) = e^{\int(-2)\,dx} = e^{-2x}$ *Integrating factor*

$y = \dfrac{1}{I(x)}\int I(x)\,g(x)\,dx = \dfrac{1}{e^{-2x}}\int e^{-2x}4x\,dx$

$\quad = 4e^{2x}\int xe^{-2x}\,dx \qquad$ (Integrate by parts)

$\quad = 4e^{2x}\left[-\dfrac{1}{2}xe^{-2x} - \dfrac{1}{4}e^{-2x} + C\right]$

$\quad = -2x - 1 + 4Ce^{2x} \qquad (A = 4C)$

$y = -2x - 1 + Ae^{2x}.$ *General solution*

29. $xy' + y = xe^x$

First write the equation in standard form: $y' + \dfrac{1}{x}y = e^x$.

Then,

$I(x) = e^{\int f(x)\,dx} = e^{\int(1/x)\,dx} = e^{\ln x} = x$ *Integrating factor*

$y = \dfrac{1}{I(x)}\int I(x)\,g(x)\,dx$

$\quad = \dfrac{1}{x}\int xe^x\,dx \qquad$ (Integrate by parts)

$\quad = \dfrac{1}{x}[xe^x - e^x + C]$

$y = e^x - \dfrac{e^x}{x} + \dfrac{C}{x}.$ *General solution*

31. $xy' + y = x \ln x$

First write the equation in standard form: $y' + \dfrac{1}{x}y = \ln x$

Then,

$y' + \dfrac{1}{x}y = \ln x$

$I(x) = e^{\int f(x)\,dx} = e^{\int (1/x)\,dx} = e^{\ln x} = x$ *Integrating factor*

$y = \dfrac{1}{I(x)}\int I(x)g(x)\,dx$

$ = \dfrac{1}{x}\int x \ln x\,dx$ (Integrate by parts)

$ = \dfrac{1}{x}\left[\dfrac{x^2}{2}\ln x - \dfrac{1}{4}x^2 + C\right]$

$ = \dfrac{1}{2}x \ln x - \dfrac{1}{4}x + \dfrac{C}{x}.$ *General solution*

33. $2xy' + 3y = 20x$

First write the equation in standard form

$\qquad y' + \dfrac{3}{2x}y = 10$

Then,

$I(x) = e^{\int f(x)\,dx} = e^{\int (3/2x)\,dx} = e^{(3/2)\ln x}$

$\qquad\qquad\qquad\qquad = e^{\ln x^{3/2}} = x^{3/2}$ *Integrating factor*

$y = \dfrac{1}{I(x)}\int I(x)g(x)\,dx = \dfrac{1}{x^{3/2}}\int x^{3/2}10\,dx$

$\qquad\qquad = 10x^{-3/2}\int x^{3/2}\,dx$

$\qquad\qquad = 10x^{-3/2}\left[\dfrac{2}{5}x^{5/2} + C\right]$

$\qquad\qquad = 4x + 10Cx^{-3/2}$ $(A = 10C)$

$\qquad\qquad = 4x + Ax^{-3/2}$ *General solution*

35. (A) Substitute $y = \dfrac{1}{3}(x + 1)^3 + C$; $y' = (x + 1)^2$ into the differential

equation to determine whether these substitutions reduce the equation to an identity.

(B) The solution is wrong:

$\qquad \dfrac{1}{x}\int x(x + 1)^2\,dx \neq \int (x + 1)^2\,dx$

(C) $y = \dfrac{1}{x}\int x(x + 1)^2 \, dx = \dfrac{1}{x}\int (x^3 + 2x^2 + x)\, dx$

$$= \dfrac{1}{x}\left[\dfrac{1}{4}x^4 + \dfrac{2}{3}x^3 + \dfrac{1}{2}x^2 + C\right]$$

$$= \dfrac{1}{4}x^3 + \dfrac{2}{3}x^2 + \dfrac{1}{2}x + \dfrac{C}{x}$$

Thus, $\quad y = \dfrac{1}{4}x^3 + \dfrac{2}{3}x^2 + \dfrac{1}{2}x + \dfrac{C}{x}$ *General solution*

Substituting y and $y' = \dfrac{3}{4}x^2 + \dfrac{4}{3}x + \dfrac{1}{2} - \dfrac{C}{x^2}$

into the differential equation yields:

$$\dfrac{3}{4}x^2 + \dfrac{4}{3}x + \dfrac{1}{2} - \dfrac{C}{x^2} + \dfrac{1}{x}\left(\dfrac{1}{4}x^3 + \dfrac{2}{3}x^2 + \dfrac{1}{2}x + \dfrac{C}{x}\right) = x^2 + 2x + 1$$

$$= (x + 1)^2$$

37. (A) Substitute $y = \dfrac{1}{2}e^{-x}$, $y' = -\dfrac{1}{2}e^{-x}$ into the differential equation to determine whether these substitutions reduce the equation to an identity.

(B) $y = \dfrac{1}{2}e^{-x}$ is **not** the general solution since the constant of integration has been omitted. However, $y = \dfrac{1}{2}e^{-x}$ is a particular solution.

(C) $y = \dfrac{1}{e^{3x}}\int e^{2x}\, dx = \dfrac{1}{e^{3x}}\left[\dfrac{1}{2}e^{2x} + C\right]$

$$= \dfrac{1}{2}e^{-x} + Ce^{-3x}$$

Thus, $\quad y = \dfrac{1}{2}e^{-x} + Ce^{-3x}$ *General solution*

Substituting y and $y' = -\dfrac{1}{2}e^{-x} - 3Ce^{-3x}$ into the differential equation yields:

$$-\dfrac{1}{2}e^{-x} - 3Ce^{-3x} + 3\left(\dfrac{1}{2}e^{-x} + Ce^{-3x}\right) = e^{-x}$$

39. $y' = \dfrac{1 - y}{x}$

This equation can be rewritten as a first-order linear differential equation in the standard form.

(A) $y' + \dfrac{1}{x}y = \dfrac{1}{x}$.

Then $f(x) = \dfrac{1}{x}$ and the integrating factor is

$I(x) = e^{\int(1/x)dx} = e^{\ln x} = x$.

Thus, $y = \dfrac{1}{x}\int x \cdot \dfrac{1}{x}\,dx = \dfrac{1}{x}\int dx = \dfrac{1}{x}(x + C) = 1 + \dfrac{C}{x}$.

(B) Using separation of variables on the original equation, we have:

$\dfrac{y'}{1 - y} = \dfrac{1}{x}$

$\int \dfrac{dy}{1 - y} = \int \dfrac{1}{x}\,dx$

$-\ln(1 - y) = \ln(x) + C$ \qquad (assuming $1 - y > 0$ and $x > 0$)

$\ln(1 - y) = -\ln(x) - C$

$1 - y = e^{-\ln x - C}$

$1 - y = e^{-C}e^{\ln x^{-1}}$

$1 - y = \dfrac{K}{x}$ \qquad $\left(e^{\ln x^{-1}} = \dfrac{1}{x}\right)$

$y = 1 + \dfrac{K}{x}$

41. $y' = \dfrac{2x + 2xy}{1 + x^2}$

This equation can be rewritten as a first-order linear differential equation in the standard form.

(A) $y' - \dfrac{2x + 2xy}{1 + x^2}y = \dfrac{2x}{1 + x^2}$.

Then, $f(x) = \dfrac{-2x}{1 + x^2}$ and the integrating factor is:

$I(x) = e^{\int(-2x/1 + x^2)dx} = e^{-\ln(1 + x^2)} = \dfrac{1}{1 + x^2}$

Thus, $y = \dfrac{1}{\dfrac{1}{1 + x^2}}\int \dfrac{1}{1 + x^2} \cdot \dfrac{2x}{1 + x^2}\,dx$

$= (1 + x^2)\int \dfrac{2x}{(1 + x^2)^2}\,dx = (1 + x^2)\left[\dfrac{-1}{1 + x^2} + C\right]$

and \quad $y = -1 + C(1 + x^2)$.

(B) Using separation of variables on the original equation, we have:

$$\frac{y'}{1 + y} = \frac{2x}{1 + x^2}$$

$$\int \frac{dy}{1 + y} = \int \frac{2x}{1 + x^2} \, dx$$

$$\ln|1 + y| = \ln(1 + x^2) + C$$

$$1 + y = e^{\ln(1+x^2)+C}$$

$$1 + y = e^C e^{\ln(1+x^2)}$$

$$1 + y = K(1 + x^2) \qquad (e^{\ln(1+x^2)} = 1 + x^2)$$

$$y = -1 + K(1 + x^2)$$

43. $y' = 2x(y + 1)$

This equation can be rewritten as a first-order linear differential equation in the standard form.

(A) $y' - 2xy = 2x$

Then, $f(x) = -2x$ and the integrating factor is:

$$I(x) = e^{\int -2x \, dx} = e^{-x^2}$$

Thus, $y = \dfrac{1}{e^{-x^2}} \int e^{-x^2} \, 2x \, dx = e^{x^2} \int 2x e^{-x^2} \, dx = e^{x^2} [-e^{-x^2} + C]$

and $y = -1 + Ce^{x^2}$.

(B) Using separation of variables on the original equation, we have:

$$\frac{y'}{y + 1} = 2x$$

$$\int \frac{dy}{1 + y} = \int 2x \, dx$$

$$\ln|y + 1| = x^2 + C$$

$$y + 1 = e^{x^2 + C}$$

$$y + 1 = e^C e^{x^2}$$

$$= Ke^{x^2}$$

Thus, $y = -1 + Ke^{x^2}$.

45. $\dfrac{dy}{dt} = ky.$

This equation can be rewritten as

$$\frac{dy}{dt} - ky = 0$$

Here $f(t) = -k$ and the integrating factor is:

$$I(t) = e^{\int -k \, dt} = e^{-kt}$$

Thus, $y = \dfrac{1}{e^{-kt}} \int e^{-kt} \cdot 0 \, dt = e^{kt} \int 0 \, dt = e^{kt} C$

and $y = Ce^{kt}$.

47. If $f(x) = a \neq 0$ and $g(x) = b$, a, b constant, then $y' + f(x)y = g(x)$ becomes $y' + ay = b$.

The integrating factor is: $I(x) = e^{\int a\, dx} = e^{ax}$, and

$$e^{ax}y' + ae^{ax}y = be^{ax}$$

$$(e^{ax}y)' = be^{ax}$$

$$\int (e^{ax}y)'\, dx = be^{ax}\, dx$$

$$e^{ax}y = \frac{b}{a}e^{ax} + C$$

$$y = \frac{b}{a} + Ce^{-ax} \qquad \text{(General solution)}$$

49. The amount A in the account at any time t must satisfy
$$\frac{dA}{dt} - 0.048A = -3000.$$

Now $f(t) = -0.048$ and the integrating factor is:

$$I(t) = e^{\int (-0.048)\, dt} = e^{-0.048t}$$

Thus, $A = \dfrac{1}{e^{-0.048t}}\displaystyle\int -3000e^{-0.048t}\, dt$

$$= e^{0.048t}\left[\frac{-3000e^{-0.048t}}{-0.048} + C \right]$$

$$A = 62{,}500 + Ce^{0.048t} \qquad \textit{General solution}$$

Applying the initial condition $A(0) = 20{,}000$ yields:
$$A(0) = 62{,}500 + Ce^0 = 20{,}000 \quad \text{and} \quad C = -42{,}500$$
Thus, the amount in the account at any time t is:
$$A(t) = 62{,}500 - 42{,}500e^{0.048t}$$

To determine when the amount in the account is 0, we must solve $A(t) = 0$ for t:

$$62{,}500 - 42{,}500e^{0.048t} = 0$$
$$42{,}500e^{0.048t} = 62{,}500$$
$$e^{0.048t} = 1.4706$$

$$t = \frac{\ln 1.4706}{0.048} \approx 8.035$$

Thus, the account is depleted after 8.035 years. The total amount withdrawn from the account is:
$$3000(8.035) = \$24{,}105.$$

51. The amount in the account at any time t must satisfy
$$\frac{dA}{dt} - 0.0475A = -1900.$$
Now $f(t) = -0.0475$ and the integrating factor is:
$$I(t) = e^{\int (-0.0475)dt} = e^{-0.0475t}$$
Thus,
$$A = \frac{1}{e^{-0.0475t}}\int -1900e^{-0.0475t} \, dt = e^{0.0475t}\left[\frac{-1900e^{-0.0475t}}{-0.0475} + C\right]$$
$$= 40,000 + Ce^{0.0475t} \qquad \textit{General solution}$$

Applying the initial condition $A(0) = P$ yields:
$$40,000 + C = P$$
$$C = P - 40,000$$

Thus, the amount in the account at any time t is:
$$A(t) = 40,000 + (P - 40,000)e^{0.0475t}$$

Since $A(10) = 0$, we have:
$$0 = 40,000 + (P - 40,000)e^{0.0475(10)}$$
$$(P - 40,000)e^{0.475} = -40,000$$

Solving for the initial deposit P yields:
$$P = \frac{-40,000}{e^{0.475}} + 40,000 = 40,000(1 - e^{-0.475}) \approx 15,124.60$$

Thus, the initial deposit was $15,124.60.

53. The amount in the account at any time t must satisfy
$$\frac{dA}{dt} - 0.07A = 2100.$$
Now $f(t) = -0.07$ and the integrating factor is
$$I(t) = e^{\int (-0.07)dt} = e^{-0.07t}$$
Thus,
$$A = \frac{1}{e^{-0.07t}}\int 2100e^{-0.07t} \, dt = e^{0.07t}\left[\frac{2100e^{-0.07t}}{-0.07} + C\right]$$
$$= -30,000 + Ce^{0.07t}$$

Applying the initial condition $A(0) = 5000$ yields:
$$5000 = -30,000 + C$$
and $\quad C = 35,000$

Thus, the amount in the account at any time t is:
$$A(t) = 35,000e^{0.07t} - 30,000$$

After 5 years, the amount in the account is
$$A(5) = 35,000e^{0.07(5)} - 30,000 = 35,000e^{0.35} - 30,000$$
$$\approx \$19,667.36$$

55. Let r (expressed as a decimal) be the interest rate. Then the amount in the account at any time t must satisfy

$$\frac{dA}{dt} - rA = 1{,}000$$

Now, $f(t) = -r$ and the integrating factor is:

$$I(t) = e^{\int -r\ dt} = e^{-rt}$$

Thus,

$$A(t) = \frac{1}{e^{-rt}}\int 1{,}000e^{-rt}\ dt$$

$$= \frac{1{,}000}{e^{-rt}}\left[-\frac{1}{r}e^{-rt} + C\right]$$

$$= Ce^{rt} - \frac{1{,}000}{r}$$

Since $A(0) = 10{,}000$, we have

$$10{,}000 = Ce^{0} - \frac{1{,}000}{r}$$

and $\quad C = 10{,}000 + \dfrac{1{,}000}{r}$

Therefore,

$$A(t) = 10{,}000e^{rt} + \frac{1{,}000}{r}(e^{rt} - 1)$$

Now, at $t = 10$, we have

$$30{,}000 = 10{,}000e^{10r} + \frac{1{,}000}{r}(e^{10r} - 1)$$

Solving this equation for r using a graphing utility, we find that $r \approx 0.0523$. Expressed as a percentage, $r = 5.23\%$.

57. The equilibrium price at time t is the solution of the equation

$$95 - 5p(t) + 2p'(t) = 35 - 2p(t) + 3p'(t)$$

which satisfies the initial condition $p(0) = 30$.

The equation simplifies to

$$p'(t) + 3p(t) = 60,$$

a first-order linear equation. The integrating factor is:

$$I(t) = e^{\int 3\ dt} = e^{3t}$$

Thus,

$$p(t) = \frac{1}{e^{3t}}\int 60e^{3t}\ dt = e^{-3t}\left[\frac{60e^{3t}}{3} + C\right]$$

$$= 20 + Ce^{-3t} \qquad \textit{General solution}$$

Applying the initial condition yields

$$p(0) = 20 + C = 30$$
$$C = 10$$

Thus, the equilibrium price at time t is:

$$p(t) = 20 + 10e^{-3t}$$

The long-range equilibrium price is:

$$\overline{p} = \lim_{t \to \infty}(20 + 10e^{-3t}) = 20$$

59. Let $p(t)$ be the amount of pollutants in the tank at time t. The initial amount of pollutants in the tank is $p(0) = 2 \cdot 200 = 400$ pounds.

Pollutants are entering the tank at the constant rate of $3 \cdot 75 = 225$ pounds per hour.

The amount of water in the tank at time t is $200 + 25t$.

The amount of pollutants in each gallon of water at time t is $\dfrac{p(t)}{200 + 25t}$.

The rate at which pollutants are leaving the tank is

$$\frac{50p(t)}{200 + 25t} = \frac{2p(t)}{8 + t}.$$

Thus, the model for this problem is

$$p'(t) = 225 - \frac{2p(t)}{8 + t}; \quad p(0) = 400 \quad \text{or} \quad p'(t) + \frac{2p(t)}{8 + t} = 225; \quad p(0) = 400.$$

Now $f(t) = \dfrac{2}{8 + t}$ and the integrating factor is:

$$I(t) = e^{\int(2/8+t))dt} = e^{2\,\ln(8+t)} = e^{\ln(8+t)^2} = (8 + t)^2$$

Thus,

$$p(t) = \frac{1}{(8 + t)^2}\int 225(8 + t)^2 dt = \frac{1}{(8 + t)^2}\left[225\frac{(8 + t)^3}{3} + C\right]$$

$$p(t) = 75(8 + t) + \frac{C}{(8 + t)^2}. \quad \textit{General solution}$$

We use the initial condition $p(0) = 400$ to evaluate the constant C.

$$p(0) = 400 = 75(8) + \frac{C}{8^2}$$

$$\frac{C}{64} = -200$$

$$C = -12{,}800$$

$$p(t) = 75(8 + t) - \frac{12{,}800}{(8 + t)^2}. \quad \textit{Particular solution}$$

To find the total amount of pollutants in the tank after two hours, we evaluate $p(2)$:

$$p(2) = 75(10) - \frac{12{,}800}{(10)^2} = 750 - 128 = 622$$

After two hours, the tank contains 250 gallons of water. Thus, the rate at which pollutants are being released is

$$\frac{622}{250} \approx 2.5 \text{ pounds per gallon.}$$

61. Let $p(t)$ be the amount of pollutants in the tank at time t. The initial amount of pollutants in the tank is $p(0) = 2 \cdot 200 = 400$ pounds.

Pollutants are entering the tank at the constant rate of $3(50) = 150$ pounds per hour.

Since water is entering and leaving the tank at the same rate, the amount of water in the tank at all times t is 200 gallons.

The amount of pollutants in each gallon of water at time t is $\dfrac{p(t)}{200}$.

The rate at which pollutants are leaving the tank is $\dfrac{50p(t)}{200} = \dfrac{p(t)}{4}$.

Thus, the model for this problem is:
$$p'(t) = 150 - \frac{p(t)}{4}; \quad p(0) = 400 \quad \text{or} \quad p'(t) + \frac{1}{4}p(t) = 150; \quad p(0) = 400$$

Now $f(t) = \dfrac{1}{4}$ and the integrating factor is:
$$I(t) = e^{\int (1/4)\,dt} = e^{t/4}$$

Thus, $p(t) = \dfrac{1}{e^{t/4}} \int e^{t/4}(150)\,dt$

$$= 150e^{-t/4} \int e^{t/4}\,dt = 150e^{-t/4}[4e^{t/4} + C]$$

$$= 600 + 150Ce^{-t/4} \qquad (A = 150C)$$

$$p(t) = 600 + Ae^{-t/4} . \textit{General solution}$$

We use the initial condition $p(0) = 400$ to evaluate the constant A.
$$p(0) = 400 = 600 + Ae^0, \quad A = -200$$

Therefore, $p(t) = 600 - 200e^{-t/4}$.   *Particular solution*

To find the amount of pollutants in the tank after two hours, we evaluate $p(2)$:

$$p(2) = 600 - 200e^{-1/2} \approx 479 \text{ pounds}$$

The rate at which pollutants are being released after two hours is

$$\frac{600 - 200e^{-1/2}}{200} = 3 - e^{-1/2} \approx 2.4 \text{ pounds per gallon.}$$

63. From Problem 59, the amount of pollutants in the tank at time t is given by:

$$p(t) = 75(8 + t) - \frac{12,800}{(8 + t)^2}$$

To find the time t when the tank contains 1,000 pounds of pollutants, we solve the equation:

$$75(8 + t) - \frac{12,800}{(8 + t)^2} = 1,000$$

Using a graphing utility, we find that
$t \approx 6.2$ hrs.
The graphs of $p(t)$ and $p = 1,000$ are shown above.

65. The model for this problem is:

$$\frac{dw}{dt} + 0.005w = \frac{2100}{3500} \quad \text{or} \quad \frac{dw}{dt} + 0.005w = \frac{3}{5}$$

Now $f(t) = 0.005$, and the integrating factor is:

$$I(t) = e^{\int 0.005 dt} = e^{0.005t}$$

Thus, $w(t) = \dfrac{1}{e^{0.005t}} \displaystyle\int \frac{3}{5} e^{0.005t} \, dt$

$$= \frac{3}{5} e^{-0.005t} \left[\frac{e^{0.005t}}{0.005} + k \right]$$

$$= 120 + \frac{3}{5} k e^{-0.005t}$$

$$= 120 + A e^{-0.005t} \qquad \textit{General solution}$$

Applying the initial condition $w(0) = 160$, we have:

$$160 = 120 + A e^0$$
$$A = 40$$

Thus, $w(t) = 120 + 40 e^{-0.005t}$.
How much will a person weigh after 30 days on the diet?

$$w(30) = 120 + 40 e^{(-0.005)(30)} \approx 154 \text{ pounds}$$

Now, we want to find t such that $w(t) = 150$.

$$150 = 120 + 40 e^{-0.005t}$$
$$40 e^{-0.005t} = 30$$
$$e^{-0.005t} = \frac{3}{4}$$
$$-0.005t = \ln\left(\frac{3}{4}\right)$$
$$t = \frac{-\ln\left(\frac{3}{4}\right)}{0.005} \approx 58$$

Thus, it will take 58 days to lose 10 pounds.

Finally, $\lim\limits_{t \to \infty} w(t) = \lim\limits_{t \to \infty} (120 + 40 e^{-0.005t}) = 120$, since $\lim\limits_{t \to \infty} e^{-0.005t} = 0$.
Therefore, the person's weight will approach 120 pounds if this diet is maintained for a long period.

67. The model for this problem is
$$\frac{dw}{dt} + 0.005w = \frac{1}{3500}C,$$
where C is to be determined.

Now, $f(t) = 0.005$, and the integrating factor is:
$$I(t) = e^{\int 0.005\,dt} = e^{0.005t}$$

Thus, $w(t) = \dfrac{1}{e^{0.005t}}\displaystyle\int \dfrac{C}{3500} e^{0.005t}\,dt$

$$= \frac{C}{3500} e^{-0.005t}\left[\frac{e^{0.005t}}{0.005} + k\right]$$

$$= \frac{C}{17.5} + \frac{Ck}{3500} e^{-0.005t}$$

$$= \frac{C}{17.5} + Ae^{-0.005t} \qquad \textit{General solution}$$

Applying the initial condition $w(0) = 130$, we have
$$130 = \frac{C}{17.5} + Ae^0$$

$$A = 130 - \frac{C}{17.5}$$

and
$$w(t) = \frac{C}{17.5} + \left(130 - \frac{C}{17.5}\right)e^{-0.005t}$$

Now, we want to determine C such that $w(30) = 125$.
$$125 = \frac{C}{17.5} + \left(130 - \frac{C}{17.5}\right)e^{-0.005(30)}$$

$$125 = \frac{C}{17.5} + \left(130 - \frac{C}{17.5}\right)e^{-0.15}$$

$$\frac{C}{17.5}(1 - e^{-0.15}) = 125 - 130e^{-0.15}$$

$$C = \frac{17.5(125 - 130e^{-0.15})}{1 - e^{-0.15}} \approx 1{,}647$$

Thus, the person should consume 1,647 calories per day.

69. The model for this problem is
$$\frac{dk}{dt} + \ell k = \lambda\ell$$
where ℓ and λ are constants.

Now, $f(t) = \ell$, and the integrating factor is:
$$I(t) = e^{\int \ell\,dt} = e^{\ell t}$$
Thus,

$$k(t) = \frac{1}{e^{\ell t}}\int \lambda\ell e^{\ell t}\,dt = e^{-\ell t}\left[\ell\lambda\,\frac{e^{\ell t}}{\ell} + C\right] = \lambda + \frac{C}{\ell}e^{-\ell t}$$

$$= \lambda + Me^{-\ell t} \quad \textit{General solution}$$

For Student A, $\ell = 0.8$ and $\lambda = 0.9$. Thus,

$\quad k(t) = 0.9 + Me^{-0.8t}$.

Applying the initial condition $k(0) = 0.1$ yields:

$\quad 0.1 = 0.9 + Me^0$ or $M = -0.8$

and $k(t) = 0.9 - 0.8e^{-0.8t}$.

When $t = 6$, we have:

$\quad k(6) = 0.9 - 0.8e^{-0.8(6)} = 0.9 - 0.8e^{-4.8} \approx 0.8934$ or 89.34%

For Student B, $\ell = 0.8$ and $\lambda = 0.7$. Thus,

$\quad k(t) = 0.7 + Me^{-0.8t}$.

Applying the initial condition $k(0) = 0.4$ yields:

$\quad 0.4 = 0.7 + Me^0$ or $M = -0.3$

and $k(t) = 0.7 - 0.3e^{-0.8t}$

When $t = 6$, we have:

$\quad k(6) = 0.7 - 0.3e^{-0.8(6)} = 0.7 - 0.3e^{-4.8} \approx 0.6975$ or 69.75%

CHAPTER 1 REVIEW

1. Substitute $y = C\sqrt{x}$, $y' = \dfrac{C}{2\sqrt{x}}$ into the given differential equation:

$$2x\left(\frac{C}{2\sqrt{x}}\right) = C\sqrt{x}$$

$$C\sqrt{x} = C\sqrt{x}$$

Thus, $y = C\sqrt{x}$ is the general solution. $\hfill$ (1.1)

2. Substitute $y = 1 + Ce^{-x/3}$, $y' = -\dfrac{C}{3}e^{-x/3}$ into the given differential equation:

$$3\left(-\frac{C}{3}e^{-x/3}\right) + 1 + Ce^{-x/3} = 1$$

$$-Ce^{-x/3} + 1 + Ce^{-x/3} = 1$$

$$1 = 1$$

Thus, $y = 1 + Ce^{-x/3}$ is the general solution. $\hfill$ (1.1)

3. (B) $\hfill$ (1.1) $\qquad$ 4. (A) $\hfill$ (1.1)

5.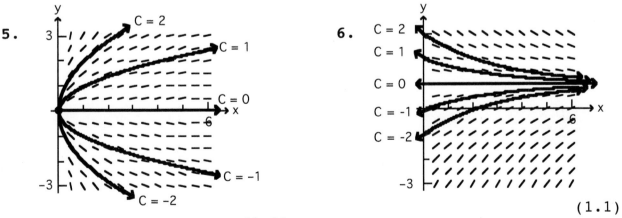

(1.1)

6.

(1.1)

7. $\dfrac{dy}{dt} = -k(y - 5), \; k < 0$ (1.2)   **8.** $\dfrac{dy}{dt} = ky, \; k > 0$ (1.2)

9. A single person began the spread of a disease; the disease is spreading at a rate that is proportional to the product of the number of people who have the disease and the number who don't have it. (1.2)

10. There are 100 grams of a radioactive material at the instant a nuclear accident occurs, and the material is decaying at a rate proportional to the amount present.   (1.2)

11. $y' + 3x^2 y + 9 = e^x(1 - x + y) = e^x - xe^x + ye^x$
$y' + (3x^2 - e^x)y = (1 - x)e^x - 9$
The differential equation is first-order linear.   (1.2, 1.3)

12. $y' + 10y + 25 = 5xy^2$
The $5xy^2$ term implies that the equation is not first-order linear. Also, the equation cannot be written in the form $f(y)y' = g(x)$. (1.2, 1

13. $y' + 3y = xy + 2x - 6$
$\quad\quad\quad y' = (x - 3)y + 2(x - 3) = (y + 2)(x - 3)$
Separation of variables form: $\dfrac{1}{y + 2}y' = x - 3$.

Also, the equation can be written in first-order linear form:
$y' + (3 - x)y = 2x - 6$ (1.2, 1.3)

14. $y^2 y' = 4xe^{x-y} = 4xe^x e^{-y}$
Separation of variables form: $y^2 e^y y' = 4xe^{-x}$
The equation is **not** first-order linear.   (1.2, 1.3)

15. $y' = -\dfrac{4y}{x}$

$\dfrac{y'}{y} = \dfrac{-4}{x}$ Separate the variables

$\displaystyle\int \dfrac{dy}{y} = \int \dfrac{-4}{x}\,dx$

$\ln|y| = -4\ln|x| + C = \ln x^{-4} + C$

$\quad\quad y = e^{\ln x^{-4} + C}$

$\quad\quad\quad = e^C e^{\ln x^{-4}}$

$\quad\quad y = Ax^{-4} = \dfrac{A}{x^4}$ *General solution*   (1.2)

16. $y' = \dfrac{-4y}{x} + x$

$y' + \dfrac{4}{x}y = x$ First-order linear equation

Integrating factor: $I(x) = e^{\int f(x)\,dx} = e^{\int (4/x)\,dx} = e^{4 \ln x} = e^{\ln x^4} = x^4$
Therefore,

$y = \dfrac{1}{I(x)}\displaystyle\int I(x)g(x)\,dx, \quad g(x) = x$

$\quad = \dfrac{1}{x^4}\displaystyle\int x^4 x\ dx = \dfrac{1}{x^4}\displaystyle\int x^5\ dx = \dfrac{1}{x^4}\left[\dfrac{x^6}{6} + C\right]$

$y = \dfrac{x^2}{6} + \dfrac{C}{x^4}$ *General solution*   (1.3)

17. $y' = 3x^2 y^2$

$\dfrac{y'}{y^2} = 3x^2$ Separate the variables

$\displaystyle\int \dfrac{dy}{y^2} = \int 3x^2\ dx$

$-\dfrac{1}{y} = x^3 + C$

$y = \dfrac{-1}{x^3 + C}$ *General solution*   (1.2)

18. $y' = 2y - e^x$

$y' - 2y = -e^x$ First-order linear equation

Integrating factor: $I(x) = e^{\int (-2)\,dx} = e^{-2x}$

$y = \dfrac{1}{I(x)}\displaystyle\int I(x)g(x)\,dx, \quad g(x) = -e^x$

$\quad = \dfrac{1}{e^{-2x}}\displaystyle\int e^{-2x}(-e^x)\,dx = e^{2x}\displaystyle\int -e^{-x}\ dx = e^{2x}[e^{-x} + C]$

$y = e^x + Ce^{2x}$ *General solution*   (1.3)

19. $y' = \dfrac{5}{x}y + x^6$

$y' - \dfrac{5}{x}y = x^6$ First-order linear equation

Integrating factor: $I(x) = e^{\int (-5/x)\,dx} = e^{-5 \ln x} = e^{\ln x^{-5}} = x^{-5}$

$y = \dfrac{1}{I(x)}\displaystyle\int I(x)g(x)\,dx, \quad g(x) = x^6$

$\quad = \dfrac{1}{x^{-5}}\displaystyle\int x^{-5}x^6\ dx = x^5\displaystyle\int x\ dx = x^5$

$y = \dfrac{x^7}{2} + Cx^5$ *General solution*   (1.3)

20. $y' = \dfrac{3 + y}{2 + x}$

$\dfrac{y'}{3 + y} = \dfrac{1}{2 + x}$　　　Separate the variables

$\displaystyle\int\dfrac{dy}{3 + y} = \int\dfrac{dx}{2 + x}$

$\ln|3 + y| = \ln(2 + x) + C$　　　(Note: $2 + x > 0$.)

$3 + y = e^{\ln(2+x)+C} = e^C(2 + x) = A(2 + x)$

$y = A(2 + x) - 3$　　　*General solution*　　　　　　　　　(1.2)

21. $y' = 10 - y$; $y(0) = 0$

$\dfrac{y'}{10 - y} = 1$　　　Separate the variables

$\displaystyle\int\dfrac{dy}{10 - y} = \int dx$

$-\ln|10 - y| = x + C$

$\ln|10 - y| = -x - C$

$10 - y = e^{-x-C}$

$\quad = e^{-C}e^{-x} = Ae^{-x}$

$y = 10 - Ae^{-x}$. *General solution*

Applying the initial condition $y(0) = 0$, we have:

$0 = 10 - Ae^0$, $A = 10$

Thus, $y = 10 - 10e^{-x}$.　　　*Particular solution*　　　(1.2 or 1.3)

22. $y' + y = x$; $y(0) = 0$

Integrating factor: $I(x) = e^{\int 1 \, dx} = e^x$

Thus, $y = \dfrac{1}{I(x)}\int I(x)g(x)\,dx$, $g(x) = x$

$\quad = \dfrac{1}{e^x}\int e^x x \, dx = e^{-x}\int xe^x \, dx = e^{-x}[xe^x - e^x + C]$

$y = x - 1 + Ce^{-x}$.　　　*General solution*

Applying the initial condition $y(0) = 0$, we have:

$0 = 0 - 1 + Ce^0$, $C = 1$

Therefore, $y = x - 1 + e^{-x}$. *Particular solution*　　　　　(1.3)

23. $y' = 2ye^{-x}$; $y(0) = 1$

$\dfrac{y'}{y} = 2e^{-x}$　　　Separate the variables

$\displaystyle\int\dfrac{dy}{y} = \int 2e^{-x} \, dx$

$\ln|y| = -2e^{-x} + C$

$y = e^{-2e^{-x}+C} = e^0 e^{-2e^{-x}}$

$y = Ae^{-2e^{-x}}$　　　　　*General solution*

Applying the initial condition $y(0) = 1$, we have:

$1 = Ae^{-2e^0} = Ae^{-2}$, $A = e^2$

Thus, $y = e^2 e^{-2e^{-x}}$.   *Particular solution*   (1.2)

24. $y' = \dfrac{2x - y}{x + 4}$; $y(0) = 1$

$y' + \dfrac{1}{x + 4}y = \dfrac{2x}{x + 4}$ First-order linear equation

Integrating factor: $I(x) = e^{\int(1/(x+4))dx} = e^{\ln(x+4)} = x + 4$

Thus, $y = \dfrac{1}{I(x)}\int I(x)g(x)\,dx$, $g(x) = \dfrac{2x}{x + 4}$

$\quad = \dfrac{1}{x + 4}\int(x + 4)\dfrac{2x}{x + 4}\,dx = \dfrac{1}{x + 4}\int 2x\,dx = \dfrac{1}{x + 4}[x^2 + C]$

$\quad y = \dfrac{x^2}{x + 4} + \dfrac{C}{x + 4}$.   *General solution*

Applying the initial condition $y(0) = 1$, we have:

$1 = 0 + \dfrac{C}{4}$, $C = 4$

Therefore, $y = \dfrac{x^2}{x + 4} + \dfrac{4}{x + 4} = \dfrac{x^2 + 4}{x + 4}$.   *Particular solution*   (1.3)

25. $y' = \dfrac{x}{y + 4}$; $y(0) = 0$

$(y + 4)y' = x$ Separate the variables

$\int(y + 4)\,dy = \int x\,dx$

$\quad \dfrac{(y + 4)^2}{2} = \dfrac{x^2}{2} + C$

$\quad (y + 4)^2 = x^2 + 2C$

or $(y + 4)^2 = x^2 + A$.   *General solution, implicit form*

Solving for y and applying the initial condition $y(0) = 0$, we have:

$y + 4 = \sqrt{x^2 + A}$

$0 + 4 = \sqrt{0 + A}$

$\quad A = 16$

Therefore, $y = \sqrt{x^2 + 16} - 4$.   *Particular solution*   (1.2)

26. $y' + \dfrac{2}{x}y = \ln x; \quad y(1) = 2$

Integrating factor: $I(x) = e^{\int(2/x)dx} = e^{2\ln x} = e^{\ln x^2} = x^2$

Thus, $y = \dfrac{1}{I(x)}\int I(x)g(x)dx, \quad g(x) = \ln x$

$\qquad = \dfrac{1}{x^2}\int x^2 \ln x\, dx \quad$ (Integrate by parts)

$\qquad = \dfrac{1}{x^2}\left[\dfrac{1}{3}x^3 \ln x - \dfrac{x^3}{9} + C\right]$

$\qquad y = \dfrac{1}{3}x \ln x - \dfrac{x}{9} + \dfrac{C}{x^2}. \qquad$ *General solution*

Applying the initial condition $y(1) = 2$, we have:

$2 = \dfrac{1}{3}(1)\ln 1 - \dfrac{1}{9} + C, \quad C = \dfrac{19}{9}$

Therefore, $y = \dfrac{1}{3}x \ln x - \dfrac{x}{9} + \dfrac{19}{9x^2}.$ *Particular solution* $\qquad$ (1.3)

27. $yy' = \dfrac{x(1 + y^2)}{1 + x^2}; \quad y(0) = 1$

$\dfrac{yy'}{1 + y^2} = \dfrac{x}{1 + x^2} \qquad$ Separate the variables

$\displaystyle\int \dfrac{y\, dy}{1 + y^2} = \int \dfrac{x\, dx}{1 + x^2}$

$\dfrac{1}{2}\ln(1 + y^2) = \dfrac{1}{2}\ln(1 + x^2) + C$

$\ln(1 + y^2) = \ln(1 + x^2) + 2C$

$1 + y^2 = e^{\ln(1+x^2) + 2C}$

$\qquad = e^{2C}e^{\ln(1+x^2)}$

$\qquad = A(1 + x^2)$

$\qquad y^2 = A(1 + x^2) - 1. \quad$ *General solution, implicit form*

Solving this equation for y and applying the initial condition $y(0) = 1$, we have:

$\qquad y = \sqrt{A(1 + x^2) - 1}$

$\qquad 1 = \sqrt{A - 1}$

$A - 1 = 1$

$\qquad A = 2$

Thus, $y = \sqrt{2(1 + x^2) - 1} = \sqrt{1 + 2x^2}. \qquad$ *Particular solution* $\qquad$ (1.2)

28. $y' + 2xy = 2e^{-x^2}$; $y(0) = 1$

Integrating factor: $I(x) = e^{\int 2x\, dx} = e^{x^2}$

Thus, $y = \dfrac{1}{I(x)}\int I(x)\,g(x)\,dx$, $g(x) = 2e^{-x^2}$

$\qquad = \dfrac{1}{e^{x^2}}\int e^{x^2}\,2e^{-x^2}\,dx = e^{-x^2}\int 2\ dx = e^{-x^2}[2x + C]$

$\qquad y = 2xe^{-x^2} + Ce^{-x^2}.$ *General solution*

Applying the initial condition $y(0) = 1$, we have:

$1 = 2\cdot 0\cdot e^0 + Ce^0$, $C = 1$

Therefore, $y = 2xe^{-x^2} + e^{-x^2} = (2x + 1)e^{-x^2}$. *Particular solution*

(1.3)

29. $xy' - 4y = 8$

(A) <u>Solution using an integrating factor:</u>

<u>Step 1</u>: Write the differential equation in standard form:
Multiply both sides of the equation by $\dfrac{1}{x}$

$\qquad\qquad y' - \dfrac{4}{x}y = \dfrac{8}{x}$

<u>Step 2</u>: Find the integrating factor:
$\qquad f(x) = -\dfrac{4}{x}$, $I(x) = e^{\int f(x)\,dx} = e^{\int (-4/x)\,dx}$

$\qquad\qquad\qquad\qquad\qquad = e^{-4\ln x}$

$\qquad\qquad\qquad\qquad\qquad = e^{\ln(x^{-4})}$

$\qquad\qquad\qquad\qquad\qquad = x^{-4}$

<u>Step 3</u>: Multiply both sides of the equation by the integrating factor:
$\qquad\qquad x^{-4}(y' - 4x^{-1}y) = (8x^{-1})x^{-4}$

$\qquad\qquad\qquad x^{-4}y' - 4x^{-5}y = 8x^{-5}$

$\qquad\qquad\qquad\qquad [x^{-4}y]' = 8x^{-5}$

<u>Step 4</u>: Integrate both sides:
$\qquad\qquad \int [x^{-4}y]'\,dx = \int 8x^{-5}\,dx$

$\qquad\qquad\qquad x^{-4}y = -2x^{-4} + C$

<u>Step 5</u>: Solve for y:
$\qquad\qquad y = -2 + Cx^4$ *General solution*

(B) <u>Solution using separation of variables</u>

$$xy' - 4y = 8$$
$$xy' = 4y + 8$$
$$\frac{1}{4y + 8} y' = \frac{1}{x}$$
$$\int \frac{1}{4y + 8} dy = \int \frac{1}{x} dx$$
$$\frac{1}{4} \ln|4y + 8| = \ln|x| + K$$
$$\ln|4y + 8| = 4 \ln|x| + L \qquad (L = 4K)$$
$$\ln|4y + 8| = \ln x^4 + L$$
$$|4y + 8| = e^{\ln x^4 + L} = e^L x^4$$
$$4y + 8 = Mx^4 \qquad\qquad (M = \pm e^L)$$
$$y = Cx^4 - 2 \qquad\qquad (C = M/4) \qquad\qquad (1.2,\ 1.3)$$

30. The equation $y' + y = x$ can be solved using an integrating factor; it cannot be solved by separating the variables.

Integrating factor:
$$f(x) = 1, \quad I(x) = e^{\int dx} = e^x$$
Multiply by e^x:
$$e^x y' + e^x y = xe^x$$
$$[e^x y]' = xe^x$$
Integrate:
$$e^x y = xe^x - e^x + C$$
Solve for y:
$$y = Ce^{-x} + x - 1 \qquad\qquad (1.3)$$

31. The equation $y' = xy^2$ can be solved by separating the variables; it cannot be solved using an integrating factor

$$y' = xy^2$$
$$\frac{1}{y^2} y' = x$$
$$\int \frac{1}{y^2} dy = \int x\ dx$$
$$-\frac{1}{y} = \frac{1}{2} x^2 + K$$
$$y = \frac{-1}{\frac{1}{2} x^2 + K} = \frac{-2}{x^2 + 2K}$$
$$y = \frac{-2}{x^2 + C} \qquad (C = 2K) \qquad\qquad (1.2)$$

32. $xy' - 5y = -10$

   Step 1: Write the differential equation in standard form:
   $$y' - \frac{5}{x}y = -\frac{10}{x}$$

   Step 2: Find an integrating factor:
   $$f(x) = -\frac{5}{x} \quad ; \quad I(x) = e^{\int (-5/x)\,dx} = e^{-5 \ln x}$$
   $$= e^{\ln x^{-5}} = x^{-5}$$

   Step 3: Multiply by the integrating factor:
   $$x^{-5}(y' - 5x^{-1}y) = x^{-5}(-10x^{-1})$$
   $$x^{-5}y' - 5x^{-6}y = -10x^{-6}$$
   $$(x^{-5}y)' = -10x^{-6}$$

   Step 4: Integrate both sides:
   $$\int (x^{-5}y)'\,dx = \int -10x^{-6}\,dx$$
   $$x^{-5}y = 2x^{-5} + C$$

   Step 5: Solve for y:
   $$y = 2 + Cx^5 \qquad \textit{General solution}$$

   (A) Applying the initial condition $y(0) = 2$, we have:
   $$2 = 2 + 0 = 2$$
   Thus, $y = 2 + Cx^5$ satisfies $y(0) = 2$ for all values of C.

   (B) Applying the initial condition $y(0) = 0$, we have:
   $$0 = 2 + 0 \quad \text{or} \quad 2 = 0$$
   Thus, there is **no** particular solution that satisfies $y(0) = 0$.

   (C) Applying the initial condition $y(1) = 1$, we have:
   $$1 = 2 + C(1) \quad \text{and} \quad C = -1$$
   Thus, $y = 2 - x^5$ is the particular solution that satisfies
   $y(1) = 1$. (1.3)

33.
   $$yy' = x$$
   $$\int y\,dy = \int x\,dx$$
   $$\frac{1}{2}y^2 = \frac{1}{2}x^2 + K$$

   or $\qquad y^2 = x^2 + C \quad (C = 2K) \qquad \textit{General solution}$

   Applying the initial condition $y(0) = 4$, we have:
   $$16 = 0^2 + C \quad \text{and} \quad C = 16$$
   Thus, $y^2 = x^2 + 16$ and $y = \sqrt{x^2 + 16}$ $\qquad$ *Particular solution* $\qquad$ (1.2)

34. (A)

(B) The graphs are increasing and cross the x axis only at $x = 0$.

(C)

(D) The graphs have a local maximum, a local minimum, and cross the x axis three times.

(1.1)

35. $y = M(1 - e^{-kt})$, $M > 0$, $k > 0$

(A) At $t = 2$, $4 = M(1 - e^{-2k})$ so $M = \dfrac{4}{1 - e^{-2k}}$

At $t = 5$, $7 = M(1 - e^{-5k})$ so $M = \dfrac{7}{1 - e^{-5k}}$

(B) Using a graphing utility to graph the two equations in part (A), we find that $M \approx 9.2$.

(1.2)

36. Let $V(t)$ denote the value of the refrigerator at time t. Then the model for this problem is: $\dfrac{dV}{dt} = kV$; $V(0) = 500$, $V(20) = 25$

$$\frac{dV}{dt} - kV = 0$$

Integrating factor: $I(t) = e^{\int (-k)\,dt} = e^{-kt}$

Thus, $V = \dfrac{1}{I(t)}\int I(t)g(t)\,dt$, $g(t) = 0$

$\qquad = \dfrac{1}{e^{-kt}}\int e^{-kt}\cdot 0\ dt = e^{kt}\int 0\ dt$

$V = Ce^{kt}$. *General solution*

Applying the conditions $V(0) = 500$ and $V(20) = 25$, we have:

$V(0) = 500 = Ce^{0}$, $C = 500$

Therefore, $V(t) = 500e^{kt}$.

$V(20) = 25 = 500e^{k(20)}$

$\qquad e^{20k} = \dfrac{25}{500} = \dfrac{1}{20}$

$\qquad 20k = \ln\!\left(\dfrac{1}{20}\right)$

$\qquad\quad k = \dfrac{1}{20}\ln\!\left(\dfrac{1}{20}\right)$

Therefore, $V(t) = 500e^{(1/20)\ln(1/20)t}$.

Finally, we want to calculate V when $t = 5$:

$V(5) = 500e^{(1/20)\ln(1/20)5} = 500e^{(1/4)\ln(1/20)} = 500e^{-0.25\ln 20} \approx \$236.44$

(1.2 or 1.3)

37. The model for this problem is:

$$\frac{ds}{dt} = k(200{,}000 - s); \quad s(0) = 0, \; s(1) = 50{,}000, \; k > 0$$

(A) $\dfrac{ds}{200{,}000 - s} = k \, dt$ Separate the variables

$$\int \frac{ds}{200{,}000 - s} = \int k \, dt$$

$$-\ln(200{,}000 - s) = kt + C \qquad (0 < s < 200{,}000)$$

$$200{,}000 - s = e^{-kt-C}$$

$$= e^{-C}e^{-kt}$$

$$= Ae^{-kt}$$

$$s = 200{,}000 - Ae^{-kt} \qquad \textit{General solution}$$

We use the conditions $s(0) = 0$ and $s(1) = 50{,}000$ to evaluate the constants A and k.

$$s(0) = 0 = 200{,}000 - Ae^0$$

$$A = 200{,}000$$

Thus, $s = 200{,}000 - 200{,}000e^{-kt}$.

$$s(1) = 50{,}000 = 200{,}000 - 200{,}000e^{-k}$$

$$200{,}000e^{-k} = 150{,}000$$

$$e^{-k} = \frac{150{,}000}{200{,}000} = \frac{3}{4}$$

$$-k = \ln\left(\frac{3}{4}\right)$$

Therefore, $s = 200{,}000 - 200{,}000e^{\ln(3/4)t}$.

Finally, we determine t such that $s(t) = 150{,}000$.

$$150{,}000 = 200{,}000 - 200{,}000e^{\ln(3/4)t}$$

$$200{,}000e^{\ln(3/4)t} = 50{,}000$$

$$e^{\ln(3/4)t} = \frac{50{,}000}{200{,}000} = \frac{1}{4}$$

$$\ln\left(\frac{3}{4}\right)t = \ln\left(\frac{1}{4}\right)$$

$$t = \frac{\ln(1/4)}{\ln(3/4)} \approx 5 \text{ years}$$

(B) From part (A), we know that

$$S(t) = 200{,}000 - 200{,}000e^{-kt}$$

Since we want the sales to be \$150,000 after 3 years, we have

$$150{,}000 = 200{,}000 - 200{,}000e^{-3k}$$

$$200{,}000e^{-3k} = 50{,}000$$

$$e^{-3k} = 0.25$$

$$-3k = \ln 0.25$$

$$k = -\frac{\ln(0.25)}{3}$$

Thus, $s(t) = 200{,}000 - 200{,}000e^{(t/3)\ln 0.25}$

Now, $s(1) = 200{,}000 - 200{,}000e^{(1/3)\ln 0.25} \approx 74{,}000$

Therefore, the sales in the first year should be $74,000 to ensure that the sales after 3 years will be $150,000. (1.2)

38. (A) The equilibrium price $p(t)$ at time t satisfies
$S = D$; $p(0) = 75$. Thus, $100 + p + p' = 200 - p' - p$
$$2p' + 2p = 100$$
$$p' + p = 50$$

Integrating factor: $I(t) = e^{\int f(t)\,dt} = e^{\int 1\,dt} = e^t$

Thus, $p = \dfrac{1}{I(t)}\int I(t)g(t)\,dt$, $\quad g(t) = 50$

$\qquad = \dfrac{1}{e^t}\int e^t \cdot 50\ dt = 50e^{-t}[e^t + C]$

$\qquad = 50 + 50Ce^{-t} \qquad (A = 50C)$

$\qquad p = 50 + Ae^{-t}$. $\qquad$ *General solution*

(B) The equilibrium price $\bar{p}$ is given by
$$\bar{p} = \lim_{t\to\infty}(50 + 25e^{-t}) = 50 + 25\lim_{t\to\infty}e^{-t} = 50.$$

(C) Applying the initial condition $p(0) = 75$, we have:
$$75 = 50 + Ae^0 \quad \text{and} \quad A = 25$$
Therefore, $p_1 = 50 + 25e^{-t}$ $\quad$ *Particular solution*

Applying the initial condition $p(0) = 25$, we have
$$25 = 50 + Ae^0 \quad \text{and} \quad A = -25$$

Therefore, $p_2 = 50 - 25e^{-t}$ $\quad$ *Particular solution*

The graphs of p_1 and p_2 are shown at the right.

(D) For an initial price above the equilibrium price $\bar{p} = 50$, the price of the commodity decreases toward $\bar{p}$. For an initial price below the equilibrium price $\bar{p}$, the price of the commodity increases toward $\bar{p}$. (1.1, 1.2)

39. The amount in the account at any time t must satisfy
$$\frac{dA}{dt} - 0.05A = -5000.$$
Now, $f(t) = -0.05$, and the integrating factor is:
$I(t) = e^{\int(-0.05)\,dt} = e^{-0.05t}$

Thus, $A = \dfrac{1}{e^{-0.05t}}\int -5000e^{-0.05t}\,dt = e^{0.05t}\left[-5000\dfrac{e^{-0.05t}}{-0.05} + C\right]$

$\qquad A = 100{,}000 + Ce^{0.05t}$ $\quad$ *General solution*

Applying the initial condition $A(0) = 60{,}000$ yields:
$A(0) = 100{,}000 + Ce^0 = 60{,}000$
$$C = -40{,}000$$
Thus, the amount in the account at any time t is:
$A(t) = 100{,}000 - 40{,}000e^{0.05t}$
To determine when the amount in the account is 0, we must solve $A(t) = 0$ for t:
$100{,}000 - 40{,}000e^{0.05t} = 0$
$$e^{0.05t} = \frac{100{,}000}{40{,}000} = \frac{5}{2}$$
$$t = \frac{\ln\left(\frac{5}{2}\right)}{0.05} \approx 18.326$$

Thus, the account will be depleted after 18.326 years. The total amount withdrawn from the account is: $5000(18.326) = \$91{,}630$ (1.3)

40. Let r be the continuous compound rate of interest (expressed in decimal form). Then the amount in the account at any time t is given by:
$$\frac{dA}{dt} = rA + 2{,}000$$
or $\dfrac{dA}{dt} - rA = 2{,}000$

(Note: the method of separation of variables could also have been used to solve the equation.)

Now, $f(t) = -r$ and the integrating factor is:
$$I(t) = e^{\int -r \, dt} = e^{-rt}$$
Thus,
$$A = \frac{1}{e^{-rt}} \int 2{,}000 e^{-rt} \, dt$$
$$= e^{rt}\left[-\frac{2{,}000}{r} e^{-rt} + C \right]$$
and $A = Ce^{rt} - \dfrac{2{,}000}{r}$ *General solution*

Applying the initial condition $A(0) = 15{,}000$ yields:
$$A(0) = 15{,}000 = Ce^0 - \frac{2{,}000}{r}$$
$$C = 15{,}000 + \frac{2{,}000}{r}$$
Thus, the amount in the account at any time t is:
$$A(t) = \left(15{,}000 + \frac{2{,}000}{r} \right) e^{rt} - \frac{2{,}000}{r}$$

Now, at $t = 10$, $A(10) = 50{,}000$. Therefore, we have
$$50{,}000 = \left(15{,}000 + \frac{2{,}000}{r} \right) e^{10r} - \frac{2{,}000}{r}$$
Using a graphing utility to solve this equation for r, we find that $r = 0.0482$. Expressed as a percentage, $r = 4.82\%$.   (1.2 or 1.3)

41. $\dfrac{dy}{dt} = 100 + e^{-t} - y; \quad y(0) = 0$

$\dfrac{dy}{dt} + y = 100 + e^{-t}$

Integrating factor: $I(t) = e^{\int 1\, dt} = e^{t}$

Thus, $y = \dfrac{1}{I(t)}\int I(t)g(t)\,dt, \quad g(t) = 100 + e^{-t}$

$\qquad = \dfrac{1}{e^{t}}\int e^{t}(100 + e^{-t})\,dt = e^{-t}\int(100e^{t} + 1)\,dt = e^{-t}[100e^{t} + t + C]$

$\qquad y = 100 + te^{-t} + Ce^{-t}. \qquad \textit{General solution}$

Applying the initial condition, we have:

$0 = 100 + 0e^{0} + Ce^{0}, \quad C = -100$

Therefore, $y = 100 + te^{-t} - 100e^{-t}. \qquad \textit{Particular solution}$ $\qquad\qquad$ (1.3)

42. Let $p(t)$ be the amount of pollutants in the tank at time t. At $t = 0$, we have $p(0) = 0$.

Pollutants are entering the tank at the constant rate $2(75) = 150$ pounds per hour. The amount of water in the tank at time t is:

$\qquad 100 + 75t - 50t = 100 + 25t$

The amount of pollutants in each gallon of water at time t is:

$\qquad \dfrac{p(t)}{100 + 25t}$

The rate at which pollutants are leaving the tank at time t is:

$\qquad 50\left(\dfrac{p(t)}{100 + 25t}\right) = \dfrac{2p(t)}{4 + t}$

The mathematical model for this problem is:

$\qquad \dfrac{dp}{dt} = 150 - \dfrac{2p}{4 + t}; \quad p(0) = 0$

(A) In standard form, the differential equation is:

$\qquad \dfrac{dp}{dt} + \dfrac{2}{4 + t}p = 150$

Now, $f(t) = \dfrac{2}{4 + t}$ and $I(t) = e^{\int [2/(4+t)]\,dt} = e^{2\ln(4 + t)}$

$\qquad\qquad\qquad\qquad\qquad\qquad\qquad = e^{\ln(4 + t)^{2}}$

$\qquad\qquad\qquad\qquad\qquad\qquad\qquad = (4 + t)^{2}$

Thus, $p(t) = \dfrac{1}{I(t)}\int I(t)g(t)\,dt, \quad g(t) = 150$

$\qquad\quad = \dfrac{1}{(4 + t)^{2}}\int(4 + t)^{2}\,150\,dt$

$\qquad\quad = \dfrac{150}{(4 + t)^{2}}\left[\dfrac{(4 + t)^{3}}{3} + K\right]$

$\qquad\quad = 50(4 + t) + \dfrac{C}{(4 + t)^{2}} \qquad (C = 150K) \qquad \textit{General solution}$

Applying the initial condition $p(0) = 0$, we have

$$0 = 50(4) + \frac{C}{(4)^2} \quad \text{and} \quad C = -3,200$$

Therefore, $p(t) = 50(4 + t) - \dfrac{3,200}{(4 + t)^2}$ *Particular solution*

Now, at $t = 2$,

$$p(2) = 50(6) - \frac{3,200}{6^2} \approx 211.1$$

There are approximately 211.1 pounds of pollutants in the tank after 2 hours.

(B) To find how long it will take for the tank to contain 700 pounds of pollutants, we solve the equation

$$50(4 + t) - \frac{3,200}{(4 + t)^2} = 700$$

for t using a graphing utility. The result is $t \approx 10.3$ hours. (1.3)

43. Let $p(t)$ be the bird population at time t. Then $\dfrac{dp}{dt} = k(p - 200)$, $k < 0$ constant.

(Note: this equation can be solved either by separating the variables or as a first order linear equation; we'll illustrate the latter.)

(A) $\dfrac{dp}{dt} = kp - 200k$, $p(0) = 500$

In standard form, the differential equation is:

$$\frac{dp}{dt} - kp = -200k, \quad k < 0 \text{ constant}$$

Now, $f(t) = -k$ and $I(t) = e^{\int -k\, dt} = e^{-kt}$

Thus, $p(t) = \dfrac{1}{e^{-kt}} \int e^{-kt}(-200k)\, dt$

$$= e^{kt}[200e^{-kt} + C]$$

and $p(t) = 200 + Ce^{kt}$ *General solution*

Applying the initial condition $p(0) = 500$, yields

$$500 = 200 + C \quad \text{and} \quad C = 300$$

Therefore, $p(t) = 200 + 300e^{kt}$

Now, at $t = -5$, $p(-5) = 1,000$ and

$$1000 = 200 + 300e^{-5k}$$

$$e^{-5k} = \frac{8}{3}$$

$$-5k = \ln\left(\frac{8}{3}\right)$$

$$k = \frac{\ln(8/3)}{-5}$$

Thus, the bird population at any time t is:

$$p(t) = 200 + 300e^{-(t/5)\ln(8/3)}$$

The bird population 4 years from now will be:

$$p(4) = 200 + 300e^{-(4/5)\ln(8/3)} \approx 337 \text{ birds}$$

(B) From part (A), the general solution of
$$\frac{dp}{dt} = k(p - M), \; k < 0 \text{ constant}$$
is $p(t) = M + Ce^{kt}$

Applying the initial condition $p(0) = 500$, we have
$$500 = M + C \quad \text{and} \quad C = 500 - M$$

Therefore,
$$p(t) = M + (500 - M)e^{kt}$$

Now, at $t = -5$, $p(-5) = 1,000$ and
$$1,000 = M + (500 - M)e^{-5k}$$
$$e^{-5k} = \frac{1,000 - M}{500 - M}$$
$$-5k = \ln\left(\frac{1,000 - M}{500 - M}\right)$$
$$k = -\frac{1}{5}\ln\left(\frac{1,000 - M}{500 - M}\right)$$

Thus, the bird population at any time t is
$$p(t) = M + (500 - M)e^{-(t/5)\ln[(1000 - M)/(500 - M)]}$$
$$= M + (500 - M)\left(\frac{1,000 - M}{500 - M}\right)^{-t/5}$$

Now, at $t = 4$, $p(4) = 400$. Using a graphing calculator to solve
$$400 = M + (500 - M)\left(\frac{1,000 - M}{500 - M}\right)^{-4/5}$$
we get $M \approx 357$ birds   (1.2 or 1.3)

44. Let $p(t)$ denote the number of people who have heard the rumor at time t. Then the model for this problem is:
$$\frac{dp}{dt} = k(200 - p); \; p(0) = 1, \; p(2) = 10$$
$$\frac{dp}{200 - p} = k \, dt \qquad \text{Separating the variables}$$
$$\int \frac{dp}{200 - p} = \int k \, dt$$
$$-\ln(200 - p) = kt + C$$
$$\ln(200 - p) = -kt - C$$
$$200 - p = e^{-kt-C}$$
$$= e^{-C}e^{-kt}$$
$$= Ae^{-kt}$$
$$p = 200 - Ae^{-kt} \qquad \textit{General solution}$$

Apply the conditions $p(0) = 1$ and $p(2) = 10$ to evaluate the constants A and k: $p(0) = 1 = 200 - Ae^0$, $A = 199$

Thus, $p = 200 - 199e^{-kt}$.

$$p(2) = 10 = 200 - 199e^{-2k}$$
$$199e^{-2k} = 190$$
$$e^{-2k} = \frac{190}{199}$$
$$-2k = \ln\left(\frac{190}{199}\right)$$
$$k = \frac{-1}{2}\ln\left(\frac{190}{199}\right)$$

Therefore, $p = 200 - 199e^{(1/2)\ln(190/199)t}$.   *Particular solution*

(A) When $t = 5$,
$$p(5) = 200 - 199e^{(1/2)\ln(190/199)5}$$
$$= 200 - 199e^{(5/2)\ln(190/199)} \approx 23 \text{ people}$$

(B) Find t such that $p(t) = 100$.
$$100 = 200 - 199e^{(1/2)\ln(190/199)t}$$
$$199e^{(1/2)\ln(190/199)t} = 100$$
$$e^{(1/2)\ln(190/199)t} = \frac{100}{199}$$
$$\frac{1}{2}\ln\left(\frac{190}{199}\right)t = \ln\left(\frac{100}{199}\right)$$
$$t = \frac{2\ln\left(\frac{100}{199}\right)}{\ln\left(\frac{190}{199}\right)} \approx 30 \text{ days} \tag{1.2}$$

2 TAYLOR POLYNOMIALS AND INFINITE SERIES

EXERCISE 2.1

1. $f(x) = \dfrac{1}{x} = x^{-1}$

$f'(x) = -x^{-2}$ (Using Power Rule)

$f''(x) = 2x^{-3}$

$f^{(3)}(x) = -6x^{-4} = -\dfrac{6}{x^4}$

3. $f(x) = e^{-x}$

$f'(x) = -e^{-x}$

$f''(x) = e^{-x}$

$f^{(3)}(x) = -e^{-x}$

5. $f(x) = \ln(1 + 3x)$

$f'(x) = \dfrac{3}{1 + 3x} = 3(1 + 3x)^{-1}$

$f''(x) = 3(-1)(3)(1 + 3x)^{-2} = -9(1 + 3x)^{-2}$ (Using Power Rule)

$f^{(3)}(x) = (-9)(-2)(3)(1 + 3x)^{-3} = 54(1 + 3x)^{-3}$

$f^{(4)}(x) = (54)(-3)(3)(1 + 3x)^{-4} = -486(1 + 3x)^{-4} = -\dfrac{486}{(1 + 3x)^4}$

7. $f(x) = \sqrt{1 + x} = (1 + x)^{1/2}$

$f'(x) = \dfrac{1}{2}(1 + x)^{-1/2}$ (Using Power Rule)

$f''(x) = \left(\dfrac{1}{2}\right)\left(-\dfrac{1}{2}\right)(1 + x)^{-3/2} = -\dfrac{1}{4}(1 + x)^{-3/2}$

$f^{(3)}(x) = \left(-\dfrac{1}{4}\right)\left(-\dfrac{3}{2}\right)(1 + x)^{-5/2} = \dfrac{3}{8}(1 + x)^{-5/2}$

$f^{(4)}(x) = \left(\dfrac{3}{8}\right)\left(-\dfrac{5}{2}\right)(1 + x)^{-7/2} = -\dfrac{15}{16}(1 + x)^{-7/2}$

9. $f(x) = e^{-x}$ $\qquad\qquad f(0) = e^{-0} = 1$

$f'(x) = -e^{-x}$ $\qquad\qquad f'(0) = -e^{-0} = -1$

$f''(x) = e^{-x}$ $\qquad\qquad f''(0) = e^{-0} = 1$

$f^{(3)}(x) = -e^{-x}$ $\qquad\qquad f^{(3)}(0) = -e^{-0} = -1$

$f^{(4)}(x) = e^{-x}$ $\qquad\qquad f^{(4)}(0) = e^{-0} = 1$

Using $\underline{2}$,

$$p_4(x) = f(0) + f'(0)x + \dfrac{f''(0)}{2!}x^2 + \dfrac{f^{(3)}(0)}{3!}x^3 + \dfrac{f^{(4)}(0)}{4!}x^4$$

Thus,

$$p_4(x) = 1 - x + \dfrac{1}{2!}x^2 - \dfrac{1}{3!}x^3 + \dfrac{1}{4!}x^4 = 1 - x + \dfrac{1}{2}x^2 - \dfrac{1}{6}x^3 + \dfrac{1}{24}x^4$$

58

11.

$$f(x) = (x + 1)^3, \qquad f(0) = 1$$
$$f'(x) = 3(x + 1)^2, \qquad f'(0) = 3$$
$$f''(x) = 6(x + 1), \qquad f''(0) = 6$$
$$f^{(3)}(x) = 6, \qquad f^{(3)}(0) = 6$$
$$f^{(4)}(x) = 0 \qquad f^{(4)}(0) = 0$$

$$p_4(x) = 1 + 3x + \frac{6}{2!}x^2 + \frac{6}{3!}x^3 = 1 + 3x + 3x^2 + x^3$$

13.

$$f(x) = \ln(1 + 2x) \qquad\qquad f(0) = \ln(1) = 0$$
$$f'(x) = \frac{1}{1 + 2x}(2) = \frac{2}{1 + 2x} \qquad\qquad f'(0) = \frac{2}{1 + 2 \cdot 0} = 2$$
$$f''(x) = -2(1 + 2x)^{-2}(2) = \frac{-4}{(1 + 2x)^2} \qquad f''(0) = -4$$
$$f^{(3)}(x) = 8(1 + 2x)^{-3}(2) = \frac{16}{(1 + 2x)^3} \qquad f^{(3)}(0) = 16$$

Using 2, $p_3(x) = f(0) + f'(0)x + \dfrac{f''(0)}{2!}x^2 + \dfrac{f^{(3)}(0)}{3!}x^3$

Thus, $p_3(x) = 0 + 2x - \dfrac{4}{2!}x^2 + \dfrac{16}{3!}x^3 = 2x - 2x^2 + \dfrac{8}{3}x^3$

15.

$$f(x) = \sqrt[3]{x + 1} = (x + 1)^{1/3} \qquad f(0) = \sqrt[3]{1} = 1$$
$$f'(x) = \frac{1}{3(x + 1)^{2/3}} \qquad\qquad f'(0) = \frac{1}{3}$$
$$f''(x) = \frac{-2}{9(x + 1)^{5/3}} \qquad\qquad f''(0) = -\frac{2}{9}$$
$$f^{(3)}(x) = \frac{10}{27(x + 1)^{8/3}} \qquad f^{(3)}(0) = \frac{10}{27}$$

$$p_3(x) = f(0) + f'(0)x + \frac{f''(0)}{2!}x^2 + \frac{f^{(3)}(0)}{3!}x^3$$

Thus, $p_3(x) = 1 + \dfrac{1}{3}x - \dfrac{2}{9 \cdot 2!}x^2 + \dfrac{10}{27 \cdot 3!}x^3 = 1 + \dfrac{1}{3}x - \dfrac{1}{9}x^2 + \dfrac{5}{81}x^3$

17. (A)

$$f(x) = x^4 - 1 \qquad\qquad f(0) = -1$$
$$f'(x) = 4x^3 \qquad\qquad f'(0) = 0$$
$$f''(x) = 12x^2 \qquad\qquad f''(0) = 0$$
$$f^{(3)}(x) = 24x \qquad\qquad f^{(3)}(0) = 0$$

Using 2, $p_3(x) = f(0) + f'(0)x + \dfrac{f''(0)}{2!}x^2 + \dfrac{f^{(3)}(0)}{3!}x^3$

Thus, $p_3(x) = -1$

Now $|p_3(x) - f(x)| = |-1 - (x^4 - 1)| = |x^4| = |x|^4$

and $|x|^4 < 0.1$ implies $|x| < (0.1)^{1/4} \approx 0.562$

Therefore, $-0.562 < x < 0.562$

(B) From part (A),
$$f^{(4)}(x) = 24 \qquad\qquad f^{(4)}(0) = 24$$

Using $\underline{2}$, $p_4(x) = f(0) + f'(0)x + \dfrac{f''(0)}{2!}x^2 + \dfrac{f^{(3)}(0)}{3!}x^3 + \dfrac{f^{(4)}(0)}{4!}x^4$

Thus, $p_4(x) = -1 + \dfrac{24}{4!}x^4 = -1 + x^4 = x^4 - 1 = f(x)$

and $\ |p_4(x) - f(x)| = 0 < 0.1$ for all x.

19.
$$\begin{array}{ll} f(x) = e^{x-1} & f(1) = 1 \\ f'(x) = e^{x-1} & f'(1) = 1 \\ f''(x) = e^{x-1} & f''(1) = 1 \\ f^{(3)}(x) = e^{x-1} & f^{(3)}(1) = 1 \\ f^{(4)}(x) = e^{x-1} & f^{(4)}(1) = 1 \end{array}$$

Thus, using $\underline{3}$,

$$p_4(x) = f(1) + f'(1)(x-1) + \dfrac{f''(1)}{2!}(x-1)^2 + \dfrac{f^{(3)}(1)}{3!}(x-1)^3 + \dfrac{f^{(4)}(1)}{4!}(x-1)^4$$
$$= 1 + (x-1) + \dfrac{1}{2!}(x-1)^2 + \dfrac{1}{3!}(x-1)^3 + \dfrac{1}{4!}(x-1)^4$$
$$= 1 + (x-1) + \dfrac{1}{2}(x-1)^2 + \dfrac{1}{6}(x-1)^3 + \dfrac{1}{24}(x-1)^4$$

21.
$$\begin{array}{ll} f(x) = x^3 & f(1) = 1 \\ f'(x) = 3x^2 & f'(1) = 3 \\ f''(x) = 6x & f''(1) = 6 \\ f^{(3)}(x) = 6 & f^{(3)}(1) = 6 \end{array}$$
$$p_3(x) = 1 + 3(x-1) + \dfrac{6}{2!}(x-1)^2 + \dfrac{6}{3!}(x-1)^3$$
$$= 1 + 3(x-1) + 3(x-1)^2 + (x-1)^3$$

23.
$$\begin{array}{ll} f(x) = \ln 3x & f\left(\dfrac{1}{3}\right) = \ln 1 = 0 \\[2mm] f'(x) = \dfrac{3}{3x} = \dfrac{1}{x} & f'\left(\dfrac{1}{3}\right) = 3 \\[2mm] f''(x) = -\dfrac{1}{x^2} & f''\left(\dfrac{1}{3}\right) = -9 \\[2mm] f^{(3)}(x) = \dfrac{2}{x^3} & f^{(3)}\left(\dfrac{1}{3}\right) = 54 \end{array}$$

Thus, using $\underline{3}$,

$$p_3(x) = f\left(\dfrac{1}{3}\right) + f'\left(\dfrac{1}{3}\right)\left(x - \dfrac{1}{3}\right) + \dfrac{f''\left(\frac{1}{3}\right)}{2!}\left(x - \dfrac{1}{3}\right)^2 + \dfrac{f^{(3)}\left(\frac{1}{3}\right)}{3!}\left(x - \dfrac{1}{3}\right)^3$$
$$= 0 + 3\left(x - \dfrac{1}{3}\right) - \dfrac{9}{2!}\left(x - \dfrac{1}{3}\right)^2 + \dfrac{54}{3!}\left(x - \dfrac{1}{3}\right)^3$$
$$= 3\left(x - \dfrac{1}{3}\right) - \dfrac{9}{2}\left(x - \dfrac{1}{3}\right)^2 + 9\left(x - \dfrac{1}{3}\right)^3$$

25.
$$f(x) = e^{-2x} \qquad\qquad f(0) = 1$$
$$f'(x) = -2e^{-2x} \qquad\qquad f'(0) = -2$$
$$f''(x) = 4e^{-2x} \qquad\qquad f''(0) = 4$$
$$f^{(3)}(x) = -8e^{-2x} \qquad\qquad f^{(3)}(0) = -8$$

Using $\underline{2}$, $p_3(x) = f(0) + f'(0)x + \dfrac{f''(0)}{2!}x^2 + \dfrac{f^{(3)}(0)}{3!}x^3$

Thus, $p_3(x) = 1 - 2x + \dfrac{4}{2!}x^2 - \dfrac{8}{3!}x^3 = 1 - 2x + 2x^2 - \dfrac{4}{3}x^3.$

Now, $e^{-0.5} = e^{-2(0.25)} = f(0.25) \approx p_3(0.25)$

$$= 1 - 2(0.25) + 2(0.25)^2 - \dfrac{4}{3}(0.25)^3 = 0.60416667.$$

27.
$$f(x) = \sqrt{x+16} = (x+16)^{1/2} \qquad\qquad f(0) = 4$$
$$f'(x) = \dfrac{1}{2}(x+16)^{-1/2} = \dfrac{1}{2\sqrt{x+16}} \qquad\qquad f'(0) = \dfrac{1}{8}$$
$$f''(x) = \dfrac{-1}{4}(x+16)^{-3/2} = \dfrac{-1}{4(x+16)^{3/2}} \qquad\qquad f''(0) = \dfrac{-1}{256}$$

$$p_2(x) = f(0) + f'(0) + \dfrac{f''(0)}{2!}x^2 = 4 + \dfrac{1}{8}x - \dfrac{1}{256\cdot2!}x^2 = 4 + \dfrac{1}{8}x - \dfrac{1}{512}x^2.$$

Now, $\sqrt{17} = \sqrt{1+16} = f(1) \approx p_2(1) = 4 + \dfrac{1}{8}(1) - \dfrac{1}{512}(1)^2 = 4.1230469.$

29.
$$f(x) = \sqrt{x} = x^{1/2} \qquad\qquad f(1) = 1$$
$$f'(x) = \dfrac{1}{2}x^{-1/2} \qquad\qquad f'(1) = \dfrac{1}{2}$$
$$f''(x) = -\dfrac{1}{4}x^{-3/2} \qquad\qquad f''(1) = -\dfrac{1}{4}$$
$$f^{(3)}(x) = \dfrac{3}{8}x^{-5/2} \qquad\qquad f^{(3)}(1) = \dfrac{3}{8}$$
$$f^{(4)}(x) = -\dfrac{15}{16}x^{-7/2} \qquad\qquad f^{(4)}(1) = -\dfrac{15}{16}$$

Thus,

$$p_4(x) = f(1) + f'(1)(x-1) + \dfrac{f''(1)}{2!}(x-1)^2 + \dfrac{f^{(3)}(1)}{3!}(x-1)^3 + \dfrac{f^{(4)}(1)}{4!}(x-1)^4$$

$$= 1 + \dfrac{1}{2}(x-1) - \dfrac{1}{4\cdot2!}(x-1)^2 + \dfrac{3}{8\cdot3!}(x-1)^3 - \dfrac{15}{16\cdot4!}(x-1)^4$$

$$= 1 + \dfrac{1}{2}(x-1) - \dfrac{1}{8}(x-1)^2 + \dfrac{1}{16}(x-1)^3 - \dfrac{5}{128}(x-1)^4.$$

Now,

$$\sqrt{1.2} = f(1.2) \approx p_4(1.2)$$

$$= 1 + \dfrac{1}{2}(1.2-1) - \dfrac{1}{8}(1.2-1)^2 + \dfrac{1}{16}(1.2-1)^3 - \dfrac{5}{128}(1.2-1)^4$$

$$= 1 + \dfrac{1}{2}(0.2) - \dfrac{1}{8}(0.2)^2 + \dfrac{1}{16}(0.2)^3 - \dfrac{5}{128}(0.2)^4 = 1.0954375.$$

31. $f(x) = \dfrac{1}{4 - x} = (4 - x)^{-1}$

$\quad f'(x) = -1(4 - x)^{-2}(-1) = (4 - x)^{-2}$

$\quad f''(x) = -2(4 - x)^{-3}(-1) = 1 \cdot 2(4 - x)^{-3}$

$\quad f^{(3)}(x) = 2(-3)(4 - x)^{-4}(-1) = 1 \cdot 2 \cdot 3(1 - x)^{-4}$

$\quad f^{(4)}(x) = 2 \cdot 3(-4)(4 - x)^{-5}(-1) = 1 \cdot 2 \cdot 3 \cdot 4(1 - x)^{-5}$

$\quad \vdots$

$\quad f^{(n)}(x) = n!(4 - x)^{-(n+1)}$

33. $f(x) = e^{3x}$

$\quad f'(x) = e^{3x}(3) = 3e^{3x}$

$\quad f''(x) = 3e^{3x}(3) = 9e^{3x} = 3^2 e^{3x}$

$\quad f^{(3)}(x) = 9e^{3x}(3) = 27e^{3x} = 3^3 e^{3x}$

$\quad f^{(4)}(x) = 27e^{3x}(3) = 81e^{3x} = 3^4 e^{3x}$

$\quad \vdots$

$\quad f^{(n)}(x) = 3^n e^{3x}$

35. $f(x) = \ln(6 - x)$

$\quad f'(x) = \dfrac{1}{6 - x}(-1) = -\dfrac{1}{6 - x} = -(6 - x)^{-1}$

$\quad f''(x) = (6 - x)^{-2}(-1) = -(6 - x)^{-2}$

$\quad f^{(3)}(x) = 2(6 - x)^{-3}(-1) = -1 \cdot 2(6 - x)^{-3}$

$\quad f^{(4)}(x) = 1 \cdot 2 \cdot 3(6 - x)^{-4}(-1) = -1 \cdot 2 \cdot 3(6 - x)^{-4}$

$\quad \vdots$

$\quad f^{(n)}(x) = -(n - 1)!(6 - x)^{-n}$

37. From Problem 31,

$\quad f(0) = \dfrac{1}{4}, \ f'(0) = \dfrac{1}{4^2}, \ f''(0) = \dfrac{2!}{4^3}, \ f^{(3)}(0) = \dfrac{3!}{4^4}, \ \ldots, \ f^{(n)}(0) = \dfrac{n!}{4^{n+1}}$

$\quad$ Thus,

$$p_n(x) = \dfrac{1}{4} + \dfrac{1}{4^2}x + \dfrac{1}{4^3}x^2 + \dfrac{1}{4^4}x^3 + \ldots + \dfrac{1}{4^{n+1}}x^n.$$

39. From Problem 33,

$\quad f(0) = e^0 = 1, \ f'(0) = 3e^0 = 3, \ f''(0) = 3^2 e^0 = 3^2,$

$\quad f^{(3)}(0) = 3^3 e^0 = 3^3, \ \ldots, \ f^{(n)}(0) = 3^n e^0 = 3^n$

$\quad$ Thus,

$$p_n(x) = 1 + 3x + \dfrac{3^2}{2!}x^2 + \dfrac{3^3}{3!}x^3 + \ldots + \dfrac{3^n}{n!}x^n.$$

41. From Problem 35,

$$f(0) = \ln 6, \quad f'(0) = -\frac{1}{6}, \quad f''(0) = -\frac{1}{6^2}, \quad f^{(3)}(0) = -\frac{2!}{6^3}, \quad ..., \quad f^{(n)}(0) = -\frac{(n-1)!}{6^n}$$

Thus,

$$p_n(x) = \ln 6 - \frac{1}{6}x - \frac{1}{2 \cdot 6^2}x^2 - \frac{1}{3 \cdot 6^3}x^3 - ... - \frac{1}{n \cdot 6^n}x^n.$$

43. Step 1.

$$f(x) = \frac{1}{x}$$

$$f'(x) = -\frac{1}{x^2}$$

$$f''(x) = \frac{2}{x^3}$$

$$f^{(3)}(x) = -\frac{3!}{x^4}$$

$$f^{(4)}(x) = \frac{4!}{x^5}$$

$$\vdots$$

$$f^{(n)} = \frac{(-1)^n n!}{x^n}$$

Step 2.

$$f(-1) = -1$$

$$f'(-1) = -1$$

$$f''(-1) = -2!$$

$$f^{(3)}(-1) = -3!$$

$$f^{(4)}(-1) = -4!$$

$$\vdots$$

$$f^{(n)}(-1) = -n!$$

Step 3.

$$a_0 = f(-1) = -1$$

$$a_1 = f'(-1) = -1$$

$$a_2 = \frac{f''(-1)}{2!} = -\frac{2!}{2!} = -1$$

$$a_3 = \frac{f^{(3)}(-1)}{3!} = -\frac{3!}{3!} = -1$$

$$a_4 = \frac{f^{(4)}(-1)}{4!} = -\frac{4!}{4!} = -1$$

$$\vdots$$

$$a_n = \frac{f^{(n)}(-1)}{n!} = -\frac{n!}{n!} = -1$$

Step 4. The nth degree Taylor polynomial is:

$$p_n(x) = -1 - (x+1) - (x+1)^2 - (x+1)^3 - (x+1)^4 - ... - (x+1)^n.$$

45. Step 1.

$$f(x) = \ln x$$

$$f'(x) = \frac{1}{x}$$

$$f''(x) = -\frac{1}{x^2}$$

$$f^{(3)}(x) = \frac{2}{x^3}$$

$$f^{(4)}(x) = -\frac{2 \cdot 3}{x^4}$$

$$\vdots$$

$$f^{(n)}(x) =$$

$$\frac{(-1)^{n+1}(n-1)!}{x^n}$$

Step 2.

$$f(1) = 0$$

$$f'(1) = 1$$

$$f''(1) = -1$$

$$f^{(3)}(1) = 2$$

$$f^{(4)}(1) = -3!$$

$$\vdots$$

$$f^{(n)}(1) =$$

$$(-1)^{n+1}(n-1)!$$

Step 3.

$$a_0 = f(1) = 0$$

$$a_1 = f'(1) = 1$$

$$a_2 = \frac{f''(1)}{2!} = -\frac{1}{2!} = -\frac{1}{2}$$

$$a_3 = \frac{f^{(3)}(1)}{3!} = \frac{2}{3!} = \frac{1}{3}$$

$$a_4 = \frac{f^{(4)}(1)}{4!} = -\frac{3!}{4!} = -\frac{1}{4}$$

$$\vdots$$

$$a_n =$$

$$\frac{f^{(n)}(1)}{n!} = \frac{(-1)^{n+1}(n-1)!}{n!} = \frac{(-1)^{n+1}}{n}$$

Step 4. The nth degree Taylor polynomial is:

$$p_n(x) = (x-1) - \frac{1}{2}(x-1)^2 + \frac{1}{3}(x-1)^3 - \frac{1}{4}(x-1)^4 + ... + \frac{(-1)^{n+1}}{n}(x-1)^n.$$

47. <u>Step 1.</u>

$f(x) = e^{-x}$

$f'(x) = -e^{-x}$

$f''(x) = e^{-x}$

$f^{(3)}(x) = -e^{-x}$

$f^{(4)}(x) = e^{-x}$

$\vdots$

$f^{(n)}(x) = (-1)^n e^{-x}$

<u>Step 2.</u>

$f(2) = \dfrac{1}{e^2}$

$f'(2) = -\dfrac{1}{e^2}$

$f''(2) = \dfrac{1}{e^2}$

$f^{(3)}(2) = -\dfrac{1}{e^2}$

$f^{(4)}(2) = \dfrac{1}{e^2}$

$\vdots$

$f^{(n)}(2) = \dfrac{(-1)^n}{e^2}$

<u>Step 3.</u>

$a_0 = f(2) = \dfrac{1}{e^2}$

$a_1 = f'(2) = -\dfrac{1}{e^2}$

$a_2 = \dfrac{f''(2)}{2!} = \dfrac{1}{2!\,e^2}$

$a_3 = \dfrac{f^{(3)}(2)}{3!} = \dfrac{-1}{3!\,e^2}$

$a_4 = \dfrac{f^{(4)}(2)}{4!} = \dfrac{1}{4!\,e^2}$

$\vdots$

$a_n = \dfrac{f^{(n)}(2)}{n!} = \dfrac{(-1)^n}{n!\,e^2}$

<u>Step 4.</u> The nth degree Taylor polynomial is:

$$p_n(x) = \frac{1}{e^2} - \frac{1}{e^2}(x-2) + \frac{1}{2!\,e^2}(x-2)^2 - \frac{1}{3!\,e^2}(x-2)^3$$

$$+ \frac{1}{4!\,e^2}(x-2)^4 - \ldots + \frac{(-1)^n}{n!\,e^2}(x-2)^n$$

49. <u>Step 1.</u>

$f(x) = x \ln x$

$f'(x) = 1 + \ln x$

$f''(x) = \dfrac{1}{x}$

$f^{(3)}(x) = -\dfrac{1}{x^2}$

$f^{(4)}(x) = \dfrac{2}{x^3}$

$\vdots$

$f^{(n)}(x) = \dfrac{(-1)^n(n-2)!}{x^{n-1}}$

<u>Step 2.</u>

$f(3) = 3 \ln 3$

$f'(3) = 1 + \ln 3$

$f''(3) = \dfrac{1}{3}$

$f^{(3)}(3) = -\dfrac{1}{3^2}$

$f^{(4)}(3) = \dfrac{2}{3^3}$

$\vdots$

$f^{(n)}(3) = \dfrac{(-1)^n(n-2)!}{3^{n-1}}$

<u>Step 3.</u>

$a_0 = 3 \ln 3$

$a_1 = 1 + \ln 3$

$a_2 = \dfrac{f''(3)}{2!} = \dfrac{1}{3 \cdot 2}$

$a_3 = \dfrac{f^{(3)}(3)}{3!} = \dfrac{-1}{3^2 \cdot 2 \cdot 3}$

$a_4 = \dfrac{f^{(4)}(3)}{4!} = \dfrac{1}{3^3 \cdot 3 \cdot 4}$

$\vdots$

$a_n = \dfrac{f^{(n)}(3)}{n!} = \dfrac{(-1)^n}{3^{n-1}(n-1)n}$

<u>Step 4.</u> The nth degree Taylor polynomial is:

$$p_n(x) = 3 \ln 3 + (1 + \ln 3)(x-3) + \frac{1}{3 \cdot 2}(x-3)^2 - \frac{1}{3^2 \cdot 2 \cdot 3}(x-3)^3$$

$$+ \frac{1}{3^3 \cdot 3 \cdot 4}(x-3)^4 - \ldots + \frac{(-1)^n}{3^{n-1}(n-1)n}(x-3)^n.$$

51. $f(x) = x^4 + 5x^2 + 1$

(A) Third-degree Taylor polynomial $p_3(x)$ for f at 0 is:

$$p_3(x) = f(0) + \frac{f'(0)}{1!}x + \frac{f''(0)}{2!}x^2 + \frac{f^{(3)}(0)}{3!}x^3$$

$f(0) = 1$

$f'(x) = 4x^3 + 10x$; $f'(0) = 0$

$f''(x) = 12x^2 + 10$; $f''(0) = 10$

$f^{(3)}(x) = 24x$; $f^{(3)}(0) = 0$

Thus,

$$p_3(x) = 1 + \frac{10}{2!}x^2 = 1 + 5x^2 = 5x^2 + 1$$

(B) The degree of the polynomial is 2.

53. $f(x) = x^6 + 2x^3 + 1$

$f(0) = 1$

$f'(x) = 6x^5 + 6x^2$; $f'(0) = 0$

$f''(x) = 30x^4 + 12x$; $f''(0) = 0$

$f^{(3)}(x) = 120x^3 + 12$; $f^{(3)}(0) = 12$

$f^{(4)}(x) = 360x^2$; $f^{(4)}(0) = 0$

$f^{(5)}(x) = 720x$; $f^{(5)}(0) = 0$

$f^{(6)}(x) = 720$; $f^{(6)}(0) = 720$

$f^{(n)}(x) = 0$ for $n \geq 7$.

Thus, for $n = 0$, 3 and 6, the nth-degree Taylor polynomial for f at 0 has degree n.

55.

$f(x) = \ln(1 + x)$ $f(0) = 0$

$f'(x) = \dfrac{1}{1 + x}$ $f'(0) = 1$

$f''(x) = \dfrac{-1}{(1 + x)^2}$ $f''(0) = -1$

$f^{(3)}(x) = \dfrac{2}{(1 + x)^3}$ $f^{(3)}(0) = 2$

Thus,

$$p_1(x) = x, \quad p_2(x) = x - \frac{x^2}{2}, \quad p_3(x) = x - \frac{x^2}{2} + \frac{x^3}{3}.$$

x	$p_1(x)$	$p_2(x)$	$p_3(x)$	$f(x)$
-0.2	-0.2	-0.22	-0.222667	-0.223144
-0.1	-0.1	-0.105	-0.105333	-0.105361
0	0	0	0	0
0.1	0.1	0.095	0.095333	0.09531
0.2	0.2	0.18	0.182667	0.182322

x	$\left\lvert p_1(x) - f(x) \right\rvert$	$\left\lvert p_2(x) - f(x) \right\rvert$	$\left\lvert p_3(x) - f(x) \right\rvert$
-0.2	0.023144	0.003144	0.000477
-0.1	0.005361	0.000361	0.000028
0	0	0	0
0.1	0.00469	0.00031	0.000023
0.2	0.017678	0.002322	0.000345

57. From Problem 55, the first three Taylor polynomials for $f(x) = \ln(1 + x)$ are:

$$p_1(x) = x, \qquad p_2(x) = x - \frac{x^2}{2},$$

$$p_3(x) = x - \frac{x^2}{2} + \frac{x^3}{3}$$

The graphs of f, p_1, p_2, and p_3 are shown at the right.

59. From the text we know that
$$p_3(x) = 1 + x + \frac{1}{2}x^2 + \frac{1}{6}x^3$$
Using a graphing utility, we find that
$$\left\lvert p_3(x) - e^x \right\rvert < 0.1 \quad \text{for} \quad -1.323 < x < 1.168$$

61.
$$
\begin{array}{ll}
f(x) = e^x & f(a) = e^a \\
f'(x) = e^x & f'(a) = e^a \\
f''(x) = e^x & f''(a) = e^a \\
f^{(3)}(x) = e^x & f^{(3)}(a) = e^a \\
\vdots & \vdots \\
f^{(n)}(x) = e^x & f^{(n)}(a) = e^a
\end{array}
$$

Thus,

$$p_n(x) = f(a) + f'(a)(x - a) + \frac{f''(a)}{2!}(x - a)^2 + \frac{f^{(3)}(a)}{3!}(x - a)^3$$

$$+ \cdots + \frac{f^{(n)}(a)}{n!}(x - a)^n$$

$$= e^a + e^a(x - a) + \frac{e^a}{2!}(x - a)^2 + \frac{e^a}{3!}(x - a)^3 + \cdots + \frac{e^a}{n!}(x - a)^n$$

$$= e^a\left[1 + (x - a) + \frac{1}{2!}(x - a)^2 + \frac{1}{3!}(x - a)^3 + \cdots + \frac{1}{n!}(x - a)^n\right]$$

$$= e^a \sum_{k=0}^{n} \frac{1}{k!}(x - a)^k$$

63.

$$f(x) = \frac{1}{x} \qquad\qquad f(a) = \frac{1}{a}$$

$$f'(x) = \frac{-1}{x^2} \qquad\qquad f'(a) = \frac{-1}{a^2}$$

$$f''(x) = \frac{2}{x^3} \qquad\qquad f''(a) = \frac{2}{a^3}$$

$$f^{(3)}(x) = \frac{-2 \cdot 3}{x^4} = \frac{-3!}{x^4} \qquad\qquad f^{(3)}(a) = \frac{-3!}{a^4}$$

$$\vdots \qquad\qquad\qquad\qquad \vdots$$

$$f^{(n)}(x) = \frac{(-1)^n\, n!}{x^{n+1}} \qquad\qquad f^{(n)}(a) = \frac{(-1)^n\, n!}{a^{n+1}}$$

Thus,

$$p_n(x) = f(a) + f'(a)(x - a) + \frac{f''(a)}{2!}(x - a)^2 + \frac{f^{(3)}(a)}{3!}(x - a)^3$$
$$+ \; \dots \; + \frac{f^{(n)}(a)}{n!}(x - a)^n$$

$$= \frac{1}{a} - \frac{1}{a^2}(x - a) + \frac{2}{a^3} \cdot \frac{1}{2!}(x - a)^2 - \frac{3!}{a^4} \cdot \frac{1}{3!}(x - a)^3$$
$$+ \; \dots \; + \frac{(-1)^n\, n!}{a^{n+1}} \cdot \frac{1}{n!}(x - a)^n$$

$$= \frac{1}{a} - \frac{1}{a^2}(x - a) + \frac{1}{a^3}(x - a)^2 - \frac{1}{a^4}(x - a)^3 + \; \dots \; + \frac{(-1)^n}{a^{n+1}}(x - a)^n$$

$$= \sum_{k=0}^{n} \frac{(-1)^k}{a^{k+1}}(x - a)^k$$

65. Let $f(x)$ be a polynomial of degree k, $k \ge 0$. Then

$$f(x) = a_0 + a_1 x + a_2 x^2 + a_3 x^3 + \dots + a_k x^k \qquad f(0) = a_0$$

$$f'(x) = a_1 + 2a_2 x + 3a_3 x^2 + \dots + k a_k x^{k-1} \qquad f'(0) = a_1$$

$$f''(x) = 2a_2 + 6a_3 x + \dots + k(k - 1)a_k x^{k-2} \qquad f''(0) = 2a_2 + 2!a_2$$

$$f^{(3)}(x) = 6a_3 + \dots + k(k - 1)(k - 2)a_k x^{k-3} \qquad f^{(3)}(0) = 6a_3 = 3!a_3$$

$$\vdots \qquad\qquad\qquad\qquad \vdots$$

In general,

$$f^{(m)}(0) = \begin{cases} m!\, a_m & \text{for } m = 0, 1, 2, \dots k \\ 0 & \text{for } m > k \end{cases}$$

Since $p_n(x) = f(0) + f'(0)x + \dfrac{f''(0)}{2!}x^2 + \dfrac{f^{(3)}(0)}{3!}x^3 + \dots + \dfrac{f^{(n)}(0)}{n!}x^n$

it follows that $p_n(x) = f(x)$ for all $n \ge k$.

67. $f(x) = e^x$

$f(0) = 1$

$f'(x) = e^x$; $f'(0) = 1$

$f''(x) = e^x$; $f''(0) = 1$

$\vdots$

$f^{(k)}(x) = e^x$; $f^{(k)}(0) = 1$

Therefore,

$$p_{10}(x) = 1 + \frac{1}{1!}x + \frac{1}{2!}x^2 + \dots + \frac{1}{10!}x^{10}$$

$$p_{11}(x) = 1 + \frac{1}{1!}x + \frac{1}{2!}x^2 + \dots + \frac{1}{10!}x^{10} + \frac{1}{11!}x^{11}$$

For $x > 0$, $e^x > p_{11}(x)$ and hence

$$e^x - p_{10}(x) > p_{11}(x) - p_{10}(x) = \frac{1}{11!}x^{11}$$

Take $x = 2(11!)^{1/11}$, then

$$e^x - p_{10}(x) > \frac{1}{11!}(2(11!)^{1/11})^{11} = 2^{11} = 2048.$$

So, there exist values of x for which

$$|p_{10}(x) - e^x| = |e^x - p_{10}(x)| \geq 100.$$

69. $D(x) = \dfrac{1}{10}\sqrt{10,000 - x^2} = \dfrac{1}{10}(10,000 - x^2)^{1/2}$ $\qquad D(0) = \dfrac{1}{10}(100) = 10$

$D'(x) = \dfrac{1}{10}\left(\dfrac{1}{2}\right)(10,000 - x^2)^{-1/2}(-2x)$

$\qquad = \dfrac{-x}{10}(10,000 - x^2)^{-1/2}$ $\qquad\qquad\qquad\qquad D'(0) = 0$

$D''(x) = -\dfrac{1}{10}(10,000 - x^2)^{-1/2} + \dfrac{x}{20}(10,000 - x^2)^{-3/2}(-2x)$

$\qquad = -\dfrac{1}{10}(10,000 - x^2)^{-1/2} - \dfrac{x^2}{10}(10,000 - x^2)^{-3/2}$ $\quad D''(0) = \dfrac{-1}{10(100)}$

$\qquad = \dfrac{-1}{10(10,000 - x^2)^{1/2}} - \dfrac{x^2}{10(10,000 - x^2)^{3/2}}$ $\qquad\qquad = \dfrac{-1}{1000}$

Thus,

$$p_2(x) = D(0) + D'(0)x + \frac{D''(0)}{2!}x^2 = 10 - \frac{1}{2000}x^2 = 10 - 0.0005x^2.$$

Average price on [0, 30]:

$$\frac{1}{30 - 0}\int_0^{30} D(x)\,dx \approx \frac{1}{30}\int_0^{30}(10 - 0.0005x^2)\,dx$$

$$= \frac{1}{30}\left[\left(10x - \frac{0.0005x^3}{3}\right)\Big|_0^{30}\right] = \frac{1}{30}\left[10(30) - \frac{0.0005(30)^3}{3}\right]$$

$$= \frac{1}{30}[300 - 4.5] = \$9.85$$

71.
$$D(x) = \frac{1}{10}\sqrt{10,000 - x^2}$$

$$= \frac{1}{10}(10,000 - x^2)^{1/2}$$

$$D'(x) = \frac{1}{10}\left(\frac{1}{2}\right)(10,000 - x^2)^{-1/2}(-2x)$$

$$= \frac{1}{10}(-x)(10,000 - x^2)^{-1/2}$$

$$= \frac{-x}{10(10,000 - x^2)^{1/2}}$$

$$D''(x) = -\frac{1}{10}(10,000 - x^2)^{-1/2}$$

$$+ \frac{1}{20}x(10,000 - x^2)^{-3/2}(-2x)$$

$$= \frac{-1}{10(10,000 - x^2)^{1/2}} - \frac{x^2}{10(10,000 - x^2)^{3/2}}$$

$$D(60) = \frac{1}{10}\sqrt{10,000 - (60)^2}$$

$$= \frac{1}{10}\sqrt{6400} = 8$$

$$D'(60) = \frac{-60}{10 \cdot 80} = \frac{-3}{40}$$

$$D''(60) = \frac{-1}{10 \cdot 80} - \frac{3600}{10(80)^3}$$

$$= \frac{-1}{512}$$

Thus,

$$P_2(x) = D(60) + D'(60)(x - 60) + \frac{D''(60)}{2!}(x - 60)^2$$

$$= 8 - \frac{3}{40}(x - 60) - \frac{1}{1024}(x - 60)^2.$$

Average price on [60, 80]:

$$\frac{1}{80 - 60}\int_{60}^{80} D(x)\,dx \approx \frac{1}{20}\int_{60}^{80}\left[8 - \frac{3}{40}(x - 60) - \frac{1}{1024}(x - 60)^2\right]dx$$

$$= \frac{1}{20}\left[8x - \frac{3}{40}\cdot\frac{(x-60)^2}{2} - \frac{1}{1024}\cdot\frac{(x-60)^3}{3}\right]\Big|_{60}^{80}$$

$$= \frac{1}{20}\left[640 - \frac{3}{40}\cdot\frac{400}{2} - \frac{1}{1024}\cdot\frac{8000}{3}\right] - \frac{1}{20}(480)$$

$$= \$7.12$$

73.
$$R(t) = 2 + 8e^{-0.1t^2}$$

$$R'(t) = -1.6te^{-0.1t^2}$$

$$R''(t) = -1.6e^{-0.1t^2} + 0.32t^2e^{-0.1t^2}$$

$$R(0) = 10$$

$$R'(0) = 0$$

$$R''(0) = -1.6$$

Thus,

$$P_2(t) = R(0) + R'(0)t + \frac{R''(0)}{2!}t^2$$

$$= 10 - 0.8t^2$$

Now, the total production during the first two years is

$$P = \int_0^2 R(t)\,dt \approx \int_0^2 (10 - 0.8t^2)\,dt$$

$$= \left(10t - \frac{0.8t^3}{3}\right)\Big|_0^2$$

$$\approx 17.87 \text{ or } \$18 \text{ million}$$

75. Let $A'(t) = F(t) = \dfrac{-75}{t^2 + 25}$ $\qquad\qquad\qquad F(0) = -3$

$$F'(t) = \frac{75(2t)}{(t^2 + 25)^2} = \frac{150t}{(t^2 + 25)^2} \qquad\qquad F'(0) = 0$$

$$F''(t) = \frac{(t + 25)^2(150) - 150t(2)(t^2 + 25)(2t)}{(t + 25)^4} \qquad F''(0) = \frac{6}{25}$$

$$= \frac{150(t^2 + 25) - 600t^2}{(t^2 + 25)^3}$$

Thus, $p_2(t) = F(0) + F'(0)t + \dfrac{F''(0)}{2!}t^2 = -3 + \dfrac{3}{25}t^2.$

Therefore,

$$A(t) = \int A'(t)\,dt \approx \int p_2(t)\,dt = \int\left[-3 + \frac{3}{25}t^2\right]dt = -3t + \frac{1}{25}t^3 + C.$$

Now, $A(0) = 12$. Therefore, $C = 12$ and $A(t) \approx -3t + \dfrac{1}{25}t^3 + 12$;

thus, $A(2) \approx -6 + \dfrac{8}{25} + 12 = 6.32$ square centimeters.

77. $P(x) = 20\sqrt{3x^2 + 25} - 80$ $\qquad\qquad P(5) = 20(3\cdot 5^2 + 25)^{1/2} - 80$

$\qquad\quad = 20(3x^2 + 25)^{1/2} - 80$ $\qquad\qquad\qquad = 120$

$$P'(x) = 20\left(\frac{1}{2}\right)(3x^2 + 25)^{-1/2}(6x) \qquad P'(5) = \frac{60(5)}{10} = 30$$

$$= 60x(3x^2 + 25)^{-1/2} = \frac{60x}{(3x^2 + 25)^{1/2}}$$

$$P''(x) = 60(3x^2 + 25)^{-1/2} \qquad\qquad P''(5) = \frac{60}{10} - \frac{180(5)^2}{1000}$$

$$+ 60x\left(\frac{1}{2}\right)(3x^2 + 25)^{-3/2}(6x) \qquad\qquad = 6 - \frac{9}{2} = \frac{3}{2}$$

$$= \frac{60}{(3x^2 + 25)^{1/2}} - \frac{180x^2}{(3x^2 + 25)^{3/2}}$$

Thus, $p_2(x) = P(5) + P'(5)(x - 5) + \dfrac{P''(5)}{2!}(x - 5)^2$

$$= 120 + 30(x - 5) + \frac{3}{4}(x - 5)^2$$

Average pollution:

$$\frac{1}{10 - 0}\int_0^{10} P(x)\,dx \approx \frac{1}{10}\int_0^{10}\left[120 + 30(x - 5) + \frac{3}{4}(x - 5)^2\right]dx$$

$$= \frac{1}{10}\left[120x + 15(x - 5)^2 + \frac{1}{4}(x - 5)^3\right]\Big|_0^{10}$$

$$= \frac{1}{10}\left[1200 + 375 + \frac{125}{4}\right] - \frac{1}{10}\left[375 - \frac{125}{4}\right]$$

$$= 120 + 6.25 = 126.25 \text{ parts per million}$$

79. Let $N'(t) = F(t) = 6e^{-0.01t^2}$ $\qquad\qquad\qquad F(0) = 6$

$\qquad F'(t) = 6e^{-0.01t^2}(-0.02t) = -0.12te^{-0.01t^2}$ $\qquad F'(0) = 0$

$\qquad F''(t) = -0.12e^{-0.01t^2} - 0.12te^{-0.01t^2}(-0.02t)$ $\qquad F''(0) = -0.12$

$\qquad\qquad = -0.12e^{-0.01t^2} + 0.0024t^2e^{-0.01t^2}$

Thus,

$$p_2(t) = F(0) + F'(0)t + \frac{F''(0)}{2!}t^2 = 6 - 0.06t^2.$$

Therefore,

$$N(t) = \int N'(t)\,dt \approx \int p_2(t)\,dt = \int(6 - 0.06t^2)\,dt = 6t - 0.02t^3 + C.$$

Now, $N(0) = 40$. Therefore, $C = 40$ and
$N(t) \approx 6t - 0.02t^3 + 40$.
Thus, $N(5) \approx 30 - 0.02(5)^3 + 40 = 67.5$ words per minute and the improvement is $N(5) - N(0) = 67.5 - 40 = 27.5$ words per minute.

81. From Problem 69,

$D(x) = \dfrac{1}{10}\sqrt{10,000 - x^2}$ and

$p_2(x) = 10 - 0.0005x^2$.

The graphs of D and p_2 are shown at the right.

83. From Problem 73, $R(t) = 2 + 8e^{-0.1t^2}$ and $p_2(t) = 10 - 0.8t^2$. The graphs of R and p_2 are shown at the right.

85. From Problem 77,

$P(x) = 20\sqrt{3x^2 + 25} - 80$ and

$p_2(x) = 120 + 30(x - 5) + \dfrac{3}{4}(x - 5)^2$.

The graphs of P and p_2 are shown at the right.

87. From Problem 79,

$N'(t) = 6e^{-0.01t^2}$ and $p_2(t) = 6 - 0.06t^2$.
The graphs of N' and p_2 are shown at the right.

1. $\dfrac{4}{1-x} = 4 + 4x + 4x^2 + \ldots + 4x^n + \ldots$

$a_n = 4$

$a_{n+1} = 4$

$\dfrac{a_{n+1}}{a_n} = 1$, so $\displaystyle\lim_{n\to\infty}\left|\dfrac{a_{n+1}}{a_n}\right| = 1.$

Thus, $R = \dfrac{1}{L} = 1$ and the series converges for $|x| < 1$ or $-1 < x < 1$.

3. $\dfrac{1}{1+7x} = 1 - 7x + 7^2 x^2 - \ldots + (-1)^n 7^n x^n + \ldots$

$a_n = (-1)^n 7^n$

$a_{n+1} = (-1)^{n+1} 7^{n+1}$

$\dfrac{a_{n+1}}{a_n} = \dfrac{(-1)^{n+1} 7^{n+1}}{(-1)^n 7^n} = -7$

$\displaystyle\lim_{n\to\infty}\left|\dfrac{a_{n+1}}{a_n}\right| = 7$, thus $R = \dfrac{1}{L} = \dfrac{1}{7}$ and the series converges for $|x| < \dfrac{1}{7}$

or $-\dfrac{1}{7} < x < \dfrac{1}{7}.$

5. $\dfrac{1}{6-x} = \dfrac{1}{6} + \dfrac{1}{6^2}x + \dfrac{1}{6^3}x^2 + \ldots + \dfrac{1}{6^{n+1}}x^n + \ldots$

$a_n = \dfrac{1}{6^{n+1}}$

$a_{n+1} = \dfrac{1}{6^{n+2}}$

$\dfrac{a_{n+1}}{a_n} = \dfrac{\frac{1}{6^{n+2}}}{\frac{1}{6^{n+1}}} = \dfrac{1}{6}$

$\displaystyle\lim_{n\to\infty}\left|\dfrac{a_{n+1}}{a_n}\right| = \dfrac{1}{6}$, thus $R = \dfrac{1}{L} = 6$ and the series converges for $|x| < 6$

or $-6 < x < 6.$

7. $\ln(1 + x) = x - \dfrac{1}{2}x^2 + \dfrac{1}{3}x^3 - \cdots + \dfrac{(-1)^{n-1}}{n}x^n + \cdots$

We have $a = 0$ and

$$a_n = \frac{(-1)^{n-1}}{n}$$

$$a_{n+1} = \frac{(-1)^n}{n + 1}$$

Thus, $\dfrac{a_{n+1}}{a_n} = \dfrac{\dfrac{(-1)^n}{n+1}}{\dfrac{(-1)^{n-1}}{n}} = -\dfrac{n}{n+1}$ and $\lim\limits_{n \to \infty}\left|\dfrac{a_{n+1}}{a_n}\right| = \lim\limits_{n \to \infty}\left|\dfrac{-n}{n+1}\right| = 1.$

Therefore, Case (a) of $\underline{2}$ applies. We have $L = 1$, $R = \dfrac{1}{1} = 1$, and the series converges for $|x - 0| < 1$. Thus, the interval of convergence is:

$|x| < 1$ or $-1 < x < 1$

9. $\dfrac{1}{(1 + x)^2} = 1 - 2x + 3x^2 - \cdots + (-1)^n(n + 1)x^n + \cdots$

We have $a = 0$ and

$$a_n = (-1)^n(n + 1)$$

$$a_{n+1} = (-1)^{n+1}(n + 2)$$

Thus, $\dfrac{a_{n+1}}{a_n} = \dfrac{(-1)^{n+1}(n+2)}{(-1)^n(n+1)} = -\dfrac{(n+2)}{n+1}$ and $\lim\limits_{n \to \infty}\left|\dfrac{a_{n+1}}{a_n}\right| = \lim\limits_{n \to \infty}\left|\dfrac{-(n+2)}{(n+1)}\right| = 1.$

Therefore, Case (a) of $\underline{2}$ applies. We have $L = 1$, $R = \dfrac{1}{1} = 1$, and the series converges for $|x - 0| < 1$. Thus, the interval of convergence is:

$|x| < 1$ or $-1 < x < 1$

11. $e^x = 1 + x + \dfrac{1}{2!}x^2 + \cdots + \dfrac{1}{n!}x^n + \cdots$

We have $a = 0$ and $a_n = \dfrac{1}{n!}$

$$a_{n+1} = \frac{1}{(n + 1)!}$$

Thus, $\dfrac{a_{n+1}}{a_n} = \dfrac{\dfrac{1}{(n+1)!}}{\dfrac{1}{n!}} = \dfrac{n!}{(n+1)!} = \dfrac{1}{n+1}$ and $\lim\limits_{n \to \infty}\left|\dfrac{a_{n+1}}{a_n}\right| = \lim\limits_{n \to \infty}\left|\dfrac{1}{n+1}\right| = 0.$

Therefore, Case (b) of $\underline{2}$ applies and the series converges for all x. The interval of convergence is:

$-\infty < x < \infty$.

13. (A) Using a calculator, $e^2 \approx 7.3891$.
Now

$$p_1(x) = 1 + x \qquad\qquad\qquad\qquad p_1(2) = 3$$

$$p_2(x) = 1 + x + \frac{1}{2!}x^2 \qquad\qquad\qquad p_2(2) = 5$$

$$p_3(x) = 1 + x + \frac{1}{2!}x^2 + \frac{1}{3!}x^3 \qquad\qquad p_3(2) \approx 6.3333$$

$$p_4(x) = 1 + x + \frac{1}{2!}x^2 + \frac{1}{3!}x^3 + \frac{1}{4!}x^4 \qquad p_4(2) = 7$$

$$p_5(x) = 1 + x + \frac{1}{2!}x^2 + \dots + \frac{1}{5!}x^5 \qquad p_5(2) \approx 7.2667$$

$$p_6(x) = 1 + x + \frac{1}{2!}x^2 + \dots + \frac{1}{6!}x^6 \qquad p_6(2) \approx 7.3556$$

Thus, the smallest n such that $|p_n(2) - e^2| < 0.1$ is $n = 6$.

(B) Since the interval of convergence for e^x at 0 is $-\infty < x < \infty$, it follows from $\underline{3}$ that

$$\lim_{n \to \infty} p_n(x) = e^x$$

for every x. Therefore,

$$\lim_{n \to \infty} p_n(100) = e^{100}$$

and there does exist a positive integer n such that $|p_n(100) - e^{100}| < 0.1$

15. $\ln(4 + x) = (x + 3) - \frac{1}{2}(x + 3)^2 + \frac{1}{3}(x + 3)^3 - \dots + \frac{(-1)^{n+1}}{n}(x + 3)^n + \dots$

$$a_n = \frac{(-1)^{n+1}}{n}, \quad a_{n+1} = \frac{(-1)^{n+2}}{n + 1}$$

$$\frac{a_{n+1}}{a_n} = \frac{\frac{(-1)^{n+2}}{n + 1}}{\frac{(-1)^{n+1}}{n}} = \frac{(-1)^{n+2}}{n + 1} \cdot \frac{n}{(-1)^{n+1}} = -\frac{n}{n + 1}$$

$$\lim_{n \to \infty} \left| \frac{a_{n+1}}{a_n} \right| = \lim_{n \to \infty} \left| \frac{-n}{n + 1} \right| = \lim_{n \to \infty} \frac{n}{n + 1} = \lim_{n \to \infty} \frac{1}{1 + \frac{1}{n}} = 1$$

Thus, $L = 1$, $R = \frac{1}{L} = \frac{1}{1} = 1$, and the series converges for $|x + 3| < 1$.
The interval of convergence is: $|x + 3| < 1$ or $-4 < x < -2$.

17. $e^{2x} = 1 + 2x + \dfrac{2^2}{2!}x^2 + \dfrac{2^3}{3!}x^3 + \dots + \dfrac{2^n}{n!}x^n + \dots$

$a_n = \dfrac{2^n}{n!}, \quad a_{n+1} = \dfrac{2^{n+1}}{(n+1)!}$

$\dfrac{a_{n+1}}{a_n} = \dfrac{\dfrac{2^{n+1}}{(n+1)!}}{\dfrac{2^n}{n!}} = \dfrac{2^{n+1}}{(n+1)!} \cdot \dfrac{n!}{2^n} = \dfrac{2}{n+1}$

$\lim\limits_{n \to \infty} \left| \dfrac{a_{n+1}}{a_n} \right| = \lim\limits_{n \to \infty} \left| \dfrac{2}{n+1} \right| = \lim\limits_{n \to \infty} \dfrac{2}{n+1} = 0$

The series converges for all values of x. The interval of convergence is: $-\infty < x < \infty$.

19. $\dfrac{1}{6-x} = \dfrac{1}{4} + \dfrac{1}{4^2}(x-2) + \dfrac{1}{4^3}(x-2)^2 + \dots + \dfrac{1}{4^{n+1}}(x-2)^n + \dots$

$a_n = \dfrac{1}{4^{n+1}}, \quad a_{n+1} = \dfrac{1}{4^{n+2}}$

$\dfrac{a_{n+1}}{a_n} = \dfrac{\dfrac{1}{4^{n+2}}}{\dfrac{1}{4^{n+1}}} = \dfrac{1}{4^{n+2}} \cdot \dfrac{4^{n+1}}{1} = \dfrac{1}{4}$

$\lim\limits_{n \to \infty} \left| \dfrac{a_{n+1}}{a_n} \right| = \lim\limits_{n \to \infty} \left| \dfrac{1}{4} \right| = \lim\limits_{n \to \infty} \dfrac{1}{4} = \dfrac{1}{4}$

Thus, $L = \dfrac{1}{4}$, $R = \dfrac{1}{L} = 4$, and the interval of convergence is: $|x-2| < 4$ or $-2 < x < 6$.

21. $\dfrac{1}{6-x} = -\dfrac{1}{2} + \dfrac{1}{2^2}(x-8) - \dfrac{1}{2^3}(x-8)^2 + \dots + \dfrac{(-1)^n}{2^{n+1}}(x-8)^n$

$a_n = \dfrac{(-1)^n}{2^{n+1}}, \quad a_{n+1} = \dfrac{(-1)^{n+1}}{2^{n+2}}$

$\dfrac{a_{n+1}}{a_n} = \dfrac{\dfrac{(-1)^{n+1}}{2^{n+2}}}{\dfrac{(-1)^n}{2^{n+1}}} = \dfrac{(-1)^{n+1}}{2^{n+2}} \cdot \dfrac{2^{n+1}}{(-1)^n} = -\dfrac{1}{2}$

$\lim\limits_{n \to \infty} \left| \dfrac{a_{n+1}}{a_n} \right| = \lim\limits_{n \to \infty} \left| -\dfrac{1}{2} \right| = \dfrac{1}{2}$

Thus, $L = \dfrac{1}{2}$, $R = 2$, and the interval of convergence is: $|x-8| < 2$ or $6 < x < 10$.

23. **(A)**

Based on these graphs it appears that the interval of convergence will be $-\infty < x < \infty$.

(B) The Taylor series at 0 for $f(x) = e^x$ is:

$$e^x = 1 + x + \frac{1}{2!}x^2 + \dots + \frac{1}{n!}x^n + \dots$$

By Problem 11, the interval of convergence is $-\infty < x < \infty$.

25. $f(x) = e^{4x}$

(A)

Step 1:	Step 2:	Step 3:
$f(x) = e^{4x}$	$f(0) = 1$	$a_0 = f(0) = 1$
$f'(x) = 4e^{4x}$	$f'(0) = 4$	$a_1 = f'(0) = 4$
$f''(x) = 4^2 e^{4x}$	$f''(0) = 4^2$	$a_2 = \dfrac{f''(0)}{2!} = \dfrac{4^2}{2}$
$\vdots$	$\vdots$	$\vdots$
$f^{(n)}(x) = 4^n e^{4x}$	$f^{(n)}(0) = 4^n$	$a_n = \dfrac{f^{(n)}(0)}{n!} = \dfrac{4^n}{n!}$

Step 4: The nth-degree Taylor polynomial at $a = 0$ for $f(x) = e^{4x}$ is:

$$p_n(x) = 1 + 4x + \frac{4^2}{2}x^2 + \dots + \frac{4^n}{n!}x^n$$

(B) The Taylor series at $a = 0$ for f is:

$$\lim_{n \to \infty} p_n(x) = 1 + 4x + \frac{4^2}{2!}x^2 + \dots + \frac{4^n}{n!}x^n + \dots$$

(C) From part (A):

$$a_n = \frac{4^n}{n!}$$

$$a_{n+1} = \frac{4^{n+1}}{(n+1)!}$$

Thus, $\dfrac{a_{n+1}}{a_n} = \dfrac{\dfrac{4^{n+1}}{(n+1)!}}{\dfrac{4^n}{n!}} = \dfrac{4^{n+1}}{4^n} \cdot \dfrac{n!}{(n+1)!} = \dfrac{4}{n+1}$ and

$$\lim_{n \to \infty} \left| \frac{a_{n+1}}{a_n} \right| = \lim_{n \to \infty} \left| \frac{4}{n+1} \right| = 0.$$

Therefore, the series converges for all x, and the interval of convergence is: $-\infty < x < \infty$.

27. $f(x) = \ln(1 + 2x)$

(A) <u>Step 1</u>:

$$f(x) = \ln(1 + 2x)$$

$$f'(x) = \frac{1}{1 + 2x}(2) = 2(1 + 2x)^{-1}$$

$$f''(x) = -2(1 + 2x)^{-2}(2) = -2^2(1 + 2x)^{-2}$$

$$f^{(3)}(x) = -2^2(-2)(1 + 2x)^{-3}(2) = 2^3(2)(1 + 2x)^{-3}$$

$$f^{(4)}(x) = 2^3(2)(-3)(1 + 2x)^{-4}(2) = -2^4(3 \cdot 2)(1 + 2x)^{-4}$$

$$\vdots$$

$$f^{(n)}(x) = (-1)^{n-1}2^n(n - 1)!(1 + 2x)^{-n}$$

<u>Step 2</u>:   <u>Step 3</u>:

$f(0) = \ln 1 = 0$ $a_0 = f(0) = 0$

$f'(0) = 2$ $a_1 = f'(0) = 2$

$f''(0) = -2^2$ $a_2 = \dfrac{f''(0)}{2!} = \dfrac{-2^2}{2}$

$f^{(3)}(0) = 2^3 \cdot 2$ $a_3 = \dfrac{f^{(3)}(0)}{3!} = \dfrac{2^3}{3}$

$f^{(4)}(0) = -2^4 \cdot 3!$ $a_4 = \dfrac{f^{(4)}(0)}{4!} = \dfrac{-2^4}{4}$

$\vdots$ $\vdots$

$f^{(n)}(0) = (-1)^{n-1}2^n(n - 1)!$ $a_n = \dfrac{f^{(n)}(0)}{n!} = \dfrac{(-1)^{n-1}2^n}{n}$

<u>Step 4</u>: The nth-degree Taylor polynomial at $a = 0$ for $f(x) = \ln(1 + 2x)$ is:

$$p_n(x) = 2x - \frac{2^2}{2}x^2 + \frac{2^3}{3}x^3 - \frac{2^4}{4}x^4 + \cdots + \frac{(-1)^{n-1}2^n}{n}x^n$$

(B) The Taylor series at $a = 0$ for f is

$$\lim_{n \to \infty} p_n(x) = 2x - \frac{2^2}{2}x^2 + \frac{2^3}{3}x^3 - \frac{2^4}{4}x^4 + \cdots + \frac{(-1)^{n-1}2^n}{n}x^n + \cdots$$

(C) From part (A):

$$a_n = \frac{(-1)^{n-1}2^n}{n}$$

$$a_{n+1} = \frac{(-1)^n 2^{n+1}}{n + 1}$$

Thus, $\dfrac{a_{n+1}}{a_n} = \dfrac{\dfrac{(-1)^n 2^{n+1}}{n + 1}}{\dfrac{(-1)^{n+1}2^n}{n}} = \dfrac{-2n}{n + 1}$ and $\lim\limits_{n \to \infty}\left|\dfrac{a_{n+1}}{a_n}\right| = \lim\limits_{n \to \infty}\left|\dfrac{-2n}{n + 1}\right| = 2.$

Therefore, $L = 2$, $R = \dfrac{1}{2}$, and the series converges for

$|x| < \dfrac{1}{2}$ or $-\dfrac{1}{2} < x < \dfrac{1}{2}.$

29. $f(x) = \dfrac{2}{2 - x}$

(A)   Step 1:

$$f(x) = \frac{2}{2 - x} = 2(2 - x)^{-1}$$

$$f'(x) = 2(-1)(2 - x)^{-2}(-1)$$
$$= 2(2 - x)^{-2}$$

$$f''(x) = 2(-2)(2 - x)^{-3}(-1)$$
$$= 2(2)(2 - x)^{-3}$$

$$f^{(3)}(x) = 2(2)(-3)(2 - x)^{-4}(-1)$$
$$= 2(3 \cdot 2)(2 - x)^{-4}$$

$$\vdots$$

$$f^{(n)}(x) = 2(n!)(2 - x)^{-(n+1)}$$

Step 2:

$$f(0) = 1$$

$$f'(0) = \frac{2}{2^2} = \frac{1}{2}$$

$$f''(0) = \frac{2!}{2^2} = \frac{1}{2}$$

$$f^{(3)}(0) = \frac{3!}{2^3}$$

$$\vdots$$

$$f^{(n)}(0) = \frac{n!}{2^n}$$

Step 3:

$$a_0 = f(0) = 1$$

$$a_1 = f'(0) = \frac{1}{2}$$

$$a_2 = \frac{f''(0)}{2!} = \frac{1}{2^2}$$

$$a_3 = \frac{f^{(3)}(0)}{3!} = \frac{1}{2^3}$$

$$\vdots$$

$$a_n = \frac{f^{(n)}(0)}{n!} = \frac{1}{2^n}$$

Step 4: The nth-degree Taylor polynomial at $a = 0$ for
$$f(x) = \frac{2}{2 - x} \text{ is:}$$

$$p_n(x) = 1 + \frac{1}{2}x + \frac{1}{2^2}x^2 + \cdots + \frac{1}{2^n}x^n$$

(B) The Taylor series at $a = 0$ for f is:

$$\lim_{n \to \infty} p_n(x) = 1 + \frac{1}{2}x + \frac{1}{2^2}x^2 + \cdots + \frac{1}{2^n}x^n + \cdots$$

(C) From part (A):

$$a_n = \frac{1}{2^n}$$

$$a_{n+1} = \frac{1}{2^{n+1}}$$

Thus, $\dfrac{a_{n+1}}{a_n} = \dfrac{\frac{1}{2^{n+1}}}{\frac{1}{2^n}} = \dfrac{1}{2}$ and $\displaystyle\lim_{n \to \infty} \left| \dfrac{a_{n+1}}{a_n} \right| = \lim_{n \to \infty} \left| \dfrac{1}{2} \right| = \dfrac{1}{2}$.

Therefore, $L = \dfrac{1}{2}$, $R = \dfrac{1}{\frac{1}{2}} = 2$, and the series converges for:

$$|x| < 2 \quad \text{or} \quad -2 < x < 2.$$

31. $f(x) = \ln(2 - x)$, $a = 1$.

(A) <u>Step 1:</u> <u>Step 2:</u> <u>Step 3:</u>

$$f(x) = \ln(2 - x)$$

$$f'(x) = \frac{1}{2 - x}(-1)$$
$$= -(2 - x)^{-1}$$

$$f''(x) = (2 - x)^{-2}(-1)$$
$$= -(2 - x)^{-2}$$

$$f^{(3)}(x) = 2(2 - x)^{-3}(-1)$$
$$= -2(2 - x)^{-3}$$

$$f^{(4)}(x) = 3\cdot 2(2 - x)^{-4}(-1)$$
$$= -3!(2 - x)^{-4}$$

$$\vdots$$

$$f^{(n)}(x) = -(n - 1)!(2 - x)^{-n}$$

Step 2:

$$f(1) = \ln 1 = 0$$

$$f'(1) = -1$$

$$f''(1) = -1$$

$$f^{(3)}(1) = -2$$

$$f^{(4)}(1) = -3!$$

$$\vdots$$

$$f^{(n)}(1) = -(n - 1)!$$

Step 3:

$$a_0 = f(1) = 0$$

$$a_1 = f'(1) = -1$$

$$a_2 = \frac{f''(1)}{2!} = -\frac{1}{2}$$

$$a_3 = \frac{f^{(3)}(1)}{3!} = -\frac{1}{3}$$

$$a_4 = \frac{f^{(4)}(1)}{4!} = -\frac{1}{4}$$

$$\vdots$$

$$a_n = \frac{f^{(n)}(1)}{n!} = -\frac{1}{n}$$

<u>Step 4:</u> The nth-degree Taylor polynomial at $a = 1$ for $f(x) = \ln(2 - x)$ is:

$$p_n(x) = -(x - 1) - \frac{1}{2}(x - 1)^2 - \frac{1}{3}(x - 1)^3 - \cdots - \frac{1}{n}(x - 1)^n$$

(B) The Taylor series at $a = 1$ for f is:

$$\lim_{n \to \infty} p_n(x) = -(x - 1) - \frac{1}{2}(x - 1)^2 - \frac{1}{3}(x - 1)^3 - \cdots - \frac{1}{n}(x - 1)^n - \cdots$$

(C) From part (A):

$$a_n = -\frac{1}{n}$$

$$a_{n+1} = -\frac{1}{n + 1}$$

Thus, $\dfrac{a_{n+1}}{a_n} = \dfrac{-\dfrac{1}{n + 1}}{-\dfrac{1}{n}} = \dfrac{n}{n + 1}$ and $\lim\limits_{n \to \infty}\left|\dfrac{a_{n+1}}{a_n}\right| = \lim\limits_{n \to \infty}\left|\dfrac{n}{n + 1}\right| = 1.$

Therefore, $L = 1$, $R = \dfrac{1}{1} = 1$, and the series converges for:

$|x - 1| < 1$ or $0 < x < 2$.

33. $f(x) = \dfrac{1}{1 - x}$, $a = 2$.

(A)

Step 1:

$$f(x) = \dfrac{1}{1 - x}$$
$$= (1 - x)^{-1}$$
$$f'(x) = -(1 - x)^{-2}(-1)$$
$$= (1 - x)^{-2}$$
$$f''(x) = -2(1 - x)^{-3}(-1)$$
$$= 2(1 - x)^{-3}$$
$$f^{(3)}(x) = 2(-3)(1 - x)^{-4}(-1)$$
$$= 3!(1 - x)^{-4}$$
$$\vdots$$
$$f^{(n)}(x) = n!(1 - x)^{-(n+1)}$$

Step 2:

$$f(2) = -1$$

$$f'(2) = 1$$

$$f''(2) = -2$$

$$f^{(3)}(2) = 3!$$

$$\vdots$$

$$f^{(n)}(2) = (-1)^{n-1}n!$$

Step 3:

$$a_0 = f(2) = -1$$

$$a_1 = f'(2) = 1$$

$$a_2 = \dfrac{f''(2)}{2!} = -1$$

$$a_3 = \dfrac{f^{(3)}(2)}{3!} = 1$$

$$\vdots$$

$$a_n = \dfrac{f^{(n)}(2)}{n!}$$
$$= (-1)^{n-1}$$

Step 4: The nth-degree Taylor polynomial at $a = 2$ for
$f(x) = \dfrac{1}{1 - x}$ is:

$$p_n(x) = -1 + (x - 2) - (x - 2)^2 + (x - 2)^3 - \cdots + (-1)^{n-1}(x - 2)^n$$

(B) The Taylor series at $a = 2$ for f is:

$$\lim_{n \to \infty} p_n(x) = -1 + (x - 2) - (x - 2)^2 + (x - 2)^3 - \cdots$$
$$+ (-1)^{n-1}(x - 2)^n + \cdots$$

(C) From part (A): $a_n = (-1)^{n-1}$

$$a_{n+1} = (-1)^n$$

Thus, $\dfrac{a_{n+1}}{a_n} = \dfrac{(-1)^n}{(-1)^{n-1}} = -1$ and $\lim_{n \to \infty}\left|\dfrac{a_{n+1}}{a_n}\right| = \lim_{n \to \infty}|-1| = 1$.

Therefore, $L = 1$, $R = \dfrac{1}{1} = 1$, and the series converges for:
$|x - 2| < 1$ or $1 < x < 3$.

35. (A) $\dfrac{1}{4 - x} = \dfrac{1}{4} + \dfrac{1}{4^2}x + \dfrac{1}{4^3}x^2 + \cdots + \dfrac{1}{4^{n+1}}x^n + \cdots$
We have $a = 0$ and
$$a_n = \dfrac{1}{4^{n+1}}; \quad a_{n+1} = \dfrac{1}{4^{n+2}}$$

Thus, $\dfrac{a_{n+1}}{a_n} = \dfrac{\dfrac{1}{4^{n+2}}}{\dfrac{1}{4^{n+1}}} = \dfrac{4^{n+1}}{4^{n+2}} = \dfrac{1}{4}$ and

$$\lim_{n \to \infty} \left| \frac{a_{n+1}}{a_n} \right| = \lim_{n \to \infty} \left| \frac{1}{4} \right| = \frac{1}{4}.$$

Therefore, $L = \frac{1}{4}$, $R = 4$ and the interval of convergence is $|x - 0| < 4$; that is, $|x| < 4$ or $-4 < x < 4$.

(B) $\dfrac{1}{4 - x^2} = \dfrac{1}{4} + \dfrac{1}{4^2}x^2 + \dfrac{1}{4^3}x^4 + \cdots + \dfrac{1}{4^{n+1}}x^{2n} + \cdots$

Theorem 1 is not directly applicable because the coefficients of the odd powers of x are 0.

(C) If we let $t = x^2$, then the Taylor series in (B) becomes

$$\frac{1}{4 - x^2} = \frac{1}{4 - t} = \frac{1}{4} + \frac{1}{4^2}t + \frac{1}{4^3}t^2 + \cdots + \frac{1}{4^{n+1}}t^n + \cdots$$

From the result in part (A), this series converges for $|t| < 4$. Expressed in terms of x, we have $|x^2| < 4$ which implies $|x| < 2$. Thus, the interval of convergence is $|x| < 2$ or $-2 < x < 2$.

37. (A) $\dfrac{1}{1 - x} + \dfrac{1}{1 - x^2} = 2 + x + 2x^2 + x^3 + 2x^4 + x^5 + \cdots$

We have $a = 0$ and

$$a_n = \begin{cases} 2 & \text{if } n \text{ is even} \\ 1 & \text{if } n \text{ is odd} \end{cases}$$

Therefore, $\dfrac{a_{n+1}}{a_n} = \begin{cases} \dfrac{1}{2} & \text{if } n \text{ is even} \\ 2 & \text{if } n \text{ is odd} \end{cases}$

and $\lim\limits_{n \to \infty} \left| \dfrac{a_{n+1}}{a_n} \right|$ does not exist. Thus, Theorem 1 does not apply.

(B) $\dfrac{1}{1 - x} = 1 + x + x^2 + x^3 + \cdots + x^n + \cdots$

We have $a = 0$ and $a_n = a_{n+1} = 1$.

Thus, $\dfrac{a_{n+1}}{a_n} = 1$ and $\lim\limits_{n \to \infty} \left| \dfrac{a_{n+1}}{a_n} \right| = 1$.

Therefore, $L = R = 1$ and the interval of convergence is $|x| < 1$ or $-1 < x < 1$.

$$\frac{1}{1 - x^2} = 1 + x^2 + x^4 + x^6 + \cdots + x^{2n} + \cdots$$

If we let $t = x^2$, then

$$\frac{1}{1 - x^2} = \frac{1}{1 - t} = 1 + t + t^2 + t^3 + \cdots + t^n + \cdots$$

and the interval of convergence is $|t| < 1$. In terms of x, the interval of convergence is $|x^2| < 1$ which implies $|x| < 1$ or $-1 < x < 1$. Thus, both series have the same interval of convergence, $-1 < x < 1$, and so this is the interval of convergence of their sum.

1. $f(x) = \dfrac{1}{1 - x} + \dfrac{1}{1 + x}$

$\dfrac{1}{1 - x} = 1 + x + x^2 + \dots + x^n + \dots \qquad ; \quad -1 < x < 1$

$\dfrac{1}{1 + x} = 1 - x + x^2 - \dots + (-1)^n x^n + \dots \; ; \quad -1 < x < 1$

$\dfrac{1}{1 - x} + \dfrac{1}{1 + x} = 2 + 2x^2 + 2x^4 + \dots + 2x^{2n} + \dots$

$a_n = 2; \; a_{n+1} = 2$

$\displaystyle \lim_{n \to \infty} \left| \dfrac{a_{n+1}}{a_n} \right| = 1$, thus $R = \dfrac{1}{L} = 1$ and hence $-1 < x < 1$.

Note: Since the interval of convergence for each series is $(-1, 1)$, we could have concluded that the interval of convergence for the sum of them is also $(-1, 1)$.

3. $f(x) = \dfrac{1}{1 - x} + e^{-x}$

$\dfrac{1}{1 - x} = 1 + x + x^2 + \dots + x^n + \dots \qquad ; \quad -1 < x < 1$

$e^{-x} = 1 - x + \dfrac{1}{2!} x^2 - \dots + \dfrac{(-1)^n}{n!} x^n + \dots ; \quad -\infty < x < \infty$

$\dfrac{1}{1 - x} + e^{-x} = 2 + \dfrac{3}{2} x^2 + \dfrac{1}{12} x^4 + \dots + \left[1 + \dfrac{(-1)^n}{n!} \right] x^n + \dots$

$a_n = 1 + \dfrac{(-1)^n}{n!}$

$a_{n+1} = 1 + \dfrac{(-1)^{n+1}}{(n + 1)!}$

$\displaystyle \lim_{n \to \infty} \left| \dfrac{a_{n+1}}{a_n} \right| = 1$ and hence $R = 1$ or $(-1, 1)$ is the interval of convergence.

Note: We could have concluded that the interval of convergence of the sum of the two series is the intersection of the two interval of convergence, which is $(-1, 1)$.

5. $f(x) = \dfrac{x^3}{1 + x}$

$\dfrac{1}{1 + x} = 1 - x + x^2 - \dots + (-1)^n x^n + \dots \quad ; \quad -1 < x < 1$

$\dfrac{x^3}{1 + x} = x^3 - x^4 + x^5 - \dots + (-1)^n x^{n+3} + \dots$

$a_n = (-1)^n; \; a_{n+1} = (-1)^{n+1}$

$\displaystyle \lim_{n \to \infty} \left| \dfrac{a_{n+1}}{a_n} \right| = 1$ and hence the series is convergent for $|x| < 1$ or $-1 < x < 1$.

7. $f(x) = x^2 \ln(1 - x)$

$\ln(1 - x) = -x - \dfrac{x^2}{2} - \dfrac{x^3}{3} - \ldots - \dfrac{x^n}{n} - \ldots \quad , \quad -1 < x < 1$

$x^2 \ln(1 - x) = -x^3 - \dfrac{x^4}{2} - \dfrac{x^5}{5} - \ldots - \dfrac{x^{n+2}}{n} - \ldots$

$a_n = -\dfrac{1}{n}$

$a_{n+1} = -\dfrac{1}{n + 1}$

$\lim\limits_{n \to \infty} \left| \dfrac{a_{n+1}}{a_n} \right| = \lim\limits_{n \to \infty} \dfrac{n}{n + 1} = 1.$ Thus the series is convergent for $|x| < 1$
or $-1 < x < 1$.

9. $f(x) = e^{x^2}$

$e^u = 1 + u + \dfrac{1}{2!}u^2 + \ldots + \dfrac{1}{n!}u^n + \ldots \quad ; \quad -\infty < u < \infty$

Let $u = x^2$, then

$e^{x^2} = 1 + x^2 + \dfrac{1}{2!}x^4 + \ldots + \dfrac{1}{n!}x^{2n} + \ldots \quad ; \quad -\infty < x < \infty$

11. $f(x) = \ln(1 + 3x)$

$\ln(1 + u) = u - \dfrac{1}{2}u^2 + \ldots + \dfrac{(-1)^{n-1}}{n}u^n + \ldots \quad ; \quad -1 < u < 1$

Let $u = 3x$, then

$\ln(1 + 3x) = 3x - \dfrac{9}{2}x^2 + 9x^3 - \ldots + (-1)^{n-1}\dfrac{3^n}{n}x^n + \ldots$

Note that

$-1 < 3x < 1 \quad \text{or} \quad -\dfrac{1}{3} < x < \dfrac{1}{3},$

and hence the interval of convergence is $\left(-\dfrac{1}{3}, \dfrac{1}{3} \right)$.

13. From Table 1,

$\dfrac{1}{1 - x} = 1 + x + x^2 + \ldots + x^n + \ldots \quad (-1 < x < 1).$

Now, $f(x) = \dfrac{1}{2 - x} = \dfrac{1}{2\left(1 - \dfrac{x}{2}\right)} = \dfrac{1}{2} \cdot \dfrac{1}{1 - \dfrac{x}{2}}.$

Substituting $\dfrac{x}{2}$ for x in the series for $\dfrac{1}{1 - x}$, and using Property $\underline{2}$,
we have

$$f(x) = \frac{1}{2 - x} = \frac{1}{2}\left(\frac{1}{1 - x/2}\right) = \frac{1}{2}\left(1 + \frac{x}{2} + \left(\frac{x}{2}\right)^2 + \cdots + \left(\frac{x}{2}\right)^n + \cdots\right)$$

$$= \frac{1}{2}\left(1 + \frac{x}{2} + \frac{x^2}{2^2} + \cdots + \frac{x^n}{2^n} + \cdots\right)$$

$$= \frac{1}{2} + \frac{x}{2^2} + \frac{x^2}{2^3} + \cdots + \frac{x^n}{2^{n+1}} + \cdots$$

The interval of convergence is $-1 < \dfrac{x}{2} < 1$ or $-2 < x < 2$.

15. From Table 1,

$$\frac{1}{1 - x} = 1 + x + x^2 + \cdots + x^n + \cdots \qquad (-1 < x < 1).$$

Substituting $8x^3$ for x, we have

$$f(x) = \frac{1}{1 - 8x^3} = 1 + 8x^3 + [8x^3]^2 + \cdots + [8x^3]^n + \cdots$$

$$= 1 + 8x^3 + 8^2 x^6 + \cdots + 8^n x^{3n} + \cdots .$$

The interval of convergence is $-1 < 8x^3 < 1$, which is
$\dfrac{-1}{8} < x^3 < \dfrac{1}{8}$ or $\dfrac{-1}{2} < x < \dfrac{1}{2}$.

17. $f(x) = 10^x = e^{x \ln 10}$
From Table 1,

$$e^x = 1 + x + \frac{1}{2!}x^2 + \cdots + \frac{1}{n!}x^n + \cdots \qquad (-\infty < x < \infty)$$

Substituting $x \ln 10$ for x, we have

$$10^x = e^{x \ln 10} = 1 + (\ln 10)x + \frac{(\ln 10)^2}{2!}x^2 + \frac{(\ln 10)^3}{3!}x^3 + \cdots$$

$$+ \frac{(\ln 10)^n}{n!}x^n + \cdots .$$

The interval of convergence is $-\infty < x < \infty$.

19. $f(x) = \log_2(1 - x) = \dfrac{1}{\ln 2}\ln(1 - x)$
From Table 1,

$$\ln(1 - x) = -x - \frac{1}{2}x^2 - \frac{1}{3}x^3 - \cdots - \frac{1}{n}x^n - \cdots, \quad -1 < x < 1.$$

Therefore, the Taylor series for $f(x) = \log_2(1 - x)$ is:

$$\log_2(1 - x) = \frac{-1}{\ln 2}x - \frac{1}{2 \ln 2}x^2 - \frac{1}{3 \ln 2}x^3 - \frac{1}{n \ln 2}x^n - \cdots, \quad -1 < x < 1.$$

21. From Table 1,

$$\frac{1}{1+x} = 1 - x + x^2 - x^3 + \cdots + (-1)^n x^n + \cdots \quad (-1 < x < 1).$$

Now, $f(x) = \dfrac{1}{4+x^2} = \dfrac{1}{4\left(1 + \dfrac{x^2}{4}\right)} = \dfrac{1}{4} \cdot \dfrac{1}{1 + \left(\dfrac{x}{2}\right)^2}.$

Thus, substituting $\left(\dfrac{x}{2}\right)^2 = \dfrac{x^2}{4}$ for x in the series for $\dfrac{1}{1+x}$, we have

$$f(x) = \frac{1}{4+x^2} = \frac{1}{4}\left[\frac{1}{1 + x^2/4}\right] = \frac{1}{4}\left(1 - \frac{x^2}{4} + \left[\frac{x^2}{4}\right]^2 - \cdots + (-1)^n \left[\frac{x^2}{4}\right]^n + \cdots\right)$$

$$= \frac{1}{4}\left(1 - \frac{x^2}{4} + \frac{x^4}{4^2} - \cdots + (-1)^n \frac{x^{2n}}{4^n} + \cdots\right)$$

$$= \frac{1}{4} - \frac{x^2}{4^2} + \frac{x^4}{4^3} - \cdots + (-1)^n \frac{x^{2n}}{4^{n+1}} + \cdots.$$

The interval of convergence is $-1 < \dfrac{x^2}{4} < 1$ or $-4 < x^2 < 4$, which is $-2 < x < 2$.

23. (A) The Taylor series at 0 for e^x converges for all x. Since the odd powers of $\sqrt{x} = x^{1/2}$ are defined only for $x \geq 0$, the formula

$$e^{\sqrt{x}} = 1 + x^{1/2} + \frac{1}{2!}x + \frac{1}{3!}x^{3/2} + \cdots + \frac{1}{n!}x^{n/2} + \cdots$$

is valid only for $x \geq 0$.

(B) The formula for $e^{\sqrt{x}}$ is **not** a Taylor series at 0 because some (in fact, half) of the powers of x are not non-negative integers.

25. (A) From Table 1,

$$\frac{1}{1-x} = 1 + x + x^2 + x^3 + \cdots + x^n + \cdots \quad (-1 < x < 1).$$

Substituting x^2 for x, we have

$$f(x) = \frac{1}{1-x^2} = 1 + x^2 + (x^2)^2 + (x^2)^3 + \cdots + (x^2)^n + \cdots$$

$$= 1 + x^2 + x^4 + x^6 + \cdots + x^{2n} + \cdots \quad (-1 < x < 1).$$

(B) Using Property 3,

$$f'(x) = 2x + 4x^3 + 6x^5 + \cdots + 2nx^{2n-1} + \cdots \quad (-1 < x < 1).$$

On the other hand, differentiating $f(x) = \dfrac{1}{1-x^2}$, we have

$$f'(x) = \frac{2x}{(1-x^2)^2}.$$

Thus, the Taylor series at 0 for $g(x) = \dfrac{2x}{(1-x^2)^2}$ is

$$g(x) = 2x + 4x^3 + 6x^5 + \cdots + 2nx^{2n-1} + \cdots \quad (-1 < x < 1).$$

27. From Table 1,

$$\frac{1}{1+x} = 1 - x + x^2 - x^3 + \cdots + (-1)^n x^n + \cdots \qquad (-1 < x < 1).$$

Thus,

$$f'(x) = \frac{1}{1+x^2} = 1 - x^2 + x^4 - x^6 + \cdots + (-1)^n x^{2n} + \cdots \qquad (-1 < x < 1),$$

substituting x^2 for x in the series for $\dfrac{1}{1+x}$. Now, using Property 4,

$$f(x) = \int f(x)\,dx = \int [1 - x^2 + x^4 - x^6 + \cdots + (-1)^n x^{2n} + \cdots]\,dx$$

$$= C + x - \frac{x^3}{3} + \frac{x^5}{5} - \frac{x^7}{7} + \cdots + \frac{(-1)^n}{2n+1} x^{2n+1} + \cdots .$$

Applying the initial condition $f(0) = 0$, we have

$$0 = C + 0 - \frac{0^3}{3} + \cdots + \frac{(-1)^n}{2n+1} 0^{2n+1} + \cdots,$$

$C = 0$.

Thus,

$$f(x) = x - \frac{x^3}{3} + \frac{x^5}{5} - \frac{x^7}{7} + \cdots + \frac{(-1)^n}{2n+1} x^{2n+1} + \cdots \qquad (-1 < x < 1).$$

29. From Table 1

$$\ln(1 - x) = -x - \frac{1}{2}x^2 - \frac{1}{3}x^3 - \cdots - \frac{1}{n}x^n - \cdots \qquad -1 < x < 1$$

Therefore,

$$f'(x) = x^2\left[-x - \frac{1}{2}x^2 - \frac{1}{3}x^3 - \cdots - \frac{1}{n}x^n - \cdots\right]$$

$$= -x^3 - \frac{1}{2}x^4 - \frac{1}{3}x^5 - \cdots - \frac{1}{n}x^{n+2} - \cdots, \qquad -1 < x < 1$$

and

$$f(x) = \int f'(x)\,dx = \int\left[-x^3 - \frac{1}{2}x^4 - \frac{1}{3}x^5 - \cdots - \frac{1}{n}x^{n+2} - \cdots\right]dx$$

$$= -\int x^3\,dx - \frac{1}{2}\int x^4\,dx - \frac{1}{3}\int x^5\,dx - \cdots - \frac{1}{n}\int x^{n+2}\,dx - \cdots$$

$$= C - \frac{1}{4}x^4 - \frac{1}{10}x^5 - \frac{1}{18}x^6 - \cdots - \frac{1}{n(n+3)}x^{n+3} - \cdots$$

$$= C - \frac{1}{4}x^4 - \frac{1}{10}x^5 - \frac{1}{18}x^6 - \cdots - \frac{1}{n(n-3)}x^n - \cdots$$

Since $f(0) = 5$, we have

$$f(0) = 5 = C - 0 - 0 - \cdots - 0 - \cdots$$
$$= C$$

Thus

$$f(x) = 5 - \frac{1}{4}x^4 - \frac{1}{10}x^5 - \frac{1}{18}x^6 - \cdots - \frac{1}{n(n-3)}x^n - \cdots$$

Since the series for f' converges for $-1 < x < 1$, the series for f converges for $-1 < x < 1$.

31. (A)

(B) $\sinh x = x + \dfrac{1}{3!}x^3 + \dfrac{1}{5!}x^5 + \cdots + \dfrac{1}{(2n+1)!}x^{2n+1} + \cdots,\ -\infty < x < \infty.$

Since $\dfrac{d^2}{dx^2}(x) = 0,\ \dfrac{d^2}{dx^2}\left(\dfrac{1}{3!}x^3\right) = x,$

$\dfrac{d^2}{dx^2}\left(\dfrac{1}{5!}x^5\right) = \dfrac{1}{3!}x^3,$ and, in general,

$\dfrac{d^2}{dx^2}\left[\dfrac{1}{(2k+1)!}x^{2k+1}\right] = \dfrac{1}{(2k-1)!}x^{2k-1},\ k = 1, 2, \cdots,$

it follows that $\dfrac{d^2}{dx^2}(\sinh x) = \sinh x.$

33. Let $t = x - 3$. Then $x = t + 3$ and

$\dfrac{1}{4-x} = \dfrac{1}{4-(t+3)} = \dfrac{1}{1-t} = f(t).$

From Table 1,

$\dfrac{1}{1-t} = 1 + t + t^2 + t^3 + \cdots + t^n + \cdots \quad (-1 < t < 1).$

Substituting $x - 3$ for t in this series, we have

$f(x) = \dfrac{1}{4-x} = 1 + (x-3) + (x-3)^2 + (x-3)^3 + \cdots + (x-3)^n + \cdots.$

The interval of convergence is $-1 < x - 3 < 1$ or $2 < x < 4$.

35. Let $t = x - 1$. Then $x = 1 + t$ and

$\ln x = \ln(1+t) = t - \dfrac{1}{2}t^2 + \dfrac{1}{3}t^3 - \cdots + \dfrac{(-1)^{n-1}}{n}t^n + \cdots \quad (-1 < t < 1)$

from Table 1. Substituting $x - 1$ for t in this series, we have

$f(x) = \ln x = (x-1) - \dfrac{1}{2}(x-1)^2 + \dfrac{1}{3}(x-1)^3 - \cdots + \dfrac{(-1)^{n-1}}{n}(x-1)^n + \cdots.$

The interval of convergence is $-1 < x - 1 < 1$ or $0 < x < 2$.

37. Let $t = x - 1$. Then $x = t + 1$ and

$\dfrac{1}{4-3x} = \dfrac{1}{4-3(t+1)} = \dfrac{1}{1-3t}.$

Now, from Table 1,

$\dfrac{1}{1-u} = 1 + u + u^2 + u^3 + \cdots + u^n + \cdots \quad (-1 < u < 1).$

Substituting $3t$ for u in this series, we have

$$\frac{1}{1 - 3t} = 1 + (3t) + (3t)^2 + (3t)^3 + \cdots + (3t)^n + \cdots$$

$$= 1 + 3t + 3^2 t^2 + 3^3 t^3 + \cdots + 3^n t^n + \cdots,$$

and the interval of convergence is $-1 < 3t < 1$ or $-\frac{1}{3} < t < \frac{1}{3}$.

Finally, replacing t by $x - 1$, we obtain

$$\frac{1}{4 - 3x} = 1 + 3(x - 1) + 3^2(x - 1)^2 + 3^3(x - 1)^3 + \cdots + 3^n(x - 1)^n + \cdots$$

and the interval of convergence is $-\frac{1}{3} < x - 1 < \frac{1}{3}$ or $\frac{2}{3} < x < \frac{4}{3}$.

39. From Table 1,

$$F(x) = \frac{1}{1 - x} = 1 + x + x^2 + x^3 + x^4 + \cdots + x^n + \cdots \qquad (-1 < x < 1).$$

Now, using Property 3,

$$F'(x) = \frac{1}{(1 - x)^2} = 1 + 2x + 3x^2 + 4x^3 + \cdots + nx^{n-1} + \cdots \qquad (-1 < x < 1)$$

and

$$F''(x) = \frac{2}{(1 - x)^3} = 2 + 3 \cdot 2x + 4 \cdot 3x^2 + \cdots + n(n - 1)x^{n-2} + \cdots \quad (-1 < x < 1).$$

Thus,

$$f(x) = \frac{1}{(1 - x)^3} = \frac{1}{2} \cdot \frac{2}{(1 - x)^3}$$

$$= \frac{1}{2}[2 + 3 \cdot 2x + 4 \cdot 3x^2 + \cdots + n(n - 1)x^{n-2} + \cdots]$$

$$= 1 + 3x + 6x^2 + \cdots + \frac{n(n - 1)}{2}x^{n-2} + \cdots \quad (-1 < x < 1).$$

41. $f(x) = x + \frac{1}{3}x^3 + \frac{1}{5}x^5 + \cdots + \frac{1}{2n + 1}x^{2n + 1} + \cdots, \ -1 < x < 1.$

(A) Since $\dfrac{d}{dx}\left[\dfrac{1}{2k + 1}x^{2k+1}\right] = x^{2k}$ for $k = 1, 2, \cdots,$

it follows from Property 3 that

$f'(x) = 1 + x^2 + x^4 + \cdots + x^{2n} + \cdots, \ -1 < x < 1.$

(B) From Table 1,

$$\frac{1}{1 - x} = 1 + x + x^2 + \cdots + x^n + \cdots, \ -1 < x < 1$$

Substituting x^2 for x, the Taylor series for $\dfrac{1}{1 - x^2}$ at 0 is:

$$\frac{1}{1 - x^2} = 1 + x^2 + x^4 + \cdots + x^{2n} + \cdots, \ -1 < x < 1.$$

Therefore, $f'(x)$ and $\dfrac{1}{1 - x^2}$ have the same Taylor series at 0 and

so

$$f'(x) = \frac{1}{1 - x^2} \text{ for } -1 < x < 1.$$

43. Using Table 1 and Property 2, we have

$$\frac{1}{1-x} = 1 + x + x^2 + x^3 + \cdots + x^n + \cdots \qquad (-1 < x < 1)$$

$$\frac{x}{1-x} = x\left(\frac{1}{1-x}\right) = x + x^2 + x^3 + x^4 + \cdots + x^{n+1} + \cdots \qquad (-1 < x < 1).$$

Thus, by Property 1,

$$\frac{1+x}{1-x} = \frac{1}{1-x} + \frac{x}{1-x} = 1 + 2x + 2x^2 + 2x^3 + \cdots + 2x^n + \cdots$$

and the interval of convergence is $-1 < x < 1$.

45. Using Table 1 and Property 2, we have

$$\ln(1+x) = x - \frac{1}{2}x^2 + \frac{1}{3}x^3 - \cdots + \frac{(-1)^{n+1}}{n}x^n + \cdots \qquad (-1 < x < 1)$$

$$-\ln(1-x) = x + \frac{1}{2}x^2 + \frac{1}{3}x^3 + \cdots + \frac{1}{n}x^n + \cdots \qquad (-1 < x < 1).$$

Thus, by Property 1,

$$\ln\frac{1+x}{1-x} = \ln(1+x) - \ln(1-x) = 2x + \frac{2}{3}x^3 + \cdots + \frac{2}{2n+1}x^{2n+1} + \cdots$$

$$(-1 < x < 1),$$

so, by Property 2,

$$\frac{1}{2}\ln\frac{1+x}{1-x} = x + \frac{1}{3}x^3 + \frac{1}{5}x^5 + \cdots + \frac{1}{2n+1}x^{2n+1} + \cdots \qquad (-1 < x < 1).$$

47. From Table 1,

$$e^x = 1 + x + \frac{x^2}{2!} + \frac{x^3}{3!} + \cdots + \frac{x^n}{n!} + \cdots \qquad (-\infty < x < \infty)$$

and

$$e^{-x} = 1 - x + \frac{x^2}{2!} - \frac{x^3}{3!} + \cdots + \frac{(-1)^n}{n!}x^n + \cdots \qquad (-\infty < x < \infty).$$

Thus, using Properties 1 and 2,

$$f(x) = \frac{e^x + e^{-x}}{2} = \frac{1}{2}(e^x + e^{-x}) = \frac{1}{2}\left(2 + \frac{2}{2!}x^2 + \frac{2}{4!}x^4 + \cdots + \frac{2}{(2n)!}x^{2n} + \cdots\right)$$

and

$$f(x) = 1 + \frac{1}{2!}x^2 + \frac{1}{4!}x^4 + \cdots + \frac{1}{(2n)!}x^{2n} + \cdots \qquad (-\infty < x < \infty).$$

49. From Table 1,

$$f''(x) = \ln(1+x) = x - \frac{1}{2}x^2 + \frac{1}{3}x^3 - \cdots + \frac{(-1)^{n-1}}{n}x^n + \cdots \qquad (-1 < x < 1)$$

Therefore

$$f'(x) = \int f''(x)\,dx = \int\left[x - \frac{1}{2}x^2 + \frac{1}{3}x^3 - \cdots + \frac{(-1)^{n-1}}{n}x^n + \cdots\right]dx$$

$$= \int x\,dx - \frac{1}{2}\int x^2\,dx + \frac{1}{3}\int x^3\,dx - \cdots + \frac{(-1)^{n-1}}{n}\int x^n\,dx + \cdots$$

$$= C_1 + \frac{1}{2}x^2 - \frac{1}{6}x^3 + \frac{1}{12}x^4 - \cdots + \frac{(-1)^{n-1}}{n(n+1)}x^{n+1} + \cdots$$

$$= C_1 + \frac{1}{2}x^2 - \frac{1}{6}x^3 + \frac{1}{12}x^4 - \cdots + \frac{(-1)^n}{n(n-1)}x^n + \cdots$$

Now,
$$f'(0) = 3 = C_1 + 0 - 0 + 0 - \cdots$$
$$= C_1$$

Thus
$$f'(x) = 3 + \frac{1}{2}x^2 - \frac{1}{6}x^3 + \frac{1}{12}x^4 - \cdots + \frac{(-1)^n}{n(n-1)}x^n + \cdots \qquad (-1 < x < 1)$$

Continuing,
$$f(x) = \int f'(x)\,dx = \int \left[3 + \frac{1}{2}x^2 - \frac{1}{6}x^3 + \frac{1}{12}x^4 - \cdots + \frac{(-1)^n}{n(n-1)}x^n + \cdots \right] dx$$

$$= \int 3\,dx + \frac{1}{2}\int x^2\,dx - \frac{1}{6}\int x^3\,dx + \cdots + \frac{(-1)^n}{n(n-1)}\int x^n\,dx + \cdots$$

$$= C_2 + 3x + \frac{1}{6}x^3 - \frac{1}{24}x^4 + \cdots + \frac{(-1)^n}{n(n-1)(n+1)}x^{n+1} + \cdots$$

$$= C_2 + 3x + \frac{1}{6}x^3 - \frac{1}{24}x^4 + \cdots + \frac{(-1)^{n+1}}{n(n-1)(n-2)}x^n + \cdots$$

Now
$$f(0) = -2 = C_2 + 0 + 0 - 0 + \cdots$$
$$= C_2$$

Thus,
$$f(x) = -2 + 3x + \frac{1}{6}x^3 - \frac{1}{24}x^4 + \cdots + \frac{(-1)^{n+1}}{n(n-1)(n-2)}x^n + \cdots, \quad -1 < x < 1.$$

51. From Table 1,
$$\frac{1}{1+t} = 1 - t + t^2 - t^3 + \cdots + (-1)^n t^n + \cdots \qquad (-1 < t < 1).$$

Now, $\dfrac{1}{x} = \dfrac{1}{a + (x-a)} = \dfrac{1}{a\left[1 + \dfrac{x-a}{a}\right]} = \dfrac{1}{a} \cdot \dfrac{1}{1 + \left(\dfrac{x-a}{a}\right)}.$

Substituting $\dfrac{x-a}{a}$ for t in the series for $\dfrac{1}{1+t}$ and using Property 2, we have

$$\frac{1}{x} = \frac{1}{a}\left[1 - \frac{x-a}{a} + \left(\frac{x-a}{a}\right)^2 - \left(\frac{x-a}{a}\right)^3 + \cdots + (-1)^n\left(\frac{x-a}{a}\right)^n + \cdots \right]$$

$$= \frac{1}{a} - \frac{1}{a^2}(x-a) + \frac{1}{a^3}(x-a)^2 - \frac{1}{a^4}(x-a)^3 + \cdots + \frac{(-1)^n}{a^{n+1}}(x-a)^n + \cdots,$$

and the interval of convergence is $-1 < \dfrac{x-a}{a} < 1$ or $-a < x - a < a$, which is $0 < x < 2a$.

Now, $\ln x = \int \frac{1}{x}\, dx =$

$$\int \left(\frac{1}{a} - \frac{1}{a^2}(x-a) + \frac{1}{a^3}(x-a)^2 - \ldots + \frac{(-1)^n}{a^{n+1}}(x-a)^n + \ldots \right) dx$$

$$= C + \frac{1}{a}(x-a) - \frac{1}{2a^2}(x-a)^2 + \frac{1}{3a^3}(x-a)^3 - \ldots$$

$$+ \frac{(-1)^n}{(n+1)a^{n+1}}(x-a)^{n+1} + \ldots \qquad (0 < x < 2a).$$

Evaluating this equation at $x = a$ gives $\ln a = C$.

Therefore, $\ln x = \ln a + \frac{1}{a}(x-a) - \frac{1}{2a^2}(x-a)^2 + \frac{1}{3a^3}(x-a)^3 - \ldots$

$$+ \frac{(-1)^n}{(n+1)a^{n+1}}(x-a)^{n+1} + \ldots \qquad (0 < x < 2a).$$

Equivalently, this can be written:

$\ln x = \ln a + \frac{1}{a}(x-a) - \frac{1}{2a^2}(x-a)^2 + \frac{1}{3a^3}(x-a)^3 - \ldots$

$$+ \frac{(-1)^{n-1}}{na^n}(x-a)^n + \ldots \qquad (0 < x < 2a).$$

53. From Table 1,

$$\frac{1}{1-x} = 1 + x + x^2 + x^3 + \ldots + x^n + \ldots \qquad -1 < x < 1$$

Therefore, if α and β are constants, then:

$$\frac{1}{\alpha - \beta x} = \frac{1}{\alpha \left[1 - \frac{\beta}{\alpha} x \right]} = \frac{1}{\alpha} \left[1 + \frac{\beta}{\alpha} x + \frac{\beta^2}{\alpha^2} x^2 + \frac{\beta^3}{\alpha^3} x^3 + \ldots + \frac{\beta^n}{\alpha^n} x^n + \ldots \right]$$

$$= \frac{1}{\alpha} + \frac{\beta}{\alpha^2} x + \frac{\beta^2}{\alpha^3} x^2 + \frac{\beta^3}{\alpha^4} x^3 + \ldots + \frac{\beta^n}{\alpha^{n+1}} x^n + \ldots$$

$$\left| \frac{\beta}{\alpha} x \right| < 1 \quad \text{or} \quad |x| < \left| \frac{\alpha}{\beta} \right|$$

Finally, replacing x by $x - a$, we have

$$\frac{1}{\alpha - \beta(x-a)} = \frac{1}{\alpha} + \frac{\beta}{\alpha^2}(x-a) + \frac{\beta^2}{\alpha^3}(x-a)^2$$

$$+ \ldots + \frac{\beta^n}{\alpha^{n+1}}(x-a)^n + \ldots ,$$

$$|x - a| < \left| \frac{\alpha}{\beta} \right|$$

Now, $f(x) = \frac{1}{1-bx} = \frac{1}{1 - ab - b(x-a)}, \quad ab \neq 1$

$$= \frac{1}{1-ab} + \frac{b}{(1-ab)^2} x + \frac{b^2}{(1-ab)^3} x^2 + \ldots + \frac{b^n}{(1-ab)^{n+1}} x^n + \ldots ,$$

$$|x - a| < \left| \frac{1-ab}{b} \right| \text{ by our result above.}$$

1. Using $\underline{3}$ with $n = 1$, we have
   $e^{-0.6} \approx 1 - 0.6 = 0.4$
   and $\left|R_1(0.6)\right| < 0.18$.

3. Using $\underline{3}$ with $n = 3$, we have
   $e^{-0.6} \approx 1 - 0.6 + 0.18 - 0.036 = 0.544$
   and $\left|R_3(0.6)\right| < 0.0054$.

5. Using $\underline{3}$ with $n = 2$, we have
   $\ln 1.3 \approx 0.3 - 0.045 = 0.255$
   and $\left|R_2(0.3)\right| < 0.009$.

7. Using $\underline{3}$ with $n = 4$, we have
   $\ln 1.3 \approx 0.3 - 0.045 + 0.009 - 0.00203$
   $= 0.261975$
   and $\left|R_4(0.3)\right| < 0.000486$.

For Problems 9 and 11: $e^{-x} = 1 - x + \dfrac{x^2}{2!} - \dfrac{x^3}{3!} + \dfrac{x^4}{4!} - \dots$

and $\qquad p_3(x) = 1 - x + \dfrac{x^2}{2!} - \dfrac{x^3}{3!}$.

9. Let $x = 0.2$. Then

$$e^{-0.2} \approx p_3(0.2) = 1 - 0.2 + \frac{(0.2)^2}{2!} - \frac{(0.2)^3}{3!}$$
$$= 1 - 0.2 + 0.02 - 0.001333$$
$$= 0.818667$$

and $\left|R_3(0.2)\right| < \left|\dfrac{(0.2)^4}{4!}\right| = 0.000067$.

11. Let $x = 0.03$. Then

$$e^{-0.03} \approx p_3(0.03) = 1 - 0.03 + \frac{(0.03)^2}{2!} - \frac{(0.03)^3}{3!}$$
$$= 1 - 0.03 + 0.00045 - 0.000005$$
$$= 0.970446$$

and $\left|R_3(0.03)\right| < \left|\dfrac{(0.03)^4}{4!}\right| = 0.000000033$.

For Problems 13 and 15: $\ln(1 + x) = x - \dfrac{x^2}{2} + \dfrac{x^3}{3} - \dfrac{x^4}{4} + \dots$

$$p_3(x) = x - \frac{x^2}{2} + \frac{x^3}{3}.$$

13. Let $x = 0.6$. Then

$$\ln(1.6) \approx p_3(0.6) = 0.6 - \frac{(0.6)^2}{2} + \frac{(0.6)^3}{3}$$
$$= 0.6 - 0.18 + 0.072 = 0.492$$

and $\left|R_3(0.6)\right| < \left|\dfrac{-(0.6)^4}{4}\right| = 0.0324$.

15. Let $x = 0.06$. Then

$$\ln(1.06) \approx p_3(0.06) = 0.06 - \frac{(0.06)^2}{2} + \frac{(0.06)^3}{3}$$

$$= 0.06 - 0.0018 + 0.000072 = 0.058272$$

and $\left| R_3(0.06) \right| < \left| \frac{-(0.06)^4}{4} \right| = 0.00000324$.

17. $e^{-0.1}$

Let $f(x) = e^{-x}$, then

$$f'(x) = -e^{-x}$$

$$f''(x) = e^{-x}$$

$$\vdots$$

$$f^{(n)}(x) = (-1)^n e^{-x}$$

$$\vdots$$

$$R_n(x) = \frac{f^{(n+1)}(t)x^{n+1}}{(n+1)!} \text{ for some } t \text{ between } 0 \text{ and } x.$$

Note that $f^{(n+1)}(t) = (-1)^{n+1} e^{-t}$ and hence

$$\left| f^{(n+1)}(t) \right| = \left| (-1)^{n+1} e^{-t} \right| = e^{-t} < 1 \text{ for } t > 0.$$

Therefore, $\left| R_n(x) \right| = \left| \frac{f^{(n+1)}(t)x^{n+1}}{(n+1)!} \right| < \frac{|x|^{n+1}}{(n+1)!}$ and $\left| R_n(0.1) \right| < \frac{(0.1)^{n+1}}{(n+1)!}$.

For $n = 3$, $\frac{(0.1)^4}{4!} < 0.0000042 < 0.000005$,

and hence $\left| R_3(0.1) \right| < 0.000005$. Thus, the polynomial of the lowest degree is

$$p_3(x) = 1 - x + \frac{1}{2!}x^2 - \frac{1}{3!}x^3 \text{ which has degree 3.}$$

$$e^{-0.1} \approx p_3(0.1) = 1 - 0.1 + \frac{1}{2}(0.1)^2 - \frac{1}{6}(0.1)^3 = 0.904833.$$

19. $e^{-0.01}$

From Problem 17 we have

$$\left| R_n(x) \right| < \frac{|x|^{n+1}}{(n+1)!}$$

For $x = 0.01$,

$$\left| R_n(0.01) \right| < \frac{(0.01)^{n+1}}{(n+1)!}$$

Now, for $n = 2$, $\frac{(0.01)^3}{3!} < 0.000002 < 0.000005$, and hence

$\left| R_2(0.01) \right| < 0.000005$. Thus, the polynomial with the lowest degree is

$$p_2(x) = 1 - x + \frac{1}{2!}x^2 \text{ which has degree 2.}$$

$$e^{-0.01} \approx p_2(0.01) = 1 - 0.01 + \frac{1}{2}(0.01)^2 = 0.990050.$$

21. ln 1.2

Let $f(x) = \ln(1 + x)$

$$f'(x) = \frac{1}{1 + x} = (1 + x)^{-1}$$

$$f''(x) = -(1 + x)^{-2}$$

$$f^{(3)}(x) = 2(1 + x)^{-3}$$

$$\vdots$$

$$f^{(n)}(x) = (n - 1)!(-1)^{n-1}(1 + x)^{-n}$$

$$\vdots$$

$$R_n(x) = \frac{f^{(n+1)}(t)x^{n+1}}{(n + 1)!} \text{ for some } t \text{ between } 0 \text{ and } x.$$

Note that $f^{(n+1)}(t) = n!(-1)^n(1 + t)^{-(n+1)}$ and hence

$$|f^{(n+1)}(t)| = |n!(-1)^n(1 + t)^{-(n+1)}| = n!(1 + t)^{-(n+1)}$$
$$< n! \text{ for } t > 0.$$

Therefore,

$$|R_n(x)| = \left|\frac{f^{(n+1)}(t)x^{n+1}}{(n + 1)!}\right| < \frac{n!\,|x|^{n+1}}{(n + 1)!} = \frac{|x|^{n+1}}{n + 1}, \text{ and } R_n(0.2) < \frac{(0.2)^{n+1}}{n + 1}.$$

For $n = 6$, $|R_6(0.2)| < \frac{(0.2)^7}{8} < 0.000002 < 0.000005$,

and hence the polynomial with the lowest degree is

$$p_6(x) = x - \frac{1}{2}x^2 + \frac{1}{3}x^3 - \frac{1}{4}x^4 + \frac{1}{5}x^5 - \frac{1}{6}x^6$$

which has degree 6.

$$\ln(1.2) \approx p_6(0.2) = 0.2 - \frac{1}{2}(0.2)^2 + \frac{1}{3}(0.2)^3 - \frac{1}{4}(0.2)^4$$
$$+ \frac{1}{5}(0.2)^5 - \frac{1}{6}(0.2)^6 = 0.182320.$$

23. ln(1.02)

From Problem 21 we have

$$|R_n(x)| < \frac{|x|^{n+1}}{n + 1}$$

For $x = 0.02$,

$$|R_n(0.02)| < \frac{(0.02)^{n+1}}{n + 1}$$

Now, for $n = 2$, $\frac{(0.02)^3}{3} < 0.000003 < 0.000005$, and hence

$|R_2(0.02)| < 0.000005$. Thus, the polynomial with the lowest degree is

$p_2(x) = x - \frac{1}{2}x^2$ which has degree 2.

$$\ln(1.02) \approx p_2(0.02) = 0.02 - \frac{1}{2}(0.02)^2 = 0.019800.$$

25. The Taylor series at 0 for $f(x) = \dfrac{1}{1 + x^2}$ is

$$\frac{1}{1 + x^2} = 1 - x^2 + x^4 - x^6 + \cdots + (-1)^n x^{2n} + \cdots \qquad (-1 < x < 1).$$

[<u>Note</u>: Use the Taylor series at 0 for $\dfrac{1}{1 + x^2}$ and substitute x^2 for x.]

Thus,

$$\int \frac{1}{1 + x^2}\,dx = C + x - \frac{x^3}{3} + \frac{x^5}{5} - \frac{x^7}{7} + \cdots + \frac{(-1)^n}{2n + 1}x^{2n+1} + \cdots \ (-1 < x < 1)$$

and

$$\int_0^{0.2} \frac{1}{1 + x^2}\,dx = \left[x - \frac{x^3}{3} + \frac{x^5}{5} - \frac{x^7}{7} + \cdots + \frac{(-1)^n}{2n + 1}x^{2n+1} + \cdots \right]\Big|_0^{0.2}$$

$$= 0.2 - \frac{(0.2)^3}{3} + \frac{(0.2)^5}{5} - \frac{(0.2)^7}{7} + \cdots$$

$$= 0.2 - 0.00267 + 0.000064 - \cdots.$$

Now, <u>3</u> applies and the error in using the first two terms in this series will be less than 0.000064. Thus,

$$\int_0^{0.2} \frac{1}{1 + x^2}\,dx \approx 0.19733.$$

27. The Taylor series at 0 for $f(x) = \ln(1 + x^2)$ is

$$\ln(1 + x^2) = x^2 - \frac{1}{2}x^4 + \frac{1}{3}x^6 - \cdots + \frac{(-1)^{n+1}}{n}x^{2n} + \cdots \qquad (-1 < x < 1).$$

[<u>Note</u>: Use the Taylor series at 0 for $\ln(1 + x)$ and substitute x^2 for x.]

Thus,

$$\int \ln(1 + x^2)\,dx = C + \frac{x^3}{3} - \frac{x^5}{10} + \frac{x^7}{21} - \cdots + \frac{(-1)^{n+1}}{n(2n + 1)}x^{2n+1} + \cdots$$

and

$$\int_0^{0.6} \ln(1 + x^2)\,dx = \left[\frac{x^3}{3} - \frac{x^5}{10} + \frac{x^7}{21} - \cdots + \frac{(-1)^{n+1}}{n(2n + 1)}x^{2n+1} + \cdots \right]\Big|_0^{0.6}$$

$$= 0.072 - 0.00778 + 0.00133 - 0.00028 + \cdots$$

Now, <u>3</u> applies and the error in using the first three terms in this series will be less than 0.00028. Therefore,

$$\int_0^{0.6} \ln(1 + x^2)\,dx \approx 0.0656.$$

29. The Taylor series at 0 for $f(x) = x^2 e^{-x^2}$ is

$$x^2 e^{-x^2} = x^2 - x^4 + \frac{1}{2!}x^6 - \cdots + \frac{(-1)^n}{n!}x^{2n+2} + \cdots \qquad (-\infty < x < \infty).$$

[<u>Note</u>: Use the Taylor series at 0 for e^{-x}, substitute x^2 for x, and multiply the resulting series by x^2.]

Thus,

$$\int x^2 e^{-x^2}\, dx = C + \frac{x^3}{3} - \frac{x^5}{5} + \frac{1}{7 \cdot 2!} x^7 - \cdots + \frac{(-1)^n}{(2n+3)n!} x^{2n+3} + \cdots$$

and

$$\int_0^{0.4} x^2 e^{-x^2}\, dx = \left[\frac{x^3}{3} - \frac{x^5}{5} + \frac{1}{14} x^7 - \cdots + \frac{(-1)^n}{(2n+3)n!} x^{2n+3} + \cdots \right]\Bigg|_0^{0.4}$$

$$= 0.02133 - 0.00205 + 0.00012 - \cdots .$$

Now, $\underline{3}$ applies and the error in using the first two terms in this series will be less than 0.00012. Therefore,

$$\int_0^{0.4} x^2 e^{-x^2}\, dx \approx 0.01928.$$

31. From Taylor's formula for the remainder,

$$R_n(2) = \frac{f^{(n+1)}(t)}{(n+1)!} 2^{n+1}$$

where t is some number between 0 and 2. Since $|f^{n+1}(t)| \le 1$, we have

$$|R_n(2)| = \left| \frac{f^{(n+1)}(t)}{(n+1)!} 2^{n+1} \right| = \frac{|f^{(n+1)}(t)|}{(n+1)!} 2^{n+1} \le \frac{2^{n+1}}{(n+1)!}$$

Now, we want $|R_n(2)| < 0.001$ which will be true if

$$\frac{2^{n+1}}{(n+1)!} < 0.001$$

which implies $(n+1)! > \frac{1}{0.001} 2^{n+1} = 1000(2^{n+1})$.

The smallest n that satisfies this inequality is $n = 9$.

33. From Taylor's formula for the remainder,

$$R_5(x) = \frac{f^{(6)}(t)}{6!} x^6$$

where t is between 0 and x. Now

$$|R_6(x)| = \left| \frac{f^{(6)}(t)}{6!} x^6 \right| \le \frac{|x^6|}{6!} = \frac{|x|^6}{720} < 0.05$$

implies $|x|^6 < 720(0.05) = 36$

Therefore, $|x| < (36)^{1/6} \approx 1.817$.

The error in the approximation of $f(x)$ by $P_5(x)$ will be less than 0.05 if $|x| < 1.817$.

35. Since $xe^x = x\left(1 + x + \dfrac{1}{2!}x^2 + \ldots + \dfrac{1}{n!}x^n + \ldots\right)$

$$= x + x^2 + \frac{1}{2!}x^3 + \ldots + \frac{1}{n!}x^{n+1} + \ldots, \quad -\infty < x < \infty,$$

it follows that

$$p_3(x) = x + x^2 + \frac{1}{2!}x^3$$

Using a graphing utility to graph

$$\left|p_3(x) - xe^x\right|$$

we find that

$$\left|p_3(x) - xe^x\right| < 0.005$$

for $-0.427 < x < 0.405$

37. From Section 2.3, Table 1, the Taylor series at 0 for $f(x) = e^x$ is

$$e^x = 1 + x + \frac{x^2}{2!} + \frac{x^3}{3!} + \ldots + \frac{x^n}{n!} + \ldots \quad (-\infty < x < \infty).$$

Thus, the second-degree polynomial at 0 is

$$p_2(x) = 1 + x + \frac{x^2}{2!} = 1 + x + \frac{x^2}{2}$$

and

$$e^{-0.3} = f(-0.3) \approx p_2(-0.3) = 1 - 0.3 + \frac{(-0.3)^2}{2} = 0.745.$$

To estimate the error, we use the formula in **2**:

$$R_2(-0.3) = \frac{f^{(3)}(t)}{3!}(-0.3)^3, \text{ where } -0.3 < t < 0.$$

Now, $\quad f(x) = e^x$

$$f'(x) = e^x$$
$$f''(x) = e^x$$
$$f^{(3)}(x) = e^x.$$

Therefore, $R_2(-0.3) = \dfrac{e^t}{3!}(-0.3)^3, \; -0.3 < t < 0,$ and the error $\left|R_2(-0.3)\right|$

satisfies $\left|R_2(-0.3)\right| = \left|\dfrac{e^t}{3!}(-0.3)^3\right| = \dfrac{e^t}{6}(.027) < \dfrac{1}{6}(.027) = 0.0045.$

[Note: Here we used $e^t \leq e^0 = 1, \; -0.3 < t < 0.$]

39. The second-degree Taylor polynomial at 0 for $f(x) = e^x$ is

$$p_2(x) = 1 + x + \frac{x^2}{2!} = 1 + x + \frac{x^2}{2}.$$

Now,

$$e^{0.05} = f(0.05) \approx p_2(0.05) = 1 + 0.05 + \frac{(0.05)^2}{2} = 1.05125.$$

The remainder $R_2(0.05)$ is given by

$$R_2(0.05) = \frac{f^{(3)}(t)}{3!}(0.05)^3, \text{ where } 0 < t < 0.05.$$

Since $f^{(3)}(x) = e^x$, we have

$$R_2(0.05) = \frac{e^t}{3!}(0.05)^3, \text{ where } 0 < t < 0.05,$$

and the error $\left|R_2(0.05)\right|$ satisfies

$$\left|R_2(0.05)\right| = \left|\frac{e^t}{3!}(0.05)^3\right| = \frac{e^t}{6}(0.000125) < \frac{3}{6}(0.000125) = 0.0000625.$$

[Note: Here we used $e^t < e = 2.71828... < 3$, $0 < t < 0.05$.]

41. $f(x) = \sqrt{16 + x} = (16 + x)^{1/2}$

$$p_2(x) = f(0) + f'(0)x + \frac{f''(0)}{2!}x^2.$$

Now,

$$f(x) = (16 + x)^{1/2} \qquad\qquad f(0) = 16^{1/2} = 4$$

$$f'(x) = \frac{1}{2}(16 + x)^{-1/2} = \frac{1}{2(16 + x)^{1/2}} \qquad f'(0) = \frac{1}{2 \cdot 16^{1/2}} = \frac{1}{8}$$

$$f''(x) = -\frac{1}{4}(16 + x)^{-3/2} = \frac{-1}{4(16 + x)^{3/2}} \qquad f''(0) = \frac{-1}{4 \cdot 16^{3/2}} = \frac{-1}{256}$$

Thus, $p_2(x) = 4 + \frac{1}{8}x - \frac{1}{2!} \cdot \frac{1}{256}x^2 = 4 + \frac{1}{8}x - \frac{1}{512}x^2$

and $\sqrt{17} = f(1) \approx P_2(1) = 4 + \frac{1}{8} - \frac{1}{512} = 4 + .125 - 0.00195 = 4.12305.$

The error in this approximation is

$$\left|R_2(1)\right| = \left|\frac{f^{(3)}(t)}{3!}(1)^3\right| \qquad 0 < t < 1$$

$$= \frac{\left|f^{(3)}(t)\right|}{3!}.$$

Now, $f^{(3)}(x) = \frac{3}{8}(16 + x)^{-5/2} = \frac{3}{8(16 + x)^{5/2}}.$

Since the maximum value of $\dfrac{3}{8(16 + t)^{5/2}}$ on $[0, 1]$ occurs at $t = 0$ and

is $\dfrac{3}{8(16)^{5/2}} = \dfrac{3}{8 \cdot 4^5},$

we have

$$\left|R_2(1)\right| = \frac{\left|f^{(3)}(t)\right|}{3!} \le \frac{\frac{3}{8 \cdot 4^5}}{3!} = \frac{1}{16 \cdot 4^5} = \frac{1}{4^7} = \frac{1}{16,384} = 0.000061.$$

43. The Taylor series for $f(x) = \dfrac{1}{1 - x}$ at 0

is $\dfrac{1}{1 - x} = 1 + x + x^2 + \cdots + x^n + \cdots$,

with interval of convergence $-1 < x < 1$.
Since the lower limit of integration, -2, lies outside the interval of convergence, the Taylor series cannot be used to approximate the integral $\int_{-2}^{0} \dfrac{1}{1 - x}\, dx$.

The second computation:

$$\int_{-2}^{0} \dfrac{1}{1 - x}\, dx = -\ln(1 - x)\Big|_{-2}^{0} = -\ln 1 + \ln 3 = \ln 3 \approx 1.099$$

is correct.

45. (A) The Taylor series at 0 for $f(x) = e^x$ is:

$$e^x = 1 + x + \dfrac{x^2}{2!} + \dfrac{x^3}{3!} + \cdots + \dfrac{x^n}{n!} + \cdots \quad (-\infty < x < \infty)$$

Thus, $p_2(x) = 1 + x + \dfrac{1}{2!}x^2$

The quadratic regression polynomial $q_2(x)$ for the points

$(-0.1, e^{-0.1})$, $(0, e^0)$, $(0.1, e^{0.1})$ is shown at the right.

```
QuadReg
y=ax²+bx+c
a=.5004168056
b=1.0016675
c=1
R²=1
```

(B) Max $|f(x) - p_2(x)| < 0.000171$
Max $|f(x) - q_2(x)| < 0.000065$

(C) $q_2(x)$ will give a better approximation to $\int_{-0.1}^{0.1} e^x\, dx$.

47. Index of income concentration $= 2\int_{0}^{1} [x - f(x)]\, dx = 2\int_{0}^{1} \left[x - \dfrac{5x^6}{4 + x^2}\right] dx$

$= \int_{0}^{1} 2x\, dx - \int_{0}^{1} \dfrac{10x^6}{4 + x^2}\, dx = x^2\Big|_{0}^{1} - \int_{0}^{1} \dfrac{10x^6}{4 + x^2}\, dx = 1 - \int_{0}^{1} \dfrac{10x^6}{4 + x^2}\, dx.$

Step 1: Find the Taylor series for the integrand.

$$\dfrac{10x^6}{4 + x^2} = \dfrac{10x^6}{4} \cdot \dfrac{1}{1 + \dfrac{x^2}{4}}$$

$$= \dfrac{5x^6}{2}\left[1 - \dfrac{x^2}{4} + \dfrac{x^4}{16} - \dfrac{x^6}{64} + \cdots + \dfrac{(-1)^n x^{2n}}{4^n} + \cdots\right]$$

[substitute $\dfrac{x^2}{4}$ into the series for $\dfrac{1}{1+x}$]

$$= 5\left[\dfrac{x^6}{2} - \dfrac{x^8}{8} + \dfrac{x^{10}}{32} - \dfrac{x^{12}}{128} + \cdots + \dfrac{(-1)^n x^{2n+6}}{2 \cdot 4^n} + \cdots\right].$$

This series converges for $\left|\dfrac{x^2}{4}\right| < 1$ or $-2 < x < 2$.

Step 2: Find the Taylor series for the antiderivative.

$$\int \frac{10x^6}{4 + x^2}\,dx = \int 5\left[\frac{x^6}{2} - \frac{x^8}{8} + \frac{x^{10}}{32} - \frac{x^{12}}{128} + \cdots + \frac{(-1)^n x^{2n+6}}{2 \cdot 4^n} + \cdots\right]dx$$

$$= C + 5\left[\frac{x^7}{14} - \frac{x^9}{72} + \frac{x^{11}}{352} - \frac{x^{13}}{1664} + \cdots + \frac{(-1)^n x^{2n+7}}{2 \cdot 4^n(2n + 7)} + \cdots\right].$$

Step 3: Approximate the definite integral.

Choosing $C = 0$ in the antiderivative, we have

$$\int_0^1 \frac{10x^6}{4 + x^2}\,dx = 5\left[\frac{x^7}{14} - \frac{x^9}{72} + \frac{x^{11}}{352} - \frac{x^{13}}{1664} + \cdots + \frac{(-1)^n x^{2n+7}}{2 \cdot 4^n(2n + 7)} + \cdots\right]\Bigg|_0^1$$

$$= \frac{5}{14} - \frac{5}{72} + \frac{5}{352} - \frac{5}{1664} + \cdots$$

$$= 0.3571 - 0.0694 + 0.0142 - 0.003 + \cdots .$$

Since the terms are alternating in sign and decreasing in absolute value, and since the fourth term is less than 0.005, we can use the first three terms of this series to approximate the definite integral to the specified accuracy:

$$\int_0^1 \frac{10x^6}{4 + x^2}\,dx \approx 0.3571 - 0.0694 + 0.0142 = 0.3019 \approx 0.302$$

Finally, the index of income concentration is:

$$2\int_0^1 \left[x - \frac{10x^6}{4 + x^2}\right]dx \approx 1 - 0.302 = 0.698$$

49. Total Sales $= \int_0^4 S'(t)\,dt = \int_0^4 [10 - 10e^{-0.01t^2}]\,dt$

Step 1: Find the fourth-degree Taylor polynomial at 0 for its integrand. Substituting $0.01t^2 = \left(\frac{t}{10}\right)^2$ into the Taylor series at 0 for e^{-x}, we have:

$$e^{-0.01t^2} = 1 - \left(\frac{t}{10}\right)^2 + \frac{1}{2!}\left(\frac{t}{10}\right)^4 - \frac{1}{3!}\left(\frac{t}{10}\right)^6 + \cdots + \frac{(-1)^n}{n!}\left(\frac{t}{10}\right)^{2n} + \cdots$$

Thus,

$$10 - 10e^{-0.01t^2} = 10 - 10\left[1 - \frac{t^2}{(10)^2} + \frac{1}{2!}\frac{t^4}{(10)^4} - \frac{1}{3!}\frac{t^6}{(10)^6} + \cdots\right.$$

$$\left. + \frac{(-1)^n}{n!}\frac{t^{2n}}{(10)^{2n}} + \cdots\right]$$

$$= \frac{t^2}{10} - \frac{t^4}{2!(10)^3} + \frac{t^6}{3!(10)^5} - \cdots + \frac{(-1)^{n+1}t^{2n}}{n!(10)^{2n-1}} + \cdots$$

and $p_4(t) = \dfrac{t^2}{10} - \dfrac{t^4}{2!(10)^3} = 0.1t^2 - 0.0005t^4.$

<u>Step 2</u>: Approximate the definite integral.

$$\int_0^4 S'(t)\,dt \approx \int_0^4 p_4(t)\,dt = \int_0^4 (0.1t^2 - 0.0005t^4)\,dt$$

$$= \left(\frac{0.1t^3}{3} - 0.0001t^5 \right)\Big|_0^4$$

$$= \frac{0.1(4)^3}{3} - 0.0001(4^5) = 2.1333 - 0.1024$$

$$= 2.0309 \approx 2.031$$

Therefore, $S(4) \approx 2.031$ and total sales during the first four months are approximately $\$2,031,000$.

<u>Step 3</u>: Estimate the error in this approximation.

From Steps 1 and 2, the Taylor series at 0 for $S(t)$ is:

$$S(t) = \frac{t^3}{3(10)} - \frac{t^5}{5 \cdot 2!\,(10)^3} + \frac{t^7}{7 \cdot 3!\,(10)^5} - \ldots + \frac{(-1)^n t^{2n+1}}{(2n+1)n!\,(10)^{2n-1}} + \ldots$$

and

$$S(4) = \frac{(4)^3}{3(10)} - \frac{(4)^5}{5 \cdot 2!\,(10)^3} + \frac{(4)^7}{7 \cdot 3!\,(10)^5} - \ldots + \frac{(-1)^n (4)^{2n+1}}{(2n+1)n!\,(10)^{2n-1}} + \ldots .$$

Since the terms alternate in sign and decrease in absolute value, the error in this approximation is less than

$$\left| \frac{(4)^7}{7 \cdot 3!\,(10)^5} \right| \approx 0.004.$$

Thus, $S(4) = 2.031$ to within ± 0.004 or $S(4) = \$2,031,000$ to within $\pm\$4000$.

51. To find the useful life, set $C'(t) = R'(t)$ and solve for t:

$$4 = \frac{80}{16 + t^2}$$

$$4t^2 + 64 = 80$$

$$t^2 = 4$$

and $\quad t = 2$ or -2

Thus, the useful life of the system is 2 years. The total profit of the system is given by the definite integral

Total Profit $= \int_0^2 [R'(t) - C'(t)]\,dt$

<u>Step 1</u>: Find the Taylor series for the integrand.

$$R'(t) = \frac{80}{16 + t^2} = \frac{80}{16} \cdot \frac{1}{1 + \dfrac{t^2}{16}} = 5 \cdot \frac{1}{1 + \left(\dfrac{t}{4}\right)^2}$$

$$= 5\left[1 - \frac{t^2}{4^2} + \frac{t^4}{4^4} - \frac{t^6}{4^6} + \ldots + (-1)^n \frac{t^{2n}}{4^{2n}} + \ldots \right]$$

(substitute $\left(\frac{t}{4}\right)^2$ into the series for $\frac{1}{1+x}$)

Thus,

$$R'(t) - C'(t) = 5\left[1 - \frac{t^2}{4^2} + \frac{t^4}{4^4} - \frac{t^6}{4^6} + \ldots + (-1)^n \frac{t^{2n}}{4^{2n}} + \ldots\right] - 4$$

$$= 1 - \frac{5t^2}{4^2} + \frac{5t^4}{t^4} - \frac{5t^6}{4^6} + \ldots + (-1)^n \frac{5t^{2n}}{4^{2n}} + \ldots$$

Step 2: Find the Taylor series for the antiderivative.

$$\int\left[1 - \frac{5t^2}{4^2} + \frac{5t^4}{4^4} - \frac{5t^6}{4^6} + \ldots + (-1)^n \frac{5t^{2n}}{4^{2n}} + \ldots\right] dt$$

$$= C + t - \frac{5t^3}{3 \cdot 4^2} + \frac{t^5}{4^4} - \frac{5t^7}{7 \cdot 4^6} + \ldots + (-1)^n \frac{5t^{2n+1}}{(2n+1)4^{2n}} + \ldots$$

Step 3: Approximate the definite integral. Let $C = 0$. Then

$$\int_0^2 [R'(t) - C'(t)]\,dt = \left[t - \frac{5t^3}{3 \cdot 4^2} + \frac{t^5}{4^4} - \frac{5t^7}{7 \cdot 4^6} + \ldots \right.$$

$$\left. + (-1)^n \frac{5t^{2n+1}}{(2n+1)4^{2n}} + \ldots \right]\Bigg|_0^2$$

$$= 2 - \frac{5 \cdot 2^3}{3 \cdot 4^2} + \frac{2^5}{4^4} - \frac{5 \cdot 2^7}{7 \cdot 4^6} + \frac{5 \cdot 2^9}{9 \cdot 4^8} - \ldots$$

$$= 2 - \frac{5}{6} + \frac{1}{8} - \frac{5}{224} + \frac{5}{1152} - \ldots$$

Since the terms are alternating in sign and decreasing in absolute value, and since $\frac{5}{1152} \approx 0.0043$ is less than 0.005, we can use the first four terms of this series. Thus,

Total Profit $\approx 2 - \frac{5}{6} + \frac{1}{8} - \frac{5}{224} \approx 1.270$ thousand or \$1,270.

53. $C(t) = 20 + 800 \ln\left(1 + \frac{t^2}{100}\right)$, $0 \le t \le 2$.

Average Temperature $= \frac{1}{2-0}\int_0^2 C(t)\,dt = \frac{1}{2}\int_0^2\left[20 + 800 \ln\left(1 + \frac{t^2}{100}\right)\right] dt$.

Step 1: Determine the Taylor series at 0 for the integrand.
Substituting $\frac{t^2}{100}$ into the Taylor series at 0 for $\ln(1 + x)$, we have:

$$\ln\left(1 + \frac{t^2}{100}\right) = \frac{t^2}{100} - \frac{1}{2}\left(\frac{t^2}{100}\right)^2 + \frac{1}{3}\left(\frac{t^2}{100}\right)^3 - \ldots + (-1)^{n+1}\frac{1}{n}\left(\frac{t^2}{100}\right)^n + \ldots$$

$$= \frac{t^2}{100} - \frac{1}{2 \cdot 10^4}t^4 + \frac{1}{3 \cdot 10^6}t^6 - \ldots$$

$$+ (-1)^{n+1}\frac{1}{n \cdot 10^{2n}}t^{2n} + \ldots .$$

Thus,

$$20 + 8 \cdot 10^2 \ln\left(1 + \frac{t^2}{100}\right) = 20 + 8t^2 - \frac{8}{2 \cdot 10^2}t^4 + \frac{8}{3 \cdot 10^4}t^6 - \cdots$$

$$+ (-1)^{n+1}\frac{8}{n \cdot 10^{2n-2}}t^{2n} + \cdots .$$

Step 2: Calculate the definite integral.

Average Temperature $= \frac{1}{2}\int_0^2 C(t)\,dt$

$$= \frac{1}{2}\int_0^2 20\ dt + \frac{1}{2}\int\left[8t^2 - \frac{8}{2 \cdot 10^2}t^4 + \frac{8}{3 \cdot 10^4}t^6 - \cdots\right.$$

$$\left. + \frac{(-1)^{n+1}8}{n \cdot 10^{2n-2}}t^{2n} + \cdots\right]dt$$

$$= 10t\bigg|_0^2 + \frac{1}{2}\left[\frac{8}{3}t^3 - \frac{8}{2 \cdot 5 \cdot 10^2}t^5 + \frac{8}{3 \cdot 7 \cdot 10^4}t^7 - \cdots\right.$$

$$\left. + \frac{(-1)^{n+1}8}{n(2n+1)10^{2n-2}}t^{2n+1} + \cdots\right]\bigg|_0^2$$

$$= 20 + \frac{1}{2}\left[\frac{8}{3}(2)^3 - \frac{8}{2 \cdot 5 \cdot 10^2}(2)^5 + \frac{8}{3 \cdot 7 \cdot 10^4}(2)^7 - \cdots\right.$$

$$\left. + \frac{(-1)^{n+1}8}{n(2n+1)10^{2n-2}}(2)^{2n+1} + \cdots\right]$$

$$= 20 + \frac{1}{2}\left[\frac{2^6}{3} - \frac{2^8}{2 \cdot 5 \cdot 10^2} + \frac{2^{10}}{3 \cdot 7 \cdot 10^4} - \cdots + \frac{(-1)^{n+1}2^{2n+4}}{n(2n+1)10^{2n-2}} + \cdots\right]$$

$$= 20 + \frac{2^5}{3} - \frac{2^7}{2 \cdot 5 \cdot 10^2} + \frac{2^9}{3 \cdot 7 \cdot 10^4} - \cdots + \frac{(-1)^{n+1}2^{2n+3}}{n(2n+1)10^{2n-2}} + \cdots$$

Step 3: Approximate the definite integral to within ±0.005.

Since the terms are alternating in sign and decreasing in absolute value, and since the fourth term

$$\frac{2^9}{3 \cdot 7 \cdot 10^4} = \frac{512}{210,000} = 0.0024 < 0.005,$$

the approximate average temperature is:

$$20 + \frac{2^5}{3} - \frac{2^7}{2 \cdot 5 \cdot 10^2} = 30.539°C$$

55. $A'(t) = \dfrac{-75}{t^2 + 25}$

Step 1: Find the second-degree Taylor polynomial at 0 for

$$A'(t) = \frac{-75}{t^2 + 25} = -3\frac{1}{1 + \left(\dfrac{t}{5}\right)^2}$$

Substituting $\dfrac{t^2}{25}$ into the Taylor series at 0 for $\dfrac{1}{1 + x}$, we have:

$$-3\frac{1}{1 + \left(\dfrac{t}{5}\right)^2} = -3\left[1 - \left(\frac{t}{5}\right)^2 + \left(\frac{t}{5}\right)^4 - \left(\frac{t}{5}\right)^6 + \ldots + (-1)^n\left(\frac{t}{5}\right)^{2n} + \ldots\right]$$

Thus, $p_2(t) = -3 + \dfrac{3t^2}{25}$.

Step 2: Approximate $A(t) = \int A'(t)\,dt$, and find $A(2)$.

$$A(t) = \int A'(t)\,dt \approx \int p_2(t)\,dt = \int\left[-3 + \frac{3t^2}{25}\right]dt = -3t + \frac{t^3}{25} + C.$$

Since $A(0) = 12$, we have:

$$A(t) \approx -3t + \frac{t^3}{25} + 12$$

Thus, $A(2) \approx -3 \cdot 2 + \dfrac{2^3}{25} + 12 = 6.32$ square inches.

Step 3: Estimate the error in this approximation. From Steps 1 and 2, the Taylor series at 0 for $A(t)$ is

$$A(t) = 12 - 3t + \frac{t^3}{5^2} - \frac{3t^5}{5 \cdot 5^4} + \frac{3t^7}{7 \cdot 5^6} - \ldots$$

and

$$A(2) = 12 - 6 + \frac{8}{25} - \frac{3 \cdot 2^5}{5^5} + \frac{3 \cdot 2^7}{7 \cdot 5^6} - \ldots .$$

Since the terms are alternating in sign and decreasing in absolute value, the error in the approximation is less than

$$\left|\frac{-3 \cdot 2^5}{5^5}\right| = 0.03072 \approx 0.031.$$

Thus, $A(2) = 6.32$ square cm to within ± 0.031.

57. $N'(t) = 6e^{-0.01t^2}$

Step 1: Find the second-degree polynomial at 0 for the integrand.

Substituting $0.01t^2 = \left(\dfrac{t}{10}\right)^2$ into the Taylor series at 0 for e^{-x}, we have:

$$e^{-0.01t^2} = 1 - \left(\frac{t}{10}\right)^2 + \frac{1}{2!}\left(\frac{t}{10}\right)^4 - \cdots + \frac{(-1)^n}{n!}\left(\frac{t}{10}\right)^{2n} + \cdots$$

Thus, $6e^{-0.01t^2} = 6 - \dfrac{6t^2}{(10)^2} + \dfrac{6t^4}{2!(10)^4} - \cdots + \dfrac{(-1)^n 6t^{2n}}{n!(10)^{2n}} + \cdots$

and

$$P_2(t) = 6 - \frac{6t^2}{100} = 6 - 0.06t^2.$$

Step 2: Approximate $N(t) = \int N'(t)\,dt$ and calculate $N(5)$.

$$N(t) = \int 6e^{-0.01t^2}\,dt \approx \int P_2(t)\,dt = \int [6 - 0.06t^2]\,dt$$

$$= 6t - \frac{0.06t^3}{3} + C = 6t - 0.02t^3 + C$$

Since $N(0) = 40$, we have:

$N(t) \approx 40 + 6t - 0.02t^3$.

Thus, $N(5) \approx 40 + 6(5) - 0.02(5)^3 = 67.5$ words per minute.

Step 3: Estimate the error in the approximation.

From Steps 1 and 2, the Taylor series at 0 for $N(t)$ is:

$$N(t) = 40 + 6t - 0.02t^3 + \frac{6t^5}{5 \cdot 2!(10)^4} - \cdots$$

$$+ \frac{(-1)^n 6t^{2n+1}}{(2n+1)n!(10)^{2n}} + \cdots$$

and

$$N(5) = 40 + 6(5) - 0.02(5)^3 + \frac{6(5)^5}{5 \cdot 2!(10)^4} - \cdots .$$

Since the terms are alternating in sign and decreasing in absolute value, the error in the approximation is less than

$$\left| \frac{6(5)^5}{5 \cdot 2!(10)^4} \right| = 0.1875.$$

Thus, $N(5) = 67.5$ words per minute to within ± 0.1875 and the improvement is $N(5) - N(0) = 67.5 - 40 = 27.5$ words per minute to within ± 0.1875.

1.
$$f(x) = \ln(x + 5)$$
$$f'(x) = \frac{1}{x + 5}(1) = (x + 5)^{-1}$$
$$f''(x) = -1(x + 5)^{-2}(1) = -(x + 5)^{-2} = \frac{-1}{(x + 5)^2}$$
$$f^{(3)}(x) = -(-2)(x + 5)^{-3}(1) = 2(x + 5)^{-3} = \frac{2}{(x + 5)^3}$$
$$f^{(4)}(x) = 2(-3)(x + 5)^{-4}(1) = -6(x + 5)^{-4} = \frac{-6}{(x + 5)^4}$$

(2.1)

2.
$$f(x) = \sqrt[3]{1 + x} = (1 + x)^{1/3} \qquad f(0) = 1$$
$$f'(x) = \frac{1}{3}(1 + x)^{-2/3} = \frac{1}{3(1 + x)^{2/3}} \qquad f'(0) = \frac{1}{3}$$
$$f''(x) = \frac{-2}{9}(1 + x)^{-5/3} = \frac{-2}{9(1 + x)^{5/3}} \qquad f''(0) = \frac{-2}{9}$$
$$f^{(3)}(x) = \frac{10}{27}(1 + x)^{-8/3} = \frac{10}{27(1 + x)^{8/3}} \qquad f^{(3)}(0) = \frac{10}{27}$$

Thus,

$$p_3(x) = f(0) + f'(0)x + \frac{f''(0)}{2!}x^2 + \frac{f^{(3)}(0)}{3!}x^3$$
$$= 1 + \frac{1}{3}x - \frac{2}{9 \cdot 2!}x^2 + \frac{10}{27 \cdot 3!}x^3 = 1 + \frac{1}{3}x - \frac{1}{9}x^2 + \frac{5}{81}x^3.$$

Now,

$$\sqrt[3]{1.01} = f(0.01) \approx p_3(0.01) = 1 + \frac{1}{3}(0.01) - \frac{1}{9}(0.01)^2 + \frac{5}{81}(0.01)^3$$
$$\approx 1.003322.$$

(2.1)

3.
$$f(x) = \sqrt{1 + x} = (1 + x)^{1/2} \qquad f(3) = \sqrt{4} = 2$$
$$f'(x) = \frac{1}{2}(1 + x)^{-1/2}(1) = \frac{1}{2(1 + x)^{1/2}} \qquad f'(3) = \frac{1}{4}$$
$$f''(x) = -\frac{1}{4}(1 + x)^{-3/2}(1) = \frac{-1}{4(1 + x)^{3/2}} \qquad f''(3) = -\frac{1}{32}$$
$$f^{(3)}(x) = \frac{3}{8}(1 + x)^{-5/2}(1) = \frac{3}{8(1 + x)^{5/2}} \qquad f^{(3)}(3) = \frac{3}{256}$$

Thus,

$$p_3(x) = f(3) + f'(3)(x - 3) + \frac{f''(3)}{2!}(x - 3)^2 + \frac{f^{(3)}(3)}{3!}(x - 3)^3$$
$$= 2 + \frac{1}{4}(x - 3) - \frac{1}{32 \cdot 2!}(x - 3)^2 + \frac{3}{256 \cdot 3!}(x - 3)^3$$
$$= 2 + \frac{1}{4}(x - 3) - \frac{1}{64}(x - 3)^2 + \frac{1}{512}(x - 3)^3.$$

Now, $\sqrt{3.9} = f(2.9) \approx p_3(2.9) = 2 + \frac{1}{4}(-0.1) - \frac{1}{64}(-0.1)^2 + \frac{1}{512}(-0.1)^3$
$$= 1.974842.$$

(2.1)

4. $f(x) = \sqrt{9 + x^2} = (9 + x^2)^{1/2}$ $f(0) = 3$

$f'(x) = \dfrac{1}{2}(9 + x^2)^{-1/2}(2x) = x(9 + x^2)^{-1/2}$ $f'(0) = 0$

$f''(x) = (9 + x^2)^{-1/2} - \dfrac{1}{2}x(9 + x^2)^{-3/2}(2x)$

$\qquad = (9 + x^2)^{-1/2} - x^2(9 + x^2)^{-3/2}$ $f''(0) = \dfrac{1}{3}$

Thus,

$p_2(x) = f(0) + f'(0)x + \dfrac{f''(0)}{2!}x^2 = 3 + \dfrac{\frac{1}{3}}{2!}x^2 = 3 + \dfrac{1}{6}x^2.$

Now, $\sqrt{9.1} = f(0.1) \approx p_2(0.1) = 3 + \dfrac{1}{6}(0.1)^2 = 3.001667.$ (2.1)

5. $\dfrac{1}{1 - 4x} = 1 + 4x + 4^2x^2 + \cdots + 4^nx^n + \cdots$

We have $a = 0$ and

$a_n = 4^n$

$a_{n+1} = 4^{n+1}$

Thus, $\dfrac{a_{n+1}}{a_n} = \dfrac{4^{n+1}}{4^n} = 4$ and $\lim\limits_{n \to \infty}\left|\dfrac{a_{n+1}}{a_n}\right| = \lim\limits_{n \to \infty}|4| = 4.$

Therefore, $L = 4$, $R = \dfrac{1}{4}$, and the series converges for $|x - 0| < \dfrac{1}{4}.$

The interval of convergence is:

$|x| < \dfrac{1}{4}$ or $-\dfrac{1}{4} < x < \dfrac{1}{4}$ (2.2)

6. $\dfrac{5}{x - 1} = 1 - \dfrac{1}{5}(x - 6) + \dfrac{1}{5^2}(x - 6)^2 - \cdots + \dfrac{(-1)^n}{5^n}(x - 6)^n + \cdots$

We have $a = 6$, and

$a_n = \dfrac{(-1)^n}{5^n}$

$a_{n+1} = \dfrac{(-1)^{n+1}}{5^{n+1}}$

Thus, $\dfrac{a_{n+1}}{a_n} = \dfrac{\frac{(-1)^{n+1}}{5^{n+1}}}{\frac{(-1)^n}{5^n}} = \dfrac{-5^n}{5^{n+1}} = \dfrac{-1}{5}$ and $\lim\limits_{n \to \infty}\left|\dfrac{a_{n+1}}{a_n}\right| = \lim\limits_{n \to \infty}\left|\dfrac{-1}{5}\right| = \dfrac{1}{5}.$

Therefore, $L = \dfrac{1}{5}$, $R = \dfrac{1}{\frac{1}{5}} = 5$, and the series converges for $|x - 6| < 5.$

The interval of convergence is:

$|x - 6| < 5$ or $1 < x < 11$ (2.2)

CHAPTER 2 REVIEW   **107**

7. $\dfrac{2x}{(1-x)^3} = 1 \cdot 2x + 2 \cdot 3x^2 + 3 \cdot 4x^3 + \cdots + n(n+1)x^n + \cdots$

We have $a = 0$, and

$a_n = n(n+1)$

$a_{n+1} = (n+1)(n+2)$

Thus, $\dfrac{a_{n+1}}{a_n} = \dfrac{(n+1)(n+2)}{n(n+1)} = \dfrac{n+2}{n}$ and $\displaystyle\lim_{n\to\infty}\left|\dfrac{a_{n+1}}{a_n}\right| = \lim_{n\to\infty}\left|\dfrac{n+2}{n}\right| = 1$.

Therefore, $L = 1$, $R = 1$, and the series converges for $|x - 0| < 1$. The interval of convergence is:
$|x| < 1$ or $-1 < x < 1$. (2.2)

8. $e^{10x} = 1 + 10x + \dfrac{10^2}{2!}x^2 + \cdots + \dfrac{10^n}{n!}x^n + \cdots$

We have $a = 0$ and

$a_n = \dfrac{10^n}{n!}$

$a_{n+1} = \dfrac{10^{n+1}}{(n+1)!}$

Thus, $\dfrac{a_{n+1}}{a_n} = \dfrac{\dfrac{10^{n+1}}{(n+1)!}}{\dfrac{10^n}{n!}} = \dfrac{10^{n+1}}{(n+1)!}\dfrac{n!}{10^n} = \dfrac{10}{n+1}$

and $\displaystyle\lim_{n\to\infty}\left|\dfrac{a_{n+1}}{a_n}\right| = \lim_{n\to\infty}\left|\dfrac{10}{n+1}\right| = 0$.

Therefore, the series converges for all x. The interval of convergence is: $-\infty < x < \infty$. (2.2)

9. $f(x) = e^{-9x}$

$f'(x) = e^{-9x}(-9) = -9e^{-9x}$

$f''(x) = -9e^{-9x}(-9) = 9^2e^{-9x}$

$f^{(3)}(x) = 9^2e^{-9x}(-9) = -9^3e^{-9x}$

$\vdots$

$f^{(n)}(x) = (-1)^n 9^n e^{-9x}$ (2.1)

10. $f(x) = \dfrac{1}{7-x} = (7-x)^{-1}$ $\qquad f(0) = \dfrac{1}{7}$

$f'(x) = -(7-x)^{-2}(-1) = (7-x)^{-2}$ $\qquad f'(0) = \dfrac{1}{7^2}$

$f''(x) = -2(7-x)^{-3}(-1) = 2(7-x)^{-3}$ $\qquad f''(0) = \dfrac{2}{7^3}$

$f^{(3)}(x) = -3(2)(7-x)^{-4}(-1) = 3!(7-x)^{-4}$ $\qquad f^{(3)}(0) = \dfrac{3!}{7^4}$

$\vdots$ $\qquad\qquad \vdots$

$f^{(n)}(x) = n!(7-x)^{-(n+1)}$ $\qquad f^{(n)}(0) = \dfrac{n!}{7^{n+1}}$

$$a_0 = f(0) = \frac{1}{7}$$

$$a_1 = f'(0) = \frac{1}{7^2}$$

$$a_2 = \frac{f''(0)}{2!} = \frac{2}{7^3 \cdot 2!} = \frac{1}{7^3}$$

$$a_3 = \frac{f^{(3)}(0)}{3!} = \frac{3!}{7^4 \cdot 3!} = \frac{1}{7^4}$$

$$\vdots$$

$$a_n = \frac{f^{(n)}(0)}{n!} = \frac{n!}{7^{n+1} n!} = \frac{1}{7^{n+1}}$$

The Taylor series at 0 for f is:

$$f(x) = f(0) + f'(0)x + \frac{f''(0)}{2!}x^2 + \frac{f^{(3)}(0)}{3!}x^3 + \ldots + \frac{f^{(n)}(0)}{n!}x^n + \ldots$$

$$= \frac{1}{7} + \frac{1}{7^2}x + \frac{1}{7^3}x^2 + \ldots + \frac{1}{7^{n+1}}x^n + \ldots$$

Now, $a_n = \frac{1}{7^{n+1}}$, $a_{n+1} = \frac{1}{7^{n+2}}$, and $\frac{a_{n+1}}{a_n} = \frac{\frac{1}{7^{n+2}}}{\frac{1}{7^{n+1}}} = \frac{7^{n+1}}{7^{n+2}} = \frac{1}{7}$.

Thus, $\lim\limits_{n \to \infty} \left| \frac{a_{n+1}}{a_n} \right| = \lim\limits_{n \to \infty} \left| \frac{1}{7} \right| = \frac{1}{7}$. Therefore, $L = \frac{1}{7}$, $R = \frac{1}{\frac{1}{7}} = 7$, and the

series converges for $|x| < 7$ or $-7 < x < 7$. $\hspace{2cm}$ (2.2)

11. $\quad f(x) = \ln x \hspace{5cm} f(2) = \ln 2$

$\quad f'(x) = \frac{1}{x} = x^{-1} \hspace{4cm} f'(2) = \frac{1}{2}$

$\quad f''(x) = -x^{-2} \hspace{4.3cm} f''(2) = -\frac{1}{4} = -\frac{1}{2^2}$

$\quad f^{(3)}(x) = 2x^{-3} \hspace{4.3cm} f^{(3)}(2) = \frac{2!}{2^3}$

$\quad f^{(4)}(x) = -3!x^{-4} \hspace{3.8cm} f^{(4)}(2) = \frac{-3!}{2^4}$

$\quad \vdots \hspace{7cm} \vdots$

$\quad f^{(n)}(x) = (-1)^{n-1}(n-1)!x^{-n} \hspace{1cm} f^{(n)}(2) = \frac{(-1)^{n-1}(n-1)!}{2^n}$

$$a_0 = f(2) = \ln 2$$

$$a_1 = f'(2) = \frac{1}{2}$$

$$a_2 = \frac{f''(2)}{2!} = \frac{-1}{2^2 \cdot 2!}$$

$$a_3 = \frac{f^{(3)}(2)}{3!} = \frac{2}{2^3 \cdot 3!} = \frac{1}{3 \cdot 2^3}$$

$$a_4 = \frac{f^{(4)}(2)}{4!} = \frac{-3!}{2^4 \cdot 4!} = \frac{-1}{4 \cdot 2^4}$$

$$\vdots$$

$$a_n = \frac{f^{(n)}(2)}{n!} = \frac{(-1)^{n-1}(n-1)!}{2^n \cdot n!} = \frac{(-1)^{n-1}}{n \cdot 2^n}$$

The Taylor series at 2 for f is:

$$f(x) = f(2) + f'(2)(x - 2) + \frac{f''(2)}{2!}(x - 2)^2 + \cdots + \frac{f^{(n)}(2)}{n!}(x - 2)^n + \cdots$$

$$= \ln 2 + \frac{1}{2}(x - 2) - \frac{1}{2 \cdot 2^2}(x - 2)^2 + \cdots + \frac{(-1)^{n-1}}{n \cdot 2^n}(x - 2)^n + \cdots$$

$$= \ln 2 + \frac{1}{2}(x - 2) - \frac{1}{8}(x - 2)^2 + \cdots + \frac{(-1)^{n-1}}{n \cdot 2^n}(x - 2)^n + \cdots.$$

Now, $a_n = \dfrac{(-1)^{n-1}}{n \cdot 2^n}$, $a_{n+1} = \dfrac{(-1)^n}{(n+1)2^{n+1}}$

and

$$\frac{a_{n+1}}{a_n} = \frac{\dfrac{(-1)^n}{(n+1)2^{n+1}}}{\dfrac{(-1)^{n-1}}{n \cdot 2^n}} = \frac{-n \cdot 2^n}{(n+1)2^{n+1}} = \frac{-n}{2(n+1)}.$$

Thus, $\displaystyle\lim_{n \to \infty}\left|\frac{a_{n+1}}{a_n}\right| = \lim_{n \to \infty}\left|\frac{-n}{2(n+1)}\right| = \frac{1}{2}$

Therefore, $L = \dfrac{1}{2}$, $R = \dfrac{1}{\frac{1}{2}} = 2$, and the series converges for

$|x - 2| < 2$ or $0 < x < 4$. (2.2)

12. $f(x) = \dfrac{1}{10 + x} = \dfrac{1}{10\left(1 + \dfrac{x}{10}\right)} = \dfrac{1}{10} \cdot \dfrac{1}{1 + \dfrac{x}{10}}$

From Table 1, the Taylor series at 0 for $\dfrac{1}{1 + x}$ is

$$\frac{1}{1 + x} = 1 - x + x^2 - x^3 + \cdots + (-1)^n x^n + \cdots \quad (-1 < x < 1).$$

Replacing x by $\dfrac{x}{10}$, we have

$$\frac{1}{10} \cdot \frac{1}{1 + \dfrac{x}{10}} = \frac{1}{10}\left[1 - \frac{x}{10} + \frac{x^2}{10^2} - \frac{x^3}{10^3} + \cdots + \frac{(-1)^n}{10^n}x^n + \cdots\right]$$

$$= \frac{1}{10} - \frac{x}{10^2} + \frac{x^2}{10^3} - \frac{x^3}{10^4} + \cdots + \frac{(-1)^n}{10^{n+1}}x^n + \cdots.$$

This series converges for $-1 < \dfrac{x}{10} < 1$ or $-10 < x < 10$. (2.3)

13. $f(x) = \dfrac{x^2}{4 - x^2} = \dfrac{x^2}{4\left(1 - \dfrac{x^2}{4}\right)} = \dfrac{x^2}{4} \cdot \dfrac{1}{1 - \dfrac{x^2}{4}}$

From Table 1, the Taylor series at 0 for $\dfrac{1}{1 - x}$ is

$\dfrac{1}{1 - x} = 1 + x + x^2 + x^3 + \cdots + x^n + \cdots \qquad (-1 < x < 1).$

Replacing x by $\dfrac{x^2}{4}$, we have

$\dfrac{x^2}{4} \cdot \dfrac{1}{1 - \dfrac{x^2}{4}} = \dfrac{x^2}{4}\left[1 + \dfrac{x^2}{4} + \dfrac{x^4}{4^2} + \dfrac{x^6}{4^3} + \cdots + \dfrac{x^{2n}}{4^n} + \cdots\right]$

$\qquad\qquad = \dfrac{x^2}{4} + \dfrac{x^4}{4^2} + \dfrac{x^6}{4^3} + \dfrac{x^8}{4^4} + \cdots + \dfrac{x^{2n+2}}{4^{n+1}} + \cdots$

The interval of convergence is $-1 < \dfrac{x^2}{4} < 1$ or $-2 < x < 2$. $\qquad$ (2.3)

14. $f(x) = x^2 e^{3x}$

From Table 1, the Taylor series at 0 for e^x is

$e^x = 1 + x + \dfrac{x^2}{2!} + \dfrac{x^3}{3!} + \cdots + \dfrac{x^n}{n!} + \cdots \qquad (-\infty < x < \infty).$

Replacing x by $3x$, we have

$x^2 e^{3x} = x^2\left[1 + 3x + \dfrac{(3x)^2}{2!} + \dfrac{(3x)^3}{3!} + \cdots + \dfrac{(3x)^n}{n!} + \cdots\right]$

$\qquad = x^2 + 3x^3 + \dfrac{3^2}{2!}x^4 + \dfrac{3^3}{3!}x^5 + \cdots + \dfrac{3^n}{n!}x^{n+2} + \cdots.$

The interval of convergence for this series is $-\infty < x < \infty$. $\qquad$ (2.3)

15. $f(x) = x\ln(e + x) = x\left[\ln e\left(1 + \dfrac{x}{e}\right)\right]$

$\qquad\qquad = x\left[\ln e + \ln\left(1 + \dfrac{x}{e}\right)\right] = \left[1 + \ln\left(1 + \dfrac{x}{e}\right)\right].$

The Taylor series at 0 for $\ln(1 + x)$ is

$\ln(1 + x) = x - \dfrac{x^2}{2} + \dfrac{x^3}{3} - \dfrac{x^4}{4} + \cdots + \dfrac{(-1)^{n-1}}{n}x^n + \cdots \qquad (-1 < x < 1).$

Replacing x by $\dfrac{x}{e}$, we have

$x\ln(e + x) = x\left[1 + \dfrac{1}{e}x - \dfrac{1}{2e^2}x^2 + \dfrac{1}{3e^3}x^3 - \cdots + \dfrac{(-1)^{n-1}}{ne^n}x^n + \cdots\right]$

$\qquad = x + \dfrac{1}{e}x^2 - \dfrac{1}{2e^2}x^3 + \dfrac{1}{3e^3}x^4 - \cdots + \dfrac{(-1)^{n-1}}{ne^n}x^{n+1} + \cdots.$

The interval of convergence is $-1 < \dfrac{x}{e} < 1$ or $-e < x < e$. $\qquad$ (2.3)

16. $f(x) = \dfrac{1}{4 - x} = \dfrac{1}{2 - (x - 2)} = \dfrac{1}{2} \cdot \dfrac{1}{1 - \dfrac{x - 2}{2}}$

The Taylor series at 0 for $\dfrac{1}{1 - x}$ is

$$\dfrac{1}{1 - x} = 1 + x + x^2 + x^3 + \cdots + x^n + \cdots \quad (-1 < x < 1).$$

Replacing x by $\dfrac{x - 2}{2}$, we have

$$\dfrac{1}{4 - x} = \dfrac{1}{2} \cdot \dfrac{1}{1 - \dfrac{x - 2}{2}}$$

$$= \dfrac{1}{2}\left[1 + \dfrac{x - 2}{2} + \dfrac{(x - 2)^2}{2^2} + \dfrac{(x - 2)^3}{2^3} + \cdots + \dfrac{(x - 2)^n}{2^n} + \cdots\right]$$

$$= \dfrac{1}{2} + \dfrac{x - 2}{2^2} + \dfrac{(x - 2)^2}{2^3} + \dfrac{(x - 2)^3}{2^4} + \cdots + \dfrac{(x - 2)^n}{2^{n+1}} + \cdots .$$

The interval of convergence is $-1 < \dfrac{x - 2}{2} < 1$ or $-2 < x - 2 < 2$ or

$0 < x < 4.$ (2.3)

17. (A) Theorem 1 of Section 2.2 is not applicable because the coefficients of the odd powers of x are 0.

(B) If we let $t = 5x^2$, then we have
$$\ln(1 - 5x^2) = \ln(1 - t) = -t - \dfrac{1}{2}t^2 - \dfrac{1}{3}t^3 - \cdots - \dfrac{1}{n}t^n - \cdots, \quad -1 < t < 1,$$
from Table 1, Section 2.3.

Thus, the interval of convergence for the given Taylor series is
$-1 < 5x^2 < 1$ which is the same as $-\dfrac{1}{\sqrt{5}} < x < \dfrac{1}{\sqrt{5}}$ or $-\dfrac{\sqrt{5}}{5} < x < \dfrac{\sqrt{5}}{5}.$
(2.2, 2.3)

18. (A) The Taylor series at 0 for $\dfrac{1}{1 + x}$ converges for $-1 < x < 1.$

Since the odd powers of $\sqrt{x} = x^{1/2}$ are defined only for $x \geq 0$, the formula $\dfrac{1}{1 + \sqrt{x}} = 1 - x^{1/2} + x - x^{3/2} + \cdots + (-1)^n x^{n/2} + \cdots$
is valid only for $0 \leq x < 1.$

(B) The formula for $\dfrac{1}{1 + \sqrt{x}}$ is **not** a Taylor series at 0 because some (in fact, half) of the powers of x are not non-negative integers.
(2.2, 2.3)

19. $f(x) = \dfrac{1}{2 - x} = \dfrac{1}{2} \cdot \dfrac{1}{1 - \dfrac{x}{2}}$

Use the Taylor series at 0 for $\dfrac{1}{1 - x}$ and replace x by $\dfrac{x}{2}$:

$$\dfrac{1}{2 - x} = \dfrac{1}{2} \cdot \dfrac{1}{1 - \dfrac{x}{2}} = \dfrac{1}{2}\left[1 + \dfrac{x}{2} + \dfrac{x^2}{2^2} + \cdots + \dfrac{x^n}{2^n} + \cdots\right]$$

$$= \dfrac{1}{2} + \dfrac{x}{2^2} + \dfrac{x^2}{2^3} + \cdots + \dfrac{x^n}{2^{n+1}} + \cdots.$$

The interval of convergence is $-1 < \dfrac{x}{2} < 1$ or $-2 < x < 2$.

Now, $f'(x) = \dfrac{1}{(2 - x)^2} = g(x)$.

Thus, the Taylor series at 0 for $g(x)$ can be obtained by differentiating the Taylor series for $f(x)$. We have

$$\dfrac{1}{(2 - x)^2} = f'(x) = \dfrac{1}{2^2} + \dfrac{2x}{2^3} + \dfrac{3x^2}{2^4} + \cdots + \dfrac{nx^{n-1}}{2^{n+1}} + \cdots$$

$$= \dfrac{1}{4} + \dfrac{1}{4}x + \dfrac{3}{16}x^2 + \cdots + \dfrac{n}{2^{n+1}}x^{n-1} + \cdots.$$

The interval of convergence is $-2 < x < 2$. (2.3)

20. $f(x) = \dfrac{x^2}{1 + x^2}$

Use the Taylor series at 0 for $\dfrac{1}{1 + x}$, replace x by x^2, and multiply by x^2. This yields

$$\dfrac{x^2}{1 + x^2} = x^2 \cdot \dfrac{1}{1 + x^2} = x^2[1 - x^2 + x^4 - x^6 + \cdots + (-1)^n x^{2n} + \cdots]$$

$$= x^2 - x^4 + x^6 - x^8 + \cdots + (-1)^n x^{2n+2} + \cdots.$$

The interval of convergence is $-1 < x^2 < 1$ or $-1 < x < 1$.
Now,

$$f'(x) = \dfrac{2x}{(1 + x^2)^2} = g(x).$$

Thus, we differentiate the series for $f(x)$ to obtain the series for $g(x)$.

$$\dfrac{2x}{(1 + x^2)^2} = f'(x) = 2x - 4x^3 + 6x^5 - 8x^7 + \cdots + (-1)^n(2n + 2)x^{2n+1} + \cdots.$$

The interval of convergence is $-1 < x < 1$. (2.3)

21. $f(x) = \int_0^x \frac{t^2}{9 + t^2} \, dt$

$$\frac{t^2}{9 + t^2} = \frac{t^2}{9} \cdot \frac{1}{1 + \frac{t^2}{9}}$$

Use the Taylor series at 0 for $\frac{1}{1 + x}$, replace x by $\frac{t^2}{9}$, and multiply the result by $\frac{t^2}{9}$. We obtain

$$\frac{t^2}{t^2 + 9} = \frac{t^2}{9} \cdot \frac{1}{1 + \frac{t^2}{9}} = \frac{t^2}{9}\left[1 - \frac{t^2}{9} + \frac{t^4}{9^2} - \frac{t^6}{9^3} + \dots + \frac{(-1)^n}{9^n} t^{2n} + \dots\right]$$

$$= \frac{t^2}{9} - \frac{t^4}{9^2} + \frac{t^6}{9^3} - \dots + \frac{(-1)^n}{9^{n+1}} t^{2n+2} + \dots \, .$$

The interval of convergence for this series is $-1 < \frac{t^2}{9} < 1$ or $-3 < t < 3$.

Now,
$$f(x) = \int_0^x \frac{t^2}{9 + t^2} \, dt$$

$$= \left[\frac{t^3}{3 \cdot 9} - \frac{t^5}{5 \cdot 9^2} + \frac{t^7}{7 \cdot 9^3} - \dots + \frac{(-1)^n}{(2n + 3)9^{n+1}} t^{2n+3} + \dots\right]\Big|_0^x$$

$$= \frac{1}{3 \cdot 9} x^3 - \frac{1}{5 \cdot 9^2} x^5 + \frac{1}{7 \cdot 9^3} x^7 - \dots + \frac{(-1)^n}{(2n + 3)9^{n+1}} x^{2n+3} + \dots$$

and the interval of convergence is $-3 < x < 3$. $\hspace{3cm}$ (2.3)

22. $f(x) = \int_0^x \frac{t^4}{16 - t^2} \, dt$

$$\frac{t^4}{16 - t^2} = \frac{t^4}{16} \cdot \frac{1}{1 - \frac{t^2}{16}}$$

Thus, we use the Taylor series at 0 for $\frac{1}{1 - x}$, replace x by $\frac{t^2}{16}$, and multiply the result by $\frac{t^4}{16}$. We obtain

$$\frac{t^4}{16 - t^2} = \frac{t^4}{16} \cdot \frac{1}{1 - \frac{t^2}{16}} = \frac{t^4}{16}\left[1 + \frac{t^2}{16} + \frac{t^4}{16^2} + \frac{t^6}{16^3} + \dots + \frac{t^{2n}}{16^n} + \dots\right]$$

$$= \frac{1}{16} t^4 + \frac{1}{16^2} t^6 + \frac{1}{16^3} t^8 + \dots + \frac{1}{16^{n+1}} t^{2n+4} + \dots \, .$$

The interval of convergence is $-1 < \frac{t^2}{16} < 1$ or $-4 < t < 4$.

Now,

$$f(x) = \int_0^x \frac{t^4}{16 - t^2}\, dt$$

$$= \left[\frac{1}{5 \cdot 16} t^5 + \frac{1}{7 \cdot 16^2} t^7 + \frac{1}{9 \cdot 16^3} t^9 + \dots + \frac{1}{(2n + 5)16^{n+1}} t^{2n+5} + \dots \right] \Big|_0^x$$

$$= \frac{1}{5 \cdot 16} x^5 + \frac{1}{7 \cdot 16^2} x^7 + \frac{1}{9 \cdot 16^3} x^9 + \dots + \frac{1}{(2n + 5)16^{n+1}} x^{2n+5} + \dots$$

and the interval of convergence is $-4 < x < 4$. \hfill (2.3)

23. Let $f(x) = x^3 - 3x^2 + 4$

(A) At $a = 1$:

$$
\begin{array}{ll}
f(x) = x^3 - 3x^2 + 4 & f(1) = 2 \\
f'(x) = 3x^2 - 6x & f'(1) = -3 \\
f''(x) = 6x - 6 & f''(1) = 0 \\
f^{(3)}(x) = 6 & f^{(3)}(1) = 6 \\
f^{(4)}(x) = f^{(5)}(x) = \dots = 0 & f^{(4)}(1) = f^{(5)}(1) = \dots = 0
\end{array}
$$

Thus,

$$f(x) = f(1) + f'(1)(x - 1) + \frac{f''(1)}{2!}(x - 1)^2 + \frac{f^{(3)}(1)}{3!}(x - 1)^3$$

$$= 2 - 3(x - 1) + (x - 1)^3$$

At $a = -1$:

$$
\begin{array}{l}
f(-1) = 0 \\
f'(-1) = 9 \\
f''(-1) = -12 \\
f^{(3)}(-1) = 6 \\
f^{(4)}(-1) = f^{(5)}(-1) = \dots = 0
\end{array}
$$

Thus,

$$f(x) = f(-1) + f'(-1)(x + 1) + \frac{f''(1)}{2!}(x + 1)^2 + \frac{f^{(3)}(-1)}{3!}(x + 1)^3$$

$$= 9(x + 1) - 6(x + 1)^2 + (x + 1)^3$$

(B) Each series represents $f(x) = x^3 - 3x^2 + 4$ for $-\infty < x < \infty$. \hfill (2.2)

24. (A) $f(x) = |x|$ does not have any Taylor polynomials at 0 because f is not differentiable at 0.

(B) $f(x) = |x| = \begin{cases} x & \text{if } x \geq 0 \\ -x & \text{if } x < 0 \end{cases}$

and $f'(x) = \begin{cases} 1 & \text{if } x > 0 \\ -1 & \text{if } x < 0 \end{cases}$

If $a > 0$, then $p_n(x) = a + (x - a) = x$, $n \geq 1$

If $a < 0$, then $p_n(x) = -a - (x - a) = -x$, $n \geq 1$ \hfill (2.2)

For Problems 25 and 26:

$$e^x = 1 + x + \frac{x^2}{2!} + \frac{x^3}{3!} + \cdots ,$$

$$p_2(x) = 1 + x + \frac{x^2}{2!} = 1 + x + \frac{1}{2}x^2, \text{ and}$$

$$R_2(x) = \frac{f^{(3)}(t)}{3!}x^3 = \frac{e^t}{3!}x^3, \text{ where } 0 < t < x.$$

25. Let $x = 0.6$. Then

$$e^{0.6} \approx p_2(0.6) = 1 + 0.6 + \frac{(0.6)^2}{2} = 1.78$$

and $\left| R_2(x) \right| = \left| \frac{e^t}{3!}(0.6)^3 \right| < \frac{3(0.6)^3}{3!} = 0.108.$ (2.4)

26. Let $x = 0.06$. Then

$$e^{0.06} \approx p_2(0.06) = 1 + 0.06 + \frac{(0.06)^2}{2} = 1.0618$$

and $\left| R_2(x) \right| = \left| \frac{e^t(0.06)^3}{3!} \right| < \frac{3(0.06)^3}{3!} = 0.000108.$ (2.4)

For Problems 27 and 28:

$$\ln(1 + x) = x - \frac{x^2}{2} + \frac{x^3}{3} - \frac{x^4}{4} + \frac{x^5}{5} - \cdots$$

27. Let $x = 0.3$. Then

$$\ln(1.3) = \ln(1 + 0.3) = 0.3 - \frac{(0.3)^2}{2} + \frac{(0.3)^3}{3} - \frac{(0.3)^4}{4} + \frac{(0.3)^5}{5} - \cdots$$
$$= 0.3 - 0.045 + 0.009 - 0.002025 + 0.000486 \approx 0.261975.$$

The terms are alternating in sign and decreasing in absolute value. If we use the Taylor polynomial of degree 4, then the error will be less than $0.000486 < 0.0005$. Thus, $\ln(1.3) \approx 0.261975$ to within ± 0.0005.

      (2.4)

28. Let $x = 0.03$. Then

$$\ln(1.03) = \ln(1 + 0.03) = 0.03 - \frac{(0.03)^2}{2} + \frac{(0.03)^3}{3} - \cdots$$
$$= 0.03 - 0.00045 + 0.000009 - \cdots \approx 0.03.$$

The terms are alternating in sign and decreasing in absolute value. If we use the Taylor polynomial of degree 1, then the error will be less than $0.00045 < 0.0005$. Thus, $\ln(1.03) \approx 0.03$ to within ± 0.0005.

      (2.4)

29. $f'(x) = x \ln(1 - x)$. From Table 1, Section 2.3,

$$\ln(1 - x) = -x - \frac{1}{2}x^2 - \frac{1}{3}x^3 - \dots - \frac{1}{n}x^n - \dots, \quad -1 < x < 1$$

Therefore

$$f'(x) = -x^2 - \frac{1}{2}x^3 - \frac{1}{4}x^4 - \dots - \frac{1}{n}x^{n+1} - \dots$$

and

$$f(x) = \int f'(x)\,dx = \int\left(-x^2 - \frac{1}{2}x^3 - \frac{1}{4}x^4 - \dots - \frac{1}{n}x^{n+1} - \dots\right)dx$$

$$= C - \frac{1}{3}x^3 - \frac{1}{8}x^4 - \frac{1}{20}x^5 - \dots - \frac{1}{n(n+2)}x^{n+2} - \dots$$

Since $f(0) = 5$, we have

$$5 = C - 0 - 0 - \dots \quad \text{so} \quad C = 5$$

Thus,

$$f(x) = 5 - \frac{1}{3}x^3 - \frac{1}{8}x^4 - \frac{1}{20}x^5 - \dots - \frac{1}{n(n+2)}x^{n+2} - \dots$$

$$= 5 - \frac{1}{3}x^3 - \frac{1}{8}x^4 - \frac{1}{20}x^5 - \dots - \frac{1}{(n-2)n}x^n - \dots, \quad -1 < x < 1.$$

(2.3)

30. $f''(x) = xe^{-x}$. From Table 1, Section 2.3,

$$e^{-x} = 1 - x + \frac{1}{2!}x^2 - \frac{1}{3!}x^3 + \dots + \frac{(-1)^n}{n!}x^n + \dots, \quad -\infty < x < \infty.$$

Therefore

$$f''(x) = x - x^2 + \frac{1}{2!}x^3 - \frac{1}{3!}x^4 + \dots + \frac{(-1)^n}{n!}x^{n+1} + \dots$$

and

$$f'(x) = \int f''(x)\,dx = \int\left(x - x^2 + \frac{1}{2!}x^3 - \frac{1}{3!}x^4 + \dots + \frac{(-1)^n}{n!}x^{n+1} + \dots\right)dx$$

$$= C_1 + \frac{1}{2}x^2 - \frac{1}{3}x^3 + \frac{1}{4(2!)}x^4 - \frac{1}{5(3!)}x^5 + \dots + \frac{(-1)^n}{(n+2)n!}x^{n+2} + \dots$$

Since $f'(0) = -4$, we have

$$-4 = C_1 + 0 - 0 + 0 \dots = C_1 \quad \text{so} \quad C_1 = -4$$

and

$$f'(x) = -4 + \frac{1}{2}x^2 - \frac{1}{3}x^3 + \frac{1}{4(2!)}x^4 - \dots + \frac{(-1)^n}{(n+2)n!}x^{n+2} + \dots$$

Now

$$f(x) = \int f'(x)\,dx = \int\left(-4 + \frac{1}{2}x^2 - \frac{1}{3}x^3 + \frac{1}{4(2!)}x^4 - \dots + \frac{(-1)^n}{(n+2)n!}x^{n+2} + \dots\right)dx$$

$$= C_2 - 4x + \frac{1}{6}x^3 - \frac{1}{12}x^4 + \frac{1}{4 \cdot 5(2!)}x^5 - \dots + \frac{(-1)^n}{(n+2)(n+3)n!}x^{n+3} + \dots$$

Since $f(0) = 3$, we have

$$3 = C_2 - 0 + 0 - 0 + \ldots = C_2 \quad \text{so} \quad C_2 = 3$$

and

$$f(x) = 3 - 4x + \frac{1}{6}x^3 - \frac{1}{12}x^4 + \ldots + \frac{(-1)^n}{(n+2)(n+3)n!}x^{n+3} + \ldots$$

$$= 3 - 4x + \frac{1}{6}x^3 - \frac{1}{12}x^4 + \ldots + \frac{(-1)^{n-3}}{(n-3)!(n-1)n}x^n + \ldots$$

$$\text{(replacing } n \text{ by } n - 3)$$

$$= 3 - 4x + \frac{1}{6}x^3 - \frac{1}{12}x^4 + \ldots + \frac{(-1)^{n+1}}{(n-3)!(n-1)n}x^n + \ldots \; , \quad -\infty < x < \infty.$$

$$(2.3)$$

31. Using the Taylor series at 0 for $\dfrac{1}{1+x}$, we have

$$\frac{1}{16+x^2} = \frac{1}{16} \cdot \frac{1}{1 + \dfrac{x^2}{16}}$$

$$= \frac{1}{16}\left[1 - \frac{x^2}{16} + \frac{x^4}{16^2} - \frac{x^6}{16^3} + \ldots + \frac{(-1)^n}{16^n}x^{2n} + \ldots \right]$$

$$= \frac{1}{16} - \frac{x^2}{16^2} + \frac{x^4}{16^3} - \frac{x^6}{16^4} + \ldots + \frac{(-1)^n}{16^{n+1}}x^{2n} + \ldots$$

The interval of convergence is $-1 < \dfrac{x^2}{16} < 1$ or $-4 < x < 4$. Thus,

$$\int_0^1 \frac{1}{16+x^2}\,dx = \left(\frac{1}{16}x - \frac{1}{3 \cdot 16^2}x^3 + \frac{1}{5 \cdot 16^3}x^5 - \ldots \right.$$

$$\left. + \frac{(-1)^n}{(2n+1)16^{n+1}}x^{2n+1} + \ldots \right)\Bigg|_0^1$$

$$= \frac{1}{16} - \frac{1}{3 \cdot 16^2} + \frac{1}{5 \cdot 16^3} - \ldots$$

$$= 0.0625 - 0.00130 + 0.00005 - \ldots \; .$$

Since the terms in the series are alternating in sign and decreasing in absolute value, the error in using the first two terms in this series will be less than 0.00005. Thus,

$$\int_0^1 \frac{1}{16+x^2}\,dx \approx 0.0625 - 0.00130 = 0.0612.$$

$$(2.4)$$

32. Using the Taylor series at 0 for $f(x) = e^{-x}$, we obtain

$$x^2 e^{-(0.1)x^2} = x^2\left[1 - \frac{x^2}{10} + \frac{1}{2!\,10^2}x^4 - \frac{1}{3!\,10^3}x^6 + \ldots \right]$$

$$= x^2 - \frac{x^4}{10} + \frac{1}{2!\,10^2}x^6 - \frac{1}{3!\,10^3}x^8 + \ldots \; .$$

Thus,

$$\int_0^1 x^2 e^{-(0.1)x^2}\,dx = \left(\frac{1}{3}x^3 - \frac{1}{50}x^5 + \frac{1}{7 \cdot 2! \, 10^2}x^7 - \frac{1}{9 \cdot 3! \, 10^3}x^9 + \cdots\right)\Big|_0^1$$

$$= \frac{1}{3} - \frac{1}{50} + \frac{1}{1400} - \frac{1}{54,000} + \cdots .$$

Since the terms in the series are alternating in sign and decreasing in absolute value, the error in using the first three terms in this series will be less than $\dfrac{1}{54,000} = 0.000019 < 0.0005$.

Thus,

$$\int_0^1 x^2 e^{-(0.1)x^2}\,dx \approx 0.33333 - 0.02 + 0.0071 = 0.31404. \qquad (2.4)$$

33. From Taylor's formula for the remainder,

$$R_n(0.5) = \frac{f^{(n+1)}(t)}{(n+1)!}(0.5)^{n+1}$$

where t is some number between 0 and 0.5.
Since $\left|f^{(n+1)}(t)\right| \le 10$,

$$\left|R_n(0.5)\right| = \left|\frac{f^{(n+1)}(t)}{(n+1)!}(0.5)^{n+1}\right| = \frac{\left|f^{(n+1)}(t)\right|}{(n+1)!}(0.5)^{n+1} \le \frac{10}{(n+1)!}(0.5)^{n+1}$$

Now, we want $\left|R_n(0.5)\right| < 10^{-6}$ which will be true if

$$\frac{10}{(n+1)!}(0.5)^{n+1} < 10^{-6}$$

which implies $(n+1)! > \dfrac{10(0.5)^{n+1}}{10^{-6}} = 10^7 (0.5)^{n+1} = \dfrac{10^7}{2^{n+1}}$.

The smallest n that satisfies this inequality is $n = 7$. $\qquad (2.4)$

34. From Taylor's formula for the remainder,

$$R_8(x) = \frac{f^{(9)}(t)}{9!}x^9$$

where t is between 0 and x.
Now

$$\left|R_8(x)\right| = \left|\frac{f^{(9)}(t)}{9!}x^9\right| \le \frac{10}{9!}\left|x\right|^9 < 10^{-6}$$

implies

$$\left|x\right|^9 < 9!(10)^{-7} = \frac{9!}{10^7} = 0.036288$$

Therefore

$$\left|x\right| < (0.036288)^{1/9} \approx 0.6918.$$

The error in the approximation of $f(x)$ by $P_8(x)$ will be less than 10^{-6} if $\left|x\right| < 0.6918$. $\qquad (2.4)$

35. $e^x = 1 + x + \dfrac{1}{2!}x^2 + \cdots + \dfrac{1}{n!}x^n + \cdots, \quad -\infty < x < \infty$

$e^{x^2} = 1 + x^2 + \dfrac{1}{2!}x^4 + \cdots + \dfrac{1}{n!}x^{2n} + \cdots, \quad -\infty < x < \infty.$

Thus, the fourth-degree Taylor polynomial for $f(x) = e^{x^2}$ at 0 is:

$p_4(x) = 1 + x^2 + \dfrac{1}{2}x^4$

Using a graphing utility, we find that

$|p_4(x) - e^{x^2}| < 0.01 \quad$ for $\quad -0.616 < x < 0.616.$ (2.4)

36. From Table 1, Section 2.3,

$\ln(1 - x) = -x - \dfrac{1}{2}x^2 - \dfrac{1}{3}x^3 - \cdots - \dfrac{1}{n}x^n - \cdots, \quad -1 < x < 1$

Substituting x^2 for x, we have

$f(x) = \ln(1 - x^2) = -x^2 - \dfrac{1}{2}x^4 - \dfrac{1}{3}x^6 - \cdots - \dfrac{1}{n}x^{2n} - \cdots, \quad -1 < x < 1$

Thus, the sixth-degree Taylor polynomial for f at 0 is:

$p_6(x) = -x^2 - \dfrac{1}{2}x^4 - \dfrac{1}{3}x^6$

Using a graphing utility, we find that

$|p_6(x) - \ln(1 - x^2)| < 0.001 \quad$ for $\quad -0.488 < x < 0.488.$ (2.4)

37. $\quad D(x) = \dfrac{1}{10}\sqrt{2500 - x^2} = \dfrac{1}{10}(2500 - x^2)^{1/2}, \qquad\qquad D(0) = 5$

$D'(x) = \dfrac{1}{20}(2500 - x^2)^{-1/2}(-2x) = -\dfrac{1}{10}x(2500 - x^2)^{-1/2} \quad D'(0) = 0$

$D''(x) = -\dfrac{1}{10}(2500 - x^2)^{-1/2} + \dfrac{1}{20}x(2500 - x^2)^{-3/2}(-2x) \quad D''(0) = -\dfrac{1}{500}$

$\qquad\quad = -\dfrac{1}{10}(2500 - x^2)^{-1/2} - \dfrac{1}{10}x^2(2500 - x^2)^{-3/2}$

Now, $p_2(x) = D(0) + D'(0)x + \dfrac{D''(0)}{2!}x^2 = 5 - \dfrac{1}{1000}x^2$. Therefore,

Average price $= \dfrac{1}{15 - 0}\displaystyle\int_0^{15} D(x)\,dx \approx \dfrac{1}{15}\int_0^{15} p_2(x)\,dx = \dfrac{1}{15}\int_0^{15}\left(5 - \dfrac{1}{1000}x^2\right)dx$

$\qquad\qquad = \dfrac{1}{15}\left[5x - \dfrac{1}{3000}x^3\right]\Big|_0^{15} = \dfrac{1}{15}\left(75 - \dfrac{3375}{3000}\right) = 4.925$ or \$4.93.

(2.4)

38. $R(t) = 6 + 3e^{-0.01t^2}$

Substituting $-0.01t^2$ into the Taylor series at 0 for e^x, we have

$$e^{-0.01t^2} = 1 - (0.01)t^2 + \frac{(0.01)^2}{2!}t^4 - \frac{(0.01)^3}{3!}t^6 + \dots$$

Thus, the second degree Taylor polynomial for R is:

$$p_2(t) = 6 + 3(1 - 0.01t^2) = 9 - 0.03t^2$$

The total production during the first 10 years of operation of the well is:

$$T = \int_0^{10} R(t)\,dt \approx \int_0^{10} p_2(t)\,dt = \int_0^{10} (9 - 0.03t^2)\,dt = (9t - 0.01t^3)\Big|_0^{10} = 80$$

or \$80,000

(2.4)

39. Index of income concentration $= 2\int_0^1 [x - f(x)]\,dx = 2\int_0^1 \left(x - \frac{9x^3}{8 + x^2}\right) dx$

$$= \int_0^1 2x\,dx - \int_0^1 \frac{18x^3}{8 + x^2}\,dx = x^2\Big|_0^1 - \int_0^1 \frac{18x^3}{8 + x^2}\,dx$$

$$= 1 - \int_0^1 \frac{18x^3}{8 + x^2}\,dx$$

Step 1: Find the Taylor series for the integrand.

$$\frac{18x^3}{8 + x^2} = \frac{18x^3}{8} \cdot \frac{1}{1 + \frac{x^2}{8}}$$

$$= \frac{9x^3}{4}\left[1 - \frac{x^2}{8} + \frac{x^4}{8^2} - \frac{x^6}{8^3} + \dots + \frac{(-1)^n}{8^n}x^{2n} + \dots\right]$$

$$\left[\text{Substitute } \frac{x^2}{8} \text{ into the series for } \frac{1}{1 + x}\right]$$

$$= \frac{9}{4}\left[x^3 - \frac{x^5}{8} + \frac{x^7}{8^2} - \frac{x^9}{8^3} + \dots + \frac{(-1)^n}{8^n}x^{2n+3} + \dots\right]$$

This series converges for $\left|\frac{x^2}{8}\right| < 1$ or $-\sqrt{8} < x < \sqrt{8}$.

Step 2: Find the Taylor series for the antiderivative.

$$\int \frac{18x^3}{8 + x^2}\,dx = \int \frac{9}{4}\left[x^3 - \frac{x^5}{8} + \frac{x^7}{8^2} - \frac{x^9}{8^3} + \dots + \frac{(-1)^n}{8^n}x^{2n+3} + \dots\right]dx$$

$$= C + \frac{9}{4}\left[\frac{x^4}{4} - \frac{x^6}{6 \cdot 8} + \frac{x^8}{8 \cdot 8^2} - \frac{x^{10}}{10 \cdot 8^3} + \dots + \frac{(-1)^n}{(2n + 4)8^n}x^{2n+4} + \dots\right]$$

Step 3: Approximate the definite integral.

Choosing $C = 0$ in the antiderivative, we have:

$$\int \frac{18x^3}{8 + x^2} dx = \frac{9}{4} \left[\frac{x^4}{4} - \frac{x^6}{6 \cdot 8} + \frac{x^8}{8 \cdot 8^2} - \frac{x^{10}}{10 \cdot 8^3} + \cdots \right.$$

$$\left. + \frac{(-1)^n}{(2n + 4)8^n} x^{2n+4} + \cdots \right] \Big|_0^1$$

$$= \frac{9}{4} \left(\frac{1}{4} - \frac{1}{48} + \frac{1}{512} - \frac{1}{5120} + \cdots \right)$$

$$= 0.5625 - 0.046875 + 0.004395 - \cdots$$

Since the terms are alternating in sign and decreasing in absolute value, and since the third term is less than 0.005, we can use the first two terms of this series to approximate the definite integral within the specified accuracy.

$$\int \frac{18x^3}{8 + x^2} dx \approx 0.5625 - 0.046875 = 0.515625 \approx 0.516$$

Finally, the index of income concentration is:

$$2 \int_0^1 \left(x - \frac{9x^3}{8 + x^2} \right) dx \approx 1 - 0.516 = 0.484. \tag{2.4}$$

40. Total sales $= \int_0^8 S'(t) dt = \int_0^8 [20 - 20e^{-0.001t^2}] dt.$

Step 1: Find the fourth-degree polynomial at 0 for the integrand.

Substituting $0.001t^2 = \dfrac{t^2}{10^3}$ into the Taylor series at 0 for e^{-x}, we have:

$$e^{-0.001t^2} = 1 - \frac{t^2}{10^3} + \frac{1}{2!} \cdot \frac{t^4}{10^6} - \frac{1}{3!} \cdot \frac{t^6}{10^9} + \cdots$$

Thus,

$$20 - 20e^{-0.001t^2} = \frac{20t^2}{10^3} - 20 \cdot \frac{1}{2!} \cdot \frac{t^4}{10^6} + 20 \cdot \frac{1}{3!} \cdot \frac{t^6}{10^9} + \cdots$$

$$= \frac{t^2}{50} - \frac{t^4}{10^5} + \frac{1}{3 \cdot 10^8} t^6 - \cdots$$

and $p_4(t) = \dfrac{t^2}{50} - \dfrac{t^4}{10^5}$.

Step 2: Approximate the definite integral.

$$\int_0^8 S'(t) dt \approx \int_0^8 p_4(t) dt = \int_0^8 \left(\frac{t^2}{50} - \frac{t^4}{10^5} \right) dt = \left(\frac{t^3}{150} - \frac{t^5}{5 \cdot 10^5} \right) \Big|_0^8$$

$$= \frac{8^3}{150} - \frac{8^5}{5 \cdot 10^5} \approx 3.3478$$

Therefore, $S(8) \approx 3.348$, and the total sales during the first eight months are approximately $3,348,000.

Step 3: Estimate the error in this approximation.

From Steps 1 and 2, the Taylor series at 0 for $S(t)$ is:

$$S(t) = \frac{t^3}{150} - \frac{t^5}{5 \cdot 10^5} + \frac{t^7}{3 \cdot 7 \cdot 10^8} - \cdots, \text{ and}$$

$$S(8) = \frac{8^3}{150} - \frac{8^5}{5 \cdot 10^5} + \frac{8^7}{21 \cdot 10^8} - \cdots.$$

Since the terms alternate in sign and decrease in absolute value, the error in this approximation is less than

$$\left| \frac{8^7}{21 \cdot 10^8} \right| = 0.00099 < 0.001.$$

Thus, $S(8) = 3.348$ to within ± 0.001 or $S(8) = \$3,348,000$ to within $\pm \$1000$. (2.4)

41. $A'(t) = \dfrac{-100}{t^2 + 40}$

Step 1: Find the second-degree Taylor polynomial at 0 for

$$A'(t) = \frac{-100}{t^2 + 40} = \frac{-100}{40} \cdot \frac{1}{1 + \dfrac{t^2}{40}} = \frac{-5}{2} \cdot \frac{1}{1 + \dfrac{t^2}{40}}$$

Substituting $\dfrac{t^2}{40}$ into the Taylor series at 0 for $\dfrac{1}{1 + x}$, we have:

$$-\frac{5}{2} \cdot \frac{1}{1 + \dfrac{t^2}{40}} = -\frac{5}{2}\left[1 - \frac{t^2}{40} + \frac{t^4}{(40)^2} - \frac{t^6}{(40)^3} + \cdots\right]$$

Thus, $p_2(t) = -\dfrac{5}{2} + \dfrac{5}{2} \cdot \dfrac{t^2}{40} = -\dfrac{5}{2} + \dfrac{1}{16}t^2$.

Step 2: Approximate $A(t)$ and find $A(2)$.

$$A(t) = \int A'(t)\,dt \approx \int p_2(t)\,dt = \int\left[-\frac{5}{2} + \frac{1}{16}t^2\right]dt = -\frac{5}{2}t + \frac{1}{48}t^3 + C$$

Since $A(0) = 15$, we have:

$$A(t) \approx -\frac{5}{2}t + \frac{1}{48}t^3 + 15$$

Thus, $A(2) \approx -\dfrac{5}{2}(2) + \dfrac{1}{48}(2)^3 + 15 \approx 10.16667$.

Step 3: Estimate the error in this approximation.

From Steps 1 and 2, the Taylor series at 0 for $A(t)$ is:

$$A(t) = 15 - \frac{5}{2}t + \frac{t^3}{48} - \frac{t^5}{5(40)^2} + \cdots, \text{ and}$$

$$A(2) = 15 - \frac{5}{2}(2) + \frac{2^3}{48} - \frac{2^5}{5(40)^2} + \cdots$$

$$= 15 - 5 + \frac{1}{6} - \frac{32}{8000} + \cdots .$$

Since the terms alternate in sign and decrease in absolute value, the error in this approximation is less than
$$\left|\frac{-32}{8000}\right| = 0.004 < 0.01.$$

Thus, $A(2) = 10.17$ square centimeters to within ± 0.01. (2.4)

42. The average insulin level for the five-minute interval following the injection is:
$$\frac{1}{5}\int_0^5 \frac{5000t^2}{10,000 + t^4}\, dt$$

The Taylor series at 0 for $\dfrac{5000t^2}{10,000 + t^4} = \dfrac{5000t^2}{10,000} \cdot \dfrac{1}{1 + \dfrac{t^4}{10,000}}$

$$= \frac{t^2}{2} \cdot \frac{1}{1 + \left(\dfrac{t}{10}\right)^4} \quad \text{is:}$$

$$\frac{t^2}{2}\left[1 - \left(\frac{t}{10}\right)^4 + \left(\frac{t}{10}\right)^8 - \left(\frac{t}{10}\right)^{12} + \cdots + (-1)^n\left(\frac{t}{10}\right)^{4n} + \cdots\right],$$

where $\left|\left(\dfrac{t}{10}\right)^4\right| < 1$ or $-10 < t < 10$.

$\left[\text{Substitute } \left(\dfrac{t}{10}\right)^4 \text{ into the Taylor series at 0 for } \dfrac{1}{1+x}.\right]$

Therefore, $\dfrac{5000t^2}{10,000 + t^4} = \dfrac{t^2}{2} - \dfrac{t^6}{2 \cdot 10^4} + \dfrac{t^{10}}{2 \cdot 10^8} - \cdots + \dfrac{(-1)^n t^{4n+2}}{2 \cdot 10^{4n}} + \cdots$,

and $\dfrac{1}{5}\int_0^5 \dfrac{5000t^2}{10,000 + t^4}\, dt = \dfrac{1}{5}\left[\dfrac{t^3}{6} - \dfrac{t^7}{2 \cdot 7 \cdot 10^4} + \dfrac{t^{11}}{2 \cdot 11 \cdot 10^8} - \cdots\right]\Big|_0^5$

$$= \frac{1}{5}\left(\frac{5^3}{6} - \frac{5^7}{2 \cdot 7 \cdot 10^4} + \frac{5^{11}}{2 \cdot 11 \cdot 10^8} - \cdots\right)$$

$$= 4.16667 - 0.11161 + 0.00443 - \cdots$$

Since the terms alternate in sign and decrease in absolute value, the error in using the first two terms in this series will be less than 0.00443 < 0.005. Thus, average insulin level for the first five minutes is, approximately, $4.05505 \approx 4.06$. (2.4)

43. The average number of voters in the five-year period is

$$\frac{1}{5}\int_0^5 N(t)\,dt = \frac{1}{5}\int_0^5 (10 + 2t - 5e^{-0.01t})\,dt.$$

The Taylor series at 0 for $f(t) = e^{-0.01t^2}$ is

$$e^{-0.01t^2} = 1 - (0.01)t^2 + \frac{(0.01)^2}{2!}t^4 - \frac{(0.01)^3}{3!}t^6 + \cdots.$$

[<u>Note</u>: Use the Taylor series for e^{-x} and replace x by $(0.01)t^2$.]

Thus,

$$N(t) = 10 + 2t - 5\left(1 - (0.01)t^2 + \frac{(0.01)^2}{2}t^4 - \frac{(0.01)^3}{3!}t^6 + \cdots\right)$$

$$= 5 + 2t + (0.05)t^2 - \frac{0.0005}{2}t^4 + \frac{0.000005}{6}t^6 + \cdots.$$

Therefore,

$$\frac{1}{5}\int_0^5 N(t)\,dt = \frac{1}{5}\left[5t + t^2 + \frac{(0.05)}{3}t^3 - \frac{(0.0005)}{10}t^5 + \frac{(0.000005)}{42}t^7 - \cdots\right]\Big|_0^5$$

$$= \frac{1}{5}\left[25 + 25 + \frac{(0.05)}{3}(5)^3 - \frac{(0.0005)}{10}(5)^5 + \frac{(0.000005)}{42}(5)^7 - \cdots\right]$$

$$= \frac{1}{5}(50 + 2.08333 - 0.15625 + 0.00930 - \cdots)$$

$$= 10 + 0.41667 - 0.03125 + 0.00186 - \cdots$$

$$\approx 10.41667 \approx 10.4.$$

Since the terms alternate in sign and decrease in absolute value, the error in approximating this integral with the first two terms in the series will be less than $|-0.03125| = 0.03125 < 0.05$.

Thus, the average number of voters over the interval $[0, 5]$ is 10.4 to within ± 0.05.

(2.4)

APPENDIX D   SPECIAL TOPIC

EXERCISE D.1

1. (A) $p(x) = a_0 + a_1(x - 1) + a_2(x - 1)(x - 3)$

(B) $2 = p(1) = a_0$

$6 = p(3) = a_0 + 2a_1$

$11 = p(4) = a_0 + 3a_1 + 3a_2$

(C) $a_0 = 2$

$a_1 = \dfrac{1}{2}(6 - a_0) = \dfrac{1}{2}(6 - 2) = 2$

$a_2 = \dfrac{1}{3}(11 - a_0 - 3a_1) = \dfrac{1}{3}(11 - 2 - 6) = 1$

The interpolating polynomial is:
$p(x) = 2 + 2(x - 1) + (x - 1)(x - 3)$

3. (A) $p(x) = a_0 + a_1(x + 1) + a_2(x + 1)x + a_3(x + 1)x(x - 2)$

(B) $6 = p(-1) = a_0$

$5 = p(0) = a_0 + a_1$

$15 = p(2) = a_0 + 3a_1 + 6a_2$

$-39 = p(4) = a_0 + 5a_1 + 20a_2 + 40a_3$

(C) $a_0 = 6$

$a_1 = 5 - a_0 = -1$

$a_2 = \dfrac{1}{6}(15 - a_0 - 3a_1) = \dfrac{1}{6}(15 - 6 + 3) = 2$

$a_3 = \dfrac{1}{40}(-39 - a_0 - 5a_1 - 20a_2) = \dfrac{1}{40}(-39 - 6 + 5 - 40) = -2$

The interpolating polynomial is:
$p(x) = 6 - (x + 1) + 2(x + 1)x - 2(x + 1)x(x - 2)$

5.

x	1	2	3
$f(x)$	4	8	14

x_k	y_k	FIRST DIVIDED DIFFERENCE	SECOND DIVIDED DIFFERENCE
1	4	$\dfrac{8 - 4}{2 - 1} = 4$	
2	8		$\dfrac{6 - 4}{3 - 1} = 1$
3	14	$\dfrac{14 - 8}{3 - 2} = 6$	

Interpolating polynomial: $p(x) = 4 + 4(x - 1) + (x - 1)(x - 2)$.

7.

x	-1	0	1	2
$f(x)$	-3	1	3	9

x_k	y_k	FIRST DIVIDED DIFFERENCE	SECOND DIVIDED DIFFERENCE	THIRD DIVIDED DIFFERENCE
-1	-3	$\dfrac{1-(-3)}{0-(-1)}=4$		
0	1		$\dfrac{2-4}{1-(-1)}=-1$	
1	3	$\dfrac{3-1}{1-0}=2$		$\dfrac{2-(-1)}{2-(-1)}=1$
2	9	$\dfrac{9-3}{2-1}=6$	$\dfrac{6-2}{2-0}=2$	

Interpolating polynomial:

$$p(x) = -3 + 4(x+1) - (x+1)x + (x+1)x(x-1).$$

9.

x	-2	1	2	4
$f(x)$	25	10	17	13

x_k	y_k	FIRST DIVIDED DIFFERENCE	SECOND DIVIDED DIFFERENCE	THIRD DIVIDED DIFFERENCE
-2	25	$\dfrac{10-25}{1-(-2)}=-5$		
1	10		$\dfrac{7-(-5)}{2-(-2)}=3$	
2	17	$\dfrac{17-10}{2-1}=7$		$\dfrac{-3-3}{4-(-2)}=-1$
4	13	$\dfrac{13-17}{4-2}=-2$	$\dfrac{-2-7}{4-1}=-3$	

Interpolating polynomial:

$$25 - 5(x+2) + 3(x+2)(x-1) - (x+2)(x-1)(x-2).$$

11. Given a table with 3 points, it will have a linear interpolating polynomial if the 2 first divided differences are equal. In general, it will have a quadratic polynomial. It will not have a cubic interpolating polynomial because 3 points do not determine a unique cubic.

13.

x	-4	0	4	8
$f(x)$	-64	32	0	224

x_k	y_k	FIRST DIVIDED DIFFERENCE	SECOND DIVIDED DIFFERENCE	THIRD DIVIDED DIFFERENCE
-4	-64	$\dfrac{32-(-64)}{0-(-4)}=24$		
0	32		$\dfrac{-8-24}{4-(-4)}=-4$	
		$\dfrac{0-32}{4-0}=-8$		$\dfrac{8-(-4)}{8-(-4)}=1$
4	0		$\dfrac{56-(-8)}{8-0}=8$	
		$\dfrac{224-0}{8-4}=56$		
8	224			

Interpolating polynomial:

$\quad p(x) = -64 + 24(x+4) - 4(x+4)x + (x+4)x(x-4).$

(A) $f(2) \approx p(2) = -64 + 24(6) - 4(6)(2) + (6)(2)(-2) = 8$

(B) $f(6) \approx p(6) = -64 + 24(10) - 4(10)(6) + 10(6)(2) = 56$

15.

x	-1	0	1	4
$f(x)$	0	0	0	15

x_k	y_k	FIRST DIVIDED DIFFERENCE	SECOND DIVIDED DIFFERENCE	THIRD DIVIDED DIFFERENCE
-1	0	$\dfrac{0-0}{0-(-1)}=0$		
0	0		$\dfrac{0-0}{1-(-1)}=0$	
		$\dfrac{0-0}{1-0}=0$		$\dfrac{5/4-0}{4-(-1)}=\dfrac{1}{4}$
1	0		$\dfrac{5-0}{4-0}=\dfrac{5}{4}$	
		$\dfrac{15-0}{4-1}=5$		
4	15			

Interpolating polynomial: $\dfrac{1}{4}(x+1)x(x-1).$

(A) $f(2) \approx p(2) = \dfrac{1}{4}(3)(2)(1) = \dfrac{3}{2}$

(B) $f(3) \approx p(3) = \dfrac{1}{4}(4)(3)(2) = 6$

17.

x	-4	-2	0	2	4
$f(x)$	24	2	0	-6	8

x_k	y_k	FIRST DIVIDED DIFFERENCE	SECOND DIVIDED DIFFERENCE	THIRD DIVIDED DIFFERENCE	FOURTH DIVIDED DIFFERENCE
-4	24	$\dfrac{2-24}{-2-(-4)}=-11$			
-2	2		$\dfrac{-1-(-11)}{0-(-4)}=\dfrac{5}{2}$		
		$\dfrac{0-2}{0-(-2)}=-1$		$\dfrac{-1/2-5/2}{2-(-4)}=-\dfrac{1}{2}$	
0	0		$\dfrac{-3-(-1)}{2-(-2)}=-\dfrac{1}{2}$		$\dfrac{1/2-(-1/2)}{4-(-4)}=\dfrac{1}{8}$
		$\dfrac{-6-0}{2-0}=-3$		$\dfrac{5/2-(-1/2)}{4-(-2)}=\dfrac{1}{2}$	
2	-6		$\dfrac{7-(-3)}{4-0}=\dfrac{5}{2}$		
		$\dfrac{8-(-6)}{4-2}=7$			
4	8				

Interpolating polynomial:

$$p(x) = 24 - 11(x + 4) + \frac{5}{2}(x + 4)(x + 2) - \frac{1}{2}(x + 4)(x + 2)x$$
$$+ \frac{1}{8}(x + 4)(x + 2)x(x - 2)$$

(A) $f(-3) \approx p(-3) = 24 - 11(1) + \frac{5}{2}(1)(-1) - \frac{1}{2}(1)(-1)(-3)$

$$+ \frac{1}{8}(1)(-1)(-3)(-5) = \frac{57}{8} = 7.125$$

(B) $f(1) \approx p(1) = 24 - 11(5) + \frac{5}{2}(5)(3) - \frac{1}{2}(5)(3)(1) + \frac{1}{8}(5)(3)(1)(-1)$

$$= -\frac{23}{8} = -2.875$$

19.

x	-3	-2	-1	1	2	3
$f(x)$	-24	-6	0	0	6	24

x_k	y_k	FIRST DIVIDED DIFFERENCE	SECOND DIVIDED DIFFERENCE	THIRD DIVIDED DIFFERENCE	FOURTH DIVIDED DIFFERENCE	FIFTH DIVIDED DIFFERENCE
-3	-					
		$\frac{-6 - (-24)}{-2 - (-3)} = 18$				
-2	24		$\frac{6 - 18}{-1 - (-3)} = -6$			
		$\frac{0 - (-6)}{-1 - (-2)} = 6$		$\frac{-2 - (-6)}{1 - (-3)} = 1$		
-1	-6		$\frac{0 - 6}{1 - (-2)} = -2$			
		$\frac{0 - 0}{1 - (-1)} = 0$		$\frac{2 - (-2)}{2 - (-2)} = 1$	$\frac{1 - 1}{2 - (-3)} = 0$	
1	0		$\frac{6 - 0}{2 - (-1)} = 2$			0
		$\frac{6 - 0}{2 - 1} = 6$		$\frac{6 - 2}{3 - (-1)} = 1$	$\frac{1 - 1}{3 - (-2)} = 0$	
2	0		$\frac{18 - 6}{3 - 1} = 6$			
		$\frac{24 - 6}{3 - 2} = 18$				
3	6					
	24					

Interpolating polynomial:

$$p(x) = -24 + 18(x + 3) - 6(x + 3)(x + 2) + (x + 3)(x + 2)(x + 1).$$

(A) $f(-0.5) \approx p\left(-\frac{1}{2}\right) = -24 + 18\left(\frac{5}{2}\right) - 6\left(\frac{5}{2}\right)\left(\frac{3}{2}\right) + \left(\frac{5}{2}\right)\left(\frac{3}{2}\right)\left(\frac{1}{2}\right) = \frac{3}{8} = 0.375$

(B) $f(2.5) \approx p\left(\frac{5}{2}\right) = -24 + 18\left(\frac{11}{2}\right) - 6\left(\frac{11}{2}\right)\left(\frac{9}{2}\right) + \left(\frac{11}{2}\right)\left(\frac{9}{2}\right)\left(\frac{7}{2}\right) = \frac{105}{8} = 13.125$

21.

x	-2	0	2
$f(x)$	2	0	2

x_k	y_k	FIRST DIVIDED DIFFERENCE	SECOND DIVIDED DIFFERENCE
-2	2		
		$\frac{0 - 2}{0 - (-2)} = -1$	
0	0		$\frac{1 - (-1)}{2 - (-2)} = \frac{1}{2}$
		$\frac{2 - 0}{2 - 0} = 1$	
2	2		

Interpolating polynomial:

$$p(x) = 2 - (x + 2) + \frac{1}{2}(x + 2)x = \frac{1}{2}x^2$$

23.

x	0	1	2
$f(x)$	-4	-2	0

x_k	y_k	FIRST DIVIDED DIFFERENCE	SECOND DIVIDED DIFFERENCE
0	-4		
		$\dfrac{-2-(-4)}{1-0}=2$	
1	-2		0
		$\dfrac{0-(-2)}{2-1}=2$	
2	0		

Interpolating polynomial:
$$p(x) = -4 + 2x$$

25.

x	-1	0	2	3
$f(x)$	0	2	0	-4

x_k	y_k	FIRST DIVIDED DIFFERENCE	SECOND DIVIDED DIFFERENCE	THIRD DIVIDED DIFFERENCE
-1	0			
		$\dfrac{2-0}{0-(-1)}=2$		
0	2		$\dfrac{-1-2}{2-(-1)}=-1$	
		$\dfrac{0-2}{2-0}=-1$		0
2	0		$\dfrac{-4-(-1)}{3-0}=-1$	
		$\dfrac{-4-0}{3-2}=-4$		
3	-4			

Interpolating polynomial:
$$p(x) = 2(x+1) - 1(x+1)x = 2 + x - x^2$$

27.

x	-2	-1	0	1	2
$f(x)$	1	5	3	1	5

x_k	y_k	FIRST DIVIDED DIFFERENCE	SECOND DIVIDED DIFFERENCE	THIRD DIVIDED DIFFERENCE	FOURTH DIVIDED DIFFERENCE
-2	1				
		$\dfrac{5-1}{-1-(-2)}=4$			
-1	5		$\dfrac{-2-4}{0-(-2)}=-3$		
		$\dfrac{3-5}{0-(-1)}=-2$		$\dfrac{0-(-3)}{1-(-2)}=1$	
0	3		$\dfrac{-2-(-2)}{1-(-1)}=0$		0
		$\dfrac{1-3}{1-0}=-2$		$\dfrac{3-0}{2-(-1)}=1$	
1	1		$\dfrac{4-(-2)}{2-0}=3$		
		$\dfrac{5-1}{2-1}=4$			
2	5				

Interpolating polynomial:
$$p(x) = 1 + 4(x+2) - 3(x+2)(x+1) + (x+2)(x+1)x$$
$$= x^3 - 3x + 3$$

29.

x	-2	-1	0	1	2
$f(x)$	-3	0	5	0	-3

x_k	y_k	FIRST D.D.	SECOND D.D.	THIRD D.D.	FOURTH D.D.
-2	-3	$\frac{0-(-3)}{-1-(-2)}=3$			
-1	0	$\frac{5-0}{0-(-1)}=5$	$\frac{5-3}{0-(-2)}=1$	$\frac{-5-1}{1-(-2)}=-2$	
0	5	$\frac{0-5}{1-0}=-5$	$\frac{-5-5}{1-(-1)}=-5$	$\frac{1-(-5)}{2-(-1)}=2$	$\frac{2-(-2)}{2-(-2)}=1$
1	0	$\frac{-3-0}{2-1}=-3$	$\frac{-3-(-5)}{2-0}=1$		
2	-3				

Interpolating polynomial:
$$p(x) = -3 + 3(x+2) + (x+2)(x+1) \quad -2(x+2)(x+1)x$$
$$+ (x+2)(x+1)x(x-1)$$
$$= 5 - 6x^2 + x^4$$

31. $p(x) = x^3 - 3x + 3$; the two polynomials are identical.

33. $p(x) = x^4 - 6x^2 + 5$; the two polynomials are identical.

35.

x	1	4	9
$f(x)$	1	2	3

x_k	y_k	FIRST DIVIDED DIFFERENCE	SECOND DIVIDED DIFFERENCE
1	1	$\frac{2-1}{4-1}=\frac{1}{3}$	
4	2	$\frac{3-2}{9-4}=\frac{1}{5}$	$\frac{\frac{1}{5}-\frac{1}{3}}{9-1}=-\frac{1}{60}$
9	3		

Interpolating polynomial:
$$p(x) = 1 + \frac{1}{3}(x-1) - \frac{1}{60}(x-1)(x-4)$$

x	1	2	3	4	5	6	7	8	9
$p(x)$	1	1.4	1.7	2	2.2	2.5	2.7	2.9	3
$\sqrt{x}$	1	1.4	1.7	2	2.2	2.4	2.6	2.8	3

37.

x	-2	-1	0	1	2
$f(x)$	-4	-5	0	5	4

x_k	y_k	FIRST DIVIDED DIFFERENCE	SECOND DIVIDED DIFFERENCE	THIRD DIVIDED DIFFERENCE	FOURTH DIVIDED DIFFERENCE
-2	-4	$\dfrac{-5-(-4)}{-1-(-2)} = -1$			
-1	-5	$\dfrac{0-(-5)}{0-(-1)} = 5$	$\dfrac{5-(-1)}{0-(-2)} = 3$	$\dfrac{0-3}{1-(-2)} = -1$	
0	0	$\dfrac{5-0}{1-0} = 5$	0	$\dfrac{-3-0}{2-(-1)} = -1$	0
1	5	$\dfrac{4-5}{2-1} = -1$	$\dfrac{-1-5}{2-0} = -3$		
2	4				

Interpolating polynomial:
$$p(x) = -4 - (x+2) + 3(x+2)(x+1) - (x+2)(x+1)x$$
$$= 6x - x^3$$

39.

x	$-x_1$	0	x_1
$f(x)$	y_1	y_2	y_1

x_k	y_k	FIRST DIVIDED DIFFERENCE	SECOND DIVIDED DIFFERENCE
$-x_1$	y_1	$\dfrac{y_2-y_1}{0-(-x_1)} = \dfrac{y_2-y_1}{x_1}$	$\dfrac{\dfrac{y_1-y_2}{x_1} - \dfrac{y_2-y_1}{x_1}}{x_1-(-x_1)} = \dfrac{y_1-y_2}{x_1^2}$
0	y_2	$\dfrac{y_1-y_2}{x_1-0} = \dfrac{y_1-y_2}{x_1}$	
x_1	y_1		

Interpolating polynomial:
$$p(x) = y_1 + \frac{y_2-y_1}{x_1}(x+x_1) + \frac{y_1-y_2}{x_1^2}(x+x_1)x$$
$$= y_1 + \frac{(y_2-y_1)}{x_1}x + y_2 - y_1 + \frac{y_1-y_2}{x_1^2}x^2 + \frac{(y_1-y_2)x}{x_1}$$
$$= y_2 + \frac{y_1-y_2}{x_1^2}x^2$$

41.

t	0	4	8	12
$C(t)$	2	32	38	20

(A)

t_k	y_k	FIRST DIVIDED DIFFERENCE	SECOND DIVIDED DIFFERENCE	THIRD DIVIDED DIFFERENCE
0	2	$\dfrac{32-2}{4-0} = 7.5$		
4	32	$\dfrac{38-32}{8-4} = 1.5$	$\dfrac{1.5-7.5}{8-0} = -0.75$	
8	38	$\dfrac{20-38}{12-8} = -4.5$	$\dfrac{-4.5-1.5}{12-4} = -0.75$	0
12	20			

Interpolating polynomial:

$$p(t) = 2 + 7.5t - 0.75t(t-4)$$
$$= 2 + 10.5t - 0.75t^2$$

(B) $C(6) \approx p(6) = 2 + 10.5(6) - 0.75(6^2) = 38$ or \$38,000

(C) Average cash reserves for the first quarter:

$$\frac{1}{3}\int_0^3 p(t)\,dt = \frac{1}{3}\int_0^3 (2 + 10.5t - 0.75t^2)\,dt$$

$$= \frac{1}{3}\left[2t + 5.25t^2 - 0.25t^3\right]_0^3 = 15.5$$

The average cash reserves are approximately \$15,500.

43.

x	0	0.2	0.8	1
$f(x)$	0	0.04	0.52	1

x_k	y_k	FIRST DIVIDED DIFFERENCE	SECOND DIVIDED DIFFERENCE	THIRD DIVIDED DIFFERENCE
0	0	$\dfrac{0.04-0}{0.2-0} = 0.2$		
0.2	0.04	$\dfrac{0.52-0.04}{0.8-0.2} = 0.8$	$\dfrac{0.8-0.2}{0.8-0} = 0.75$	
0.8	0.52	$\dfrac{1-0.52}{1-0.8} = 2.4$	$\dfrac{2.4-0.8}{1-0.2} = 2$	$\dfrac{2-0.75}{1} = 1.25$
1	1			

(A) Interpolating polynomial:

$$p(t) = 0.2x + 0.75x(x-0.2) + 1.25x(x-0.2)(x-0.8)$$
$$= 0.25x - 0.5x^2 + 1.25x^3$$

(B) Index of income concentration:

$$C \approx 2\int_0^1 [x - p(x)]\,dx$$

$$= 2\int_0^1 [x - (0.25x - 0.5x^2 + 1.25x^3)]\,dx$$

$$= 2\int_0^1 (0.75x + 0.5x^2 - 1.25x^3)\,dx$$

$$= 2\left[0.375x^2 + 0.1667x^3 - 0.3125x^4\right]_0^1$$

$$= 2(0.2292) = 0.4584$$

45.

x	2	4	6
$R(x)$	24.4	36	34.8

x_k	y_k	FIRST DIVIDED DIFFERENCE	SECOND DIVIDED DIFFERENCE
2	24.4	$\dfrac{36 - 24.4}{4 - 2} = 5.8$	
4	36	$\dfrac{34.8 - 36}{6 - 4} = -0.6$	$\dfrac{-0.6 - 5.8}{6 - 2} = -1.6$
6	34.8		

(A) Interpolating polynomial:

$$p(x) = 24.4 + 5.8(x - 2) - 1.6(x - 2)(x - 4)$$
$$= 15.4x - 1.6x^2$$

(B) $R(5) \approx p(5) = 15.4(5) - 1.6(5^2) = 37$ or \$37,000

(C) Production level to maximize revenue:

$$P'(x) = 15.4 - 3.2x$$
$$p'(x) = 0: \quad 15.4 - 3.2x = 0$$
$$x = 4.8125 \quad \text{(thousand lamps)}$$

To the nearest integer, the production level that will maximize the revenue is 4,813 lamps.

47.

t	0	1	2	3	4
$C(t)$	14	13	16	17	10

t_k	y_k	FIRST DIVIDED DIFFERENCE	SECOND DIVIDED DIFFERENCE	THIRD DIVIDED DIFFERENCE	FOURTH DIVIDED DIFFERENCE
0	14	$\dfrac{13 - 14}{1 - 0} = -1$			
1	13	$\dfrac{16 - 13}{2 - 1} = 3$	$\dfrac{3 - (-1)}{2 - 0} = 2$		
2	16	$\dfrac{17 - 16}{3 - 2} = 1$	$\dfrac{1 - 3}{3 - 1} = -1$	$\dfrac{-1 - 2}{3} = -1$	
3	17	$\dfrac{10 - 17}{4 - 3} = -7$	$\dfrac{-7 - 1}{4 - 2} = -4$	$\dfrac{-4 - (-1)}{4 - 1} = -1$	0
4	10				

(A) Interpolating polynomial:

$$p(t) = 14 - t + 2t(t - 1) - t(t - 1)(t - 2)$$
$$= 14 - 5t + 5t^2 - t^3$$

(B) Average temperature:

$$\frac{1}{4}\int_0^4 p(t)\,dt = \frac{1}{4}\int_0^4 (14 - 5t + 5t^2 - t^3)\,dt$$

$$= \frac{1}{4}\left[14t - \frac{5}{2}t^2 + \frac{5}{3}t^3 - \frac{1}{4}t^4\right]_0^4$$

$$= \frac{1}{4}\left(\frac{176}{3}\right) \approx 14.7°C$$

49.

t	0	2	4	6
$C(t)$	450	190	90	150

t_k	Y_k	FIRST DIVIDED DIFFERENCE	SECOND DIVIDED DIFFERENCE	THIRD DIVIDED DIFFERENCE
0	450	$\dfrac{190 - 450}{2 - 0} = -130$		
2	190	$\dfrac{90 - 190}{4 - 2} = -50$	$\dfrac{-50 - (-130)}{4 - 0} = 20$	0
4	90	$\dfrac{150 - 90}{6 - 4} = 30$	$\dfrac{30 - (-50)}{4} = 20$	
6	150			

(A) Interpolating polynomial:
$$p(t) = 450 - 130t + 20t(t - 2) = 450 - 170t + 20t^2$$

(B) Minimum concentration level:
$$p'(t) = -170 + 40t$$
$$p'(t) = 0: \quad -170 + 40t = 0$$
$$t = \frac{170}{40} = 4.25$$

The minimum concentration level will be reached in 4.25 days (approximately).

51.

t	0	10	20	30
$N(t)$	10,000	13,500	20,000	23,500

t_k	Y_k	FIRST DIVIDED DIFFERENCE	SECOND DIVIDED DIFFERENCE	THIRD DIVIDED DIFFERENCE
0	10,000	$\dfrac{13,500 - 10,000}{10 - 0} = 350$		
10	13,500	$\dfrac{20,000 - 13,500}{20 - 10} = 650$	$\dfrac{650 - 350}{20 - 0} = 15$	$\dfrac{-15 - 15}{30 - 0} = -1$
20	20,000	$\dfrac{23,500 - 20,000}{30 - 20} = 350$	$\dfrac{350 - 650}{30 - 10} = -15$	
30	23,500			

(A) Interpolating polynomial:
$$p(t) = 10,000 + 350t + 15t(t - 10) - t(t - 10)(t - 20)$$
$$= 10,000 + 45t^2 - t^3$$

(B) Average number of registered voters
$$\frac{1}{20}\int_0^{20} p(t)\,dt = \frac{1}{20}\int_0^{20} (10,000 + 45t^2 - t^3)\,dt$$
$$= \frac{1}{20}\left[10,000t + 15t^3 - \frac{1}{4}t^4\right]_0^{20}$$
$$= \frac{1}{20}(280,000) = 14,000$$

The average number of registered voters over the first 20 years is approximately 14,000.

The following text is taken from Chapter 10 of *Calculus for the Life Sciences*, Second Edition by Greenwell, Ritchey and Lial

Matrices

When stocking a lake with various species of fish, wildlife biologists need to take into account the nutrient requirements of each fish, as well as the amounts of the various nutrients available in the lake. An exercise in the first section of this chapter solves such a problem using systems of linear equations and matrices.

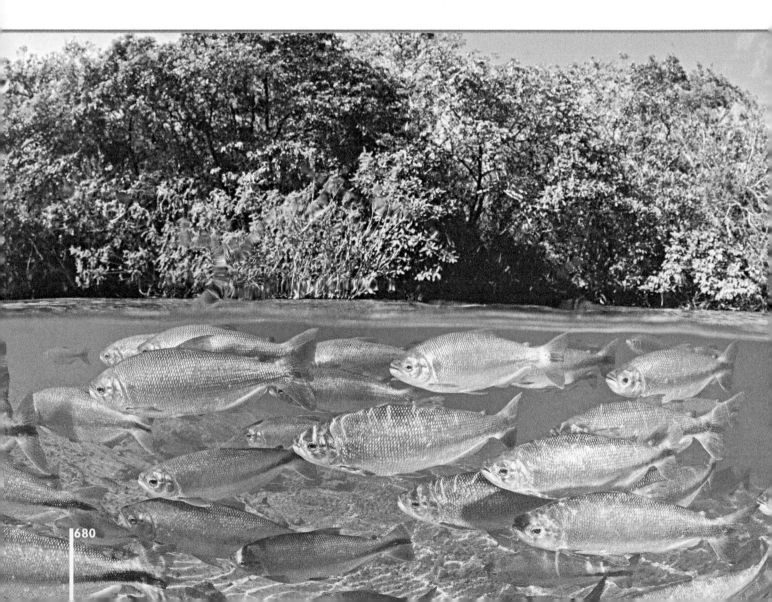

Many mathematical models require finding the solutions of two or more equations. The solutions must satisfy *all* of the equations in the model. A set of equations related in this way is called a **system of equations**. In this chapter we will discuss systems of equations, introduce the idea of a *matrix*, and then show how matrices are used to solve systems of linear equations. We will also see how matrices provide answers to important questions about population growth.

10.1 Solution of Linear Systems

APPLY IT   How much of each ingredient should be used in an animal feed to meet dietary requirements?

APPLY IT   Suppose that an animal feed is made from three ingredients: corn, soybeans, and cottonseed. One gram of each ingredient provides the number of grams of protein, fat, and fiber shown in the table. For example, the entries in the first column, 0.25, 0.4, and 0.3, indicate that one gram of corn provides twenty-five hundredths (one-fourth) of a gram of protein, four-tenths of a gram of fat, and three-tenths of a gram of fiber.

Nutritional Content of Ingredients			
	Corn	**Soybeans**	**Cottonseed**
Protein	0.25	0.4	0.2
Fat	0.4	0.2	0.3
Fiber	0.3	0.2	0.1

Now suppose we need to know the number of grams of each ingredient that should be used to make a feed that contains 22 grams of protein, 28 grams of fat, and 18 grams of fiber. To determine this, we let x represent the required number of grams of corn, y the number of grams of soybeans, and z the number of grams of cottonseed. Since each gram of corn provides 0.25 gram of protein, the amount of protein provided by x grams of corn is $0.25x$. Similarly, the amount of protein provided by y grams of soybeans is $0.4y$ and the amount of protein provided by z grams of cottonseed is $0.2z$. Since the total amount of protein is to be 22 grams,

$$0.25x + 0.4y + 0.2z = 22.$$

The feed must supply 28 grams of fat, so

$$0.4x + 0.2y + 0.3z = 28,$$

and 18 grams of fiber, so

$$0.3x + 0.2y + 0.1z = 18.$$

To solve this problem, we must find values of x, y, and z that satisfy this system of equations. Verify that $x = 40$ grams, $y = 15$ grams, and $z = 30$ grams is a solution of the system by substituting these numbers into all three equations. In fact, this is the only solution of this system, as we will see in Exercise 45 of this section. Many practical problems lead to such systems of *first-degree equations*, also known as **linear systems**.

A **first-degree equation in n unknowns** is any equation of the form

$$a_1 x_1 + a_2 x_2 + \cdots + a_n x_n = k,$$

where $a_1, a_2, \ldots, a_n$ and k are all real numbers and $x_1, x_2, \ldots, x_n$ represent variables.* Each of the three equations from the animal feed problem is a first-degree equation. For example, the first equation

$$0.25x + 0.4y + 0.2z = 22$$

is a first-degree equation with $n = 3$ where

$$a_1 = 0.25, \quad a_2 = 0.4, \quad a_3 = 0.2, \quad k = 22,$$

and the variables are $x, y,$ and z. We use $x_1, x_2,$ etc., rather than $x, y,$ etc., in the general case because we might have any number of variables. When n is no more than 4, we usually use $x, y, z,$ and w to represent $x_1, x_2, x_3,$ and x_4.

A *solution* of the first-degree equation

$$a_1 x_1 + a_2 x_2 + \cdots + a_n x_n = k$$

is a sequence of numbers $s_1, s_2, \ldots, s_n$ such that

$$a_1 s_2 + a_2 s_2 + \cdots + a_n s_n = k.$$

A solution of an equation is usually written in parentheses as $(s_1, s_2, \ldots, s_n)$. For example, $(1, 6, 2)$ is a solution of the equation $3x_1 + 2x_2 - 4x_3 = 7$, since $3(1) + 2(6) - 4(2) = 7$. This is an extension of the idea of an ordered pair. A solution of a first-degree equation in two unknowns is an ordered pair, and the graph of the equation is a straight line. For this reason, all first-degree equations are also called linear equations.

Because the graph of a linear equation in two unknowns is a straight line, there are three possibilities for the solutions of a system of two linear equations in two unknowns.

Types of Solutions for Two Equations in Two Unknowns

1. The two graphs are lines intersecting at a single point. The system has a **unique solution**, and it is given by the coordinates of this point. See Figure 1(a).

2. The graphs are distinct parallel lines. When this is the case, the system is **inconsistent**; there is no solution common to both equations. See Figure 1(b).

3. The graphs are the same line. In this case, the equations are said to be **dependent**, since any solution of one equation is also a solution of the other. There are infinitely many solutions. See Figure 1(c).

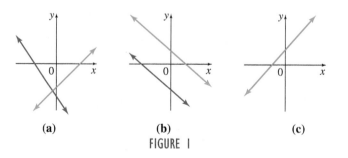

(a)   (b)   (c)

FIGURE 1

---

*a_1 is read "a-sub-one." The notation $a_1, a_2, \ldots a_n$ represents n real-number coefficients (some of which may be equal), and the notation $x_1, x_2, \ldots x_n$ represents n different variables, or unknowns.

In larger systems, with more variables or more equations (or both, as is usually the case), there also may be exactly one solution, no solution, or infinitely many solutions. With more than two variables. the geometrical interpretation becomes. more complicated, so we will consider only the geometry of two variables in two unknowns.

In this section we develop a method for solving a system of linear equations. Although the discussion will be confined to equations with only a few variables, the method of solution can be extended to systems with many variables.

When we solve a system, since the variables are in the same order in each equation, we really need to keep track of just the coefficients and the constants. For example, consider the following system of three equations in three unknowns.

$$2x + y - z = 2$$
$$x + 3y + 2z = 1$$
$$x + y + z = 2$$

This system can be written in an abbreviated form as

$$\text{Rows} \longrightarrow \begin{bmatrix} 2 & 1 & -1 & 2 \\ 1 & 3 & 2 & 1 \\ 1 & 1 & 1 & 2 \end{bmatrix}.$$

Columns

Such a rectangular array of numbers enclosed by brackets is called a **matrix** (plural: **matrices**).* Each number in the array is an **element** or **entry**. To separate the constants in the last column of the matrix from the coefficients of the variables, we use a vertical line, producing the following **augmented matrix**.

$$\begin{bmatrix} 2 & 1 & -1 & | & 2 \\ 1 & 3 & 2 & | & 1 \\ 1 & 1 & 1 & | & 2 \end{bmatrix}$$

Any algebraic operation done to the equations of a linear system is equivalent to performing the same operation on the rows of the augmented matrix, since the matrix is just a shorter way of writing the system. The following **row operations** on the augmented matrix transform the system of equations into an **equivalent system**, that is, one that has the same solutions as the original system.

Row Operations

For any augmented matrix of a system of equations, the following operations produce the augmented matrix of an equivalent system:

1. interchanging any two rows;
2. multiplying the elements of a row by any nonzero real number;
3. adding a nonzero multiple of the elements of one row to the corresponding elements of a nonzero multiple of some other row.

In steps 2 and 3, we are replacing a row with a new, modified row, which the old row helped to form. This is equivalent to replacing an equation with a new, modified equation.

---

*The word *matrix*, Latin for "womb," was coined by James Joseph Sylvester (1814–1897) and made popular by his friend Arthur Cayley (1821–1895). Both mathematicians were English, although Sylvester spent much of his life in the United States.

Row operations, like the transformations of systems of equations, are reversible. If they are used to change matrix A to matrix B, then it is possible to use row operations to transform B back into A.

By the first row operation, we can interchange rows 1 and 2, for example, which we will indicate by the notation $R_2 \to R_1$ and $R_1 \to R_2$. (R stands for row.) Row 3 is left unchanged. Thus

$$\begin{bmatrix} 0 & 1 & 2 & | & 3 \\ -2 & -6 & -10 & | & -12 \\ 2 & 1 & -2 & | & -5 \end{bmatrix} \quad \text{becomes} \quad \begin{bmatrix} -2 & -6 & -10 & | & -12 \\ 0 & 1 & 2 & | & 3 \\ 2 & 1 & -2 & | & -5 \end{bmatrix} \begin{array}{l} R_2 \to R_1 \\ R_1 \to R_2 \end{array}$$

by interchanging the first two rows. Row 3 is left unchanged.

The second row operation, multiplying a row by a number, allows us to change

$$\begin{bmatrix} -2 & -6 & -10 & | & -12 \\ 0 & 1 & 2 & | & 3 \\ 2 & 1 & -2 & | & -5 \end{bmatrix} \quad \text{to} \quad \begin{bmatrix} 1 & 3 & 5 & | & 6 \\ 0 & 1 & 2 & | & 3 \\ 2 & 1 & -2 & | & -5 \end{bmatrix} \quad (-1/2)R_1 \to R_1$$

by multiplying the elements of row 1 of the original matrix by $-1/2$. Note that rows 2 and 3 are left unchanged. This operation is helpful in converting all entries in a matrix to integers, which can simplify the calculations. It is also useful for dividing a common factor out of a row, which makes the numbers smaller and hence easier to work with.

Using the third row operation, adding a multiple of one row to another, we change

$$\begin{bmatrix} 1 & 3 & 5 & | & 6 \\ 0 & 1 & 2 & | & 3 \\ 2 & 1 & -2 & | & -5 \end{bmatrix} \quad \text{to} \quad \begin{bmatrix} 1 & 3 & 5 & | & 6 \\ 0 & 1 & 2 & | & 3 \\ 0 & -5 & -12 & | & -17 \end{bmatrix} \quad -2R_1 + R_3 \to R_3$$

by first multiplying each element in row 1 of the original matrix by -2 and then adding the results to the corresponding elements in the third row of that matrix. Work as follows.

$$\begin{bmatrix} 1 & 3 & 5 & | & 6 \\ 0 & 1 & 2 & | & 3 \\ (-2)1+2 & (-2)3+1 & (-2)5-2 & | & (-2)6-5 \end{bmatrix} = \begin{bmatrix} 1 & 3 & 5 & | & 6 \\ 0 & 1 & 2 & | & 3 \\ 0 & -5 & -12 & | & -17 \end{bmatrix}$$

Notice that rows 1 and 2 are left unchanged, *even though the elements of row 1 were used to transform row 3*. This operation is very useful for converting an element in a matrix to 0.

The Gauss-Jordan Method

The **Gauss-Jordan Method** uses the row operations just described to transform a system of equations into one from which the solution can be immediately read.* Before the Gauss-Jordan method can be used, the system must be in proper form: the terms with variables should be on the left and the constants on the right in each equation, with the variables in the same order in each equation.

The system is then written as an augmented matrix. Using row operations, the goal is to transform the matrix so that it has zeros above and below a diagonal of 1's on the left of the vertical bar. Once this is accomplished, the final solution can be read directly from the last matrix. The following example illustrates the use of the Gauss-Jordan method to solve a system of equations.

---

*The great German mathematician Carl Friedrich Gauss (1777–1855), sometimes referred to as the "Prince of Mathematicians," originally developed his elimination method for use in finding least squares coefficients. (See Section 1.2.) The German geodesist Wilhelm Jordan (1842–1899) improved his method and used it in surveying problems. Gauss's method had been known to the Chinese at least 1800 years earlier and was described in the *Jiuahang Suanshu (Nine Chapters on the Mathematical Art)*.

EXAMPLE 1 Gauss-Jordan Method

Solve the system

$$3x - 4y = 1 \tag{1}$$

$$5x + 2y = 19. \tag{2}$$

SOLUTION

Method 1
1's on Diagonal

The system is already in the proper form to use the Gauss-Jordan method. Our goal is to transform this matrix, if possible, into the form

$$\begin{bmatrix} 1 & 0 & m \\ 0 & 1 & n \end{bmatrix},$$

where m and n are real numbers. To begin, we change the 3 in the first row to 1 using the second row operation.

$$\begin{bmatrix} 3 & -4 & 1 \\ 5 & 2 & 19 \end{bmatrix} \quad \text{Augmented matrix}$$

$$\tfrac{1}{3}R_1 \to R_1 \quad \begin{bmatrix} 1 & -\tfrac{4}{3} & \tfrac{1}{3} \\ 5 & 2 & 19 \end{bmatrix}$$

Using the third row operation, we change the 5 in row 2 to 0.

$$-5R_1 + R_2 \to R_2 \quad \begin{bmatrix} 1 & -\tfrac{4}{3} & \tfrac{1}{3} \\ 0 & \tfrac{26}{3} & \tfrac{52}{3} \end{bmatrix}$$

We now change 26/3 in row 2 to 1 to complete the diagonal of 1's.

$$\tfrac{3}{26}R_2 \to R_2 \quad \begin{bmatrix} 1 & -\tfrac{4}{3} & \tfrac{1}{3} \\ 0 & 1 & 2 \end{bmatrix}$$

The final transformation is to change the $-4/3$ in row 1 to 0.

$$\tfrac{4}{3}R_2 + R_1 \to R_1 \quad \begin{bmatrix} 1 & 0 & 3 \\ 0 & 1 & 2 \end{bmatrix}$$

The last matrix corresponds to the system

$$x = 3$$
$$y = 2,$$

so we can read the solution directly from the last column of the final matrix. Check that $(3, 2)$ is the solution by substitution in the equations of the original system.

Method 2
Fraction-Free

An alternate form of Gauss-Jordan is to first transform the matrix so that it contains zeros above and below the main diagonal. Then, use the second transformation to get the required 1's. When doing calculations by hand, this second method simplifies the calculations by avoiding fractions and decimals. We will use this method when doing calculations by hand throughout the remainder of this chapter.

To begin, we change the 5 in row 2 to 0.

$$\begin{bmatrix} 3 & -4 & 1 \\ 5 & 2 & 19 \end{bmatrix} \quad \text{Augmented matrix}$$

$$5R_1 + (-3)R_2 \to R_2 \quad \begin{bmatrix} 3 & -4 & 1 \\ 0 & -26 & -52 \end{bmatrix}$$

We change the -4 in row 1 to 0.

$$-2R_2 + 13R_1 \to R_1 \quad \begin{bmatrix} 39 & 0 & 117 \\ 0 & -26 & -52 \end{bmatrix}$$

YOUR TURN 1 Use the Gauss-Jordan method to solve the system

$4x + 5y = 10$

$7x + 8y = 19.$

Then we change the first nonzero number in each row to 1.

$$\begin{matrix} \frac{1}{39}R_1 \rightarrow R_1 \\ -\frac{1}{26}R_2 \rightarrow R_2 \end{matrix} \quad \begin{bmatrix} 1 & 0 & | & 3 \\ 0 & 1 & | & 2 \end{bmatrix}$$

The solution is read directly from this last matrix: $x = 3$ and $y = 2$, or $(3, 2)$.

TRY YOUR TURN 1

NOTE If your solution does not check, the most efficient way to find the error is to substitute back through the equations that correspond to each matrix, starting with the last matrix. When you find a system that is not satisfied by your (incorrect) answers, you have probably reached the matrix just before the error occurred. Look for the error in the transformation to the next matrix. For example, if you erroneously wrote the 2 as -2 in the final matrix of the fraction-free method of Example 1, you would find that $(3, -2)$ was not a solution of the system represented by the previous matrix because $-26(-2) \neq -52$, telling you that your error occurred between this matrix and the final one.

When the Gauss-Jordan method is used to solve a system, the final matrix will always have zeros above and below the diagonal of 1's on the left of the vertical bar. To transform the matrix, it is best to work column by column from left to right. Such an orderly method avoids confusion and working in circles. For each column, first perform the steps that give the zeros. When all columns have zeros in place, multiply each row by the reciprocal of the coefficient of the remaining nonzero number in that row to get the required 1's. With dependent equations or inconsistent systems, it will not be possible to get the complete diagonal of 1's.

We will demonstrate the method in an example with three variables and three equations, after which we will summarize the steps.

EXAMPLE 2 Gauss-Jordan Method

Use the Gauss-Jordan method to solve the system

$$x + 5z = -6 + y$$
$$3x + 3y = 10 + z$$
$$x + 3y + 2z = 5.$$

Method 1
Calculating by Hand

SOLUTION

First, rewrite the system in proper form, as follows.

$$x - y + 5z = -6$$
$$3x + 3y - z = 10$$
$$x + 3y + 2z = 5$$

Begin to find the solution by writing the augmented matrix of the linear system.

$$\begin{bmatrix} 1 & -1 & 5 & | & -6 \\ 3 & 3 & -1 & | & 10 \\ 1 & 3 & 2 & | & 5 \end{bmatrix}$$

Row transformations will be used to rewrite this matrix in the form

$$\begin{bmatrix} 1 & 0 & 0 & | & m \\ 0 & 1 & 0 & | & n \\ 0 & 0 & 1 & | & p \end{bmatrix},$$

where m, n, and p are real numbers (if this form is possible). From this final form of the matrix, the solution can be read: $x = m$, $y = n$, $z = p$, or (m, n, p).

In the first column, we need zeros in the second and third rows. Multiply the first row by -3 and add to the second row to get a zero there. Then multiply the first row by -1 and add to the third row to get that zero.

$$\begin{array}{c} -3R_1 + R_2 \rightarrow R_2 \\ \\ -1R_1 + R_3 \rightarrow R_3 \end{array} \quad \begin{bmatrix} 1 & -1 & 5 & | & -6 \\ 0 & 6 & -16 & | & 28 \\ 0 & 4 & -3 & | & 11 \end{bmatrix}$$

Now get zeros in the second column in a similar way. We want zeros in the first and third rows. Row 2 will not change.

$$\begin{array}{c} R_2 + 6R_1 \rightarrow R_1 \\ \\ 2R_2 + (-3)R_3 \rightarrow R_3 \end{array} \quad \begin{bmatrix} 6 & 0 & 14 & | & -8 \\ 0 & 6 & -16 & | & 28 \\ 0 & 0 & -23 & | & 23 \end{bmatrix}$$

In transforming the third row, you may have used the operation $4R_2 + (-6)R_3 \rightarrow R_3$ instead of $2R_2 + (-3)R_3 \rightarrow R_3$. This is perfectly fine; the last row would then have -46 and 46 in place of -23 and 23. To avoid errors, it helps to keep the numbers as small as possible. We observe at this point that all of the numbers can be reduced in size by multiplying each row by an appropriate constant. This next step is not essential, but it simplifies the arithmetic.

$$\begin{array}{c} \frac{1}{2}R_1 \rightarrow R_1 \\ \frac{1}{2}R_2 \rightarrow R_2 \\ -\frac{1}{23}R_3 \rightarrow R_3 \end{array} \quad \begin{bmatrix} 3 & 0 & 7 & | & -4 \\ 0 & 3 & -8 & | & 14 \\ 0 & 0 & 1 & | & -1 \end{bmatrix}$$

Next, we want zeros in the first and second rows of the third column. Row 3 will not change.

$$\begin{array}{c} -7R_3 + R_1 \rightarrow R_1 \\ 8R_3 + R_2 \rightarrow R_2 \end{array} \quad \begin{bmatrix} 3 & 0 & 0 & | & 3 \\ 0 & 3 & 0 & | & 6 \\ 0 & 0 & 1 & | & -1 \end{bmatrix}$$

Finally, get 1's in each row by multiplying the row by the reciprocal of (or dividing the row by) the number in the diagonal position.

$$\begin{array}{c} \frac{1}{3}R_1 \rightarrow R_1 \\ \frac{1}{3}R_2 \rightarrow R_2 \end{array} \quad \begin{bmatrix} 1 & 0 & 0 & | & 1 \\ 0 & 1 & 0 & | & 2 \\ 0 & 0 & 1 & | & -1 \end{bmatrix}$$

The linear system associated with the final augmented matrix is

$$\begin{aligned} x &= 1 \\ y &= 2 \\ z &= -1, \end{aligned}$$

and the solution is $(1, 2, -1)$. Verify that this is the solution to the original system of equations.

CAUTION   Notice that we have performed two or three operations on the same matrix in one step. This is permissible as long as we do not use a row that we are changing as part of another row operation. For example, when we changed row 2 in the first step, we could not use row 2 to transform row 3 in the same step. To avoid difficulty, use *only* row 1 to get zeros in column 1, row 2 to get zeros in column 2, and so on.

Method 2
Graphing Calculator

The row operations of the Gauss-Jordan method can also be done on a graphing calculator. For example, Figure 2 on the next page shows the result when the augmented matrix is entered into a TI-84 Plus. Figures 3 and 4 show how row operations can be used to get zeros in rows 2 and 3 of the first column.

FIGURE 2　　　　　FIGURE 3　　　　　FIGURE 4

Calculators typically do not allow any multiple of a row to be added to any multiple of another row, such as in the operation $2R_2 + 6R_1 \rightarrow R_1$. They normally allow a multiple of a row to be added only to another unmodified row. To get around this restriction, we can convert the diagonal element to a 1 before changing the other elements in the column to 0, as we did in the first method of Example 1. In this example, we change the 6 in row 2, column 2, to a 1 by dividing by 6. The result is shown in Figure 5. (The right side of the matrix is not visible but can be seen by pressing the right arrow key.) Notice that this operation introduces decimals. Converting to fractions is preferable on calculators that have that option; 1/3 is certainly more concise than 0.3333333333. Figure 6 shows such a conversion on the TI-84 Plus.

When performing row operations without a graphing calculator, it is best to avoid fractions and decimals, because these make the operations more difficult and more prone to error. A calculator, on the other hand, encounters no such difficulties.

Continuing in the same manner, the solution $(1, 2, -1)$ is found as shown in Figure 7.

FIGURE 7

Some calculators can do the entire Gauss-Jordan process with a single command; on the TI-84 Plus, for example, this is done with the `rref` command. This is very useful in practice, although it does not show any of the intermediate steps. For more details, see the *Graphing Calculator and Excel Spreadsheet Manual* available with this book.

FIGURE 5

FIGURE 6

Method 3　Spreadsheet

The Gauss-Jordan method can be done using a spreadsheet either by using a macro or by performing row operations using formulas with the copy and paste commands. However, spreadsheets also have built-in methods to solve systems of equations. Although these solvers do not usually employ the Gauss-Jordan method for solving systems of equations, they are, nonetheless, efficient and practical to use.

The Solver included with Excel can solve systems of equations that are both linear and nonlinear. The Solver is located in the Tools menu and requires that cells be identified ahead of time for each variable in the problem. It also requires that the left-hand side of each equation be placed in the spreadsheet as a formula. For example, to solve the above problem, we could identify cells A1, B1, and C1 for the variables x, y, and z, respectively. The Solver requires that we place a guess for the answer in these cells. It is convenient to place a zero in each of these cells. The left-hand side of each equation must be placed in a cell. We could choose A3, A4, and A5 to hold each of these formulas. Thus, in cell A3, we would type "=A1 − B1 + 5*C1" and put the other two equations in cells A4 and A5.

We now click on the Tools menu and choose Solver. (In some versions, it may be necessary to install the Solver. For more details, see the *Graphing Calculator and Excel Spreadsheet Manual* available with this book.) Since this solver attempts to find a solution that is best in some way, we are required to identify a cell with a formula in it that we want to optimize. In this case, it is convenient to use the cell with the left-hand side of the first constraint in it, A3. Figure 8 illustrates the Solver box and the items placed in it.

FIGURE 8

YOUR TURN 2 Use the Gauss-Jordan method to solve the system

$$x + 2y + 3z = 2$$
$$2x + 2y - 3z = 27$$
$$3x + 2y + 5z = 10.$$

To obtain a solution, click on Solve. The approximate solution is located in cells A1, B1, and C1, and these correspond to x, y, and z, respectively.

TRY YOUR TURN 2

In summary, the Gauss-Jordan method of solving a linear system requires the following steps.

Gauss-Jordan Method of Solving a Linear System

1. Write each equation so that variable terms are in the same order on the left side of the equal sign and constants are on the right.

2. Write the augmented matrix that corresponds to the system.

3. Use row operations to transform the first column so that all elements except the element in the first row are zero.

4. Use row operations to transform the second column so that all elements except the element in the second row are zero.

5. Use row operations to transform the third column so that all elements except the element in the third row are zero.

6. Continue in this way, when possible, until the last row is written in the form

$$[0 \quad 0 \quad 0 \quad \cdots \quad 0 \quad j \mid k],$$

where j and k are constants with $j \neq 0$. When this is not possible, continue until every row has more zeros on the left than the previous row (except possibly for any rows of all zeros at the bottom of the matrix), and the first nonzero entry in each row is the only nonzero entry in its column.

7. Multiply each row by the reciprocal of the nonzero element in that row.

Systems without a Unique Solution

In the previous examples, we were able to get the last row in the form $[0 \quad 0 \quad 0 \quad \cdots \quad 0 \quad j \mid k]$, where j and k are constants with $j \neq 0$. We will now look at examples where this is not the case.

EXAMPLE 3 Solving a System of Equations with No Solution

Use the Gauss-Jordan method to solve the system

$$x - 2y = 2$$
$$3x - 6y = 5.$$

SOLUTION Begin by writing the augmented matrix.

$$\begin{bmatrix} 1 & -2 & | & 2 \\ 3 & -6 & | & 5 \end{bmatrix}$$

To get a zero for the second element in column 1, multiply the numbers in row 1 by -3 and add the results to the corresponding elements in row 2.

$$-3R_1 + R_2 \rightarrow R_2 \quad \begin{bmatrix} 1 & -2 & | & 2 \\ 0 & 0 & | & -1 \end{bmatrix}$$

This matrix corresponds to the system

$$x - 2y = 2$$
$$0x + 0y = -1.$$

Since the second equation is $0 = -1$, the system is inconsistent and, therefore, has no solution. The row $[0 \quad 0 \mid k]$ for any nonzero k is a signal that the given system is inconsistent.

EXAMPLE 4 Solving a System of Equations with an Infinite Number of Solutions

Use the Gauss-Jordan method to solve the system

$$x + 2y - z = 0$$
$$3x - y + z = 6$$
$$-2x - 4y + 2z = 0.$$

SOLUTION The augmented matrix is

$$\begin{bmatrix} 1 & 2 & -1 & | & 0 \\ 3 & -1 & 1 & | & 6 \\ -2 & -4 & 2 & | & 0 \end{bmatrix}.$$

We first get zeros in the second and third rows of column 1.

$$\begin{matrix} -3R_1 + R_2 \rightarrow R_2 \\ 2R_1 + R_3 \rightarrow R_3 \end{matrix} \quad \begin{bmatrix} 1 & 2 & -1 & | & 0 \\ 0 & -7 & 4 & | & 6 \\ 0 & 0 & 0 & | & 0 \end{bmatrix}$$

To continue, we get a zero in the first row of column 2 using the second row, as usual.

$$2R_2 + 7R_1 \rightarrow R_1 \quad \begin{bmatrix} 7 & 0 & 1 & | & 12 \\ 0 & -7 & 4 & | & 6 \\ 0 & 0 & 0 & | & 0 \end{bmatrix}$$

We cannot get a zero for the first-row, third-column element without changing the form of the first two columns. We must multiply each of the first two rows by the reciprocal of the first nonzero number.

$$\begin{matrix} \frac{1}{7}R_1 \to R_1 \\ -\frac{1}{7}R_2 \to R_2 \\ \\ \end{matrix} \begin{bmatrix} 1 & 0 & \frac{1}{7} & \Big| & \frac{12}{7} \\ 0 & 1 & -\frac{4}{7} & \Big| & -\frac{6}{7} \\ 0 & 0 & 0 & \Big| & 0 \end{bmatrix}$$

To complete the solution, write the equations that correspond to the first two rows of the matrix.

$$x + \frac{1}{7}z = \frac{12}{7}$$
$$y - \frac{4}{7}z = -\frac{6}{7}$$

The third equation of this system, $0 = 0$, gives us no information. Usually the third equation gives us the value of z. In this case, z can be any real number. This system is dependent and has an infinite number of solutions, corresponding to the infinite number of values of z. The variable z in this case is called a **parameter**. Solve the first equation for x and the second for y to get

$$x = \frac{12 - z}{7} \quad \text{and} \quad y = \frac{4z - 6}{7}.$$

The general solution is written

$$\left(\frac{12 - z}{7}, \frac{4z - 6}{7}, z \right),$$

where z is any real number. For example, $z = 2$ and $z = 12$ lead to the solutions $(10/7, 2/7, 2)$ and $(0, 6, 12)$.

EXAMPLE 5 **Solving a System of Equations with an Infinite Number of Solutions**

Consider the following system of equations.

$$\begin{aligned} x + 2y + 3z - w &= 4 \\ 2x + 3y + w &= -3 \\ 3x + 5y + 3z &= 1 \end{aligned}$$

(a) Write this system as an augmented matrix, and verify that the result after the Gauss-Jordan method is

$$\begin{bmatrix} 1 & 0 & -9 & 5 & \Big| & -18 \\ 0 & 1 & 6 & -3 & \Big| & 11 \\ 0 & 0 & 0 & 0 & \Big| & 0 \end{bmatrix}.$$

(b) Find the solution to this system of equations.

SOLUTION To complete the solution, write the equations that correspond to the first two rows of the matrix.

$$\begin{aligned} x - 9z + 5w &= -18 \\ y + 6z - 3w &= 11 \end{aligned}$$

Because both equations involve both z and w, let z and w be parameters. There are an infinite number of solutions, corresponding to the infinite number of values of z and w. Solve the first equation for x and the second for y to get

$$x = -18 + 9z - 5w \quad \text{and} \quad y = 11 - 6z + 3w.$$

YOUR TURN 3 Use the Gauss-Jordan method to solve the system
$2x - 2y + 3z - 4w = 6$
$3x + 2y + 5z - 3w = 7$
$4x + y + 2z - 2w = 8$.

In an analogous manner to problems with a single parameter, the general solution is written

$$(-18 + 9z - 5w, 11 - 6z + 3w, z, w),$$

where z and w are any real numbers. For example, $z = 1$ and $w = -2$ leads to the solution $(1, -1, 1, -2)$.
TRY YOUR TURN 3

Although the examples have used only systems with two equations in two unknowns, three equations in three unknowns, or three equations in four unknowns, the Gauss-Jordan method can be used for any system with n equations and m unknowns. The method becomes tedious with more than three equations in three unknowns; on the other hand, it is very suitable for use with graphing calculators and computers, which can solve fairly large systems quickly. Sophisticated computer programs modify the method to reduce round-off error. Other methods used for special types of large matrices are studied in a course on numerical analysis.

EXAMPLE 6   Rats

A lab has a group of young rats, adult female rats, and adult male rats to be used for experiments. There are 23 rats in all. The rats consume 376 g of food and 56.9 mL of water each day.

(a) Suppose that a young rat consumes 12 g of food and 2 mL of water each day. The corresponding values for an adult female are 16 and 2.5, and for an adult male are 20 and 2.8. How many young rats, adult females, and adult males are there?

SOLUTION   We have organized the information in a table.

Lab Rats				
	Young	**Female**	**Male**	**Total**
Number	x	y	z	23
Food (g)	12	16	20	376
Water (mL)	2.0	2.5	2.8	56.9

The three rows of the table lead to three equations: one for the total number of rats, one for the food, and one for the water.

$$x + y + z = 23$$
$$12x + 16y + 20z = 376$$
$$2.0x + 2.5y + 2.8z = 56.9$$

Represent this system by an augmented matrix, and verify that the result after the Gauss-Jordan method is

$$\begin{bmatrix} 1 & 0 & 0 & | & 6 \\ 0 & 1 & 0 & | & 9 \\ 0 & 0 & 1 & | & 8 \end{bmatrix}.$$

There are 6 young rats, 9 adult females, and 8 adult males.

(b) Suppose the amounts of water that young rats, adult females, and adult males consume in a new experiment are 2 mL, 4 mL, and 6 mL, respectively, but all other information remains the same. How many young rats, adult females, and adult males are there?

SOLUTION Change the third equation to

$$2x + 4y + 6z = 56.9$$

and use the Gauss-Jordan method again. The result is

$$\begin{bmatrix} 1 & 0 & -1 & | & 2 \\ 0 & 1 & 2 & | & 25 \\ 0 & 0 & 0 & | & -37.1 \end{bmatrix}.$$

(If you do the row operations in a different order in this example, you will have different numbers in the last column.) The last row of this matrix says that $0 = -37.1$, so the system is inconsistent and has no solution. (In retrospect, this is clear, because each rat consumes a whole number of mL of water, and the total amount of water consumed is not a whole number. In general, however, it is not easy to tell whether a system of equations has a solution or not by just looking at it.)

(c) Suppose the amounts of water consumed by each rat are the same as in part (b), but the total amount of water consumed is 96 mL. Now how many young rats, adult females, and adult males are there?

SOLUTION The third equation becomes

$$2x + 4y + 6z = 96,$$

and the Gauss-Jordan method leads to

$$\begin{bmatrix} 1 & 0 & -1 & | & -2 \\ 0 & 1 & 2 & | & 25 \\ 0 & 0 & 0 & | & 0 \end{bmatrix}.$$

The system is dependent, similar to Example 4. Let z be the parameter, and solve the first two equations for x and y, yielding

$$x = z - 2 \quad \text{and} \quad y = 25 - 2z.$$

Since x, y, and z represent numbers of rats, they must be nonnegative integers. From the equation for x, we must have

$$z - 2 \geq 0, \quad \text{or} \quad z \geq 2,$$

and from the equation for y, we must have

$$25 - 2z \geq 0,$$

from which we find

$$z \leq 12.5.$$

We therefore have 11 solutions, corresponding to $z = 2, 3, \ldots, 12$.

(d) Give the solutions from part (c) that have the smallest and the largest number of adult males.

SOLUTION For the smallest number of adult males, let $z = 2$, giving $x = 2 - 2 = 0$ and $y = 25 - 2(2) = 21$. There are 0 young rats, 21 adult females, and 2 adult males.

For the largest number of adult males, let $z = 12$, giving $x = 12 - 2 = 10$ and $y = 25 - 2(12) = 1$. There are 10 young rats, 1 adult female, and 12 adult males.

10.1 EXERCISES

Write the augmented matrix for each system. Do not solve.

1. $3x + y = 6$
$2x + 5y = 15$

2. $4x - 2y = 8$
$-7y = -12$

3. $2x + y + z = 3$
$3x - 4y + 2z = -7$
$x + y + z = 2$

4. $2x - 5y + 3z = 4$
$-4x + 2y - 7z = -5$
$3x - y = 8$

Write the system of equations associated with each augmented matrix.

5. $\begin{bmatrix} 1 & 0 & | & 2 \\ 0 & 1 & | & 3 \end{bmatrix}$

6. $\begin{bmatrix} 1 & 0 & | & 5 \\ 0 & 1 & | & -3 \end{bmatrix}$

7. $\begin{bmatrix} 1 & 0 & 0 & | & 4 \\ 0 & 1 & 0 & | & -5 \\ 0 & 0 & 1 & | & 1 \end{bmatrix}$

8. $\begin{bmatrix} 1 & 0 & 0 & | & 4 \\ 0 & 1 & 0 & | & 2 \\ 0 & 0 & 1 & | & 3 \end{bmatrix}$

9. _____ on a matrix correspond to transformations of a system of equations.

10. Describe in your own words what $2R_1 + R_3 \rightarrow R_3$ means.

Use the indicated row operations to change each matrix.

11. Replace R_2 by $R_1 + (-3)R_2$.

$\begin{bmatrix} 3 & 7 & 4 & | & 10 \\ 1 & 2 & 3 & | & 6 \\ 0 & 4 & 5 & | & 11 \end{bmatrix}$

12. Replace R_3 by $(-1)R_1 + 3R_3$.

$\begin{bmatrix} 3 & 2 & 6 & | & 18 \\ 2 & -2 & 5 & | & 7 \\ 1 & 0 & 5 & | & 20 \end{bmatrix}$

13. Replace R_1 by $(-2)R_2 + R_1$.

$\begin{bmatrix} 1 & 6 & 4 & | & 7 \\ 0 & 3 & 2 & | & 5 \\ 0 & 5 & 3 & | & 7 \end{bmatrix}$

14. Replace R_1 by $R_3 + (-3)R_1$.

$\begin{bmatrix} 1 & 0 & 4 & | & 21 \\ 0 & 6 & 5 & | & 30 \\ 0 & 0 & 12 & | & 15 \end{bmatrix}$

15. Replace R_1 by $\frac{1}{3}R_1$.

$\begin{bmatrix} 3 & 0 & 0 & | & 18 \\ 0 & 5 & 0 & | & 9 \\ 0 & 0 & 4 & | & 8 \end{bmatrix}$

16. Replace R_3 by $\frac{1}{6}R_3$.

$\begin{bmatrix} 1 & 0 & 0 & | & 30 \\ 0 & 1 & 0 & | & 17 \\ 0 & 0 & 6 & | & 162 \end{bmatrix}$

Use the Gauss-Jordan method to solve each system of equations.

17. $x + y = 5$
$3x + 2y = 12$

18. $x + 2y = 5$
$2x + y = -2$

19. $x + y = 7$
$4x + 3y = 22$

20. $4x - 2y = 3$
$-2x + 3y = 1$

21. $2x - 3y = 2$
$4x - 6y = 1$

22. $2x + 3y = 9$
$4x + 6y = 7$

23. $6x - 3y = 1$
$-12x + 6y = -2$

24. $x - y = 1$
$-x + y = -1$

25. $y = x - 3$
$y = 1 + z$
$z = 4 - x$

26. $x = 1 - y$
$2x = z$
$2z = -2 - y$

27. $2x - 2y = -5$
$2y + z = 0$
$2x + z = -7$

28. $x - z = -3$
$y + z = 9$
$-2x + 3y + 5z = 33$

29. $4x + 4y - 4z = 24$
$2x - y + z = -9$
$x - 2y + 3z = 1$

30. $x + 2y - 7z = -2$
$-2x - 5y + 2z = 1$
$3x + 5y + 4z = -9$

31. $3x + 5y - z = 0$
$4x - y + 2z = 1$
$7x + 4y + z = 1$

32. $3x - 6y + 3z = 11$
$2x + y - z = 2$
$5x - 5y + 2z = 6$

33. $5x - 4y + 2z = 6$
$5x + 3y - z = 11$
$15x - 5y + 3z = 23$

34. $3x + 2y - z = -16$
$6x - 4y + 3z = 12$
$5x - 2y + 2z = 4$

35. $2x + 3y + z = 9$
$4x + 6y + 2z = 18$
$-\frac{1}{2}x - \frac{3}{4}y - \frac{1}{4}z = -\frac{9}{4}$

36. $3x - 5y - 2z = -9$
$-4x + 3y + z = 11$
$8x - 5y + 4z = 6$

37. $x + 2y - w = 3$
$2x + 4z + 2w = -6$
$x + 2y - z = 6$
$2x - y + z + w = -3$

38. $x + 3y - 2z - w = 9$
$2x + 4y + 2w = 10$
$-3x - 5y + 2z - w = -15$
$x - y - 3z + 2w = 6$

39. $x + y - z + 2w = -20$
$2x - y + z + w = 11$
$3x - 2y + z - 2w = 27$

40. $4x - 3y + z + w = 21$
$-2x - y + 2z + 7w = 2$
$10x - 5z - 20w = 15$

41. $10.47x + 3.52y + 2.58z - 6.42w = 218.65$

$\quad\ \ 8.62x - 4.93y - 1.75z + 2.83w = 157.03$

$\quad\ \ 4.92x + 6.83y - 2.97z + 2.65w = 462.3$

$\quad\ \ 2.86x + 19.10y - 6.24z - 8.73w = 398.4$

42. $28.6x + 94.5y + 16.0z - 2.94w = 198.3$

$\quad\ \ 16.7x + 44.3y - 27.3z + 8.9w = 254.7$

$\quad\ \ 12.5x - 38.7y + 92.5z + 22.4w = 562.7$

$\quad\ \ 40.1x - 28.3y + 17.5z - 10.2w = 375.4$

43. On National Public Radio, the "Weekend Edition" program on Sunday, July 29, 2001, posed the following puzzle: Draw a three-by-three square (three boxes across by three boxes down). Put the fraction 3/8 in the first square in the first row. Put the fraction 1/4 in the last square in the second row. The object is to put a fraction in each of the remaining boxes, so the three numbers in each row, each column, and each of the long diagonals add up to 1. Solve this puzzle by letting seven variables represent the seven unknown fractions, writing eight equations for the eight sums, and solving by the Gauss-Jordan method.

LIFE SCIENCE APPLICATIONS

44. Birds The date of the first sighting of robins has been occurring earlier each spring over the past 25 years at the Rocky Mountain Biological Laboratory. Scientists from this laboratory have developed two linear equations that estimate the date of the first sighting of robins:

$$y = 759 - 0.338x$$
$$y = 1637 - 0.779x,$$

where x is the year and y is the estimated number of days into the year when a robin can be expected. *Source: Proceedings of the National Academy of Science.*

a. Compare the date of first sighting in 2015 for each of these equations.

b. Solve this system of equations to find the year in which the two estimates agree.

45. Animal Feed Solve the animal feed problem posed at the beginning of this section.

46. Animal Breeding An animal breeder can buy four types of food for Vietnamese pot-bellied pigs. Each case of Brand A contains 25 units of fiber, 30 units of protein, and 30 units of fat. Each case of Brand B contains 50 units of fiber, 30 units of protein, and 20 units of fat. Each case of Brand C contains 75 units of fiber, 30 units of protein, and 20 units of fat. Each case of Brand D contains 100 units of fiber, 60 units of protein, and 30 units of fat. How many cases of each should the breeder mix together to obtain a food that provides 1200 units of fiber, 600 units of protein, and 400 units of fat?

47. Dietetics A hospital dietician is planning a special diet for a certain patient. The total amount per meal of food groups A, B, and C must equal 400 grams. The diet should include one-third as much of group A as of group B, and the sum of the amounts

of group A and group C should equal twice the amount of group B.

a. How many grams of each food group should be included?

b. Suppose we drop the requirement that the diet include one-third as much of group A as of group B. Describe the set of all possible solutions.

c. Suppose that, in addition to the conditions given in the original problem, foods A and B cost 2 cents per gram and food C costs 3 cents per gram, and that a meal must cost $8. Is a solution possible?

48. Bacterial Food Requirements Three species of bacteria are fed three foods, I, II, and III. A bacterium of the first species consumes 1.3 units each of foods I and II and 2.3 units of food III each day. A bacterium of the second species consumes 1.1 units of food I, 2.4 units of food II, and 3.7 units of food III each day. A bacterium of the third species consumes 8.1 units of I, 2.9 units of II, and 5.1 units of III each day. If 16,000 units of I, 28,000 units of II, and 44,000 units of III are supplied each day, how many of each species can be maintained in this environment?

49. Fish Food Requirements A lake is stocked each spring with three species of fish, A, B, and C. Three foods, I, II, and III, are available in the lake. Each fish of species A requires an average of 1.32 units of food I, 2.9 units of food II, and 1.75 units of food III each day. Species B fish each require 2.1 units of food I, 0.95 unit of food II, and 0.6 unit of food III daily. Species C fish require 0.86, 1.52, and 2.01 units of I, II, and III per day, respectively. If 490 units of food I, 897 units of food II, and 653 units of food III are available daily, how many of each species should be stocked?

50. Agriculture According to data from a Texas agricultural report, the amount of nitrogen (in lb/acre), phosphate (in lb/acre), and labor (in hr/acre) needed to grow honeydews, yellow onions, and lettuce is given by the following table. *Source: The AMATYC Review.*

	Honeydews	**Yellow Onions**	**Lettuce**
Nitrogen	120	150	180
Phosphate	180	80	80
Labor	4.97	4.45	4.65

a. If the farmer has 220 acres, 29,100 lb of nitrogen, 32,600 lb of phosphate, and 480 hours of labor, is it possible to use all resources completely? If so, how many acres should he allot for each crop?

b. Suppose everything is the same as in part a, except that 1061 hours of labor are available. Is it possible to use all resources completely? If so, how many acres should he allot for each crop?

51. Mixing Plant Foods Natural Brand plant food is made from three chemicals. The mix must include 10.8% of the first chemical, and the other two chemicals must be in a ratio of 4 to 3 as measured by weight. How much of each chemical is required to make 750 kg of the plant food?

52. Health The U.S. National Center for Health Statistics tracks the major causes of death in the United States. After a steady increase, the death rate by cancer has decreased since the early 1990s. The table lists the age-adjusted death rate per 100,000 people for 4 years. *Source: The New York Times 2010 Almanac.*

Year	Rate
1980	183.9
1990	203.3
2000	196.5
2010	186.2

a. If the relationship between the death rate R and the year t is expressed as $R = at^2 + bt + c$, where $t = 0$ corresponds to 1980, use data from 1980, 1990, and 2000 and a linear system of equations to determine the constants a, b, and c.

b. Use the equation from part a to predict the rate in 2010, and compare the result with the actual rate of 186.2. *Source: National Vital Statistics Reports.*

c. If the relationship between the death rate R and the year t is expressed as $R = at^3 + bt^2 + ct + d$, where $t = 0$ corresponds to 1980, use all four data points and a linear system of equations to determine the constants a, b, c, and d.

d. Discuss the appropriateness of the functions used in parts a and c to model this data.

53. Archimedes' Problem Bovinum Archimedes is credited with the authorship of a famous problem involving the number of cattle of the sun god. A simplified version of the problem is stated as follows:

> *The sun god had a herd of cattle consisting of bulls and cows, one part of which was white, a second black, a third spotted, and a fourth brown.*
>
> *Among the bulls, the number of white ones was one-half plus one-third the number of the black greater than the brown; the number of the black, one-quarter plus one-fifth the number of the spotted greater than the brown; the number of the spotted, one-sixth and one-seventh the number of the white greater than the brown.*
>
> *Among the cows, the number of white ones was one-third plus one-quarter of the total black cattle; the number of the black, one-quarter plus one-fifth the total of the spotted cattle; the number of the spotted, one-fifth plus one-sixth the total of the brown cattle; the number of the brown, one-sixth plus one-seventh the total of the white cattle.*
>
> *What was the composition of the herd?*

Source: 100 Great Problems of Elementary Mathematics.
The problem can be solved by converting the statements into two systems of equations, using X, Y, Z, and T for the number of white, black, spotted, and brown bulls, respectively, and x, y, z, and t for the number of white, black, spotted, and brown cows, respectively. For example, the first statement can be written as $X = (1/2 + 1/3)Y + T$ and then reduced. The result is the following two systems of equations:

$$6X - 5Y = 6T \qquad\qquad 12x - 7y = 7Y$$
$$20Y - 9Z = 20T \quad \text{and} \quad 20y - 9z = 9Z$$
$$42Z - 13X = 42T \qquad\qquad 30z - 11t = 11T$$
$$\qquad\qquad\qquad\qquad -13x + 42t = 13X$$

a. Show that these two systems of equations represent Archimedes' Problem Bovinum.

b. If it is known that the number of brown bulls, T, is 4,149,387, use the Gauss-Jordan method to first find a solution to the 3×3 system and then use these values and the Gauss-Jordan method to find a solution to the 4×4 system of equations.

OTHER APPLICATIONS

54. Banking A bank teller has a total of 70 bills in five-, ten-, and twenty-dollar denominations. The total value of the money is $960.

a. Find the total number of solutions.

b. Find the solution with the smallest number of five-dollar bills.

c. Find the solution with the largest number of five-dollar bills.

55. Surveys The president of Sam's Supermarkets plans to hire two public relations firms to survey 500 customers by phone, 750 by mail, and 250 by in-person interviews. The Garcia firm has personnel to do 10 phone surveys, 30 mail surveys, and 5 interviews per hour. The Wong firm can handle 20 phone surveys, 10 mail surveys, and 10 interviews per hour. For how many hours should each firm be hired to produce the exact number of surveys needed?

56. Manufacturing Fred's Furniture Factory has 1950 machine hours available each week in the cutting department, 1490 hours in the assembly department, and 2160 in the finishing department. Manufacturing a chair requires 0.2 hour of cutting, 0.3 hour of assembly, and 0.1 hour of finishing. A cabinet requires 0.5 hour of cutting, 0.4 hour of assembly, and 0.6 hour of finishing. A buffet requires 0.3 hour of cutting, 0.1 hour of assembly, and 0.4 hour of finishing. How many chairs, cabinets, and buffets should be produced in order to use all the available production capacity?

57. Manufacturing Nadir, Inc. produces three models of television sets: deluxe, super-deluxe, and ultra. Each deluxe set requires 2 hours of electronics work, 3 hours of assembly time, and 5 hours of finishing time. Each super-deluxe requires 1, 3, and 2 hours of electronics, assembly, and finishing time, respectively. Each ultra requires 2, 2, and 6 hours of the same work, respectively.

a. There are 54 hours available for electronics, 72 hours available for assembly, and 148 hours available for finishing per week. How many of each model should be produced each week if all available time is to be used?

b. Suppose everything is the same as in part a, but a super-deluxe set requires 1, rather than 2, hours of finishing time. How many solutions are there now?

c. Suppose everything is the same as in part b, but the total hours available for finishing changes from 148 hours to 144 hours. Now how many solutions are there?

58. Transportation An electronics company produces three models of stereo speakers, models A, B, and C, and can deliver them by truck, van, or SUV. A truck holds 2 boxes of model A, 2 of model B, and 3 of model C. A van holds 3 boxes of model A, 4 boxes of model B, and 2 boxes of model C. An SUV holds 3 boxes of model A, 5 boxes of model B, and 1 box of model C.

    a. If 25 boxes of model A, 33 boxes of model B, and 22 boxes of model C are to be delivered, how many vehicles of each type should be used so that all operate at full capacity?

    b. Model C has been discontinued. If 25 boxes of model A and 33 boxes of model B are to be delivered, how many vehicles of each type should be used so that all operate at full capacity?

59. Loans To get the necessary funds for a planned expansion, a small company took out three loans totaling $25,000. Company owners were able to get interest rates of 8%, 9%, and 10%. They borrowed $1000 more at 9% than they borrowed at 10%. The total annual interest on the loans was $2190.

    a. How much did they borrow at each rate?

    b. Suppose we drop the condition that they borrowed $1000 more at 9% than at 10%. What can you say about the amount borrowed at 10%? What is the solution if the amount borrowed at 10% is $5000?

    c. Suppose the bank sets a maximum of $10,000 at the lowest interest rate of 8%. Is a solution possible that still meets all of the original conditions?

    d. Explain why $10,000 at 8%, $8000 at 9%, and $7000 at 10% is not a feasible solution for part c.

60. Transportation A manufacturer purchases a part for use at both of its plants—one at Roseville, California, the other at Akron, Ohio. The part is available in limited quantities from two suppliers. Each supplier has 75 units available. The Roseville plant needs 40 units, and the Akron plant requires 75 units. The first supplier charges $70 per unit delivered to Roseville and $90 per unit delivered to Akron. Corresponding costs from the second supplier are $80 and $120. The manufacturer wants to order a total of 75 units from the first, less expensive supplier, with the remaining 40 units to come from the second supplier. If the company spends $10,750 to purchase the required number of units for the two plants, find the number of units that should be sent from each supplier to each plant.

61. Broadway Economics When Neil Simon opens a new play, he has to decide whether to open the show on Broadway or Off Broadway. For example, in his play *London Suite*, he decided to open it Off Broadway. From information provided by Emanuel Azenberg, his producer, the following equations were developed:

$$43,500x - y = 1,295,000$$
$$27,000x - y = 440,000,$$

where x represents the number of weeks that the show has run and y represents the profit or loss from the show (first equation is for Broadway and second equation is for Off Broadway). *Source: The Mathematics Teacher.*

    a. Solve this system of equations to determine when the profit/loss from the show will be equal for each venue. What is the profit at that point?

    b. Discuss which venue is favorable for the show.

62. Snack Food According to the nutrition labels on the package, a single serving of Oreos® has 10 g of fat, 36 g of carbohydrates, 2 g of protein, and 240 calories. The figures for a single serving of Twix® are 14 g, 37 g, 3 g, and 280 calories. The figures for a single serving of trail mix are 20 g, 23 g, 11 g, and 295 calories. How many calories are in each gram of fat, carbohydrate, and protein? *Source: The Mathematics Teacher.**

63. Basketball Wilt Chamberlain holds the record for the highest number of points scored in a single NBA basketball game. Chamberlain scored 100 points for Philadelphia against the New York Knicks on March 2, 1962. This is an amazing feat, considering he scored all of his points without the help of three-point shots. Chamberlain made a total of 64 baskets, consisting of field goals (worth two points) and foul shots (worth one point). Find the number of field goals and the number of foul shots that Chamberlain made. *Source: ESPN.*

64. Basketball Kobe Bryant has the second highest single game point total in the NBA. Bryant scored 81 points for the Los Angeles Lakers on January 22, 2006, against the Toronto Raptors. Bryant made a total of 46 baskets, including foul shots (worth one point), field goals (worth two points), and three-point shots (worth three points). The number of field goal shots he made is equal to three times the number of three pointers he made. Find the number of foul shots, field goals, and three pointers Bryant made. *Source: ESPN.*

65. Baseball Ichiro Suzuki holds the American League record for the most hits in a single baseball season. In 2004, Suzuki had a total of 262 hits for the Seattle Mariners. He hit three fewer triples than home runs, and he hit three times as many doubles as home runs. Suzuki also hit 45 times as many singles as triples. Find the number of singles, doubles, triples, and home runs hit by Suzuki during the season. *Source: Baseball Almanac.*

66. Toys One hundred toys are to be given out to a group of children. A ball costs $2, a doll costs $3, and a car costs $4. A total of $295 was spent on the toys.

    a. A ball weighs 12 oz, a doll 16 oz, and a car 18 oz. The total weight of all the toys is 1542 oz. Find how many of each toy there are.

    b. Now suppose the weight of a ball, doll, and car are 11, 15, and 19 oz, respectively. If the total weight is still 1542 oz, how many solutions are there now?

    c. Keep the weights as in part b, but change the total weight to 1480 oz. How many solutions are there?

    d. Give the solution to part c that has the smallest number of cars.

    e. Give the solution to part c that has the largest number of cars.

*For a discussion of some complications that can come up in solving linear systems, read the original article: Szydlik, Stephen D., "The Problem with the Snack Food Problem," *The Mathematics Teacher*, Vol. 103, No. 1, Aug. 2009, pp. 18–28.

67. Ice Cream Researchers have determined that the amount of sugar contained in ice cream helps to determine the overall "degree of like" that a consumer has toward that particular flavor. They have also determined that too much or too little sugar will have the same negative affect on the "degree of like" and that this relationship follows a quadratic function. In an experiment conducted at Pennsylvania State University, the following condensed table was obtained. *Source: Journal of Food Science.*

Percentage of Sugar	Degree of Like
8	5.4
13	6.3
18	5.6

a. Use this information and the Gauss-Jordan method to determine the coefficients a, b, c, of the quadratic equation

$$y = ax^2 + bx + c,$$

where y is the "degree of like" and x is the percentage of sugar in the ice cream mix.

b. Repeat part a by using the quadratic regression feature on a graphing calculator. Compare your answers.

68. Modeling War One of the factors that contribute to the success or failure of a particular army during war is its ability to get new troops ready for service. It is possible to analyze the rate of change in the number of troops of two hypothetical armies with the following simplified model,

Rate of increase (RED ARMY) $= 200{,}000 - 0.5r - 0.3b$

Rate of increase (BLUE ARMY) $= 350{,}000 - 0.5r - 0.7b$,

where r is the number of soldiers in the Red Army at a given time and b is the number of soldiers in the Blue Army at a given time. The factors 0.5 and 0.7 represent each army's efficiency of bringing new soldiers to the fight. *Source: Journal of Peace Research.*

a. Solve this system of equations to determine the number of soldiers in each army when the rate of increase for each is zero.

b. Describe what might be going on in a war when the rate of increase is zero.

69. Traffic Control At rush hours, substantial traffic congestion is encountered at the traffic intersections shown in the figure. (The streets are one-way, as shown by the arrows.)

The city wishes to improve the signals at these corners so as to speed the flow of traffic. The traffic engineers first gather data. As the figure shows, 700 cars per hour come down M Street to intersection A, and 300 cars per hour come down 10th

Street to intersection A. A total of x_1 of these cars leave A on M Street, and x_4 cars leave A on 10th Street. The number of cars entering A must equal the number leaving, so that

$$x_1 + x_4 = 700 + 300$$

or

$$x_1 + x_4 = 1000.$$

For intersection B, x_1 cars enter on M Street and x_2 on 11th Street. The figure shows that 900 cars leave B on 11th and 200 on M. Thus,

$$x_1 + x_2 = 900 + 200$$
$$x_1 + x_2 = 1100.$$

a. Write two equations representing the traffic entering and leaving intersections C and D.

b. Use the four equations to set up an augmented matrix, and solve the system by the Gauss-Jordan method, using x_4 as the parameter.

c. Based on your solution to part b, what are the largest and smallest possible values for the number of cars leaving intersection A on 10th Street?

d. Answer the question in part c for the other three variables.

e. Verify that you could have discarded any one of the four original equations without changing the solution. What does this tell you about the original problem?

70. Lights Out The Tiger Electronics' game, Lights Out, consists of five rows of five lighted buttons. When a button is pushed, it changes the on/off status of it and the status of all of its vertical and horizontal neighbors. For any given situation where some of the lights are on and some are off, the goal of the game is to push buttons until all of the lights are turned off. It turns out that for any given array of lights, solving a system of equations can be used to develop a strategy for turning the lights out. The following system of equations can be used to solve the problem for a simplified version of the game with 2 rows of 2 buttons where all of the lights are initially turned on:

$$x_{11} + x_{12} + x_{21} = 1$$
$$x_{11} + x_{12} + x_{22} = 1$$
$$x_{11} + x_{21} + x_{22} = 1$$
$$x_{12} + x_{21} + x_{22} = 1,$$

where $x_{ij} = 1$ if the light in row i, column j, is on and $x_{ij} = 0$ when it is off. The order in which the buttons are pushed does not matter, so we are only seeking which buttons should be pushed. *Source: Mathematics Magazine.*

a. Solve this system of equations and determine a strategy to turn the lights out. (*Hint:* While doing row operations, if an odd number is found, immediately replace this value with a 1; if an even number is found, then immediately replace that number with a zero. This is called modulo 2 arithmetic, and it is necessary in problems dealing with on/off switches.)

b. Resolve the equation with the right side changed to $(0, 1, 1, 0)$.

YOUR TURN ANSWERS

1. $(5, -2)$ **2.** $(7, 2, -3)$

3. $(17/9 + w/3, -4/9 - 2w/3, 4/9 + 2w/3, w)$

10.2 Addition and Subtraction of Matrices

APPLY IT

A pharmaceutical company manufactures different products at its plants in several cities. How might the company keep track of its production most efficiently?

In the previous section, matrices were used to store information about systems of linear equations. In this section, we begin to study calculations with matrices, which we will use in Examples 1, 5, and 7 to answer the question posed above.

The use of matrices has increased in importance in the fields of management, natural science, and social science because matrices provide a convenient way to organize data, as Example 1 demonstrates.

EXAMPLE 1 Pharmaceutical Manufacturing

The Wellbeing Pharmaceutical Company manufactures decongestants and pain relievers in three forms: capsules, softgels, and tablets. The company has regional manufacturing plants in New York, Chicago, and San Francisco. In August, the New York plant manufactured 10 cases of decongestant capsules, 12 cases of decongestant softgels, and 5 cases of decongestant tablets, as well as 15 cases of pain reliever capsules, 20 cases of pain reliever softgels, and 8 cases of pain reliever tablets. Organize this information in a more readable format.

APPLY IT   **SOLUTION**   To organize this data, we might tabulate the data in a chart.

Number of Cases of Pharmaceuticals			
	Capsules	**Softgels**	**Tablets**
Decongestants	10	12	5
Pain relievers	15	20	8

With the understanding that the numbers in each row refer to the pharmaceutical type (decongestants, pain relievers), and the numbers in each column refer to the form (capsule, softgel, tablet), the same information can be given by a matrix, as follows.

$$M = \begin{bmatrix} 10 & 12 & 5 \\ 15 & 20 & 8 \end{bmatrix}$$

Matrices often are named with capital letters, as in Example 1. Matrices are classified by **size**; that is, by the number of rows and columns they contain. For example, matrix M above has two rows and three columns. This matrix is a 2×3 (read "2 by 3") matrix. By definition, a matrix with m rows and n columns is an $m \times n$ matrix. The number of rows is always given first.

EXAMPLE 2 Matrix Size

(a) The matrix $\begin{bmatrix} -3 & 5 \\ 2 & 0 \\ 5 & -1 \end{bmatrix}$ is a 3×2 matrix.   **(b)** $\begin{bmatrix} 0.5 & 8 & 0.9 \\ 0 & 5.1 & -3 \\ -4 & 0 & 5 \end{bmatrix}$ is a 3×3 matrix.

(c) $\begin{bmatrix} 1 & 6 & 5 & -2 & 5 \end{bmatrix}$ is a 1×5 matrix.   **(d)** $\begin{bmatrix} 3 \\ -5 \\ 0 \\ 2 \end{bmatrix}$ is a 4×1 matrix.

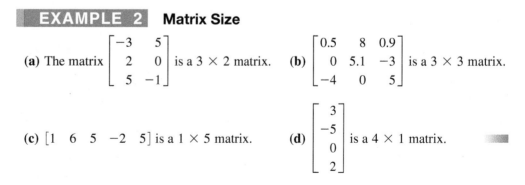

A matrix with the same number of rows as columns is called a **square matrix**. The matrix in Example 2(b) is a square matrix.

A matrix containing only one row is called a **row matrix** or a **row vector**. The matrix in Example 2(c) is a row matrix, as are

$$\begin{bmatrix} 5 & 8 \end{bmatrix}, \quad \begin{bmatrix} 6 & -9 & 2 \end{bmatrix}, \quad \text{and} \quad \begin{bmatrix} -4 & 0 & 0 & 0 \end{bmatrix}.$$

A matrix of only one column, as in Example 2(d), is a **column matrix** or a **column vector**.

Equality for matrices is defined as follows.

Matrix Equality

Two matrices are equal if they are the same size and if each pair of corresponding elements is equal.

By this definition,

$$\begin{bmatrix} 2 & 1 \\ 3 & -5 \end{bmatrix} \quad \text{and} \quad \begin{bmatrix} 1 & 2 \\ -5 & 3 \end{bmatrix}$$

are not equal (even though they contain the same elements and are the same size) since the corresponding elements differ.

EXAMPLE 3 Matrix Equality

(a) From the definition of matrix equality given above, the only way that the statement

$$\begin{bmatrix} 2 & 1 \\ p & q \end{bmatrix} = \begin{bmatrix} x & y \\ -1 & 0 \end{bmatrix}$$

can be true is if $2 = x$, $1 = y$, $p = -1$, and $q = 0$.

(b) The statement

$$\begin{bmatrix} x \\ y \end{bmatrix} = \begin{bmatrix} 1 \\ -3 \\ 0 \end{bmatrix}$$

can never be true, since the two matrices are different sizes. (One is 2×1 and the other is 3×1.)

Addition   The matrix given in Example 1,

$$M = \begin{bmatrix} 10 & 12 & 5 \\ 15 & 20 & 8 \end{bmatrix},$$

shows the number of cases of decongestants and pain relievers in each of the three forms manufactured by the New York plant of the Wellbeing Pharmaceutical Company in August. If matrix N below gives the amounts manufactured in September, what are the total amounts manufactured over these two months?

$$N = \begin{bmatrix} 45 & 35 & 20 \\ 65 & 40 & 35 \end{bmatrix}$$

If 10 cases of decongestant capsules were manufactured in August and 45 in September, then altogether $10 + 45 = 55$ cases were manufactured in the two months. The other corresponding entries can be added in a similar way to get a new matrix Q, which represents the total amounts manufactured over the two months.

$$Q = \begin{bmatrix} 55 & 47 & 25 \\ 80 & 60 & 43 \end{bmatrix}$$

It is convenient to refer to Q as the sum of M and N.

The way these two matrices were added illustrates the following definition of addition of matrices.

Adding Matrices

The sum of two $m \times n$ matrices X and Y is the $m \times n$ matrix $X + Y$ in which each element is the sum of the corresponding elements of X and Y.

| CAUTION | It is important to remember that only matrices that are the same size can be added.

EXAMPLE 4 Adding Matrices

Find each sum, if possible.

SOLUTION

YOUR TURN 1 Find each sum, if possible.

(a) $\begin{bmatrix} 3 & 4 & 5 & 6 \\ 1 & 2 & 3 & 4 \end{bmatrix} + \begin{bmatrix} 1 & -2 & 4 \\ -2 & -4 & 8 \end{bmatrix}$

(b) $\begin{bmatrix} 3 & 4 & 5 \\ 1 & 2 & 3 \end{bmatrix} + \begin{bmatrix} 1 & -2 & 4 \\ -2 & -4 & 8 \end{bmatrix}$

(a) $\begin{bmatrix} 5 & -6 \\ 8 & 9 \end{bmatrix} + \begin{bmatrix} -4 & 6 \\ 8 & -3 \end{bmatrix} = \begin{bmatrix} 5 + (-4) & -6 + 6 \\ 8 + 8 & 9 + (-3) \end{bmatrix} = \begin{bmatrix} 1 & 0 \\ 16 & 6 \end{bmatrix}$

(b) The matrices

$$A = \begin{bmatrix} 5 & -8 \\ 6 & 2 \end{bmatrix} \quad \text{and} \quad B = \begin{bmatrix} 3 & -9 & 1 \\ 4 & 2 & -5 \end{bmatrix}$$

are different sizes. Therefore, the sum $A + B$ does not exist.   **TRY YOUR TURN 1**

EXAMPLE 5 Pharmaceutical Manufacturing

The number of cases manufactured by the Wellbeing Pharmaceutical Company in September at the New York, San Francisco, and Chicago manufacturing plants are given in matrices N, S, and C below.

$$N = \begin{bmatrix} 45 & 35 & 20 \\ 65 & 40 & 35 \end{bmatrix} \quad S = \begin{bmatrix} 30 & 32 & 28 \\ 43 & 47 & 30 \end{bmatrix} \quad C = \begin{bmatrix} 22 & 25 & 38 \\ 31 & 34 & 35 \end{bmatrix}$$

What was the total amount manufactured at the three plants in September?

 APPLY IT

SOLUTION   The total amount manufactured in September is represented by the sum of the three matrices N, S, and C.

$$N + S + C = \begin{bmatrix} 45 & 35 & 20 \\ 65 & 40 & 35 \end{bmatrix} + \begin{bmatrix} 30 & 32 & 28 \\ 43 & 47 & 30 \end{bmatrix} + \begin{bmatrix} 22 & 25 & 38 \\ 31 & 34 & 35 \end{bmatrix}$$

$$= \begin{bmatrix} 97 & 92 & 86 \\ 139 & 121 & 100 \end{bmatrix}$$

For example, this sum shows that the total number of cases of decongestants in tablet form manufactured at the three plants in September was 86.

Subtraction   Subtraction of matrices is defined similarly to addition.

Subtracting Matrices

The difference of two $m \times n$ matrices X and Y is the $m \times n$ matrix $X - Y$ in which each element is the difference of the corresponding elements of X and Y.

EXAMPLE 6   Subtracting Matrices

Subtract each pair of matrices, if possible.

SOLUTION

(a) $\begin{bmatrix} 8 & 6 & -4 \\ -2 & 7 & 5 \end{bmatrix} - \begin{bmatrix} 3 & 5 & -8 \\ -4 & 2 & 9 \end{bmatrix} = \begin{bmatrix} 8-3 & 6-5 & -4-(-8) \\ -2-(-4) & 7-2 & 5-9 \end{bmatrix} = \begin{bmatrix} 5 & 1 & 4 \\ 2 & 5 & -4 \end{bmatrix}.$

(b) The matrices

$$\begin{bmatrix} -2 & 5 \\ 0 & 1 \end{bmatrix} \quad \text{and} \quad \begin{bmatrix} 3 \\ 5 \end{bmatrix}$$

YOUR TURN 2   Calculate
$\begin{bmatrix} 3 & 4 & 5 \\ 1 & 2 & 3 \end{bmatrix} - \begin{bmatrix} 1 & -2 & 4 \\ -2 & -4 & 8 \end{bmatrix}.$

are different sizes and cannot be subtracted.   **TRY YOUR TURN 2**

EXAMPLE 7   Pharmaceutical Manufacturing

APPLY IT

During September the Chicago manufacturing plant of the Wellbeing Pharmaceutical Company shipped out the following number of cases of each pharmaceutical.

$$K = \begin{bmatrix} 5 & 10 & 8 \\ 11 & 14 & 15 \end{bmatrix}$$

How many cases were left at the plant on October 1, taking into account only the cases manufactured and sent out during the month?

Method 1
Calculating by Hand

SOLUTION   The number of cases of each pharmaceutical manufactured by the Chicago plant during September is given by matrix C from Example 5; the number of cases of each pharmaceutical shipped out during September is given by matrix K. The October 1 inventory will be represented by the matrix $C - K$:

[A]−[B]
$\begin{bmatrix} 17 & 15 & 30 \\ 20 & 20 & 20 \end{bmatrix}$

$$\begin{bmatrix} 22 & 25 & 38 \\ 31 & 34 & 35 \end{bmatrix} - \begin{bmatrix} 5 & 10 & 8 \\ 11 & 14 & 15 \end{bmatrix} = \begin{bmatrix} 17 & 15 & 30 \\ 20 & 20 & 20 \end{bmatrix}.$$

FIGURE 9

Method 2
Graphing Calculator

Matrix operations are easily performed on a graphing calculator. Figure 9 shows the previous operation; the matrices A and B were already entered into the calculator.

TECHNOLOGY NOTE

Spreadsheet programs are designed to effectively organize data that can be represented in rows and columns. Accordingly, matrix operations are also easily performed on spreadsheets. See the *Graphing Calculator and Excel Spreadsheet Manual* available with this book for details.

10.2 EXERCISES

Decide whether each statement is true or false. If false, tell why.

1. $\begin{bmatrix} 1 & 3 \\ 5 & 7 \end{bmatrix} = \begin{bmatrix} 1 & 5 \\ 3 & 7 \end{bmatrix}$

2. $\begin{bmatrix} 1 \\ 2 \\ 3 \end{bmatrix} = \begin{bmatrix} 1 & 2 & 3 \end{bmatrix}$

3. $\begin{bmatrix} x \\ y \end{bmatrix} = \begin{bmatrix} -2 \\ 8 \end{bmatrix}$ if $x = -2$ and $y = 8$.

4. $\begin{bmatrix} 3 & 5 & 2 & 8 \\ 1 & -1 & 4 & 0 \end{bmatrix}$ is a 4 × 2 matrix.

5. $\begin{bmatrix} 1 & 9 & -4 \\ 3 & 7 & 2 \\ -1 & 1 & 0 \end{bmatrix}$ is a square matrix.

6. $\begin{bmatrix} 2 & 4 & -1 \\ 3 & 7 & 5 \\ 0 & 0 & 0 \end{bmatrix} = \begin{bmatrix} 2 & 4 & -1 \\ 3 & 7 & 5 \end{bmatrix}$

Find the size of each matrix. Identify any square, column, or row matrices.

7. $\begin{bmatrix} -4 & 8 \\ 2 & 3 \end{bmatrix}$

8. $\begin{bmatrix} 2 & -3 & 7 \\ 1 & 0 & 4 \end{bmatrix}$

9. $\begin{bmatrix} -6 & 8 & 0 & 0 \\ 4 & 1 & 9 & 2 \\ 3 & -5 & 7 & 1 \end{bmatrix}$

10. $\begin{bmatrix} 8 & -2 & 4 & 6 & 3 \end{bmatrix}$

11. $\begin{bmatrix} -7 \\ 5 \end{bmatrix}$

12. $\begin{bmatrix} -9 \end{bmatrix}$

13. The sum of an $n \times m$ matrix and an $m \times n$ matrix, where $m \neq n$, is _____.

14. If A is a 5×2 matrix and $A + K = A$, what do you know about K?

Find the values of the variables in each equation.

15. $\begin{bmatrix} 3 & 4 \\ -8 & 1 \end{bmatrix} = \begin{bmatrix} 3 & x \\ y & z \end{bmatrix}$

16. $\begin{bmatrix} -5 \\ y \end{bmatrix} = \begin{bmatrix} -5 \\ 8 \end{bmatrix}$

17. $\begin{bmatrix} s-4 & t+2 \\ -5 & 7 \end{bmatrix} = \begin{bmatrix} 6 & 2 \\ -5 & r \end{bmatrix}$

18. $\begin{bmatrix} 9 & 7 \\ r & 0 \end{bmatrix} = \begin{bmatrix} m-3 & n+5 \\ 8 & 0 \end{bmatrix}$

19. $\begin{bmatrix} a+2 & 3b & 4c \\ d & 7f & 8 \end{bmatrix} + \begin{bmatrix} -7 & 2b & 6 \\ -3d & -6 & -2 \end{bmatrix} = \begin{bmatrix} 15 & 25 & 6 \\ -8 & 1 & 6 \end{bmatrix}$

20. $\begin{bmatrix} a+2 & 3z+1 & 5m \\ 4k & 0 & 3 \end{bmatrix} + \begin{bmatrix} 3a & 2z & 5m \\ 2k & 5 & 6 \end{bmatrix} = \begin{bmatrix} 10 & -14 & 80 \\ 10 & 5 & 9 \end{bmatrix}$

Perform the indicated operations, where possible.

21. $\begin{bmatrix} 2 & 4 & 5 & -7 \\ 6 & -3 & 12 & 0 \end{bmatrix} + \begin{bmatrix} 8 & 0 & -10 & 1 \\ -2 & 8 & -9 & 11 \end{bmatrix}$

22. $\begin{bmatrix} 1 & 5 \\ 2 & -3 \\ 3 & 7 \end{bmatrix} + \begin{bmatrix} 2 & 3 \\ 8 & 5 \\ -1 & 9 \end{bmatrix}$

23. $\begin{bmatrix} 1 & 3 & -2 \\ 4 & 7 & 1 \end{bmatrix} + \begin{bmatrix} 3 & 0 \\ 6 & 4 \\ -5 & 2 \end{bmatrix}$

24. $\begin{bmatrix} 8 & 0 & -3 \\ 1 & 19 & -5 \end{bmatrix} - \begin{bmatrix} 1 & -5 & 2 \\ 3 & 9 & -8 \end{bmatrix}$

25. $\begin{bmatrix} 2 & 8 & 12 & 0 \\ 7 & 4 & -1 & 5 \\ 1 & 2 & 0 & 10 \end{bmatrix} - \begin{bmatrix} 1 & 3 & 6 & 9 \\ 2 & -3 & -3 & 4 \\ 8 & 0 & -2 & 17 \end{bmatrix}$

26. $\begin{bmatrix} 2 & 1 \\ 5 & -3 \\ -7 & 2 \\ 9 & 0 \end{bmatrix} + \begin{bmatrix} 1 & -8 & 0 \\ 5 & 3 & 2 \\ -6 & 7 & -5 \\ 2 & -1 & 0 \end{bmatrix}$

27. $\begin{bmatrix} 2 & 3 \\ -2 & 4 \end{bmatrix} + \begin{bmatrix} 4 & 3 \\ 7 & 8 \end{bmatrix} - \begin{bmatrix} 3 & 2 \\ 1 & 4 \end{bmatrix}$

28. $\begin{bmatrix} 4 & 3 \\ 1 & 2 \end{bmatrix} - \begin{bmatrix} 1 & 1 \\ 1 & 0 \end{bmatrix} + \begin{bmatrix} 1 & 1 \\ 1 & 4 \end{bmatrix}$

29. $\begin{bmatrix} 2 & -1 \\ 0 & 13 \end{bmatrix} - \begin{bmatrix} 4 & 8 \\ -5 & 7 \end{bmatrix} + \begin{bmatrix} 12 & 7 \\ 5 & 3 \end{bmatrix}$

30. $\begin{bmatrix} 5 & 8 \\ -3 & 1 \end{bmatrix} + \begin{bmatrix} 0 & 1 \\ -2 & -2 \end{bmatrix} + \begin{bmatrix} -5 & -8 \\ 6 & 1 \end{bmatrix}$

31. $\begin{bmatrix} -4x+2y & -3x+y \\ 6x-3y & 2x-5y \end{bmatrix} + \begin{bmatrix} -8x+6y & 2x \\ 3y-5x & 6x+4y \end{bmatrix}$

32. $\begin{bmatrix} 4k-8y \\ 6z-3x \\ 2k+5a \\ -4m+2n \end{bmatrix} - \begin{bmatrix} 5k+6y \\ 2z+5x \\ 4k+6a \\ 4m-2n \end{bmatrix}$

33. For matrices $X = \begin{bmatrix} x & y \\ z & w \end{bmatrix}$ and $0 = \begin{bmatrix} 0 & 0 \\ 0 & 0 \end{bmatrix}$, find the matrix $0 - X$.

Using matrices $O = \begin{bmatrix} 0 & 0 \\ 0 & 0 \end{bmatrix}$, $P = \begin{bmatrix} m & n \\ p & q \end{bmatrix}$, $T = \begin{bmatrix} r & s \\ t & u \end{bmatrix}$, and $X = \begin{bmatrix} x & y \\ z & w \end{bmatrix}$, **verify the statements in Exercises 34–37.**

34. $X + T = T + X$ (commutative property of addition of matrices)

35. $X + (T + P) = (X + T) + P$ (associative property of addition of matrices)

36. $X - X = O$ (inverse property of addition of matrices)

37. $P + O = P$ (identity property of addition of matrices)

38. Which of the above properties are valid for matrices that are not square?

LIFE SCIENCE APPLICATIONS

39. **Dietetics** A dietician prepares a diet specifying the amounts a patient should eat of four basic food groups: group I, meats; group II, fruits and vegetables; group III, breads and starches; group IV, milk products. Amounts are given in "exchanges" that represent 1 oz (meat), 1/2 cup (fruits and vegetables), 1 slice (bread), 8 oz (milk), or other suitable measurements.

   a. The number of "exchanges" for breakfast for each of the four food groups, respectively, are 2, 1, 2, and 1; for lunch, 3, 2, 2, and 1; and for dinner, 4, 3, 2, and 1. Write a 3×4 matrix using this information.

   b. The amounts of fat, carbohydrates, and protein (in appropriate units) in each food group, respectively, are as follows.

      Fat: 5, 0, 0, 10

      Carbohydrates: 0, 10, 15, 12

      Protein: 7, 1, 2, 8

      Use this information to write a 4×3 matrix.

   c. There are 8 calories per exchange of fat, 4 calories per exchange of carbohydrates, and 5 calories per exchange of protein. Summarize this data in a 3×1 matrix.

40. Animal Growth At the beginning of a laboratory experiment, five baby rats measured 5.6, 6.4, 6.9, 7.6, and 6.1 cm in length, and weighed 144, 138, 149, 152, and 146 g, respectively.

a. Write a 2 × 5 matrix using this information.

b. At the end of two weeks, their lengths (in centimeters) were 10.2, 11.4, 11.4, 12.7, and 10.8 and their weights (in grams) were 196, 196, 225, 250, and 230. Write a 2 × 5 matrix with this information.

c. Use matrix subtraction and the matrices found in parts a and b to write a matrix that gives the amount of change in length and weight for each rat.

d. During the third week, the rats grew by the amounts shown in the matrix below.

What were their lengths and weights at the end of this week?

41. Testing Medication A drug company is testing 200 patients to see if Painfree (a new headache medicine) is effective. Half the patients receive Painfree and half receive a placebo. The data on the first 50 patients is summarized in this matrix:

$$\begin{array}{c} \text{Pain Relief Obtained} \\ \begin{array}{cc} \text{Yes} & \text{No} \end{array} \\ \begin{array}{c} \text{Painfree} \\ \text{Placebo} \end{array} \begin{bmatrix} 22 & 3 \\ 8 & 17 \end{bmatrix}. \end{array}$$

a. Of those who took the placebo, how many got relief?

b. Of those who took the new medication, how many got no relief?

c. The test was repeated on three more groups of 50 patients each, with the results summarized by these matrices.

$$\begin{bmatrix} 21 & 4 \\ 6 & 19 \end{bmatrix} \quad \begin{bmatrix} 19 & 6 \\ 10 & 15 \end{bmatrix} \quad \begin{bmatrix} 23 & 2 \\ 3 & 22 \end{bmatrix}$$

Find the total results for all 200 patients.

d. On the basis of these results, does it appear that Painfree is effective?

OTHER APPLICATIONS

42. Motorcycle Helmets The following table shows the percentage of motorcyclists in various regions of the country who used helmets compliant with federal safety regulations and the percentage who used helmets that were noncompliant in two recent years. *Source: NHTSA.*

2008	**Compliant**	**Noncompliant**
Northeast	45	8
Midwest	67	16
South	61	14
West	71	5

2009	**Compliant**	**Noncompliant**
Northeast	61	15
Midwest	67	8
South	65	6
West	83	4

a. Write two matrices for the 2008 and 2009 helmet usage.

b. Use the two matrices from part a to write a matrix showing the change in helmet usage from 2008 to 2009.

c. Analyze the results from part b and discuss the extent to which changes from 2008 to 2009 differ from one region to another.

43. Life Expectancy The following table gives the life expectancy of African American males and females and white American males and females at the beginning of each decade since 1970. *Source: National Center for Health Statistics.*

	African American		**White American**	
Year	**Male**	**Female**	**Male**	**Female**
1970	60.0	68.3	68.0	75.6
1980	63.8	72.5	70.7	78.1
1990	64.5	73.6	72.7	79.4
2000	68.2	75.1	74.7	79.9
2010	71.8	78.0	76.5	81.3

a. Write a matrix for the life expectancy of African Americans.

b. Write a matrix for the life expectancy of white Americans.

c. Use the matrices from parts a and b to write a matrix showing the difference between the two groups.

d. Analyze the results from part c and discuss any noticeable trends.

44. Educational Attainment The table below gives the educational attainment of the U.S. population 25 years and older since 1970. *Source: U.S. Census Bureau.*

	Male		**Female**	
Year	**Percentage with 4 Years of High School or More**	**Percentage with 4 Years of College or More**	**Percentage with 4 Years of High School or More**	**Percentage with 4 Years of College or More**
1970	55.0	14.1	55.4	8.2
1980	69.2	20.9	68.1	13.6
1990	77.7	24.4	77.5	18.4
2000	84.2	27.8	84.0	23.6
2010	86.6	30.3	87.6	29.6

a. Write a matrix for the educational attainment of males.

b. Write a matrix for the educational attainment of females.

c. Use the matrices from parts a and b to write a matrix showing the difference in educational attainment between males and females since 1970.

45. Educational Attainment The following table gives the educational attainment of African Americans and Hispanic Americans 25 years and older since 1980. *Source: U.S. Census Bureau.*

	African American		Hispanic American	
Year	Percentage with 4 Years of High School or More	Percentage with 4 Years of College or More	Percentage with 4 Years of High School or More	Percentage with 4 Years of College or More
1980	51.2	7.9	45.3	7.9
1985	59.8	11.1	47.9	8.5
1990	66.2	11.3	50.8	9.2
1995	73.8	13.2	53.4	9.3
2000	78.5	16.5	57.0	10.6
2010	84.2	19.8	62.9	13.9

a. Write a matrix for the educational attainment of African Americans.

b. Write a matrix for the educational attainment of Hispanic Americans.

c. Use the matrices from parts a and b to write a matrix showing the difference in educational attainment between African and Hispanic Americans.

46. Animal Interactions When two kittens named Cauchy and Cliché were introduced into a household with Jamie (an older cat) and Musk (a dog), the interactions among animals were complicated. The two kittens liked each other and Jamie, but didn't like Musk. Musk liked everybody, but Jamie didn't like any of the other animals.

a. Write a 4 × 4 matrix in which rows (and columns) 1, 2, 3, and 4 refer to Musk, Jamie, Cauchy, and Cliché. Make an element a 1 if the animal for that row likes the animal for that column, and otherwise make the element a 0. Assume every animal likes herself.

b. Within a few days, Cauchy and Cliché decided that they liked Musk after all. Write a 4 × 4 matrix, as you did in part a, representing the new situation.

47. Car Accidents The tables in the next column give the death rates, per million person trips, for male and female drivers for various ages and number of passengers. *Source: JAMA.*

Male Drivers	Number of Passengers			
Age	0	1	2	≥ 3
16	2.61	4.39	6.29	9.08
17	1.63	2.77	4.61	6.92
30–59	0.92	0.75	0.62	0.54

Female Drivers	Number of Passengers			
Age	0	1	2	≥ 3
16	1.38	1.72	1.94	3.31
17	1.26	1.48	2.82	2.28
30–59	0.41	0.33	0.27	0.40

a. Write a matrix for the death rate of male drivers.

b. Write a matrix for the death rate of female drivers.

c. Use the matrices from parts a and b to write a matrix showing the difference between the death rates of males and females.

d. Analyze the results of part c and make some suggestions on how to reduce the rates.

48. Management A toy company has plants in Boston, Chicago, and Seattle that manufacture toy phones and calculators. The following matrix gives the production costs (in dollars) for each item at the Boston plant:

$$\begin{array}{cc} & \text{Phones} \quad \text{Calculators} \\ \begin{matrix} \text{Material} \\ \text{Labor} \end{matrix} & \begin{bmatrix} 4.27 & 6.94 \\ 3.45 & 3.65 \end{bmatrix} \end{array}$$

a. In Chicago, a phone costs $4.05 for material and $3.27 for labor; a calculator costs $7.01 for material and $3.51 for labor. In Seattle, material costs are $4.40 for a phone and $6.90 for a calculator; labor costs are $3.54 for a phone and $3.76 for a calculator. Write the production cost matrices for Chicago and Seattle.

b. Suppose labor costs increase by $0.11 per item in Chicago and material costs there increase by $0.37 for a phone and $0.42 for a calculator. What is the new production cost matrix for Chicago?

49. Management There are three convenience stores in Folsom. This week, store I sold 88 loaves of bread, 48 qt of milk, 16 jars of peanut butter, and 112 lb of cold cuts. Store II sold 105 loaves of bread, 72 qt of milk, 21 jars of peanut butter, and 147 lb of cold cuts. Store III sold 60 loaves of bread, 40 qt of milk, no peanut butter, and 50 lb of cold cuts.

a. Use a 4 × 3 matrix to express the sales information for the three stores.

b. During the following week, sales on these products at store I increased by 25%; sales at store II increased by 1/3; and sales at store III increased by 10%. Write the sales matrix for that week.

c. Write a matrix that represents total sales over the two-week period.

YOUR TURN ANSWERS

1. (a) Does not exist (b) $\begin{bmatrix} 4 & 2 & 9 \\ -1 & -2 & 11 \end{bmatrix}$ **2.** $\begin{bmatrix} 2 & 6 & 1 \\ 3 & 6 & -5 \end{bmatrix}$

10.3 Multiplication of Matrices

What is a wildlife center's total cost of seed for each season of the year for various species of birds?
Matrix multiplication will be used to answer this question in Example 6.

We begin by defining the product of a real number and a matrix. In work with matrices, a real number is called a **scalar**.

Product of a Matrix and a Scalar
The product of a scalar k and a matrix X is the matrix kX, in which each element is k times the corresponding element of X.

EXAMPLE 1 Scalar Product of a Matrix

Calculate $-5A$, where $A = \begin{bmatrix} 3 & 4 \\ 0 & -1 \end{bmatrix}$.

SOLUTION

$$(-5)\begin{bmatrix} 3 & 4 \\ 0 & -1 \end{bmatrix} = \begin{bmatrix} (-5)(3) & (-5)(4) \\ (-5)(0) & (-5)(-1) \end{bmatrix} = \begin{bmatrix} -15 & -20 \\ 0 & 5 \end{bmatrix}$$

Finding the product of two matrices is more involved, but such multiplication is important in solving practical problems. To understand the reasoning behind matrix multiplication, it may be helpful to consider another example concerning Wellbeing Pharmaceutical Company discussed in the previous section. Suppose Wellbeing makes three antibiotics, which we will label A, B, and C. Matrix W shows the number of cases of each antibiotic manufactured in a month at each plant.

$$\begin{array}{c} \\ \text{New York} \\ \text{Chicago} \\ \text{San Francisco} \end{array} \begin{array}{ccc} A & B & C \\ \end{array} \\ \begin{bmatrix} 10 & 7 & 3 \\ 5 & 9 & 6 \\ 4 & 8 & 2 \end{bmatrix} = W$$

If the selling price for a case of antibiotic A is $800, for a case of antibiotic B is $1000, and for a case of antibiotic C is $1200, the total value of the antibiotics manufactured at the New York plant is found as follows.

Value of Antibiotic				
Antibiotic	Number of Cases	Price of Case		Total
A	10	× $800	=	$8000
B	7	× $1000	=	$7000
C	3	× $1200	=	$3600
	(Total for New York)			$18,600

The total value of the three kinds of antibiotics manufactured in New York is $18,600.
The work done in the table is summarized as follows:

$$10(\$800) + 7(\$1000) + 3(\$1200) = \$18,600.$$

In the same way, we find that the Chicago antibiotics have a total value of

$$5(\$800) + 9(\$1000) + 6(\$1200) = \$20{,}200,$$

and in San Francisco, the total value of the antibiotics is

$$4(\$800) + 8(\$1000) + 2(\$1200) = \$13{,}600.$$

The selling prices can be written as a column matrix P, and the total value in each location as another column matrix, V.

$$\begin{bmatrix} 800 \\ 1000 \\ 1200 \end{bmatrix} = P \qquad \begin{bmatrix} 18{,}600 \\ 20{,}200 \\ 13{,}600 \end{bmatrix} = V$$

Look at the elements of W and P below; multiplying the first, second, and third elements of the first row of W by the first, second, and third elements, respectively, of the column matrix P and then adding these products gives the first element in V. Doing the same thing with the second row of W gives the second element of V; the third row of W leads to the third element of V, suggesting that it is reasonable to write the product of matrices

$$W = \begin{bmatrix} 10 & 7 & 3 \\ 5 & 9 & 6 \\ 4 & 8 & 2 \end{bmatrix} \quad \text{and} \quad P = \begin{bmatrix} 800 \\ 1000 \\ 1200 \end{bmatrix}$$

as

$$WP = \begin{bmatrix} 10 & 7 & 3 \\ 5 & 9 & 6 \\ 4 & 8 & 2 \end{bmatrix} \begin{bmatrix} 800 \\ 1000 \\ 1200 \end{bmatrix} = \begin{bmatrix} 18{,}600 \\ 20{,}200 \\ 13{,}600 \end{bmatrix} = V.$$

The product was found by multiplying the elements of *rows* of the matrix on the left and the corresponding elements of the *column* of the matrix on the right, and then finding the sum of these separate products. Notice that the product of a 3×3 matrix and a 3×1 matrix is a 3×1 matrix. Notice also that each element of the product of two matrices is a sum of products. This is exactly what you do when you go to the store and buy 8 candy bars at $0.80 each, 4 bottles of water at $1.25 each, and so forth, and calculate the total as $8 \times 0.80 + 4 \times 1.25 + \cdots.$

The product AB of an $m \times n$ matrix A and an $n \times k$ matrix B is found as follows. Multiply each element of the *first row* of A by the corresponding element of the *first column* of B. The sum of these n products is the *first-row, first-column* element of AB. Similarly, the sum of the products found by multiplying the elements of the *first row* of A by the corresponding elements of the *second column* of B gives the *first-row, second-column* element of AB, and so on.

Product of Two Matrices

Let A be an $m \times n$ matrix and let B be an $n \times k$ matrix. To find the element in the ith row and jth column of the **product matrix** AB, multiply each element in the ith row of A by the corresponding element in the jth column of B, and then add these products. The product matrix AB is an $m \times k$ matrix.

EXAMPLE 2 Matrix Product

Find the product AB of matrices

$$A = \begin{bmatrix} 2 & 3 & -1 \\ 4 & 2 & 2 \end{bmatrix} \quad \text{and} \quad B = \begin{bmatrix} 1 \\ 8 \\ 6 \end{bmatrix}.$$

SOLUTION   Since A is 2×3 and B is 3×1, we can find the product matrix AB.

Step 1   Multiply the elements of the first row of A and the corresponding elements of the column of B.

$$\begin{bmatrix} 2 & 3 & -1 \\ 4 & 2 & 2 \end{bmatrix} \begin{bmatrix} 1 \\ 8 \\ 6 \end{bmatrix} \qquad 2 \cdot 1 + 3 \cdot 8 + (-1) \cdot 6 = 20$$

Thus, 20 is the first-row entry of the product matrix AB.

Step 2   Multiply the elements of the second row of A and the corresponding elements of B.

$$\begin{bmatrix} 2 & 3 & -1 \\ 4 & 2 & 2 \end{bmatrix} \begin{bmatrix} 1 \\ 8 \\ 6 \end{bmatrix} \qquad 4 \cdot 1 + 2 \cdot 8 + 2 \cdot 6 = 32$$

The second-row entry of the product matrix AB is 32.

Step 3   Write the product as a column matrix using the two entries found above.

$$AB = \begin{bmatrix} 2 & 3 & -1 \\ 4 & 2 & 2 \end{bmatrix} \begin{bmatrix} 1 \\ 8 \\ 6 \end{bmatrix} = \begin{bmatrix} 20 \\ 32 \end{bmatrix}$$

Note that the product of a 2×3 matrix and a 3×1 matrix is a 2×1 matrix.

EXAMPLE 3   Matrix Product

Find the product CD of matrices

$$C = \begin{bmatrix} -3 & 4 & 2 \\ 5 & 0 & 4 \end{bmatrix} \quad \text{and} \quad D = \begin{bmatrix} -6 & 4 \\ 2 & 3 \\ 3 & -2 \end{bmatrix}.$$

SOLUTION   Since C is 2×3 and D is 3×2, we can find the product matrix CD.

Step 1

$$\begin{bmatrix} -3 & 4 & 2 \\ 5 & 0 & 4 \end{bmatrix} \begin{bmatrix} -6 & 4 \\ 2 & 3 \\ 3 & -2 \end{bmatrix} \qquad (-3) \cdot (-6) + 4 \cdot 2 + 2 \cdot 3 = 32$$

Step 2

$$\begin{bmatrix} -3 & 4 & 2 \\ 5 & 0 & 4 \end{bmatrix} \begin{bmatrix} -6 & 4 \\ 2 & 3 \\ 3 & -2 \end{bmatrix} \qquad (-3) \cdot 4 + 4 \cdot 3 + 2 \cdot (-2) = -4$$

Step 3

$$\begin{bmatrix} -3 & 4 & 2 \\ 5 & 0 & 4 \end{bmatrix} \begin{bmatrix} -6 & 4 \\ 2 & 3 \\ 3 & -2 \end{bmatrix} \qquad 5 \cdot (-6) + 0 \cdot 2 + 4 \cdot 3 = -18$$

Step 4

$$\begin{bmatrix} -3 & 4 & 2 \\ 5 & 0 & 4 \end{bmatrix} \begin{bmatrix} -6 & 4 \\ 2 & 3 \\ 3 & -2 \end{bmatrix} \qquad 5 \cdot 4 + 0 \cdot 3 + 4 \cdot (-2) = 12$$

YOUR TURN 1 Calculate the
product AB where $A = \begin{bmatrix} 3 & 4 \\ 1 & 2 \end{bmatrix}$ and
$B = \begin{bmatrix} 1 & -2 \\ -2 & -4 \end{bmatrix}$.

Step 5 The product is

$$CD = \begin{bmatrix} -3 & 4 & 2 \\ 5 & 0 & 4 \end{bmatrix} \begin{bmatrix} -6 & 4 \\ 2 & 3 \\ 3 & -2 \end{bmatrix} = \begin{bmatrix} 32 & -4 \\ -18 & 12 \end{bmatrix}.$$

Here the product of a 2 × 3 matrix and a 3 × 2 matrix is a 2 × 2 matrix.

TRY YOUR TURN 1

NOTE One way to avoid errors in matrix multiplication is to lower the first matrix so it is below and to the left of the second matrix, and then write the product in the space between the two matrices. For example, to multiply the matrices in Example 3, we could rewrite the product as shown.

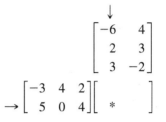

To find the entry where the * is, for example, multiply the row and the column indicated by the arrows: $5 \cdot (-6) + 0 \cdot 2 + 4 \cdot 3 = -18$.

As the definition of matrix multiplication shows,

> the product AB of two matrices A and B can be found only if the number of columns of A is the same as the number of rows of B.

The final product will have as many rows as A and as many columns as B.

EXAMPLE 4   Matrix Product

Suppose matrix A is 2 × 2 and matrix B is 2 × 4. Can the products AB and BA be calculated? If so, what is the size of each product?

SOLUTION The following diagram helps decide the answers to these questions.

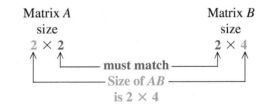

The product of A and B can be found because A has two columns and B has two rows. The size of the product is 2 × 4.

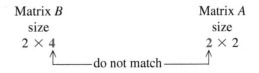

The product BA cannot be found because B has 4 columns and A has 2 rows.

> **EXAMPLE 5** **Comparing Matrix Products *AB* and *BA***
>
> Find AB and BA, given
>
> $$A = \begin{bmatrix} 1 & -3 \\ 7 & 2 \\ -2 & 5 \end{bmatrix} \quad \text{and} \quad B = \begin{bmatrix} 1 & 0 & -1 \\ 3 & 1 & 4 \end{bmatrix}.$$

SOLUTION

Method 1
Calculating by Hand

$$AB = \begin{bmatrix} 1 & -3 \\ 7 & 2 \\ -2 & 5 \end{bmatrix} \begin{bmatrix} 1 & 0 & -1 \\ 3 & 1 & 4 \end{bmatrix}$$

$$= \begin{bmatrix} -8 & -3 & -13 \\ 13 & 2 & 1 \\ 13 & 5 & 22 \end{bmatrix}$$

YOUR TURN 2 Calculate each product AB and BA, if possible, where $A = \begin{bmatrix} 3 & 5 & -1 \\ 2 & 4 & -2 \end{bmatrix}$ and $B = \begin{bmatrix} 3 & -4 \\ -5 & -3 \end{bmatrix}$.

$$BA = \begin{bmatrix} 1 & 0 & -1 \\ 3 & 1 & 4 \end{bmatrix} \begin{bmatrix} 1 & -3 \\ 7 & 2 \\ -2 & 5 \end{bmatrix}$$

$$= \begin{bmatrix} 3 & -8 \\ 2 & 13 \end{bmatrix}$$

Method 2
Graphing Calculator

Matrix multiplication is easily performed on a graphing calculator. Figure 10 in the margin below shows the results. The matrices A and B were already entered into the calculator.

TRY YOUR TURN 2

> **TECHNOLOGY NOTE**
>
> Matrix multiplication can also be easily done with a spreadsheet. See the *Graphing Calculator and Excel Spreadsheet Manual* available with this textbook for details.

```
[A]*[B]
       [-8   -3   -13]
       [13    2     1]
       [13    5    22]
[B]*[A]
          [3   -8]
          [2   13]
```

FIGURE 10

Notice in Example 5 that $AB \neq BA$; matrices AB and BA aren't even the same size. In Example 4, we showed that they may not both exist. This means that matrix multiplication is *not* commutative. Even if both A and B are square matrices, in general, matrices AB and BA are not equal. (See Exercise 31.) Of course, there may be special cases in which they are equal, but this is not true in general.

> **CAUTION** Since matrix multiplication is not commutative, always be careful to multiply matrices in the correct order.

Matrix multiplication *is* associative, however. For example, if

$$C = \begin{bmatrix} 3 & 2 \\ 0 & -4 \\ -1 & 1 \end{bmatrix},$$

then $(AB)C = A(BC)$, where A and B are the matrices given in Example 5. (Verify this.) Also, there is a distributive property of matrices such that, for appropriate matrices A, B, and C,

$$A(B + C) = AB + AC.$$

(See Exercises 32 and 33.) Other properties of matrix multiplication involving scalars are included in the exercises. Multiplicative inverses and multiplicative identities are defined in the next section.

> ### EXAMPLE 6   Bird Feeding

A wildlife center finds that the number of cardinals and finches that visit a bird feeder on a regular basis varies with the season, as shown in the matrix P below.

$$
\begin{array}{c}
\text{Spring} \\
\text{Summer} \\
\text{Fall} \\
\text{Winter}
\end{array}
\overset{\text{Cardinals Finches}}{
\begin{bmatrix}
25 & 31 \\
20 & 35 \\
22 & 29 \\
36 & 20
\end{bmatrix}}
= P
$$

The wildlife center has also found that cardinals and finches eat different amounts of sunflower seed, corn, and millet (in grams) when they visit the feeder. The matrix Q shows how much one bird of each species eats over an entire season.

$$
\begin{array}{c}
\text{Cardinals} \\
\text{Finches}
\end{array}
\overset{\text{Sunflower Corn Millet}}{
\begin{bmatrix}
32 & 10 & 30 \\
10 & 18 & 27
\end{bmatrix}}
= Q
$$

The cost (in cents) per gram of each type of seed is shown in the matrix R.

$$
\begin{array}{c}
\text{Sunflower} \\
\text{Corn} \\
\text{Millet}
\end{array}
\overset{\text{Cost}}{
\begin{bmatrix}
3 \\
2 \\
1
\end{bmatrix}}
= R
$$

(a) What is the total cost of seed for each season of the year to feed the cardinals and finches that regularly visit the feeder?

APPLY IT

SOLUTION   To find the total cost for each season, first find PQ, which shows how much of each type of seed is eaten each season of the year.

$$
PQ =
\begin{bmatrix}
25 & 31 \\
20 & 35 \\
22 & 29 \\
36 & 20
\end{bmatrix}
\begin{bmatrix}
32 & 10 & 30 \\
10 & 18 & 27
\end{bmatrix}
$$

$$
=
\overset{\text{Sunflower Corn Millet}}{
\begin{bmatrix}
1110 & 808 & 1587 \\
990 & 830 & 1545 \\
994 & 742 & 1443 \\
1352 & 720 & 1620
\end{bmatrix}}
\begin{array}{c}
\text{Spring} \\
\text{Summer} \\
\text{Fall} \\
\text{Winter}
\end{array}
$$

Now multiply PQ by R, the cost matrix, to get the total cost of seed for each season.

$$
\begin{bmatrix}
1110 & 808 & 1587 \\
990 & 830 & 1545 \\
994 & 742 & 1443 \\
1352 & 720 & 1620
\end{bmatrix}
\begin{bmatrix}
3 \\
2 \\
1
\end{bmatrix}
=
\overset{\text{Cost}}{
\begin{bmatrix}
6533 \\
6175 \\
5909 \\
7116
\end{bmatrix}}
\begin{array}{c}
\text{Spring} \\
\text{Summer} \\
\text{Fall} \\
\text{Winter}
\end{array}
$$

These costs are in cents, so multiply by 0.01 to convert to dollars. The total cost of seed is $65.33 in spring, $61.75 in summer, $59.09 in fall, and $71.16 in winter.

(b) How many grams of each kind of seed are used over an entire year?

SOLUTION   The totals of the columns of matrix PQ give a matrix whose elements represent the total number of grams of each seed used over an entire year. Call this matrix T, and write it as a row matrix.

$$
T = \begin{bmatrix} 4446 & 3100 & 6195 \end{bmatrix}
$$

Thus, 4446 grams of sunflower seed, 3100 grams of corn, and 6195 grams of millet are used over an entire year.

(c) What is the total cost of seed in a year?

SOLUTION For the total cost of seed in a year, find the product of the matrix T, the matrix showing the total amount of each seed, and matrix R, the cost matrix. (To multiply these and get a 1×1 matrix representing total cost, we need a 1×4 matrix multiplied by a 4×1 matrix. This is why T was written as a row matrix in (b) above.)

$$TR = \begin{bmatrix} 4446 & 3100 & 6195 \end{bmatrix} \begin{bmatrix} 3 \\ 2 \\ 1 \end{bmatrix} = \begin{bmatrix} 25{,}733 \end{bmatrix}$$

The total cost is $257.33. Of course, we could have calculated this same answer by adding the amounts found in part (a).

(d) Suppose the wildlife center puts bird feeders in four more locations, for a total of five feeders. The locations are very distant from each other, but have similar habitats, so the number of birds and the amount they eat is expected to be the same as at the original feeder. Calculate the total amount of each type of seed expected to be used in each season.

SOLUTION Multiply PQ by the scalar 5, as follows.

$$5(PQ) = 5\begin{bmatrix} 1110 & 808 & 1587 \\ 990 & 830 & 1545 \\ 994 & 742 & 1443 \\ 1352 & 720 & 1620 \end{bmatrix} = \begin{bmatrix} 5550 & 4040 & 7935 \\ 4950 & 4150 & 7725 \\ 4970 & 3710 & 7215 \\ 6760 & 3600 & 8100 \end{bmatrix}$$

The total amount of corn used in fall, for example, is 3710 grams.

Meaning of a Matrix Product

It is helpful to use a notation that keeps track of the quantities a matrix represents. We will use the notation

$$\text{meaning of the rows/meaning of the columns,}$$

that is, writing the meaning of the rows first, followed by the meaning of the columns. In Example 6, we would use the notation seasons/birds for matrix P, birds/seeds for matrix Q, and seeds/cost for matrix R. In multiplying PQ, we are multiplying seasons/birds by birds/seeds. The result is seasons/seeds. Notice that birds, the common quantity in both P and Q, was eliminated in the product PQ. By this method, the product $(PQ)R$ represents seasons/cost.

In practical problems this notation helps us decide in which order to multiply matrices so that the results are meaningful. In Example 6(c) either RT or TR can be calculated. Since T represents year/seeds and R represents seeds/cost, the product TR gives year/cost, while the product RT is meaningless.

10.3 EXERCISES

Let $A = \begin{bmatrix} -2 & 4 \\ 0 & 3 \end{bmatrix}$ and $B = \begin{bmatrix} -6 & 2 \\ 4 & 0 \end{bmatrix}$. Find each value.

1. $2A$

2. $-3B$

3. $-6A$

4. $5B$

5. $-4A + 5B$

6. $7B - 3A$

In Exercises 7–12, the sizes of two matrices A and B are given. Find the sizes of the product AB and the product BA, whenever these products exist.

7. A is 2×2, and B is 2×2.

8. A is 3×3, and B is 3×3.

9. A is 3×4, and B is 4×4.

10. A is 4×3, and B is 3×6.

11. A is 4×2, and B is 3×4.

12. A is 3×2, and B is 1×3.

13. To find the product matrix AB, the number of _____ of A must be the same as the number of _____ of B.

14. The product matrix AB has the same number of _____ as A and the same number of _____ as B.

Find each matrix product, if possible.

15. $\begin{bmatrix} 2 & -1 \\ 5 & 8 \end{bmatrix} \begin{bmatrix} 3 \\ -2 \end{bmatrix}$

16. $\begin{bmatrix} -1 & 5 \\ 7 & 0 \end{bmatrix} \begin{bmatrix} 6 \\ 2 \end{bmatrix}$

17. $\begin{bmatrix} 2 & -1 & 7 \\ -3 & 0 & -4 \end{bmatrix} \begin{bmatrix} 5 \\ 10 \\ 2 \end{bmatrix}$

18. $\begin{bmatrix} 5 & 2 \\ 7 & 6 \\ 1 & 0 \end{bmatrix} \begin{bmatrix} 1 & 4 & 0 \\ 2 & -1 & 2 \end{bmatrix}$

19. $\begin{bmatrix} 2 & -1 \\ 3 & 6 \end{bmatrix} \begin{bmatrix} -1 & 0 & 4 \\ 5 & -2 & 0 \end{bmatrix}$

20. $\begin{bmatrix} 6 & 0 & -4 \\ 1 & 2 & 5 \\ 10 & -1 & 3 \end{bmatrix} \begin{bmatrix} 1 \\ 2 \\ 0 \end{bmatrix}$

21. $\begin{bmatrix} 2 & 2 & -1 \\ 3 & 0 & 1 \end{bmatrix} \begin{bmatrix} 0 & 2 \\ -1 & 4 \\ 0 & 2 \end{bmatrix}$

22. $\begin{bmatrix} -3 & 1 & 0 \\ 6 & 0 & 8 \end{bmatrix} \begin{bmatrix} 3 \\ -1 \\ -2 \end{bmatrix}$

23. $\begin{bmatrix} 1 & 2 \\ 3 & 4 \end{bmatrix} \begin{bmatrix} -1 & 5 \\ 7 & 0 \end{bmatrix}$

24. $\begin{bmatrix} 2 & 8 \\ -7 & 5 \end{bmatrix} \begin{bmatrix} 1 & 0 \\ 0 & 1 \end{bmatrix}$

25. $\begin{bmatrix} -2 & -3 & 7 \\ 1 & 5 & 6 \end{bmatrix} \begin{bmatrix} 1 \\ 2 \\ 3 \end{bmatrix}$

26. $\begin{bmatrix} 2 \\ -9 \\ 12 \end{bmatrix} \begin{bmatrix} 1 & 0 & -1 \end{bmatrix}$

27. $\left(\begin{bmatrix} 2 & 1 \\ -3 & -6 \\ 4 & 0 \end{bmatrix} \begin{bmatrix} 1 & -2 \\ 2 & -1 \end{bmatrix} \right) \begin{bmatrix} 3 \\ 1 \end{bmatrix}$

28. $\begin{bmatrix} 2 & 1 \\ -3 & -6 \\ 4 & 0 \end{bmatrix} \left(\begin{bmatrix} 1 & -2 \\ 2 & -1 \end{bmatrix} \begin{bmatrix} 3 \\ 1 \end{bmatrix} \right)$

29. $\begin{bmatrix} 2 & -2 \\ 1 & -1 \end{bmatrix} \left(\begin{bmatrix} 4 & 3 \\ 1 & 2 \end{bmatrix} + \begin{bmatrix} 7 & 0 \\ -1 & 5 \end{bmatrix} \right)$

30. $\begin{bmatrix} 2 & -2 \\ 1 & -1 \end{bmatrix} \begin{bmatrix} 4 & 3 \\ 1 & 2 \end{bmatrix} + \begin{bmatrix} 2 & -2 \\ 1 & -1 \end{bmatrix} \begin{bmatrix} 7 & 0 \\ -1 & 5 \end{bmatrix}$

31. Let $A = \begin{bmatrix} -2 & 4 \\ 1 & 3 \end{bmatrix}$ and $B = \begin{bmatrix} -2 & 1 \\ 3 & 6 \end{bmatrix}$.

  a. Find AB.   **b.** Find BA.

  c. Did you get the same answer in parts a and b?

  d. In general, for matrices A and B such that AB and BA both exist, does AB always equal BA?

Given matrices $P = \begin{bmatrix} m & n \\ p & q \end{bmatrix}$, $X = \begin{bmatrix} x & y \\ z & w \end{bmatrix}$, and $T = \begin{bmatrix} r & s \\ t & u \end{bmatrix}$, verify that the statements in Exercises 32–35 are true. The statements are valid for any matrices whenever matrix multiplication and addition can be carried out. This, of course, depends on the size of the matrices.

32. $(PX)T = P(XT)$ (associative property: see Exercises 27 and 28)

33. $P(X + T) = PX + PT$ (distributive property: see Exercises 29 and 30)

34. $k(X + T) = kX + kT$ for any real number k.

35. $(k + h)P = kP + hP$ for any real numbers k and h.

36. Let I be the matrix $I = \begin{bmatrix} 1 & 0 \\ 0 & 1 \end{bmatrix}$, and let matrices P, X, and T be defined as for Exercises 32–35.

  a. Find IP, PI, and IX.

  b. Without calculating, guess what the matrix IT might be.

  c. Suggest a reason for naming a matrix such as I an *identity matrix*.

37. Show that the system of linear equations

$$2x_1 + 3x_2 + x_3 = 5$$
$$x_1 - 4x_2 + 5x_3 = 8$$

can be written as the matrix equation

$$\begin{bmatrix} 2 & 3 & 1 \\ 1 & -4 & 5 \end{bmatrix} \begin{bmatrix} x_1 \\ x_2 \\ x_3 \end{bmatrix} = \begin{bmatrix} 5 \\ 8 \end{bmatrix}.$$

38. Let $A = \begin{bmatrix} 1 & 2 \\ -3 & 5 \end{bmatrix}$, $X = \begin{bmatrix} x_1 \\ x_2 \end{bmatrix}$, and $B = \begin{bmatrix} -4 \\ 12 \end{bmatrix}$. Show that the equation $AX = B$ represents a linear system of two equations in two unknowns. Solve the system and substitute into the matrix equation to check your results.

Use a computer or graphing calculator and the following matrices to find the matrix products and sums in Exercises 39–41.

$$A = \begin{bmatrix} 2 & 3 & -1 & 5 & 10 \\ 2 & 8 & 7 & 4 & 3 \\ -1 & -4 & -12 & 6 & 8 \\ 2 & 5 & 7 & 1 & 4 \end{bmatrix} \quad B = \begin{bmatrix} 9 & 3 & 7 & -6 \\ -1 & 0 & 4 & 2 \\ -10 & -7 & 6 & 9 \\ 8 & 4 & 2 & -1 \\ 2 & -5 & 3 & 7 \end{bmatrix}$$

$$C = \begin{bmatrix} -6 & 8 & 2 & 4 & -3 \\ 1 & 9 & 7 & -12 & 5 \\ 15 & 2 & -8 & 10 & 11 \\ 4 & 7 & 9 & 6 & -2 \\ 1 & 3 & 8 & 23 & 4 \end{bmatrix} \quad D = \begin{bmatrix} 5 & -3 & 7 & 9 & 2 \\ 6 & 8 & -5 & 2 & 1 \\ 3 & 7 & -4 & 2 & 11 \\ 5 & -3 & 9 & 4 & -1 \\ 0 & 3 & 2 & 5 & 1 \end{bmatrix}$$

39. a. Find AC.

  b. Find CA.

  c. Does $AC = CA$?

40. a. Find CD.

  b. Find DC.

  c. Does $CD = DC$?

41. a. Find $C + D$.

  b. Find $(C + D)B$.

  c. Find CB.

  d. Find DB.

  e. Find $CB + DB$.

  f. Does $(C + D)B = CB + DB$?

42. Which property of matrices does Exercise 41 illustrate?

LIFE SCIENCE APPLICATIONS

43. Dietetics In Exercise 39 from Section 10.2, label the matrices

$$\begin{bmatrix} 2 & 1 & 2 & 1 \\ 3 & 2 & 2 & 1 \\ 4 & 3 & 2 & 1 \end{bmatrix}, \quad \begin{bmatrix} 5 & 0 & 7 \\ 0 & 10 & 1 \\ 0 & 15 & 2 \\ 10 & 12 & 8 \end{bmatrix}, \quad \text{and} \quad \begin{bmatrix} 8 \\ 4 \\ 5 \end{bmatrix}$$

found in parts a, b, and c, respectively, X, Y, and Z.

  a. Find the product matrix XY. What do the entries of this matrix represent?

  b. Find the product matrix YZ. What do the entries represent?

  c. Find the products $(XY)Z$ and $X(YZ)$ and verify that they are equal. What do the entries represent?

44. Motorcycle Helmets In Exercise 42 from Section 10.2, you constructed matrices that represented usage of motorcycle helmets for 2008 and 2009. Use matrix operations to combine these two matrices to form one matrix that represents the average of the two years.

45. Life Expectancy In Exercise 43 from Section 10.2, you constructed matrices that represent the life expectancy of African American and white American males and females. Use matrix operations to combine these two matrices to form one matrix that represents the combined life expectancy of both races at the beginning of each decade since 1970. Use the fact that of the combined African and white American population, African Americans are about one-sixth of the total and white Americans about five-sixths. (*Hint:* Multiply the matrix for African Americans by 1/6 and the matrix for the white Americans by 5/6, and then add the results.)

46. Car Accidents In Exercise 47 from Section 10.2, you constructed matrices that represent the death rates, per million person trips, for both male and female drivers for various ages and number of passengers. Use matrix operations to combine these two matrices to form one matrix that represents the combined death rates for males and females, per million person trips, of drivers of various ages and number of passengers. (*Hint:* Add the two matrices together and then multiply the resulting matrix by the scalar 1/2.)

47. Northern Spotted Owl Population In an attempt to save the endangered northern spotted owl, the U.S. Fish and Wildlife Service imposed strict guidelines for the use of 12 million acres of Pacific Northwest forest. This decision led to a national debate between the logging industry and environmentalists. Mathematical ecologists have created a mathematical model to analyze population dynamics of the northern spotted owl by dividing the female owl population into three categories: juvenile (up to 1 year old), subadult (1 to 2 years), and adult (over 2 years old). By analyzing these three subgroups, it is possible to use the number of females in each subgroup at time n to estimate the number of females in each group at any time $n + 1$ with the following matrix equation:

$$\begin{bmatrix} j_{n+1} \\ s_{n+1} \\ a_{n+1} \end{bmatrix} = \begin{bmatrix} 0 & 0 & 0.33 \\ 0.18 & 0 & 0 \\ 0 & 0.71 & 0.94 \end{bmatrix} \begin{bmatrix} j_n \\ s_n \\ a_n \end{bmatrix},$$

where j_n is the number of juveniles, s_n is the number of subadults, and a_n is the number of adults at time n. *Source: Conservation Biology.*

  a. If there are currently 4000 female northern spotted owls made up of 900 juveniles, 500 subadults, and 2600 adults, use a graphing calculator or spreadsheet and matrix operations to determine the total number of female owls for each of the next 5 years. (*Hint:* Round each answer to the nearest whole number after each matrix multiplication.)

  b. With advanced techniques from linear algebra, it is possible to show that in the long run, the following holds.

$$\begin{bmatrix} j_{n+1} \\ s_{n+1} \\ a_{n+1} \end{bmatrix} \approx 0.98359 \begin{bmatrix} j_n \\ s_n \\ a_n \end{bmatrix}$$

  What can we conclude about the long-term survival of the northern spotted owl?

  c. Notice that only 18 percent of the juveniles become subadults. Assuming that, through better habitat management, this number could be increased to 40 percent, rework part a. Discuss possible reasons why only 18 percent of the juveniles become subadults. Under the new assumption, what can you conclude about the long-term survival of the northern spotted owl?

48. World Population The 2010 birth and death rates per million for several regions and the world population (in millions) by region are given in the following tables. *Source: U.S. Census Bureau.*

	Births	**Deaths**
Africa	0.0346	0.0118
Asia	0.0174	0.0073
Latin America	0.0189	0.0059
North America	0.0135	0.0083
Europe	0.0099	0.0103

		Population (millions)			
Year	Africa	Asia	Latin America	North America	Europe
1970	361	2038	286	227	460
1980	473	2494	362	252	484
1990	627	2978	443	278	499
2000	803	3435	524	314	511
2010	1013	3824	591	344	522

a. Write the information in each table as a matrix.

b. Use the matrices from part a to find the total number (in millions) of births and deaths in each year (assuming birth and death rates for all years are close to these in 2010).

c. Using the results of part b, compare the number of births in 1970 and in 2010. Also compare the birth rates from part a. Which gives better information?

d. Using the results of part b, compare the number of deaths in 1980 and in 2010. Discuss how this comparison differs from a comparison of death rates from part a.

49. Bird Feeding Consider the matrices P, Q, and R given in Example 6.

a. Find and interpret the matrix product QR.

b. Verify that $P(QR)$ is equal to $(PQ)R$ calculated in Example 6.

OTHER APPLICATIONS

50. Cost Analysis The four departments of Spangler Enterprises need to order the following amounts of the same products.

	Paper	Tape	Binders	Memo Pads	Pens
Department 1	10	4	3	5	6
Department 2	7	2	2	3	8
Department 3	4	5	1	0	10
Department 4	0	3	4	5	5

The unit price (in dollars) of each product is given below for two suppliers.

	Supplier A	Supplier B
Paper	2	3
Tape	1	1
Binders	4	3
Memo Pads	3	3
Pens	1	2

a. Use matrix multiplication to get a matrix showing the comparative costs for each department for the products from the two suppliers.

b. Find the total cost over all departments to buy products from each supplier. From which supplier should the company make the purchase?

51. Cost Analysis The Mundo Candy Company makes three types of chocolate candy: Cheery Cherry, Mucho Mocha, and Almond Delight. The company produces its products in San Diego, Mexico City, and Managua using two main ingredients: chocolate and sugar.

a. Each kilogram of Cheery Cherry requires 0.5 kg of sugar and 0.2 kg of chocolate; each kilogram of Mucho Mocha requires 0.4 kg of sugar and 0.3 kg of chocolate; and each kilogram of Almond Delight requires 0.3 kg of sugar and 0.3 kg of chocolate. Put this information into a 2×3 matrix called A, labeling the rows and columns.

b. The cost of 1 kg of sugar is $4 in San Diego, $2 in Mexico City, and $1 in Managua. The cost of 1 kg of chocolate is $3 in San Diego, $5 in Mexico City, and $7 in Managua. Put this information into a matrix called C in such a way that when you multiply it with your matrix from part a, you get a matrix representing the ingredient cost of producing each type of candy in each city.

c. Only one of the two products AC and CA is meaningful. Determine which one it is, calculate the product, and describe what the entries represent.

d. From your answer to part c, what is the combined sugar-and-chocolate cost to produce 1 kg of Mucho Mocha in Managua?

e. Mundo Candy needs to quickly produce a special shipment of 100 kg of Cheery Cherry, 200 kg of Mucho Mocha, and 500 kg of Almond Delight, and it decides to select one factory to fill the entire order. Use matrix multiplication to determine in which city the total sugar-and-chocolate cost to produce the order is the smallest.

52. Shoe Sales Sal's Shoes and Fred's Footwear both have outlets in California and Arizona. Sal's sells shoes for $80, sandals for $40, and boots for $120. Fred's prices are $60, $30, and $150 for shoes, sandals, and boots, respectively. Half of all sales in California stores are shoes, 1/4 are sandals, and 1/4 are boots. In Arizona the fractions are 1/5 shoes, 1/5 sandals, and 3/5 boots.

a. Write a 2×3 matrix called P representing prices for the two stores and three types of footwear.

b. Write a 3×2 matrix called F representing the fraction of each type of footwear sold in each state.

c. Only one of the two products PF and FP is meaningful. Determine which one it is, calculate the product, and describe what the entries represent.

d. From your answer to part c, what is the average price for a pair of footwear at an outlet of Fred's in Arizona?

YOUR TURN ANSWERS

1. $\begin{bmatrix} -5 & -22 \\ -3 & -10 \end{bmatrix}$ **2.** AB does not exist; $BA = \begin{bmatrix} 1 & -1 & 5 \\ -21 & -37 & 11 \end{bmatrix}$

10.4   Matrix Inverses

APPLY IT

How can we determine the amount of various kinds of fertilizers to use on a farm, given the requirements for the soil?
This question is answered in Example 5.

In this section, we introduce the idea of a matrix inverse, which is comparable to the reciprocal of a real number. This will allow us to solve a matrix equation.

The real number 1 is the *multiplicative* identity for real numbers: for any real number a, we have $a \cdot 1 = 1 \cdot a = a$. In this section, we define a *multiplicative identity matrix I* that has properties similar to those of the number 1. We then use the definition of matrix I to find the *multiplicative inverse* of any square matrix that has an inverse.

If I is to be the identity matrix, both of the products AI and IA must equal A. This means that an identity matrix exists only for square matrices. The 2×2 **identity matrix** that satisfies these conditions is

$$I = \begin{bmatrix} 1 & 0 \\ 0 & 1 \end{bmatrix}.$$

To check that I, as defined above, is really the 2×2 identity, let

$$A = \begin{bmatrix} a & b \\ c & d \end{bmatrix}.$$

Then AI and IA should both equal A.

$$AI = \begin{bmatrix} a & b \\ c & d \end{bmatrix} \begin{bmatrix} 1 & 0 \\ 0 & 1 \end{bmatrix} = \begin{bmatrix} a(1) + b(0) & a(0) + b(1) \\ c(1) + d(0) & c(0) + d(1) \end{bmatrix} = \begin{bmatrix} a & b \\ c & d \end{bmatrix} = A$$

$$IA = \begin{bmatrix} 1 & 0 \\ 0 & 1 \end{bmatrix} \begin{bmatrix} a & b \\ c & d \end{bmatrix} = \begin{bmatrix} 1(a) + 0(c) & 1(b) + 0(d) \\ 0(a) + 1(c) & 0(b) + 1(d) \end{bmatrix} = \begin{bmatrix} a & b \\ c & d \end{bmatrix} = A$$

This verifies that I has been defined correctly.

It is easy to verify that the identity matrix I is unique. Suppose there is another identity; call it J. Then IJ must equal I, because J is an identity, and IJ must also equal J, because I is an identity. Thus $I = J$.

The identity matrices for 3×3 matrices and 4×4 matrices, respectively, are

$$I = \begin{bmatrix} 1 & 0 & 0 \\ 0 & 1 & 0 \\ 0 & 0 & 1 \end{bmatrix} \quad \text{and} \quad I = \begin{bmatrix} 1 & 0 & 0 & 0 \\ 0 & 1 & 0 & 0 \\ 0 & 0 & 1 & 0 \\ 0 & 0 & 0 & 1 \end{bmatrix}.$$

By generalizing, we can find an $n \times n$ identity matrix for any value of n.

Recall that the multiplicative inverse of the nonzero real number a is $1/a$. The product of a and its multiplicative inverse $1/a$ is 1. Given a matrix A, can a **multiplicative inverse matrix A^{-1}** (read "A-inverse") that will satisfy both

$$AA^{-1} = I \quad \text{and} \quad A^{-1}A = I$$

be found? For a given matrix, we often can find an inverse matrix by using the row operations of Section 10.1.

NOTE A^{-1} does not mean $1/A$; here, A^{-1} is just the notation for the multiplicative inverse of matrix A. Also, only square matrices can have inverses because both $A^{-1}A$ and AA^{-1} must exist and be equal to an identity matrix of the same size.

EXAMPLE 1 Inverse Matrices

Verify that the matrices $A = \begin{bmatrix} 1 & 3 \\ 2 & 5 \end{bmatrix}$ and $B = \begin{bmatrix} -5 & 3 \\ 2 & -1 \end{bmatrix}$ are inverses of each other.

SOLUTION Multiply A times B as in the previous section:

$$AB = \begin{bmatrix} 1 & 3 \\ 2 & 5 \end{bmatrix}\begin{bmatrix} -5 & 3 \\ 2 & -1 \end{bmatrix} = \begin{bmatrix} 1 & 0 \\ 0 & 1 \end{bmatrix}.$$

Similarly,

$$BA = \begin{bmatrix} -5 & 3 \\ 2 & -1 \end{bmatrix}\begin{bmatrix} 1 & 3 \\ 2 & 5 \end{bmatrix} = \begin{bmatrix} 1 & 0 \\ 0 & 1 \end{bmatrix}.$$

Since $AB = BA = I$, A and B are inverses of each other.

If an inverse exists, it is unique. That is, any given square matrix has no more than one inverse. The proof of this is left to Exercise 50 in this section.

As an example, let us find the inverse of

$$A = \begin{bmatrix} 1 & 3 \\ -1 & 2 \end{bmatrix}.$$

Let the unknown inverse matrix be

$$A^{-1} = \begin{bmatrix} x & y \\ z & w \end{bmatrix}.$$

By the definition of matrix inverse, $AA^{-1} = I$, or

$$AA^{-1} = \begin{bmatrix} 1 & 3 \\ -1 & 2 \end{bmatrix}\begin{bmatrix} x & y \\ z & w \end{bmatrix} = \begin{bmatrix} 1 & 0 \\ 0 & 1 \end{bmatrix}.$$

By matrix multiplication,

$$\begin{bmatrix} x + 3z & y + 3w \\ -x + 2z & -y + 2w \end{bmatrix} = \begin{bmatrix} 1 & 0 \\ 0 & 1 \end{bmatrix}.$$

Setting corresponding elements equal gives the system of equations

$$x \qquad + 3z \qquad = 1 \tag{1}$$
$$y \qquad + 3w = 0 \tag{2}$$
$$-x \qquad + 2z \qquad = 0 \tag{3}$$
$$- y \qquad + 2w = 1. \tag{4}$$

Since Equations (1) and (3) involve only x and z, while Equations (2) and (4) involve only y and w, these four equations lead to two systems of equations,

$$x + 3z = 1 \qquad\qquad y + 3w = 0$$
$$\qquad\qquad\text{and}$$
$$-x + 2z = 0 \qquad\qquad -y + 2w = 1.$$

Writing the two systems as augmented matrices gives

$$\begin{bmatrix} 1 & 3 & | & 1 \\ -1 & 2 & | & 0 \end{bmatrix} \quad\text{and}\quad \begin{bmatrix} 1 & 3 & | & 0 \\ -1 & 2 & | & 1 \end{bmatrix}.$$

Each of these systems can be solved by the Gauss-Jordan method. Notice, however, that the elements to the left of the vertical bar are identical. The two systems can be combined into the single matrix

$$\begin{bmatrix} 1 & 3 & | & 1 & 0 \\ -1 & 2 & | & 0 & 1 \end{bmatrix}.$$

This is of the form $[A \mid I]$. It is solved simultaneously as follows.

$$R_1 + R_2 \rightarrow R_2 \quad \begin{bmatrix} 1 & 3 & | & 1 & 0 \\ 0 & 5 & | & 1 & 1 \end{bmatrix} \quad \text{Get 0 in the second-row,}\\ \text{first-column position.}$$

$$-3R_2 + 5R_1 \rightarrow R_1 \quad \begin{bmatrix} 5 & 0 & | & 2 & -3 \\ 0 & 5 & | & 1 & 1 \end{bmatrix} \quad \text{Get 0 in the first-row,}\\ \text{second-column position.}$$

$$\begin{matrix} \frac{1}{5}R_1 \rightarrow R_1 \\ \frac{1}{5}R_2 \rightarrow R_2 \end{matrix} \quad \begin{bmatrix} 1 & 0 & | & \frac{2}{5} & -\frac{3}{5} \\ 0 & 1 & | & \frac{1}{5} & \frac{1}{5} \end{bmatrix} \quad \text{Get 1's down the}\\ \text{diagonal.}$$

The numbers in the first column to the right of the vertical bar give the values of x and z. The second column gives the values of y and w. That is,

$$\begin{bmatrix} 1 & 0 & | & x & y \\ 0 & 1 & | & z & w \end{bmatrix} = \begin{bmatrix} 1 & 0 & | & \frac{2}{5} & -\frac{3}{5} \\ 0 & 1 & | & \frac{1}{5} & \frac{1}{5} \end{bmatrix}$$

so that

$$A^{-1} = \begin{bmatrix} x & y \\ z & w \end{bmatrix} = \begin{bmatrix} \frac{2}{5} & -\frac{3}{5} \\ \frac{1}{5} & \frac{1}{5} \end{bmatrix}.$$

To check, multiply A by A^{-1}. The result should be I.

$$AA^{-1} = \begin{bmatrix} 1 & 3 \\ -1 & 2 \end{bmatrix} \begin{bmatrix} \frac{2}{5} & -\frac{3}{5} \\ \frac{1}{5} & \frac{1}{5} \end{bmatrix} = \begin{bmatrix} \frac{2}{5} + \frac{3}{5} & -\frac{3}{5} + \frac{3}{5} \\ -\frac{2}{5} + \frac{2}{5} & \frac{3}{5} + \frac{2}{5} \end{bmatrix} = \begin{bmatrix} 1 & 0 \\ 0 & 1 \end{bmatrix} = I$$

Verify that $A^{-1}A = I$, also.

Finding a Multiplicative Inverse Matrix

To obtain A^{-1} for any $n \times n$ matrix A for which A^{-1} exists, follow these steps.

1. Form the augmented matrix $[A \mid I]$, where I is the $n \times n$ identity matrix.
2. Perform row operations on $[A \mid I]$ to get a matrix of the form $[I \mid B]$, if this is possible.
3. Matrix B is A^{-1}.

EXAMPLE 2 Inverse Matrix

Find A^{-1} if $A = \begin{bmatrix} 1 & 0 & 1 \\ 2 & -2 & -1 \\ 3 & 0 & 0 \end{bmatrix}$.

Method 1
Calculating by Hand

SOLUTION Write the augmented matrix $[A \mid I]$.

$$[A \mid I] = \begin{bmatrix} 1 & 0 & 1 & | & 1 & 0 & 0 \\ 2 & -2 & -1 & | & 0 & 1 & 0 \\ 3 & 0 & 0 & | & 0 & 0 & 1 \end{bmatrix}$$

Begin by selecting the row operation that produces a zero for the first element in row 2.

$$\begin{matrix} -2R_1 + R_2 \rightarrow R_2 \\ -3R_1 + R_3 \rightarrow R_3 \end{matrix} \quad \begin{bmatrix} 1 & 0 & 1 & | & 1 & 0 & 0 \\ 0 & -2 & -3 & | & -2 & 1 & 0 \\ 0 & 0 & -3 & | & -3 & 0 & 1 \end{bmatrix} \quad \text{Get 0's in the first column.}$$

Column 2 already has zeros in the required positions, so work on column 3.

$$
\begin{matrix}
R_3 + 3R_1 \rightarrow R_1 \\
R_3 + (-1)R_2 \rightarrow R_2
\end{matrix}
\quad
\left[\begin{array}{ccc|ccc}
3 & 0 & 0 & 0 & 0 & 1 \\
0 & 2 & 0 & -1 & -1 & 1 \\
0 & 0 & -3 & -3 & 0 & 1
\end{array}\right]
\quad \text{Get 0's in the third column.}
$$

Now get 1's down the main diagonal.

$$
\begin{matrix}
\frac{1}{3}R_1 \rightarrow R_1 \\
\frac{1}{2}R_2 \rightarrow R_2 \\
-\frac{1}{3}R_3 \rightarrow R_3
\end{matrix}
\quad
\left[\begin{array}{ccc|ccc}
1 & 0 & 0 & 0 & 0 & \frac{1}{3} \\
0 & 1 & 0 & -\frac{1}{2} & -\frac{1}{2} & \frac{1}{2} \\
0 & 0 & 1 & 1 & 0 & -\frac{1}{3}
\end{array}\right]
\quad \text{Get 1's down the diagonal.}
$$

From the last transformation, the desired inverse is

$$
A^{-1} = \begin{bmatrix}
0 & 0 & \frac{1}{3} \\
-\frac{1}{2} & -\frac{1}{2} & \frac{1}{2} \\
1 & 0 & -\frac{1}{3}
\end{bmatrix}.
$$

YOUR TURN 1 Find A^{-1} if

$$A = \begin{bmatrix} 2 & 3 & 1 \\ 1 & -2 & -1 \\ 3 & 3 & 2 \end{bmatrix}.$$

Confirm this by forming the products $A^{-1}A$ and AA^{-1}, both of which should equal I.

Method 2
Graphing Calculator

The inverse of A can also be found with a graphing calculator, as shown in Figure 11 in the margin below. (The matrix A had previously been entered into the calculator.)

TRY YOUR TURN 1

TECHNOLOGY NOTE

Spreadsheets also have the capability of calculating the inverse of a matrix with a simple command. See the *Graphing Calculator and Excel Spreadsheet Manual* available with this book for details.

[A]⁻¹▶Frac
$$\begin{bmatrix} 0 & 0 & \frac{1}{3} \\ -\frac{1}{2} & -\frac{1}{2} & \frac{1}{2} \\ 1 & 0 & -\frac{1}{3} \end{bmatrix}$$

FIGURE 11

EXAMPLE 3 **Inverse Matrix**

Find A^{-1} if $A = \begin{bmatrix} 2 & -4 \\ 1 & -2 \end{bmatrix}$.

SOLUTION Using row operations to transform the first column of the augmented matrix

$$
\left[\begin{array}{cc|cc}
2 & -4 & 1 & 0 \\
1 & -2 & 0 & 1
\end{array}\right]
$$

gives the following results.

$$
R_1 + (-2)R_2 \rightarrow R_2
\quad
\left[\begin{array}{cc|cc}
2 & -4 & 1 & 0 \\
0 & 0 & 1 & -2
\end{array}\right]
$$

Because the last row has all zeros to the left of the vertical bar, there is no way to complete the process of finding the inverse matrix. What is wrong? Just as the real number 0 has no multiplicative inverse, some matrices do not have inverses. Matrix A is an example of a matrix that has no inverse: there is no matrix A^{-1} such that $AA^{-1} = A^{-1}A = I$.

NOTE As is shown in Exercise 46, there is a quick way to find the inverse of a 2×2 matrix:

$$
\text{When } A = \begin{bmatrix} a & b \\ c & d \end{bmatrix} \text{ and } ad - bc \neq 0, \ A^{-1} = \frac{1}{ad - bc}\begin{bmatrix} d & -b \\ -c & a \end{bmatrix}.
$$

Solving Systems of Equations with Inverses

We used matrices to solve systems of linear equations by the Gauss-Jordan method in Section 10.1. Another way to use matrices to solve linear systems is to write the system as a matrix equation $AX = B$, where A is the matrix of the coefficients of the variables of the system, X is the matrix of the variables, and B is the matrix of the constants. Matrix A is called the **coefficient matrix**.

To solve the matrix equation $AX = B$, first see if A^{-1} exists. Assuming A^{-1} exists and using the facts that $A^{-1}A = I$ and $IX = X$ gives

$$AX = B$$
$$A^{-1}(AX) = A^{-1}B \quad \text{Multiply both sides by } A^{-1}.$$
$$(A^{-1}A)X = A^{-1}B \quad \text{Associative property}$$
$$IX = A^{-1}B \quad \text{Multiplicative inverse property}$$
$$X = A^{-1}B. \quad \text{Identity property}$$

CAUTION When multiplying by matrices on both sides of a matrix equation, be careful to multiply in the same order on both sides of the equation, since multiplication of matrices is not commutative (unlike multiplication of real numbers).

The work thus far leads to the following method of solving a system of equations written as a matrix equation.

Solving a System $AX = B$ Using Matrix Inverses

To solve a system of equations $AX = B$, where A is the square matrix of coefficients and A^{-1} exists, X is the matrix of variables, and B is the matrix of constants, first find A^{-1}. Then $X = A^{-1}B$.

This method is most practical in solving several systems that have the same coefficient matrix but different constants, as in Example 5 in this section. Then just one inverse matrix must be found.

EXAMPLE 4 Inverse Matrices and Systems of Equations

Use the inverse of the coefficient matrix to solve the linear system

$$2x - 3y = 4$$
$$x + 5y = 2.$$

SOLUTION To represent the system as a matrix equation, use the coefficient matrix of the system together with the matrix of variables and the matrix of constants:

$$A = \begin{bmatrix} 2 & -3 \\ 1 & 5 \end{bmatrix}, \quad X = \begin{bmatrix} x \\ y \end{bmatrix}, \quad \text{and} \quad B = \begin{bmatrix} 4 \\ 2 \end{bmatrix}.$$

The system can now be written in matrix form as the equation $AX = B$, since

$$AX = \begin{bmatrix} 2 & -3 \\ 1 & 5 \end{bmatrix} \begin{bmatrix} x \\ y \end{bmatrix} = \begin{bmatrix} 2x - 3y \\ x + 5y \end{bmatrix} = \begin{bmatrix} 4 \\ 2 \end{bmatrix} = B.$$

To solve the system, first find A^{-1}. Do this by using row operations on matrix $[A \mid I]$ to get

$$\begin{bmatrix} 1 & 0 & \frac{5}{13} & \frac{3}{13} \\ 0 & 1 & -\frac{1}{13} & \frac{2}{13} \end{bmatrix}.$$

From this result,

$$A^{-1} = \begin{bmatrix} \frac{5}{13} & \frac{3}{13} \\ -\frac{1}{13} & \frac{2}{13} \end{bmatrix}.$$

Next, find the product $A^{-1}B$.

$$A^{-1}B = \begin{bmatrix} \frac{5}{13} & \frac{3}{13} \\ -\frac{1}{13} & \frac{2}{13} \end{bmatrix} \begin{bmatrix} 4 \\ 2 \end{bmatrix} = \begin{bmatrix} 2 \\ 0 \end{bmatrix}$$

YOUR TURN 2 Use the inverse of the coefficient matrix to solve the linear system

$5x + 4y = 23$
$4x - 3y = 6.$

Since $X = A^{-1}B$,

$$X = \begin{bmatrix} x \\ y \end{bmatrix} = \begin{bmatrix} 2 \\ 0 \end{bmatrix}.$$

The solution of the system is $(2, 0)$. **TRY YOUR TURN 2**

EXAMPLE 5 Fertilizer

Three brands of fertilizer are available that provide nitrogen, phosphoric acid, and soluble potash to the soil. One bag of each brand provides the following units of each nutrient.

		Brand		
		Fertifun	Big Grow	Soakem
Nutrient	Nitrogen	1	2	3
	Phosphoric Acid	3	1	2
	Potash	2	0	1

For ideal growth, the soil on a Michigan farm needs 18 units of nitrogen, 23 units of phosphoric acid, and 13 units of potash per acre. The corresponding numbers for a California farm are 31, 24, and 11, and for a Kansas farm are 20, 19, and 15. How many bags of each brand of fertilizer should be used per acre for ideal growth on each farm?

APPLY IT **SOLUTION** Rather than solve three separate systems, we consider the single system

$$x + 2y + 3z = a$$
$$3x + y + 2z = b$$
$$2x \quad\quad + z = c,$$

where a, b, and c represent the units of nitrogen, phosphoric acid, and potash needed for the different farms. The system of equations is then of the form $AX = B$, where

$$A = \begin{bmatrix} 1 & 2 & 3 \\ 3 & 1 & 2 \\ 2 & 0 & 1 \end{bmatrix} \quad \text{and} \quad X = \begin{bmatrix} x \\ y \\ z \end{bmatrix}.$$

B has different values for the different farms. We find A^{-1} first, then use it to solve all three systems.

To find A^{-1}, we start with the matrix

$$[A\,|\,I] = \begin{bmatrix} 1 & 2 & 3 & | & 1 & 0 & 0 \\ 3 & 1 & 2 & | & 0 & 1 & 0 \\ 2 & 0 & 1 & | & 0 & 0 & 1 \end{bmatrix}$$

and use row operations to get $[I\,|\,A^{-1}]$. The result is

$$A^{-1} = \begin{bmatrix} -\frac{1}{3} & \frac{2}{3} & -\frac{1}{3} \\ -\frac{1}{3} & \frac{5}{3} & -\frac{7}{3} \\ \frac{2}{3} & -\frac{4}{3} & \frac{5}{3} \end{bmatrix}.$$

Now we can solve each of the three systems by using $X = A^{-1}B$.

For the Michigan farm, $B = \begin{bmatrix} 18 \\ 23 \\ 13 \end{bmatrix}$, and

$$X = \begin{bmatrix} -\frac{1}{3} & \frac{2}{3} & -\frac{1}{3} \\ -\frac{1}{3} & \frac{5}{3} & -\frac{7}{3} \\ \frac{2}{3} & -\frac{4}{3} & \frac{5}{3} \end{bmatrix} \begin{bmatrix} 18 \\ 23 \\ 13 \end{bmatrix} = \begin{bmatrix} 5 \\ 2 \\ 3 \end{bmatrix}.$$

Therefore, $x = 5$, $y = 2$, and $z = 3$. Buy 5 bags of Fertifun, 2 bags of Big Grow, and 3 bags of Soakem.

For the California farm, $B = \begin{bmatrix} 31 \\ 24 \\ 11 \end{bmatrix}$, and

$$X = \begin{bmatrix} -\frac{1}{3} & \frac{2}{3} & -\frac{1}{3} \\ -\frac{1}{3} & \frac{5}{3} & -\frac{7}{3} \\ \frac{2}{3} & -\frac{4}{3} & \frac{5}{3} \end{bmatrix} \begin{bmatrix} 31 \\ 24 \\ 11 \end{bmatrix} = \begin{bmatrix} 2 \\ 4 \\ 7 \end{bmatrix}.$$

Buy 2 bags of Fertifun, 4 bags of Big Grow, and 7 bags of Soakem.

For the Kansas farm, $B = \begin{bmatrix} 20 \\ 19 \\ 15 \end{bmatrix}$. Verify that this leads to $x = 1$, $y = -10$, and $z = 13$.

We cannot have a negative number of bags, so this solution is impossible. In buying enough bags to meet all of the nutrient requirements, the farmer must purchase an excess of some nutrients.

In Example 5, using the matrix inverse method of solving the systems involved considerably less work than using row operations for each of the three systems.

EXAMPLE 6   Solving an Inconsistent System of Equations

Use the inverse of the coefficient matrix to solve the system

$$2x - 4y = 13$$
$$x - 2y = 1.$$

SOLUTION   We saw in Example 3 that the coefficient matrix $\begin{bmatrix} 2 & -4 \\ 1 & -2 \end{bmatrix}$ does not have an inverse. This means that the given system either has no solution or has an infinite number of solutions. Verify that this system is inconsistent and has no solution.

NOTE   If a matrix has no inverse, then a corresponding system of equations might have either no solutions or an infinite number of solutions, and we instead use the Gauss-Jordan method. In Example 3, we saw that the matrix $\begin{bmatrix} 2 & -4 \\ 1 & -2 \end{bmatrix}$ had no inverse. The reason is that the first row of this matrix is double the second row. The system

$$2x - 4y = 2$$
$$x - 2y = 1$$

has an infinite number of solutions because the first equation is double the second equation. The system

$$2x - 4y = 13$$
$$x - 2y = 1$$

has no solutions because the left side of the first equation is double the left side of the second equation, but the right side is not.

EXAMPLE 7   Cryptography

Throughout the Cold War and as the Internet has grown and developed, the need for sophisticated methods of coding and decoding messages has increased. Although there are many methods of encrypting messages, one fairly sophisticated method uses matrix operations. This method first assigns a number to each letter of the alphabet. The simplest way to do this is to assign the number 1 to A, 2 to B, and so on, with the number 27 used to represent a space between words.

For example, the message *math is cool* can be divided into groups of three letters and spaces each and then converted into numbers as follows:

$$\begin{bmatrix} m \\ a \\ t \end{bmatrix} = \begin{bmatrix} 13 \\ 1 \\ 20 \end{bmatrix}.$$

The entire message would then consist of four 3×1 columns of numbers:

$$\begin{bmatrix} 13 \\ 1 \\ 20 \end{bmatrix}, \quad \begin{bmatrix} 8 \\ 27 \\ 9 \end{bmatrix}, \quad \begin{bmatrix} 19 \\ 27 \\ 3 \end{bmatrix}, \quad \begin{bmatrix} 15 \\ 15 \\ 12 \end{bmatrix}.$$

This code is easy to break, so we further complicate the code by choosing a matrix that has an inverse (in this case a 3×3 matrix) and calculate the products of the matrix and each of the column vectors above.

If we choose the coding matrix

$$A = \begin{bmatrix} 1 & 3 & 4 \\ 2 & 1 & 3 \\ 4 & 2 & 1 \end{bmatrix},$$

then the products of A with each of the column vectors above produce a new set of vectors

$$\begin{bmatrix} 96 \\ 87 \\ 74 \end{bmatrix}, \quad \begin{bmatrix} 125 \\ 70 \\ 95 \end{bmatrix}, \quad \begin{bmatrix} 112 \\ 74 \\ 133 \end{bmatrix}, \quad \begin{bmatrix} 108 \\ 81 \\ 102 \end{bmatrix}.$$

This set of vectors represents our coded message, and it will be transmitted as 96, 87, 74, 125 and so on.

When the intended person receives the message, it is divided into groups of three numbers, and each group is formed into a column matrix. The message is easily decoded if the receiver knows the inverse of the original matrix. The inverse of matrix A is

$$A^{-1} = \begin{bmatrix} -0.2 & 0.2 & 0.2 \\ 0.4 & -0.6 & 0.2 \\ 0 & 0.4 & -0.2 \end{bmatrix}.$$

Thus, the message is decoded by taking the product of the inverse matrix with each column vector of the received message. For example,

$$A^{-1} \begin{bmatrix} 96 \\ 87 \\ 74 \end{bmatrix} = \begin{bmatrix} 13 \\ 1 \\ 20 \end{bmatrix}.$$

YOUR TURN 3 Use the matrix A and its inverse A^{-1} in Example 7 to do the following.
(a) Encode the message "Behold."
(b) Decode the message 96, 87, 74, 141, 117, 114.

Unless the original matrix or its inverse is known, this type of code can be difficult to break. In fact, very large matrices can be used to encrypt data. It is interesting to note that many mathematicians are employed by the National Security Agency to develop encryption methods that are virtually unbreakable. **TRY YOUR TURN 3**

10.4 EXERCISES

Decide whether the given matrices are inverses of each other. (Check to see if their product is the identity matrix I.)

1. $\begin{bmatrix} 2 & 1 \\ 5 & 3 \end{bmatrix}$ and $\begin{bmatrix} 3 & -1 \\ -5 & 2 \end{bmatrix}$

2. $\begin{bmatrix} 1 & -4 \\ 2 & -7 \end{bmatrix}$ and $\begin{bmatrix} -7 & 4 \\ -2 & 1 \end{bmatrix}$

3. $\begin{bmatrix} 2 & 6 \\ 2 & 4 \end{bmatrix}$ and $\begin{bmatrix} -1 & 2 \\ 2 & -4 \end{bmatrix}$

4. $\begin{bmatrix} -1 & 2 \\ 3 & -5 \end{bmatrix}$ and $\begin{bmatrix} -5 & -2 \\ -3 & -1 \end{bmatrix}$

5. $\begin{bmatrix} 2 & 0 & 1 \\ 1 & 1 & 2 \\ 0 & 1 & 0 \end{bmatrix}$ and $\begin{bmatrix} 1 & 1 & -1 \\ 0 & 1 & 0 \\ -1 & -2 & 2 \end{bmatrix}$

6. $\begin{bmatrix} 0 & 1 & 0 \\ 0 & 0 & -2 \\ 1 & -1 & 0 \end{bmatrix}$ and $\begin{bmatrix} 1 & 0 & 1 \\ 1 & 0 & 0 \\ 0 & -1 & 0 \end{bmatrix}$

7. $\begin{bmatrix} 1 & 3 & 3 \\ 1 & 4 & 3 \\ 1 & 3 & 4 \end{bmatrix}$ and $\begin{bmatrix} 7 & -3 & -3 \\ -1 & 1 & 0 \\ -1 & 0 & 1 \end{bmatrix}$

8. $\begin{bmatrix} 1 & 0 & 0 \\ -1 & -2 & 3 \\ 0 & 1 & 0 \end{bmatrix}$ and $\begin{bmatrix} 1 & 0 & 0 \\ 0 & 0 & 1 \\ \frac{1}{3} & \frac{1}{3} & \frac{2}{3} \end{bmatrix}$

9. Does a matrix with a row of all zeros have an inverse? Why?

10. Matrix A has A^{-1} as its inverse. What does $(A^{-1})^{-1}$ equal? (*Hint:* Experiment with a few matrices to see what you get.)

Find the inverse, if it exists, for each matrix.

11. $\begin{bmatrix} 1 & -1 \\ 2 & 0 \end{bmatrix}$

12. $\begin{bmatrix} 1 & 1 \\ 2 & 3 \end{bmatrix}$

13. $\begin{bmatrix} 3 & -1 \\ -5 & 2 \end{bmatrix}$

14. $\begin{bmatrix} -3 & -8 \\ 1 & 3 \end{bmatrix}$

15. $\begin{bmatrix} 1 & -3 \\ -2 & 6 \end{bmatrix}$

16. $\begin{bmatrix} 5 & 10 \\ -3 & -6 \end{bmatrix}$

17. $\begin{bmatrix} 1 & 0 & 0 \\ 0 & -1 & 0 \\ 1 & 0 & 1 \end{bmatrix}$

18. $\begin{bmatrix} 1 & 3 & 0 \\ 0 & 2 & -1 \\ 1 & 0 & 2 \end{bmatrix}$

19. $\begin{bmatrix} -1 & -1 & -1 \\ 4 & 5 & 0 \\ 0 & 1 & -3 \end{bmatrix}$

20. $\begin{bmatrix} 2 & 1 & 0 \\ 0 & 3 & 1 \\ 4 & -1 & -3 \end{bmatrix}$

21. $\begin{bmatrix} 1 & 2 & 3 \\ -3 & -2 & -1 \\ -1 & 0 & 1 \end{bmatrix}$

22. $\begin{bmatrix} 2 & 0 & 4 \\ 1 & 0 & -1 \\ 3 & 0 & -2 \end{bmatrix}$

23. $\begin{bmatrix} 1 & 3 & -2 \\ 2 & 7 & -3 \\ 3 & 8 & -5 \end{bmatrix}$

24. $\begin{bmatrix} 4 & 1 & -4 \\ 2 & 1 & -1 \\ -2 & -4 & 5 \end{bmatrix}$

25. $\begin{bmatrix} 1 & -2 & 3 & 0 \\ 0 & 1 & -1 & 1 \\ -2 & 2 & -2 & 4 \\ 0 & 2 & -3 & 1 \end{bmatrix}$

26. $\begin{bmatrix} 1 & 1 & 0 & 2 \\ 2 & -1 & 1 & -1 \\ 3 & 3 & 2 & -2 \\ 1 & 2 & 1 & 0 \end{bmatrix}$

Solve each system of equations by using the inverse of the coefficient matrix if it exists and by the Gauss-Jordan method if the inverse doesn't exist. (The inverses for exercises 35–38 were found in Exercises 19, 20, 23, and 24.)

27. $2x + 5y = 15$
$x + 4y = 9$

28. $-x + 2y = 15$
$-2x - y = 20$

29. $2x + y = 5$
$5x + 3y = 13$

30. $-x - 2y = 8$
$3x + 4y = 24$

31. $3x - 2y = 3$
$7x - 5y = 0$

32. $3x - 6y = 1$
$-5x + 9y = -1$

33. $-x - 8y = 12$
$3x + 24y = -36$

34. $2x + 7y = 14$
$4x + 14y = 28$

35. $-x - y - z = 1$
$4x + 5y = -2$
$y - 3z = 3$

36. $2x + y = 1$
$3y + z = 8$
$4x - y - 3z = 8$

37. $x + 3y - 2z = 4$
$2x + 7y - 3z = 8$
$3x + 8y - 5z = -4$

38. $4x + y - 4z = 17$
$2x + y - z = 12$
$-2x - 4y + 5z = 17$

39. $2x - 2y = 5$
$4y + 8z = 7$
$x + 2z = 1$

40. $x + 2z = -1$
$y - z = 5$
$x + 2y = 7$

Solve each system of equations by using the inverse of the coefficient matrix. (The inverses were found in Exercises 25 and 26.)

41. $x - 2y + 3z = 4$
$y - z + w = -8$
$-2x + 2y - 2z + 4w = 12$
$2y - 3z + w = -4$

42. $x + y + 2w = 3$
$2x - y + z - w = 3$
$3x + 3y + 2z - 2w = 5$
$x + 2y + z = 3$

Let $A = \begin{bmatrix} a & b \\ c & d \end{bmatrix}$ and $0 = \begin{bmatrix} 0 & 0 \\ 0 & 0 \end{bmatrix}$ in Exercises 43–48.

43. Show that $IA = A$.

44. Show that $AI = A$.

45. Show that $A \cdot O = O$.

46. Find A^{-1}.
(Assume $ad - bc \neq 0$.)

47. Show that $A^{-1}A = I$.

48. Show that $AA^{-1} = I$.

49. Using the definition and properties listed in this section, show that for square matrices A and B of the same size, if $AB = O$ and if A^{-1} exists, then $B = O$, where O is a matrix whose elements are all zeros.

50. Prove that, if it exists, the inverse of a matrix is unique. (*Hint:* Assume there are two inverses B and C for some matrix A, so that $AB = BA = I$ and $AC = CA = I$. Multiply the first equation by C and the second by B.)

Use matrices C and D in Exercises 51–55.

$$C = \begin{bmatrix} -6 & 8 & 2 & 4 & -3 \\ 1 & 9 & 7 & -12 & 5 \\ 15 & 2 & -8 & 10 & 11 \\ 4 & 7 & 9 & 6 & -2 \\ 1 & 3 & 8 & 23 & 4 \end{bmatrix}, \quad D = \begin{bmatrix} 5 & -3 & 7 & 9 & 2 \\ 6 & 8 & -5 & 2 & 1 \\ 3 & 7 & -4 & 2 & 11 \\ 5 & -3 & 9 & 4 & -1 \\ 0 & 3 & 2 & 5 & 1 \end{bmatrix}$$

51. Find C^{-1}.

52. Find $(CD)^{-1}$.

53. Find D^{-1}.

54. Is $C^{-1}D^{-1} = (CD)^{-1}$?

55. Is $D^{-1}C^{-1} = (CD)^{-1}$?

Solve the matrix equation $AX = B$ for X by finding A^{-1}, given A and B as follows.

56. $A = \begin{bmatrix} 2 & -5 & 7 \\ 4 & -3 & 2 \\ 15 & 2 & 6 \end{bmatrix}$, $B = \begin{bmatrix} -2 \\ 5 \\ 8 \end{bmatrix}$

57. $A = \begin{bmatrix} 2 & 5 & 7 & 9 \\ 1 & 3 & -4 & 6 \\ -1 & 0 & 5 & 8 \\ 2 & -2 & 4 & 10 \end{bmatrix}$, $B = \begin{bmatrix} 3 \\ 7 \\ -1 \\ 5 \end{bmatrix}$

58. $A = \begin{bmatrix} 3 & 2 & -1 & -2 & 6 \\ -5 & 17 & 4 & 3 & 15 \\ 7 & 9 & -3 & -7 & 12 \\ 9 & -2 & 1 & 4 & 8 \\ 1 & 21 & 9 & -7 & 25 \end{bmatrix}$, $B = \begin{bmatrix} -2 \\ 5 \\ 3 \\ -8 \\ 25 \end{bmatrix}$

LIFE SCIENCE APPLICATIONS

Solve each exercise by using the inverse of the coefficient matrix to solve a system of equations.

59. Vitamins Greg Tobin mixes together three types of vitamin tablets. Each Super Vim tablet contains, among other things, 15 mg of niacin and 12 I.U. of vitamin E. The figures for a Multitab tablet are 20 mg and 15 I.U., and for a Mighty Mix are 25 mg and 35 I.U. How many of each tablet are there if the total number of tablets, total amount of niacin, and total amount of vitamin E are as follows?

a. 225 tablets, 4750 mg of niacin, and 5225 I.U. of vitamin E

b. 185 tablets, 3625 mg of niacin, and 3750 I.U. of vitamin E

c. 230 tablets, 4450 mg of niacin, and 4210 I.U. of vitamin E

60. Calorie Expenditure Jennifer Crum has an exercise regimen at the local gym that includes using a treadmill, stair machine, and cycle. According to a website, a 130-pound person like Jennifer will burn, on average, about 600 calories per hour running a moderate pace on the treadmill, about 500 calories per hour on the stair machine, and about 300 calories per hour on the cycle. *Source: Nutristrategy.*

a. Jennifer wants to spend 10 hours a week at the gym, and would like to spend twice as much time on the stair machine as the cycle. She wants to burn 5000 calories a week at the gym. Is this possible? How much time should Jennifer spend on each machine?

b. Jennifer decides to spend 15 hours this week at the gym. She still wants to spend twice as much time on the stair machine as the cycle, but wants to double the total number of calories that she burns. Is this possible?

c. Next week Jennifer can spend only 9 hours at the gym, and still wants to spend twice as much time on the stair machine as the cycle. Can she still burn 5000 total calories? If so, how much time should Jennifer spend on each machine?

OTHER APPLICATIONS

61. Analysis of Orders The Bread Box Bakery sells three types of cakes, each requiring the amounts of the basic ingredients shown in the following matrix.

		Type of Cake		
		I	II	III
	Flour (in cups)	2	4	2
Ingredient	Sugar (in cups)	2	1	2
	Eggs	2	1	3

To fill its daily orders for these three kinds of cake, the bakery uses 72 cups of flour, 48 cups of sugar, and 60 eggs.

a. Write a 3×1 matrix for the amounts used daily.

b. Let the number of daily orders for cakes be a 3×1 matrix X with entries x_1, x_2, and x_3. Write a matrix equation that can be solved for X, using the given matrix and the matrix from part a.

c. Solve the equation from part b to find the number of daily orders for each type of cake.

62. Production Requirements An electronics company produces transistors, resistors, and computer chips. Each transistor requires 3 units of copper, 1 unit of zinc, and 2 units of glass. Each resistor requires 3, 2, and 1 units of the three materials, and each computer chip requires 2, 1, and 2 units of these materials, respectively. How many of each product can be made with the following amounts of materials?

a. 810 units of copper, 410 units of zinc, and 490 units of glass

b. 765 units of copper, 385 units of zinc, and 470 units of glass

c. 1010 units of copper, 500 units of zinc, and 610 units of glass

63. Investments An investment firm recommends that a client invest in AAA-, A-, and B-rated bonds. The average yield on AAA bonds is 6%, on A bonds 6.5%, and on B bonds 8%. The client wants to invest twice as much in AAA bonds as in B bonds. How much should be invested in each type of bond under the following conditions?

a. The total investment is $25,000, and the investor wants an annual return of $1650 on the three investments.

b. The values in part a are changed to $30,000 and $1985, respectively.

c. The values in part a are changed to $40,000 and $2660, respectively.

64. Production Pretzels cost $4 per lb, dried fruit $5 per lb, and nuts $9 per lb. The three ingredients are to be combined in a trail mix containing twice the weight of pretzels as dried fruit. How many pounds of each should be used to produce the following amounts at the given cost?

a. 140 lb at $6 per lb

b. 100 lb at $7.60 per lb

c. 125 lb at $6.20 per lb

65. Encryption Use the matrices presented in Example 7 of this section to do the following:

a. Encode the message, "All is fair in love and war."

b. Decode the message 138, 81, 102, 101, 67, 109, 162, 124, 173, 210, 150, 165.

66. Encryption Use the methods presented in Example 7 along with the given matrix B to do the following.

$$B = \begin{bmatrix} 2 & 4 & 6 \\ -1 & -4 & -3 \\ 0 & 1 & -1 \end{bmatrix}$$

a. Encode the message, "To be or not to be."

b. Find the inverse of B.

c. Use the inverse of B to decode the message $116, -60, -15, 294, -197, -2, 148, -92, -9, 96, -64, 4, 264, -182, -2.$

67. Music During a marching band's half-time show, the band members generally line up in such a way that a common shape is recognized by the fans. For example, as illustrated in the figure, a band might form a letter T, where an × represents a member of the band. As the music is played, the band will either create a new shape or rotate the original shape. In doing this, each member of the band will need to move from one point on the field to another. For larger bands, keeping track of who goes where can be a daunting task. However, it is possible to use matrix inverses to make the process a bit easier. The entire process is calculated by knowing how three band members, all of whom cannot be in a straight line, will move from the current position to a new position. For example, in the figure, we can see that there are band members at $(50, 0)$, $(50, 15)$, and $(45, 20)$. We will assume that these three band members move to $(40, 10)$, $(55, 10)$, and $(60, 15)$, respectively. (Note: The x-coordinate 60 is represented by the right side's 40 yard line in the picture.) **Source: The College Mathematics Journal.**

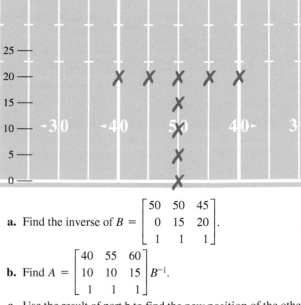

a. Find the inverse of $B = \begin{bmatrix} 50 & 50 & 45 \\ 0 & 15 & 20 \\ 1 & 1 & 1 \end{bmatrix}$.

b. Find $A = \begin{bmatrix} 40 & 55 & 60 \\ 10 & 10 & 15 \\ 1 & 1 & 1 \end{bmatrix} B^{-1}$.

c. Use the result of part b to find the new position of the other band members. What is the shape of the new position? (*Hint:* Multiply the matrix A by a 3×1 column vector with the first two components equal to the original position of each band member and the third component equal to 1. The new position of the band member is in the first two components of the product.)

YOUR TURN ANSWERS

1. $\begin{bmatrix} 1/8 & 3/8 & 1/8 \\ 5/8 & -1/8 & -3/8 \\ -9/8 & -3/8 & 7/8 \end{bmatrix}$ **2.** $(3, 2)$ **3. a.** 49, 33, 26, 67, 54, 88 **b.** matrix

10.5 Eigenvalues and Eigenvectors

APPLY IT How can we determine a population of insects that grows at a constant rate while keeping the same proportion of adults and juveniles?
This kind of question is of fundamental interest in mathematical biology, and will be answered in Example 1.

Suppose there is an insect population consisting of juveniles (insects in their first year of life) and adults (insects in their second year of life). *Source: Population Biology: Concepts and Models.* We will assume that no insects of this species live more than two years.

Let $x_1(t)$ and $x_2(t)$ be the number of juveniles and adults in year t. We will assume that a proportion s of the juveniles survive to become adults the following year. We will also assume that a proportion p of the juveniles have offspring that are juveniles the following year, and that a proportion q of the adults have offspring that are juveniles the following year. Then the number of juveniles and adults next year can be calculated from the number this year using the equation

$$x_1(t + 1) = px_1(t) + qx_2(t)$$
$$x_2(t + 1) = sx_1(t).$$

In matrix form, this is

$$\begin{bmatrix} x_1(t + 1) \\ x_2(t + 1) \end{bmatrix} = \begin{bmatrix} p & q \\ s & 0 \end{bmatrix} \begin{bmatrix} x_1(t) \\ x_2(t) \end{bmatrix},$$

which can also be written as

$$X(t + 1) = MX(t),$$

where

$$M = \begin{bmatrix} p & q \\ s & 0 \end{bmatrix}$$

and

$$X(t) = \begin{bmatrix} x_1(t) \\ x_2(t) \end{bmatrix}.$$

The advantage of this last notation is that it can be extended to any number of groups within the population. The matrix M is known as a **Leslie matrix** after P. H. Leslie, who first wrote about them in 1945. *Source: Biometrika.*

EXAMPLE 1 Insect Population Growth

Suppose

$$M = \begin{bmatrix} 0.6 & 0.8 \\ 0.9 & 0 \end{bmatrix}$$

and that the initial insect population consists of 1000 juveniles and 2000 adults. Determine the population of insects in year 1 and year 2.

APPLY IT **SOLUTION** Let $X(0)$ be the initial population, so

$$X(0) = \begin{bmatrix} 1000 \\ 2000 \end{bmatrix}.$$

To find the population in year 1, find $X(1) = MX(0)$. Therefore,

$$X(1) = \begin{bmatrix} x_1(1) \\ x_2(1) \end{bmatrix} = \begin{bmatrix} 0.6 & 0.8 \\ 0.9 & 0 \end{bmatrix} \begin{bmatrix} 1000 \\ 2000 \end{bmatrix}$$

$$= \begin{bmatrix} 2200 \\ 900 \end{bmatrix}.$$

Likewise, the population in year 2 is $X(2) = MX(1)$. Thus,

$$X(2) = \begin{bmatrix} x_1(2) \\ x_2(2) \end{bmatrix} = \begin{bmatrix} 0.6 & 0.8 \\ 0.9 & 0 \end{bmatrix} \begin{bmatrix} 2200 \\ 900 \end{bmatrix}$$

$$= \begin{bmatrix} 2040 \\ 1980 \end{bmatrix}.$$

Notice that the population of juveniles has gone from 1000 in year 0 to 2200 in year 1 to 2040 in year 2. Meanwhile, the population of adults has gone from 2000 in year 0 to 900 in year 1 to 1980 in year 2.

In many actual populations, the proportion of the population in each age group stays the same from year to year, even as the population grows. For example, if

$$X(0) = \begin{bmatrix} 400 \\ 300 \end{bmatrix},$$

then

$$X(1) = \begin{bmatrix} 0.6 & 0.8 \\ 0.9 & 0 \end{bmatrix} \begin{bmatrix} 400 \\ 300 \end{bmatrix} = \begin{bmatrix} 480 \\ 360 \end{bmatrix} = 1.2 \begin{bmatrix} 400 \\ 300 \end{bmatrix}.$$

Both the population of juveniles and adults have grown by 20%. If we denote the growth factor by the Greek letter λ (pronounced lambda), then

$$MX = \lambda X.$$

A number λ that satisfies the above equation is called an **eigenvalue**. (Eigen is the German word meaning "characteristic.") The matrix (or vector) X in the above equation is called an **eigenvector**. Eigenvalues and eigenvectors have a wide variety of applications in mathematics in addition to solving problems about populations. We will see how they are used in solving systems of differential equations. The important thing to notice here is that multiplying an eigenvector X by the matrix M has the same result as multiplying X by the scalar λ.

Now we must investigate how to find eigenvalues and eigenvectors. By subtracting λX from both sides of the equation above, we get

$$MX - \lambda X = O,$$

where O represents a square matrix with all zeros. This equation can be rewritten as

$$(M - \lambda I)X = O,$$

where I is the identity matrix. This equation has the trivial solution $X = 0$, but we are interested in nontrivial solutions. In the language of Section 10.1, the above equation would have more than one solution (in fact, an infinite number of solutions) if it describes a dependent system. So we need to know for what values of λ the above system is dependent.

We now need to stretch a little to some mathematics that is explained more fully in a text on linear algebra.* It can be shown that the above system has a nontrivial solution if something called the **determinant** of $M - \lambda I$ is zero. (For a proof of this fact in the case where M is a 2×2 matrix, see Exercise 13.) Computing the determinant of a 2×2 matrix A, denoted $\det(A)$, is easy:

$$\det(A) = \det \begin{bmatrix} a & b \\ c & d \end{bmatrix} = ad - bc.$$

*For example, see Lay, David, *Linear Algebra and Its Applications*, 4th ed., Pearson, 2011.

Recall from the previous section that the expression $ad - bc$ is part of the formula for the inverse of a 2×2 matrix. You can think of calculating the determinant by starting with the product of the numbers along the diagonal from upper left to lower right, and subtracting the product of the numbers along the diagonal from upper right to lower left:

$$\det \begin{bmatrix} a & b \\ c & d \end{bmatrix} =$$
$$-bc + ad.$$

EXAMPLE 2   Determinant of 2 × 2 Matrix

Calculate the determinant of the matrix $\begin{bmatrix} 2 & 3 \\ 4 & 5 \end{bmatrix}$.

SOLUTION   The determinant is

$$\det \begin{bmatrix} 2 & 3 \\ 4 & 5 \end{bmatrix} =$$
$$-(3 \times 4) + (2 \times 5) = -12 + 10 = -2.$$

YOUR TURN 1   Calculate the determinant of $\begin{bmatrix} 4 & 2 \\ 1 & 7 \end{bmatrix}$.

TRY YOUR TURN 1

To find the determinant of a 3×3 matrix, take the first two columns of the matrix and duplicate them on the right, as we will show in a moment. Then add the products of the numbers along each of the three diagonals going from upper left to lower right, and subtract the products of the numbers along each of the three diagonals from upper right to lower left. Here we demonstrate the process for a general 3×3 matrix.

$$\det \begin{bmatrix} a & b & c \\ d & e & f \\ g & h & i \end{bmatrix} =$$

$$-ceg - afh - bdi + aei + bfg + cdh.$$

EXAMPLE 3   Determinant of 3 × 3 Matrix

Calculate the determinant of the matrix $\begin{bmatrix} 1 & 2 & 0 \\ -1 & 3 & 4 \\ -2 & 5 & -1 \end{bmatrix}$.

YOUR TURN 2   Calculate the determinant of $\begin{bmatrix} 1 & -1 & 4 \\ 2 & 3 & 0 \\ 3 & -2 & -1 \end{bmatrix}$.

SOLUTION   The determinant is

$$\det \begin{bmatrix} 1 & 2 & 0 \\ -1 & 3 & 4 \\ -2 & 5 & -1 \end{bmatrix} =$$

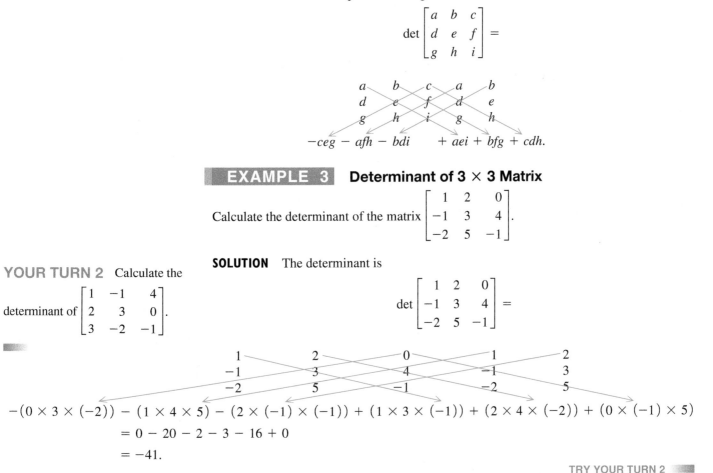

$$-(0 \times 3 \times (-2)) - (1 \times 4 \times 5) - (2 \times (-1) \times (-1)) + (1 \times 3 \times (-1)) + (2 \times 4 \times (-2)) + (0 \times (-1) \times 5)$$
$$= 0 - 20 - 2 - 3 - 16 + 0$$
$$= -41.$$

TRY YOUR TURN 2

CAUTION | The determinant of any square matrix can be calculated, but the procedure is more involved for matrices larger than 3×3, so we will not discuss those in this book.

Now we return to the problem of finding eigenvalues and their corresponding eigenvectors.

EXAMPLE 4 Eigenvalues and Eigenvectors

Find the eigenvalues and their corresponding eigenvectors for the matrix

$$M = \begin{bmatrix} 0.6 & 0.8 \\ 0.9 & 0 \end{bmatrix}, \quad \text{from Example 1.}$$

SOLUTION To find the eigenvalues, set $\det(M - \lambda I) = 0$ and solve for λ. The determinant of $M - \lambda I$ is

$$\det(M - \lambda I) = \det\left(\begin{bmatrix} 0.6 & 0.8 \\ 0.9 & 0 \end{bmatrix} - \lambda \begin{bmatrix} 1 & 0 \\ 0 & 1 \end{bmatrix} \right) = \det \begin{bmatrix} 0.6 - \lambda & 0.8 \\ 0.9 & 0 - \lambda \end{bmatrix}$$

$$= (0.6 - \lambda)(0 - \lambda) - 0.8 \times 0.9$$

$$= \lambda^2 - 0.6\lambda - 0.72.$$

We can solve $\lambda^2 - 0.6\lambda - 0.72 = 0$ with the quadratic formula.

$$\lambda = \frac{0.6 \pm \sqrt{0.6^2 - 4(-0.72)}}{2}$$

$$= \frac{0.6 \pm \sqrt{3.24}}{2}$$

$$= \frac{0.6 \pm 1.8}{2}$$

$$= 1.2, \quad -0.6$$

Therefore, since the $\det(M - \lambda I) = 0$ when $\lambda = 1.2$ and -0.6, the eigenvalues are 1.2 and -0.6.

To find the corresponding eigenvectors, substitute each eigenvalue back into the equation $(M - \lambda I)X = 0$ and solve the dependent system. First try this with $\lambda = 1.2$.

$$(M - \lambda I)X = \begin{bmatrix} 0.6 - \lambda & 0.8 \\ 0.9 & 0 - \lambda \end{bmatrix} \begin{bmatrix} x_1 \\ x_2 \end{bmatrix} \quad \text{Let } \lambda = 1.2.$$

$$= \begin{bmatrix} -0.6 & 0.8 \\ 0.9 & -1.2 \end{bmatrix} \begin{bmatrix} x_1 \\ x_2 \end{bmatrix} = \begin{bmatrix} 0 \\ 0 \end{bmatrix}$$

Now create the augmented matrix for this system.

$$\begin{bmatrix} -0.6 & 0.8 & | & 0 \\ 0.9 & -1.2 & | & 0 \end{bmatrix}$$

Before row reducing, let's simplify by getting rid of the decimals, and then dividing out any common factors.

$$\begin{matrix} -10R_1 \rightarrow R_1 \\ 10R_2 \rightarrow R_2 \end{matrix} \begin{bmatrix} 6 & -8 & | & 0 \\ 9 & -12 & | & 0 \end{bmatrix}$$

$$\begin{matrix} R_1/2 \rightarrow R_1 \\ R_2/3 \rightarrow R_2 \end{matrix} \begin{bmatrix} 3 & -4 & | & 0 \\ 3 & -4 & | & 0 \end{bmatrix}$$

Next, get a zero in row 2 of column 1.

$$-R_1 + R_2 \rightarrow R_2 \begin{bmatrix} 3 & -4 & | & 0 \\ 0 & 0 & | & 0 \end{bmatrix}$$

The zeros in row 2 indicate that we have a dependent system. Since the first row indicates that $3x_1 - 4x_2 = 0$, the simplest solution is $x_1 = 4$ and $x_2 = 3$. There are, of course, an infinite number of solutions, described by letting x_2 be an arbitrary parameter and $x_1 = 4x_2/3$, but we only need one solution. An eigenvector corresponding to $\lambda = 1.2$ is therefore

$$\begin{bmatrix} x_1 \\ x_2 \end{bmatrix} = \begin{bmatrix} 4 \\ 3 \end{bmatrix}.$$

Any multiple of this matrix is also an eigenvector.

Now find the eigenvector corresponding to $\lambda = -0.6$.

$$(M - \lambda I)X = \begin{bmatrix} 0.6 - \lambda & 0.8 \\ 0.9 & 0 - \lambda \end{bmatrix}\begin{bmatrix} x_1 \\ x_2 \end{bmatrix} \qquad \text{Let } \lambda = -0.6.$$

$$= \begin{bmatrix} 1.2 & 0.8 \\ 0.9 & 0.6 \end{bmatrix}\begin{bmatrix} x_1 \\ x_2 \end{bmatrix} = \begin{bmatrix} 0 \\ 0 \end{bmatrix}$$

Next create the augmented matrix for this system.

$$\begin{bmatrix} 1.2 & 0.8 & | & 0 \\ 0.9 & 0.6 & | & 0 \end{bmatrix}$$

YOUR TURN 3 Find the eigenvalues and their corresponding eigenvectors for the matrix

$$\begin{bmatrix} 1 & 3 \\ 2 & 0 \end{bmatrix}.$$

Verify that one solution to this system is

$$\begin{bmatrix} x_1 \\ x_2 \end{bmatrix} = \begin{bmatrix} 2 \\ -3 \end{bmatrix},$$

which is an eigenvector corresponding to $\lambda = -0.6$.

TRY YOUR TURN 3

The matrix M in Example 4 is the Leslie matrix for the insect population first introduced in Example 1. Since a population cannot have a negative value, a population with a stable structure cannot be a multiple of the second eigenvector. This eigenvector can, however, be a component of a population whose age structure is changing with time, as we shall see in Example 6.

Meanwhile, the population in which the proportion of each age group stays the same from one year to the next must be a multiple of the eigenvector

$$\begin{bmatrix} x_1 \\ x_2 \end{bmatrix} = \begin{bmatrix} 4 \\ 3 \end{bmatrix},$$

for which each year's population is 1.2 times the previous year's population. In other words, the population grows 20%, and the proportion of juveniles and adults stays the same.

For example, if we wanted to start in year 0 with a population of size 14,000, then we would take a multiple of the above eigenvector, say,

$$\begin{bmatrix} x_1 \\ x_2 \end{bmatrix} = k\begin{bmatrix} 4 \\ 3 \end{bmatrix} = \begin{bmatrix} 4k \\ 3k \end{bmatrix}.$$

The size of the population is then $4k + 3k$, or $7k$. Setting this equal to 14,000 makes $k = 2000$, so the population in year 0 is

$$\begin{bmatrix} x_1 \\ x_2 \end{bmatrix} = 2000\begin{bmatrix} 4 \\ 3 \end{bmatrix} = \begin{bmatrix} 8000 \\ 6000 \end{bmatrix}.$$

The population the next year is

$$1.2\begin{bmatrix} 8000 \\ 6000 \end{bmatrix} = \begin{bmatrix} 9600 \\ 7200 \end{bmatrix},$$

and the population the following year is

$$1.2\begin{bmatrix} 9600 \\ 7200 \end{bmatrix} = \begin{bmatrix} 11{,}520 \\ 8640 \end{bmatrix}.$$

Verify that these results are exactly what you would get by multiplying the original population vector by the matrix M, and then multiplying that result by M. It is, of course, much simpler to multiply a vector by a scalar than by a matrix, which is a nice feature of eigenvectors and eigenvalues.

| EXAMPLE 5 | **Eigenvalues and Eigenvectors** |

Find the eigenvalues and their corresponding eigenvectors for the matrix

$$M = \begin{bmatrix} 5 & 2 & 3 \\ 0 & 8 & 3 \\ 0 & 0 & 4 \end{bmatrix}.$$

SOLUTION   Calculate $\det(M - \lambda I)$.

$$\det(M - \lambda I) = \det \begin{bmatrix} 5 - \lambda & 2 & 3 \\ 0 & 8 - \lambda & 3 \\ 0 & 0 & 4 - \lambda \end{bmatrix} =$$

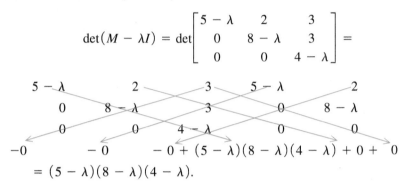

$$-0 \quad\quad -0 \quad\quad -0 + (5 - \lambda)(8 - \lambda)(4 - \lambda) + 0 + \quad 0$$

$$= (5 - \lambda)(8 - \lambda)(4 - \lambda).$$

We now see that $\det(M - \lambda I) = 0$ when $\lambda = 5$, 8, and 4. Notice that these are the values along the main diagonal of the original matrix. This will always be the case when all the values above the main diagonal or all the values below the main diagonal are 0.

To find an eigenvector corresponding to the eigenvalue $\lambda = 5$, set $\lambda = 5$ in the augmented matrix corresponding to the system $(M - \lambda I)X = 0$.

$$\begin{bmatrix} 5 - \lambda & 2 & 3 & | & 0 \\ 0 & 8 - \lambda & 3 & | & 0 \\ 0 & 0 & 4 - \lambda & | & 0 \end{bmatrix} \qquad \text{Let } \lambda = 5.$$

$$= \begin{bmatrix} 0 & 2 & 3 & | & 0 \\ 0 & 3 & 3 & | & 0 \\ 0 & 0 & -1 & | & 0 \end{bmatrix}$$

Row reduction is simplified by the fact that the first column consists entirely of zeros.

$$\begin{matrix} \\ R_2/3 \to R_2 \\ -R_3 \to R_3 \end{matrix} \begin{bmatrix} 0 & 2 & 3 & | & 0 \\ 0 & 1 & 1 & | & 0 \\ 0 & 0 & 1 & | & 0 \end{bmatrix} \qquad \text{Simplify the rows.}$$

$$\begin{matrix} -2R_2 + R_1 \to R_1 \\ \\ \end{matrix} \begin{bmatrix} 0 & 0 & 1 & | & 0 \\ 0 & 1 & 1 & | & 0 \\ 0 & 0 & 1 & | & 0 \end{bmatrix} \qquad \text{Get zeros in column 2.}$$

$$\begin{matrix} R_1 - R_3 \to R_1 \\ R_2 - R_3 \to R_2 \end{matrix} \begin{bmatrix} 0 & 0 & 0 & | & 0 \\ 0 & 1 & 0 & | & 0 \\ 0 & 0 & 1 & | & 0 \end{bmatrix} \qquad \text{Get zeros in column 3.}$$

The second row tells us that $x_2 = 0$, and the third row tells us that $x_3 = 0$. Since x_1 is arbitrary, we will let $x_1 = 1$. Therefore, an eigenvector corresponding to $\lambda = 5$ is

$$\begin{bmatrix} 1 \\ 0 \\ 0 \end{bmatrix}.$$

Similarly, when $\lambda = 8$, the augmented matrix corresponding to the system $(M - \lambda I)X = 0$ is

$$\left[\begin{array}{ccc|c} -3 & 2 & 3 & 0 \\ 0 & 0 & 3 & 0 \\ 0 & 0 & -4 & 0 \end{array}\right].$$

Verify that this augmented matrix reduces to

$$\left[\begin{array}{ccc|c} -3 & 2 & 0 & 0 \\ 0 & 0 & 1 & 0 \\ 0 & 0 & 0 & 0 \end{array}\right]$$

and that an eigenvector is

$$\begin{bmatrix} 2 \\ 3 \\ 0 \end{bmatrix}.$$

We leave it as an exercise to show that an eigenvector corresponding to $\lambda = 4$ is

$$\begin{bmatrix} 6 \\ 3 \\ -4 \end{bmatrix}.$$

The following result, mentioned in Example 5, is worth noting.

If all the values above the main diagonal or all the values below the main diagonal of a matrix are 0, the eigenvalues are the values along the main diagonal.

NOTE The eigenvalues of a matrix can be complex numbers. There can also be eigenvalues with a multiplicity greater than 1, in the sense that, rather than having two distinct eigenvalues for a 2×2 matrix or three distinct eigenvalues for a 3×3 matrix, some of the eigenvalues may be identical. In the examples and exercises in this text, the eigenvalues will be real and distinct, with the exception of Exercises 14–17 in this section.

Earlier in this section, we showed how a population described by an eigenvector has a stable distribution from one generation to the next. In the next example, we will see how eigenvalues and eigenvectors help us analyze an arbitrary population that is not an eigenvector. The key is to represent the initial population in terms of the eigenvectors.

EXAMPLE 6   **Long-term Population**

In the insect population discussed in Examples 1 and 4, recall that the Leslie matrix was $M = \begin{bmatrix} 0.6 & 0.8 \\ 0.9 & 0 \end{bmatrix}$ and that the eigenvectors $\lambda_1 = 1.2$ and $\lambda_2 = -0.6$ corresponded to the eigenvectors $V_1 = \begin{bmatrix} 4 \\ 3 \end{bmatrix}$ and $V_2 = \begin{bmatrix} 2 \\ -3 \end{bmatrix}$, respectively. Recall also that the initial population was $X(0) = \begin{bmatrix} 1000 \\ 2000 \end{bmatrix}$.

(a) Find values a and b such that $aV_1 + bV_2 = X(0)$.

SOLUTION The equation

$$a\begin{bmatrix} 4 \\ 3 \end{bmatrix} + b\begin{bmatrix} 2 \\ -3 \end{bmatrix} = \begin{bmatrix} 1000 \\ 2000 \end{bmatrix}$$

corresponds to the augmented matrix

$$\begin{bmatrix} 4 & 2 & | & 1000 \\ 3 & -3 & | & 2000 \end{bmatrix}.$$

Use the Gauss-Jordan method to reduce this matrix to

$$\begin{bmatrix} 1 & 0 & | & 3500/9 \\ 0 & 1 & | & -2500/9 \end{bmatrix}.$$

The solution is $a = 3500/9$ and $b = -2500/9$.

(b) Use the result from part (a), as well as properties of eigenvalues and eigenvectors, to find the population distribution the following year.

SOLUTION The population in the next year is given by

$$X(1) = MX(0) = M\left(\frac{3500}{9}V_1 - \frac{2500}{9}V_2\right) \qquad \text{Use the results of part (a).}$$

$$= \frac{3500}{9}MV_1 - \frac{2500}{9}MV_2$$

$$= \frac{3500}{9}\lambda_1 V_1 - \frac{2500}{9}\lambda_2 V_2 \qquad \text{Use properties of eigenvalues and eigenvectors.}$$

$$= \frac{3500}{9}(1.2)\begin{bmatrix} 4 \\ 3 \end{bmatrix} - \frac{2500}{9}(-0.6)\begin{bmatrix} 2 \\ -3 \end{bmatrix}$$

$$= \begin{bmatrix} 2200 \\ 900 \end{bmatrix}.$$

(c) Find a formula for the long-term population distribution.

SOLUTION By continuing to multiply by M, the population after n years is given by

$$X(n) = M^n X(0) = M^n\left(\frac{3500}{9}V_1 - \frac{2500}{9}V_2\right)$$

$$= \frac{3500}{9}M^n V_1 - \frac{2500}{9}M^n V_2$$

$$= \frac{3500}{9}\lambda_1^n V_1 - \frac{2500}{9}\lambda_2^n V_2$$

$$= \frac{3500}{9}(1.2)^n\begin{bmatrix} 4 \\ 3 \end{bmatrix} - \frac{2500}{9}(-0.6)^n\begin{bmatrix} 2 \\ -3 \end{bmatrix}.$$

Since $\lim_{n \to \infty} (0.6)^n = 0$, the second term becomes smaller and smaller over time. Therefore, when n is large,

$$X(n) \approx \frac{3500}{9}(1.2)^n\begin{bmatrix} 4 \\ 3 \end{bmatrix}.$$

Example 6 demonstrates an important result. Even if the initial population is not an eigenvector, the population over time approaches a multiple of one of the eigenvectors. Since any multiple of an eigenvector is itself an eigenvector, this shows that, at least in the case with two eigenvalues, one greater than 1 in magnitude and one less than 1 in magnitude, the population will approach an eigenvector over time, and that each year's population can be approximately found by multiplying the previous year's population by an eigenvalue. This behavior is typical of a large range of applications in the life sciences.

10.5 EXERCISES

Find the determinant of the following matrices.

1. $\begin{bmatrix} 3 & -1 \\ 2 & 5 \end{bmatrix}$ **2.** $\begin{bmatrix} 7 & -5 \\ -3 & -1 \end{bmatrix}$

3. $\begin{bmatrix} 4 & 1 & 0 \\ -1 & 7 & -2 \\ 2 & 3 & 5 \end{bmatrix}$ **4.** $\begin{bmatrix} -7 & -1 & 4 \\ 9 & 0 & 6 \\ 4 & 2 & 1 \end{bmatrix}$

For Exercises 5–12, find the eigenvalues and their corresponding eigenvectors.

5. $\begin{bmatrix} 5 & 0 \\ 2 & 1 \end{bmatrix}$ **6.** $\begin{bmatrix} 7 & 4 \\ -3 & -1 \end{bmatrix}$

7. $\begin{bmatrix} 3 & 2 \\ 3 & 8 \end{bmatrix}$ **8.** $\begin{bmatrix} 1 & 0 \\ 6 & -1 \end{bmatrix}$

9. $\begin{bmatrix} 4 & -3 \\ 2 & -1 \end{bmatrix}$ **10.** $\begin{bmatrix} 2 & 3 \\ 4 & 1 \end{bmatrix}$

11. $\begin{bmatrix} 4 & 0 & 0 \\ 3 & -1 & 0 \\ 2 & 5 & -3 \end{bmatrix}$ **12.** $\begin{bmatrix} -5 & 0 & 0 \\ 1 & 2 & 0 \\ -1 & 4 & 4 \end{bmatrix}$

13. Show that the system of equations

$$ax + by = 0$$
$$cx + dy = 0$$

is dependent whenever $ad - bc = 0$, that is, when the determinant of the coefficient matrix is 0. (*Hint:* Use the Gauss-Jordan method.)

In Exercises 14 and 15, each 2 × 2 matrix has only one eigenvalue. Find the eigenvalue and the corresponding eigenvector.

14. $\begin{bmatrix} 7 & -2 \\ 2 & 3 \end{bmatrix}$ **15.** $\begin{bmatrix} 10 & -9 \\ 4 & -2 \end{bmatrix}$

In Exercises 16 and 17, each matrix has complex numbers as eigenvalues. Find the eigenvalues and their corresponding eigenvectors. (Note: These exercises require a knowledge of complex numbers. Complex eigenvalues are important in biology applications.)

16. $\begin{bmatrix} 1 & -2 \\ 1 & 3 \end{bmatrix}$ **17.** $\begin{bmatrix} 1 & 5 \\ -2 & 3 \end{bmatrix}$

LIFE SCIENCE APPLICATIONS

Leslie Matrices For each of the following Leslie matrices,
(a) *find a population of size 10,000 for which the proportion of the population in each age group stays the same from one year to the next, and* **(b)** *tell by what factor the population grows or declines each year.*

18. $\begin{bmatrix} 0.7 & 0.9 \\ 1.6 & 0 \end{bmatrix}$

19. $\begin{bmatrix} 0.5 & 0.9 \\ 1.4 & 0 \end{bmatrix}$

20. $\begin{bmatrix} 0.95 & 0.03 \\ 0.05 & 0.97 \end{bmatrix}$

21. $\begin{bmatrix} 0.2 & 0.7 \\ 0.7 & 0.2 \end{bmatrix}$

22. $\begin{bmatrix} 0.7 & 0.2 \\ 0.2 & 0.4 \end{bmatrix}$

23. $\begin{bmatrix} 0.1 & 1.2 \\ 0.4 & 0.3 \end{bmatrix}$

24. Long-term Population For the matrix in Exercise 18, find an approximate expression for the population distribution after n years, given that the initial population distribution is given by $X(0) = \begin{bmatrix} 3000 \\ 1000 \end{bmatrix}$.

25. Long-term Population Repeat Exercise 24 using the matrix in Exercise 19.

26. Northern Spotted Owl Population In Exercise 47 of Section 10.3 on Multiplication of Matrices, we saw that the number of female northern spotted owls at time $n + 1$ could be estimated by the equation

$$\begin{bmatrix} j_{n+1} \\ s_{n+1} \\ a_{n+1} \end{bmatrix} = \begin{bmatrix} 0 & 0 & 0.33 \\ 0.18 & 0 & 0 \\ 0 & 0.71 & 0.94 \end{bmatrix} \begin{bmatrix} j_n \\ s_n \\ a_n \end{bmatrix},$$

where j_n is the number of juveniles, s_n is the number of sub-adults, and a_n is the number of adults at time n. In part b of that exercise, it was stated that in the long run, the following approximation holds:

$$\begin{bmatrix} j_{n+1} \\ s_{n+1} \\ a_{n+1} \end{bmatrix} \approx 0.98359 \begin{bmatrix} j_n \\ s_n \\ a_n \end{bmatrix}.$$

Use the concept of eigenvalues to show that this approximation is true if $\begin{bmatrix} j_n \\ s_n \\ a_n \end{bmatrix}$ is an eigenvector. (*Hint:* After calculating $\det(M - \lambda I)$, use a graphing calculator to plot $y = \det(M - \lambda I)$ as a function of λ, and find where $y = 0$.)

YOUR TURN ANSWERS

1. 26 **2.** −57

3. For $\lambda = 3$, the eigenvector is $\begin{bmatrix} 3 \\ 2 \end{bmatrix}$; for $\lambda = -2$, the eigenvector is $\begin{bmatrix} 1 \\ -1 \end{bmatrix}$.

10 CHAPTER REVIEW

SUMMARY

In this chapter we studied systems of linear equations and matrices. The Gauss-Jordan method was developed and used to solve systems of linear equations. We introduced matrices, which are used to store mathematical information. We saw that matrices can be combined using addition, subtraction, scalar multiplication, and matrix multiplication.

We then developed the concept of a multiplicative inverse of a matrix and used such inverses to solve systems of equations. We concluded the chapter by introducing eigenvalues and eigenvectors, which are used to solve certain types of matrix equations that arise in applications.

Row Operations For any augmented matrix of a system of equations, the following operations produce the augmented matrix of an equivalent system:

1. interchanging any two rows;
2. multiplying the elements of a row by a nonzero real number;
3. adding a nonzero multiple of the elements of one row to the corresponding elements of a nonzero multiple of some other row.

The Gauss-Jordan Method

1. Write each equation so that variable terms are in the same order on the left side of the equal sign and constants are on the right.
2. Write the augmented matrix that corresponds to the system.
3. Use row operations to transform the first column so that all elements except the element in the first row are zero.
4. Use row operations to transform the second column so that all elements except the element in the second row are zero.
5. Use row operations to transform the third column so that all elements except the element in the third row are zero.
6. Continue in this way, when possible, until the last row is written in the form

$$[0 \ 0 \ 0 \ \cdots \ 0 \ j \,|\, k],$$

where j and k are constants with $j \neq 0$. When this is not possible, continue until every row has more zeros on the left than the previous row (except possibly for any rows of all zeros at the bottom of the matrix), and the first nonzero entry in each row is the only nonzero entry in its column.
7. Multiply each row by the reciprocal of the nonzero element in that row.

Adding Matrices The sum of two $m \times n$ matrices X and Y is the $m \times n$ matrix $X + Y$ in which each element is the sum of the corresponding elements of X and Y.

Subtracting Matrices The difference of two $m \times n$ matrices X and Y is the $m \times n$ matrix $X - Y$ in which each element is the difference of the corresponding elements of X and Y.

Product of a Matrix and a Scalar The product of a scalar k and a matrix X is the matrix kX, in which each element is k times the corresponding element of X.

Product of Two Matrices Let A be an $m \times n$ matrix and let B be an $n \times k$ matrix. To find the element in the ith row and jth column of the product AB, multiply each element in the ith row of A by the corresponding element in the jth column of B, and then add these products. The product matrix AB is an $m \times k$ matrix.

Finding a Multiplicative Inverse Matrix To obtain A^{-1} for any $n \times n$ matrix A for which A^{-1} exists, follow these steps.

1. Form the augmented matrix $[A\,|\,I]$, where I is the $n \times n$ identity matrix.
2. Perform row operations on $[A\,|\,I]$ to get a matrix of the form $[I\,|\,B]$, if this is possible.
3. Matrix B is A^{-1}.

Solving a System $AX = B$ Using Matrix Inverses To solve a system of equations $AX = B$, where A is a square matrix of coefficients, X is the matrix of variables, and B is the matrix of constants, first find A^{-1}. Then, $X = A^{-1}B$.

KEY TERMS

system of equations	augmented matrix	**10.3**	**10.5**
10.1	row operations	scalar	Leslie matrix
linear systems	equivalent system	product matrix	eigenvalue
first-degree equation in n	Gauss-Jordan method		eigenvector
unknowns	parameter	**10.4**	determinant
unique solution	**10.2**	identity matrix	
inconsistent system	size	multiplicative inverse matrix	
dependent equations	square matrix	coefficient matrix	
matrix (matrices)	row matrix (row vector)		
element (entry)	column matrix (column vector)		

REVIEW EXERCISES

CONCEPT CHECK

Determine whether each of the following statements is true or false, and explain why.

1. The only solution to the system of equations

$$2x + 3y = 7$$
$$5x - 4y = 6$$

is $x = 2$ and $y = 1$.

2. If a system of equations has three equations and four unknowns, then it could have a unique solution.

3. If a system of equations has three equations and three unknowns, then it may have a unique solution, an infinite number of solutions, or no solutions.

4. When solving a system of equations by the Gauss-Jordan method, we can add a nonzero multiple of the elements of one column to the corresponding elements of some nonzero multiple of some other column.

5. If $A = \begin{bmatrix} 2 & 3 \\ 1 & -1 \end{bmatrix}$ and $B = \begin{bmatrix} 3 & 4 \\ 7 & 4 \\ 1 & 0 \end{bmatrix}$, then $A + B = \begin{bmatrix} 5 & 7 \\ 8 & 3 \\ 1 & 0 \end{bmatrix}$.

6. If A is a 2×3 matrix and B is a 3×4 matrix, then $A + B$ is a 2×4 matrix.

7. If A is an $n \times k$ matrix and B is a $k \times m$ matrix, then AB is an $n \times m$ matrix.

8. If A is a 4×4 matrix and B is a 4×4 matrix, then it is always the case that $AB = BA$.

9. Every square matrix has an inverse.

10. A 3×4 matrix could have an inverse.

11. If A, B, and C are matrices such that $AB = C$, then $B = \dfrac{C}{A}$.

12. If A and B are matrices such that $A = B^{-1}$, then $AB = BA$.

13. If A, B, and C are matrices such that $AB = CB$, then $A = C$.

14. The determinant of the matrix $\begin{bmatrix} 1 & 4 \\ 2 & 5 \end{bmatrix}$ is 3.

15. The determinant of any square matrix can be calculated.

16. The eigenvalues of the matrix $\begin{bmatrix} 1 & 0 \\ 2 & 3 \end{bmatrix}$ are $\lambda = 1$ and $\lambda = 3$.

PRACTICE AND EXPLORATIONS

17. What is true about the number of solutions to a system of m linear equations in n unknowns if $m = n$? If $m < n$? If $m > n$?

18. Suppose someone says that a more reasonable way to multiply two matrices than the method presented in the text is to multiply corresponding elements. For example, the result of

$$\begin{bmatrix} 1 & 2 \\ 3 & 4 \end{bmatrix} \cdot \begin{bmatrix} 3 & 5 \\ 7 & 11 \end{bmatrix} \quad \text{should be} \quad \begin{bmatrix} 3 & 10 \\ 21 & 44 \end{bmatrix},$$

according to this person. How would you respond?

Solve each system by the Gauss-Jordan method.

19. $2x + 4y = -6$
  $-3x - 5y = 12$

20. $x - 4y = 10$
  $5x + 3y = 119$

21. $x - y + 3z = 13$
  $4x + y + 2z = 17$
  $3x + 2y + 2z = 1$

22. $x + 2y + 3z = 9$
  $x - 2y = 4$
  $3x + 2z = 12$

23. $3x - 6y + 9z = 12$
  $-x + 2y - 3z = -4$
  $x + y + 2z = 7$

24. $x - 2z = 5$
  $3x + 2y = 8$
  $-x + 2z = 10$

Find the size of each matrix, find the values of any variables, and identify any square, row, or column matrices.

25. $\begin{bmatrix} 2 & 3 \\ 5 & q \end{bmatrix} = \begin{bmatrix} a & b \\ c & 9 \end{bmatrix}$

26. $\begin{bmatrix} 2 & x \\ y & 6 \\ 5 & z \end{bmatrix} = \begin{bmatrix} a & -1 \\ 4 & 6 \\ p & 7 \end{bmatrix}$

27. $\begin{bmatrix} 2m & 4 & 3z & -12 \end{bmatrix} = \begin{bmatrix} 12 & k+1 & -9 & r-3 \end{bmatrix}$

28. $\begin{bmatrix} a+5 & 3b & 6 \\ 4c & 2+d & -3 \\ -1 & 4p & q-1 \end{bmatrix} = \begin{bmatrix} -7 & b+2 & 2k-3 \\ 3 & 2d-1 & 4l \\ m & 12 & 8 \end{bmatrix}$

Given the matrices

$$A = \begin{bmatrix} 4 & 10 \\ -2 & -3 \\ 6 & 9 \end{bmatrix}, \quad B = \begin{bmatrix} 2 & 3 & -2 \\ 2 & 4 & 0 \\ 0 & 1 & 2 \end{bmatrix}, \quad C = \begin{bmatrix} 5 & 0 \\ -1 & 3 \\ 4 & 7 \end{bmatrix},$$

$$D = \begin{bmatrix} 6 \\ 1 \\ 0 \end{bmatrix}, \quad E = \begin{bmatrix} 1 & 3 & -4 \end{bmatrix},$$

$$F = \begin{bmatrix} -1 & 4 \\ 3 & 7 \end{bmatrix}, \quad G = \begin{bmatrix} -2 & 0 \\ 1 & 5 \end{bmatrix},$$

find each of the following, if it exists.

29. $A + C$

30. $2G - 4F$

31. $3C + 2A$

32. $B - C$

33. $2A - 5C$

34. AG

35. AC

36. DE

37. ED

38. BD

39. EC

40. F^{-1}

41. B^{-1}

42. $(A + C)^{-1}$

Find the inverse of each matrix that has an inverse.

43. $\begin{bmatrix} 1 & 3 \\ 2 & 7 \end{bmatrix}$

44. $\begin{bmatrix} -4 & 2 \\ 0 & 3 \end{bmatrix}$

45. $\begin{bmatrix} 3 & -6 \\ -4 & 8 \end{bmatrix}$

46. $\begin{bmatrix} 6 & 4 \\ 3 & 2 \end{bmatrix}$

47. $\begin{bmatrix} 2 & -1 & 0 \\ 1 & 0 & 1 \\ 1 & -2 & 0 \end{bmatrix}$

48. $\begin{bmatrix} 2 & 0 & 4 \\ 1 & -1 & 0 \\ 0 & 1 & -2 \end{bmatrix}$

49. $\begin{bmatrix} 1 & 3 & 6 \\ 4 & 0 & 9 \\ 5 & 15 & 30 \end{bmatrix}$

50. $\begin{bmatrix} 2 & -3 & 4 \\ 1 & 5 & 7 \\ -4 & 6 & -8 \end{bmatrix}$

Solve the matrix equation $AX = B$ for X using the given matrices.

51. $A = \begin{bmatrix} 5 & 1 \\ -2 & -2 \end{bmatrix}, \quad B = \begin{bmatrix} -8 \\ 24 \end{bmatrix}$

52. $A = \begin{bmatrix} 1 & 2 \\ 2 & 4 \end{bmatrix}, \quad B = \begin{bmatrix} 5 \\ 10 \end{bmatrix}$

53. $A = \begin{bmatrix} 1 & 0 & 2 \\ -1 & 1 & 0 \\ 3 & 0 & 4 \end{bmatrix}, \quad B = \begin{bmatrix} 8 \\ 4 \\ -6 \end{bmatrix}$

54. $A = \begin{bmatrix} 2 & 4 & 0 \\ 1 & -2 & 0 \\ 0 & 0 & 3 \end{bmatrix}, \quad B = \begin{bmatrix} 72 \\ -24 \\ 48 \end{bmatrix}$

Solve each system of equations by inverses.

55. $\begin{aligned} x + 2y &= 4 \\ 2x - 3y &= 1 \end{aligned}$

56. $\begin{aligned} 5x + 10y &= 80 \\ 3x - 2y &= 120 \end{aligned}$

57. $\begin{aligned} x + y + z &= 1 \\ 2x + y \phantom{{}+z} &= -2 \\ 3y + z &= 2 \end{aligned}$

58. $\begin{aligned} x - 4y + 2z &= -1 \\ -2x + y - 3z &= -9 \\ 3x + 5y - 2z &= 7 \end{aligned}$

Find the eigenvalues and their corresponding eigenvectors.

59. $\begin{bmatrix} -3 & 12 \\ -2 & 7 \end{bmatrix}$

60. $\begin{bmatrix} 5 & 3 \\ 3 & 5 \end{bmatrix}$

61. $\begin{bmatrix} 1 & 0 & 0 \\ 2 & 2 & 0 \\ 2 & 1 & -3 \end{bmatrix}$

62. $\begin{bmatrix} -2 & 0 & 0 \\ 1 & 3 & 0 \\ -1 & 1 & 2 \end{bmatrix}$

LIFE SCIENCE APPLICATIONS

63. Animal Activity The activities of a grazing animal can be classified roughly into three categories: grazing, moving, and resting. Suppose horses spend 8 hours grazing, 8 moving, and 8 resting; cattle spend 10 grazing, 5 moving, and 9 resting; sheep spend 7 grazing, 10 moving, and 7 resting; and goats spend 8 grazing, 9 moving, and 7 resting. Write this information as a 4 × 3 matrix.

64. CAT Scans Computer Aided Tomography (CAT) scanners take X-rays of a part of the body from different directions, and put the information together to create a picture of a cross section of the body. The amount by which the energy of the X-ray decreases, measured in linear-attenuation units, tells whether the X-ray has passed through healthy tissue, tumorous tissue, or bone, based on the following table. *Source: The Mathematics Teacher.*

Type of Tissue	Linear-Attenuation Values
Healthy tissue	0.1625–0.2977
Tumorous tissue	0.2679–0.3930
Bone	0.3857–0.5108

The part of the body to be scanned is divided into cells. If an X-ray passes through more than one cell, the total linear-attenuation value is the sum of the values for the cells. For example, in the figure, let a, b, and c be the values for cells A, B, and C. The attenuation value for beam 1 is $a + b$ and for beam 2 is $a + c$.

Beam 1
X-ray source

Beam 2

A
B   C

Beam 3

X-ray detector

a. Find the attenuation value for beam 3.

b. Suppose that the attenuation values are 0.8, 0.55, and 0.65 for beams 1, 2, and 3, respectively. Set up and solve the system of three equations for a, b, and c. What can you conclude about cells A, B, and C?

c. Find the inverse of the coefficient matrix from part b to find a, b, and c for the following three cases, and make conclusions about cells A, B, and C for each.

	Linear-Attenuation Values		
Patient	**Beam 1**	**Beam 2**	**Beam 3**
X	0.54	0.40	0.52
Y	0.65	0.80	0.75
Z	0.51	0.49	0.44

65. CAT Scans   (Refer to Exercise 64.) Four X-ray beams are aimed at four cells, as shown in the following figure. ***Source: The Mathematics Teacher.***

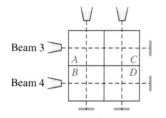

Beam 1 Beam 2

Beam 3

A   C
B   D

Beam 4

a. Suppose the attenuation values for beams 1, 2, 3, and 4 are 0.60, 0.75, 0.65, and 0.70, respectively. Do we have enough information to determine the values of a, b, c, and d? Explain.

b. Suppose we have the data from part a, as well as the following values for d. Find the values for a, b, and c, and draw conclusions about cells A, B, C, and D in each case.

(i) 0.33   **(ii)** 0.43

c. Two X-ray beams are added, as shown in the figure in the next column. In addition to the data in part a, we now have attenuation values for beams 5 and 6 of 0.85 and 0.50. Find the values for a, b, c, and d, and make conclusions about cells A, B, C, and D.

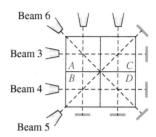

Beam 1 Beam 2

Beam 6

Beam 3

A   C
B   D

Beam 4

Beam 5

d. Six X-ray beams are not necessary because four appropriately chosen beams are sufficient. Give two examples of four beams (chosen from beams 1–6 in part c) that will give the solution. (*Note:* There are 12 possible solutions.)

e. Discuss what properties the four beams selected in part d must have in order to provide a unique solution.

66. Hockey   In a recent study, the number of head and neck injuries among hockey players wearing full face shields and half face shields were compared. The following table provides the rates per 1000 athlete-exposures for specific injuries that caused a player wearing either shield to miss one or more events. ***Source: JAMA.***

	Half Shield	**Full Shield**
Head and Face Injuries (excluding Concussions)	3.54	1.41
Concussions	1.53	1.57
Neck Injuries	0.34	0.29
Other	7.53	6.21

If an equal number of players in a large league wear each type of shield and the total number of athlete-exposures for the league in a season is 8000, use matrix operations to estimate the total number of injuries of each type.

Leslie Matrices For each of the following Leslie matrices, a. find a population of size 10,000 for which the proportion of the population in each age group stays the same from one year to the next and b. tell by what factor the population grows or declines each year.

67. $\begin{bmatrix} 0.3 & 0.2 \\ 0.3 & 0.8 \end{bmatrix}$

68. $\begin{bmatrix} 0.2 & 0.3 \\ 0.4 & 0.1 \end{bmatrix}$

69. Buffalo A mathematical model for a herd of buffalo is given by the Leslie matrix

$$\begin{bmatrix} 0.95 & 0 & 0.75 & 0 & 0 & 0 \\ 0 & 0.95 & 0 & 0.75 & 0 & 0 \\ 0 & 0 & 0 & 0 & 0.6 & 0 \\ 0 & 0 & 0 & 0 & 0 & 0.6 \\ 0 & 0.48 & 0 & 0 & 0 & 0 \\ 0 & 0.42 & 0 & 0 & 0 & 0 \end{bmatrix},$$

where the first row corresponds to the number of adult males, the second to the number of adult females, the third to the number of male yearlings, the fourth to the number of female yearlings, the fifth to the number of male calves, and the sixth to the number of female calves. *Source: UMAP.* The matrix is used to give next year's herd as a function of this year's.

a. Explain what each row of the matrix means.

b. Verify that $\lambda = 0.95$ is an eigenvalue corresponding to the eigenvector $\begin{bmatrix} k \\ 0 \\ 0 \\ 0 \\ 0 \\ 0 \end{bmatrix}$ for any constant k. Explain what this tells us about the herd.

c. The manager of a buffalo herd wants to harvest some of the herd each year. Suppose that Q is the vector describing a harvest that leaves the population for next year the same as this year's. Show that the population X must satisfy the equation

$$X = (M - I)^{-1}Q.$$

d. Suppose the manager in part c wants a harvest given by

$$Q = \begin{bmatrix} 100 \\ 100 \\ 10 \\ 10 \\ 0 \\ 0 \end{bmatrix}.$$

Find the matrix X describing the herd.

e. Suppose the manager wants the herd to increase by 10% each year while still yielding a harvest Q. Show that the population X must satisfy the equation

$$X = (M - 1.1I)^{-1}Q.$$

f. Suppose the manager in part e wants a harvest given by

$$Q = \begin{bmatrix} 100 \\ 100 \\ 10 \\ 10 \\ 0 \\ 0 \end{bmatrix}.$$

Find the matrix X describing the herd.

70. Carbon Dioxide Determining the amount of carbon dioxide in the atmosphere is important because carbon dioxide is known to be a greenhouse gas. Carbon dioxide concentrations (in parts per million) have been measured at Mauna Loa, Hawaii, for more than 40 years. The concentrations have increased quadratically. The table lists readings for 3 years. *Source: Scripps Institution of Oceanography.*

Year	CO_2
1960	317
1980	339
2010	390

a. If the relationship between the carbon dioxide concentration C and the year t is expressed as $C = at^2 + bt + c$, where $t = 0$ corresponds to 1960, use a linear system of equations to determine the constants a, b, and c.

b. Predict the year when the amount of carbon dioxide in the atmosphere will double from its 1960 level. (*Hint:* This requires solving a quadratic equation. For review on how to do this, see Section R.4.)

71. Chemistry When carbon monoxide (CO) reacts with oxygen (O_2), carbon dioxide (CO_2) is formed. This can be written as $CO + (1/2)O_2 = CO_2$ and as a matrix equation. If we form a 2×1 column matrix by letting the first element be the number of carbon atoms and the second element be the number of oxygen atoms, then CO would have the column matrix

$$\begin{bmatrix} 1 \\ 1 \end{bmatrix}$$

Similarly, O_2 and CO_2 would have the column matrices $\begin{bmatrix} 0 \\ 2 \end{bmatrix}$ and $\begin{bmatrix} 1 \\ 2 \end{bmatrix}$, respectively. *Source: Journal of Chemical Education.*

a. Use the Gauss-Jordan method to find numbers x and y (known as *stoichiometric numbers*) that solve the system of equations

$$\begin{bmatrix} 1 \\ 1 \end{bmatrix} x + \begin{bmatrix} 0 \\ 2 \end{bmatrix} y = \begin{bmatrix} 1 \\ 2 \end{bmatrix}.$$

Compare your answers to the equation written above.

b. Repeat the process for $xCO_2 + yH_2 + zCO = H_2O$, where H_2 is hydrogen and H_2O is water. In words, what does this mean?

OTHER APPLICATIONS

72. Roof Trusses Linear systems occur in the design of roof trusses for new homes and buildings. The simplest type of roof truss is a triangle. The truss shown in the figure below is used to frame roofs of small buildings. If a 100-lb force is applied at the peak of the truss, then the forces or weights W_1 and W_2 exerted parallel to each rafter of the truss are determined by the following linear system of equations.

$$\frac{\sqrt{3}}{2}(W_1 + W_2) = 100$$

$$W_1 - W_2 = 0$$

Solve the system to find W_1 and W_2. *Source: Structural Analysis.*

73. Roof Trusses (Refer to Exercise 72.) Use the following system of equations to determine the force or weights W_1 and W_2 exerted on each rafter for the truss shown in the figure.

$$\frac{1}{2}W_1 + \frac{\sqrt{2}}{2}W_2 = 150$$

$$\frac{\sqrt{3}}{2}W_1 - \frac{\sqrt{2}}{2}W_2 = 0$$

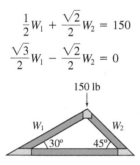

74. Scheduling Production An office supply manufacturer makes two kinds of paper clips, standard and extra large. To make 1000 standard paper clips requires 1/4 hour on a cutting machine and 1/2 hour on a machine that shapes the clips. One thousand extra large paper clips require 1/3 hour on each machine. The manager of paper clip production has 4 hours per day available on the cutting machine and 6 hours per day on the shaping machine. How many of each kind of clip can he make?

75. Production Requirements The Waputi Indians make woven blankets, rugs, and skirts. Each blanket requires 24 hours for spinning the yarn, 4 hours for dyeing the yarn, and 15 hours for weaving. Rugs require 30, 5, and 18 hours and skirts 12, 3, and 9 hours, respectively. If there are 306, 59, and 201 hours available for spinning, dyeing, and weaving, respectively, how many of each item can be made? (*Hint:* Simplify the equations you write, if possible, before solving the system.)

76. Distribution An oil refinery in Tulsa sells 50% of its production to a Chicago distributor, 20% to a Dallas distributor, and 30% to an Atlanta distributor. Another refinery in New Orleans

sells 40% of its production to the Chicago distributor, 40% to the Dallas distributor, and 20% to the Atlanta distributor. A third refinery in Ardmore sells the same distributors 30%, 40%, and 30% of its production. The three distributors received 219,000, 192,000, and 144,000 gal of oil, respectively. How many gallons of oil were produced at each of the three plants?

77. Stock Reports The New York Stock Exchange reports in daily newspapers give the dividend, price-to-earnings ratio, sales (in hundreds of shares), last price, and change in price for each company. Write the following stock reports as a 4 × 5 matrix: American Telephone & Telegraph: 1.33, 17.6, 152,000, 26.75, +1.88; General Electric: 1.00, 20.0, 238,200, 32.36, −1.50; Sara Lee: 0.79, 25.4, 39,110, 16.51, −0.89; Walt Disney Company: 0.27, 21.2, 122,500, 28.60, +0.75.

78. Filling Orders A printer has three orders for pamphlets that require three kinds of paper, as shown in the following matrix.

		Order	
	I	II	III
High-grade	10	5	8
Paper Medium-grade	12	0	4
Coated	0	10	5

The printer has on hand 3170 sheets of high-grade paper, 2360 sheets of medium-grade paper, and 1800 sheets of coated paper. All the paper must be used in preparing the order.

a. Write a 3 × 1 matrix for the amounts of paper on hand.

b. Write a matrix of variables to represent the number of pamphlets that must be printed in each of the three orders.

c. Write a matrix equation using the given matrix and your matrices from parts a and b.

d. Solve the equation from part c.

79. Students Suppose 20% of the boys and 30% of the girls in a high school like tennis, and 60% of the boys and 90% of the girls like math. If 500 students like tennis and 1500 like math, how many boys and girls are in the school? Find all possible solutions.

80. Baseball In the 2009 Major League Baseball season, slugger Ichiro Suzuki had a total of 225 hits. The number of singles he hit was 11 more than four times the combined total of doubles and home runs. The number of doubles he hit was 1 more than twice the combined total of triples and home runs. The number of singles and home runs together was 15 more than five times the combined total of doubles and triples. Find the number of singles, doubles, triples, and home runs that Suzuki hit during the season. *Source: Baseball-Reference.com.*

81. Cookies Regular Nabisco Oreo cookies are made of two chocolate cookie wafers surrounding a single layer of vanilla cream. The claim on the package states that a single serving is 34 g, which is three cookies. Nabisco Double Stuf cookies are made of the same two chocolate cookie wafers surrounding a double layer of vanilla cream. The claim on this package states that a single serving is 29 g, which is two Double Stuf cookies. If the Double Stuf cookies truly have a double layer of vanilla cream, find the weight of a single chocolate wafer and the weight of a single layer of vanilla cream.

CONTAGION

Suppose that three people have contracted a contagious disease. A second group of five people may have been in contact with the three infected persons. A third group of six people may have been in contact with the second group. We can form a 3×5 matrix P with rows representing the first group of three and columns representing the second group of five. We enter a one in the corresponding position if a person in the first group has contact with a person in the second group. These direct contacts are called *first-order contacts*. Similarly, we form a 5×6 matrix Q representing the first-order contacts between the second and third group. For example, suppose

$$P = \begin{bmatrix} 1 & 0 & 0 & 1 & 0 \\ 0 & 0 & 1 & 1 & 0 \\ 1 & 1 & 0 & 0 & 0 \end{bmatrix} \text{ and }$$

$$Q = \begin{bmatrix} 1 & 1 & 0 & 1 & 1 & 1 \\ 0 & 0 & 0 & 0 & 1 & 0 \\ 0 & 0 & 0 & 0 & 0 & 0 \\ 0 & 1 & 0 & 1 & 0 & 0 \\ 1 & 0 & 0 & 0 & 1 & 0 \end{bmatrix}.$$

From matrix P we see that the first person in the first group had contact with the first and fourth persons in the second group. Also, none of the first group had contact with the last person in the second group.

A *second-order contact* is an indirect contact between persons in the first and third groups through some person in the second group. The product matrix PQ indicates these contacts. Verify that the second-row, fourth-column entry of PQ is 1. That is, there is one second-order contact between the second person in group one and the fourth person in group three. Let a_{ij} denote the element in the ith row and jth column of the matrix PQ. By looking at the products that form a_{24} below, we see that the common contact was with the fourth individual in group two. (The p_{ij} are entries in P, and the q_{ij} are entries in Q.)

$$\begin{aligned} a_{24} &= p_{21}q_{14} + p_{22}q_{24} + p_{23}q_{34} + p_{24}q_{44} + p_{25}q_{54} \\ &= 0 \cdot 1 + 0 \cdot 0 + 1 \cdot 0 + 1 \cdot 1 + 0 \cdot 0 \\ &= 1 \end{aligned}$$

The second person in group 1 and the fourth person in group 3 both had contact with the fourth person in group 2.

This idea could be extended to third-, fourth-, and larger-order contacts. It indicates a way to use matrices to trace the spread of a contagious disease. It could also pertain to the dispersal of ideas or anything that might pass from one individual to another.

*Source: **Finite Mathematics with Applications to Business, Life Sciences, and Social Sciences.***

EXERCISES

1. Find the second-order contact matrix PQ mentioned in the text.

2. How many second-order contacts were there between the second contagious person and the third person in the third group?

3. Is there anyone in the third group who has had no contacts at all with the first group?

4. The totals of the columns in PQ give the total number of second-order contacts per person, while the column totals in P and Q give the total number of first-order contacts per person. Which person(s) in the third group had the most contacts, counting first- and second-order contacts?

5. Go to the website WolframAlpha.com and enter: "multiply matrices." Study how matrix multiplication can be performed by Wolfram|Alpha. Try Exercise 1 with Wolfram|Alpha and discuss how it compares with Microsoft Excel and with your graphing calculator.

DIRECTIONS FOR GROUP PROJECT

Assume that your group (3–5 students) is trying to map the spread of a new disease. Suppose also that the information given above has been obtained from interviews with the first three people that were hospitalized with symptoms of the disease and their contacts. Using the questions above as a guide, prepare a presentation for a public meeting that describes the method of obtaining the data and the data itself, and that addresses the spirit of each question. Formulate a strategy for how to handle the spread of this disease to other people. The presentation should be mathematically sound, grammatically correct, and professionally crafted. Use presentation software, such as Microsoft PowerPoint, to present your findings.

Answers to Selected Exercises

Chapter 10 Matrices

Exercises 10.1

1. $\begin{bmatrix} 3 & 1 & | & 6 \\ 2 & 5 & | & 15 \end{bmatrix}$

For Exercises ...	1–8, 11–16	17–20, 25, 26, 29, 30, 34, 36–38, 41, 42	21, 22, 27, 32	23, 24, 28, 31, 33, 35, 39, 40	44–70
Refer to Example ...	1–5	1, 2	3	4, 5	6

3. $\begin{bmatrix} 2 & 1 & 1 & | & 3 \\ 3 & -4 & 2 & | & -7 \\ 1 & 1 & 1 & | & 2 \end{bmatrix}$ **5.** $x = 2, y = 3$ **7.** $x = 4, y = -5, z = 1$ **9.** Row operations **11.** $\begin{bmatrix} 3 & 7 & 4 & | & 10 \\ 0 & 1 & -5 & | & -8 \\ 0 & 4 & 5 & | & 11 \end{bmatrix}$

13. $\begin{bmatrix} 1 & 0 & 0 & | & -3 \\ 0 & 3 & 2 & | & 5 \\ 0 & 5 & 3 & | & 7 \end{bmatrix}$ **15.** $\begin{bmatrix} 1 & 0 & 0 & | & 6 \\ 0 & 5 & 0 & | & 9 \\ 0 & 0 & 4 & | & 8 \end{bmatrix}$ **17.** $(2, 3)$ **19.** $(1, 6)$ **21.** No solution **23.** $((3y + 1)/6, y)$ **25.** $(4, 1, 0)$

27. No solution **29.** $(-1, 23, 16)$ **31.** $((-9z + 5)/23, (10z - 3)/23, z)$ **33.** $((-2z + 62)/35, (3z + 5)/7, z)$
35. $((9 - 3y - z)/2, y, z)$ **37.** $(0, 2, -2, 1)$; the answers are given in the order x, y, z, w. **39.** $(-w - 3, -4w - 19, -3w - 2, w)$
41. $(28.9436, 36.6326, 9.6390, 37.1036)$ **43.** row 1: 3/8, 1/6, 11/24; row 2: 5/12, 1/3, 1/4; row 3: 5/24, 1/2, 7/24 **45.** 40 units of
corn, 15 units of soybeans, and 30 units of cottonseed **47. a.** 400/9 g of group A, 400/3 g of group B, and 2000/9 g of group C
b. For any positive number z of grams of group C, there should be z grams less than 800/3 g of group A and 400/3 g of group B.
c. No **49.** About 244 fish of species A, 39 fish of species B, and 101 fish of species C **51.** 81 kg of the first chemical, 382.286 kg
of the second, and 286.714 kg of the third **53. b.** 7,206,360 white cows, 4,893,246 black cows, 3,515,820 spotted cows, and
5,439,213 brown cows **55.** Hire the Garcia firm for 20 hr and the Wong firm for 15 hr. **57. a.** 10 deluxe, 4 super-deluxe, 15 ultra
b. None **c.** 5 **59. a.** \$12,000 at 8%, \$7000 at 9%, and \$6000 at 10% **b.** The amount borrowed at 10% must be less than or
equal to \$9500. If $z = \$5000$, they borrowed \$11,000 at 8% and \$9000 at 9%. **c.** No solution **d.** The total annual interest would
be \$2220, not \$2190, as specified as one of the conditions. **61. a.** About 51.8 weeks; about \$959,091 **63.** 36 field goals, 28 foul
shots **65.** 225 singles, 24 doubles, 5 triples, and 8 home runs **67. a.** $y = -0.032x^2 + 0.852x + 0.632$
b. $y = -0.032x^2 + 0.852x + 0.632$ **69. a.** $x_2 + x_3 = 700, x_3 + x_4 = 600$ **b.** $(1000 - x_4, 100 + x_4, 600 - x_4, x_4)$
c. $0 \le x_4 \le 600$ **d.** $400 \le x_1 \le 1000, 100 \le x_2 \le 700, 0 \le x_3 \le 600$

Exercises 10.2

1. False; not all corresponding elements are equal.

For Exercises ...	1–6, 15–20	7–14	21–32	41, 48, 49	39, 46	40	42–45, 47
Refer to Example ...	3	2	4, 6	5	1	5, 7	7

3. True **5.** True **7.** 2×2; square
9. 3×4 **11.** 2×1; column **13.** Undefined **15.** $x = 4, y = -8, z = 1$ **17.** $s = 10, t = 0, r = 7$

19. $a = 20, b = 5, c = 0, d = 4, f = 1$ **21.** $\begin{bmatrix} 10 & 4 & -5 & -6 \\ 4 & 5 & 3 & 11 \end{bmatrix}$ **23.** Not possible **25.** $\begin{bmatrix} 1 & 5 & 6 & -9 \\ 5 & 7 & 2 & 1 \\ -7 & 2 & 2 & -7 \end{bmatrix}$ **27.** $\begin{bmatrix} 3 & 4 \\ 4 & 8 \end{bmatrix}$

29. $\begin{bmatrix} 10 & -2 \\ 10 & 9 \end{bmatrix}$ **31.** $\begin{bmatrix} -12x + 8y & -x + y \\ x & 8x - y \end{bmatrix}$ **33.** $\begin{bmatrix} -x & -y \\ -z & -w \end{bmatrix}$ **39. a.** $\begin{bmatrix} 2 & 1 & 2 & 1 \\ 3 & 2 & 2 & 1 \\ 4 & 3 & 2 & 1 \end{bmatrix}$ **b.** $\begin{bmatrix} 5 & 0 & 7 \\ 0 & 10 & 1 \\ 0 & 15 & 2 \\ 10 & 12 & 8 \end{bmatrix}$ **c.** $\begin{bmatrix} 8 \\ 4 \\ 5 \end{bmatrix}$

41. a. 8 **b.** 3 **c.** $\begin{bmatrix} 85 & 15 \\ 27 & 73 \end{bmatrix}$ **d.** Yes **43. a.** $\begin{bmatrix} 60.0 & 68.3 \\ 63.8 & 72.5 \\ 64.5 & 73.6 \\ 68.2 & 75.1 \\ 71.8 & 78.0 \end{bmatrix}$ **b.** $\begin{bmatrix} 68.0 & 75.6 \\ 70.7 & 78.1 \\ 72.7 & 79.4 \\ 74.7 & 79.9 \\ 76.5 & 81.3 \end{bmatrix}$ **c.** $\begin{bmatrix} -8.0 & -7.3 \\ -6.9 & -5.6 \\ -8.2 & -5.8 \\ -6.5 & -4.8 \\ -4.7 & -3.3 \end{bmatrix}$

45. a. $\begin{bmatrix} 51.2 & 7.9 \\ 59.8 & 11.1 \\ 66.2 & 11.3 \\ 73.8 & 13.2 \\ 78.5 & 16.5 \\ 84.2 & 19.8 \end{bmatrix}$ **b.** $\begin{bmatrix} 45.3 & 7.9 \\ 47.9 & 8.5 \\ 50.8 & 9.2 \\ 53.4 & 9.3 \\ 57.0 & 10.6 \\ 62.9 & 13.9 \end{bmatrix}$ **c.** $\begin{bmatrix} 5.9 & 0 \\ 11.9 & 2.6 \\ 15.4 & 2.1 \\ 20.4 & 3.9 \\ 21.5 & 5.9 \\ 21.3 & 5.9 \end{bmatrix}$ **47. a.** $\begin{bmatrix} 2.61 & 4.39 & 6.29 & 9.08 \\ 1.63 & 2.77 & 4.61 & 6.92 \\ 0.92 & 0.75 & 0.62 & 0.54 \end{bmatrix}$

b. $\begin{bmatrix} 1.38 & 1.72 & 1.94 & 3.31 \\ 1.26 & 1.48 & 2.82 & 2.28 \\ 0.41 & 0.33 & 0.27 & 0.40 \end{bmatrix}$ **c.** $\begin{bmatrix} 1.23 & 2.67 & 4.35 & 5.77 \\ 0.37 & 1.29 & 1.79 & 4.64 \\ 0.51 & 0.42 & 0.35 & 0.14 \end{bmatrix}$

49. a. $\begin{bmatrix} 88 & 105 & 60 \\ 48 & 72 & 40 \\ 16 & 21 & 0 \\ 112 & 147 & 50 \end{bmatrix}$ **b.** $\begin{bmatrix} 110 & 140 & 66 \\ 60 & 96 & 44 \\ 20 & 28 & 0 \\ 140 & 196 & 55 \end{bmatrix}$ **c.** $\begin{bmatrix} 198 & 245 & 126 \\ 108 & 168 & 84 \\ 36 & 49 & 0 \\ 252 & 343 & 105 \end{bmatrix}$

Exercises 10.3

For Exercises ...	1–6, 44–46	7–12	15–31	43, 47–52
Refer to Example ...	1	4	2, 3, 5	6

1. $\begin{bmatrix} -4 & 8 \\ 0 & 6 \end{bmatrix}$ **3.** $\begin{bmatrix} 12 & -24 \\ 0 & -18 \end{bmatrix}$ **5.** $\begin{bmatrix} -22 & -6 \\ 20 & -12 \end{bmatrix}$ **7.** $2 \times 2; 2 \times 2$

9. 3×4; BA does not exist. **11.** AB does not exist; 3×2. **13.** columns; rows **15.** $\begin{bmatrix} 8 \\ -1 \end{bmatrix}$ **17.** $\begin{bmatrix} 14 \\ -23 \end{bmatrix}$ **19.** $\begin{bmatrix} -7 & 2 & 8 \\ 27 & -12 & 12 \end{bmatrix}$

21. $\begin{bmatrix} -2 & 10 \\ 0 & 8 \end{bmatrix}$ **23.** $\begin{bmatrix} 13 & 5 \\ 25 & 15 \end{bmatrix}$ **25.** $\begin{bmatrix} 13 \\ 29 \end{bmatrix}$ **27.** $\begin{bmatrix} 7 \\ -33 \\ 4 \end{bmatrix}$ **29.** $\begin{bmatrix} 22 & -8 \\ 11 & -4 \end{bmatrix}$ **31. a.** $\begin{bmatrix} 16 & 22 \\ 7 & 19 \end{bmatrix}$ **b.** $\begin{bmatrix} 5 & -5 \\ 0 & 30 \end{bmatrix}$ **c.** No **d.** No

39. a. $\begin{bmatrix} 6 & 106 & 158 & 222 & 28 \\ 120 & 139 & 64 & 75 & 115 \\ -146 & -2 & 184 & 144 & -129 \\ 106 & 94 & 24 & 116 & 110 \end{bmatrix}$ **b.** Does not exist **c.** No

41. a. $\begin{bmatrix} -1 & 5 & 9 & 13 & -1 \\ 7 & 17 & 2 & -10 & 6 \\ 18 & 9 & -12 & 12 & 22 \\ 9 & 4 & 18 & 10 & -3 \\ 1 & 6 & 10 & 28 & 5 \end{bmatrix}$ **b.** $\begin{bmatrix} -2 & -9 & 90 & 77 \\ -42 & -63 & 127 & 62 \\ 413 & 76 & 180 & -56 \\ -29 & -44 & 198 & 85 \\ 137 & 20 & 162 & 103 \end{bmatrix}$ **c.** $\begin{bmatrix} -56 & -1 & 1 & 45 \\ -156 & -119 & 76 & 122 \\ 315 & 86 & 118 & -91 \\ -17 & -17 & 116 & 51 \\ 118 & 19 & 125 & 77 \end{bmatrix}$

d. $\begin{bmatrix} 54 & -8 & 89 & 32 \\ 114 & 56 & 51 & -60 \\ 98 & -10 & 62 & 35 \\ -12 & -27 & 82 & 34 \\ 19 & 1 & 37 & 26 \end{bmatrix}$ **e.** $\begin{bmatrix} -2 & -9 & 90 & 77 \\ -42 & -63 & 127 & 62 \\ 413 & 76 & 180 & -56 \\ -29 & -44 & 198 & 85 \\ 137 & 20 & 162 & 103 \end{bmatrix}$ **f.** Yes

43. a. $\begin{bmatrix} 20 & 52 & 27 \\ 25 & 62 & 35 \\ 30 & 72 & 43 \end{bmatrix}$; the rows give the amounts of fat, carbohydrates, and protein, respectively, in each of the daily meals.

b. $\begin{bmatrix} 75 \\ 45 \\ 70 \\ 168 \end{bmatrix}$; the rows give the number of calories in one exchange of each of the food groups. **c.** The rows give the number of calories in each meal.

45. $\begin{bmatrix} 66.7 & 74.4 \\ 69.6 & 77.2 \\ 71.3 & 78.4 \\ 73.8 & 79.3 \end{bmatrix}$ **47. a.** 3819; 3824; 3763; 3698; 3638 **b.** Extinction **c.** 4017; 4154; 4280; 4399; 4524; does not become extinct

49. a. $\begin{bmatrix} 146 \\ 93 \end{bmatrix}$; the rows represent the cost (in cents) for each type of bird.

51. a. $\begin{array}{c} \\ S \\ C \end{array} \begin{array}{c} \begin{array}{ccc} CC & MM & AD \end{array} \\ \begin{bmatrix} 0.5 & 0.4 & 0.3 \\ 0.2 & 0.3 & 0.3 \end{bmatrix} \end{array}$ **b.** $\begin{array}{c} \\ SD \\ MC \\ M \end{array} \begin{array}{c} \begin{array}{cc} S & C \end{array} \\ \begin{bmatrix} 4 & 3 \\ 2 & 5 \\ 1 & 7 \end{bmatrix} \end{array}$ **c.** $CA = \begin{array}{c} \\ SD \\ MC \\ M \end{array} \begin{array}{c} \begin{array}{ccc} CC & MM & AD \end{array} \\ \begin{bmatrix} 2.6 & 2.5 & 2.1 \\ 2 & 2.3 & 2.1 \\ 1.9 & 2.5 & 2.4 \end{bmatrix} \end{array}$ **d.** \$2.50 **e.** Mexico City

Exercises 10.4

1. Yes   **3.** No
5. No   **7.** Yes

For Exercises . . .	1–8	11–26, 51–55	27–42, 56–58	59–64, 67	65, 66
Refer to Example . . .	1	2, 3	4, 6	5	7

9. No; the row of all zeros makes it impossible to get all the 1's in the diagonal of the identity matrix, no matter what matrix is used as a candidate for the inverse.

11. $\begin{bmatrix} 0 & 1/2 \\ -1 & 1/2 \end{bmatrix}$ **13.** $\begin{bmatrix} 2 & 1 \\ 5 & 3 \end{bmatrix}$ **15.** No inverse   **17.** $\begin{bmatrix} 1 & 0 & 0 \\ 0 & -1 & 0 \\ -1 & 0 & 1 \end{bmatrix}$ **19.** $\begin{bmatrix} 15 & 4 & -5 \\ -12 & -3 & 4 \\ -4 & -1 & 1 \end{bmatrix}$ **21.** No inverse

23. $\begin{bmatrix} -11/2 & -1/2 & 5/2 \\ 1/2 & 1/2 & -1/2 \\ -5/2 & 1/2 & 1/2 \end{bmatrix}$ **25.** $\begin{bmatrix} 1/2 & 1/2 & -1/4 & 1/2 \\ -1 & 4 & -1/2 & -2 \\ -1/2 & 5/2 & -1/4 & -3/2 \\ 1/2 & -1/2 & 1/4 & 1/2 \end{bmatrix}$ **27.** $(5, 1)$ **29.** $(2, 1)$ **31.** $(15, 21)$

33. No inverse, $(-8y - 12, y)$ **35.** $(-8, 6, 1)$ **37.** $(-36, 8, -8)$ **39.** No inverse, no solution for system

41. $(-7, -34, -19, 7)$ **51.** $\begin{bmatrix} -0.0447 & -0.0230 & 0.0292 & 0.0895 & -0.0402 \\ 0.0921 & 0.0150 & 0.0321 & 0.0209 & -0.0276 \\ -0.0678 & 0.0315 & -0.0404 & 0.0326 & 0.0373 \\ 0.0171 & -0.0248 & 0.0069 & -0.0003 & 0.0246 \\ -0.0208 & 0.0740 & 0.0096 & -0.1018 & 0.0646 \end{bmatrix}$

53. $\begin{bmatrix} 0.0394 & 0.0880 & 0.0033 & 0.0530 & -0.1499 \\ -0.1492 & 0.0289 & 0.0187 & 0.1033 & 0.1668 \\ -0.1330 & -0.0543 & 0.0356 & 0.1768 & 0.1055 \\ 0.1407 & 0.0175 & -0.0453 & -0.1344 & 0.0655 \\ 0.0102 & -0.0653 & 0.0993 & 0.0085 & -0.0388 \end{bmatrix}$ **55.** Yes   **57.** $\begin{bmatrix} 1.51482 \\ 0.053479 \\ -0.637242 \\ 0.462629 \end{bmatrix}$

59. a. 50 Super Vim, 75 Multitab, and 100 Mighty Mix   **b.** 75 Super Vim, 50 Multitab, and 60 Mighty Mix   **c.** 80 Super Vim, 100 Multitab, and 50 Mighty Mix

61. a. $\begin{bmatrix} 72 \\ 48 \\ 60 \end{bmatrix}$ **b.** $\begin{bmatrix} 2 & 4 & 2 \\ 2 & 1 & 2 \\ 2 & 1 & 3 \end{bmatrix} \begin{bmatrix} x_1 \\ x_2 \\ x_3 \end{bmatrix} = \begin{bmatrix} 72 \\ 48 \\ 60 \end{bmatrix}$ **c.** 8 type I, 8 type II, and 12 type III   **63. a.** \$10,000 at 6%, \$10,000 at 6.5%, and \$5000 at 8%   **b.** \$14,000 at 6%, \$9000 at 6.5%, and \$7000 at 8%   **c.** \$24,000 at 6%, \$4000 at 6.5%, and \$12,000 at 8%

65. a. 85, 50, 40, 130, 120, 145, 49, 63, 121, 171, 117, 99, 159, 113, 91, 145, 105, 100, 90, 40, 75, 134, 113, 91, 98, 101, 112

b. I love you   **67. a.** $\begin{bmatrix} -1/15 & -1/15 & 13/3 \\ 4/15 & 1/15 & -40/3 \\ -1/5 & 0 & 10 \end{bmatrix}$ **b.** $\begin{bmatrix} 0 & 1 & 40 \\ -1 & 0 & 60 \\ 0 & 0 & 1 \end{bmatrix}$ **c.** The shape is a sideways T whose vertical and horizontal intersection is at the mark $(60, 10)$.

Exercises 10.5

1. 17   **3.** 165   **5.** 1, 5; $\begin{bmatrix} 0 \\ 1 \end{bmatrix}, \begin{bmatrix} 2 \\ 1 \end{bmatrix}$ **7.** 2, 9; $\begin{bmatrix} 2 \\ -1 \end{bmatrix}, \begin{bmatrix} 1 \\ 3 \end{bmatrix}$ **9.** 2,1; $\begin{bmatrix} 3 \\ 2 \end{bmatrix}, \begin{bmatrix} 1 \\ 1 \end{bmatrix}$

For Exercises . . .	1–4	5–23	24, 25
Refer to Example . . .	2, 3	4, 5	6

11. 4, −1, −3; $\begin{bmatrix} 35 \\ 21 \\ 25 \end{bmatrix}, \begin{bmatrix} 0 \\ 2 \\ 5 \end{bmatrix}, \begin{bmatrix} 0 \\ 0 \\ 1 \end{bmatrix}$ **15.** 4; $\begin{bmatrix} 3 \\ 2 \end{bmatrix}$ **17.** $2 + 3i, 2 - 3i$; $\begin{bmatrix} 1 - 3i \\ 2 \end{bmatrix}, \begin{bmatrix} 1 + 3i \\ 2 \end{bmatrix}$ **19. a.** $\begin{bmatrix} 5000 \\ 5000 \end{bmatrix}$ **b.** 1.4

21. a. $\begin{bmatrix} 5000 \\ 5000 \end{bmatrix}$ **b.** 0.9   **23. a.** $\begin{bmatrix} 6000 \\ 4000 \end{bmatrix}$ **b.** 0.9   **25.** $X(n) \approx (55{,}000/23) (1.4)^n \begin{bmatrix} 1 \\ 1 \end{bmatrix}$

Chapter 10 Review Exercises

1. True **2.** False **3.** True
4. False **5.** False **6.** False
7. True **8.** False **9.** False
10. False **11.** False **12.** True
13. False **14.** False **15.** True

For Exercises . . .	1–4, 19–24, 63–65, 70–76, 79–81	5–6, 25–33, 77	7–8, 34–39, 66	9–13, 40–58, 78	14–16, 59–62, 67–69
Refer to Section . . .	1	2	3	4	5

16. True **19.** $(-9, 3)$ **20.** $(22, 3)$ **21.** $(7, -9, -1)$ **22.** $(2, -1, 3)$ **23.** $(6 - 7z/3, 1 + z/3, z)$ **24.** No solution
25. 2×2 (square); $a = 2, b = 3, c = 5, q = 9$ **26.** 3×2; $a = 2, x = -1, y = 4, p = 5, z = 7$ **27.** 1×4 (row);
$m = 6, k = 3, z = -3, r = -9$ **28.** 3×3 (square); $a = -12, b = 1, k = 9/2, c = 3/4, d = 3, l = -3/4, m = -1, p = 3, q = 9$

29. $\begin{bmatrix} 9 & 10 \\ -3 & 0 \\ 10 & 16 \end{bmatrix}$ **30.** $\begin{bmatrix} 0 & -16 \\ -10 & -18 \end{bmatrix}$ **31.** $\begin{bmatrix} 23 & 20 \\ -7 & 3 \\ 24 & 39 \end{bmatrix}$ **32.** Not possible **33.** $\begin{bmatrix} -17 & 20 \\ 1 & -21 \\ -8 & -17 \end{bmatrix}$ **34.** $\begin{bmatrix} 2 & 50 \\ 1 & -15 \\ -3 & 45 \end{bmatrix}$

35. Not possible **36.** $\begin{bmatrix} 6 & 18 & -24 \\ 1 & 3 & -4 \\ 0 & 0 & 0 \end{bmatrix}$ **37.** $[9]$ **38.** $\begin{bmatrix} 15 \\ 16 \\ 1 \end{bmatrix}$ **39.** $[-14 \; -19]$ **40.** $\begin{bmatrix} -7/19 & 4/19 \\ 3/19 & 1/19 \end{bmatrix}$ **41.** No inverse

42. No inverse **43.** $\begin{bmatrix} 7 & -3 \\ -2 & 1 \end{bmatrix}$ **44.** $\begin{bmatrix} -1/4 & 1/6 \\ 0 & 1/3 \end{bmatrix}$ **45.** No inverse **46.** No inverse **47.** $\begin{bmatrix} 2/3 & 0 & -1/3 \\ 1/3 & 0 & -2/3 \\ -2/3 & 1 & 1/3 \end{bmatrix}$

48. $\begin{bmatrix} 1/4 & 1/2 & 1/2 \\ 1/4 & -1/2 & 1/2 \\ 1/8 & -1/4 & -1/4 \end{bmatrix}$ **49.** No inverse **50.** No inverse **51.** $X = \begin{bmatrix} 1 \\ -13 \end{bmatrix}$ **52.** Matrix A has no inverse. Solution: $(-2y + 5, y)$

53. $X = \begin{bmatrix} -22 \\ -18 \\ 15 \end{bmatrix}$ **54.** $X = \begin{bmatrix} 6 \\ 15 \\ 16 \end{bmatrix}$ **55.** $(2, 1)$ **56.** $(34, -9)$ **57.** $(-1, 0, 2)$ **58.** $(1, 2, 3)$ **59.** $1, 3; \begin{bmatrix} 3 \\ 1 \end{bmatrix}, \begin{bmatrix} 2 \\ 1 \end{bmatrix}$

60. $8, 2; \begin{bmatrix} 1 \\ 1 \end{bmatrix}, \begin{bmatrix} 1 \\ -1 \end{bmatrix}$ **61.** $1, 2, 3; \begin{bmatrix} 1 \\ -2 \\ 0 \end{bmatrix}, \begin{bmatrix} 0 \\ 5 \\ 1 \end{bmatrix}, \begin{bmatrix} 0 \\ 0 \\ 1 \end{bmatrix}$ **62.** $-2, 3, 2; \begin{bmatrix} 10 \\ -2 \\ 3 \end{bmatrix}, \begin{bmatrix} 0 \\ 1 \\ 1 \end{bmatrix}, \begin{bmatrix} 0 \\ 0 \\ 1 \end{bmatrix}$ **63.** $\begin{bmatrix} 8 & 8 & 8 \\ 10 & 5 & 9 \\ 7 & 10 & 7 \\ 8 & 9 & 7 \end{bmatrix}$

64. a. $b + c$ **b.** A is tumorous, B is bone, and C is healthy. **c.** For patient X, A and C are healthy; B is tumorous. For patient Y, A and B are tumorous; C is bone. For patient Z, A could be healthy or tumorous; B and C are healthy.
65. a. No **b. (i)** 0.23, 0.37, 0.42; A is healthy; B and D are tumorous; C is bone. **(ii)** 0.33, 0.27, 0.32; A and C are tumorous, B could be healthy or tumorous, D is bone. **c.** 0.2, 0.4, 0.45, 0.3; A is healthy; B and C are bone; D is tumorous. **d.** One example is to choose beams 1, 2, 3, and 6. **66.** About 20 head and face injuries, 12 concussions, 3 neck injuries, and 55 other injuries

67. $\begin{bmatrix} 2500 \\ 7500 \end{bmatrix}, 0.9$ **68.** $\begin{bmatrix} 5000 \\ 5000 \end{bmatrix}, 0.5$ **69. d.** $\begin{bmatrix} 1191 \\ 773 \\ 213 \\ 185 \\ 371 \\ 325 \end{bmatrix}$ **f.** $\begin{bmatrix} 19,797 \\ 17,233 \\ 4093 \\ 3580 \\ 7520 \\ 6580 \end{bmatrix}$ **70. a.** $C = 0.012t^2 + 0.86t + 317$ **b.** 2091

71. a. $x = 1$ and $y = 1/2$ **b.** $x = 1, y = 1$, and $z = -1$ **72.** $W_1 = W_2 = 100\sqrt{3}/3 \approx 58$ lb
73. $W_1 \approx 110$ lb and $W_2 \approx 134$ lb **74.** 8000 standard, 6000 extra large **75.** 5 blankets, 3 rugs, 8 skirts
76. 150,000 gal were produced at Tulsa, 225,000 gal at New Orleans, and 180,000 gal at Ardmore

77. $\begin{bmatrix} 1.33 & 17.6 & 152,000 & 26.75 & +1.88 \\ 1.00 & 20.0 & 238,200 & 32.36 & -1.50 \\ 0.79 & 25.4 & 39,110 & 16.51 & -0.89 \\ 0.27 & 21.2 & 122,500 & 28.60 & +0.75 \end{bmatrix}$ **78. a.** $\begin{bmatrix} 3170 \\ 2360 \\ 1800 \end{bmatrix}$ **b.** $\begin{bmatrix} x \\ y \\ z \end{bmatrix}$ **c.** $\begin{bmatrix} 10 & 5 & 8 \\ 12 & 0 & 4 \\ 0 & 10 & 5 \end{bmatrix}\begin{bmatrix} x \\ y \\ z \end{bmatrix} = \begin{bmatrix} 3170 \\ 2360 \\ 1800 \end{bmatrix}$ **d.** $\begin{bmatrix} 150 \\ 110 \\ 140 \end{bmatrix}$

79. There are y girls and $2500 - 1.5y$ boys, where y is any even integer between 0 and 1666. **80.** 179 singles, 31 doubles, 4 triples, and 11 home runs **81.** A chocolate wafer weighs 4.08 g, and a single layer of vanilla cream weighs 3.17 g.

A Library of Elementary Functions

BASIC FUNCTIONS

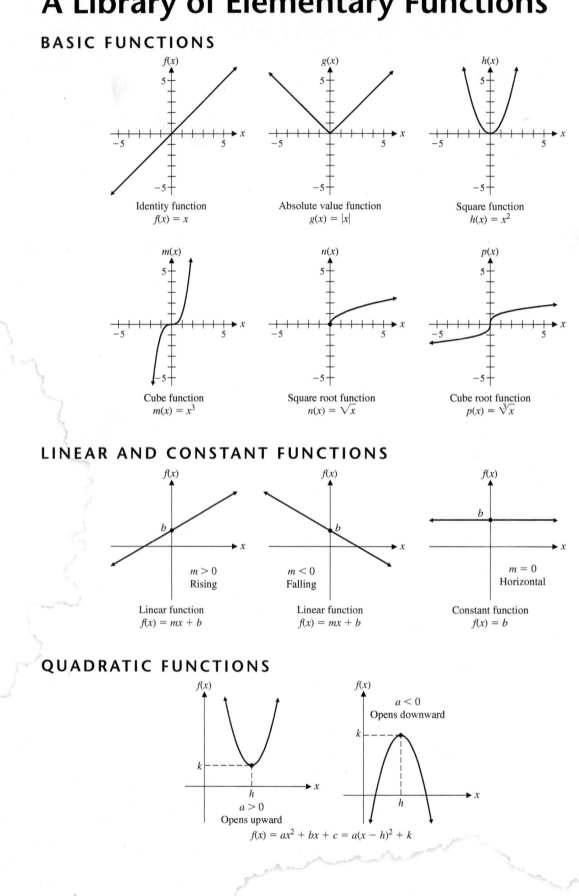

Identity function
$f(x) = x$

Absolute value function
$g(x) = |x|$

Square function
$h(x) = x^2$

Cube function
$m(x) = x^3$

Square root function
$n(x) = \sqrt{x}$

Cube root function
$p(x) = \sqrt[3]{x}$

LINEAR AND CONSTANT FUNCTIONS

$m > 0$
Rising

Linear function
$f(x) = mx + b$

$m < 0$
Falling

Linear function
$f(x) = mx + b$

$m = 0$
Horizontal

Constant function
$f(x) = b$

QUADRATIC FUNCTIONS

$a > 0$
Opens upward

$a < 0$
Opens downward

$f(x) = ax^2 + bx + c = a(x - h)^2 + k$